Biology I: Cells, Molecular Biology and Genetics Custom Text

SC/BIOL 1000 3.0

York University

NELSON

NELSON

ISBN-13: 978-0-17-672167-1
ISBN-10: 0-17-672167-3

Consists of Selections from:

Biology: Exploring the Diversity of Life, Third Canadian Edition
Peter Russell
Paul E. Hertz
Beverly McMillan
Brock Fenton
Heather Addy
Denis Maxwell
Tom Haffie
Bill Milsom
ISBN 10: 0-17-653213-7, © 2015

Biology: A Human Emphasis, 9th Edition
STARR/EVERS/STARR
ISBN 10: 1-285-42782-3, © 2015

Watson and Crick,1953. "Molecular Structure of Nucleic Acids", Nature Vol 171

Darwin,1860, On the Origin of Species

BIOLOGY: EXPLORING THE DIVERSITY OF LIFE 1CE
RUSSELL/WOLFE/HERTZ/STARR
ISBN 10: 0-17-644094-1, © 2010

Table of Contents

ORIGINS AND ORGANIZATION

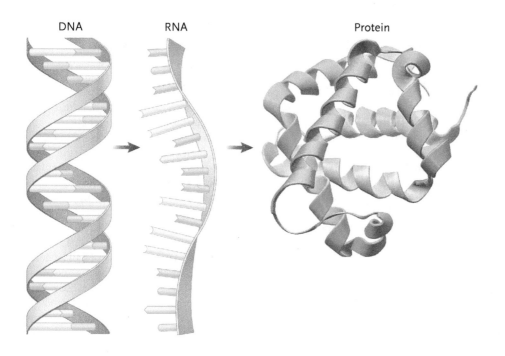

DNA   RNA   Protein

In all life, the molecule DNA carries information used to synthesize proteins through an RNA intermediate. Why do all life forms use this system and which one of the three molecules evolved first on the early Earth?

The opening volume of this textbook illustrates to us that, although life is truly astonishing in its diversity, it is equally astonishing in its similarity. From monkeys to mycoplasma to monocots, everything that is alive on Earth employs a variation on that remarkable innovation—the **cell**. No matter if that cell is communicating with other cells in the brain of a fruit fly, or capturing sunlight in a spruce needle, or driving the muscles of a sprinting cheetah, or thriving in the mineral-rich water of deep-sea vents— no matter what their role or activity, all cells, share a remarkably long list of common features that Volume 1 explores in detail.

All cells are surrounded by a bilayer of lipid molecules that allows for the development of an internal environment that is distinctly different from the outside world. All cells possess genes that are coded by the molecule DNA that through the process of transcription get copied into RNA. All cells contain ribosomes where some RNAs get translated into **proteins**, the fundamental structural, functional and regulatory molecule of the cell. All cells contain a specialized class of proteins called enzymes that have the astonishing ability to increase the rate of a chemical reaction by a billion times. We could go on and on.

The stark similarities present in all forms of life leads one logically to a single compelling conclusion—all living things on Earth are relatives of one another; ultimately sharing the same parent we call LUCA for Last Universal Common Ancestor. LUCA may have not been the first form of life, in fact there may have been hundreds of different forms that sprung up on the early Earth, but it was the most successful because it survived and, it alone, gave rise to the diversity of life we see today.

But hang on one minute—what is life anyway and how did it arise? Even at a time of unprecedented scientific achievements, arriving at an accurate yet succinct definition of life is frustratingly elusive. Defining life is not easy and at the same time exactly how life got started perhaps as early as 4 billion years ago remains one of the fundamental mysteries of science. Our understanding of how life got started would be helped immensely if we could find life some place other than Earth—perhaps on one of the thousands of habitable planets recently discovered orbiting distant stars. Maybe the **development** of life is incredibly rare or perhaps it is inevitable given the right conditions and enough time.

Although life occupies a unique spot in the natural world, cells are built of the same atoms and abide by the same laws of chemistry and physics as everything else. However, seemingly in defiance of the universal tendency towards increasing disorder, living organisms are able to maintain a complex and highly structured state. This requires cells to be constantly bringing in energy and matter from their surroundings, building more complex molecules then they take in and releasing less complex molecules and heat back into the environment. On Earth most of the energy used by living systems comes ultimately from sunlight—being harvested and converted into a useable chemical form

through the process of photosynthesis. The conversion of carbon dioxide into sugar by photosynthesis introduces chemical energy into the biosphere. The stepwise and controlled oxidation of these molecules through cellular respiration is used to generate ATP the energy currency that is universally accepted to power cells.

Genes are stretches of DNA sequence in an organism that collectively comprise a kind of library of information about how a cell functions. Recent advances in technology have made it relatively easy to determine the entire DNA sequence of an organism, including individual humans. As a result, modern biology is awash in the As, Ts, Gs and Cs of DNA sequence revealed by thousands of sequencing projects. New insights into evolutionary history as well as gene structure and function are arising from bioinformatic analysis of such extensive data sets.

The elegant double-strandedness of DNA, whereby two long strands of nucleotides are held together by hydrogen bonds formed between complementary base pairs, affords a straightforward mechanism for replication that was recognized early on by Watson and Crick. Although conceptually simple, the mechanism for unwinding the DNA **double helix** and polymerizing new complementary bases is rather complicated and managed by a suite of interacting enzymes. Again, we see that all DNA on the planet is replicated using variations on one underlying strategy.

DNA genes provide the cell with needed RNA by transcription. One remarkable feature of all protein-coding genes is that, with minor exceptions, the information they carry is specified by a universal code. That is, a gene from one organism can be "understood" by any other organism, even if only distantly related: A gene from a spider can be expressed by a goat; A gene from a jellyfish can be expressed in a flower. The field of genetic engineering is devoted to developing the tools and applications of this technology for moving genes from one organism to another.

In a story that is about to come full circle, synthetic biologists have extensively customized naturally occurring cells and have made important advances toward their ultimate goal of creating novel life forms artificially in the lab. As students of biology in the early 21st century, you can well expect to witness a momentous event in Earth's history, the creation of one life form by another.

Paintings by Claude Monet (1840–1926). Compared to his early works, including "The Water-Lily Pond" (a), his later paintings, including "The Japanese Footbridge" (b), bordered on the abstract with almost complete loss of light blue. Monet suffered from vision degenerative disease cataracts, diagnosed in 1912.

Light and Life

WHY IT MATTERS

Claude Monet (1840–1926), a French painter, is considered by many to be the master of the impressionist form that rose to prominence in the late nineteenth century. Other well-known impressionists are Edgar Degas and Paul Cézanne. Impressionism as an art movement was characterized by the use of small visible brush strokes that emphasized light and colour, rather than lines, to define an object. The artists used pure, unmixed colour, not smoothly blended, as was the custom at the time. For example, instead of physically mixing yellow and blue paint, they placed unmixed yellow paint on the canvas next to unmixed blue paint so that the colours would mingle in the eye of the viewer to create the impression of green. The impressionists found that they could capture the momentary and transient effects of sunlight and the changing colour of a scene by painting *en plein air*, in the open air, outside the studio, where they could more accurately paint the reflected light of an immediate scene.

Interestingly, compared with his early works, which included "The Water-Lily Pond" (1899), Monet's later paintings verge on the abstract, with colours bleeding into each other and a lack of rational shape and perspective. For example, "The Japanese Footbridge" is an explosion of orange, yellow, and red hues, with heavy, broad brush strokes, leaving the viewer barely able to discern the vague shape of the arched bridge. In many of Monet's later works, the colours in his paintings became more muted, far less vibrant and bright, with a pronounced colour shift from blue green to red yellow and an almost total absence of light blues. The sense of atmosphere and light that he was famous for in his earlier works disappeared.

Although the change in Monet's paintings could easily be explained by an intentional change in style or perhaps an age-related change in manual dexterity, Monet himself realized that it was not his style or dexterity that had changed but, rather, his ability to see. Monet suffered from cataracts, a vision-deteriorating disease diagnosed in both eyes by a Parisian ophthalmologist in 1912 when Monet was 72. A cataract is a change in the lens of the eye, making it more opaque. The underlying cause is a progressive denaturation of one of the proteins that make up the lens. The increased opaqueness of the lens absorbs certain **wavelengths** of light, decreasing the transmittance of blue light. Thus, to a cataract sufferer such as Monet, the world appears more yellow.

In this, the first of the 52 chapters that make up the textbook, we introduce you to the science of biology by using light as a central connecting theme. Light is arguably the most fundamental of natural phenomena, and foundational experiments into the nature of light were a key part of the scientific revolution that took place in the sixteenth and seventeenth centuries. Beyond formally defining light and discussing its properties, in this chapter we explore the huge diversity of areas of biology that light influences, from the molecular to the ecological. This introductory tour is not intended to be complete or exhaustive but to simply set the stage for the topics that come in subsequent chapters.

1.1 The Physical Nature of Light

Light serves two important functions for life on Earth. First, it is a source of energy that directly or indirectly sustains virtually all organisms. Second, light provides organisms with information about the physical world that surrounds them. An excellent example of an organism that uses light for both energy and information is the green alga *Chlamydomonas reinhardtii* **(Figure 1.1)**. *C. reinhardtii* is a single-celled photosynthetic eukaryote that is commonly found in ponds and lakes. Each cell contains a single large chloroplast that harvests light energy and uses it to make energy-rich molecules through the process of photosynthesis. In addition, each cell contains a light sensor called an eyespot that allows individual cells to gather information about the

location and intensity of a light source. With this information, cells can move toward or away from the light source, allowing them to optimize light harvesting for photosynthesis. Regardless of whether the light is used as a source of energy or as a source of information about the environment, both uses rely on the same fundamental properties of light and require the light energy to be captured by the organism.

1.1a What Is Light?

The reason there is life on Earth and, as far as we know, nowhere else in our solar system has to do with distance—specifically, the distance of 150 million kilometres separating Earth from the Sun **(Figure 1.2)**. By converting hydrogen into helium at the staggering rate of some 3.4×10^{38} hydrogen nuclei per second, the Sun converts over 4 million tonnes of matter into energy every second. This energy is given off as *electromagnetic radiation*, which travels in the form of a wave at a speed of 1 079 252 848 km/h (the speed of light) and reaches Earth in just over 8 minutes. Scientists often distinguish different types of electromagnetic radiation by their wavelength, the distance between two successive peaks **(Figure 1.3)**. The wavelength of electromagnetic radiation ranges from less than one picometre (10^{-12} m) for cosmic rays to more than a kilometre (10^6 m) for radio waves.

So what is light? **Light** is most commonly defined as the portion of the **electromagnetic spectrum** that humans can detect with their eyes. This is a very narrow portion of the total electromagnetic spectrum, only spanning the wavelengths from about 400 to 700 nm

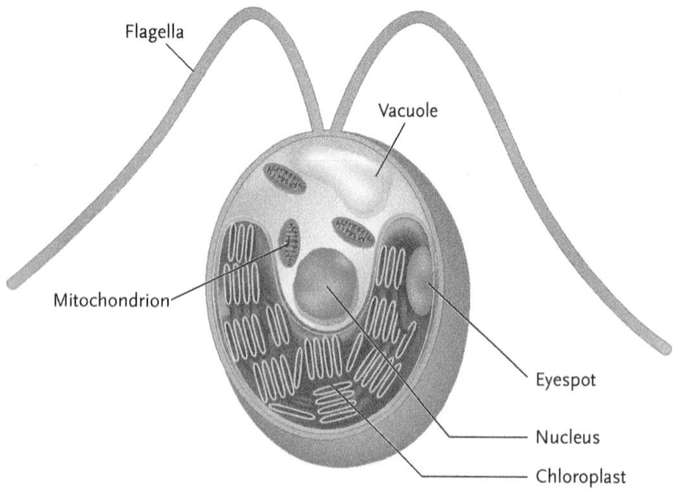

Figure 1.1
Chlamydomonas reinhardtii. Each cell contains a single chloroplast used for photosynthesis as well as an eyespot for sensing light in the environment.

Flagella

Vacuole

Mitochondrion

Eyespot

Nucleus

Chloroplast

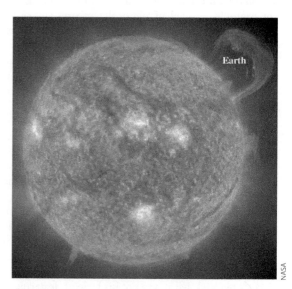

Earth

NASA

Figure 1.2
The Sun. Like most stars, the Sun generates electromagnetic radiation as a result of the nuclear fusion of hydrogen nuclei into helium. Note the superimposed image of Earth used to illustrate the relative sizes.

a. Range of the electromagnetic spectrum

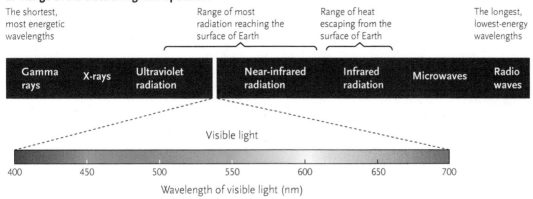

The shortest, most energetic wavelengths

Range of most radiation reaching the surface of Earth

Range of heat escaping from the surface of Earth

The longest, lowest-energy wavelengths

| Gamma rays | X-rays | Ultraviolet radiation | Near-infrared radiation | Infrared radiation | Microwaves | Radio waves |

Visible light

400   450   500   550   600   650   700

Wavelength of visible light (nm)

b. Examples of wavelengths

400 nm wavelength

700 nm wavelength

Figure 1.3
The electromagnetic spectrum. **(a)** The electromagnetic spectrum ranges from gamma rays to radio waves; visible light and the wavelengths used for photosynthesis occupy only a narrow band of the spectrum. **(b)** Examples of wavelengths, showing the difference between the longest and shortest wavelengths of visible light.

(see Figure 1.3). In physics, the definition of light often includes other regions of the electromagnetic spectrum, and thus terms such as *visible light, ultraviolet light,* and *infrared light* are commonly used.

The physical nature of light has been the focus of scientific inquiry for hundreds of years, but it is still not simple to grasp. Unlike the atoms that make up matter, light has no mass. As well, although the results of some experiments suggest that light behaves as a wave as it travels through space, the results of other experiments are best explained by light being composed of a stream of energy particles called **photons**. That light has properties of both a wave and a stream of photons is often referred to as the particle-wave duality. And so we are left with a compromise description—light is best understood as a wave of photons. The relationship between the wavelength of light and the energy of the photons it carries is an inverse one: the longer the wavelength, the lower the energy of the photons it contains. Looking at Figure 1.3, this means that shorter-wavelength blue light consists of photons of higher energy than red light, which has a longer wavelength and photons of lower energy.

1.1b Light Interacts with Matter

Although light has no mass, it is still able to interact with matter and cause change. This change is what allows the energy of light to be used by living things. When a photon of light hits an object, the photon has three possible fates: it can be reflected off the object, transmitted through the object or absorbed by the object. To be used as a source of energy or information

by an organism, absorption must take place. The absorption of light occurs when the energy of the photon is transferred to an **electron** within a molecule. This excites the electron, moving it from its ground state to a higher energy level that is referred to as an excited state **(Figure 1.4)**. An important fact to remember is that a photon can be absorbed only if the energy of the photon matches the amount of energy needed to move the electron from its ground state to a specific excited state. If the energies don't match, then the photon of light is not absorbed but instead is transmitted through the molecule or reflected. It is the excited-state electron that represents the source of energy required for processes such as photosynthesis and vision.

A major class of molecules that are very efficient at absorbing photons are called **pigments (Figure 1.5, p. 6)**. There is a large diversity of pigments, including

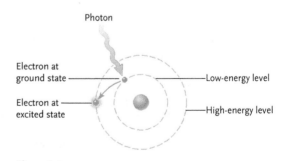

Photon

Electron at ground state — Low-energy level

Electron at excited state — High-energy level

Figure 1.4
The absorption of a photon by a molecule results in the energy being transferred to an electron. This causes the energy to move to a higher-energy excited state.

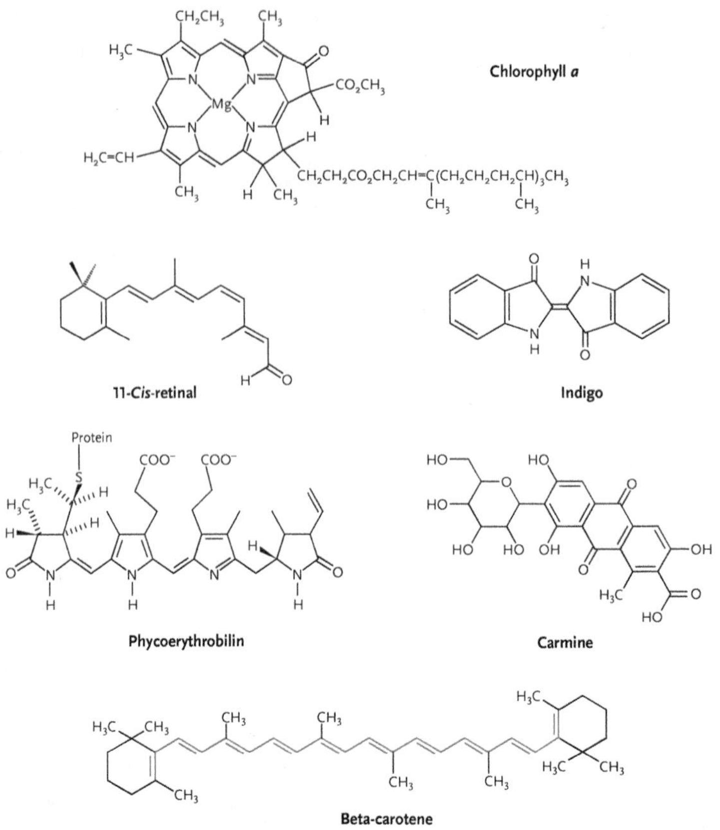

Figure 1.5

Structure of some common pigments. Chlorophyll *a*, photosynthesis. 11-*Cis*-retinal, vision. Indigo, dye. Phycoerythrobilin, red photosynthetic pigment found in red algae. Carmine, scale pigment found in some insects. Beta-carotene, an orange accessory photosynthetic pigment. A common feature of all of these pigments that is critical for light absorption is the presence of a conjugated system of double/single carbon bonds (shown in red for beta-carotene).

Chlorophyll *a*

11-*Cis*-retinal

Indigo

Phycoerythrobilin

Carmine

Beta-carotene

chlorophyll *a*, which is involved in photosynthesis; retinal, which is involved in vision; and indigo, which is used to dye jeans their distinctive blue colour.

An important question we can ask is: what is it about pigments that enable them to capture light? At first glance, the molecules shown in Figure 1.5 seem to be structurally very different from each other. However, they all have a common feature critical to light absorption: a region where carbon atoms are covalently bonded to each other with alternating single and double bonds. This bonding arrangement is called a *conjugated system,* and it results in the delocalization of electrons. None of these electrons are closely associated with a particular atom or involved in bonding and thus are available to interact with a photon of light.

Most pigments absorb light at distinctly different wavelengths. This is because the differences in chemical structure result in each pigment having distinct excited states available to its delocalized electrons. While some pigments can absorb, for example, only blue photons because they have only one high-energy excited state, others can absorb two or more different wavelengths because they have two or more excited states. Photon absorption is intimately related to the concept of colour. A pigment's colour is the result of photons of light that it *does not* absorb. Instead of being absorbed, these photons are reflected off the pigment or transmitted through the pigment to reach your eyes **(Figure 1.6).**

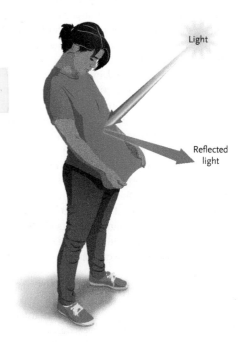

Figure 1.6

Why the t-shirt is red. Pigment molecules bound to the fabric of the shirt absorb blue, green, and yellow photons of light. Red photons are not absorbed and are instead transmitted through the shirt or reflected.

1. Define light.
2. What structural feature is common to all pigments?

1.2 Light as a Source of Energy

As we will discuss in subsequent chapters, all living things require a constant supply of energy from their surroundings. The ultimate source of this energy is light from the Sun, which is made accessible to biological systems through the ability of plants and related organisms to convert this light energy into a chemical form. Through photosynthesis, plants absorb photons of light and use the potential energy to convert carbon dioxide into sugars (carbohydrates). Energy from the Sun enters the **biosphere** through photosynthesis.

Following light absorption, the potential energy of excited electrons within **chlorophyll** is used in photosynthetic electron **transport** to synthesize the energy-rich compounds NADPH (nicotinamide adenine dinucleotide phosphate) and **ATP (adenosine triphosphate)**. These molecules are in turn consumed in the **Calvin cycle** of photosynthesis to convert carbon dioxide into carbohydrates **(Figure 1.7)**. Although the energy of one photon is very small, the photosynthetic apparatus within the chloroplast of a single *C. reinhardtii* cell absorbs millions of photons each second. And a single cell within a typical plant leaf contains hundreds of chloroplasts!

While photosynthesis converts carbon dioxide into carbohydrates, it is the process of cellular respiration that breaks down carbohydrates and other molecules, trapping the released energy as ATP (see Figure 1.7). This in turn is used in the energy-requiring metabolic and biosynthetic processes that are fundamental to life.

Not all organisms that use light as a source of energy are classified as photosynthetic. That is, some organisms do not use the light energy to convert carbon dioxide into carbohydrates. A good example is a genus of organisms within the Archaea called *Halobacterium*. These remarkable microbes thrive in habitats that contain salt levels that are lethal to most other forms of life **(Figure 1.8, p. 8)**. Species of *Halobacterium* contain a pigment–protein complex called bacteriorhodopsin, which functions as a light-driven **proton pump**. The pigment component of bacteriorhodopsin captures photons of light that provide the energy supply needed to pump protons out of the cell. The resulting difference in H$^+$ concentration across the plasma membrane represents a source of potential energy that is used by the enzyme ATP synthase to generate ATP from ADP

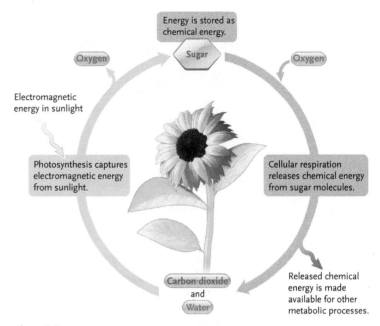

Figure 1.7

Photosynthesis converts light into a usable form of energy. Photosynthesis uses the energy in sunlight to build sugar molecules from carbon dioxide and water, releasing oxygen as a by-product. The process of cellular respiration breaks down the products of photosynthesis and releases usable energy.

(adenosine diphosphate) and inorganic phosphate (P$_i$) (see Figure 1.8, p. 8). We will discuss the mode of ATP generation in detail in Chapters 6 and 7. In Halobacteria the ATP synthesized through bacteriorhodopsin is used for a range of energy-requiring reactions—but not for the synthesis of carbohydrates from carbon dioxide.

STUDY BREAK

1. Why is the indigo pigment blue in colour?
2. How is light absorption linked to ATP synthesis in *Halobacteria*?

1.3 Light as a Source of Information

As mentioned in "Why It Matters," the deterioration of Monet's eyesight changed the way he saw the world, thus changing the way he painted. This reminds us that many organisms use light to sense their environment—to provide them with crucial information about what is around them. The experience of trying to perform even the simplest of tasks in a dark room makes one quickly realize how important the ability to sense light has become for many forms of life. The change in Monet's eyesight during his later life also suggests that not every person, and certainly not every species, sees the world in the same way.

Figure 1.8

Halobacterium is a genus of Archaea that have a light-driven proton pump. **(a)** Electron micrograph of a colony of *Halobacterium salinarum*. **(b)** Species of *Halobacterium* thrive in hypersaline environments such as Hutt Lagoon in Australia. The pink colour of the water is due to the presence of bacteriorhodopsin within individual cells. **(c)** A model of bacteriorhodopsin shows the pigment retinal bound to a protein. **(d)** Bacteriorhodopsin functions as a light-driven proton pump, the proton gradient being used to synthesize ATP.

a. *Halobacterium salinarum*

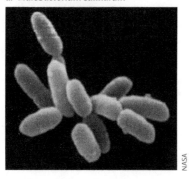

NASA

b. Hutt Lagoon, Western Australia

© J Marshall - Tribaleye Images/Alamy

c. A model of bacteriorhodopsin

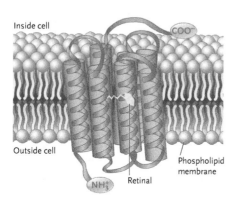

d. Bacteriorhodopsin-driven ATP formation

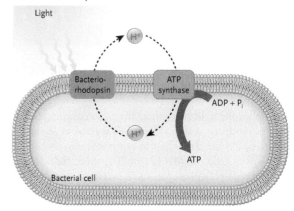

1.3a Rhodopsin, the Universal Photoreceptor

The basic light-sensing system is termed the photoreceptor. And the most common photoreceptor in nature is rhodopsin **(Figure 1.9, p. 10)**, which is the basis of vision in all animals and insects. Each rhodopsin molecule consists of a protein called opsin that binds a single pigment molecule called retinal. Opsins are membrane proteins that span a membrane multiple times and form a complex with the retinal molecule at the centre (see Figure 1.9, p. 10).

As shown in Figure 1.9, absorption of a photon of light causes the retinal pigment molecule to change shape. This change triggers alterations to the opsin protein, which, in turn, trigger downstream events, including alterations in intracellular **ion** concentrations and electrical signals. As we will see in Chapter 45, in the case of vision, these electrical signals are sent to the visual centres of the brain. In humans, light captured by the eye involves the approximately 125 million photoreceptor cells (rods and cones) that line the retina. Each photoreceptor cell contains millions of individual rhodopsin molecules.

Bacteriorhodopsin found in Halobacterium is structurally similar to the rhodopsin in the eyes of animals. As well, the eyespot of *Chlamydomonas* contains the molecule channelrhodopsin, which is used to sense light. While rhodopsin, channelrhodopsin, and bacteriorhodopsin are structurally similar (a retinal molecule bound to a protein), they do not have a similar evolutionary history. The evolutionary path leading to rhodopsin is distinctly different from the path leading to channelrhodopsin and bacteriorhodopsin.

Rhodopsin is the most common photoreceptor found in nature, but it is not the only one. Both plants and animals have a range of other photoreceptors that absorb light of particular wavelengths. However, it remains a mystery why rhodopsin became the most common photoreceptor. Perhaps its widespread occurrence is because it developed very early during the evolution of animals. Interestingly, whereas vision and smell are different senses, proteins similar to opsins are used in olfaction, suggesting that specific aspects of opsin proteins are particularly useful for sensory perception.

1.3b Sensing Light without Eyes

When we think about sensing light, we automatically think about our ability to see with our eyes. However, many organisms can sense the light in their surroundings even though they lack organs that we would consider to be eyes. These organisms include plants, algae, invertebrates, and even some bacteria. As an example,

Isaac Newton

Sir Isaac Newton (1643–1727) was an English mathematician, physicist, and astronomer and is generally regarded as one of the greatest scientists and mathematicians in history. Newton wrote the *Philosophiae Naturalis Principia Mathematica,* in which he described universal gravitation and the three laws of motion, laying the groundwork for classical mechanics. He was the first to show that the motion of objects on Earth and elsewhere in the solar system is governed by the same set of natural laws. Newton also undertook key experiments about the nature of light. In Newton's time it was thought that light from the Sun was colourless and that the colours seen in a rainbow during a rain shower, for example, were somehow made by the rain droplets. In the same way, it was thought that colours produced when light passed through a glass prism were somehow made by the prism itself. It was Newton who laid the groundwork for fundamental break-throughs in the nature of light by demonstrating through a series of experiments that these assumptions were false.

Using light entering his room through a slit in his curtains, Newton undertook a series of remarkably simple experiments that profoundly changed science. In one experiment, he passed the red light from one prism through a second prism and found the colour unchanged. From this Newton concluded that the prism does not make colour, but rather the colour is already present in the incoming light.

In Newton's "Experimentum Crucis" (shown here), he was able to use a combination of three prisms and one lens, enabling him to (from right to left) split white light into the spectrum, which was then passed through a convex lens that focused the light onto a second prism, and then reconstitute the spectrum into a single beam of white light and then split it again into the spectrum after passage through a third prism. An interesting property of light that is illustrated by a prism is that as light passes from one medium into another (e.g., air to glass), it changes speed, which causes the light to refract or bend. Light of shorter wavelength (blue) refracts to a greater degree than light of longer wavelength (red).

Newton's experiments were simple yet wonderfully elegant, leading to tremendous insight into the workings of the natural world. His experiments are classic examples of the approach to discovery that was introduced during what is called the Scientific Revolution, which swept Europe during the sixteenth and seventeenth centuries. This was a period in science when religion, superstition, and fear were replaced by reason and knowl-edge based on the observation, explanation, and prediction of real-world phenomena through experimentation (see *The Purple Pages* for more on the scientific method). Besides Newton, other key figures during this period were Francis Bacon, Johannes Kepler, Nicolaus Copernicus, René Descartes, Antonie van Leeuwen-hoek, and William Harvey.

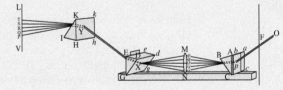

let's take a closer look at the eyespot of *C. reinhardtii.* The eyespot is a light-sensitive structure that is approximately 1 μm in diameter and is found within the chloroplast of the cell, in a region closely associated with the cell membrane **(Figure 1.10, p. 10)**. The eyespot is composed of two layers of carotenoid-rich lipid globules that play a role in focusing and directing incoming light toward the photoreceptor molecule channelrhodopsin. Although the eyespot is found within the chloroplast, it does not play a role in photosynthesis. Instead, the eyespot allows the cell to sense light direction and intensity. Using a pair of flagella, *C. reinhardtii* cells can respond to light by swimming toward or away from the light source in a process called *phototaxis.* This allows the cell to stay in the optimum light environment to maximize light capture for photosynthesis. Light absorption by the eyespot is linked to the swimming response by a **signal transduction** pathway; light absorption triggers rapid changes in the concentrations of ions, including potassium and calcium, which generate a cascade of electrical events. These, in turn, change the beating pattern of the flagella used for locomotion.

In plants, a photoreceptor called phytochrome senses the light environment and is critical for *photomorphogenesis,* the normal developmental process activated when seedlings are exposed to light **(Figure 1.11, p. 10)**. Phytochrome is present in the cytosol of all plant cells, and when a seedling is exposed to wavelengths of red light, phytochrome becomes active and initiates a signal transduction pathway that reaches the nucleus. In the nucleus, these signals activate hundreds of genes, many of which code for proteins involved in photosynthesis and leaf development. Plant development is the topic of discussion in Chapter 36.

1.3c The Eye

The **eye** can be defined as the organ animals use to sense light. It is described in detail in Chapter 45. What distinguishes the eye of an **invertebrate**, for example,

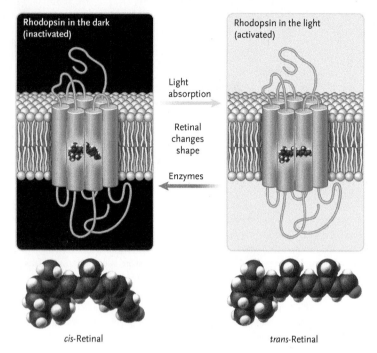

Rhodopsin in the dark (inactivated)

Rhodopsin in the light (activated)

Light absorption

Retinal changes shape

Enzymes

cis-Retinal

trans-Retinal

Figure 1.9
Model of the photoreceptor rhodopsin. Rhodopsin consists of a protein (opsin) that binds a pigment molecule (retinal). Upon absorption of a photon of light, retinal changes shape, which triggers changes to the opsin molecule. These changes trigger signalling events, which allow the organism to "see."

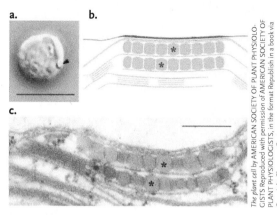

Figure 1.10
The eyespot of *Chlamydomonas*. **(a)** Light microscope image of one *Chlamydomonas* cell. Arrowhead points to the eyespot. Bar = 10 μm. **(b)** Drawing of the eyespot apparatus with the asterisks indicating the orange pigment-rich globule layers that are found inside the chloroplast outer membrane. **(c)** Transmission electron micrograph of the same area. The eyespot contains the photoreceptor molecule channelrhodopsin (not shown). Bar = 300 nm.

from the eyespot of *C. reinhardtii* is vision. The process of vision requires not only an eye to focus and absorb incoming light but also a brain or at least a simple nervous system that interprets signals sent from the eye. The eye and brain are thought to have co-evolved because detailed visual processing occurs in the brain

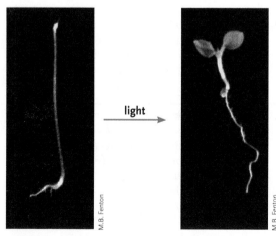

light

Figure 1.11
Photomorphogenesis. Shifting a seedling from darkness to light triggers a developmental program within the plant called photomorphogenesis. Light sensed by the photoreceptor phytochrome initiates the program that involves the activation of hundreds of genes.

rather than in the eye. Essentially, we see not with our eyes but with our brain.

The simplest eye is the *ocellus* (plural, *ocelli*), which consists of a cup or pit lined with up to 100 photoreceptor cells. Found in all forms of true eyes, the photoreceptor cell is actually a modified nerve cell that contains thousands of individual photoreceptor molecules. A common group of organisms that contain ocelli are flatworms of the genus *Planaria* **(Figure 1.12)**. Information sent to the cerebral ganglion from individual eyes enables the worms to orient themselves so that the amount of light falling on the two ocelli remains equal and diminishes as they swim. This reaction carries them directly away from the source of the light and toward darker areas, where the risk of predation is smaller. Ocelli occur in a variety of animals, including a number of insects, arthropods, and molluscs.

In many ways, the eye of a *Planaria* (plural, *Planarians*) is not much more advanced than the eyespot of *C. reinhardtii*. In both cases, the organ is used to sense light intensity and direction to a light source, but little else. The greatest advance in eye development came with the greater sophistication that produced an actual image of the lighted environment, which allowed objects and shapes to be discerned. These image-forming eyes are found in two distinctly different types: compound eyes and single-lens eyes. *Compound eyes,* which are common in arthropods such as insects and crustaceans, are built of hundreds of individual units called ommatidia (*omma* = eye) fitted closely together **(Figure 1.13).** Each ommatidium samples only a small part of the visual field, with incoming light being focused onto a bundle of photoreceptor cells. From these signals, the brain receives a mosaic image

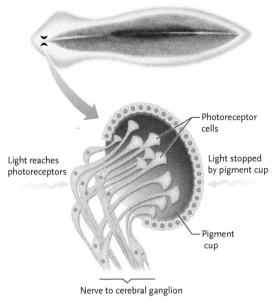

Figure 1.12
The ocellus of *Planaria*, a flatworm, and the arrangement of photoreceptor cells that allows worms to orient themselves in response to light.

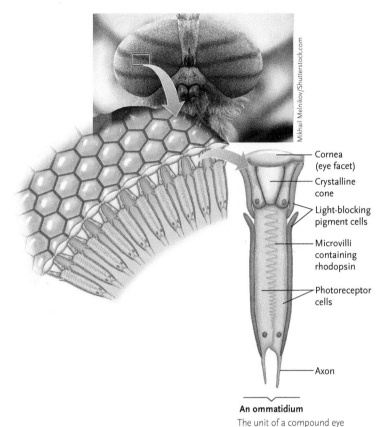

An ommatidium
The unit of a compound eye

Figure 1.13
The compound eye of a deer fly. Each ommatidium has a cornea that directs light into the crystalline cone; in turn, the cone focuses light on the photoreceptor cells. A light-blocking pigment layer at the sides of the ommatidium prevents light from scattering laterally in the compound eye.

of the world. Because even the slightest motion is detected simultaneously by many ommatidia, organisms with compound eyes are extraordinarily good at detecting movement, a lesson soon learned by fly-swatting humans.

The other major type of eye is called the *single-lens eye* **(Figure 1.14)** or camera-like eye and is found in some invertebrates and most vertebrates, including humans. Unlike compound eyes, in a single-lens eye, as light enters through the transparent cornea, a lens concentrates the light and focuses it onto a layer of photoreceptor cells at the back of the eye, the retina. The photoreceptor cells of the retina send information to the brain through the optic nerve.

1.3d Darwin and the Evolution of the Eye

When Charles Darwin presented his theory of evolution by natural selection in *On the Origin of Species by Means of Natural Selection* (1859), he recognized that

Figure 1.14
The single-lens eye of a cephalopod mollusc (an octopus).

what he called "organs of extreme perfection," such as the eye, would present a problem. He wrote:

> To suppose that the eye, with all its inimitable contrivances for adjusting the focus to different distances, for admitting different amounts of light, and for the correction of spherical and chromatic aberration, could have been formed by natural selection, seems, I freely confess, absurd in the highest possible degree. Yet reason tells me, that if numerous gradations from a perfect and complex eye to one very imperfect and simple, each grade being useful to its possessor, can be shown to exist; if further, the eye does vary ever so slightly, and the variations be inherited, which is certainly the case; and if any variation or modification in the organ be ever useful to an animal under changing conditions of life, then the difficulty of believing that a perfect and complex eye could be formed by natural selection, though insuperable by our imagination, can hardly be considered real.

Darwin proposed that the eye as it exists in humans and other animals did not appear suddenly but evolved over time from a simple, primitive eye. It now seems Darwin was very astute. Starting with a patch of light-sensitive cells on the skin, a recent study concluded that about 2000 small improvements over time would gradually yield a single-lens eye in less than 500 thousand years **(Figure 1.15)**. Considering that animals with primitive eyes appeared in the **fossil** record about 500 million years ago, the single-lens eye found in humans could have evolved more than 1000 times. This kind of timing supports fossil evidence that indicates that the eye has evolved independently at least 40 times in different animal lineages before converging into a handful of fundamental designs found today.

It is somewhat surprising that something so complex as the eye could evolve 40 or more different times. However, recently it has been shown that most eyes have fundamental similarities in their

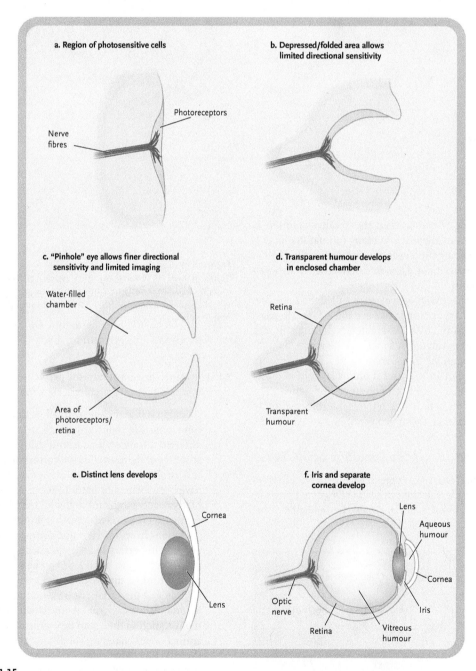

Figure 1.15

The evolution of the eye. Starting with a layer of light-sensitive cells, research suggests that a camera-like eye could evolve in less than 500 thousand years. The evolution of a more sophisticated eye can be explained by the huge advantage improved eyesight would give an organism.

underlying developmental program. For example, a diversity of organisms have recruited a similar set of highly conserved genes to orchestrate eye development. This includes a gene called *Pax6* that has been identified as a master control gene that is almost universally employed for eye formation in animals. And let's not forget that what drove eye evolution in many different animal phyla is the huge advantage eyesight, and then improved eyesight, would have to an animal. The development of heightened visual ability in a predator, as an example, would force comparable eye improvements in both prey and potentially other predators. Rapid improvements in eye development over time would therefore be critical to survival.

STUDY BREAK

1. What are the components of a photoreceptor?
2. Besides rhodopsin, what other molecules are used to sense light?
3. Differentiate between compound eyes and single-lens eyes.
4. How was Darwin able to rationalize the evolution of something so complex as the eye?

1.4 The Uniqueness of Light

Although visible light is a very small portion of the total electromagnetic spectrum, it is essential to life on Earth. In fact, it is this narrow band of energy, from a wavelength of about 400 to 700 nm, that is used for photosynthesis, vision, phototaxis, photomorphogenesis and other light-driven processes. Is it just a coincidence that all of these processes depend on such a narrow band of the electromagnetic spectrum? According to the Harvard physiologist and Nobel laureate George Wald (1906–1997), it is not a coincidence at all. Wald reasoned that visible light is used by organisms because it is the most dominant form of electromagnetic radiation reaching Earth's surface **(Figure 1.16)**. Shorter wavelengths of electromagnetic radiation are absorbed by the ozone layer high in the **atmosphere**, whereas wavelengths longer than those in the visible spectrum are absorbed by water vapour and carbon dioxide in the atmosphere.

Another reason life uses light over other wavelengths of electromagnetic radiation has to do with the energy it contains. Remember that living things are made up of molecules held together by chemical bonds (for a refresher see *The Purple Pages*). Radiation of shorter wavelengths than light contains enough energy to destroy these bonds. Alternatively, electromagnetic radiation of wavelengths longer than light are energetically relatively weak and would not supply enough

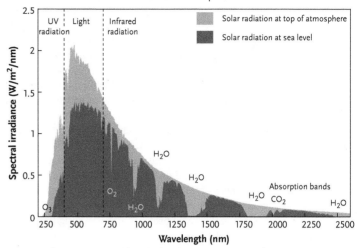

Figure 1.16

Electromagnetic radiation reaching the top of Earth's atmosphere (orange) and at sea level (red). As the energy passes through the atmosphere, short-wavelength radiation (250–300 nm) gets absorbed by ozone (O_3). Other wavelengths get partially absorbed by other gases, including O_2, H_2O, and CO_2. Compared to the electromagnetic radiation that reaches the outer atmosphere, the radiation reaching Earth's surface is reduced in both short wavelengths and long wavelengths.

energy to move an electron from a ground state to a higher, excited state. Furthermore, longer wavelengths are readily absorbed by water, which is the bulk of all living things. Given these fundamental aspects of photon energy and light absorption, it would not be at all surprising to find that life on other planets within our galaxy relied on the same narrow wavelengths of the electromagnetic spectrum for a source of energy and information.

1.5 Light Can Damage Biological Molecules

Like many forms of energy, photons of light can damage biological molecules. Recall that to be used for a source of either energy or information, photons of light must be absorbed by molecules. However, absorption of excessive light energy can result in damage that in some cases may be permanent. Of particular concern is higher-energy ultraviolet radiation, which, along with visible light, reaches Earth's surface.

1.5a Damage Is an Unavoidable Consequence of Light Absorption

The photoreceptor cells that line the human retina can be damaged by exposure to bright light. The high-energy environment associated with pigment molecules and excited electrons can result in what is referred to as photo-oxidative damage. The absorption of excess light energy can result in excited electrons reacting with O_2, producing what are called reactive oxygen species. These forms of oxygen, which include the molecule hydrogen peroxide, are particularly damaging to proteins and other biological molecules, often resulting in a loss of function. Excessive damage to photoreceptor cells can lead to the death of the cell.

Unlike eyes, the photosynthetic apparatus of plants and algae is often exposed to full sunlight for hours and thus is particularly susceptible to photooxidative damage. A typical chloroplast contains hundreds of photosystems, each one trapping the energy of thousands of photons each second, converting the light into chemical energy. Compared to the photoreceptor cells of the retina, damage to photosystems can be repaired by a very efficient mechanism that involves removing damaged proteins and replacing them with newly synthesized copies. In fact, under normal light conditions, a single photosystem II **(Figure 1.17)** complex needs to be repaired about every 20 minutes. Because damage to the photosynthetic apparatus is unavoidable, a mechanism of efficient repair must have developed early during the evolution of life so that photosynthesis could be maintained even under high light conditions.

1.5b Ultraviolet Light Is Particularly Harmful

Ultraviolet light is electromagnetic radiation that has a wavelength between blue light (400 nm) and X-rays (200 nm). Because it consists of wavelengths that are shorter than visible light, the energy of the photons of

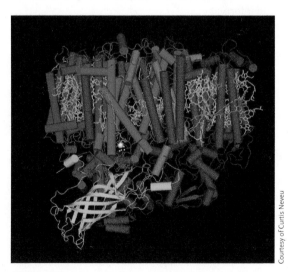

Figure 1.17
Molecular model of the structure of photosystem II. The coloured ribbons and rods represent proteins to which pigments and other cofactors are precisely bound. Light absorption results in unavoidable damage to proteins. An efficient repair system maintains photosystem function even under high light conditions.

Courtesy of Curtis Neveu

ultraviolet light is greater and more damaging to biological molecules. Life on Earth is protected from the shortest-wavelength and most damaging form of ultraviolet light by the atmosphere's ozone layer. Ozone, O_3, is produced when photons of ultraviolet light interact with molecular oxygen, O_2. While short wavelengths of ultraviolet light are absorbed by ozone, longer wavelengths of ultraviolet light reach Earth's surface.

Along with shorter-wavelength X-rays and gamma rays, ultraviolet light is classified as a form of *ionizing radiation*. The photons at these wavelengths are energetic enough to remove an electron from an atom, resulting in the formation of *ions*—atoms where the total numbers of protons and electrons are not equal. Ultraviolet light can be destructive to a range of biological molecules; however, it is the structure of DNA that is particularly susceptible to damage **(Figure 1.18)**. The interaction of ultraviolet light with nucleotide bases that make up DNA can result in the formation of a dimer—when two neighbouring bases become covalently linked together. Dimers change the shape of the double-helix structure of DNA and prevent its replication, as well as hindering gene transcription. These processes are discussed in detail in Chapter 13. Nucleotide dimers are detected and repaired by a specific enzyme. Even so, the formation of nucleotide dimers can give rise to genetic mutation and has been linked to skin cancer.

For most organisms, exposure to ultraviolet light is unavoidable. Because of this, organisms use a range of behavioural, structural, and biochemical mechanisms to protect themselves from its damaging effects. For example, many animals are protected by fur or feathers covering their skin. Organisms with naked skin, such as humans and whales, are less protected and more susceptible to sunburn due to ultraviolet light exposure.

1.5c Melanin, Suntanning, and Vitamin D

To protect cells from the harmful effects of ultraviolet light, many organisms synthesize melanin, a pigment that strongly absorbs ultraviolet light. Melanin is a remarkable pigment found in all branches of the tree of life. Along with playing a key role in ultraviolet light protection in organisms as diverse as microbes and humans, it is also the major component of the ink released by cephalopods such as squid.

Melanin is very efficient at absorbing ultraviolet light and yet it dissipates over 99% of this energy harmlessly as heat. The specific wavelength of radiation that a pigment such as melanin can absorb can be determined using an instrument called a spectrophotometer. By passing light of varying wavelengths through a solution of pure pigment, the spectrophotometer detects which wavelengths of light are transmitted through the sample and thus determines which wavelengths are absorbed by the pigment. The data from

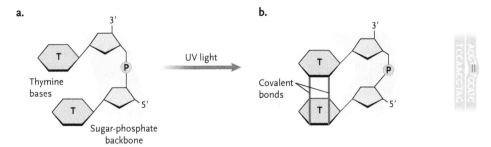

a.

T

Thymine
bases

T

3′

P

5′

Sugar-phosphate
backbone

UV light →

b.

T

3′

P

Covalent
bonds

T

5′

Figure 1.18
Ultraviolet light can damage DNA. Ultraviolet light absorbed by DNA can cause the formation of thymine dimers. Although cells have an efficient mechanism to repair damage to DNA, the formation of dimers can lead to mutation.

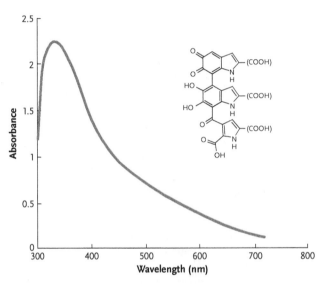

Figure 1.19
Absorption spectrum of melanin. A pure solution of melanin absorbs strongly in the ultraviolet region (300–400 nm) of the spectrum. Also shown is a portion of the chemical structure of melanin.

Figure 1.20
People differ in the amount of melanin in their skin cells.

the spectrophotometer can be used to produce an *absorption spectrum*, a plot of absorbance in relation to the wavelength of light **(Figure 1.19).**

Humans synthesize melanin in specialized skin cells called melanocytes, and melanin synthesis increases upon sun exposure, which results in the brown colour of a suntan. In general, people from countries receiving a lot of sunlight, including countries of Africa, have more melanin in their skin than people from regions receiving less direct sunlight, such as Scandinavian countries **(Figure 1.20).** Since melanin protects us from ultraviolet light, why don't all humans have high melanin levels? Although melanin filters out damaging ultraviolet wavelengths, humans require some ultraviolet radiation to synthesize vitamin D, which is critical for normal bone development. People with high melanin levels who live in regions that do not receive abundant sunlight are susceptible to vitamin D deficiency. This could occur, for example, for someone of African descent living in

Winnipeg. However, in much of the developed world, vitamin D deficiency is rare because many foods, such as milk, yogurt, and grain products, are fortified with this essential nutrient.

STUDY BREAK

1. What biological molecules are particularly susceptible to damage by ultraviolet radiation?
2. What wavelengths of electromagnetic radiation does melanin absorb?

1.6 Using Light to Tell Time

As it revolves around the Sun once a year, Earth rotates on its axis once every 24 hours. These two motions result in very predictable changes to the light and temperature at Earth's surface, giving rise to the seasons and day/night, respectively. The rhythmic and predictable nature of light and darkness during the 24 hour day has led to the evolution of many physiological and behavioural phenomena that display diurnal (*daily*) and seasonal rhythmicity.

1.6a Circadian Rhythms Are Controlled by a Biological Clock

The daily cycling of some biological phenomena is due simply to an organism responding to changes in sunlight. For example, photosynthesis and vision occur during the day and not in darkness because they both require photons of light. However, the diurnal cycling of other phenomena called **circadian** (*circa* = "around"; *diem* = "day") **rhythms** is quite different **(Figure 1.21).** Circadian rhythms are not driven by an organism constantly detecting changes in daylight but rather are governed by an internal *biological clock* (also known as the circadian clock). Phenomena that are classified as circadian rhythms and thus are controlled by a biological clock include sleep-wake cycles, body temperature, metabolic processes, cell division, and the behaviours associated with foraging for food and **mating.**

A key attribute of all biological clocks is that while they are set by the external light environment, they can run a long time independent of external conditions—a phenomenon called *free-running*. This is analogous to winding an old-fashioned wrist watch. Once it is wound it can function for a long time without being rewound. The free-running nature of circadian rhythms was first described in 1729 by the French astronomer Jean-Jacques d'Ortous de Mairan. He found that the daily rhythmic movements of certain plant leaves continued when he placed the plants in complete darkness. In humans, the free-running nature of circadian rhythms is shown by the fact that daily fluctuations in body temperature and hormone levels, for example, will occur even if an individual is subjected to conditions of constant light or darkness.

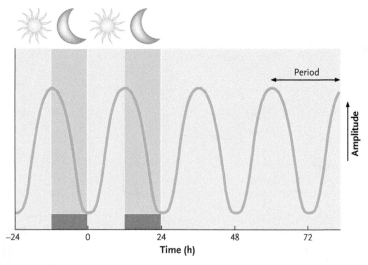

Figure 1.21

Circadian rhythms are oscillations in behaviour and physiology that have a period of approximately 24 hours. These rhythms are set by the external light environment but can run for some time (free-running) under constant conditions.

A key question we can ask at this stage is what is the physical basis of a biological clock? A requirement of anything that keeps time is the presence of something that oscillates. In the case of a traditional clock or watch it's often a crystal or a pendulum (tick, tock, tick, tock...). By comparison, a biological clock is built around a small set of so-called clock genes and clock proteins. Transcription of these genes is controlled so that the abundance of clock proteins rise and fall in a very regular pattern once every 24 hours. It is the abundance of these proteins that in turn influence various behaviours and physiological processes that show circadian rhythmicity **(Figure 1.22).**

Circadian rhythms have been found in all organisms in which they have been searched for, including species from a diverse array of phyla such as bacteria, fungi, animals, and plants. The widespread occurrence of circadian rhythms suggests that there is a selective advantage to being able to tell time. So why are circadian rhythms and the use of an underlying biological clock an advantage? The presence of biological clocks enhances an organism's ability to survive under ever-changing environments by giving them the ability to anticipate or predict when a change will occur, instead

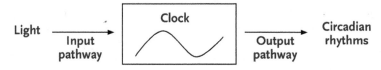

Figure 1.22

Model showing the components of circadian timekeeping. The clock is composed of a set of genes and proteins that oscillate in a very regular manner. Through an output pathway, the clock influences a wide range of behavioural and physiological phenomena. An input pathway ensures that the clock can be reset by changes to the external light environment.

of just responding after a change has occurred. This ability to predict change is seen as advantageous and increases survivability because it enables organisms to restrict their activities to specific, most beneficial, times of the day. Such activities include foraging for food, finding a mate, and avoiding predators, just to name a few. Let's work through some specific examples. In insects, emergence as adults from the pupal case is under circadian control and occurs close to dawn. This is the time of the day when the humidity in the air is highest, which is thought to prevent desiccation (drying out) of the insects, which in turn enhances their survival. In many organisms, proteins required for DNA replication are controlled by a biological clock and are synthesized at dusk. This allows for DNA replication to occur at night, which protects replicating DNA from damaging ultraviolet radiation during the day.

1.6b Biological Clocks Track the Changing Seasons

Not only are biological clocks central to diurnal behaviour and physiology, but also they have been shown to be critical to an organism's ability to keep track of the time of year. Organisms keep track of the changing seasons in part by being able to measure day length or *photoperiod*. Changes in day length and thus seasons occur because Earth is tilted on its axis as it orbits the Sun (see *The Purple Pages*). In Canada, the longest and shortest days of the year are June 21 and December 21, respectively.

Being able to determine the time of year assures that for both plants and animals certain phenomena occur under the most appropriate environmental conditions. This means that the onset of flowering occurs in the spring or summer for most angiosperm plant species, and that leaf drop followed by entrance into dormancy occurs in the autumn for trees. In animals, a huge range of phenomena are linked to being able to sense the time of year. Changes in photoperiod have been shown to provoke changes in colour of fur and feathers, and trigger migration, entry into hibernation, and changes in sexual behaviour **(Figure 1.23)**.

1.6c Jet Lag and the Need to Reset Biological Clocks

Animal cells in a range of different tissues contain clock components (genes and the proteins they encode) that regulate localized circadian-controlled processes. However, most of these so-called peripheral clocks are set by a central biological clock that is found in a very small part of the brain, the suprachiasmatic nucleus (SCN) **(Figure 1.24, p. 18)**. This central clock can receive direct light inputs through the optic nerve of the eye so that it can be reset periodically. The SCN regulates the timing of clocks in peripheral tissues in part through the release during the night of the hormone melatonin from the pineal gland.

Several conditions can interfere with normal circadian cycling. Probably the best example is jet lag, which occurs when you travel rapidly east or west across many time zones, putting your circadian cycling out of synchronization with the external light environment. As an example, let's say you take an eight-hour flight from Paris to Toronto starting at 2 p.m. **(Figure 1.25, p. 18)**. When you arrive in Toronto, your body feels like it is 10 p.m. and expects it to be dark. But because of the six-hour time zone change, when you step off the plane in Toronto it is only 4 p.m. and still daylight. The external light environment is out of synchronization with your internal biological clock. It is this confusion that results in the symptoms of jet lag, which can include lack of appetite, fatigue, insomnia, and mild depression. The clearly defined health effects of jet lag indicate that a range of behavioural and physiological processes are intimately linked to circadian timekeeping. They also show that biological clocks cannot be automatically reset to new light conditions, but instead they often take a few days to adjust. Poor synchronization between circadian clocks and the external light environment is a particular problem for shift workers (e.g., nurses, police officers, fire fighters), who usually alternate working a few weeks during the day followed by shifts at night. While there is growing evidence that this lack of synchronization is unhealthy, low-dosage melatonin given when these shift workers want to sleep seems to help.

Figure 1.23
Changes in photoperiod trigger behavioural and developmental changes. Biological clocks keep track of day length, which is critical for organisms to ensure that specific events occur only at certain times of the year. Examples of photoperiod-dependent phenomena are leaf-drop in trees and colour change in the coat of the Arctic fox (*Vulpes lagopus*).

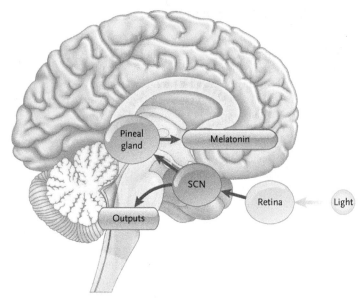

Figure 1.24
In humans central timekeeping is found in the brain. The suprachiasmatic nucleus (SCN) within the brain is the central biological clock in humans. It is set by direct light input from the eye. It controls circadian rhythms directly through an output pathway or through the synthesis of the hormone melatonin by the pineal gland.

STUDY BREAK

1. Why isn't photosynthesis considered to have a circadian rhythm?
2. What is the advantage to having a biological (circadian) clock?
3. What is the biological explanation for jet lag?

1.7 The Role of Light in Behaviour and Ecology

Nature provides a great range of light environments, ranging from the total darkness of caves and the deep ocean to the stark brightness of deserts and polar regions. Differences in the intensity and spectral composition of the light coincide with an organism's adaptations to the specific light environment of a particular habitat. For many animals, it leads to unique colorations that may serve to attract members of the same species while making them less visible to potential predators.

1.7a Using Colour as a Signal: Animals

In animals, bright coloration is thought to serve a valuable role in communication. Research suggests that what is most often communicated by the colouring is an individual's worth as a rival or as a mate. What remains unclear, and is currently being extensively studied, is what type of information is being conveyed and for which individuals the information is intended. A range of particularly colourful fish and bird species have become model systems used by ecologists investigating the role of colour in communication, while biochemists are interested in the chemistry of the actual pigments and how they are synthesized.

In the Eclectus parrot (*Eclectus roratus*), the female is more brightly coloured than the male **(Figure 1.26)**. This is an exception to the general rule that the male of a species is usually more brightly coloured and therefore more conspicuous than the female. It has been shown in a number of species, including the

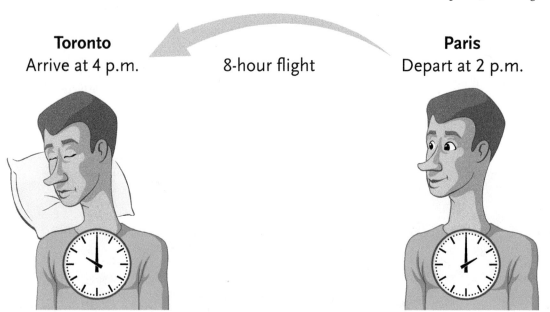

Figure 1.25
Jet lag. Flights over many time zones result in your biological clock becoming out of synchronization with the external light environment. This results in a number of unpleasant responses that are collectively referred to as *jet lag*. The effects subside as the clock within the suprachiasmatic nucleus is reset to the new light environment.

Figure 1.26
Coloured plumage of four avian species often used in studies of the role of colour in behaviour. Clockwise from top left: Eclectus parrot (*Eclectus roratus*) showing a green male and red female, European barn swallow (*Hirundo rustica rustica*), Red-winged blackbird (*Agelaius phoeniceus*), and King penguin (*Aptenodytes patagonicus*).

European barn swallow (*Hirundo rustica rustica*), that more colourful males are more likely to find a mate. An interesting finding shown for penguins has been that for both males and females, individuals with brighter yellow colouring around the eye and upper chest were found to be older and healthier and able to raise more chicks in a given year than mating pairs that were less brightly coloured (Figure 1.26).

Not only does being brightly coloured make an animal more visible, research including the study of penguins indicates that it is also a sign of being in good health. In part, this finding is based on an understanding of the pigments used for ornamentation. Many of these belong to the **carotenoid** family—the structure of beta-carotene is shown in Figure 1.5, p. 6. Unlike in plants, where carotenoids are synthesized in plant cells from precursor molecules, the carotenoids used for colouring in birds are obtained from what they eat, and then circulate in the bloodstream before being deposited in feathers. Biochemical studies have shown that carotenoids play an important role in breaking down potentially harmful reactive oxygen species. Thus, more brightly coloured individuals suggest a good diet rich in molecules that maintain good health. Besides carotenoids, different types of melanin-based pigments are also found in darker and brown colorations in birds. Finally, the dominant pigment class found in parrots, psittacofulvins, is found nowhere else in nature.

1.7b Using Colour as a Signal: Plants

Although humans marvel at the diversity of colours and patterns of flowers, botanists correctly concluded centuries ago that such displays were not designed to please humans but rather to attract pollinators. Pollination involves the movement of pollen from the anthers (male parts) of one flower to the stigma (female parts) of the same flower or other flowers to effect fertilization and production of fruit and seeds. Plant reproduction, including pollination, is discussed in more detail in Chapter 36. The goal of an insect or bird visiting a flower is not to effect pollination; it is to obtain food. This reward may be the protein-rich pollen itself, the sugar-rich nectar, or the waxes or resins found in the flower.

Plants that use animals as pollinators must attract the correct candidates to ensure efficient pollination, in part because the excess pollen or nectar can be energetically costly for the plant to produce. The dependence of a specific plant species on certain animals to act as pollinators, and the reliance of certain animals on particular flowers as a food source, has led to the co-evolution of flower–pollinator associations. Mentioned in the 1877 publication *Fertilisation of Orchids* by Charles Darwin, co-evolution refers to the fact that over evolutionary time, a change in one species triggers changes in the other. The result is that specifics of flower shape, colour, and smell make them more attractive to specific groups of potential pollinators **(Figure 1.27, p. 20)**. For example, the food reward of the flower has become an important part of the pollinator's diet, and the colour and shape of the flower coincide with the visual preferences and shape of the animal pollinator, respectively. As well, co-evolution has resulted in the breeding time of the animal often matching the flowering time of the plant.

The visual systems of pollinators differ considerably among broad groupings such as bees, bats, and birds. Thus, co-evolution has led to flower colour as a key factor that attracts specific groups of pollinators. For example, whereas hummingbirds can perceive colour across a broad range of wavelengths, bees are unable to see red. This explains why hummingbirds dominate the pollination of red-coloured flowers, whereas bees are attracted primarily to blue and yellow flowers. In

Figure 1.27
Flowering plants and their animal pollinators.

reveals patterning that is undetectable to humans. In general, it is shown that the region around the anthers and stigma is darker and thus more easily detected by the pollinating insects **(Figure 1.28)**.

1.7c Camouflage

Camouflage is a way of hiding that, in the natural world, usually involves an organism having a similar appearance to its environment. The reason for camouflage is concealment from either predators or prey. Besides simple colour, pattern and behaviour play central roles in camouflage **(Figure 1.29)**.

An excellent example of the development of camouflage is demonstrated by the peppered moth, *Biston betularia*. Before the Industrial Revolution in England, light-coloured peppered moths were far more common than the dark-coloured individuals that were prized by moth collectors. Light colour made the moths inconspicuous when resting on lichen-covered tree trunks during the day **(Figure 1.30)**. The situation changed after the Industrial Revolution, when many tree trunks became dark-coloured from deposits of soot, and air pollution killed the lichens. In this setting, light--coloured moths were easily detected by hunting birds, and dark-coloured individuals quickly became the most common form (Figure 1.30). Today, as a result of clean-air legislation and reduced air pollution, the ratio of light- to dark-coloured moths has returned to the pre-Industrial Revolution norm in some areas. The case of the peppered moth has become an often-cited example of evolution by natural selection, which is discussed further in Chapter 17.

1.7d Ecological Light Pollution

The electric light bulb is considered one of the greatest inventions because it allowed people to carry on pursuits at night that otherwise would not have been possible. However, the rapid proliferation of artificial lighting that illuminates public buildings, streets, and signs has resulted in light pollution, which has transformed the night-time environment over significant portions of Earth's surface **(Figure 1.31)**. For example, in the United States, only about 40% of people live in an area that truly gets dark at night.

Ecologists have begun to study the sometimes devastating consequences of light pollution on natural populations. The presence of artificial light disrupts orientation in nocturnal (active at night) animals otherwise accustomed to operating in the dark. For example, newly hatched sea turtles emerge from nests on sandy beaches and orient themselves and move toward the ocean because it is brighter than the silhouette of dark dunes. However, with increased beachfront lighting, hatchlings sometimes become disoriented, head inland, and die. The nocturnal lives of other animals, including many species of frogs and salamanders, have been disrupted by light pollution. As well, artificial lighting has

addition, bees and some other insects can also see in the ultraviolet region of the electromagnetic spectrum and are particularly attracted to flowers that strongly reflect ultraviolet radiation. The role of ultraviolet light in flower–pollinator interactions is widely studied and has been aided by the development of photographic approaches that readily capture the ultraviolet radiation reflected off flowers. It is striking how different flowers look that were photographed using this technique than flowers photographed using visible wavelengths. The organization of distinct ultraviolet-reflecting pigments

Figure 1.28
Two species of flowering plants (angiosperms) that are pollinated by bees. *Oenothera biennis* (top) and *Ranunculus ficaria* (bottom). Photographs capturing visible light are shown on the left, while photographs capturing only ultraviolet light are on the right.

a.

b.

c.

Figure 1.29

From a distance **(a)**, it is easy to overlook the duck (*Anas* spp.) sitting on her nest in an urban graveyard. Up close **(b)**, the pattern on her feathers breaks up her body outline, making her difficult to see, particularly when she does not move. As usual, looking for eyes can be a good way to see animals you otherwise might have overlooked, such as the Scops owl (*Otus scops*) **(c)**.

a.

b.

Figure 1.30

An example of camouflage in the peppered moth, *Biston betularia*. The moth is found in one of two forms: light-coloured and dark-coloured. During the industrial revolution, pollution darkened the bark of the trees **(a)** that were part of the moth's habitat. This resulted in increased predation of the light-coloured moth. Following antipollution measures, trees returned to being light coloured **(b)**, which resulted in an increase in the numbers of the moths that are similarly coloured.

Figure 1.31

An example of light pollution.

a negative effect on migrating birds as hundreds of thousands of migrating birds are killed each year when they collide with lighted buildings and towers. Other animals, such as bats and geckos, benefit from night lights that attract insects, effectively concentrating their prey.

1. What is a potential advantage for a parrot in being brightly coloured?
2. Explain the environmental events that drove the colour change in the peppered moth.

1.8 Life in the Dark

Humans see very well during the day, but our visual acuity quickly falters when night approaches. With decreasing light levels, we first lose our ability to see colour, followed by our ability to distinguish shapes. This is because rod photoreceptors, which do not perceive different colours, are about 100 times as sensitive to light as cone photoreceptors (see Chapter 45 for more on this topic).

Animals that are nocturnal or live in low-light conditions often display improved visual acuity under low-light conditions compared to animals that are active during the day. A good example of a nocturnal animal is the Philippine tarsier (*Tarsius syrichta*), one of the smallest primates **(Figure 1.32)**. Improved vision is often a consequence of simply having large eyes and thus being able to collect more photons, which is certainly

Figure 1.32
Philippine tarsier (*Tarsius syrichta*).

Figure 1.33
The blind mole rat (*Spalax* sp.) is subterranean and rarely ventures above ground. It is functionally blind.

the case for the tarsier as well as the giant squid (genus *Architeuthis*), which has eyes that measure over 30 cm in diameter! Deep-water crustaceans as well as nocturnal insects have specially designed compound eyes that enhance their light-gathering ability.

In some environments, such as caves and ocean depths, animals live in complete darkness. In fact over 90% of the ocean is at a depth where no light penetrates. Many of the animals that have become adapted to these environments cannot see even though their ancestors may have had functional eyes. A great example of this is the blind mole rat (genus *Spalax*), which spends its life in underground darkness, only rarely venturing above ground **(Figure 1.33)**. Twenty-five million years of adaptation to life in the dark has resulted in the natural degeneration of the *Spalax* visual system to the point that it is effectively blind. Their eyes are not only small (less than 1 mm in diameter), but they are also covered by several layers of tissue. Behavioural and physiological studies have shown that the photoreceptors of the eye remain functional even though the image-forming part of the brain is dramatically reduced. So what purpose do these functional photoreceptors have? Since individual mole rats are exposed to brief periods of natural light, it is thought that the maintenance of functional photoreceptors allows for the proper setting of biological clocks necessary for the regulation of circadian rhythms. This is supported by the finding that while the image-forming portion of the brain is small, SCN (see Section 1.6) is well developed.

Another good example of the degeneration of the eye over time is found in the Mexican cavefish, which occurs as two morphological types: a surface-water form that has eyes and skin pigment and a cave-dwelling form that lacks eyes and pigment **(Figure 1.34)**. The ancestors of the cavefish lived on the surface, and both eyes and pigment have been lost over approximately 10 000 years.

1. Why do you think that the blind mole rat is still able to detect light?

a.

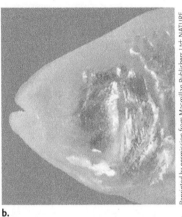

Reprinted by permission from Macmillan Publishers Ltd: NATURE, Yoshiyuki Yamamoto, David W. Stock and William R. Jeffery, "Hedgehog signalling controls eye degeneration in blind cavefish," vol. 431, 844–847, copyright 2004.

b.

Figure 1.34
An example of eye degeneration in the Mexican cave fish, *Astyanax mexicanus*. The single species exists as a surface-dwelling form **(a)** and a blind cave-dwelling form **(b)**.

1.9 Organisms Making Their Own Light: Bioluminescence

Many organisms, including certain bacteria, algae, fungi, insects, squid, and fish, are able to make their own light, a process called bioluminescence **(Figure 1.35)**. Recall from Section 1.1 that in the process of light absorption by a pigment, the energy of a photon is transferred to an electron, raising it from the ground state to an excited state. Bioluminescence is essentially the same process in reverse (see Figure 1.35). Chemical energy in the form of ATP is used to excite an electron in a **substrate** molecule from the ground state to a higher excited state, and when the electron returns to the ground state, the energy is released as a photon of light. The conversion of the chemical energy in ATP into light is very efficient. Considering that up to 95% of the energy of a light bulb is lost as heat, it is remarkable that less than 5% of the energy in ATP is lost as heat during the process of bioluminescent light production. This extraordinary efficiency is essential because high heat production would be incompatible with life.

Bioluminescent organisms generate light for a range of uses. These include attracting a mate or prey, camouflage, and communication. For example, dinoflagellates, which are unicellular algae, use bioluminescence as an alarm mechanism to scare off potential predators. In these tiny organisms, bioluminescence is triggered simply by a disturbance of the water surrounding them. When a predator such as a small fish swims close to a dinoflagellate at night, the resulting burst of light produced by all the dinoflagellates in the vicinity lights up the water around the fish. This defensive behaviour makes the fish clearly visible to its own predators.

Some marine bacteria use bioluminescence in a type of communication called *quorum sensing*. Individual bacteria often release compounds into their environment at concentrations too low to elicit a response from their neighbours. However, as a bacterial population grows, its size reaches a threshold, a quorum, whereby the concentration of compounds is high enough to elicit a physiological response in all members of the population. The response results in the activation of certain genes, including those that encode for proteins required for bioluminescence. Quorum sensing is now believed to be the basis for what are termed "milky seas" (see **Figure 1.36, p. 24**). This strange phenomenon of light on the surface of the ocean has been reported many times over the past several hundred

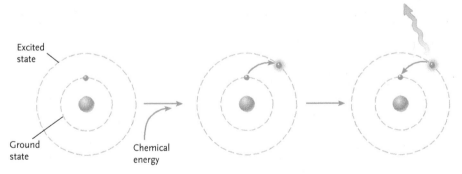

Excited state

Ground state

Chemical energy

Figure 1.35
Bioluminescence. Chemical energy is used to excite an electron in a molecule. A photon of light is released when the electron decays back down to the ground state.

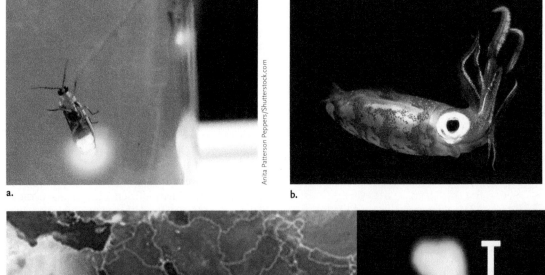

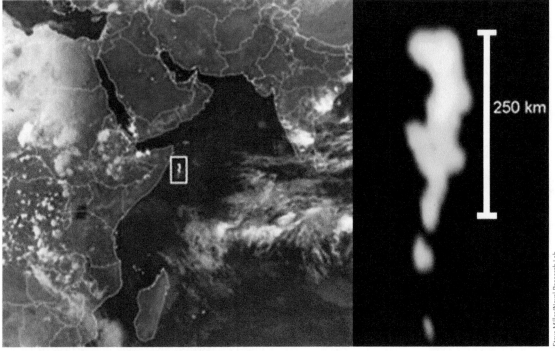

Figure 1.36

Examples of bioluminescence. **(a)** Bioluminescent insect. **(b)** Bioluminescent squid. **(c)** Satellite image of a "milky sea," a bloom of bioluminescent bacteria off the east coast of Africa.

years by sailors and is mentioned in Jules Verne's classic book *Twenty Thousand Leagues under the Sea.*

Many bioluminescent organisms are marine and are most abundant below 800 m, a depth to which sunlight does not penetrate. Bioluminescence has not been reported in land plants or higher vertebrates. Why is bioluminescence absent in these organisms? We do not yet have the answers to this or other questions about bioluminescence, reminding us how much there is still to discover about life on Earth.

In closing, this introductory chapter discussed one phenomenon, light, and how it affects the biology of Earth. From absorption of a single photon by a pigment molecule in a single cell to affecting the composition of entire ecosystems, the influence of light spans all levels of biological organization. This chapter touched on many topics, including physics and chemistry, photosynthesis, genes and proteins, evolution and natural selection, and ecology and behaviour. As you work through the remaining chapters of this textbook, you will learn much more about these topics.

STUDY BREAK

1. Compare and contrast bioluminescence with light absorption.
2. Given that bioluminescence takes energy on the part of the organism, what are some roles that it may serve?

Review

aplia

To access course materials such as Aplia and other companion resources, please visit www.NELSONbrain.com.

1.1 The Physical Nature of Light

- For organisms, light serves as a source of energy and as a source of information.
- Light can be defined as electromagnetic radiation that humans can detect with their eyes.
- Light can be thought of as a wave of discrete particles called photons.
- To be used, light energy must be absorbed by molecules called pigments.
- The colour of a pigment includes all wavelengths of light that are not absorbed.

1.2 Light as a Source of Energy

- The absorption of light by a pigment results in electrons becoming excited. This represents a source of potential energy.
- Photosynthesis is the dominant process on Earth that uses pigments to capture light energy and uses this energy to convert carbon dioxide into energy-rich carbohydrates.
- *Halobacteria* use bacteriorhodopsin to harvest light energy and to generate ATP.

1.3 Light as a Source of Information

- A photoreceptor (e.g., rhodopsin) consists of a pigment molecule (retinal) bound to a protein (opsin).
- The *C. reinhardtii* eyespot allows the organism to sense both light direction and intensity and respond by swimming toward or away from the light (phototaxis).
- The eye can be defined as the organ animals use to sense light. Vision requires a brain to interpret signals sent from the eye.
- The simplest eye is the ocellus found in planarians. It enables the sensing of light direction and intensity.
- Image-forming eyes include compound eyes found in arthropods and single-lens eyes found in some invertebrates and most vertebrates, including humans.
- Because the eye was thought to be an organ of "extreme perfection," Darwin initially had a difficult time explaining how it could have arisen by evolution.
- The relatively rapid evolution of the eye is explained by the huge advantage an improved eye would give an organism.

1.4 The Uniqueness of Light

- Photosynthesis, vision, and most other light-driven processes use only a narrow band of the electromagnetic spectrum. This may be because shorter wavelengths are more harmful (higher energy)

and longer wavelengths tend not to reach Earth's surface.

1.5 Light Can Damage Biological Molecules

- Light is a form of energy; thus the absorption of too much light can damage biological molecules.
- The photosynthetic apparatus is constantly being damaged by light, and the damage repaired.
- Ultraviolet radiation, because of its high energy, is particularly harmful to biological molecules, particularly DNA.
- Human skin cells are protected by the pigment melanin, which absorbs ultraviolet radiation.

1.6 Using Light to Tell Time

- Many physiological and behavioural responses are geared to the daily changes in light and darkness and are called circadian rhythms.
- Circadian rhythms are found in all forms of life and evolved to enable organisms to anticipate changes in the light environment.
- Jet lag is caused when your biological clock is out of synchronization with the external light environment.

1.7 The Role of Light in Behaviour and Ecology

- Many organisms use colour to attract, warn, or hide from other organisms.
- Bright coloration is thought to convey good health.
- The widespread use of artificial lighting has been shown to disrupt numerous biological phenomena, including bird migration and the orientation of nocturnal animals.

1.8 Life in the Dark

- Unlike humans, many nocturnal animals (moths, fish, bats, frogs) see very well under dim light conditions.
- Some animals, such as the blind mole rat, are functionally blind yet are descended from ancestors that had functional eyes.

1.9 Organisms Making Their Own Light: Bioluminescence

- A range of organisms can use chemical energy to make light—this is called bioluminescence.
- Bioluminescent organisms use light to attract a mate, for camouflage, to attract prey, or to communicate.

Questions

Self-Test Questions

1. Which of the following statements about light is correct?
   a. Like sound, light is a form of electromagnetic radiation.
   b. Light of a longer wavelength contains more energy.
   c. Visible light is more energetic than radio waves.
   d. A photon of red light contains more energy than a photon of blue light.

2. For a photon of light to be used by an organism, what must occur?
   a. The photon must be absorbed.
   b. The photon must be reflected off a substance.
   c. The photon must interact with a protein in the plasma membrane.
   d. The photon must have sufficient energy to oxidize a molecule.

3. What are the components of a photoreceptor?
   a. a pigment molecule bound to a protein
   b. a protein that is involved in photosynthesis
   c. a group of many pigment molecules
   d. a molecule of chlorophyll

4. Which of the following is true for an eye, but NOT about the eyespot of *Chlamydomonas reinhardtii*?
   a. It can generate a image.
   b. It is composed of photoreceptors.
   c. It can detect changes in light intensity.
   d. It can activate a signal transduction pathway when it absorbs light.

5. Which of the following statements regarding the harmful effects of light is correct?
   a. Visible light is more harmful than ultraviolet light.
   b. Damage to the photosynthetic apparatus caused by excess light cannot be repaired.
   c. Melanin protects skins cells because it specifically absorbs ultraviolet light.
   d. Ultraviolet light specifically damages proteins.

6. Light represents only a very narrow region of the electromagnetic spectrum. However, why is it the dominant form of electromagnetic radiation used in biology?
   a. Light contains the most energy per photon.
   b. Light can excite electrons within molecules without destroying them.
   c. Light is the only form of electromagnetic radiation to reach Earth's surface.
   d. All other wavelengths of electromagnetic radiation are too destructive to biological molecules.

7. Which of the following statements is correct about a biological process that is under circadian control?
   a. A mutation to a single gene could never destroy the circadian cycling of a biological process.
   b. The amplitude of the biological process oscillates with a period of approximately 12 hours.
   c. Circadian cycling of biological processes rarely follows the actual cycling of day and night.
   d. The oscillating nature of the phenomenon continues if the organism is placed in complete darkness.

8. Which of the following statements about jet lag is correct?
   a. Someone who is blind because of non-functioning optic nerves would still experience jet lag.
   b. Jet lag occurs even when the external environment and the SCN are synchronized.
   c. Taking melatonin pills would have no effect on experiencing jet lag.
   d. Jet lag is more severe after travelling by airplane from Toronto to Hawaii than from Toronto to Lima, Peru.

9. Which of the following is illustrated by the Mexican cavefish?
   a. You don't need eyes for vision.
   b. Animals can still see in complete darkness.
   c. Eyes can still function without photoreceptors.
   d. Organs that are no longer of use can degenerate over time.

10. Which of the following is correct about bioluminescence?
    a. It requires ATP.
    b. It cannot occur in complete darkness.
    c. It is found only in bacteria and archaea.
    d. Like vision, it requires the absorption of a photon of light.

Questions for Discussion

1. Nothing ruins a coloured shirt like accidentally adding bleach when washing it. What do you think bleach does?

2. In writing this chapter, the authors found it difficult to define the "eye." Why do you think this was difficult?

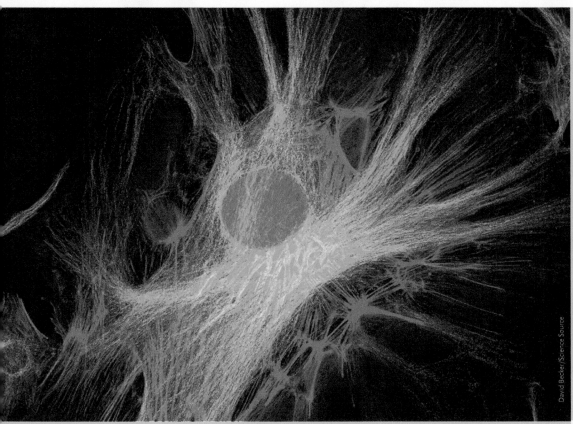

Cells fluorescently labelled to visualize their internal structure (confocal light micrograph). Cell nuclei are shown in blue and parts of the cytoskeleton in red and green.

The Cell: An Overview

WHY IT MATTERS

In the mid-1600s, Robert Hooke, Curator of Instruments for the Royal Society of England, was at the forefront of studies applying the newly invented light microscopes to biological materials. When Hooke looked at thinly sliced cork from a mature tree through a microscope, he observed tiny compartments **(Figure 2.1a, p. 28).** He gave them the Latin name *cellulae,* meaning "small rooms"—giving us the biological term *cell.* Hooke was actually looking at the walls of dead cells, which is what cork consists of.

Reports of cells also came from other sources. By the late 1600s, Anton van Leeuwenhoek (Figure 2.1b), a Dutch shopkeeper, observed "many very little animalcules, very prettily a-moving" using a single-lens microscope of his own construction. Leeuwenhoek discovered and described diverse protists, sperm cells, and even bacteria, organisms so small that they would not be seen by others for another two centuries.

In the 1820s, improvements in microscopes brought cells into sharper focus. Robert Brown, an English botanist, noticed a discrete, spherical body inside some cells; he called it a *nucleus.* In 1838, a German botanist, Matthias Schleiden, speculated that the nucleus had something to do with the development of a cell. The following year, the zoologist Theodor Schwann of Germany expanded Schleiden's idea to propose that all animals and plants consist of cells that contain a nucleus. He also proposed that even when a cell forms part of a larger organism, it has an individual life of its own. However, an important question remained: Where do cells come from? A decade later, the German physiologist Rudolf Virchow answered this question. From his studies of cell growth and reproduction, Virchow proposed that cells arise only from pre-existing cells by a process of division.

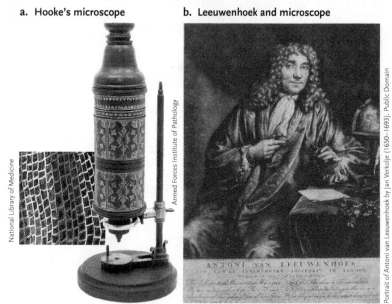

a. Hooke's microscope

National Library of Medicine

b. Leeuwenhoek and microscope

Armed Forces Institute of Pathology

Portrait of Antoni van Leeuwenhoek by Jan Verkolje (1650–1693). Public Domain

Figure 2.1

Investigations leading to the first descriptions of cells. **(a)** The cork cells drawn by Robert Hooke and the compound microscope he used to examine them. **(b)** Anton van Leeuwenhoek holding his microscope, which consisted of a single small sphere of glass fixed in a holder. He viewed objects by holding them close to one side of the glass sphere and looking at them through the other side.

Thus, by the middle of the nineteenth century, microscopic observations had yielded three profound generalizations, which together constitute what is now known as the **cell theory:**

1. All organisms are composed of one or more cells.
2. The cell is the basic structural and functional unit of all living organisms.
3. Cells arise only from the division of pre-existing cells.

These tenets were fundamental to the development of biological science.

This chapter provides an overview of our current understanding of the structure and functions of cells, emphasizing both the similarities among all cells and some of the most basic differences among cells of various organisms. The variations in cells that help make particular groups of organisms distinctive are discussed in later chapters. This chapter also introduces some of the modern microscopes that enable us to learn more about cell structure.

2.1 Basic Features of Cell Structure and Function

As the basic structural and functional units of all living organisms, cells carry out the essential processes of life. They contain highly organized systems of molecules, including the nucleic acids DNA and **RNA**, which carry hereditary information and direct the manufacture of cellular molecules. Cells use chemical molecules or light as energy sources for their activities. Cells also respond to changes in their external environment by altering their internal reactions. Further, cells duplicate and pass on their hereditary information as part of cellular reproduction. All of these activities occur in cells that, in most cases, are invisible to the naked eye.

Some types of organisms, including almost all bacteria and archaea; some protists, such as amoebas; and some fungi, such as **yeasts**, are unicellular. Each of these cells is a functionally independent organism capable of carrying out all activities necessary for its life. In more complex **multicellular organisms**, including plants and animals, the activities of life are divided among varying numbers of specialized cells. However, individual cells of multicellular organisms are potentially capable of surviving by themselves if placed in a chemical medium that can sustain them. If cells are broken open, the property of life is lost: they are unable to grow, reproduce, or respond to outside stimuli in a coordinated, potentially independent fashion. This fact confirms the second tenet of the cell theory: Life as we know it does not exist in units simpler than individual cells.

2.1a Cells Are Small and Can Only Be Seen Using a Microscope

As discussed in more detail in Chapter 3 and subsequent chapters, all forms of life are grouped into one of three domains: the Bacteria, the Archaea, and the Eukarya. Until very recently, bacteria and archaea were grouped into a single domain: the Prokaryota (**prokaryotes**); however, this domain is no longer considered to be accurate as recent research has shown that bacteria and archaea are not evolutionarily related.

As shown in **Figure 2.2**, cells representing all three domains of life assume a wide variety of forms. Individual cells range in size from tiny bacteria to an egg yolk, a single cell that can be several centimetres in diameter. Yet, all cells are organized according to the same basic plan, and all have structures that perform similar activities.

Most cells are too small to be seen by the unaided eye: Humans cannot see objects smaller than about 0.1 mm in diameter. The smallest bacteria have diameters of about 0.5 μm (a micrometre is one thousandth of a millimetre). The cells of multicellular animals range from about 5 to 30 μm in diameter. Your red blood cells are 7 to 8 μm across—a string of 2500 of these cells is needed to span the width of your thumbnail. Plant cells range from about 10 μm to a few hundred micrometres in diameter. (**Figure 2.3** explains the units of measurement used in biology to study molecules and cells.)

To see cells and the structures within them we use **microscopy**, a technique for producing visible images of objects, biological or otherwise, that are too small to be seen by the human eye (**Figure 2.4, p. 30**). The

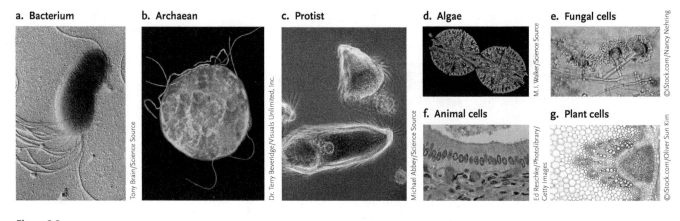

a. Bacterium **b. Archaean** **c. Protist** **d. Algae** **e. Fungal cells**

f. Animal cells

g. Plant cells

Figure 2.2

Examples of the various kinds of cells. **(a)** A bacterial cell with flagella, *Pseudomonas fluorescens*. **(b)** An archaean, the extremophile *Sulfolobus acidocaldarius*. **(c)** *Trichonympha*, a protist that lives in a termite's gut. **(d)** Two cells of *Micrasterias*, an algal protist. **(e)** Fungal cells of the bread mould *Aspergillus*. **(f)** Cells of a surface layer in the human kidney. **(g)** Cells in the stem of a sunflower, *Helianthus annuus*.

instrument of microscopy is the **microscope**. The two common types of microscopes are **light microscopes**, which use light to illuminate the specimen (the object being viewed), and **electron microscopes**, which use electrons to illuminate the specimen. Different types of microscopes give different magnification and resolution of the specimen. Just as for a camera or a pair of binoculars, **magnification** is the ratio of the object as viewed to its real size, usually given as something like 400:1. **Resolution** is the minimum distance by which two points in the specimen can be separated and still be seen as two points. Resolution depends primarily on the wavelength of light or electrons used to illuminate the specimen: the shorter the wavelength, the better the resolution. Hence, electron microscopes have higher resolution than light microscopes. Biologists choose the type of microscopy technique based on what they need to see in the specimen; selected examples are shown in Figure 2.4.

Why are most cells so small? The answer depends partly on the change in the surface area–to–volume ratio of an object as its size increases **(Figure 2.5, p. 31)**. For example, doubling the diameter of a cell multiplies its volume by eight but multiplies its surface area by only four. The significance of this relationship is that the volume of a cell determines the amount of chemical activity that can take place within it, whereas the surface area determines the amount of substances that can be exchanged between the inside of the cell and the outside environment. Nutrients must constantly enter cells, and wastes must constantly leave; however, past a certain point, increasing the diameter of a cell gives a surface area that is insufficient to maintain an adequate nutrient–waste exchange for its entire volume.

Some cells increase their ability to exchange materials with their surroundings by flattening or by developing surface folds or extensions that increase their surface area. For example, human intestinal cells have

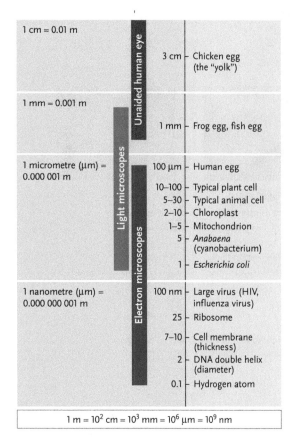

Figure 2.3

Units of measure and the ranges in which they are used in the study of molecules and cells. The vertical scale in each box is logarithmic.

closely packed, fingerlike extensions that increase their surface area, which greatly enhances their ability to absorb digested food molecules.

2.1b Cells Have a DNA-Containing Central Region That Is Surrounded by Cytoplasm

All cells are bounded by the **plasma membrane**, a **bilayer** made of lipids with embedded protein molecules **(Figure 2.6, p. 31)**. The lipid bilayer is a

Light microscopy
Micrographs are of the protist *Paramecium*.

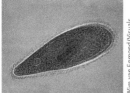

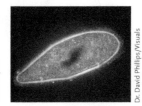

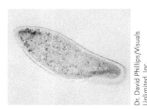

Electron microscopy
Micrographs are of the green alga *Scenedesmus*.

Wim van Egmond/Visuals Unlimited, Inc.

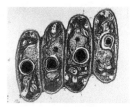

Bright field microscopy: Light passes directly through the specimen. Many cell structures have insufficient contrast to be discerned. Staining with a dye is used to enhance contrast in a specimen, as shown here, but this treatment usually fixes and kills the cells.

Dr. David Phillips/Visuals Unlimited, Inc.

Dark field microscopy: Light illuminates the specimen at an angle, and only light scattered by the specimen reaches the viewing lens of the microscope. This gives a bright image of the cell against a black background.

Dr. David Phillips/Visuals Unlimited, Inc.

Phase-contrast microscopy: Differences in refraction (the way light is bent) caused by variations in the density of the specimen are visualized as differences in contrast. Otherwise invisible structures are revealed with this technique, and living cells in action can be photographed or filmed.

Jeremy Pickett-Heaps, University of Colorado

Transmission electron microscopy (TEM): A beam of electrons is focused on a thin section of a specimen in a vacuum. Electrons that pass through form the image; structures that scatter electrons appear dark. TEM is used primarily to examine structures within cells. Various staining and fixing methods are used to highlight structures of interest.

Lebendkulturen.de/Shutterstock.com

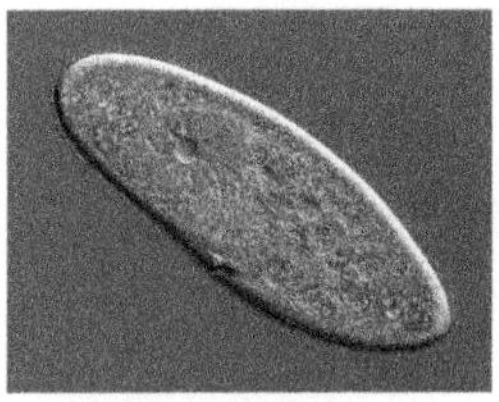

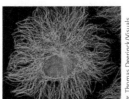

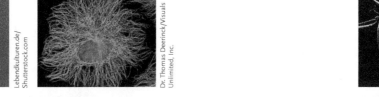

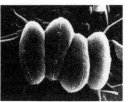

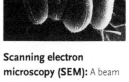

Nomarski (differential interference contrast): Similarly to phase-contrast microscopy, special lenses enhance differences in density, giving a cell a 3D appearance.

Dr. Thomas Deerinck/Visuals Unlimited, Inc.

Confocal laser scanning microscopy: Lasers scan across a fluorescently stained specimen, and a computer focuses the light to show a single plane through the cell. This provides a sharper 3D image than other light microscopy techniques.

Jeremy Pickett-Heaps, University of Colorado

Scanning electron microscopy (SEM): A beam of electrons is scanned across a whole cell or organism, and the electrons excited on the specimen surface are converted to a 3D-appearing image.

Research Method Figure 2.4 Different techniques of light and electron microscopy. Each technique produces images that reveal different structures or functions of the specimen. A micrograph is a photograph of an image formed by a microscope.

hydrophobic barrier to the passage of water-soluble substances, but selected water-soluble substances can penetrate cell membranes through **transport protein** channels. The selective movement of ions and water-soluble molecules through the transport proteins maintains the specialized internal ionic and molecular environments required for cellular life. (Membrane structure and functions are discussed further in Chapter 5.)

The central region of all cells contains DNA molecules, which store hereditary information. The hereditary information is organized in the form of **genes**—segments of DNA that code for individual proteins. The central region also contains proteins that help maintain the DNA structure and enzymes that duplicate DNA and copy its information into RNA.

All parts of the cell between the plasma membrane and the central region make up the **cytoplasm.** The cytoplasm contains the *organelles,* the *cytosol,* and the *cytoskeleton.* The **organelles** ("little organs") are small, organized structures important for cell function. The **cytosol** is an aqueous (water) solution containing ions and various **organic molecules.** The **cytoskeleton** is a protein-based framework of filamentous structures that, among other things, helps maintain proper cell shape and plays key roles in cell division and chromosome

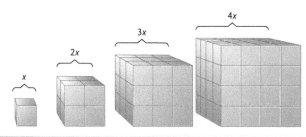

Total surface area	$6x^2$	$6(2x)^2 = 24x^2$	$6(3x)^2 = 54x^2$	$6(4x)^2 = 96x^2$
Total volume	x^3	$(2x)^3 = 8x^3$	$(3x)^3 = 27x^3$	$(4x)^3 = 64x^3$
Surface area/ volume ratio	6:1	3:1	2:1	1.5:1

Figure 2.5

Relationship between surface area and volume. The surface area of an object increases as the square of the linear dimension, whereas the volume increases as the cube of that dimension.

segregation from cell generation to cell generation. The cytoskeleton was once thought to be specific to eukaryotes, but recent research has shown that all major eukaryotic cytoskeletal proteins have functional equivalents in prokaryotes.

Many of the cell's vital activities occur in the cytoplasm, including the synthesis and assembly of most of the molecules required for growth and reproduction (except those made in the central region) and the conversion of chemical and light energy into forms that can be used by cells. The cytoplasm also conducts stimulatory signals from the outside into the cell interior and carries out chemical reactions that respond to these signals.

2.1c Cells Occur in Prokaryotic and Eukaryotic Forms, Each with Distinctive Structures and Organization

There are two fundamentally different types of cells: prokaryotic (*pro* = before; *karyon* = nucleus) and eukaryotic. As we discussed earlier in this chapter, the term *prokaryote* to describe a unique group of evolutionarily related organisms has fallen out of use by microbiologists as bacteria and archaea are seen as evolutionarily distinct. However, the term *prokaryotic cell* is still used as it refers not to a single group of organisms but rather to a particular cell architecture, that is, one lacking a nucleus. Within the prokaryotic cell that is a characteristic of both bacteria and archaea, the DNA-containing central region of the cell, the **nucleoid**, has no boundary membrane separating it from the cytoplasm. Many species of archaea and bacteria contain few if any internal membranes, but a number of other species of both groups contain extensive internal membranes.

The **eukaryotes** (*eu* = true) make up the domain Eukarya and are defined by having cells where DNA is contained within a membrane-bound compartment called the **nucleus.** The cytoplasm of eukaryotic cells typically contains extensive membrane systems that form organelles with their own distinct environments and specialized functions. As in archaea and bacteria, a plasma membrane surrounds eukaryotic cells as the outer limit of the cytoplasm.

The remainder of this chapter surveys the components of prokaryotic and eukaryotic cells in more detail.

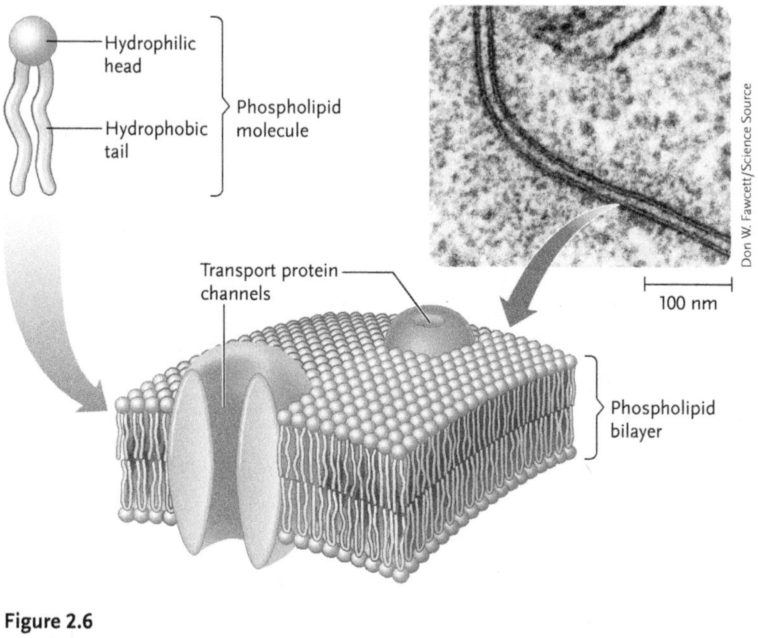

Figure 2.6

The plasma membrane consists of a phospholipid bilayer, an arrangement of phospholipids two molecules thick, which provides the framework for all biological membranes. Water-soluble substances cannot pass through the phospholipid part of the membrane. Instead, they pass through protein channels in the membrane; two proteins that transport substances across the membrane are shown. Other types of proteins are also associated with the plasma membrane. (*Inset*) Electron micrograph showing the plasma membranes of two adjacent animal cells.

Hydrophilic head

Hydrophobic tail

Phospholipid molecule

Transport protein channels

Phospholipid bilayer

Don W. Fawcett/Science Source

100 nm

STUDY BREAK

What is the plasma membrane, and what are its main functions?

2.2 Prokaryotic Cells

Most prokaryotic cells are relatively small, usually not much more than a few micrometres in length and a micrometre or less in diameter. A typical human cell has about 10 times the diameter and over 8000 times the volume of an average prokaryotic cell.

The three shapes most common among prokaryotes are spherical, rodlike, and spiral. *Escherichia coli* (*E. coli*), a normal inhabitant of the mammalian **intestine** that has been studied extensively as a model organism in genetics, molecular biology, and genomics research, is rodlike in shape. **Figure 2.7** shows an electron micrograph and a diagram of *E. coli* to illustrate the basic features of prokaryotic cell structure. More detail about prokaryotic cell structure and function, as well as about the diversity of prokaryotic organisms, is presented in Chapter 22.

The genetic material of archaea and bacteria is located in the nucleoid; in an electron microscope, that region of the cell is seen to contain a highly folded mass of DNA (see Figure 2.7). For most species, the DNA is a single, circular molecule that unfolds when released from the cell. This DNA molecule is the **prokaryotic chromosome**, the organization and regulation of which are detailed in Chapters 13 and 14.

Individual genes in the DNA molecule encode the information required to make proteins. This information is copied into a type of RNA molecule called *messenger RNA* (mRNA). Small, roughly spherical particles in the cytoplasm, the **ribosomes**, use the information in the mRNA to assemble **amino acids** into proteins. A prokaryotic ribosome consists of a large and a small subunit, each formed from a combination of **ribosomal RNA (rRNA)** and protein molecules. Each prokaryotic ribosome contains three types of rRNA molecules, which are also copied from the DNA, and more than 50 proteins.

In almost all prokaryotic cells, the plasma membrane is surrounded by a rigid external layer of material, the cell wall, which ranges in thickness from 15 to 100 nm or more (a nanometre is one-billionth of a metre). The **cell wall** provides rigidity to prokaryotic cells and, with the capsule, protects the cell from physical damage. In many prokaryotic cells, the wall is coated with an external layer of **polysaccharides** called the **glycocalyx** (a "sugar coating" from *glykys* = sweet; *calyx* = cup or vessel). When the glycocalyx is diffuse and loosely associated with the cells, it is a **slime layer;** when it is gelatinous and more firmly attached to cells, it is a **capsule.** The glycocalyx helps protect prokaryotic cells from physical damage and desiccation and may enable a cell to attach to a surface, such as other prokaryotic cells (as in forming a colony), eukaryotic cells (as in *Streptococcus pneumoniae* attaching to lung cells), or nonliving substrate (such as a rock).

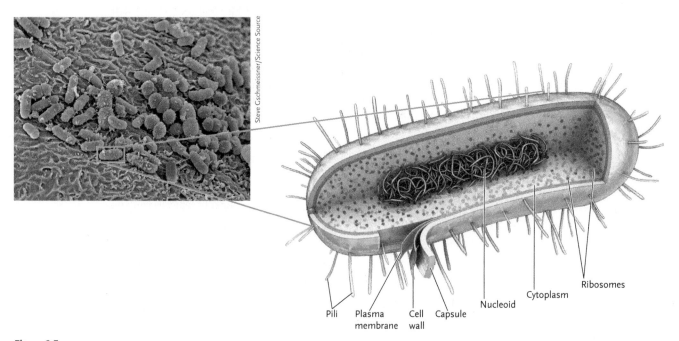

Steve Gschmeissner/Science Source

Figure 2.7

Prokaryotic cell structure. An electron micrograph (left) and a diagram (right) of the bacterium *Escherichia coli*. The pili extending from the cell wall attach bacterial cells to other cells of the same species or to eukaryotic cells as a part of infection. A typical *E. coli* has four flagella.

The plasma membrane itself performs several vital functions in both bacteria and archaea. Besides transporting materials into and out of the cells, it contains most of the molecular systems that metabolize food molecules into the chemical energy of ATP. In photosynthetic bacteria, the molecules that absorb light energy and convert it to the chemical energy of ATP are also associated with the plasma membrane or with internal, saclike membranes derived from the plasma membrane.

The cells of bacteria and archaea contain few if any internal membranes; in such cells, most cellular functions occur either on the plasma membrane or in the cytoplasm. But some archaea and bacteria have more extensive internal membrane structures. For example, photosynthetic bacteria have complex layers of intracellular membranes formed by **invaginations** of the plasma membrane on which photosynthesis takes place.

As mentioned earlier, prokaryotic cells have filamentous cytoskeletal structures with functions similar to those in eukaryotes. Prokaryotic cytoskeletons play important roles in creating and maintaining the proper shape of cells; in cell division; and, for certain bacteria, in determining the polarity of the cells.

Many bacteria and archaea can move through liquids and across wet surfaces. Most commonly they do so using long, threadlike protein fibres called **flagella** (singular, *flagellum* = whip), which extend from the cell surface (see Figure 2.2a, p. 29). The **bacterial flagellum**, which is helically shaped, rotates in a socket in the plasma membrane and cell wall to push the cell through a liquid medium (see Chapter 22). In *E. coli*, for instance, rotating bundles of flagella propel the bacterium. Archaeal flagella function similarly to bacterial flagella, but the two types differ significantly in their structures and mechanisms of action. Both types of prokaryotic flagella are also fundamentally different from the much larger and more complex flagella of eukaryotic cells, which are described in Section 2.3.

Some bacteria and archaea have hairlike shafts of protein called **pili** (singular, *pilus*) extending from their cell walls. The main function of pili is attaching the cell to surfaces or other cells. A special type of pilus, the *sex pilus*, attaches one bacterium to another during mating (see Chapter 9).

STUDY BREAK

Where in a prokaryotic cell is DNA found? How is that DNA organized?

2.3 Eukaryotic Cells

The domain of the eukaryotes, Eukarya, is divided into four major groups: protists, fungi, animals, and plants. The rest of the chapter focuses on the cell components that are common to all large groups of eukaryotic organisms.

2.3a Eukaryotic Cells Have a True Nucleus and Cytoplasmic Organelles Enclosed within a Plasma Membrane

The cells of all eukaryotes have a true nucleus enclosed by membranes. The cytoplasm surrounding the nucleus contains a remarkable system of membranous organelles, each specialized to carry out one or more major functions of energy metabolism and molecular synthesis, storage, and transport. The cytosol, the cytoplasmic solution surrounding the organelles, participates in energy metabolism and molecular synthesis and performs specialized functions in support and motility.

The eukaryotic plasma membrane carries out various functions through several types of embedded proteins. Some of these proteins form channels through the plasma membrane that transport substances into and out of the cell. Other proteins in the plasma membrane act as receptors; they recognize and bind specific signal molecules in the cellular environment and trigger internal responses. In some eukaryotes, particularly animals, plasma membrane proteins recognize and adhere to molecules on the surfaces of other cells. Yet other plasma membrane proteins are important markers in the immune system, labelling cells as "self," that is, belonging to the organism. Therefore, the immune system can identify cells without those markers as being foreign, most likely *pathogens* (disease-causing organisms or viruses).

A supportive cell wall surrounds the plasma membrane of fungal, plant, and many protist cells. Because the cell wall lies outside the plasma membrane, it is an *extracellular* structure (*extra* = outside). Although animal cells do not have cell walls, they also form extracellular material with supportive and other functions.

Figure 2.8, p. 34, presents a diagram of a representative animal cell and **Figure 2.9, p. 34**, presents a diagram of a representative plant cell to show where the nucleus, cytoplasmic organelles, and other structures are located. The following sections discuss the structure and function of eukaryotic cell parts in more detail, beginning with the nucleus.

2.3b The Eukaryotic Nucleus Contains Much More DNA Than the Prokaryotic Nucleoid

The nucleus (see Figures 2.8 and 2.9, p. 34) is separated from the cytoplasm by the **nuclear envelope**, which consists of two membranes, one layered just inside the other and separated by a narrow space **(Figure 2.10, p. 35)**. A network of protein filaments called *lamins* lines and reinforces the inner surface of the nuclear envelope in animal cells. Lamins are a type of

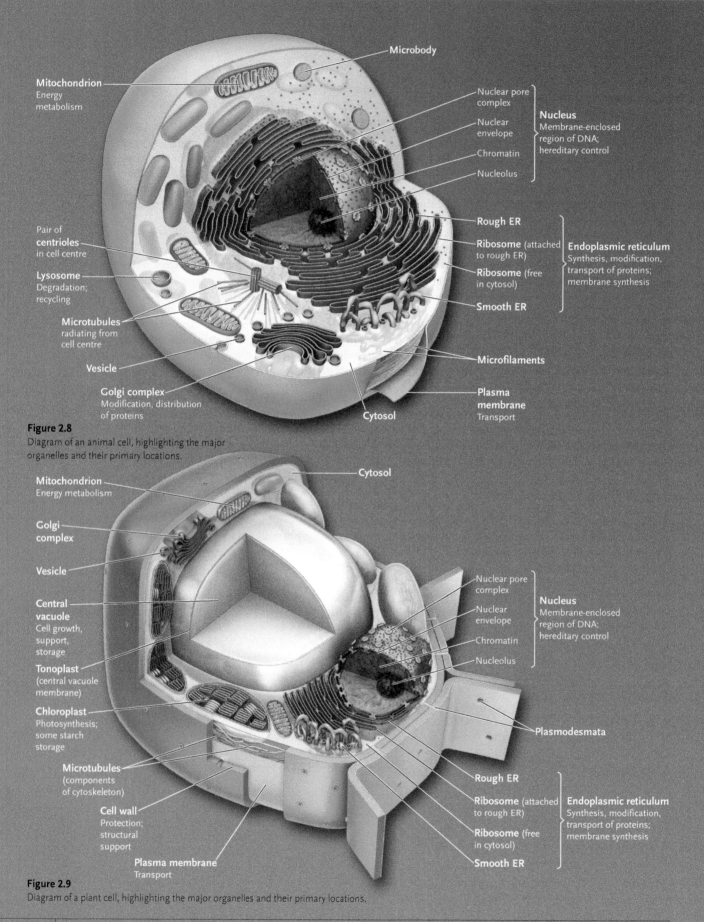

Mitochondrion
Energy
metabolism

Microbody

Nuclear pore
complex

Nuclear
envelope

Chromatin

Nucleolus

Nucleus
Membrane-enclosed
region of DNA;
hereditary control

Pair of
centrioles
in cell centre

Lysosome
Degradation;
recycling

Microtubules
radiating from
cell centre

Vesicle

Golgi complex
Modification, distribution
of proteins

Rough ER

Ribosome (attached
to rough ER)

Ribosome (free
in cytosol)

Smooth ER

Endoplasmic reticulum
Synthesis, modification,
transport of proteins;
membrane synthesis

Microfilaments

Plasma
membrane
Transport

Cytosol

Figure 2.8
Diagram of an animal cell, highlighting the major
organelles and their primary locations.

Cytosol

Mitochondrion
Energy metabolism

Golgi
complex

Vesicle

Central
vacuole
Cell growth,
support,
storage

Tonoplast
(central vacuole
membrane)

Chloroplast
Photosynthesis;
some starch
storage

Microtubules
(components
of cytoskeleton)

Cell wall
Protection;
structural
support

Plasma membrane
Transport

Nuclear pore
complex

Nuclear
envelope

Chromatin

Nucleolus

Nucleus
Membrane-enclosed
region of DNA;
hereditary control

Plasmodesmata

Rough ER

Ribosome (attached
to rough ER)

Ribosome (free
in cytosol)

Smooth ER

Endoplasmic reticulum
Synthesis, modification,
transport of proteins;
membrane synthesis

Figure 2.9
Diagram of a plant cell, highlighting the major organelles and their primary locations.

intermediate filament (see later in this section). Unrelated proteins line the inner surface of the nuclear envelope in protists, fungi, and plants.

Embedded in the nuclear envelope are many hundreds of nuclear pore complexes. A **nuclear pore complex** is a large, octagonally symmetrical, cylindrical structure formed of many types of proteins, called the *nucleoporins.* Probably the largest protein complex in the cell, it exchanges components between the nucleus and cytoplasm and prevents the transport of material not meant to cross the nuclear membrane. A channel through the nuclear pore complex—a **nuclear pore**—is the path for the assisted exchange of large molecules such as proteins and RNA molecules with the cytoplasm, whereas small molecules simply pass through unassisted. A protein or RNA molecule (called the *cargo*) associates with a transport protein acting as a chaperone to shuttle the cargo through the pore.

Some proteins—for instance, the enzymes for replicating and repairing DNA—must be imported into the nucleus to carry out their functions. Proteins to be imported into the nucleus are distinguished from those that function in the cytosol by the presence of a special short amino acid sequence called a nuclear localization signal. A specific protein in the cytosol recognizes and binds to the signal and moves the protein containing it to the nuclear pore complex, where it is transported through the pore into the nucleus.

The liquid or semi-liquid substance within the nucleus is called the **nucleoplasm.** Most of the space inside the nucleus is filled with **chromatin,** a combination of DNA and proteins. By contrast with most bacteria and archaea, most of the hereditary information of a eukaryote is distributed among several to many linear DNA molecules in the nucleus. Each individual DNA molecule with its associated proteins is a **eukaryotic chromosome.** The terms *chromatin* and *chromosome* are similar but have distinct meanings. *Chromatin* refers to any collection of eukaryotic DNA molecules with their associated proteins. *Chromosome* refers to one complete DNA molecule with its associated proteins.

Eukaryotic nuclei contain much more DNA than do prokaryotic nucleoids. For example, the entire complement of 46 chromosomes in the nucleus of a human cell has a total DNA length of about 2 m, compared with about 1.5 m in prokaryotic cells with the most DNA. Some eukaryotic cells contain even more DNA; for example, a single frog or salamander nucleus, although of microscopic diameter, is packed with about 10 m of DNA!

A eukaryotic nucleus also contains one or more **nucleoli** (singular, *nucleolus*), which look like irregular masses of small fibres and granules (see Figures 2.9, p. 34, and 2.10). These structures form around the genes coding for the rRNA molecules of ribosomes.

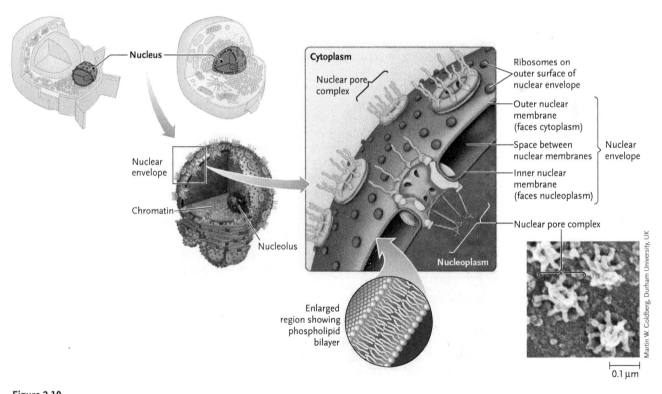

Figure 2.10

The nuclear envelope, which consists of a system of two concentric membranes with nuclear pore complexes embedded. Nuclear pore complexes are octagonally symmetrical protein structures with a channel—the nuclear pore—through the centre. They control the transport of molecules between the nucleus and the cytoplasm.

Within the nucleolus, the information in rRNA genes is copied into rRNA molecules, which combine with proteins to form ribosomal subunits. The ribosomal subunits then leave the nucleoli and exit the nucleus through the nuclear pore complexes to enter the cytoplasm, where they join on mRNAs to form complete ribosomes.

The genes for most of the proteins that the organism can make are found within the chromatin, as are the genes for specialized RNA molecules such as rRNA molecules. Expression of these genes is carefully controlled as required for the function of each cell. (The other proteins in the cell are specified by DNA in the mitochondria and chloroplasts.)

2.3c Eukaryotic Ribosomes Are Either Free in the Cytosol or Attached to Membranes

Like prokaryotic ribosomes, a eukaryotic ribosome consists of a large and a small subunit **(Figure 2.11)**. However, the structures of bacterial, archaeal, and eukaryotic ribosomes, although similar, are not identical. In general, eukaryotic ribosomes are larger than either bacterial or archaeal ribosomes; they contain 4 types of rRNA molecules and more than 80 proteins. Their function is identical to that of prokaryotic ribosomes: they use the information in mRNA to assemble amino acids into proteins.

Some eukaryotic ribosomes are freely suspended in the cytosol; others are attached to membranes. Proteins made on free ribosomes in the cytosol may remain in the cytosol; pass through the nuclear pores into the nucleus; or become parts of mitochondria,

chloroplasts, the cytoskeleton, or other cytoplasmic structures. Proteins that enter the nucleus become part of chromatin, line the nuclear envelope (the lamins), or remain in solution in the nucleoplasm.

Many ribosomes are attached to membranes. Some ribosomes are attached to the nuclear envelope, but most are attached to a network of membranes in the cytosol called the *endoplasmic reticulum* (ER) (described in more detail next). The proteins made on ribosomes attached to the ER follow a special path to other organelles within the cell.

2.3d An Endomembrane System Divides the Cytoplasm into Functional and Structural Compartments

Eukaryotic cells are characterized by an **endomembrane system** (*endo* = within), a collection of interrelated internal membranous sacs that divide the cell into functional and structural compartments. The endomembrane system has a number of functions, including the synthesis and modification of proteins and their transport into membranes and organelles or to the outside of the cell, the synthesis of lipids, and the detoxification of some toxins. The membranes of the system are connected either directly in the physical sense or indirectly by **vesicles**, which are small membrane-bound compartments that transfer substances between parts of the system.

The components of the endomembrane system include the nuclear envelope, endoplasmic reticulum, Golgi complex, lysosomes, vesicles, and plasma membrane. The plasma membrane and the nuclear envelope were discussed earlier in this chapter. The functions of the other organelles are described in the following sections.

Endoplasmic Reticulum. The **endoplasmic reticulum** (ER) is an extensive interconnected network (*reticulum* = little net) of membranous channels and vesicles called **cisternae** (singular, *cisterna*). Each cisterna is formed by a single membrane that surrounds an enclosed space called the **ER lumen (Figure 2.12)**. The ER occurs in two forms: rough ER and smooth ER, each with specialized structure and function.

The **rough ER** (see Figure 2.12a) gets its name from the many ribosomes that stud its outer surface. The proteins made on ribosomes attached to the ER enter the ER lumen, where they fold into their final form. Chemical modifications of these proteins, such as addition of carbohydrate groups to produce glycoproteins, occur in the lumen. The proteins are then delivered to other regions of the cell within small vesicles that pinch off from the ER, travel through the cytosol, and join with the organelle that performs the next steps in their modification and distribution. For most of the proteins made on the rough ER, the next destination is the Golgi complex,

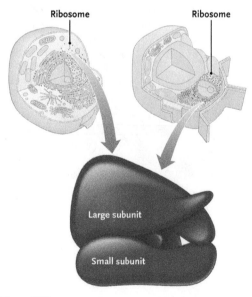

Figure 2.11

A ribosome. The diagram shows the structures of the two ribosomal subunits of mammalian ribosomes and how they come together to form the whole ribosome.

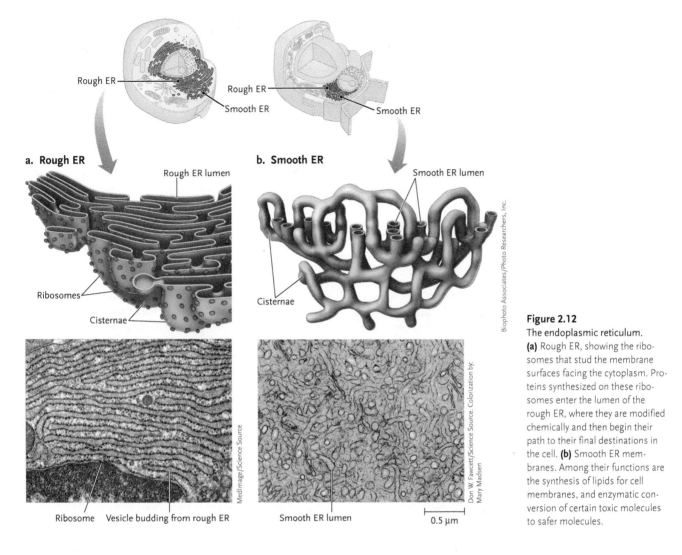

a. Rough ER

Rough ER lumen

Ribosomes

Cisternae

Ribosome   Vesicle budding from rough ER

MedImage/Science Source

b. Smooth ER

Smooth ER lumen

Cisternae

Smooth ER lumen

0.5 µm

Biophoto Associates/Photo Researchers, Inc.

Don W. Fawcett/Science Source. Colorization by:
Mary Madsen

Figure 2.12
The endoplasmic reticulum.
(a) Rough ER, showing the ribosomes that stud the membrane surfaces facing the cytoplasm. Proteins synthesized on these ribosomes enter the lumen of the rough ER, where they are modified chemically and then begin their path to their final destinations in the cell. **(b)** Smooth ER membranes. Among their functions are the synthesis of lipids for cell membranes, and enzymatic conversion of certain toxic molecules to safer molecules.

which packages and sorts them for delivery to their final destinations.

The outer membrane of the nuclear envelope is closely related in structure and function to the rough ER, to which it is connected. This membrane is also a rough membrane, studded with ribosomes attached to the surface facing the cytoplasm. The proteins made on these ribosomes enter the space between the two nuclear envelope membranes. From there, the proteins can move into the ER and on to other cellular locations.

The **smooth ER** (see Figure 2.12b) is so called because its membranes have no ribosomes attached to their surfaces. The smooth ER has various functions in the cytoplasm, including synthesis of lipids that become part of cell membranes. In some cells, such as those of the liver, smooth ER membranes contain enzymes that convert drugs, poisons, and toxic by-products of cellular metabolism into substances that can be tolerated or more easily removed from the body.

The rough and smooth ER membranes are often connected, making the entire ER system a continuous network of interconnected channels in the cytoplasm. The relative proportions of rough and smooth ER reflect cellular activities in protein and lipid synthesis. Cells that are highly active in making proteins to be released outside the cell, such as pancreatic cells that make digestive enzymes, are packed with rough ER but have relatively little smooth ER. By contrast, cells that primarily synthesize lipids or break down toxic substances are packed with smooth ER but contain little rough ER.

Golgi Complex. Camillo Golgi, a late-nineteenth-century Italian neuroscientist and Nobel laureate, discovered the **Golgi complex.** The Golgi complex consists of a stack of flattened, membranous sacs (without attached ribosomes) known as cisternae **(Figure 2.13, p. 38).** In most cells, the complex looks like a stack of cupped pancakes, and like pancakes, they are separate sacs, not interconnected as the ER cisternae are. Typically there are between three and eight cisternae, but some organisms have Golgi complexes with several tens of cisternae. The number and size of Golgi complexes can vary with cell type and the metabolic activity of the cell. Some cells have a single complex, whereas cells highly active in secreting proteins from the cell can have hundreds of complexes. Golgi complexes are usually located near concentrations of rough ER membranes, between the ER and the plasma membrane.

The Golgi complex receives proteins that were made in the ER and transported to the complex in vesicles. When the vesicles contact the *cis* face of the complex (which faces the nucleus), they fuse with the Golgi membrane and release their contents directly into the cisternal (see Figure 2.13). Within the Golgi complex, the proteins are chemically modified, for example, by removing segments of the amino acid chain, adding small functional groups, or adding lipid or carbohydrate units. The modified proteins are transported within the Golgi to the *trans* face of the complex (which faces the plasma membrane), where they are sorted into vesicles that bud off from the margins of the Golgi (see Figure 2.13). The content of a vesicle is kept separate from the cytosol by the vesicle membrane. Three quite different models have been proposed for how proteins move through the Golgi complex. The mechanism is a subject of active current research.

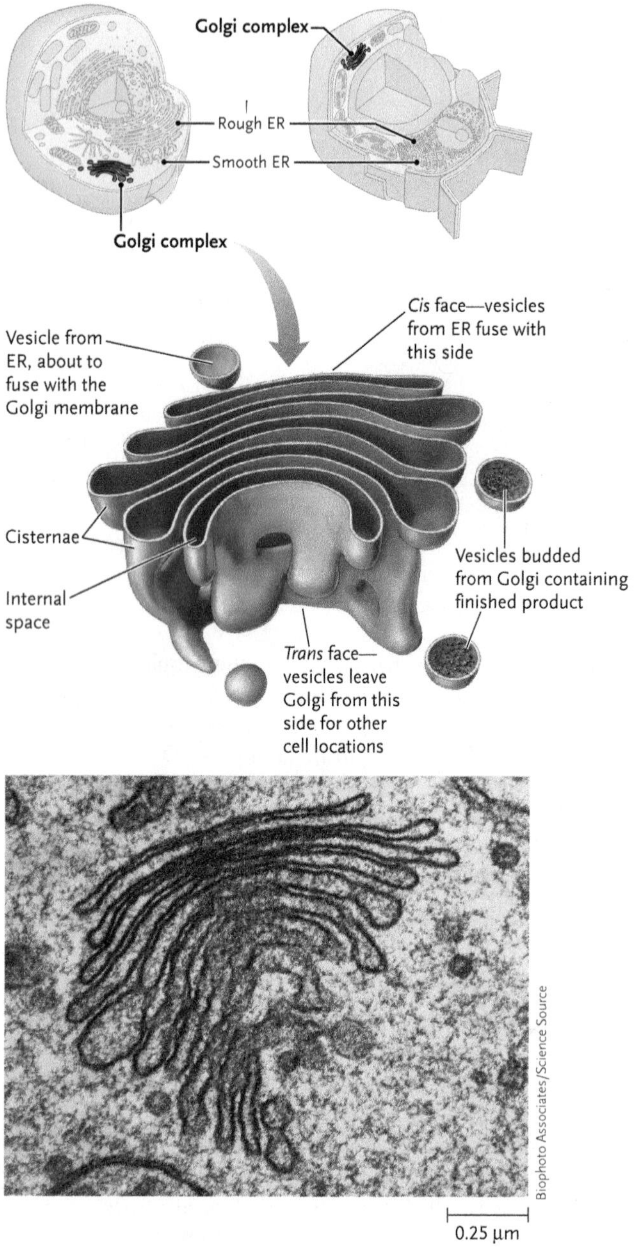

The Golgi complex regulates the movement of several types of proteins. Some are secreted from the cell, others become embedded in the plasma membrane as integral membrane proteins, and yet others are placed in lysosomes. The modifications of the proteins within the Golgi complex include adding "postal codes" to the proteins, tagging them for sorting to their final destinations. For instance, proteins secreted from the cell are transported to the plasma membrane in **secretory vesicles**, which release their contents to the exterior by **exocytosis (Figure 2.14a)**. In this process, a secretory vesicle fuses with the plasma membrane and spills the vesicle contents to the outside. The contents of secretory vesicles vary, including signalling molecules such as hormones and neurotransmitters (see Chapter 5), waste products or toxic substances, and enzymes (such as from cells lining the intestine). The membrane of a vesicle that fuses with the plasma membrane becomes part of the plasma membrane. In fact, this process is used to expand the surface of the cell during cell growth.

Vesicles may also form by the reverse process, called **endocytosis**, which brings molecules into the cell from the exterior (Figure 2.14b). In this process, the plasma membrane forms a pocket, which bulges inward and pinches off into the cytoplasm as an **endocytic vesicle**. Once in the cytoplasm, endocytic vesicles, which contain segments of the plasma membrane as well as proteins and other molecules, are carried to the Golgi complex or to other destinations such as lysosomes in animal cells. The substances carried to the Golgi complex are sorted and placed into vesicles for routing to other locations, which may include lysosomes. Those routed to lysosomes are digested into molecular subunits that may be recycled as building blocks for the biological molecules of the cell. Exocytosis and endocytosis are discussed in more detail in Chapters 43 and 44.

Lysosomes. **Lysosomes** (*lys* = breakdown; *some* = body) are small, membrane-bound vesicles that contain more than 30 hydrolytic enzymes for the digestion of many complex molecules, including proteins, lipids, nucleic acids, and polysaccharides **(Figure 2.15)**. The cell recycles the subunits of these molecules.

Golgi complex
Rough ER
Smooth ER
Golgi complex

Vesicle from ER, about to fuse with the Golgi membrane

Cis face—vesicles from ER fuse with this side

Cisternae

Internal space

Vesicles budded from Golgi containing finished product

Trans face—vesicles leave Golgi from this side for other cell locations

Biophoto Associates/Science Source

0.25 µm

Figure 2.13
The Golgi complex.

a. Exocytosis: A secretory vesicle fuses with the plasma membrane, releasing the vesicle contents to the cell exterior. The vesicle membrane becomes part of the plasma membrane.

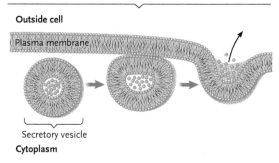

Outside cell

Plasma membrane

Secretory vesicle

Cytoplasm

b. Endocytosis: Materials from the cell exterior are enclosed in a segment of the plasma membrane that pockets inward and pinches off as an endocytic vesicle.

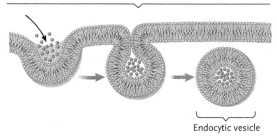

Endocytic vesicle

Figure 2.14
Exocytosis and endocytosis.

Lysosomes are found in animals but not in plants. The functions of lysosomes in plants are carried out by the central vacuole (see Section 2.4). Depending on the contents they are digesting, lysosomes assume a variety of sizes and shapes instead of a uniform struc-

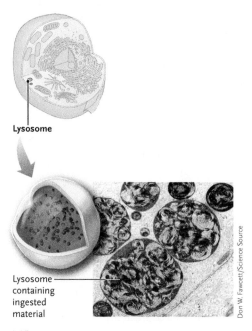

Lysosome

Lysosome containing ingested material

Don W. Fawcett/Science Source

Figure 2.15
A lysosome.

ture as is characteristic of other organelles. Most commonly, lysosomes are small (0.1–0.5 μm in diameter) oval or spherical bodies. A human cell contains about 300 lysosomes.

Lysosomes are formed by budding from the Golgi complex. Their hydrolytic enzymes are synthesized in the rough ER, modified in the lumen of the ER to identify them as being bound for a lysosome, transported to the Golgi complex in a vesicle, and then packaged in the budding lysosome.

The pH within lysosomes is acidic (pH = 5) and is significantly lower than the pH of the cytosol (pH = 7.2). The hydrolytic enzymes in the lysosomes function optimally at the acidic pH within the organelle, but they do not function well at the pH of the cytosol; this difference reduces the risk to the viability of the cell should the enzymes be released from the vesicle.

Lysosomal enzymes can digest several types of materials. They digest food molecules entering the cell by endocytosis when an endocytic vesicle fuses with a lysosome. In a process called *autophagy*, they digest organelles that are not functioning correctly. A membrane surrounds the defective organelle, forming a large vesicle that fuses with one or more lysosomes; the organelle is then degraded by the hydrolytic enzymes. They also play a role in **phagocytosis**, a process in which some types of cells engulf bacteria or other cellular debris to break them down. These cells include the white blood cells known as *phagocytes*, which play an important role in the immune system (see Chapter 5). Phagocytosis produces a large vesicle that contains the engulfed materials until lysosomes fuse with the vesicle and release the hydrolytic enzymes necessary for degrading them.

In certain human genetic diseases known as *lysosomal storage diseases*, one of the hydrolytic enzymes normally found in the lysosome is absent. As a result, the substrate of that enzyme accumulates in the lysosomes, and this accumulation eventually interferes with normal cellular activities. An example is Tay–Sachs disease, a fatal disease of the central nervous system caused by the failure to synthesize the enzyme needed for hydrolysis of **fatty acid** derivatives found in brain and nerve cells.

Summary. In summary, the endomembrane system is a major traffic network for proteins and other substances within the cell. The Golgi complex in particular is a key distribution station for membranes and proteins **(Figure 2.16, p. 40)**. From the Golgi complex, lipids and proteins may move to storage or secretory vesicles, and from the secretory vesicles, they may move to the cell exterior by exocytosis. Membranes and proteins may also move between the nuclear envelope and the endomembrane system. Proteins and other materials that enter cells by endocytosis also enter the endomembrane system to travel to the Golgi complex for sorting and distribution to other locations.

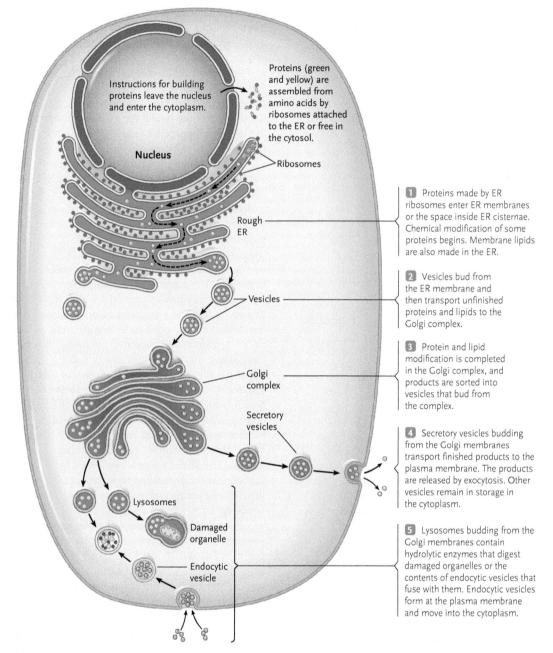

Instructions for building proteins leave the nucleus and enter the cytoplasm.

Proteins (green and yellow) are assembled from amino acids by ribosomes attached to the ER or free in the cytosol.

Nucleus

Ribosomes

Rough ER

Vesicles

Golgi complex

Secretory vesicles

Lysosomes

Damaged organelle

Endocytic vesicle

1 Proteins made by ER ribosomes enter ER membranes or the space inside ER cisternae. Chemical modification of some proteins begins. Membrane lipids are also made in the ER.

2 Vesicles bud from the ER membrane and then transport unfinished proteins and lipids to the Golgi complex.

3 Protein and lipid modification is completed in the Golgi complex, and products are sorted into vesicles that bud from the complex.

4 Secretory vesicles budding from the Golgi membranes transport finished products to the plasma membrane. The products are released by exocytosis. Other vesicles remain in storage in the cytoplasm.

5 Lysosomes budding from the Golgi membranes contain hydrolytic enzymes that digest damaged organelles or the contents of endocytic vesicles that fuse with them. Endocytic vesicles form at the plasma membrane and move into the cytoplasm.

Figure 2.16

Vesicle traffic in the cytoplasm. The ER and Golgi complex are part of the endomembrane system, which releases proteins and other substances to the cell exterior and gathers materials from outside the cell.

2.3e Mitochondria Are the Organelles in Which Cellular Respiration Occurs

Mitochondria (singular, *mitochondrion*) are the membrane-bound organelles in which cellular respiration occurs. *Cellular respiration* is the process by which energy-rich molecules such as sugars, fats, and other fuels are broken down to water and carbon dioxide by mitochondrial reactions, with the release of energy.

Much of the energy released by the breakdown is captured in ATP. In fact, mitochondria generate most of the ATP of the cell. Mitochondria require oxygen for cellular respiration—when you breathe, you are taking in oxygen primarily for your mitochondrial reactions (see Chapter 6).

Mitochondria are enclosed by two membranes **(Figure 2.17)**. The **outer mitochondrial membrane** is smooth and covers the outside of the organelle. The

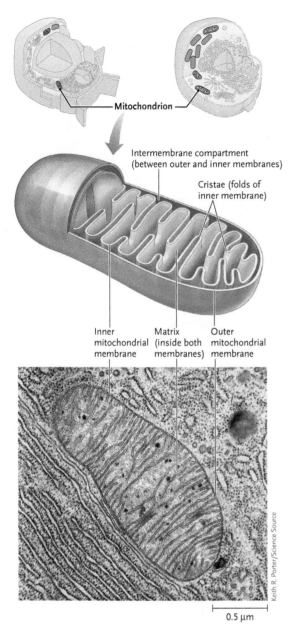

became permanent residents of the cytoplasm during the evolution of eukaryotic cells. This is discussed in more detail in Chapter 3.

2.3f The Cytoskeleton Supports and Moves Cell Structures

The characteristic shape and internal organization of each type of cell is maintained in part by its cytoskeleton, the interconnected system of protein fibres and tubes that extends throughout the cytoplasm. The cytoskeleton also reinforces the plasma membrane and functions in movement, both of structures within the cell and of the cell as a whole. It is most highly developed in animal cells, in which it fills and supports the cytoplasm from the plasma membrane to the nuclear envelope **(Figure 2.18, p. 42)**. Although cytoskeletal structures are also present in plant cells, the fibres and tubes of the system are less prominent; much of cellular support in plants is provided by the cell wall and a large central vacuole (described in Section 2.4).

The cytoskeleton of animal cells contains structural elements of three major types: *microtubules, intermediate filaments,* and *microfilaments.* Plant cytoskeletons likewise contain the same three structural elements. Microtubules are the largest cytoskeletal elements, and microfilaments are the smallest. Each cytoskeletal element is assembled from proteins—microtubules from *tubulins,* intermediate filaments from a large and varied group of *intermediate filament proteins,* and microfilaments from *actins* **(Figure 2.19, p. 42)**. The keratins of animal hair, nails, and claws contain a common form of intermediate filament proteins known as *cytokeratins.* For example, human hair consists of thick bundles of cytokeratin fibres extruded from hair follicle cells. The lamins that line the inner surface of the nuclear envelope in animal cells are also assembled from intermediate filament proteins.

Microtubules (Figure 2.19a, p. 42) are microscopic tubes with an outer diameter of about 25 nm and an inner diameter of about 15 nm; they function much like the tubes used by human engineers to construct supportive structures. Microtubules vary widely in length from less than 200 nm to several micrometres. The wall of the microtubule consists of 13 protein filaments arranged side by side. A filament is a linear polymer of tubulin dimers, each dimer consisting of one α-tubulin and one β-tubulin subunit bound noncovalently together. The dimers are organized head to tail in each filament, giving the microtubule a polarity, meaning that the two ends are different. One end, called the 1 (plus) end, has α-tubulin subunits at the ends of the filaments; the other end, called the 2 (minus) end, has β-tubulin subunits at the ends of the filaments. Microtubules are dynamic structures, changing their lengths as required by their functions. This is seen readily in animal cells that are changing shape. Microtubules change length by the addition or removal of tubulin dimers; this occurs

Figure 2.17
Mitochondria. The electron micrograph shows a mitochondrion from a bat pancreas, surrounded by cytoplasm containing rough ER. Cristae extend into the interior of the mitochondrion as folds from the inner mitochondrial membrane. The darkly stained granules inside the mitochondrion are probably lipid deposits.

surface area of the **inner mitochondrial membrane** is expanded by folds called **cristae** (singular, *crista*). Both membranes surround the innermost compartment of the mitochondrion, called the **mitochondrial matrix.** The ATP-generating reactions of mitochondria occur in the cristae and matrix.

The mitochondrial matrix also contains DNA and ribosomes that resemble the equivalent structures in bacteria. These and other similarities suggest that mitochondria originated from ancient bacteria that

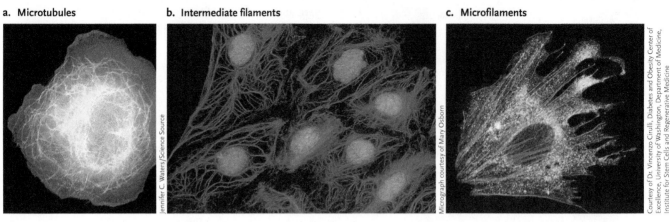

a. Microtubules

b. Intermediate filaments

c. Microfilaments

Figure 2.18
Cytoskeletons of eukaryotic cells, as seen in cells stained for light microscopy. **(a)** Microtubules (yellow) and microfilaments (red) in a pancreatic cell.
(b) Keratin intermediate filaments viewed by immunofluorescence microscopy in the rat kangaroo cell line PtK2. The nucleus is stained blue in these cells.
(c) Microfilaments (red) in a migrating mammalian cell.

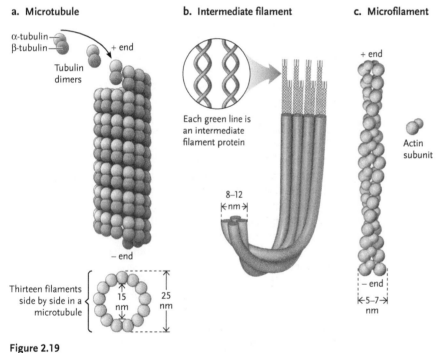

a. Microtubule

α-tubulin
β-tubulin

Tubulin dimers

+ end

– end

Thirteen filaments side by side in a microtubule
15 nm
25 nm

b. Intermediate filament

Each green line is an intermediate filament protein

8–12 nm

c. Microfilament

+ end

Actin subunit

– end

5–7 nm

Figure 2.19
The major components of the cytoskeleton. **(a)** A microtubule, assembled from dimers of α- and β-tubulin proteins. **(b)** An intermediate filament. Eight protein chains wind together to form each subunit, shown as a green cylinder. **(c)** A microfilament, assembled from two linear polymers of actin proteins wound around each other into a helical spiral.

asymmetrically, with dimers adding or detaching more rapidly at the 1 end than at the 2 end. The lengths of microtubules are tightly regulated in the cell.

Many of the cytoskeletal microtubules in animal cells are formed and radiate outward from a site near the nucleus termed the **cell centre** or **centrosome** (see Figure 2.8, p. 34). At its midpoint are two short, barrel-shaped structures also formed from microtubules called the **centrioles** (see **Figure 2.23, p. 45**). Often,

intermediate filaments also extend from the cell centre, apparently held in the same radiating pattern by linkage to microtubules. Microtubules that radiate from the cell centre anchor the ER, Golgi complex, lysosomes, secretory vesicles, and at least some mitochondria in position. The microtubules also provide tracks along which vesicles move from the cell interior to the plasma membrane and in the reverse direction. The intermediate filaments probably add support to the microtubule arrays.

Microtubules play other key roles, for instance, in separating and moving chromosomes during cell division, determining the orientation for growth of the new cell wall during plant cell division, maintaining the shape of animal cells, and moving animal cells themselves. Animal cell movements are generated by "motor" proteins that push or pull against microtubules or microfilaments, much as our muscles produce body movements by acting on bones of the skeleton. One end of a motor protein is firmly fixed to a cell structure such as a vesicle or to a microtubule or microfilament. The other end has reactive groups that "walk" along another microtubule or microfilament by making an attachment, forcefully swivelling a short distance, and then releasing **(Figure 2.20)**. ATP supplies the energy for the walking movements. The motor proteins that walk along microfilaments are called *myosins,* and the ones that walk along microtubules are called *dyneins* and *kinesins.* Some cell movements, such as the whipping motions of sperm tails, depend entirely on microtubules and their motor proteins.

a. "Walking" end of a kinesin molecule

Connects to cell structure
such as a vesicle

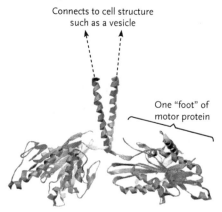

One "foot" of
motor protein

b. How a kinesin molecule "walks"

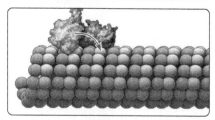

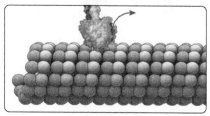

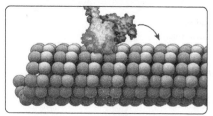

Figure 2.20

The microtubule motor protein kinesin. **(a)** Structure of the end of a kinesin molecule that "walks" along a microtubule, with α-helical segments shown as spirals and β strands as flat ribbons. **(b)** How a kinesin molecule walks along the surface of a molecule by alternately attaching and releasing its "feet."

Intermediate filaments (Figure 2.19b) are fibres with diameters of about 8 to 12 nm. ("Intermediate" signifies, in fact, that these filaments are intermediate in size between microtubules and microfilaments.) These fibres occur singly, in parallel bundles, and in interlinked networks, either alone or in combination with microtubules, microfilaments, or both. Intermediate filaments are only found in multicellular organisms. Moreover, whereas microtubules and microfilaments are the same in all tissues, intermediate filaments are tissue specific in their protein composition. Despite the molecular diversity of intermediate filaments, however, they all play similar roles in the cell, providing structural support in many cells and tissues. For example, the nucleus in epithelial cells is held within the cell by a basketlike network of intermediate filaments made of keratins.

Microfilaments (Figure 2.19c) are thin protein fibres 5 to 7 nm in diameter that consist of two polymers of actin subunits wound around each other in a long helical spiral. The actin subunits are asymmetrical in shape, and they are all oriented in the same way in the polymer chains of a microfilament. Thus, as for microtubules, microfilaments have a polarity: the two ends are designated 1 (plus) and 2 (minus). And, as for microtubules, growth and disassembly occur more rapidly at the 1 end than at the 2 end.

Microfilaments occur in almost all eukaryotic cells and are involved in many processes, including a number of structural and locomotor functions. Microfilaments are best known as one of the two components of the contractile elements in muscle fibres of vertebrates (the roles of myosin and microfilaments in muscle contraction are discussed in Chapter 46). Microfilaments are involved in the actively flowing motion of cytoplasm called **cytoplasmic streaming**, which can transport nutrients, proteins, and organelles in both animal and plant cells, and which is responsible for amoeboid movement. When animal cells divide, microfilaments are responsible for dividing the cytoplasm (see Chapter 9 for further discussion).

2.3g Flagella Propel Cells, and Cilia Move Materials over the Cell Surface

Flagella and **cilia** (singular, *cilium*) are elongated, slender, motile structures that extend from the cell surface. They are identical in structure except that cilia are usually shorter than flagella and occur on cells in greater numbers. The whiplike or oarlike movements of a flagellum propel a cell through a watery medium, and cilia move fluids over the cell surface.

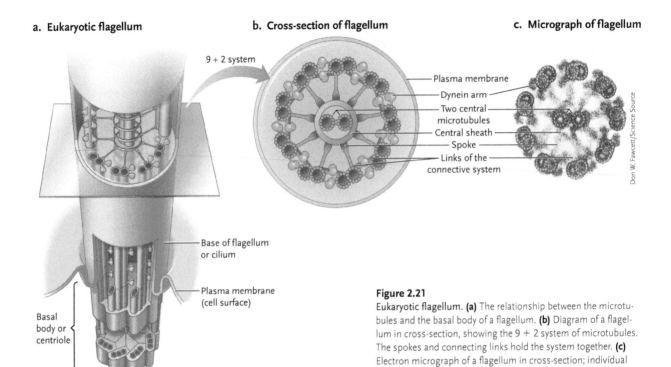

a. Eukaryotic flagellum

9 + 2 system

Base of flagellum
or cilium

Plasma membrane
(cell surface)

Basal
body or
centriole

b. Cross-section of flagellum

Plasma membrane
Dynein arm
Two central
microtubules
Central sheath
Spoke
Links of the
connective system

c. Micrograph of flagellum

Don W. Fawcett/Science Source

Figure 2.21
Eukaryotic flagellum. **(a)** The relationship between the microtubules and the basal body of a flagellum. **(b)** Diagram of a flagellum in cross-section, showing the 9 + 2 system of microtubules. The spokes and connecting links hold the system together. **(c)** Electron micrograph of a flagellum in cross-section; individual tubulin molecules are visible in the microtubule walls.

A bundle of microtubules extends from the base to the tip of a flagellum or cilium **(Figure 2.21)**. In the bundle, a circle of nine double microtubules surrounds a central pair of single microtubules, forming what is known as the 9 + 2 complex. Dynein motor proteins slide the microtubules of the 9 + 2 complex over each other to produce the movements of a flagellum or cilium **(Figure 2.22)**.

Flagella and cilia arise from the centrioles. These barrel-shaped structures contain a bundle of microtubules similar to the 9 + 2 complex, except that the central pair of microtubules is missing and the outer circle is formed from a ring of nine triple rather than double microtubules (compare Figure 2.21 and Figure 2.23, p. 45).

During the formation of a flagellum or cilium, a centriole moves to a position just under the plasma membrane. Then two of the three microtubules of each triplet grow outward from one end of the centriole to form the ring of nine double microtubules. The two central microtubules of the 9 + 2 complex also grow from the end of the centriole, but without direct

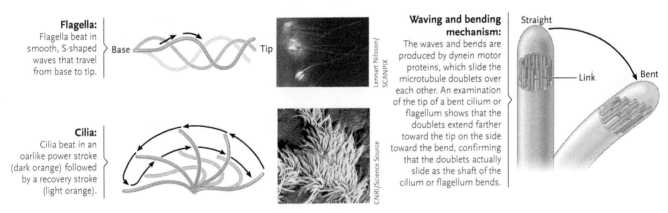

Flagella:
Flagella beat in smooth, S-shaped waves that travel from base to tip.

Base

Tip

Lennart Nilsson/SCANPIX

Cilia:
Cilia beat in an oarlike power stroke (dark orange) followed by a recovery stroke (light orange).

CNRI/Science Source

Waving and bending mechanism:
The waves and bends are produced by dynein motor proteins, which slide the microtubule doublets over each other. An examination of the tip of a bent cilium or flagellum shows that the doublets extend farther toward the tip on the side toward the bend, confirming that the doublets actually slide as the shaft of the cilium or flagellum bends.

Straight

Link

Bent

Figure 2.22
Flagellar and ciliary beating patterns. The micrographs show a few human sperm, each with a flagellum (top), and cilia from the lining of an airway in the lungs (bottom).

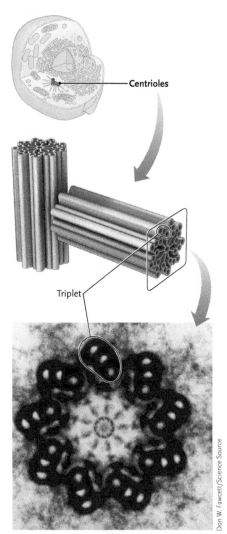

Centrioles

Triplet

Don W. Fawcett/Science Source

Figure 2.23

Centrioles. The two centrioles of the pair at the cell centre usually lie at right angles to each other as shown. The electron micrograph shows a centriole from a mouse cell in cross-section. A centriole gives rise to the 9 + 2 system of a flagellum and persists as the basal body at the inner end of the flagellum.

connection to any centriole microtubules. The centriole remains at the innermost end of a flagellum or cilium when its development is complete as the **basal body** of the structure (see Figure 2.21).

Cilia and flagella are found in protozoa and algae, and many types of animal cells have flagella—the tail of a sperm cell is a flagellum—as do the reproductive cells of some plants. In humans, cilia cover the surfaces of cells lining cavities or tubes in some parts of the body. For example, cilia on cells lining the ventricles (cavities) of the brain circulate fluid through the brain, and cilia in the oviducts conduct eggs from the ovaries to the uterus. Cilia covering cells that line the air passages of the lungs sweep out mucus containing bacteria, dust particles, and other contaminants.

Although the purpose of the eukaryotic flagellum is the same as that of prokaryotic flagella, the genes that encode the components of the flagellar apparatus of cells of Bacteria, Archaea, and Eukarya are different in each case. Thus, as mentioned earlier in the chapter, the three types of flagella are analogous, not homologous, structures, and they must have evolved independently.

With a few exceptions, the cell structures described so far in this chapter occur in all eukaryotic cells. The major exception is lysosomes, which appear to be restricted to animal cells. The next section describes three additional structures that are characteristic of plant cells.

STUDY BREAK

1. Where in a eukaryotic cell is DNA found? How is that DNA organized?
2. What is the nucleolus, and what is its function?
3. Explain the structure and function of the endomembrane system.
4. What are the structure and function of a mitochondrion?
5. What are the structure and function of the cytoskeleton?

2.4 Specialized Structures of Plant Cells

Chloroplasts, large and highly specialized central vacuoles, and cell walls give plant cells their distinctive characteristics, but these structures also occur in some other eukaryotes—for example, chloroplasts in algal protists and cell walls in algal protists and fungi.

2.4a Chloroplasts Are Biochemical Factories Powered by Sunlight

Chloroplasts (*chloro* = yellow-green), the sites of photosynthesis in plant cells, are members of a family of plant organelles known collectively as **plastids.** Other members of the family include amyloplasts and chromoplasts. **Amyloplasts** (*amylo* = starch) are colourless plastids that store **starch,** a product of photosynthesis. They occur in great numbers in the roots or tubers of some plants, such as the potato. **Chromoplasts** (*chromo* = colour) contain red and yellow pigments and are responsible for the colours of ripening fruits or autumn leaves. All plastids contain DNA genomes and molecular machinery for gene expression and the synthesis of proteins on ribosomes. Some of the proteins within plastids are encoded by their genomes; others are encoded by nuclear genes and are imported into the organelles.

Chloroplasts, like mitochondria, are usually lens or disc shaped and are surrounded by a smooth **outer boundary membrane** and an **inner boundary membrane**, which lies just inside the outer membrane **(Figure 2.24)**. These two boundary membranes completely enclose an inner compartment, the **stroma**. Within the stroma is a third membrane system that consists of flattened, closed sacs called **thylakoids**. In higher plants, the thylakoids are stacked, one on top of another, forming structures called **grana** (singular, *granum*).

The thylakoid membranes contain molecules that absorb light energy and convert it to chemical energy in photosynthesis. The primary molecule absorbing light is *chlorophyll,* a green pigment that is present in all chloroplasts. The chemical energy is used by enzymes in the stroma to make carbohydrates and other complex organic molecules from water, carbon dioxide, and other simple inorganic precursors. The organic molecules produced in chloroplasts, or from biochemical building blocks made in chloroplasts, are the ultimate food source for most organisms. (The physical and biochemical reactions of chloroplasts are described in Chapter 7.)

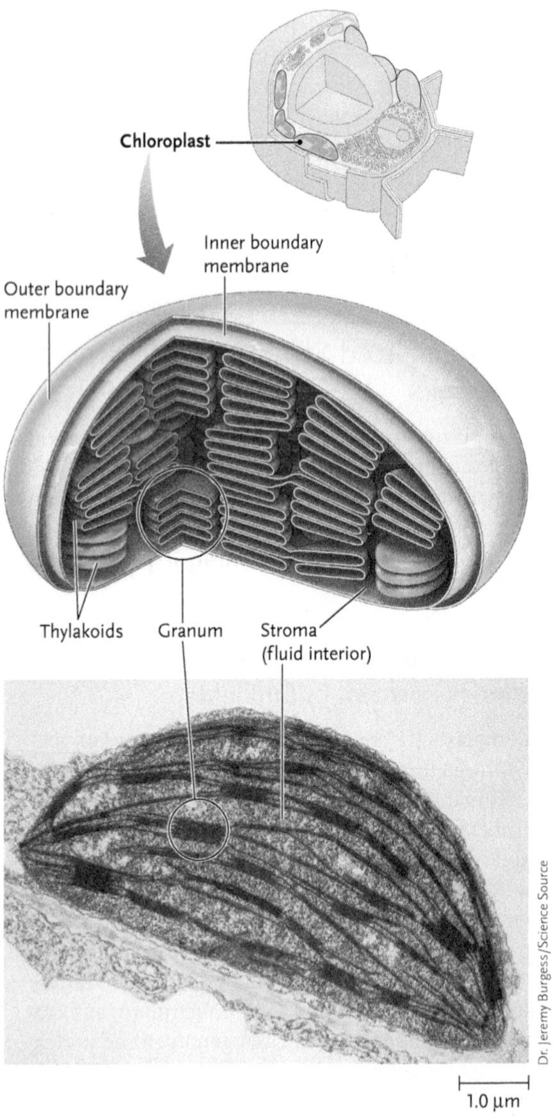

The chloroplast stroma contains DNA and ribosomes that resemble those of certain photosynthetic bacteria. Because of these similarities, chloroplasts, like mitochondria, are believed to have originated from ancient bacteria that became permanent residents of the eukaryotic cells ancestral to the plant lineage (see Chapter 3 for further discussion).

2.4b Central Vacuoles Have Diverse Roles in Storage, Structural Support, and Cell Growth

Central vacuoles (see Figure 2.9, p. 34) are large vesicles identified as distinct organelles of plant cells because they perform specialized functions unique to plants. In a mature plant cell, 90% or more of the cell's volume may be occupied by one or more large central vacuoles. The remainder of the cytoplasm and the nucleus of these cells is restricted to a narrow zone between the central vacuole and the plasma membrane. The pressure within the central vacuole supports the cells.

The membrane that surrounds the central vacuole, the **tonoplast**, contains transport proteins that move substances into and out of the central vacuole. As plant cells mature, they grow primarily by increases in the pressure and volume of the central vacuole.

Central vacuoles conduct other vital functions. They store salts, organic acids, sugars, storage proteins, pigments, and, in some cells, waste products. Pigments concentrated in the vacuoles produce the colours of many flowers. Enzymes capable of breaking down biological molecules are present in some central vacuoles, giving them some of the properties of lysosomes. Molecules that provide chemical defences against pathogenic organisms also occur in the central vacuoles of some plants.

2.4c Cell Walls Support and Protect Plant Cells

The cell walls of plants are extracellular structures because they are located outside the plasma membrane **(Figure 2.25)**. Cell walls provide support to individual cells, contain the pressure produced in the central vacuole, and protect cells against invading bacteria and fungi. Cell walls consist of cellulose fibres, which give tensile strength to the walls, embedded in a network of highly branched carbohydrates. Cell walls are perforated by minute channels,

Figure 2.24

Chloroplast structure. The electron micrograph shows a maize (corn) chloroplast.

Chloroplast

Inner boundary membrane

Outer boundary membrane

Thylakoids   Granum   Stroma (fluid interior)

Dr. Jeremy Burgess/Science Source

1.0 µm

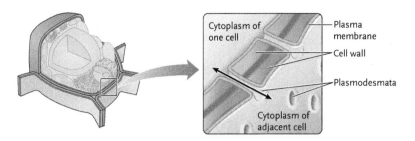

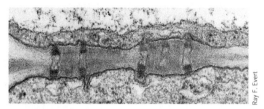

Section through five plasmodesmata that bridge the walls of two plant cells.

Figure 2.25

Cell wall structure in plants. The right diagram and electron micrograph show plasmodesmata, which form openings in the cell wall that directly connect the cytoplasm of adjacent cells.

the plasmodesmata (singular, *plasmodesma;* see Figure 2.25). A typical plant cell has between 1000 and 100 000 plasmodesmata connecting it to abutting cells. These cytosol-filled channels are lined by plasma membranes, so that connected cells essentially all have one continuous surface membrane. Most plasmodesmata also contain a narrow tubelike structure derived from the smooth ER of the connected cells. Plasmodesmata allow ions and small molecules to move directly from one cell to another through the connecting cytosol, without having to penetrate the plasma membranes or cell walls. Proteins and nucleic acids move through some plasmodesmata using energy-dependent processes.

Cell walls also surround the cells of fungi and algal protists. Carbohydrate molecules form the major framework of cell walls in most of these organisms, as they do in plants. In some, the wall fibres contain **chitin** instead of cellulose. Details of cell wall structure in the algal protists and fungi, as well as in different subgroups of the plants, are presented in later chapters devoted to these organisms. As noted earlier, animal cells do not form rigid, external, layered structures equivalent to the walls of plant cells. However, most animal cells secrete extracellular material and have other structures at the cell surface that play vital roles in the support and organization of animal body structures. The next section describes these and other surface structures of animal cells.

2.5 The Animal Cell Surface

Animal cells have specialized structures that help hold cells together, produce avenues of communication between cells, and organize body structures. Molecular systems that perform these functions are organized at three levels: individual **cell adhesion molecules** bind cells together, more complex **cell junctions** seal the spaces between cells and provide direct communication between cells, and the **extracellular matrix** (ECM) supports and protects cells and provides mechanical linkages, such as those between muscles and bone.

2.5a Cell Adhesion Molecules Organize Animal Cells into Tissues and Organs

Cell adhesion molecules are glycoproteins embedded in the plasma membrane. They help maintain body form and structure in animals ranging from sponges to the most complex invertebrates and vertebrates. Rather than acting as a generalized intercellular glue, cell adhesion molecules bind to specific molecules on other cells. Most cells in solid body tissues are held together by many different cell adhesion molecules.

Cell adhesion molecules make initial connections between cells early in embryonic development, but then attachments are broken and remade, as individual cells or tissues change position in the developing **embryo.** As an embryo develops into an adult, the connections become permanent and are reinforced by cell junctions. Cancer cells typically lose these **adhesions,** allowing them to break loose from their original locations, migrate to new locations, and form additional tumours.

Some bacteria and viruses—such as the virus that causes the common cold—target cell adhesion molecules as attachment sites during infection. Cell adhesion molecules are also partially responsible for the ability of cells to recognize one another as being part of the same individual or foreign to that individual. For example, rejection of organ transplants in mammals results from an immune response triggered by the foreign cell surface molecules.

2.5b Cell Junctions Reinforce Cell Adhesions and Provide Avenues of Communication

Three types of cell junctions are common in animal tissues **(Figure 2.26, p. 48). Anchoring junctions** form buttonlike spots, or belts, that run entirely around cells, "welding" adjacent cells together. For some anchoring junctions known as **desmosomes,** intermediate filaments anchor the junction in the underlying cytoplasm; in other anchoring junctions known as **adherens junctions,** microfilaments are the anchoring cytoskeletal component. Anchoring junctions are most common in tissues that are subject to stretching, shear,

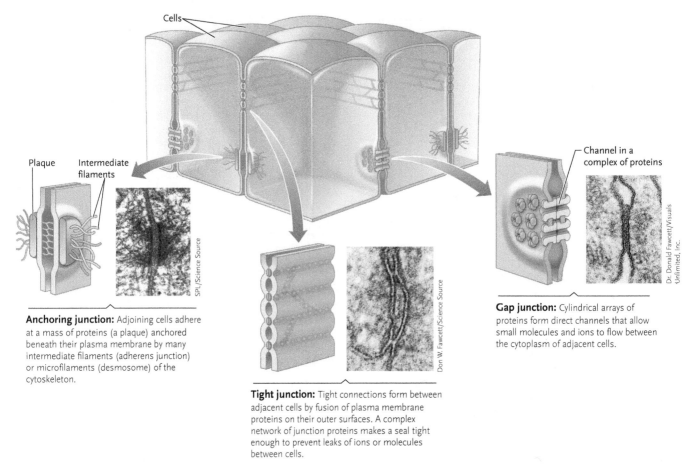

Cells

Plaque   Intermediate
filaments

SPL/Science Source

Anchoring junction: Adjoining cells adhere at a mass of proteins (a plaque) anchored beneath their plasma membrane by many intermediate filaments (adherens junction) or microfilaments (desmosome) of the cytoskeleton.

Don W. Fawcett/Science Source

Tight junction: Tight connections form between adjacent cells by fusion of plasma membrane proteins on their outer surfaces. A complex network of junction proteins makes a seal tight enough to prevent leaks of ions or molecules between cells.

Channel in a complex of proteins

Dr. Donald Fawcett/Visuals Unlimited, Inc.

Gap junction: Cylindrical arrays of proteins form direct channels that allow small molecules and ions to flow between the cytoplasm of adjacent cells.

Figure 2.26
Anchoring junctions, tight junctions, and gap junctions, which connect cells in animal tissues. Anchoring junctions reinforce the cell-to-cell connections made by cell adhesion molecules, tight junctions seal the spaces between cells, and gap junctions create direct channels of communication between animal cells.

or other mechanical forces—for example, heart muscle, skin, and the cell layers that cover organs or line body cavities and ducts.

Tight junctions, as the name indicates, are regions of tight connections between membranes of adjacent cells (see Figure 2.26). The connection is so tight that it can keep particles as small as ions from moving between the cells in the layers.

Tight junctions seal the spaces between cells in the cell layers that cover internal organs and the outer surface of the body, or the layers that line internal cavities and ducts. For example, tight junctions between cells that line the **stomach,** intestine, and bladder keep the contents of these body cavities from leaking into surrounding tissues.

A tight junction is formed by direct fusion of proteins on the outer surfaces of the two plasma membranes of adjacent cells. Strands of the tight junction proteins form a complex network that gives the appearance of stitch work holding the cells together. Within a tight junction, the plasma membrane is not joined continuously; instead, there are regions of intercellular space. Nonetheless, the network of junction proteins

is sufficient to make the tight cell connections characteristic of these junctions.

Gap junctions open direct channels that allow ions and small molecules to pass directly from one cell to another (see Figure 2.26). Hollow protein cylinders embedded in the plasma membranes of adjacent cells line up and form a sort of pipeline that connects the cytoplasm of one cell with the cytoplasm of the next. The flow of ions and small molecules through the channels provides almost instantaneous communication between animal cells, similar to the communication that plasmodesmata provide between plant cells.

In vertebrates, gap junctions occur between cells within almost all body tissues, but not between cells of different tissues. These junctions are particularly important in heart muscle tissues and in the smooth muscle tissues that form the uterus, where their pathways of communication allow the cells of the organ to operate as a coordinated unit. Although most nerve tissues do not have gap junctions, nerve cells in dental pulp are connected by gap junctions; they are responsible for the discomfort you feel if your teeth are disturbed or damaged, or when a dentist pokes a probe into a cavity.

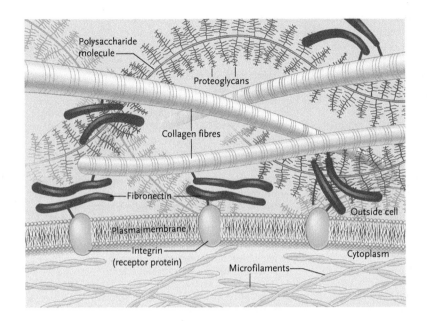

Polysaccharide molecule
Proteoglycans
Collagen fibres
Fibronectin
Outside cell
Plasma membrane
Integrin (receptor protein)
Cytoplasm
Microfilaments

Figure 2.27
Components of the ECM in an animal cell.

2.5c The Extracellular Matrix Organizes the Cell Exterior

Many types of animal cells are embedded in an ECM that consists of proteins and polysaccharides secreted by the cells themselves **(Figure 2.27)**. The primary function of the ECM is protection and support. The ECM forms the mass of skin, bones, and tendons; it also forms many highly specialized extracellular structures, such as the cornea of the eye and filtering networks in the kidney. The ECM also affects cell division, adhesion, motility, and embryonic development, and it takes part in reactions to wounds and disease.

Glycoproteins are the main component of the ECM. In most animals, the most abundant ECM glycoprotein is *collagen,* which forms fibres with great tensile strength and elasticity. In vertebrates, the collagens of tendons, cartilage, and bone are the most abundant proteins of the body, making up about half of the total body protein by weight. (Collagens and their roles in body structures are described in further detail in Chapter 39.)

The consistency of the matrix, which may range from soft and jellylike to hard and elastic, depends on a network of proteoglycans that surrounds the collagen fibres. *Proteoglycans* are glycoproteins that consist of small proteins noncovalently attached to long polysaccharide molecules. Matrix consistency depends on the number of interlinks in this network, which

determines how much water can be trapped in it. For example, cartilage, which contains a high proportion of interlinked glycoproteins, is relatively soft. Tendons, which are almost pure collagen, are tough and elastic. In bone, the glycoprotein network that surrounds collagen fibres is impregnated with mineral crystals, producing a dense and hard—but still elastic—structure that is about as strong as fibreglass or reinforced concrete.

Yet another class of glycoproteins is *fibronectins,* which aid in organizing the ECM and help cells attach to it. Fibronectins bind to **receptor proteins** called *integrins* that span the plasma membrane. On the cytoplasmic side of the plasma membrane, the integrins bind to microfilaments of the cytoskeleton. Integrins integrate changes outside and inside the cell by communicating changes in the ECM to the cytoskeleton.

Having laid the groundwork for cell structure and function in this chapter, we next take up further details of individual cell structures, beginning with the roles of cell membranes in transport in the next chapter.

STUDY BREAK

1. Distinguish between anchoring junctions, tight junctions, and gap junctions.
2. What is the structure and function of the ECM?

Review

aplia

To access course materials such as Aplia and
other companion resources, please visit
www.NELSONbrain.com.

2.1 Basic Features of Cell Structure and Function

- According to the cell theory, (1) all living organisms are composed of cells, (2) cells are the structural and functional units of life, and (3) cells arise only from the division of pre-existing cells.
- Cells of all kinds are divided internally into a central region containing the genetic material and the cytoplasm, which consists of the cytosol, the cytoskeleton, and organelles and is bounded by the plasma membrane.
- The plasma membrane is a lipid bilayer in which transport proteins are embedded (Figure 2.6).
- In the cytoplasm, proteins are made, most of the other molecules required for growth and reproduction are assembled, and energy absorbed from the surroundings is converted into energy usable by the cell.

2.2 Prokaryotic Cells

- Prokaryotic cells are surrounded by a plasma membrane and, in most groups, are enclosed by a cell wall. The genetic material, typically a single, circular DNA molecule, is located in the nucleoid. The cytoplasm contains masses of ribosomes (Figure 2.7).

2.3 Eukaryotic Cells

- Eukaryotic cells have a true nucleus, which is separated from the cytoplasm by the nuclear envelope perforated by nuclear pores. A plasma membrane forms the outer boundary of the cell. Other membrane systems enclose specialized compartments as organelles in the cytoplasm (Figures 2.8 and 2.9).
- The eukaryotic nucleus contains chromatin, a combination of DNA and proteins. A specialized segment of the chromatin forms the nucleolus, where ribosomal RNA molecules are made and combined with ribosomal proteins to make ribosomes. The nuclear envelope contains nuclear pore complexes with pores that allow passive or assisted transport of molecules between the nucleus and the cytoplasm (Figure 2.10).
- Eukaryotic cytoplasm contains ribosomes (Figure 2.11), an endomembrane system, mitochondria, microbodies, the cytoskeleton, and some organelles specific to certain organisms. The endomembrane system includes the nuclear envelope, the endoplasmic reticulum (ER), the Golgi complex, lysosomes, vesicles, and the plasma membrane.
- The ER occurs in two forms: rough and smooth ER. The ribosome-studded rough ER makes proteins that become part of cell membranes or are released from the cell. Smooth ER synthesizes lipids and breaks down toxic substances (Figure 2.12).
- The Golgi complex chemically modifies proteins made in the rough ER and sorts finished proteins to be secreted from the cell, embedded in the plasma membrane, or included in lysosomes (Figure 2.13).
- Lysosomes, specialized vesicles that contain hydrolytic enzymes, digest complex molecules such as food molecules that enter the cell by endocytosis, cellular organelles that are no longer functioning correctly, and engulfed bacteria and cell debris (Figure 2.15).
- Mitochondria carry out cellular respiration, the conversion of fuel molecules into the energy of ATP (Figure 2.17).
- The cytoskeleton is a supportive structure built from microtubules, intermediate filaments, and microfilaments. Motor proteins walking along microtubules and microfilaments produce most movements of animal cells (Figures 2.18–2.20).
- Motor protein–controlled sliding of microtubules generates the movements of flagella and cilia. Flagella and cilia arise from centrioles (Figures 2.21–2.23).

2.4 Specialized Structures of Plant Cells

- Plant cells contain all the eukaryotic structures found in animal cells except for lysosomes. They also contain three structures not found in animal cells: chloroplasts, a central vacuole, and a cell wall (Figure 2.9).
- Chloroplasts contain pigments and molecular systems that absorb light energy and convert it to chemical energy. The chemical energy is used inside the chloroplasts to assemble carbohydrates and other organic molecules from simple inorganic raw materials (Figure 2.24).
- The large central vacuole, which consists of a tonoplast enclosing an inner space, develops pressure that supports plant cells, accounts for much of cellular growth by enlarging as cells mature, and serves as a storage site for substances including waste materials (Figure 2.9).
- A cellulose cell wall surrounds plant cells, providing support and protection. Plant cell walls are perforated by plasmodesmata, channels that provide direct pathways of communication between the cytoplasm of adjacent cells (Figure 2.25).

2.5 The Animal Cell Surface

- Animal cells have specialized surface molecules and structures that function in cell adhesion, communication, and support.
- Cell adhesion molecules bind to specific molecules on other cells. The adhesions organize and hold together cells of the same type in body tissues.
- Cell adhesions are reinforced by various junctions. Anchoring junctions hold cells together. Tight junctions seal together the plasma membranes of adjacent cells, preventing ions and molecules from moving between the cells. Gap junctions open direct channels between the cytoplasm of adjacent cells (Figure 2.26).
- The extracellular matrix (ECM), formed from collagen proteins embedded in a matrix of branched glycoproteins, functions primarily in cell and body protection and support but also affects cell division, motility, embryonic development, and wound healing (Figure 2.27).

Questions

Self-Test Questions

1. Suppose you are examining a cell from a crime scene using an electron microscope, and you find it contains ribosomes, DNA, a plasma membrane, a cell wall, and mitochondria. What type of cell is it?
   a. a lung cell
   b. a plant cell
   c. a prokaryotic cell
   d. a cell from the surface of a human fingernail
   e. a sperm cell

2. A bacterium converts food energy into the chemical energy of ATP using proteins that are found on what part of the cell?
   a. Golgi complex
   b. flagellum
   c. ribosome
   d. cell wall
   e. plasma membrane

3. Which of the following is present in members of the domain Archaea?
   a. nuclear envelope
   b. chloroplast
   c. microtubules
   d. ribosomes
   e. plasmodesmata

4. Which statement about cell size is correct?
   a. As cell size increases, its surface area/volume ratio increases.
   b. A typical animal cell is about 1000 times the size of a bacterium.
   c. The surface area of a cell increases as the cube of the linear dimension.
   d. Increasing membrane surface area allows for a cell to maintain a larger volume.

5. How does a large nuclear-localized protein such as a transcription factor get into the nucleus?
   a. It diffuses across the lipid bilayer of the nuclear envelope.
   b. It is translated on ribosomes that are already within the nucleus.
   c. It contains a nuclear localization signal that is recognized by the nuclear pore complex.
   d. It is synthesized in the cytosol as a set of small polypeptides that diffuse into the nuceus prior to assembly.

6. Which structure is *not* used in eukaryotic protein manufacture and secretion?
   a. ribosome
   b. lysosome
   c. rough ER
   d. secretory vesicle
   e. Golgi complex

7. Suppose an electron micrograph shows that a cell has extensive amounts of smooth ER throughout. What can you deduce about the cell?
   a. The cell is synthesizing ATP.
   b. The cell is metabolically inactive.
   c. The cell is synthesizing and secreting proteins.
   d. The cell is synthesizing and metabolizing lipids.

8. Which of the following contributes to sealing the lining of the digestive track so that it can retain food?
   a. tight junctions formed by direct fusion of proteins
   b. plasmodesmata that help cells communicate their activities
   c. desmosomes forming buttonlike spots or a belt to keep cells joined
   d. gap junctions that communicate between cells of the stomach lining and its muscular wall

9. Which of the following statements about proteins is correct?
   a. Proteins are transported to the rough ER for use within the cell.
   b. Lipids and carbohydrates are added to proteins by the Golgi complex.
   c. Proteins are transported directly into the cytosol for secretion from the cell.
   d. Proteins that are to be stored by the cell are moved to the rough ER.
   e. Proteins are synthesized in vesicles.

10. Which of the following are NOT a component of the cytoskeleton?
    a. cilia
    b. actins
    c. microfilaments
    d. microtubules
    e. cytokeratins

Questions for Discussion

1. Many compound microscopes have a filter that eliminates all wavelengths except that of blue light, thereby allowing only blue light to pass through the microscope. Use the spectrum of visible light (see Figure 7.5 in Chapter 7) to explain why the filter improves the resolution of light microscopes.

2. Explain why aliens invading Earth are not likely to be giant cells the size of humans.

3. An electron micrograph of a cell shows the cytoplasm packed with rough ER membranes, a Golgi complex, and mitochondria. What activities might this cell concentrate on? Why would large numbers of mitochondria be required for these activities?

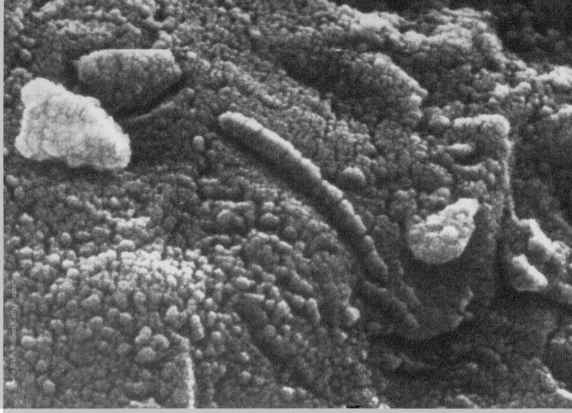

3

Scanning electron microscope image of a portion of the meteorite ALH84001. The elongate structure in the centre may be fossilized microorganism.

Defining Life and Its Origins

WHY IT MATTERS

In 1984, a group of scientists in the Antarctic discovered a 1.9 kg meteorite that they catalogued as ALH84001. Initial studies of the meteorite showed that it was about 4.5 billion years old, which is about the same age as the solar system. Its chemical composition indicated that it had originated from Mars and had impacted Earth approximately 13 thousand years ago. The meteorite garnered headlines around the world in 1996 when an article was published in the prestigious journal *Science* with evidence that ALH84001 contained distinct evidence that life had at one time existed on Mars.

Chemical analysis showed that, when on Mars, ALH84001 had at one time been fractured and subsequently infiltrated by liquid water. Using scanning electron microscopy, the coauthors of the article observed very small, elliptical, ropelike, and tubular structures in the fractured surfaces of ALH84001 that look very similar to fossilized prokaryotic cells. Furthermore, the scientists found microscopic mineral "globules," which bear strong resemblance to mineral alterations caused by primitive cells on Earth.

The analysis of meteorites for microfossils continues and remains controversial. In 2011, an article published in the *Journal of Cosmology* provided additional evidence of bacteria-like fossils within meteorites. Using sophisticated electron microscopy techniques and chemical analysis on three freshly fractured carbonaceous meteorites, data are presented in the article that show the presence of filaments that are strikingly similar in shape to cyanobacteria, a dominant form of photosynthetic bacteria on Earth. The difficulty of unequivocally assigning these structures as remnants of ancient life will continue to make the conclusions of such analyses controversial.

In this chapter, we explore two of the most basic of biological questions: What is life, and how did life evolve? After introducing the fundamental characteristics that all organisms share, we work through a discussion of the origins of life. Starting with how biologically important molecules could have been synthesized in the absence of life, we move through hypotheses regarding the first cells, to evolution of various **macromolecules** (DNA, RNA, proteins), and finally to what drove the evolution of the eukaryotic cell. The chapter closes where it begins in "Why It Matters," with a discussion on the possibility of life existing elsewhere in the galaxy.

Figure 3.1
Red-eyed tree frog on a rock.

3.1 What Is Life?

As we saw in the last chapter, all life is composed of cells—the fundamental unit of all life. But what is life? How can we define it? Picture a frog sitting on a rock, slowly shifting its head to follow the movements of insects flying nearby **(Figure 3.1).** You know instinctively that the frog is alive and the rock is not. But if you examine both at the atomic level, you will find that the difference between them is lost. The types of elements and atoms found in living things are also found in nonliving forms of matter. As well, living cells obey the same fundamental laws of physics and chemistry as the **abiotic** (nonliving) world. For example, the biochemical reactions that take place within living cells, although remarkable, are only modifications of chemical reactions that occur outside cells.

3.1a Seven Characteristics Shared by All Life-Forms

Although life seems relatively easy to recognize, it is not easy to define using a single sentence or even two. Life is defined most effectively by a list of attributes that all forms of life possess. As detailed in **Figure 3.2, p. 54,** all life displays order, harnesses and utilizes energy, reproduces, responds to stimuli, exhibits homeostasis, grows and develops, and evolves.

There are a small number of biological systems that straddle the line between the **biotic** and abiotic worlds. The best example of this is a virus **(Figure 3.3, p. 54).** Viruses are very small infectious agents that you will learn more about in Chapter 23. They display many of the properties of life, including the ability to reproduce and evolve over time. However, the characteristics of life that a virus has are based on its ability to infect cells. For example, although viruses contain nucleic acids (DNA and RNA), they lack the cellular machinery and metabolism to use that genetic information to synthesize their

own proteins. To make proteins, they have to infect living cells and essentially hijack their translational machinery and metabolism to reproduce. For this reason, most scientists do not consider viruses to be alive.

3.1b The Characteristics of Life Are Emergent

Each of the characteristics of life depicted in Figure 3.2 reflects a remarkable complexity resulting from a hierarchy of interactions that begins with atoms and progresses through molecules to macromolecules and cells. Depending upon the organism, this hierarchy may continue upward in complexity and include organelles, tissues, and organs. The seven properties of life shown in Figure 3.2 are called emergent because they come about, or emerge, from many simpler interactions that, in themselves, do not have the properties found at the higher levels. For example, the ability to harness and utilize energy is not a property of molecules or proteins or biological membranes in isolation; rather the ability emerges from the interactions of all three of these as part of a metabolic process. In this way, not only is the structural or functional complexity of living systems more than the sum of the parts, but it is fundamentally different.

A classic example that illustrates the concept of emergence is a type of termite nest called a cathedral **(Figure 3.4, p. 55).** These elegantly complex structures, most common in Australia, can grow to over 3 m tall and are the product of the activities of thousands of termites. Remarkably, there is no master plan that is followed or "queen" that gives instructions. Termites build up the mound cell by cell, based on local conditions, totally unaware of the overall structure that emerges.

a. Display order: All forms of life including this flower are arranged in a highly ordered manner, with the cell being the fundamental unit of life.

harmeet/StockXchng

b. Harness and utilize energy: Like this hummingbird, all forms of life acquire energy from the environment and use it to maintain their highly ordered state.

Steve Byland/Shutterstock.com

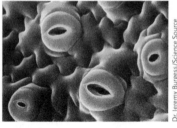

c. Reproduce: All organisms have the ability to make more of their own kind. Here, some of the bacteria have just divided into two daughter cells.

SCIMAT/Science Source

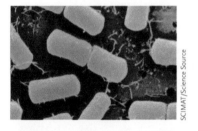

d. Respond to stimuli: Organisms can make adjustments to their structure, function, and behaviour in response to changes to the external environment. A plant can adjust the size of the pores (stomata) on the surface of its leaves to regulate gas exchange.

Dr. Jeremy Burgess/Science Source

e. Exhibit homeostasis: Organisms are able to regulate their internal environment such that conditions remain relatively constant. Sweating is one way in which the human body attempts to remove heat and thereby maintain a constant temperature.

© Tim Pannell/CORBIS

f. Grow and develop: All organisms increase their size by increasing the size and/or number of cells. Many organisms also change over time.

© Karin Duthie/Alamy

g. Evolve: Populations of living organisms change over the course of generations to become better adapted to their environment. The snowy owl illustrates this perfectly.

Stanislav Duben/Shutterstock.com

Figure 3.2
The seven characteristics of life.

STUDY BREAK

1. List the seven fundamental characteristics common to all life.
2. What does it mean that life displays emergent properties?

3.2 The Chemical Origins of Life

Recall from Chapter 2 that one of the tenets of the cell theory states that cells arise only from the growth and division of pre-existing cells. This tenet has probably been true for hundreds of millions of years, yet there must have been a time when this was not the case. There must have been a time when no cells existed, when there was no life. It is thought that over the course of hundreds of millions of years, cells with the characteristics of life arose out of a mixture of molecules that existed on primordial Earth. In this section we discuss the formation of the solar system and present hypotheses for how biologically important molecules could have been synthesized on early Earth in the absence of life.

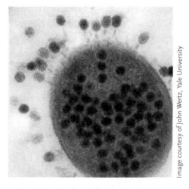

Image courtesy of John Wertz, Yale University

Figure 3.3
Bacteriophage infecting a bacterium. Notice bacteriophage on the cell surface as well as inside the bacterium. A bacteriophage is a type of virus. Viruses are generally not considered to be alive.

Figure 3.4
A termite cathedral. The sophisticated structure of a termite nest emerges from the simple work of thousands of individual termites. In a similar way, the complex properties of life emerge from much simpler molecular interactions.

3.2a Earth Is 4.6 Billion Years Old

Before we discuss the origins of life, we present in **Figure 3.5** a timeline of the evolution of major present-day organisms. Each date is still the subject of some debate within the scientific community and is based primarily on **radiometric dating** methods (see *The Purple Pages, p. F-50*). A more complete presentation of the timeline for the evolution of organismal life is found in *The Purple Pages, p. F-50*. An overview of the fossil record from which the dating and thus ordering of the major events is obtained is presented in Chapter 17. This is followed in later chapters by in-depth discussions of the evolution of the major groups of organisms, including, for example, land plants (Chapter 26), birds (Chapter 28), and mammals (Chapter 28).

Earth was formed approximately 4.6 billion years ago. To give us some sense of just how long 4.6 billion years is, as well as the relative timing of some major events in the history of life on Earth, **Figure 3.6, p. 56,** condenses the entire history of Earth into a unit of time that we are more familiar with—one year. With 4.6 billion years condensed into a single year, each day represents an interval of 12.6 million years!

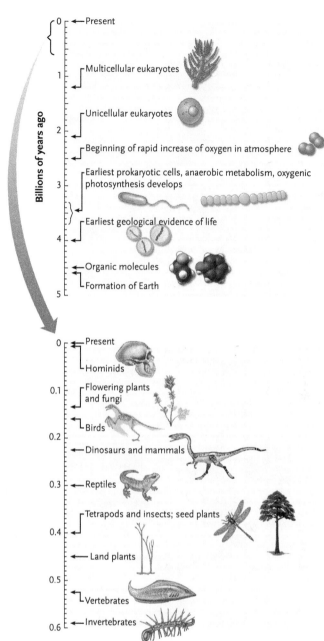

Figure 3.5
A timeline for the evolution of major forms of life. The dates presented are derived mostly from geological evidence.

Using our condensed version of the history of Earth, we set the date of the formation of Earth as January 1 at 12:00 a.m. Based on chemical evidence, life may have started as early as 4.0 billion years ago. This translates to mid-March in our one-year calendar. The first clear fossil evidence of prokaryotic cells occurs in late March or about 3.5 billion years ago. Fossil evidence of eukaryotes has been dated to about 2 billion years ago, which is not until early July using our one-year analogy. Perhaps surprisingly, animals do not make an appearance until mid-October (about 525 million years

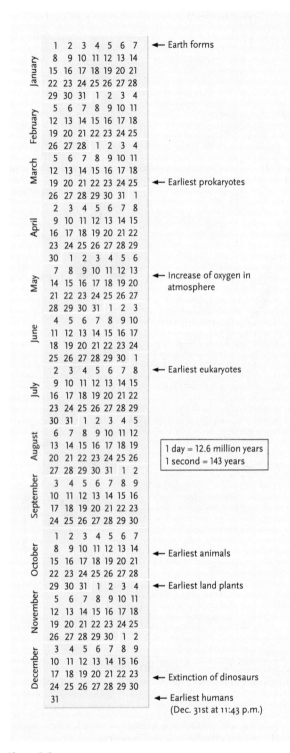

January
1 2 3 4 5 6 7
8 9 10 11 12 13 14   ← Earth forms
15 16 17 18 19 20 21
22 23 24 25 26 27 28
29 30 31 1 2 3 4

February
5 6 7 8 9 10 11
12 13 14 15 16 17 18
19 20 21 22 23 24 25
26 27 28 1 2 3 4

March
5 6 7 8 9 10 11
12 13 14 15 16 17 18
19 20 21 22 23 24 25   ← Earliest prokaryotes
26 27 28 29 30 31 1

April
2 3 4 5 6 7 8
9 10 11 12 13 14 15
16 17 18 19 20 21 22
23 24 25 26 27 28 29
30 1 2 3 4 5 6

May
7 8 9 10 11 12 13
14 15 16 17 18 19 20   ← Increase of oxygen in atmosphere
21 22 23 24 25 26 27
28 29 30 31 1 2 3

June
4 5 6 7 8 9 10
11 12 13 14 15 16 17
18 19 20 21 22 23 24
25 26 27 28 29 30 1

July
2 3 4 5 6 7 8   ← Earliest eukaryotes
9 10 11 12 13 14 15
16 17 18 19 20 21 22
23 24 25 26 27 28 29
30 31 1 2 3 4 5

August
6 7 8 9 10 11 12
13 14 15 16 17 18 19
20 21 22 23 24 25 26
27 28 29 30 31 1 2

September
3 4 5 6 7 8 9
10 11 12 13 14 15 16
17 18 19 20 21 22 23
24 25 26 27 28 29 30

October
1 2 3 4 5 6 7
8 9 10 11 12 13 14   ← Earliest animals
15 16 17 18 19 20 21
22 23 24 25 26 27 28
29 30 31 1 2 3 4   ← Earliest land plants

November
5 6 7 8 9 10 11
12 13 14 15 16 17 18
19 20 21 22 23 24 25
26 27 28 29 30 1 2

December
3 4 5 6 7 8 9
10 11 12 13 14 15 16
17 18 19 20 21 22 23   ← Extinction of dinosaurs
24 25 26 27 28 29 30
31   ← Earliest humans
(Dec. 31st at 11:43 p.m.)

1 day = 12.6 million years
1 second = 143 years

Figure 3.6
The history of Earth condensed into one year.

ago) and land plants until the following month. The extinction of dinosaurs, which was completed by about 65 million years ago, does not occur until late December. What about humans? We may think humans, *Homo sapiens*, have been around a long time, but relative to other forms of life, the roughly 150 thousand years that modern humans have existed is a very short period of time—a blip on our time-scale. Using our year analogy, modern humans have existed only since December 31—more precisely, December 31 at 11:43 p.m.!

3.2b Earth Lies within the Habitable Zone around the Sun

According to the most widely accepted hypothesis, all components of the solar system were formed at the same time by the gravitational condensation of matter present in an interstellar cloud, which initially consisted mostly of hydrogen. Intense heat and pressure generated in the central region of the cloud formed the Sun, whereas the remainder of the spiralling dust and gas condensed into the planets. Astronomers agree that this series of events is probably typical for the vast majority of the stars and planetary systems in our galaxy, the Milky Way.

Once Earth was formed, its early history was marked by bombardment of rock from the still-forming solar system and extensive volcanic and seismic activity **(Figure 3.7)**. Over time, Earth radiated away some of its heat, and surface layers cooled and solidified into the rocks of the crust. Because of its size, Earth's gravitational pull was strong enough to hold an atmosphere around the planet. The atmosphere was derived partly from the original dust cloud and partly from gases released from Earth's interior as it cooled. It is estimated that it took approximately 500 million years for Earth to cool to temperatures that could nurture the development of life.

Within the Solar System, there is currently no conclusive evidence that a planet other than Earth harbours life. The primary reason for this is that, unlike the other planets, Earth is situated at a position where heat from the Sun allows for surface temperatures to be within a range that allows water to exist in a liquid state. Interestingly, recent data from NASA's Mars Reconnaissance Orbiter suggest that some liquid water may exist on Mars as well. It is the presence of liquid water that is seen as a fundamental prerequisite for the development of life (see *The Purple Pages* for more on the structure and unique properties of water). Because of the importance of water for the development of life, the region of space around a star where temperatures would allow for liquid water is termed the *habitable zone* **(Figure 3.8)**. As you would expect, the precise distance from the star that defines the habitable zone will vary depending upon the type of star and how much energy it emits.

3.2c Biologically Important Molecules Can Be Synthesized Outside Living Cells

All forms of life are composed of the major macromolecules nucleic acids, proteins, lipids, and carbohydrates (see *The Purple Pages* for an overview of these

Figure 3.7
An artist's depiction of the primordial Earth.

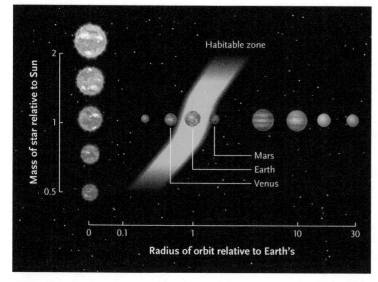

Figure 3.8
The habitable zone. The region around a star where water would exist in a liquid state and thus be conducive to the development of life is termed the *habitable zone* (shown in green). The distance from the star where the zone occurs varies depending upon the energy output of the parent star. The Sun, which is considered an average star, is shown as 1 on the scale at the left.

two scientists, Aleksander Oparin and John Haldane, independently proposed that organic molecules, essential to the formation of life, could have formed in the atmosphere of primordial Earth. A critical aspect of what is known as the Oparin–Haldane hypothesis is that the early atmosphere was a *reducing atmosphere* because of the presence of large concentrations of molecules such as hydrogen, methane, and ammonia. These molecules contain an abundance of electrons and hydrogen and would have entered into reactions with one another that would have yielded larger and more complex organic molecules.

In comparison to the proposed reducing atmosphere of primordial Earth, today's atmosphere is classified as an *oxidizing atmosphere*. The presence of high levels of oxygen prevents complex, electron-rich molecules from being formed because oxygen is a particularly strong oxidizing molecule and would itself accept the electrons from organic molecules and be reduced to water. Besides allowing for the build-up of electron-rich molecules, the lack of oxygen in the primordial atmosphere also meant that there was no ozone (O_3) layer, which only developed after oxygen levels in the atmosphere began to increase. Both Oparin and Haldane hypothesized that without the ozone layer, energetic ultraviolet light was able to reach the lower atmosphere and, along with abundant lightning, provided the energy needed to drive the formation of biologically important molecules.

Experimental evidence in support of the Oparin–Haldane hypothesis came in 1953 when Stanley Miller, a graduate student of Harold Urey's at the University of Chicago, created a laboratory simulation of the reducing atmosphere believed to have existed on early Earth. Miller placed components of a reducing atmosphere—hydrogen, methane, ammonia, and water vapour—in a closed apparatus and exposed the gases to an energy source in the form of continuously sparking electrodes **(Figure 3.9, p. 58)**. Water vapour was added to the "atmosphere" in one part of the apparatus and subsequently condensed back into water by cooling in another part. After running the experiment for one week, Miller found a large assortment of organic compounds including urea; amino acids; and lactic, formic,

molecules). With the exception of lipids, these macromolecules are derived from simpler molecules such as nucleotides, amino acids, and sugars that in modern-day cells are the products of complex metabolic pathways. But how were these molecules formed in the absence of life? There are three major hypotheses.

Hypothesis 1: Reducing Atmosphere. The atmosphere of 4 billion years ago was vastly different from the one today. The primordial atmosphere probably contained an abundance of water vapour from the evaporation of water at the surface, as well as large quantities of hydrogen (H_2), carbon dioxide (CO_2), ammonia (NH_3), and methane (CH_4). There was an almost complete absence of oxygen (O_2). In the 1920s,

Figure 3.9

The Miller–Urey experiment. Using this apparatus, Stanley Miller, a graduate student, demonstrated that organic molecules can be synthesized under conditions simulating primordial Earth.

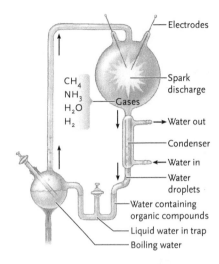

Figure 3.10

Deep-sea vent. Researchers from the Woods Hole Oceanographic Institute watch from inside the submersible Alvin as a "black smoker" chimney erupts from a seafloor vent. The regions surrounding these vents have been found to be teeming with a diversity of life.

and acetic acids after condensing the atmosphere into a liquid. In fact, as much as 15% of the carbon that was originally in the methane at the start of the experiment ended up in molecules that are common in living organisms.

Other chemicals have been tested in the Miller–Urey apparatus, including hydrogen cyanide (HCN) and formaldehyde (CH_2O), which are considered to have been among the substances formed in the primitive atmosphere. When cyanide and formaldehyde were added to the simulated primitive atmosphere in Miller's apparatus, all the building blocks of complex biological molecules were produced—amino acids; fatty acids; the **purine** and **pyrimidine** components of nucleic acids; sugars such as glyceraldehyde, ribose, glucose, and fructose; and phospholipids, which form the lipid bilayers of biological membranes.

Over the years since the Miller–Urey experiment was first conducted, considerable debate has developed in the scientific community over whether the atmosphere of primitive Earth contained enough methane and ammonia to be considered reducing. Some geologists have suggested that based on the analysis of volcanic activity, primitive Earth was probably somewhat less reactive—neither reducing nor oxidizing—with molecules including nitrogen gases (N_2), carbon monoxide (CO), and carbon dioxide (CO_2) the most dominant. Even with this composition, scientists have been able to successfully synthesize the same crucial building blocks of life in the laboratory. Regardless of the actual composition of the atmosphere on primordial Earth, the significance of the Miller–Urey experiment cannot be overstated. It was the first experiment to demonstrate the abiotic formation of molecules critical to life, such as amino acids, nucleotides, and simple sugars, and it showed that they could be produced relatively easily. At the time, this remarkable finding laid the groundwork for further research into the origins of life.

Hypothesis 2: Deep-Sea Vents. Besides the atmosphere, an **alternative hypothesis** maintains that the complex organic molecules necessary for life could have originated on the ocean floor at the site of deep-sea (hydrothermal) vents. These cracks are found around the globe near sites of volcanic or tectonic activity and release superheated nutrient-rich water at temperatures in excess of 300°C, as well as reduced molecules including methane, ammonia, and hydrogen sulfide (H_2S) **(Figure 3.10)**. Today, the areas around these vents support a remarkable diversity of life. Many of these life forms are of tremendous scientific interest because of their ability to thrive in an environment that is characterized by extreme pressure and the total absence of light.

Hypothesis 3: Extraterrestrial Origins. It is entirely possible that the key organic molecules required for life to begin came from space. Each year more than 500 meteorites impact the Earth, many of which belong to the class called carbonaceous chondrites, which are particularly rich in organic molecules. One of the most famous is the Murchison meteorite that landed in Murchison, Victoria, Australia, in 1969 **(Figure 3.11)**. Analysis of the Murchison meteorite showed that it contains an assortment of biologically important molecules including a range of amino acids such as glycine, glutamic acid, and alanine, as well as purines and pyrimidines.

3.2d Life Requires the Synthesis of Polymers

Primordial Earth contained very little oxygen, and because of this, complex organic molecules could have existed for much longer than would be possible in today's oxygen-rich world. Even if they did accumulate on early Earth, molecules such as amino acids and

Figure 3.11

The Murchison meteorite. Many meteorites have been shown to contain a range of biologically important molecules, including a number of amino acids.

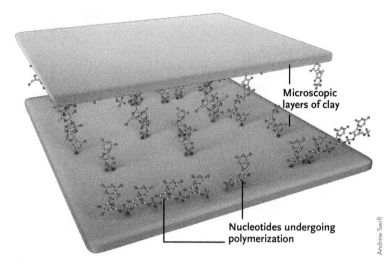

Microscopic layers of clay

Nucleotides undergoing polymerization

Andrew Swift

Figure 3.12

Clay surfaces catalyze polymerization. The charged microscopic layered structure of clay allows for the formation of relatively short polymers of proteins and nucleic acids.

nucleotides are **monomers**, which are simpler and easier to synthesize than the key chemical components of life, such as nucleic acids and proteins, which are polymers—macromolecules formed from the bonding together of individual monomers. Nucleic acids are polymers of nucleotides, proteins are polymers of amino acids, and many carbohydrates are polymers of simple sugars. Polymers are synthesized by dehydration synthesis, which is discussed in *The Purple Pages*.

Today, the synthesis of proteins and nucleic acids requires protein-based catalysts called enzymes and results in macromolecules that often consist of hundreds to many thousands of monomers linked together. So how do you make the polymers that are required for life without sophisticated enzymes? The basis of a working hypothesis to address this question must be built from the supposition that the very earliest forms of life must have been very simple—far simpler than a modern bacterium, for example. Scientists hypothesize that a polymer that consists of even 10 to 50 monomers may have been of sufficient length to impart a specific function (like a protein) or store sufficient information (like a nucleic acid) to make their formation advantageous to an organism. It is, however, doubtful that polymerization could have occurred in the aqueous environment of early Earth, as it would be very rare for monomers to interact precisely enough with one another to polymerize. It is more likely that solid surfaces, especially clays, could have provided the type of environment necessary for polymerization to occur **(Figure 3.12)**. Clays consist of very thin layers of minerals separated by layers of water only a few nanometres thick. The layered structure of clay is also

charged, allowing for molecular adhesion forces to bring monomers together in precise orientations that could more readily lead to polymer formation. Clays can also store the potential energy that may have been used for energy-requiring polymerization reactions. This *clay hypothesis* is supported by laboratory experiments that demonstrate that the formation of short nucleic acid chains and polypeptides can be synthesized on a clay surface.

STUDY BREAK

1. For understanding the origins of life, what was the significance of the Miller–Urey experiment?
2. What is the difference between a reducing atmosphere and an oxidizing atmosphere?

3.3　From Macromolecules to Life

In the previous section, we discussed how processes present on early Earth could have generated macromolecules crucial to the development of life. However, if we are to develop a comprehensive model for the origin of life, we need to explain the evolution of three key attributes of a modern cell: (1) a membrane-defined compartment—the cell, (2) a system to store genetic information and use it to guide the synthesis of specific proteins, and (3) energy-transforming pathways to bring in energy from the surroundings and harness it to sustain life. In this section, we discuss possible scenarios for the evolution of these key attributes and consider a number of hypotheses, some of which are supported by laboratory experiments.

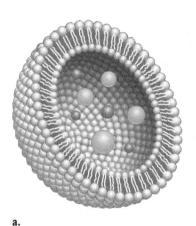
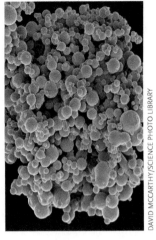

a. b.

Figure 3.13

Liposome. **(a)** An artist's rendition of a liposome, which is composed of a lipid bilayer. Liposomes can assemble spontaneously under simulated primordial conditions. **(b)** Phase micrograph of lipid vesicles assembled from phospholipids in the laboratory.

3.3a Lipid Spheres May Have Led to the Development of Cells

A critical step along the path to life is the formation of a membrane-defined compartment. Such a compartment would allow for primitive metabolic reactions to take place in an environment that is distinctly different than the external surroundings; the concentration of key molecules could be higher, and greater complexity could be maintained in a closed space. **Protobiont** is the term given to a group of abiotically produced organic molecules that are surrounded by a membrane or membranelike structure. Laboratory experiments have shown that protobionts could have formed spontaneously, that is, without any input of energy, given the conditions on primordial Earth. An early type of protobiont could have been similar to a liposome, which is a lipid vesicle in which the lipid molecules form a bilayer very similar to a cell membrane **(Figure 3.13)**. Liposomes can easily be made in the laboratory and are **selectively permeable**, allowing only some molecules to move in and out. As well, liposomes can swell and contract depending on the osmotic conditions of their environment.

Recent research from the laboratory of Jack Szostak at Harvard University has shown that the presence of clay not only catalyzes the polymerization of nucleic acids (see Section 3.2) but also accelerates the formation of lipid vesicles. As well, clay particles often become encapsulated in these vesicles, which would provide catalytically active surfaces within membrane vesicles upon which key reactions could take place. Researchers continue to experiment with producing different types of protobionts in the laboratory as a step toward understanding the origins of the first living cell. Present-day thinking is that a lipid membrane system must have evolved simultaneously with a genetic information system (see below).

3.3b RNA Can Carry Information and Catalyze Reactions

As discussed in Chapter 2, DNA is the molecule that provides every cell with the genetic instructions necessary to function. Recall as well that the information in DNA is copied into RNA, which directs protein synthesis on ribosomes. Even the simplest prokaryotic cell contains thousands of proteins, each coded by a unique DNA sequence, a gene. The flow of information from DNA to RNA to protein is common to all forms of life and is referred to as the central dogma **(Figure 3.14)**. Each step of the information flow requires the involvement of a group of proteins called enzymes, which catalyze the transcription of DNA into RNA and the translation of the RNA into protein. Enzymes are discussed in detail in Chapter 4.

A fundamental question about the flow of information from DNA to RNA to protein is: how did such a

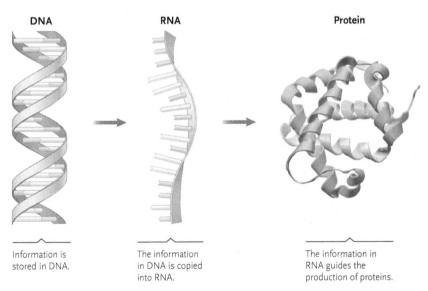

DNA	RNA	Protein
Information is stored in DNA.	The information in DNA is copied into RNA.	The information in RNA guides the production of proteins.

Figure 3.14

The central dogma. Information in DNA is used to synthesize proteins through an RNA intermediate. How did such a system evolve when the product, proteins, is required in modern-day cells to catalyze each step?

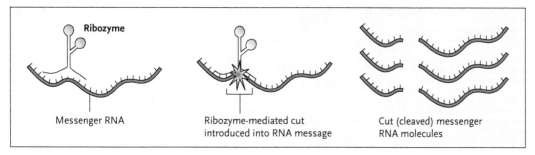

Figure 3.15

Ribozyme. An example of a ribozyme binding to an RNA molecule and catalyzing its breakage. Within a modern-day cell, such reactions may help control gene expression by altering the abundance of functional messenger RNA (mRNA) molecules.

In figure: Ribozyme / Messenger RNA / Ribozyme-mediated cut introduced into RNA message / Cut (cleaved) messenger RNA molecules

system evolve when the products of the process, proteins, are required to catalyze each step of the process? A breakthrough in our understanding of how such a system may have evolved came in the early 1980s when Thomas Cech and Sydney Altman, working independently, discovered a group of RNA molecules that could themselves act as catalysts. This group of RNA catalysts, called **ribozymes**, can catalyze reactions on the precursor RNA molecules that lead to their own synthesis, as well as on unrelated RNA molecules **(Figure 3.15)**. Ribozymes have catalytic properties because these single-stranded molecules can fold into very specific shapes based on intramolecular hydrogen bonding or base pairing. The fact that specificity in folding imparts specificity in function is very common to proteins, especially enzymes, where precise three-dimensional shape is critical for reacting with substrate molecules. Protein folding is discussed in more detail in *The Purple Pages*.

The discovery of ribozymes revolutionized thinking about the origin of life. Instead of the contemporary system that requires all three molecules—DNA, RNA, and protein—early life may have existed in an "RNA world," where a single type of molecule, RNA, could serve as a carrier of information (due to its nucleotide sequence) and a structural/functional molecule similar to a protein (due to its ability to form unique three-dimensional shapes). Before the discovery of ribozymes, enzymes were the only known biological catalysts. For their remarkable discovery, Sydney Altman and Thomas Cech, shared the Nobel Prize in Chemistry in 1989.

3.3c RNA Is Replaced by DNA for Information Storage and Proteins for Catalysis

If life developed in an RNA world, where RNA served as both an information carrier and a catalyst, why is it that in all contemporary organisms genetic information is stored in DNA, and why do enzymes (proteins) catalyze the vast majority of biological reactions? The simple answer is that they do the respective jobs of information storage (DNA) and catalysis (protein) far better than RNA does by itself; thus, the evolution of these

molecules would have given organisms that had them a distinct advantage over others that relied solely on RNA.

A possible scenario for the development of today's system of information transfer is shown in **Figure 3.16.** The first cells may have contained only RNA, which was self-replicating and could catalyze a small number of reactions critical for survival. It is hypothesized that a small population of RNA molecules then evolved that could catalyze the formation of very short proteins before the development of ribosomes. Recall from Chapter 2 that the ribosome is the organelle in contemporary organisms required for protein synthesis. It is interesting to note that the ribosome, which plays a key role as an intermediate between RNA and protein, is composed of about two-thirds RNA and one-third protein. In fact, it is the RNA component of the ribosome, not the protein, that actually catalyzes the incorporation of amino acids onto a growing peptide chain. Thus, the ribosome can be considered a type of ribozyme.

Cells that evolved the ability to use the information present in RNA to direct the synthesis of even small proteins would be at a tremendous advantage because proteins are far more versatile than RNA molecules—for three reasons. First, the catalytic power of most enzymes is much greater than that of a ribozyme. A typical enzyme can catalyze the same reaction using

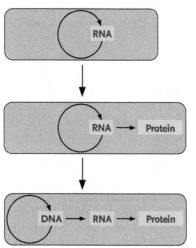

Figure 3.16

Possible scenario for the evolution of the flow of information from DNA to RNA to protein.

In figure: RNA / RNA → Protein / DNA → RNA → Protein

L1 Ligase Ribozyme

In the RNA world, RNA served as the molecule of information storage as well as structure and catalysis. To replicate RNA, individual nucleotide triphosphate monomers need to be joined, or ligated, together to form the RNA polymer. Today, this ligation reaction, carried out by a group of protein enzymes called polymerases, can result in RNA strands being many thousands of nucleotides in length. How this polymerization reaction would have been catalyzed in an RNA-only world stumped scientists for years.

Using what is called *in vitro* evolution and selection, scientists recently produced a range of synthetic ribozymes that do not currently exist in nature. One of these synthetic ribozymes is called the L1 ligase ribozyme, and it has been shown to catalyze the joining of two RNA monomers. This finding clearly suggests that, although not currently found in nature, a ribozyme capable of ligating nucleotides together may have existed on primitive Earth.

a pool of substrate molecules many thousands of times a second. By comparison, the rate of catalysis of most ribozymes is one-tenth to one-hundredth that of enzymes. Second, while the number of ribozymes is very small, a typical cell synthesizes a huge array of different proteins. Twenty different kinds of amino acids, in different arrangements, can be incorporated into a protein, whereas an RNA molecule is composed of different combinations of only four nucleotides. Third, amino acids can interact chemically with each other in bonding arrangements not possible between nucleotides. For these reasons, proteins are the dominant structural and functional molecule of a modern cell.

Continuing with the possible scenario shown in Figure 3.16, the evolution of DNA would have followed that of proteins. Compared with RNA, molecules of DNA are more structurally complex. Not only is DNA double stranded, but it also contains the sugar deoxyribose, which is more difficult to synthesize than the ribose found in molecules of RNA. A possible sequence begins with DNA nucleotides being produced by random removal of an oxygen atom from the ribose subunits of RNA nucleotides. At some point, the DNA nucleotides paired with the RNA informational molecules and were assembled into complementary copies of the RNA sequences. Some modern-day viruses carry out this RNA-to-DNA reaction using the enzyme reverse transcriptase (see Chapter 23). Once the DNA copies were made, selection may have favoured DNA, as it is a much better way to store information than RNA, for three main reasons:

- Each strand of DNA is chemically more stable, and less likely to degrade, than a strand of RNA.
- The base uracil found in RNA is not found in DNA; it has been replaced by thymine. This may be because the conversion of cytosine to uracil is a common mutation in DNA. By utilizing thymine in DNA, any uracil is easily recognized as a damaged cytosine that needs to be repaired.
- DNA is double stranded, so in the case of a mutation to one of the stands, the information contained on the complementary strand can be used to correctly repair the damaged strand.

The stability of DNA is illustrated by the fact that intact DNA can be successfully extracted from tissues that are many thousands of years old. The well-known novel and movie *Jurassic Park* are based on this demonstrated ability. By comparison, RNA needs to be quickly isolated, even from freshly isolated cells, using a strict protocol to prevent its degradation.

3.3d Simple Oxidation–Reduction Reactions Probably Preceded Metabolism

Hypotheses concerning the evolution of energy transduction and metabolism have been particularly difficult to test. Oxidation–reduction reactions were probably among the first energy-releasing reactions of the primitive cells. In our cells, we *oxidize* food molecules (e.g., sugars) and use some of the liberated energy (in the form of electrons) to *reduce* other molecules. In primitive cells, the electrons removed in an **oxidation** reaction would have been transferred in a one-step process to the substances being reduced. This, however, is not very efficient and leads to a lot of wasted energy. Over time, multi-step processes would have evolved, whereby the energy from oxidation is slowly released. A good example of the slow release of energy is cellular respiration, which is discussed in Chapter 6. The greater efficiency of stepwise energy release would have favoured development of intermediate carriers and opened the way for primitive electron transport chains.

As part of the energy-harnessing reactions, adenosine triphosphate (ATP) became established as the coupling agent that links energy-releasing reactions to those requiring energy. ATP may have first entered early cells as one of many organic molecules absorbed from the primitive environment. Initially, it was probably simply hydrolyzed into adenosine diphosphate (ADP) and inorganic phosphate, resulting in the release of energy. Later, as early cells evolved, some of the energy released during electron transfer was probably used to synthesize ATP directly from ADP and inorganic phosphate. Because of the efficiency and versatility of energy transfer by ATP, it gradually became the primary substance connecting energy-releasing and energy-requiring reactions in early cells.

STUDY BREAK

1. What are ribozymes, and what is their significance in our understanding of the origins of life?
2. In what ways is DNA better than RNA for storing genetic information?

3.4 The Earliest Forms of Life

Given hypotheses proposed for how they may have developed, what do we actually know about the earliest forms of life? In this section, we look at geological and fossil records for the earliest evidence of life. As discussed in Chapter 2, because the architecture of prokaryotic cells is the simplest known, they were most probably the first types of cells to evolve.

3.4a The Earliest Evidence of Life Is Found in Fossils

The earliest conclusive evidence of life is found in the fossilized remains of structures called stromatolites, the oldest being formed about 3.5 billion years ago. **Stromatolites** are a type of layered rock that is formed when microorganisms bind particles of sediment together, forming thin sheets **(Figure 3.17)**. Stromatolites are found in habitats characterized by warm shallow water and are most common in Australia. Modern-day stromatolites are formed by the action of a specific group of photosynthetic bacteria called cyanobacteria. Because they possess a sophisticated metabolism (discussed below), cyanobacteria do not represent the earliest forms of life but rather were preceded by much simpler organisms.

Indirect (nonfossil) evidence of life existing before 3.5 billion years ago comes from research looking at the carbon composition of ancient rocks. Early photosynthetic organisms would have had the ability to take CO_2 from the atmosphere and use it to synthesize various organic molecules (sugars, amino acids, etc.). During this process, organisms would have preferentially incorporated the carbon-12 isotope (^{12}C) over other isotopes such as carbon-13 (^{13}C) (see *The Purple Pages* for a discussion of isotopes). Researchers have discovered sedimentary rocks originating from the ocean floor that contain deposits that have lower levels of the ^{13}C isotope than expected. The most likely explanation is that the deposits are actually the remains of ancient microbes. These sediments have been dated to approximately 3.9 billion years ago. If correct, this would push the origins of life to perhaps as early as 4 billion years ago—approximately 600 million years after the formation of the planet.

3.4b The First Cells Relied on Anaerobic Metabolism

The earliest forms of life were most likely **heterotrophs**, which are organisms that obtain carbon from organic molecules. Modern animals, including humans, are examples of heterotrophs; we extract energy from organic molecules such as sugars, proteins, and fats. Since the early atmosphere contained only trace amounts of oxygen, the earliest heterotrophs must have relied on anaerobic (without oxygen) forms of respiration and fermentative pathways to extract energy from organic molecules (these forms of metabolism are discussed in Chapter 6).

Compared to heterotrophs, **autotrophs** obtain carbon from the environment in an inorganic form, most often carbon dioxide. Plants and other photosynthetic organisms are the dominant autotrophs today. The earliest type of photosynthesis, which probably developed soon after heterotrophy, was *anoxygenic photosynthesis*. Today this form of autotrophy is found only in some groups of bacteria. In anoxygenic photosynthesis, compounds such as

a.

Bill Bachmann/Science Source

b.

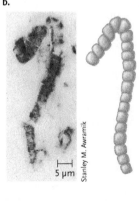

Stanley M. Awramik

⊢—⊣ 5 μm

Figure 3.17
Early fossil evidence of life.
(a) Stromatolites exposed at low tide in Western Australia's Shark Bay. These mounds, which consist of mineral deposits made by photosynthetic cyanobacteria, are about 2000 years old; they are highly similar in structure to fossil stromatolites that formed more than 3 billion years ago. **(b)** Structures that are believed to be a strand of fossil prokaryote cells in a rock sample that is 3.5 billion years old.

hydrogen sulfide and ferrous iron (Fe^{2+}) are used as electron donors for the light reactions of photosynthesis. As we will discuss in detail in Chapter 7, the products of the light reactions, ATP and NADPH, are used to synthesize organic molecules from CO_2.

3.4c Oxygenic Photosynthesis Led to the Rise in Oxygen in the Atmosphere

Starting about 2.5 billion years ago, oxygen (O_2) levels in the atmosphere began increasing. Evidence for this comes from dating a type of sedimentary rock called banded iron **(Figure 3.18)**. Geologists believe that these distinctive striped rocks were formed in the sediments of lakes and oceans when dissolved oxygen reacted with the iron in the water, forming a red-coloured precipitate, iron oxide (rust), which ended up being incorporated into the resulting sedimentary rock formations (see Figure 3.18).

An obvious question to ask is: where did the oxygen come from? Recall from the last section that ancient stromatolites were most probably formed by the action of a group of bacteria called cyanobacteria. Unlike other autotrophs that used hydrogen sulfide or Fe^{2+} as an electron donor for photosynthesis, cyanobacteria had the remarkable ability to use an electron donor that was far more common—water **(Figure 3.19)**. The oxidation of water releases not only electrons, which can be used for photosynthetic electron transport, but also molecular oxygen. It is thought that initially the free oxygen was incorporated into mineral deposits including iron. It was only after these reservoirs became full that the oxygen started to accumulate in the atmosphere. Because it releases oxygen, photosynthesis that relies on the oxidation of water as the source of electrons is termed *oxygenic photosynthesis*.

Unlike organisms that use hydrogen sulfide or Fe^{2+}, the ability to oxidize water meant that cyanobacteria could thrive almost anywhere on the planet where there was sunlight. After all, when was the last time you crossed campus and stepped in a puddle of hydrogen sulfide? As a result of the huge ecological advantage that came with being able to oxidize water, the abundance of cyanobacteria on the planet exploded and they quickly became a dominant form of life. Astonishingly, although it evolved perhaps as early as 3.5 billion years

Figure 3.18
Banded iron. The rust layers in banded iron formations provide evidence for the rise of atmospheric oxygen.

b. $2H_2O + \dfrac{\text{light}}{\text{energy}} \longrightarrow 4H^+ + 4e^- + O_2$

Figure 3.19
Cyanobacteria. **(a)** Micrograph of a filamentous cyanobacterium of the genus *Nostoc*. **(b)** Ancient cyanobacteria, like modern photosynthetic organisms, were able to use water as an electron donor for photosynthesis. A consequence was the formation of oxygen (O_2), which accumulated in the atmosphere.

ago, oxygenic photosynthesis remains the dominant form of photosynthesis and is used by all plants and algae, as well as present-day cyanobacteria.

3.4d Could Life Have Come to Earth from Space?

Some scientists believe that instead of the evolution of life through processes mentioned above, life on Earth had an extraterrestrial origin. Panspermia is the name given to the hypothesis that very simple forms of life are present in outer space and that these may have "seeded" early Earth. As scientists have never found any life existing outside of Earth, there is no evidence to directly support this hypothesis. However, two points of discussion lend support to the idea of an extraterrestrial origin of life on Earth.

First, although life seems very complex, it arose relatively quickly after the formation of Earth. Earth formed 4.6 billion years ago, and we have clear fossil evidence of life dated to about 3.5 billion years ago and chemical evidence to about 3.9 billion years ago. Given that primordial Earth had to cool after being formed before life could develop, some scientists argue that this represents too short a period of time for life to develop solely by abiotic processes occurring on the cooling planet.

Second, research in the past few decades has shown that life is far more resilient than previously thought and could possibly survive for millennia in space. An *extremophile* is the general term given to an organism that is found growing in environments that are lethal to most other organisms. Most extremophiles—mainly bacteria and archaea—can thrive under conditions such as extreme temperature, high pressure, high salinity, and high radiation levels. Research on extremophiles in recent years has shown that life is far more resilient than previously thought and thus it is quite possible that organisms may be able to survive in a dormant state in interstellar space. Prolonged dormancy is a property of reproductive structures called spores, which are produced

Lyle Whyte, Astrobiologist, *McGill University*

The heightened research interest into extremophiles coupled with technological advances that are driving the robotic exploration of Mars and other planets has spurred the development of the multidisciplinary science of astrobiology. Broadly defined, astrobiology is the study of the origin, evolution, distribution, and future of life in the universe. The field encompasses the search for habitable environments within and outside our solar system and the search for evidence of prebiotic chemistry and life on Mars and elsewhere. As well, astrobiology includes laboratory and field research into the origins and early evolution of life on Earth and studies of the potential for life to adapt to challenges on Earth and in space.

Canada is at the forefront of astrobiology research, as the government has recently established the Canadian Astrobiology Training Program. The program will create the first cross-disciplinary, multi-institutional undergraduate, graduate, and postdoctoral training program in astrobiology. This initiative brings together researchers at five institutions (McGill University, McMaster University, Western University, University of Winnipeg, and University of Toronto) with expertise in fields as diverse as geology, chemistry, physics, astronomy, microbiology, and robotics.

The head of the Canadian Astrobiology Training Program is Lyle Whyte of McGill University. Whyte is a Canada Research Chair in Environmental Microbiology. His research examines microbial biodiversity and ecology in unique Canadian high-Arctic ecosystems and is contributing significantly to the knowledge of the diversity, abundance, and critical roles played by microorganisms in polar regions. His research is providing new insights into microbial life at subzero temperatures and their role in global biogeochemical cycling. Whyte and his colleagues do considerable field research in the Canadian Arctic, which is considered by NASA and the Canadian Space Agency to be one of the best sites around the globe to mimic conditions on Mars.

by a number of bacteria and simple eukaryotes. Bacterial spores, in particular, are highly resistant to changes in the external environment and can be restored to active growth after exposure to water and moderate temperatures. Extremophiles have become a major area of research and have led, in part, to the development of the science of astrobiology (see "People behind Biology," Box 3.2).

3.4e All Present-Day Organisms Are Descended from a Common Ancestor

Based on comparing the sequence of ribosomal RNA, all present-day organisms can be categorized into one of three *domains:* Archaea, Bacteria, and Eukarya **(Figure 3.20).** Because both archaea and bacteria share

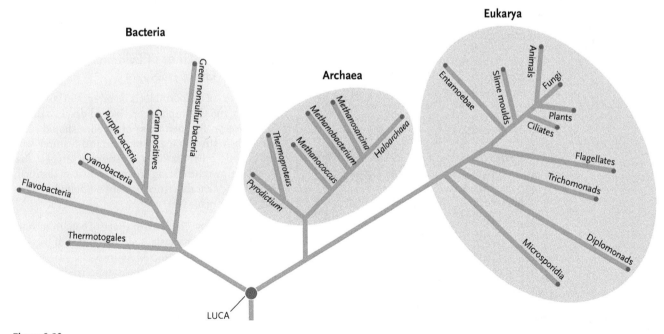

Figure 3.20
The three domains of life: Bacteria, Archaea, and Eukarya. This evolutionary tree is based on the sequencing of ribosomal RNA. All present-day organisms are thought to be descended from a common ancestor—the last universal common ancestor or LUCA.

a similar cell architecture (see Chapter 2), including the lack of a nucleus, they are often referred to as prokaryotes. But as discussed in detail in Chapter 22, archaea and bacteria are quite distinct, and evidence indicates that they are not evolutionarily closely related. In fact, molecular evidence indicates that archaea are more closely related to eukaryotes (the Eukarya) than to bacteria (see Figure 3.20, p. 65).

As will be discussed in detail in subsequent chapters, there are clear distinctions in structure and function among archaea, bacteria, and eukaryotes. This said, all life-forms currently on Earth share a remarkable set of common attributes. Perhaps the most fundamental of these are the following: (1) cells made of lipid molecules brought together forming a bilayer; (2) a genetic system based on DNA; (3) a system of information transfer—DNA to RNA to protein; (4) a system of protein assembly from a pool of amino acids by translation using messenger RNA (mRNA) and **transfer RNA** (tRNA) using ribosomes; (5) reliance on proteins as the major structural and catalytic molecule; (6) use of ATP as the molecule of chemical energy; and (7) the breakdown of glucose by the metabolic pathway of glycolysis to generate ATP.

The fact that these seven attributes are shared by all life on Earth suggests that all present-day organisms descended from a common ancestor (Figure 3.20, p. 65) that had all of these attributes. This is not to say that life evolved only once. It is quite possible that life arose many times on early Earth, each form perhaps having some of the attributes listed above. The similarities across all domains of life present today indicate, however, that only one of these primitive life-forms has descendants that survive today. We call the original life-form from which all archaea, bacteria, and eukaryotes are descended LUCA for last universal common ancestor (see Figure 3.20). Recent sequence analysis of certain proteins that have representatives in all three domains of life has given strong quantitative support to the common-ancestry hypothesis.

STUDY BREAK

1. Compared to anoxygenic photosynthesis, what is the ecological advantage to an organism of oxygenic photosynthesis?
2. What is meant by the term *last universal common ancestor (LUCA)*?

3.5 The Eukaryotic Cell and the Rise of Multicellularity

There is general agreement within the scientific community that the oldest fossils of eukaryotes are about 2.1 billion years old. Understandably, the very first eukaryotes may have appeared earlier. In fact, there is chemical evidence of eukaryotes existing as early as 2.5 billion years ago.

Present-day eukaryotic cells have two major characteristics that distinguish them from either the archaea or bacteria: (1) the separation of DNA and cytoplasm by a nuclear envelope and (2) the presence in the cytoplasm of membrane-bound compartments with specialized metabolic and synthetic functions—mitochondria, chloroplasts, the endoplasmic reticulum (ER), and the Golgi complex, among others. Hypotheses for how various eukaryotic structures and functions arose abound, some with very strong scientific evidence, others backed mostly with conjecture. In this section, we discuss how eukaryotes most probably evolved from associations of prokaryotic cells, ending with a discussion of the rise of multicellular eukaryotes.

3.5a The Theory of Endosymbiosis Suggests That Mitochondria and Chloroplasts Evolved from Ingested Prokaryotes

One feature that is found in virtually all eukaryotic cells is energy-transforming organelles: mitochondria and chloroplasts. A large amount of evidence indicates that mitochondria and chloroplasts are actually descended from free-living prokaryotic cells **(Figure 3.21):** mitochondria are descended from aerobic (with oxygen) bacteria, while chloroplasts are descended from cyanobacteria. The established model of **endosymbiosis** states that the prokaryotic ancestors of modern mitochondria and chloroplasts were engulfed by larger prokaryotic cells, forming a mutually advantageous relationship called a **symbiosis.** Slowly, over time, the **host** cell and the endosymbionts became inseparable parts of the same organism.

3.5b Several Lines of Evidence Support the Theory of Endosymbiosis

If the theory of endosymbiosis is correct and both mitochondria and chloroplasts are indeed descendants of prokaryotic cells, then these organelles should share some clear structural and biochemical features with prokaryotic cells. Six lines of evidence suggest that these energy-transducing organelles do have distinctly prokaryotic characteristics that are not found in other eukaryotic organelles:

1. **Morphology.** The form or shape of both mitochondria and chloroplasts is similar to that of bacteria and archaea.
2. **Reproduction.** A cell cannot synthesize a mitochondrion or a chloroplast. Just like free-living prokaryotic cells, mitochondria and chloroplasts are derived only from pre-existing mitochondria and chloroplasts. Both chloroplasts and mitochondria divide by binary fission, which is how bacteria and archaea divide (see Chapter 22).

3. **Genetic information.** If the ancestors of mitochondria and chloroplasts were free-living cells, then these organelles should contain their own DNA. This is indeed the case. Both mitochondria and chloroplasts contain their own DNA, which contains protein-coding genes that are essential for organelle function. As with bacteria and archaea, the DNA molecule in mitochondria and chloroplasts is circular, while the DNA molecules in the nucleus are linear.

4. **Transcription and translation.** Both chloroplasts and mitochondria contain a complete transcription and translational machinery: genes encoded by the organelle genomes are translated into mRNA and translated on the ribosomes, messenger RNA (mRNA), and transfer RNA (tRNA) necessary to synthesize the proteins encoded by their DNA. The ribosomes of mitochondria and chloroplasts are very similar to the type found in bacteria (see point 6 on this page).

5. **Electron transport.** Similar to free-living prokaryotic cells, both mitochondria and chloroplasts have electron transport chains (ETCs) used to generate chemical energy. The ETCs of bacteria and archaea are found in the plasma membrane, and for such cells, swallowed up by endosymbiosis, this membrane is inside the membrane of the endocytic vesicle. Indeed, both mitochondria and chloroplasts have double membranes, and it is the inner membrane that contains the ETC.

6. **Sequence analysis.** Sequencing of the RNA that makes up the ribosomes of chloroplasts and mitochondria firmly establishes that they belong on the bacterial branch of the tree of life (see Figure 3.20, p. 65). Chloroplast ribosomal RNA is most similar to that of cyanobacteria, while mitochondrial ribosomal RNA is most similar to that of proteobacteria.

Whereas virtually all eukaryotic cells contain mitochondria, only plants and algae contain both mitochondria and chloroplasts. This fact indicates that endosymbiosis occurred in stages (see Figure 3.21), with the event leading to the evolution of mitochondria occurring first. Once eukaryotic cells with the ability for aerobic respiration developed, some of these became photosynthetic after taking up cyanobacteria, evolving into the plants and algae of today.

3.5c Horizontal Gene Transfer Followed Endosymbiosis

The term **genome** is defined as the complete complement of an organism's genetic material. For eukaryotes, it is common to distinguish between the DNA found in the nucleus (the nuclear genome) and the DNA that resides in either the mitochondrion (mitochondrial genome) or the chloroplast (chloroplast genome).

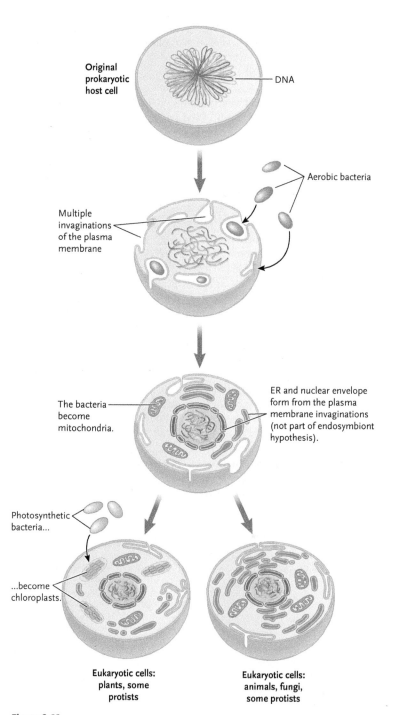

Figure 3.21
The theory of endosymbiosis. The mitochondrion is thought to have originated from an aerobic prokaryote that lived as an endosymbiont within an anaerobic prokaryote. The chloroplast is thought to have originated from a photosynthetic prokaryote that became an endosymbiont within an aerobic cell that had mitochondria.

A typical bacterium has a genome that contains about 3000 protein-coding genes. If both mitochondria and chloroplasts had once been free-living prokaryotic cells, then their genomes should have roughly the same number of genes—interestingly, they don't. The human mitochondrial genome comprises only 37 genes, and the chloroplast genome of the green alga *Chlamydomonas reinhardtii* has 99 genes. What happened to all those other genes?

Following endosymbiosis, the early eukaryotic cell would have contained at least two (nucleus and protomitochondria) and perhaps three (nucleus, protomitochondria, and protochloroplast) compartments—each with its own complete genome. These compartments and genomes would have functioned independently, each coding for proteins required for their own structure and function, just like free-living organisms. This contrasts strongly with a modern eukaryotic cell, where the function of the cell is highly integrated—mitochondrial function, for example, is strongly linked to the overall metabolism of the cell. Two major processes led to this integration. First, some of the genes that were within the protomitochondrion or protochloroplast were lost. Many of these genes would have been redundant, as the nucleus would already have genes that encode proteins with the same function. Second, many of the genes within the protomitochondria and protochloroplast were relocated to the nucleus. This process, called horizontal gene transfer (HGT), is thought to have occurred because of the evolutionary advantage that the early eukaryotic cell would gain by centralizing crucial genetic information in one place, the nucleus. It's important to realize that the outcome of HGT was not a change in gene function, only a change in the location of the gene—the nucleus as opposed to the mitochondrion or chloroplast **(Figure 3.22)**. As a side note, HGT doesn't pertain only to endosymbiotic gene transfer but to any movement of genes between organisms other than to offspring. HGT is seen as a major mechanism of diversification of genomes and thus evolution, especially in archaea and bacteria.

In a typical eukaryotic cell today, over 90% of the proteins required for mitochondrial or chloroplast function are encoded by genes that are found in the nucleus. To go along with this change of location, a large protein trafficking and sorting machinery had to evolve (Figure 3.22). Following transcription in the nucleus and translation on cytosolic ribosomes, proteins destined for the chloroplast or mitochondrion need to be correctly sorted and imported into these energy-transducing organelles, where they are trafficked to the correct location.

A major unanswered question that is being actively studied is: why do both mitochondria and chloroplasts still retain a genome—why haven't all genes moved to the nucleus? One possibility is that perhaps gene transfer is not yet complete. This seems to be the case for many chloroplast genomes. Related plant species can differ with regard to the location of a particular gene. It is not uncommon for one species to have the gene in the nucleus and a related species to have the same gene localized to the chloroplast. Another hypothesis is that since most of the genes that are retained by the mitochondrion or chloroplast code for proteins involved in electron transport, the tight regulation of these genes, which is difficult to do if the genes are in the nucleus, is essential to maintaining optimal rates of energy transformation.

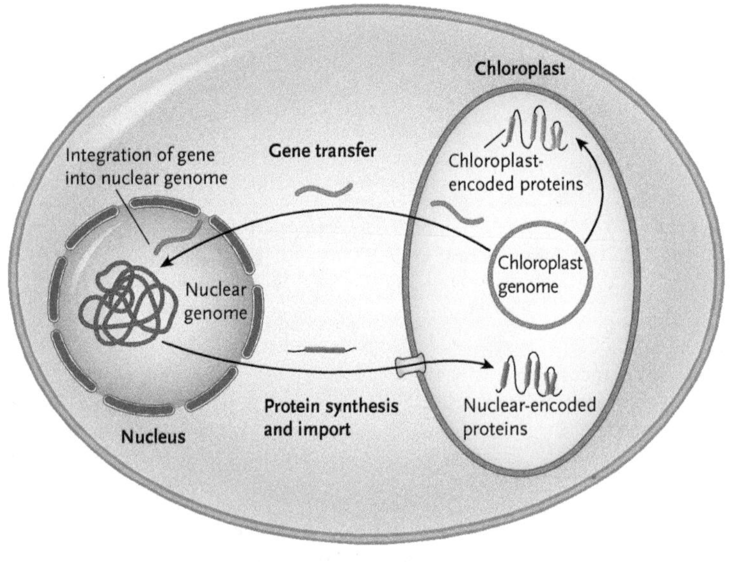

Figure 3.22
Horizontal gene transfer. Over evolutionary time, some protein-coding genes that were once part of the chloroplast or mitochondrial genome have been relocated to the nuclear genome. Following transcription of these genes, translation occurs in the cytosol before protein import into the organelle (mitochondrion or chloroplast).

3.5d The Endomembrane System May Be Derived from the Plasma Membrane

Recall from Chapter 2 that in addition to energy-transforming organelles (mitochondria and chloroplasts), eukaryotic cells are characterized by an **endomembrane system**—a collection of internal membranes that divide the cell into structural and functional regions. These include the nuclear envelope, the ER, and the Golgi complex. As we have just seen, there is very strong evidence in support of the endosymbiotic origin of chloroplasts and mitochondria; however, the origin of the endomembrane system remains unclear. The most widely held hypothesis is that it is derived from the infolding of the plasma membrane **(Figure 3.23)**. Researchers hypothesize that in cell lines leading from prokaryotic cells to eukaryotes, pockets of the plasma membrane may have extended inward and surrounded the nuclear region. Some of these membranes fused around the DNA, forming the nuclear envelope, which defines the nucleus. The remaining membranes formed vesicles in the cytoplasm that gave rise to the ER and the Golgi complex.

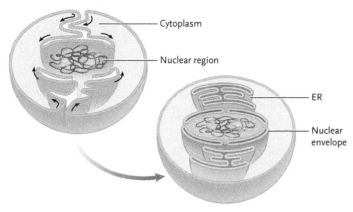

Figure 3.23

A hypothetical route for formation of the nuclear envelope and ER, through segments of the plasma membrane that were brought into the cytoplasm by endocytosis.

Cytoplasm

Nuclear region

ER

Nuclear envelope

3.5e Solving an Energy Crisis May Have Led to Eukaryotes

Bacteria and archaea outnumber eukaryotes on the planet by a huge margin. Compared to eukaryotes, archaea and bacteria show remarkable biochemical flexibility, being able to use an assortment of molecules as sources of energy and carbon and thrive in harsh environments uninhabitable to eukaryotes. That said, prokaryotic cells are simple—they lack the complexity of eukaryotes, which evolved into a tremendous diversity of forms, including plants, fungi, and animals. Within each of these groups are cells with remarkable specialization in form and function. Contrast this to archaea and bacteria, which have remained remarkably simple even though they evolved as early as 4 billion years ago.

The reason that bacteria and archaea have remained very simple is that increased complexity requires increased energy, and while eukaryotic cells can generate huge amounts of it, prokaryotic cells cannot. Mitochondria, like their aerobic progenitor bacteria, undergo aerobic respiration, which generates much greater amounts of ATP from the breakdown of organic molecules than pathways of anaerobic metabolism (this is discussed further in Chapter 6). As well, while a typical aerobic bacterium relies on its plasma membrane for many functions, including nutrient and waste transport and energy production, a typical eukaryotic cell contains hundreds of mitochondria, each having a huge internal membrane surface area dedicated to generating ATP.

The ability of early eukaryotes to generate more ATP led to remarkable changes. Cells could become larger, as now there was enough energy to support a greater volume. And cells could become more complex. This complexity comes about by being able to support a larger genome that codes for a greater number of proteins. By overcoming the energy

barrier, eukaryotes had the energy to support a wider variety of genes that led to what we know today to be eukaryotic-specific traits such as the **cell cycle**, sexual reproduction, phagocytosis, endomembrane trafficking, the nucleus, and multicellularity.

3.5f The Evolution of Multicellular Eukaryotes Led to Increased Specialization

One of the most profound transitions in the history of life was the evolution of multicellular eukaryotes. Clear evidence of multicellular eukaryotes, primarily small algae, appears in the fossil record starting about 1.2 billion years ago. It is easy to see how multicellularity could have developed. Perhaps a group of individual cells of a species came together to form a colony, or a single cell divided and the resulting two cells remained together. In the most simplest of multicellular organisms, all cells are structurally and functionally autonomous (independent). This gave way to a key trait of more advanced multicellular organisms: division of labour. That is, the cells were not functionally identical and thus usually not structurally similar. Some cells may specialize in harvesting energy, for example, whereas others may serve a specific role in the motility of the organism. In a multicellular system, the cells cooperate with one another for the benefit of the entire organism. Over evolutionary time, this specialization of cell function led to the development of the specialized tissues and organs that are so clearly evident in larger eukaryotes.

Like the earliest forms of life, there is little, if any, evidence in the fossil record of the earliest multicellular organisms. How they arose and developed is still an area of intense research. It is thought, however, that multicellularity arose more than once, most probably independently along the lineages leading to fungi, plants, and animals. A very useful model for the study of multicellularity is found in a group of green algae called the volvocine. All of the members of this group are evolutionarily closely related and span the full range of size and complexity, from the unicellular *Chlamydomonas*, through various colonial genera, to the multicellular *Volvox* **(Figure 3.24, p. 70)**. Unlike a true multicellular organism, a cell colony is a group of cells that are all of one type; there is no specialization in cell structure or function. *Volvox* consists of a sphere of two to three thousand small, flagellated *Chlamydomonas*-like cells that provide the individual *Volvox* with the ability to move. In addition, within the sphere lie about 16 large nonmotile cells that serve a specialized role in reproduction.

Figure 3.24
Differences in degree
of multicellularity
among volvocine algae.

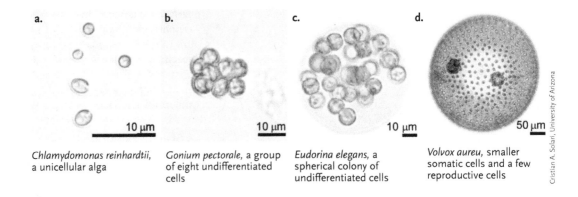

a. *Chlamydomonas reinhardtii*, a unicellular alga

b. *Gonium pectorale*, a group of eight undifferentiated cells

c. *Eudorina elegans*, a spherical colony of undifferentiated cells

d. *Volvox aureu*, smaller somatic cells and a few reproductive cells

Cristian A. Solari, University of Arizona

3.6 The Search for Extraterrestrial Life

Overall, the events outlined in this chapter may seem highly improbable: the formation of a habitable planet, followed by the abiotic synthesis of organic molecules, the development of the first cells, the development of DNA, RNA, proteins, and pathways of energy acquisition—all the way to the development of multicellular eukaryotes. Improbable? Perhaps. But we must keep in mind that these events took place over an almost unimaginable length of time—4.6 billion years! And as scientist and author George Wald of Harvard University put it, given so much time "the impossible becomes possible, the possible probable, and the probable virtually certain."

Most scientists maintain that the evolution of life on Earth was an inevitable outcome of the initial physical and chemical conditions on primordial Earth, brought about by its position relative to the Sun. If that is the case—that all you need is a planet in the habitable zone, then what is the probability of life existing elsewhere in our galaxy? Let's do a little arithmetic. The Milky Way galaxy contains an estimated 100 billion stars. Because the formation of planetary systems is thought to be a normal consequence of star formation, let's conservatively estimate that 50% of stars in the galaxy have planets. That would give us about 50 billion planetary systems. Given that perhaps two planets around each star would fall within

the habitable zone, this would put the total number of planets able to support life within our galaxy at 100 billion! Now of course the number of those planets that actually go on to develop life would be much less and the proportion that develop intelligent life and communicating civilizations would reduce the number even further. But even still, it is distinctly possible that

a.

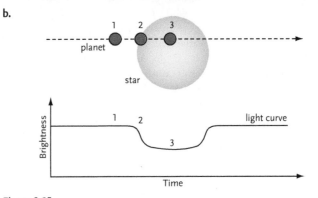

b.

Figure 3.25
Search for Earth-like planets. **(a)** Artist's depiction of the Kepler spacecraft, which is equipped with a photometer to detect Earth-like planets. **(b)** The transit method relies on measuring the very small but regular changes in the brightness of a star caused by an orbiting (transiting) planet.

the galaxy is teeming with advanced civilizations. Now what about finding them.

The search for extraterrestrial life is hampered by the incredible vastness of space. The closest star outside our solar system is some 40 trillion kilometres away, and using the fastest spacecraft humankind currently has, it would take a staggering 150 thousand years to get there! For this reason, the search for extraterrestrial life, which started about 50 years ago, has primarily focused on listening for the distinct signals of a communicating civilization using the science of radio astronomy. This type of detection has a huge advantage over spaceflight because radio waves travel at the speed of light. While using radio astronomy to detect signals from extraterrestrial civilizations continues, more recent initiatives are centred on the detection of Earth-like planets orbiting other stars. One method for this is employed in the NASA Kepler Mission that was launched in 2009 (Figure 3.25, p. 70). This project, named after the German astronomer Johannes Kepler, is a space observatory designed to continuously monitor the brightness of over 145 thousand stars. Armed with a powerful photometer, the observatory can detect the very faint but regular fluctuations in the brightness of stars. In what is termed the *transit method*, the photometer detects the slight but very regular changes in brightness of a star that are caused by a planet moving in front of and then behind the star relative to the position of the detector. Even before the Kepler Mission started, Earthbound observatories had identified over 400 extrasolar planets (planets outside our solar system). As of 2013, the Kepler mission had identified over 2740 planets, 618 of which are part of systems containing multiple planets.

STUDY BREAK

1. What is the evidence in support of endosymbiosis?
2. What are the key traits of a multicellular organism?

Review

To access course materials such as Aplia and other companion resources, please visit www.NELSONbrain.com.

3.1 What Is Life?

- All forms of life share seven characteristics: order, energy utilization, homeostasis, response to stimuli, growth and development, reproduction, and evolution.
- While a virus has some of the characteristics of life, these require it to infect living cells. Because of this it is not considered a form of life.
- The characteristics of life are referred to as emergent because they come about, or emerge, from many simpler interactions that, in themselves, do not have the properties found at the higher levels.

3.2 The Chemical Origins of Life

- Earth and the rest of the solar system were formed about 4.6 billion years ago.
- Life evolved on Earth in part because the planet is situated at a distance from the Sun so that water can exist in a liquid state. Earth is within the habitable zone of the solar system.
- The Oparin–Haldane hypothesis maintains that the organic molecules that formed the building blocks of life, such as amino acids, could have been formed given the conditions that prevailed on primitive Earth, including a reducing atmosphere that lacked oxygen.
- The Miller–Urey experiment demonstrated that abiotic synthesis of biologically important molecules is possible.

- The key macromolecules of life, such as proteins and nucleic acids, are polymers that were not formed by the Miller–Urey experiment. Instead, it is thought that polymerization reactions could have occurred on solid surfaces, such as clay.

3.3 From Macromolecules to Life

- The spontaneous formation of lipid vesicles (liposomes) may have served as the first membrane-bound compartments that developed into the first cells.
- Ribozymes are a group of RNA molecules that can catalyze specific reactions. Because they can store information and drive catalysis, it is thought that RNA was the first molecule.
- Because of their greater diversity and much higher rate of catalysis, proteins became the dominant structural and functional macromolecule of all cells.
- DNA is more stable than RNA and thus evolved as a better repository of genetic information.
- Early metabolism was probably based on simple oxidation–reduction reactions.

3.4 The Earliest Forms of Life

- Stromatolites dated to as early as 3.5 billion years ago represent the earliest fossil evidence of life. Chemical evidence suggests life may have originated 3.9 billion years ago.
- Panspermia is the hypothesis that very simple forms of life are present in space and seeded Earth soon after it cooled.
- Some early cells developed the capacity to carry out photosynthesis using water as an electron donor; the oxygen produced as a by-product accumulated, and

the oxidizing character of Earth's atmosphere increased. From this time on, organic molecules produced in the environment were quickly broken down by oxidation, and life could arise only from pre-existing life, as in today's world.

3.5 The Eukaryotic Cell and the Rise of Multicellularity

- The energy-transducing organelles—the chloroplasts and the mitochondria—are thought to have been derived from free-living prokaryotic cells.
- According to the theory of endosymbiosis, mitochondria developed from ingested aerobic bacteria; chloroplasts developed from ingested cyanobacteria.
- Following endosymbiosis, genes residing in the mitochondria and chloroplasts moved to the nucleus. This is a type of horizontal gene transfer (HGT).
- Eukaryotic cells possess an endomembrane system that probably evolved from infolding of the plasma membrane. The endomembrane system consists of the nuclear envelope, the endoplasmic reticulum (ER), and the Golgi complex.

- Eukaryotic cells are more complex than bacteria or archaea because mitochondria provide them with more energy.
- Multicellular eukaryotes probably evolved by differentiation of cells of the same species that had congregated into colonies. Multicellularity evolved several times, producing lineages of several algae and ancestors of fungi, plants, and animals.

3.6 The Search for Extraterrestrial Life

- The Milky Way galaxy contains about 100 billion stars. If 50% of those had planetary systems, and in each system 2 planets were within the habitable zone, that's potentially 100 billion planets able to sustain life.
- Interstellar distances are too great to use spacecraft to search for extraterrestrial life. Instead radio astronomy is used to listen for signals of intelligent civilization.
- Using powerful photometers, observatories in space and on the ground search for extrasolar planets by detecting the small but very regular changes in the brightness of a star caused by a transiting planet.

Questions

Self-Test Questions

1. Why are viruses not considered a form of life?
   a. They don't have a nucleus.
   b. They are not made of protein.
   c. They lack ribosomes.
   d. They cannot evolve.
   e. Thy lack nucleic acid.

2. According to the Oparin–Haldane hypothesis, what was the composition of the primordial atmosphere?
   a. water, molecular nitrogen (N_2), and carbon dioxide
   b. molecular hydrogen (H_2), water, ammonia, and methane
   c. water, molecular oxygen (O_2), and ammonia
   d. water, argon, and neon

3. Clay may have played an important role in what aspect of the development of life?
   a. formation of monomers such as amino acids
   b. formation of polymers such as short proteins or nucleic acids
   c. formation of membrane-bound compartments such as liposomes
   d. formation of multicellular organisms
   e. Both a and c are correct.

4. The Miller–Urey experiment was a huge breakthrough in our understanding of the origins of life. What was its major conclusion?
   a. Abiotic synthesis of molecules requires oxygen (O_2).
   b. Biological molecules could be formed without energy.
   c. Proteins could be synthesized without ribosomes.
   d. Abiotic synthesis of amino acids was possible.

5. Which of the following list of events is in the correct order of first appearance?
   a. O_2 in the atmosphere, anoxygenic photosynthesis, aerobic respiration, oxygenic photosynthesis
   b. oxygenic photosynthesis, anoxygenic photosynthesis, aerobic respiration, O_2 in the atmosphere
   c. anoxygenic photosynthesis, oxygenic photosynthesis, O_2 in the atmosphere, aerobic respiration
   d. aerobic respiration, O_2 in the atmosphere, oxygenic photosynthesis, anoxygenic photosynthesis

6. Which of the following statements about ribozymes is correct?
   a. They are composed of only RNA.
   b. They are able to catalyze reactions faster than enzymes.
   c. They were present only in ancient cells.
   d. Like proteins they are polymers of amino acids.

7. Why did DNA replace RNA as the means to store genetic information?
   a. The sugar ribose, present in DNA but not RNA, is less prone to breakdown.
   b. DNA contains uracil, which is more stable than the thymine present in RNA.
   c. Unlike RNA, DNA can exist in very complex three-dimensional shapes, which are very stable.
   d. The presence of complementary strands in DNA means that single base mutations can be easily repaired.

8. As part of the evolution of eukaryotic cells, infolding of the plasma membrane is thought to have led to the formation of which of the following?
   a. ribosomes
   b. microtubules
   c. mitochondria
   d. chromosomes
   e. ER

9. Which of the following statements supports the theory of endosymbiosis?
   a. Mitochondria contain proteins.
   b. Both mitochondria and chloroplasts possess their own genomes.
   c. Both mitochondria and chloroplasts are surrounded by a membrane.
   d. The nuclear envelope is derived from infolding of the plasma membrane.

10. What was an outcome of HGT?
    a. import of proteins into mitochondria
    b. increase in size of the chloroplast genome

c. relocation of proteins once localized to the mitochondria to the nucleus
d. decrease in the number of proteins in the chloroplast

Questions for Discussion

1. What evidence supports the idea that life originated through abiotic chemical processes?

2. Most scientists agree that life on Earth can arise only from pre-existing life, but also that life could have originated spontaneously on primordial Earth. Can you reconcile these seemingly contradictory statements?

3. What conditions would likely be necessary for a planet located elsewhere in the universe to evolve life similar to that on Earth?

4. What drove the evolution of the eukaryotic cell?

4

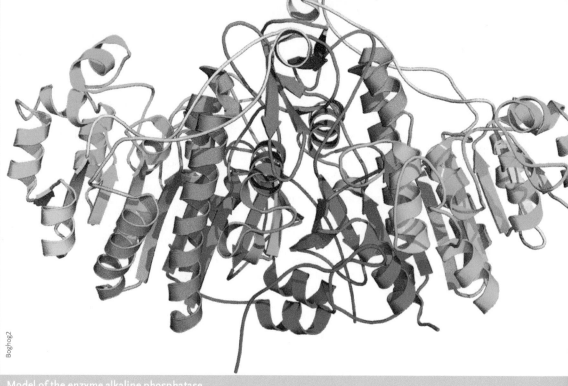

Boghog2

Energy and Enzymes

WHY IT MATTERS

Earth is a cold place—at least when it comes to chemical reactions. Life cannot survive at the high temperatures routinely used in industry for chemical synthesis. Instead, life relies on a group of catalysts called enzymes that speed up the rates of chemical reactions without the need for an increase in temperature.

Until recently, just how good enzymes are at speeding up reaction rates was not fully appreciated. Richard Wolfenden and his colleagues at the University of North Carolina experimentally measured the rates of a range of uncatalyzed and enzyme-catalyzed biochemical reactions. The prize for the greatest difference between the uncatalyzed rate and the enzyme-catalyzed rate goes to a reaction that simply removes a **phosphate group**. In the cell, a group of enzymes called phosphatases catalyze the removal of phosphate groups from a range of molecules, including proteins. The reversible addition and removal of a phosphate group from particular proteins is a central mechanism of intracellular communication in almost all cells (Chapter 5).

In the presence of the phosphatase enzyme the removal of the phosphate takes approximately 10 milliseconds. Wolfenden's research group calculated that in an aqueous environment such as within a cell, in the absence of an enzyme, the phosphate removal reaction would take over 1 trillion (10^{12}) years to occur. This exceeds the current estimate for the age of the universe! This makes the difference between the enzyme-catalyzed and uncatalyzed rates 21 orders of magnitude (10^{21}). For most reactions, the rate of the enzyme-catalyzed rate is many millions (10^6) of times faster than the uncatalyzed rate.

The high rates of catalysis brought about by the evolution of enzymes was of critical importance to the evolution of life on a relatively cold planet.

Enzymes are key players in the metabolic reactions that collectively accomplish the activities we associate with life, such as growth, reproduction, movement, and the ability to respond to stimuli. Central to these processes is the ability of organisms to harness and utilize energy from the surroundings, and thus this chapter starts with an overview of the principles of energy flow as governed by the laws of thermodynamics. This is followed by a focused discussion on the factors that govern chemical reactions and the central role played by **free energy**. We finish with an in-depth discussion of enzymes—the fundamental biological catalysts—which enable life to exist on this cold planet.

4.1 Energy and the Laws of Thermodynamics

Life, like all chemical and physical activities, is an energy-driven process. **Energy** is most conveniently defined as the capacity to do work. For example, it takes energy to move a car on a highway and it takes energy to climb a mountain. It also takes energy to build a protein from a group of amino acids or pump sucrose across a cell membrane.

4.1a Energy Exists in Different Forms

Energy can exist in many different forms, including chemical, electrical, and mechanical. Electromagnetic radiation, including visible, infrared, and ultraviolet light, is also a form of energy. While energy exists in many different forms, these can be transformed readily from one to another. The chemical energy present in a flashlight battery, for example, is converted into electrical energy that passes through the flashlight bulb, where it is transformed into light and heat.

All forms of energy can be grouped into one of two different types: kinetic and potential. **Kinetic energy** is the energy possessed by an object because it is in motion. Obvious examples of objects that possess kinetic energy are waves in the ocean, a falling rock, or a kicked football. A less obvious example is the kinetic energy of electricity, which is a flow of electrons. Photons of light are also a form of kinetic energy. The movement associated with kinetic energy is of use because it can perform work by making other objects move. **Potential energy** is stored energy, the energy an object has because of its position or chemical structure. A boulder at the top of a cliff has potential energy because of its position in the gravitational field of Earth. Likewise, a molecule has potential energy because of the specific arrangement of its atoms—this is also referred to as chemical energy.

So what is it about certain molecules that make them high in potential energy? The chemical energy present in a molecule has to do with the position of electrons within its atoms. In a way analogous to a boulder placed at different heights above the ground, the farther away an electron is from the nucleus of an atom the greater potential energy that electron possesses **(Figure 4.1)**. An electron, which is negatively charged, is attracted to the positively charged nucleus,

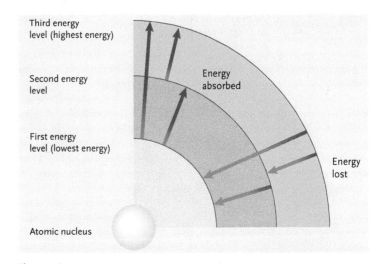

Figure 4.1

Energy levels of the electrons of an atom. Electrons can exist only in discrete energy states. When an electron gains energy it moves to a higher energy level that is farther away from the nucleus. When an electron loses energy it moves to a lower energy level closer to the nucleus.

and as it moves closer to the nucleus it loses energy. An electron moves to a higher energy level, farther from the nucleus, when it gains energy. The electronegativity of an atom strongly influences the potential energy it possesses. Atoms such as oxygen and nitrogen hold their electrons more tightly to their nucleus and thus contain less potential energy than less electronegative atoms, such as carbon and hydrogen.

4.1b The Laws of Thermodynamics Describe Energy and Its Transformation

The branch of science that concerns energy and how it changes during chemical and physical transformations is called **thermodynamics**. When discussing thermodynamics, it is important to define something called the system, which is the object being studied. A system can be anything—a single atom, one cell, or a planet. Everything outside the system is called the surroundings. The universe, in this context, is the total of the system and the surroundings. As well, it is important that we distinguish between three different types of systems: isolated, open, and closed **(Figure 4.2, p. 76)**.

- An *isolated system* is one that does not exchange matter or energy with its surroundings. The only truly isolated system is the universe itself. An insulated Thermos bottle is close to being an isolated system, as very little energy or matter is exchanged with the environment.
- A *closed system* can exchange energy, but not matter, with its surroundings. A saucepan of water with a lid heating on a stove is a good example of a closed system. Earth is also considered to be a closed

Figure 4.2
Isolated, closed, and open systems in thermodynamics.

a. Isolated system: does not exchange matter or energy with its surroundings

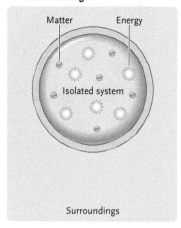

b. Closed system: exchanges energy with its surroundings

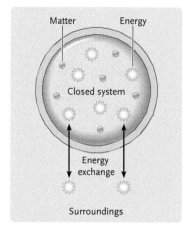

c. Open system: exchanges both energy and matter with its surroundings

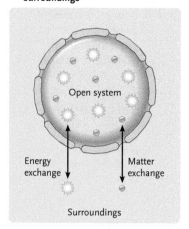

system—it takes in an enormous amount of energy generated by the Sun and releases heat, but no matter is exchanged between Earth and the rest of the universe. Each year a few meteorites hit Earth, but essentially we can consider it a closed system.

- In an *open system,* both energy and matter can move freely between the system and the surroundings. An ocean is a great example of an open system—it absorbs and releases energy, and, as a component of the hydrological cycle, water is constantly being lost and gained by the ocean through evaporation and precipitation.

4.1c The First Law of Thermodynamics: Energy Can Be Transformed but Not Created or Destroyed

Research by physicists and chemists in the nineteenth century concerning energy flow between systems and the surroundings led to the formulation of two fundamental laws of thermodynamics that apply to all systems, both living and nonliving. According to the **first law of thermodynamics,** *energy can be transformed from one form into another or transferred from one place to another, but it cannot be created or destroyed.* The first law of thermodynamics is illustrated nicely by Niagara Falls **(Figure 4.3a).** Water at the top of the falls has high potential energy because of its location in Earth's gravitational field. As the water moves over the waterfall, its potential energy is converted into kinetic

a.

b.

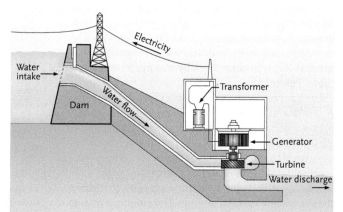

Figure 4.3
Niagara Falls. **(a)** The potential energy of the water is converted into kinetic energy as it moves over the falls. **(b)** A small portion of this kinetic energy is used to turn hydroelectric turbines, converting the gravitational energy into electrical energy. In accordance with the first law of thermodynamics, energy hasn't been gained or lost but has changed form. Niagara Falls generates approximately 4.4 gigawatts of power each year.

energy. The higher the waterfall, the more kinetic energy the water will possess. When the water reaches the bottom of the waterfall, its kinetic energy is transformed into other types of energy: heat, sound, and mechanical energy (causing weathering of the rocks). For thousands of years, the kinetic energy of waterfalls has been harnessed by people to do work. At Niagara Falls today, some of the kinetic energy in the moving water is converted into electricity through the use of hydroelectric turbines (Figure 4.3b) for the use of thousands of homes and businesses.

4.1d The Second Law of Thermodynamics: Energy Moves from Being Localized to Being Dispersed

Another important principle of thermodynamics is that the energy of a system tends to disperse or spread out. Many everyday situations illustrate this. For example, let's say you heat a pan on a stove and then switch the stove off **(Figure 4.4)**. At first the heat energy is concentrated very close to the pan, but slowly the heat energy disperses throughout the kitchen. This energy dispersal continues until no part of the room contains more energy than any other. This spreading out of energy is inevitable—it will happen.

In thermodynamics, the tendency of energy to become dispersed or spread out is defined as **entropy**, which is abbreviated S (think S for Spreading out). You may have been taught in high school that entropy is a measure of the *disorder* in a system. For example, a messy room has more entropy than a tidy room. But thinking of entropy as disorder is problematic for a couple of reasons. First, the idea of disorder cannot be applied scientifically in a precise way. Second, equating entropy with disorder gives you the impression that

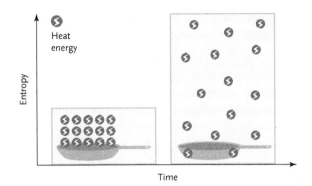

Figure 4.4

Energy tends to spread out, to become more dispersed over time. The thermodynamic measure of energy dispersal is called *entropy*.

From STARR/TAGGART/Evers/Starr, *Biology*, 12E. © 2009 Cengage Learning.

entropy is governed by spatial regularity (order), but it isn't. Thermodynamics deals specifically with energy, not with objects.

The concept of entropy forms the basis of the **second law of thermodynamics**, *the entropy of a system and the surroundings will increase—energy will always become more spread out.* Entropy is the measure of how much energy has flowed from being localized to becoming more widely dispersed.

The tendency of energy to spread out is the underlying reason that machines can never be 100% efficient. Although energy can be transformed from one form into another, a portion of the energy will always be lost to the surroundings by the tendency of energy to spread out. For example, the engine of a car only converts a portion of the energy in gasoline to the kinetic energy that powers the wheels **(Figure 4.5a)**. Likewise, only a portion of the energy in a notebook computer battery is used to run the computer. If you touch a car engine that has just been turned off

Figure 4.5

Two examples of thermodynamic systems that display the second law of thermodynamics. **(a)** A car engine converts only about 25% of the available energy in gasoline into mechanical energy. **(b)** A runner can access only about 40% of the energy in glucose to do the work of muscle contraction. In both cases, a significant portion of the energy localized in the fuel molecules is lost to the environment as heat and gases.

or put a notebook computer on your lap for an extended period of time, it is obvious where a lot of the energy is going. It is being lost to the surroundings as *heat,* which is the energy associated with random molecular motion. The inefficiency of energy transformations also applies to living cells. For example, cellular respiration converts less than half the potential energy in glucose into a form usable for metabolism (Figure 4.5b, p. 77). We will come back to and reinforce the link between thermodynamics and life later in this chapter.

STUDY BREAK

1. What is the underlying reason that atoms differ in potential energy?
2. What is the difference between a closed and an open system? Give some examples.

4.2 Free Energy and Spontaneous Processes

The reaction between molecules of carbon dioxide and water that produces glucose and oxygen requires energy to occur, but the reverse reaction can take place all by itself. Why is that? Likewise, O_2 will readily diffuse into a region where its concentration is lower, but it will never diffuse into a region where its concentration is higher. Why not? In this section we tackle one of the basics of thermodynamics, the factors that determine if a given reaction will occur by itself or whether it needs an input of energy. A process that can occur without energy input is referred to as a *spontaneous process* (we will refine this definition later in this section). It is important to remember that in the context of thermodynamics, the term *spontaneous* does not refer to how fast a reaction will occur. As discussed in "Why It Matters," some spontaneous reactions take a millisecond to occur, others a million years. Note: We use the terms *transformation, process,* and *reaction* interchangeably to include both chemical reactions (where bonds break and form) and physical transformations such as evaporation.

4.2a Energy Content and Entropy Contribute to Making a Reaction Spontaneous

The total potential energy of a system is called its **enthalpy,** or *H.* Transformations that absorb energy from the surroundings are termed **endothermic** and result in the products having more potential energy than the starting molecules. The overall

change in enthalpy ($\Delta H = H_{products} - H_{reactants}$) of an endothermic process is positive. The melting of ice is a simple example of an endothermic process. Compared to an endothermic process, a process that releases energy is called **exothermic**, as the products have less potential energy than the starting molecules (ΔH is negative). The burning of wood is a simple example of an exothermic process.

The change in enthalpy of a reaction is an important factor to evaluate to determine whether or not a reaction will occur spontaneously—however, it is not the only factor. The change in entropy is also an important consideration. Here we consider how changes in both enthalpy and entropy influence the spontaneity of a reaction.

1. *Reactions tend to be spontaneous if they are exothermic—the products have less potential energy than the reactants.* In chemical reactions the change in potential energy between products and reactants reflects a change in how tightly electrons are held by the atoms making up the molecules involved. As an example, let's look at the combustion of methane (natural gas) in air **(Figure 4.6).** The reaction is spontaneous because the reactants (methane and O_2) have greater potential energy than the products (carbon dioxide and water). The products have lower potential energy because the electrons are more tightly held by the atoms of the products than in the atoms of the reactants.

2. *Reactions tend to be spontaneous when the entropy of the products is greater than the entropy of the reactants.* Transformations tend to occur spontaneously if the energy of the products is more spread out than the energy in the starting molecules. As an example, let's look at the breakdown of glucose, a central feature of cellular respiration:

$$C_6H_{12}O_6 \text{ (s)} + 6O_2 \text{ (g)} \rightarrow 6CO_2 \text{ (g)} + 6H_2O \quad \text{(l)}$$

The reaction is spontaneous in part because of a change in enthalpy. However, its spontaneous nature is also because the entropy of the products is greater than the entropy of the reactants. But how do we know that the entropy increases simply by looking at the reaction?

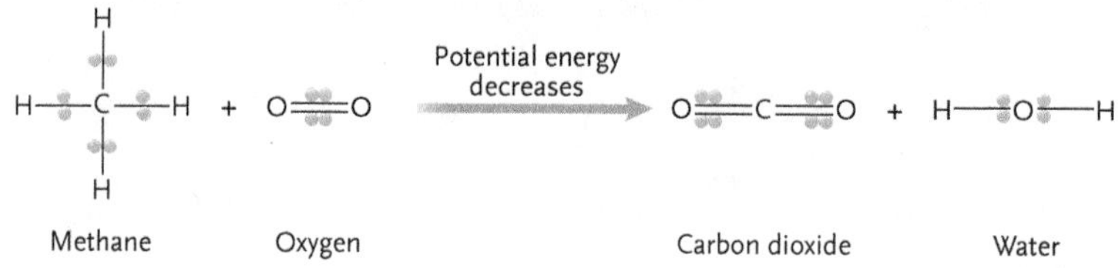

Methane   Oxygen   Carbon dioxide   Water

Figure 4.6

Combustion of methane is spontaneous because the products have less potential energy than the reactants. Compared to the reactants, the electronegative oxygen atoms in carbon dioxide and water hold the electrons more closely.

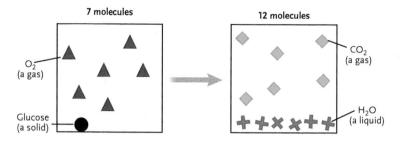

7 molecules

12 molecules

O_2
(a gas)

Glucose
(a solid)

CO_2
(a gas)

H_2O
(a liquid)

Figure 4.7

The breakdown of glucose results in an increase in entropy. This is because **(a)** the number of molecules increases and **(b)** a phase change has occurred (e.g., solid → liquid → gas).

Based on *Lehninger Principles of Biochemistry* (4th Ed.) Nelson, D., and Cox, M.; W.H. Freeman and Company, New York, 2005.

As illustrated in **Figure 4.7,** whenever a chemical reaction results in an increase in the number of molecules, entropy increases. In the example of the breakdown of glucose, 7 reacting molecules are transformed into 12 molecules of product. The entropy has increased because the energy has spread out over a greater number of molecules. Entropy also increases when a solid is converted into a liquid or a liquid into a gas. Energy spreads out more readily as matter undergoes these phase changes. In the example of the breakdown of glucose, 6 molecules of a gas and one molecule of a solid are converted into six molecules of a gas and six molecules of a liquid (Figure 4.7). A phase change in the other direction—gas to liquid or liquid to solid—decreases the entropy as the energy becomes more localized.

4.2b The Change in Free Energy Indicates Whether a Process Is Spontaneous

From our previous discussion we know that both enthalpy and entropy need to be considered to determine if a reaction is spontaneous. It was the American physicist Josiah Gibbs who arrived at the mathematical relationship of how entropy and enthalpy relate to reaction spontaneity. This is referred to as Gibbs free energy (G). The change in free energy ($\Delta G = G_{products} - G_{reactants}$) is a measure of whether or not a process is spontaneous. It can be calculated for any specific transformation using the formula

$$\Delta G = \Delta H - T\Delta S$$

where ΔH is the change in the enthalpy, ΔS is the change in the entropy of the system over the course of the reaction, and T is the temperature in degrees Kelvin (K). T is part of the entropy term because energy spreading increases as temperature increases.

Recall from the introduction to Section 4.2 that we referred to a *spontaneous* process as one that will occur by itself without any external input of energy. Now that we have introduced the concept of free energy, we can be more precise with our definition: a **spontaneous reaction** is one where the free energy of the products is less than the free energy of the reactants, ΔG is negative. A spontaneous process is also referred to as an **exergonic process (Figure 4.8a).** Similarly, a nonspontaneous process is one where the free energy of the products is greater than the free energy of the reactants, ΔG is positive. A nonspontaneous reaction is also referred to as an **endergonic process** (Figure 4.8b).

The formula $\Delta G = \Delta H - T\Delta S$ tells us that both the change in enthalpy and the change in entropy can influence the overall ΔG of a reaction. In many processes, like the breakdown of glucose, the change in enthalpy (ΔH is negative) and the change in entropy (ΔS is positive) both contribute to making the reaction exergonic. But this does not have to be the case. Let's consider a very interesting thermodynamic system: the ice cube. At room temperature, ice will spontaneously melt because the ice is absorbing energy from the surroundings. Since water has greater potential energy than ice, the melting of ice is an endothermic process (ΔH is positive)—and yet the process is exergonic (ΔG is negative). What

a. Exergonic reaction: Free energy is released, products have less free energy than reactants, and the reaction proceeds spontaneously.

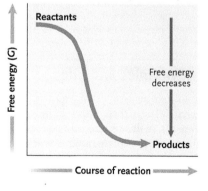

b. Endergonic reaction: Free energy is gained, products have more free energy than reactants, and the reaction is not spontaneous.

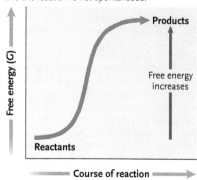

Figure 4.8

Exergonic and endergonic reactions.

explains the spontaneous melting of ice is the large increase in entropy as the solid ice changes into liquid water. The large positive $T\Delta S$ is greater than ΔH, making ΔG for the reaction negative.

Let's look at one more example of a spontaneous process: diffusion of molecules across a membrane. As illustrated in **Figure 4.9,** any molecule that can cross a membrane will move spontaneously from a compartment where it is at a higher concentration to a compartment where its concentration is lower. The spontaneous nature of diffusion is explained solely by the increase in entropy as the molecules and their associated energy spread out. Although there is no change in enthalpy (ΔH), the release of free energy during diffusion can be harnessed by the cell to do work. How this is accomplished is discussed in subsequent chapters.

4.2c Exergonic Processes Reach Equilibrium Rather Than Going to Completion

In the late nineteenth century, chemists were surprised to find that many chemical reactions never went to completion. The products were always "contaminated" with molecules of reactant. More shocking was the finding that regardless of the amount of reactants and products in the initial mixture, the system reached the same state, in which the proportion of products to reactants was a constant. As an example, consider a chemical reaction in which glucose 1-phosphate is converted into glucose 6-phosphate **(Figure 4.10)**. Starting with 0.02 M glucose 1-phosphate, the reaction will proceed spontaneously until there is 0.019 M of glucose 6-phosphate (product) and 0.001 M of glucose 1-phosphate (reactant) in the solution. In fact, regardless of the amounts of each you start with, the reaction will reach a point at which there is 95% glucose 6-phosphate and 5% glucose 1-phosphate.

The point at which there is no longer any overall change in the concentration of products and reactants is called the point of chemical equilibrium. In this state, molecules do not stop reacting; rather the rate of the forward reaction equals the rate of the backward

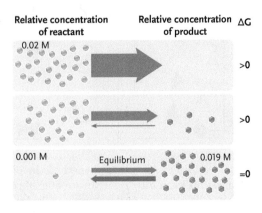

Figure 4.10
Chemical reactions run to equilibrium. No matter what quantities of glucose 1-phosphate and glucose 6-phosphate are dissolved in water, when equilibrium is attained, there will always be 95% glucose 6-phosphate and 5% glucose 1-phosphate. At equilibrium, the number of reactant molecules being converted to products equals the number of product molecules being converted back to reactants.

reaction. As a system moves toward equilibrium, the free energy of the system becomes progressively lower and reaches its lowest point when the system is at equilibrium. It is at this point that there is no tendency for spontaneous change in either the forward or the reverse direction. The system reaches a state of maximum stability, it has no capacity to do work, and $\Delta G = 0$.

The point of equilibrium is related to ΔG for the reaction, in that the more negative ΔG, the farther toward completion the reaction will move before equilibrium is established. Many reactions have a ΔG that is near zero and are thus readily **reversible** by adjusting the concentrations of products and reactants slightly.

STUDY BREAK

1. What is the difference between a reaction that is exothermic and one that is exergonic?
2. What is the thermodynamic reason that molecules spontaneously diffuse across a membrane?
3. True or false: In a reaction that has a negative ΔG, all of the reactants are converted into products.

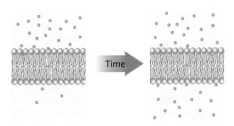

Figure 4.9
Diffusion across a membrane is driven by the increase in entropy. Molecules will move spontaneously across a membrane from a region of high concentration to a region of lower concentration because the energy associated with the molecules becomes more dispersed.

4.3 Thermodynamics and Life

In Chapter 3 we introduced seven characteristics that all forms of life share. One of these is the ability to harness and utilize energy. In this section we focus on how living things abide by the laws of thermodynamics and yet are able to maintain a highly organized state. We expand our discussion to illustrate how energy flows through the biosphere—the regions of Earth occupied by life.

4.3a Life Does Not Go against the Second Law of Thermodynamics

At first glance, living systems seem to go against the second law of thermodynamics and its foundational concept that the entropy of a system and its surroundings must always increase. It is easy to think this because organisms are able to maintain themselves in a highly organized state with energy being concentrated in complex molecules. Cells can synthesize molecules like proteins and nucleic acids and are filled with intricate structures such as microtubules, ribosomes, mitochondria, and chromosomes, to name a few. How is all of this possible without going against the second law?

Organisms can maintain a highly organized state because they are open systems and thus are constantly using energy and matter that they bring in from the environment to keep a low-entropy state. But according to thermodynamics isn't entropy always supposed to increase? The second law states that the entropy of a system *plus its surroundings* must increase—and this holds for living systems as well. As illustrated in **Figure 4.11**, organisms bring in energy and matter, but as a result of the thousands of chemical reactions that take place within cells, organisms also give off heat and by-products of metabolism, such as water and carbon dioxide, that spread out, increasing the entropy of the surroundings. The entropy of a system can be maintained in a low state but only because the entropy of its surroundings is constantly increasing.

But why do living systems have to keep consuming energy? Once all the proteins that are required to sustain life are synthesized, why can't the energy requiring process of protein synthesis stop? Once a human has fully developed and stopped growing, why can't we stop eating? Organisms need to constantly bring in energy and matter because at a cellular level the tendency of energy to spread out means that cellular components (proteins, organelles, etc.) are constantly becoming damaged and breaking down (Figure 4.11). Just like a car that needs to be taken to a mechanic to have new parts installed and others repaired, the breakdown of cellular systems is an inevitable consequence of the Second Law and increasing entropy. New cells need to be made and old ones maintained by the continued synthesis of proteins, carbohydrates, and a myriad of other molecules. Metabolism can never stop, and living cells never reach chemical equilibrium ($\Delta G = 0$); life requires a constant supply of energy. So, while it is easy to see why elite athletes need to eat a lot, people who don't exercise at all also need to ingest well over a thousand kilocalories every day. Although some of this food supplies us with the energy to use our muscles, much of the food energy we ingest is

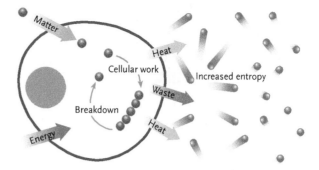

Figure 4.11

Cells are open systems. By bringing in energy and matter from their surroundings they can maintain an ordered state. The release of heat and waste gases into the environment increases the entropy of the surroundings.

used simply to maintain our low-entropy, highly organized state (Figure 4.11). We eat to maintain low entropy **(Figure 4.12)**.

4.3b The Flow of Energy through the Biosphere

Recall that Earth does not exchange matter with the rest of the universe, but it does exchange a huge amount of energy. Life exists on Earth because its position in the Solar System allowed for heat from the Sun to maintain Earth at a temperature that allowed life to evolve (see Chapter 3). But it is not the heat from the Sun that the biosphere relies on as an energy source to maintain it organized state—it's the light, which is a very concentrated form of energy that exists in packets called photons.

Figure 4.12

Why do we need to eat? The average person needs to ingest about 1500 kcal per day. A significant amount of this energy is needed to maintain the low entropy state of our cells.

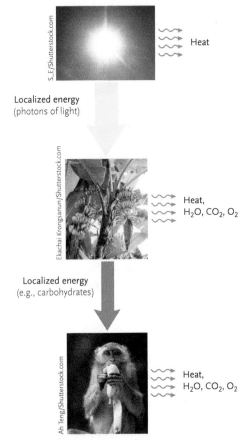

Heat

Localized energy
(photons of light)

Heat,
H_2O, CO_2, O_2

Localized energy
(e.g., carbohydrates)

Heat,
H_2O, CO_2, O_2

Figure 4.13
Flow of energy from the Sun through the biosphere. Living systems constantly bring in concentrated forms of energy and use them to do the work required to maintain a highly organized state. Organisms give off heat and gases (high-entropy energy).

Energy enters the biosphere when light energy from the Sun is transformed into chemical energy through the process of photosynthesis. By absorbing photons of light and using them to do work, photosynthetic organisms can transform molecules of CO_2 and water into high energy–containing molecules such as glucose. The energy in glucose in turn can drive the synthesis of a wide range of other organic molecules. As illustrated in **Figure 4.13,** the remainder of the biosphere (e.g., animals, fungi) is sustained by consuming the various forms of chemical energy produced by photosynthetic organisms.

STUDY BREAK

1. Why may someone think that life goes against the second law of thermodynamics?
2. Why can't we consume all the chemical energy produced by a plant through photosynthesis?
3. Explain in thermodynamic terms why if you stopped eating you would die.

4.4 Overview of Metabolism

The collection of all the chemical reactions present within a cell or organism is defined as **metabolism.** Many different metabolic reactions take place within a cell, resulting in the synthesis or breakdown of a huge variety of molecules. Most metabolic reactions fall into pathways and there are two fundamental types of pathways: those that require energy to build molecules and those that release energy by breaking molecules down. A lot of the metabolism of the biosphere involves the energy transformation reactions of two metabolic pathways: respiration and photosynthesis. The details of these processes, as well as others, such as protein synthesis, are the focus of later chapters. In this section, our attention is more broad as we look at the central features of how energy is transformed during metabolism.

4.4a Metabolism Consists of Catabolic and Anabolic Pathways

The individual reactions that make up metabolism are grouped into *pathways*—starting molecules undergo stepwise transformation, one reaction at a time, generating one or more final products. For example, the hormone testosterone is the end-product of a five-reaction pathway that starts with the molecule cholesterol.

A series of chemical reactions that results in the breakdown of larger, more-complex molecules into smaller, less-complex ones is called a **catabolic pathway.** Energy is released in a catabolic pathway because overall the free energy of the final product(s) of the pathway is less than the free energy of the starting molecule(s) **(Figure 4.14).** Perhaps the best example of a catabolic pathway is cellular respiration: energy-rich food molecules are converted into simpler, lower-energy molecules such as H_2O and CO_2. An **anabolic pathway,** on the other hand, is a series of reactions that results in the synthesis of larger, more-complex molecules from simpler starting molecules (Figure 4.14). Anabolic pathways, which are often called biosynthetic pathway, require energy because overall the free energy of the product(s) of the pathway is greater than the free energy of the starting molecule(s). The biosynthesis of specific carbohydrates, proteins, and nucleic acids are all products of anabolic pathways, as is photosynthesis.

A key feature of metabolism also shown in Figure 4.14 is that catabolic and anabolic pathways are linked through chemical energy. Because biosynthetic (anabolic) reactions result in the formation of new covalent bonds, they require a source of chemical energy. The energy comes from the catabolic breakdown of high-energy molecules. The specific form of chemical energy that most often links the two types of pathways is the molecule adenosine triphosphate (ATP).

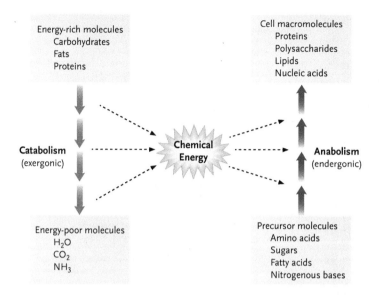

Figure 4.14

Energy relationships between the pathways of catabolism and anabolism. Energy released from the breakdown of energy-rich molecules can be harnessed by anabolic reactions, which use the energy to generate macromolecules.

From Garrett/Grisham, *Biochemistry*, 5E. © 2013 Cengage Learning.

4.4b ATP Hydrolysis Releases Free Energy

All forms of life require a readily usable form of chemical energy. Like using dollars as an accepted currency to buy goods, it would be advantageous to the cell if there were a single, widely accepted form of energy currency. Not only would this chemical currency be used for biosynthetic reactions, but ideally it could be readily transformed into mechanical energy required for muscle contraction or electrical energy required for the conduction of nerve impulses. The nucleotide ATP is that energy currency.

As shown in **Figure 4.15a**, ATP consists of a five-carbon sugar, ribose, linked to the **nitrogenous base** adenine joined to a chain of three phosphate groups. ATP is a source of free energy as a result of its reaction with water (Figure 4.15b). In this *hydrolysis* reaction, the terminal phosphate bond is broken, resulting in the formation of adenosine diphosphate and a molecule of inorganic phosphate (abbreviated P_i):

$$ATP + H_2O \rightarrow ADP + P_i$$
$$\Delta G = -7.3 \text{ kcal/mol}$$

So what is it about the chemistry of ATP that explains the negative ΔG when it is hydrolyzed? The exergonic nature of ATP hydrolysis is because of both (i) a decrease in potential energy and (ii) an increase in entropy. There is less potential energy in ADP than in ATP because the loss of the terminal phosphate has decreased the electrical repulsion among the negatively charged oxygen atoms of the phosphate groups. The hydrolysis of ATP is also spontaneous because of an increase in entropy as energy moves from being localized on one molecule (ATP) to being spread out on two molecules (ADP and P_i) (Figure 4.15b).

a. Chemical structure of ATP

Sugar (ribose)

b. Hydrolysis reaction

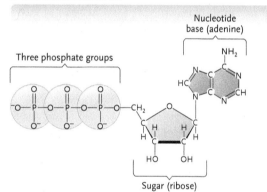

Figure 4.15

ATP, the primary molecule used to supply the energy for biosynthetic reactions. **(a)** Structure of one ATP molecule. **(b)** Reaction of ATP hydrolysis. Energy is released during the formation of ADP and P_i.

⬤ CONCEPT FIX You may have the idea that the energy associated with ATP is the result of a "high-energy phosphate bond" that releases energy when it is broken. This thinking, however, is incorrect. A foundational concept of chemistry is that energy is never released when bonds break; in fact, energy is *required*. Energy is released when ATP is hydrolyzed only because the bonds formed in the products are of lower energy than the bonds in the reactant molecules that were broken. ⬢

The fact that all forms of life use ATP as their dominant energy currency is another piece of evidence that points to all forms of life sharing a common ancestor (see Chapter 3). This is because there is nothing particularly unique to ATP. There are a number of other phosphate-containing compounds, including the other nucleotide triphosphates (GTP, CTP, TTP) (see *The Purple Pages*) that liberate comparable free energy to ATP when they are hydrolyzed. Thus, the fact that life adopted ATP doesn't reflect a unique capability of ATP but rather perhaps simply a chance event that occurred as early as 3.5 billion years ago.

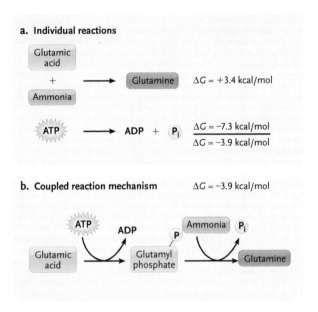

Figure 4.16
An example of energy coupling. The exergonic breakdown of ATP is linked to the endergonic biosynthesis of glutamine, a spontaneous process.

4.4c Energy Coupling Links the Energy of ATP to Other Molecules

Although ATP releases free energy when it is hydrolyzed, this does not mean that it is an especially reactive molecule. In fact, the rate of ATP hydrolysis in an aqueous environment such as the cytosol of a cell is slow. If ATP were very reactive, it would be impossible for metabolism involving ATP to be tightly controlled. Its rapid hydrolysis would simply release heat, and not only can cells not use heat to do work, too much heat can cause damage and even cell death.

So how do cells harness the free energy available from ATP hydrolysis to do cellular work? To help answer this question, let's look at a very common anabolic reaction: the synthesis of glutamine. This amino acid is synthesized from glutamic acid and ammonia:

$$\text{glutamic acid} + NH_3 \rightarrow \text{glutamine} + H_2O$$
$$\Delta G = +3.4 \text{ kcal/mol}$$

The positive ΔG shows that the reaction will not occur as written—and yet molecules of glutamine are synthesized within your cells all the time. How is that possible? During metabolism, glutamine is synthesized through a process called **energy coupling**: an endergonic reaction occurs by being coupled to an exergonic reaction **(Figure 4.16)**. For the majority of energy coupling reactions, the energy is provided by the exergonic breakdown of ATP.

Looking at Figure 4.16a, it is easiest to think of energy coupling as the joining of two independent reactions, one spontaneous (exergonic) and the other nonspontaneous (endergonic). The free-energy changes of the two reactions can be added to yield the

free-energy change of the **coupled reaction.** The sum of the two reaction free energies, ATP breakdown ($\Delta G = -7.3$ kcal/mol) and glutamine synthesis ($\Delta G = 3.4$ kcal/mol), yields -3.9 kcal/mol. This tells us that the coupled reaction will be spontaneous.

Within a cell, the actual reaction mechanism of the coupled reaction is distinctly different from the two independent reactions shown in Figure 4.16a although the overall ΔG remains simply the sum of the two reactions. Energy coupling during metabolism (Figure 4.16b) requires an enzyme that binds both a molecule of ATP and a molecule of substrate and facilitates the transfer of the terminal phosphate group from ATP to the substrate. The addition of phosphate to the substrate increases its free energy and makes it more reactive, allowing the second reaction to occur spontaneously (Figure 4.16b). An important aspect of energy coupling is that the inclusion of an enzyme facilitates the movement of potential energy from a molecule of ATP to the substrate molecule through transfer of the terminal phosphate group. The energy-wasting hydrolysis of ATP is prevented in the first reaction shown in Figure 4.16b because water cannot access the site of catalysis on the enzyme. The hydrolysis of ATP is not complete until P_i is released in the second reaction.

4.4d Cells also Couple Reactions to Regenerate ATP

We have just seen how the hydrolysis of ATP is an exergonic reaction that can be harnessed through energy coupling reactions to make biosynthetic reactions

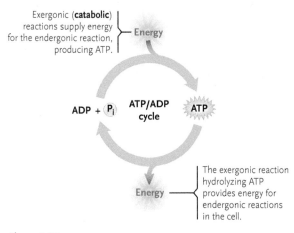

The exergonic reaction hydrolyzing ATP provides energy for endergonic reactions in the cell.

Figure 4.17
The ATP/ADP cycle that couples reactions releasing free energy and reactions requiring free energy.

proceed spontaneously. These coupling reactions occur continuously in living cells consuming a tremendous amount of ATP. So where does the ATP for these processes come from? Some ATP is synthesized using a biosynthetic pathway that includes reactions that join ribose, adenine, and phosphate groups together. However, the vast majority of ATP is generated from recombining ADP and P_i.

If ATP breakdown is an exergonic process, then ATP synthesis from ADP and P_i is an endergonic process. The free energy required for ATP synthesis comes from the catabolism of molecules that contain an abundance of energy. For animals, these molecules are food—carbohydrates, fats, and proteins—all abundant sources of energy. In photosynthetic organisms, the capture of light energy is used to synthesize ATP from ADP and P_i.

The continuous breakdown and resynthesis of ATP is called the **ATP cycle (Figure 4.17)**. Approximately 10 million ATP molecules are broken down and resynthesized each second in a typical cell, illustrating that this cycle operates at an astonishing rate. In fact, if ATP were not regenerated from ADP and P_i, it is estimated that the average human would use an estimated 75 kg of ATP per day. It makes sense that cells should never be limited in their availability of ATP. In fact, a typical cell maintains an ATP concentration that is about 1000 times greater than that of ADP.

STUDY BREAK

1. In what ways do the end-products of catabolic pathways differ from their starting molecules?
2. In an energy coupling reaction, trace the fate of the terminal phosphate group of ATP.

4.5 The Role of Enzymes in Biological Reactions

So far in this chapter we have focused on the thermodynamics of energy transformation: exergonic and endergonic reactions and factors that determine whether a particular reaction will occur without an input of energy. We have avoided discussing anything about the rate of a reaction because, in fact, the laws of thermodynamics do not address how fast a process will occur, just whether or not it will occur. But the rate of a reaction is of fundamental importance to life, because most reactions must occur at very high rates for life to be sustained. In this section, we discuss the factors that control the rate of a chemical reaction and the central role played by enzymes in increasing reaction rates.

4.5a The Activation Energy of a Reaction Represents a Kinetic Barrier

The conversion of table sugar (sucrose) into the **monosaccharides** glucose and fructose is a spontaneous reaction, and yet a bag of sugar can sit around for decades without any detectable fructose or glucose being formed. So what is preventing this spontaneous reaction from occurring rapidly? Forget sugar, what about the planet—given the large amounts of energy trapped in the wood of trees, and the coal and oil underground, why doesn't Earth just go up in flames?

For chemical reactions to occur, established bonds need to be broken and new bonds need to be formed. For bonds to be broken, they must first be strained or otherwise made less stable, which requires a small input of energy. The initial energy investment required to start a reaction is called the **activation energy** (E_a) **(Figure 4.18a, p. 86)**. Molecules that gain the necessary activation energy occupy what is called the **transition state**, where bonds are unstable and are ready to be broken.

What provides the activation energy for chemical reactions? The molecules taking part in chemical reactions are in constant motion, and reacting molecules may periodically gain enough energy to reach the transition state. But for the molecules of sucrose on the kitchen shelf, reaching the transition state is a very rare event. Supplying larger amounts of energy would allow more molecules to gain the activation energy necessary to react. A good example of this is a propane torch **(Figure 4.19, p. 86)**. Propane is a molecule that contains an abundance of free energy. In the presence of air, it spontaneously decomposes into carbon dioxide and water. However, the reaction proceeds very slowly—the propane in a torch can sit for years and remain unchanged. This is because if left undisturbed, it is a rare event for molecules of propane to acquire the energy needed for combustion. Yet if you supply a stream of propane gas with a spark

CHAPTER 4 ENERGY AND ENZYMES | 85

a.

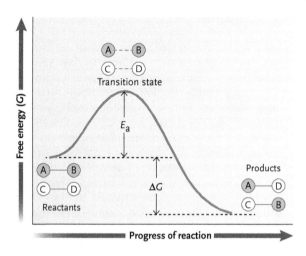

b. "Activation energy" barrier in the movement of a rock downhill

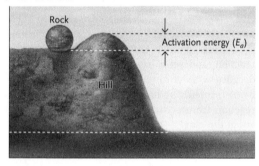

Figure 4.18
The concept of activation energy (E_a) for an exergonic reaction.

(see Figure 4.19), then you provide the molecules with the energy necessary to reach the transition state, resulting in combustion. The heat released from the initial combustion event sustains the continuous burning of the propane stream.

4.5b Enzymes Accelerate Reactions by Reducing the Activation Energy

If you walk through a typical undergraduate chemistry lab, you will find that the benches have Bunsen burners, which are used to provide the heat for a range of chemical reactions. Chemists routinely use heat to provide the energy needed for reactant molecules to get to the transition state and thus speed up the rate of a reaction. In biology, using heat to speed up a reaction is problematic for two reasons: First, high temperatures destroy the structural components of cells, particularly proteins, and can result in cell death. Second, an increase in temperature would speed up all possible chemical reactions in a cell, and thus the precise regulation of metabolic pathways would be lost. So how can you increase the rate of specific reactions without raising the temperature? You can use a **catalyst**, which is a chemical agent that speeds up the rate of a reaction without itself taking part in the reaction. The most common biological catalyst is a group of proteins called **enzymes.**

Looking back at Figure 4.18, you can think of the transition state as a kinetic barrier—it is what prevents spontaneous reactions from occurring rapidly, because so few molecules at a given time acquire the energy necessary to get to the transition state. If you could lower this energy requirement, then many more molecules would react. This is exactly what enzymes do—they increase the rate of a reaction by decreasing the activation energy **(Figure 4.20).** Since the rate of a reaction (i.e., number of molecules of product made per second) is proportional to the number of reactant molecules that can get to the transition state, lowering the transition state results in a higher rate of reaction.

CONCEPT FIX There are two common misconceptions about the role of enzymes in biochemical reactions that we need to fix before moving on. First, although enzymes decrease the activation energy of a reaction, they do not alter the thermodynamics of a reaction. The change in

Figure 4.19
Combustion of propane. **(a)** The combustion of propane is a spontaneous reaction; however, the activation energy is a barrier that prevents its rapid breakdown. **(b)** When a spark is provided, propane obtains the energy required to attain the transition state. **(c)** The initial heat generated sustains continuous propane burning.

a.

b.

c.

Denis Maxwell

Maud Menten (1879–1960)

A fundamental topic covered in almost all introductory biochemistry courses is the Michaelis–Menten equation. First stated in 1913, the equation represents one of the fundamental concepts of biochemistry, providing a mathematical description of the kinetics of an enzyme-catalyzed reaction.

The name Menten of the equation refers to Maud Menten, who was born in 1879, in Port Lambton, Ontario. After completing secondary school, Menten attended the University of Toronto and earned a bachelor of arts degree in 1904, followed by a master's degree in physiology in 1907. In the same year, Menten was appointed a fellow at the Rockefeller Institute for Medical Research in New York City, where she studied the effect of radium bromide on cancerous tumours in rats. A year later, she returned to the University of Toronto and in 1911 became one of the first Canadian women to receive a doctor of medicine degree.

In 1912, Menten travelled to Germany to work with Leonor Michaelis, a biochemist who shared her interest in understanding enzyme kinetics. After a year of research, the two scientists coauthored a paper that put forward a description of the basis of enzyme-catalyzed chemical kinetics. The paper introduced the Michaelis–Menten equation as a tool for measuring the rates of enzyme reactions. The formula gave scientists a way to record how enzymes worked and is the standard for most enzyme-kinetic measurements. Michaelis and Menten were able to demonstrate that each enzyme, given enough substrate, has its own rate of causing that substrate to undergo chemical change. The Michaelis–Menten equation profoundly changed the study of biochemistry and earned Menten and Michaelis worldwide recognition.

When Menten returned from Berlin, she enrolled at the University of Chicago, where she obtained a Ph.D. in biochemistry in 1916. Unable to find an academic position in her native Canada, in 1918 she joined the medical school faculty at the University of Pittsburgh. While maintaining an active research program, she was also known as an avid mountain climber who went on several expeditions to the Arctic. As well, she spoke numerous languages, loved to paint, and played the clarinet. Over the years, Menten authored more than 70 publications, including discoveries related to blood sugar, hemoglobin, and kidney functions. In so-called retirement, she returned to British Columbia to do research at the British Columbia Medical Research Institute, almost until her death. A plaque commemorating the life and work of Maud Menten is located in the Medical Sciences Building, University of Toronto, Queen's Park.

free energy (ΔG) of a reaction is not altered by the presence of an enzyme. Second, enzymes do not supply energy to a reaction. Although enzymes are involved in energy coupling reactions (see Section 4.4c), the chemical energy is supplied by ATP, not by the enzyme. ⬡

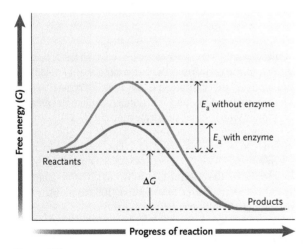

Figure 4.20

Enzymes lower the activation energy (E_a) of a reaction.

4.5c Enzymes Combine with Reactants and Are Released Unchanged

In biochemical reactions, an enzyme combines briefly with reacting molecules and is released unchanged when the reaction is complete. For example, the enzyme hexokinase **(Figure 4.21, p. 88)**, catalyzes the following reaction:

glucose + ATP → glucose 6-phosphate + ADP

The reactant that an enzyme acts on is called the enzyme's substrate, or substrates if the enzyme binds two or more molecules. Each type of enzyme catalyzes the reaction of only a single type of molecule or a group of closely related molecules. This enzyme specificity explains why the metabolism of a typical cell involves thousands of different enzymes. Notice in Figure 4.21 that the enzyme is much larger than the substrate. As well, the substrate interacts with only a very small region of the enzyme. This region is called the **active site**—the specific site on an enzyme where catalysis takes place. The active site is usually a pocket or groove that is formed when, following protein synthesis, the newly synthesized enzyme folds into its three-dimensional shape.

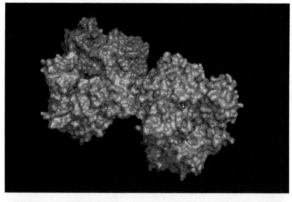

a. Like other enzymes, hexokinase has an active site where specific substrates bind and where catalysis occurs. As shown at left, the active site is a very small region of the overall enzyme.

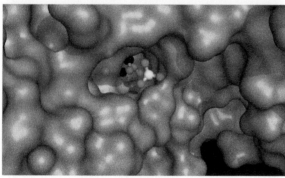

b. A close-up showing glucose and phosphate within the active site.

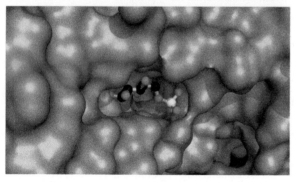

c. The glucose has bonded with the phosphate. The product of the reaction, glucose-6-phosphate, is shown leaving the active site.

Figure 4.21
Model of the enzyme hexokinase showing the catalysis of glucose with phosphate forming glucose-6-phosphate. The glucose is represented by black (carbon) and red (oxygen) spheres, while the phosphate group is shown with the phosphorus atom (yellow sphere) bonded to four oxygens (red).

From STARR/TAGGART/Evers/Starr. Biology, 12E. © 2009 Brooks/Cole, a part of Cengage Learning, Inc. Reproduced by permission. www.cengage.com/permissions

In the early twentieth century, biochemists proposed the *lock-and-key hypothesis* to explain the specificity of the substrate–enzyme interaction. The analogy worked well to explain how even somewhat similar substrates (keys) were unable to bind to the same enzyme (lock) to cause catalysis (unlocking of the door). However, more recently, this hypothesis has been superseded by what has become known as the *induced-fit hypothesis*. Research has shown that unlike locks, enzymes are not rigid objects but instead are flexible. Just before substrate binding, the enzyme changes its shape (**conformation**) so that the active site becomes even more precise in its ability to bind the substrate.

As shown in **Figure 4.22,** the enzyme binds to the substrate, forming an enzyme–substrate complex.

Catalysis occurs when the two are joined, with the action of the enzyme converting the substrate (or substrates) into one or more products. Because enzymes are released unchanged after a reaction, enzyme molecules can rapidly bind to other substrate molecules, catalyzing the same reaction again, repeating what is called the enzyme cycle (see Figure 4.22). The rate at which enzymes catalyze reactions varies widely depending on the specifics of the enzyme and substrates involved, but typical rates vary from a low of about 100 reactions up to a high of 10 million reactions per second.

Many enzymes require a **cofactor,** a nonprotein group that binds very precisely to the enzyme. Cofactors are often metals, such as iron, copper, zinc, or manganese. Although most cells need very small

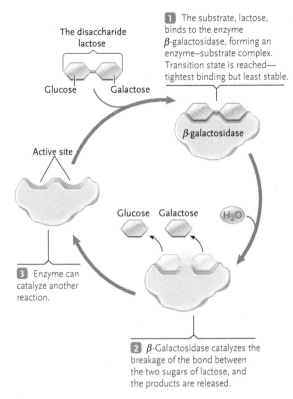

The disaccharide lactose

Glucose   Galactose

1 The substrate, lactose, binds to the enzyme β-galactosidase, forming an enzyme–substrate complex. Transition state is reached—tightest binding but least stable.

β-galactosidase

Active site

Glucose   Galactose   (H₂O)

3 Enzyme can catalyze another reaction.

2 β-Galactosidase catalyzes the breakage of the bond between the two sugars of lactose, and the products are released.

Figure 4.22
The catalytic cycle of an enzyme. Shown is the enzyme β-galactosidase, which cleaves the sugar lactose to produce glucose and galactose.

amounts of these metals, they are absolutely essential for the catalytic activity of the enzyme to which they bind. Some cofactors, called **coenzymes**, are organic molecules that are often derived from vitamins.

4.5d Enzymes Reduce the Activation Energy by Inducing the Transition State

We know that enzymes reduce the activation energy of a reaction, but how do they do it? An enzyme uses one of three basic mechanisms to lower the energy required to get to the transition state. These mechanisms are shown in **Figure 4.23**.

1. *Bringing the reacting molecules together.* Reacting molecules can assume the transition state only when they collide. Binding to an enzyme's active site brings the reactants together in the right orientation for catalysis to occur.

Bring reacting molecules close together

2. *Exposing the reactant molecule to altered charge environments that promote catalysis.* In some systems, the active site of the enzyme may contain ionic groups whose positive or negative charges alter the substrate in a way that favours catalysis.

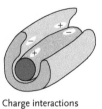

Charge interactions

3. *Changing the shape of a substrate molecule.* The active site may strain or distort substrate molecules into a conformation that mimics the transition state.

Distort or strain substrate molecules

Figure 4.23
The binding of substrate(s) to an active site results in the substrate's acquiring the transition state conformation.

Regardless of the mechanism used by a specific enzyme, the binding of the substrate to the active site results in the substrate's attaining the transition state conformation—its bonds strained and ready to be broken. Without the enzyme, substrate molecules would also be able to acquire the transition state, it's just that for most reactions would not occur very often. The addition of an enzyme simply enables many more molecules to reach the transition state. This is fundamentally why enzymes increase the rate of a reaction.

STUDY BREAK

1. Distinguish between the activation energy of a reaction and the transition state.
2. Which of the following aspects of a reaction is changed by the addition of an enzyme: free energy of products, ΔG, requirement for energy, or rate?
3. A mutation to the gene that codes for the enzyme hexokinase may result in the enzyme that is synthesized being unable to bind glucose. Why might this be the case?

4.6 Factors That Affect Enzyme Activity

Enzymes play a critical role in metabolism. Because of this, regulating how they operate is central to controlling metabolism. As you would expect, a number of factors can change the activity of a particular enzyme, including changes in the concentration of substrate and other molecules that bind to enzymes. As well, changes in environmental factors, including temperature and pH, can also effect enzyme activity.

4.6a Enzyme and Substrate Concentrations Can Change the Rate of Catalysis

Biochemists use a wide range of approaches to studying an enzyme. These span from using the tools of molecular biology and genetics to study the structure and regulation of the gene that encodes the enzyme to sophisticated computer programs for modelling the three-dimensional structure of the enzyme and its active site. However, the most fundamental and central approach has been to determine the rate of the specific reaction catalyzed by a particular enzyme and how the rate changes in response to altering certain experimental parameters. This usually requires purifying the enzyme from the remainder of the cell, incubating it in an appropriate buffered solution, and supplying the reaction mixture with substrate. With these constituents, one can then determine the rate of catalysis, which is most often done by measuring the rate at which product of the reaction is formed—so, for example, micromoles of product per second.

As shown in **Figure 4.24a**, in the presence of excess substrate, the rate of catalysis is proportional to the amount of enzyme. As enzyme concentration increases, the rate of product formation increases. In this system, where substrate concentration is high, what is limiting the rate of the reaction is the amount of enzyme in the reaction mixture. Look at what happens if we instead keep the enzyme constant at some intermediate concentration and change the substrate concentration from low to high. At very low concentrations, substrate molecules collide so infrequently with enzyme molecules that the rate at which the product is formed is slow (Figure 4.24b). As the substrate concentration increases, the reaction rate initially increases linearly as enzyme and substrate molecules collide more frequently. But as the constant number of enzyme molecules approaches the maximum rate at which they can combine with reactants and release products, increasing the substrate concentration has a smaller and smaller effect, and the rate of reaction eventually levels off. When the catalytic cycle (see Figure 4.22) is turning as fast as possible, further increases in substrate concentration have no effect on the reaction rate. At this point, the enzyme is said to be saturated with substrate.

4.6b Enzyme Activity Can Be Altered by Competitive and Noncompetitive Interactions

The rate of an enzyme-catalyzed reaction can be altered by a wide range of molecules that bind to the enzyme. A number of molecules that alter enzyme activity do so because they are structurally similar to the normal substrate of the enzyme and therefore can bind to the active site. Regulation of this type is called competitive regulation because the molecule competes with the substrate for the active site **(Figure 4.25a)**. Competitive regulation is often referred to as **competitive inhibition** because the presence of the competitor decreases the rate of the normal substrate-dependent reaction.

Competitive regulators differ in how strongly they bind to the active site. Some molecules bind through covalent bonding, resulting in enzyme inhibition that is irreversible. However, many inhibitors bind to the active site weakly, through noncovalent interactions, resulting in inhibition that is readily reversible. As

Figure 4.24

Effect of increasing **(a)** enzyme concentration or **(b)** substrate concentration on the rate of an enzyme-catalyzed reaction.

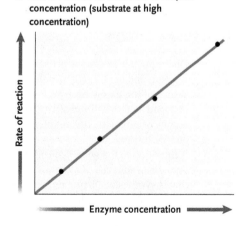

a. Rate of reaction as a function of enzyme concentration (substrate at high concentration)

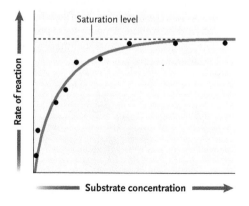

b. Rate of reaction as a function of substrate concentration (enzyme amount constant)

Penicillin: A Competitive Inhibitor of Enzyme Action

Penicillin is an antibiotic that is used in the treatment of bacterial infections. It was first discovered by Alexander Fleming, who isolated it from the mould *Penicillium* after he accidentally found that the presence of the mould inhibited the growth of bacteria on a Petri plate. Following the development of methods for its mass production, penicillin became a true wonder drug that was effective at treating a wide range of bacterial infections that in the past often led to death.

Penicillin acts by inhibiting the synthesis of peptidoglycan, a key component of the bacterial cell wall. Peptidoglycan is a complex polymer consisting of sugars and amino acids that forms a meshlike structure outside the plasma membrane. As such, peptidoglycan provides structural strength and protects the bacterial cell from osmotic changes that would otherwise cause the cell to burst. If a bacterium is unable to synthesize components necessary for its cell wall, it is unable to grow and divide.

A key factor that is required for the synthesis of peptidoglycan is the enzyme transpeptidase, which catalyzes the formation of a peptide bond between two amino acids, effectively linking two portions of the peptidoglycan together. Penicillin inhibits peptidoglycan synthesis because it is a competitive inhibitor of transpeptidase activity. The structure of penicillin mimics that of the two amino acids, which are normally brought together by the active site. Penicillin binds irreversibly to the active site of transpeptidase, effectively destroying the molecule. Given the concentrations of penicillin usually administered to a patient, this leads to total inhibition of all transpeptidase activity.

Although penicillin was widely employed in the 1950s and 1960s, most infections today involve bacteria that have acquired resistance to the drug. New antibiotics are constantly being developed to try to stop the growing problem of antibiotic-resistant bacteria.

---

shown in Figure 4.25b, one trait of reversible competitive inhibition is that it can be overcome by a high substrate concentration.

Because of their ability to act on critical enzymes, many inhibitor molecules can be toxic. For example, cyanide is a potent poison because it is a competitive inhibitor of cytochrome oxidase, an enzyme involved in cellular respiration (see Chapter 6). Interestingly, many drugs act by inhibiting specific enzymes. For example, a number of antibiotics, including penicillin, are effective because they target and inhibit specific bacterial enzymes (see "Molecule behind Biology").

Some regulatory molecules do not interact with the active site, but rather alter enzyme function by binding to another location on the enzyme. These regulatory molecules do not compete with substrate molecules and result in what is referred to as noncompetitive regulation **(Figure 4.26, p. 92)**. While competitive regulation results in inhibition of normal enzyme function, in noncompetitive regulation molecules that interact with the enzyme can cause an increase or decrease in enzyme function depending upon the molecule and the enzyme.

In noncompetitive regulation, enzyme activity is controlled by the reversible binding of a regulatory molecule to what is often referred to as the **allosteric site**, a location on the enzyme outside the active site. Enzymes controlled by noncompetitive regulation are often referred to as allosteric enzymes and typically have two alternative conformations controlled from the allosteric site. In one conformation, called the *high-affinity state*, the enzyme binds strongly to its substrate; in the other conformation, the *low-affinity state*,

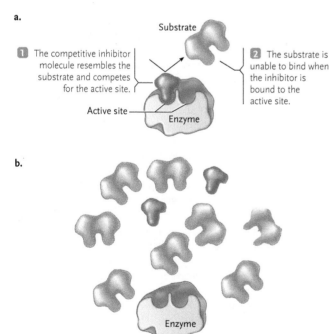

a.

① The competitive inhibitor molecule resembles the substrate and competes for the active site.

Substrate

② The substrate is unable to bind when the inhibitor is bound to the active site.

Active site

Enzyme

b.

Enzyme

Figure 4.25
(a) Competitive regulation of enzyme activity. **(b)** The inhibition of enzyme activity by a competitive inhibitor can be overcome by increasing the amount of substrate relative to inhibitor.

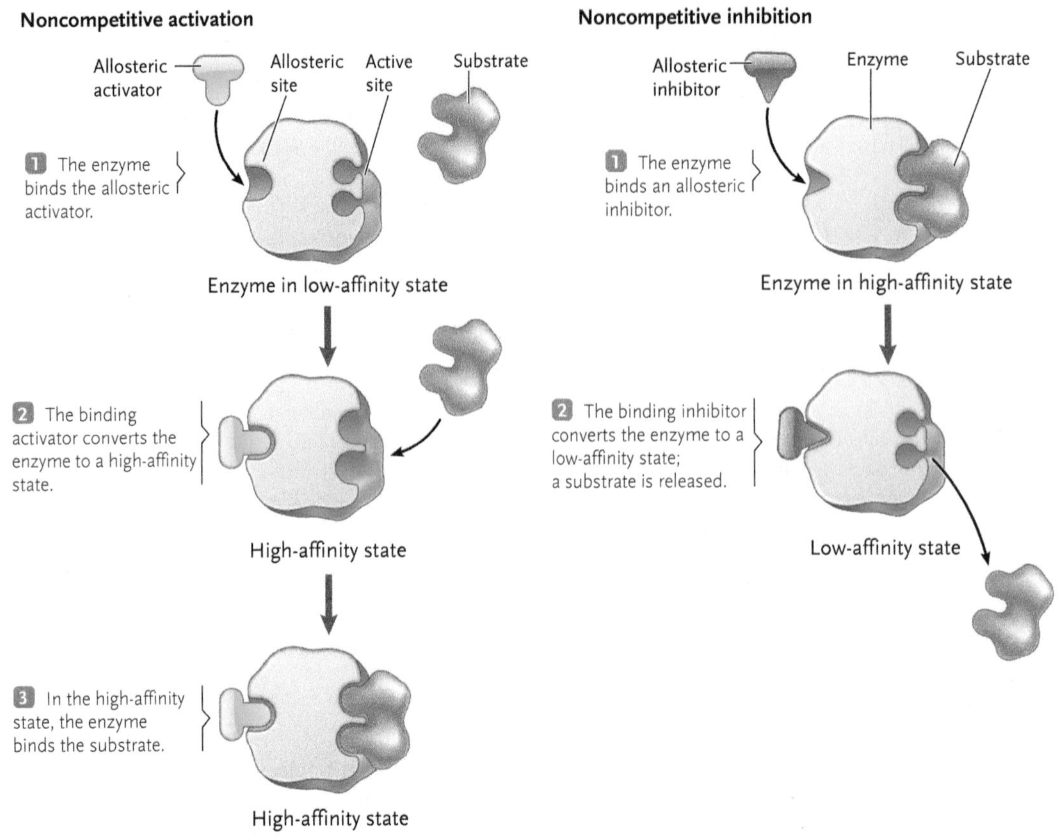

Noncompetitive activation

Allosteric activator — Allosteric site — Active site — Substrate

1 The enzyme binds the allosteric activator.

Enzyme in low-affinity state

2 The binding activator converts the enzyme to a high-affinity state.

High-affinity state

3 In the high-affinity state, the enzyme binds the substrate.

High-affinity state

Noncompetitive inhibition

Allosteric inhibitor — Enzyme — Substrate

1 The enzyme binds an allosteric inhibitor.

Enzyme in high-affinity state

2 The binding inhibitor converts the enzyme to a low-affinity state; a substrate is released.

Low-affinity state

Figure 4.26
Noncompetitive (**allosteric**) **regulation**.

the enzyme binds the substrate weakly or not at all. Binding with regulatory substances may induce either state: an **allosteric inhibitor** converts an enzyme from the high- to the low-affinity state, while an **allosteric activator** converts it from the low- to the high-affinity state (see Figure 4.26).

4.6c Metabolism Is Finely Controlled by Noncompetitive Regulation

For metabolism to work efficiently, the activity of enzymes needs to be adjusted upward or downward so that the amount of product synthesized by any reaction matches the needs of the cell for the product. Considering that a typical cell contains thousands of enzymes that collectively catalyze a huge range of reactions, a key question to address is how enzyme activity is controlled to regulate overall metabolism. One mechanism of regulation is to control the abundance of specific enzymes. Since enzymes are proteins, this can be facilitated by regulating gene expression (transcription) and protein synthesis (translation). But this type of regulation lacks fine control—metabolic pathways are often adjusted in seconds, yet changes in enzyme abundance can take 30 minutes or more to occur. In addition to transcriptional and translational control,

the cell is able to very rapidly regulate metabolic pathways by directly affecting enzyme activity. Two major mechanisms it uses to achieve this are allosteric control and covalent modification.

Frequently, allosteric inhibitors are a product of the metabolic pathway that they regulate. If the product accumulates in excess, its effect as an inhibitor automatically slows or stops the enzymatic reaction producing it. Accordingly, if the product becomes too scarce, the inhibition is reduced, and the product begins to accumulate again. This type of metabolic regulation, in which the product of a reaction acts to inhibit its own synthesis, is termed **feedback inhibition**. In multireaction pathways, feedback inhibition usually involves the final product inhibiting the enzyme that catalyzes one of the early reactions in the pathway. In this way, cellular resources are not wasted in producing intermediates that are not needed.

The biochemical pathway that makes the amino acid isoleucine from threonine is an excellent example of feedback inhibition. The pathway proceeds in five steps, each catalyzed by an enzyme (**Figure 4.27**). The end-product of the pathway, isoleucine, is an allosteric inhibitor of the first enzyme of the pathway, threonine deaminase. If the cell makes more isoleucine than it needs, isoleucine combines reversibly with

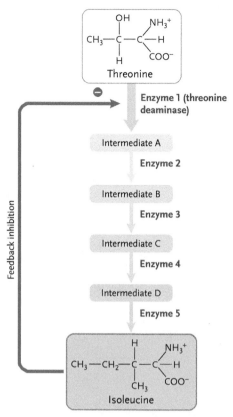

Figure 4.27
Feedback inhibition in the pathway that produces isoleucine from threonine. If the product of the pathway, isoleucine, accumulates in excess, it slows or stops the pathway by acting as an allosteric inhibitor of the enzyme that catalyzes the first step in the pathway.

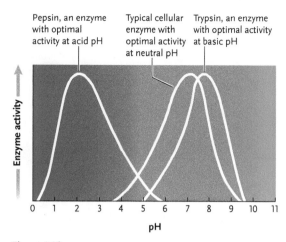

Figure 4.28
Effects of pH on enzyme activity. An enzyme typically has an optimal pH at which it is most active; at pH values above or below the optimum, the rate of enzyme activity drops off. At extreme pH values, the rate drops to zero.

threonine deaminase at its allosteric site, converting the enzyme to the low-affinity state and inhibiting its ability to combine with threonine, the substrate for the first reaction in the pathway. If isoleucine levels drop too low, the allosteric site of threonine deaminase is vacated, the enzyme is converted to the high-affinity state, and isoleucine production increases.

4.6d Temperature and pH Are Key Factors Affecting Enzyme Activity

The activity of most enzymes is strongly altered by changes in pH and temperature. Characteristically, enzymes reach maximal activity within a narrow range of temperature or pH; at levels outside this range, enzyme activity drops off. These effects produce a typically peaked curve when enzyme activity is plotted, with the peak where temperature or pH produces maximal activity.

Effects of pH Changes. Typically, each enzyme has an optimal pH where it operates at peak efficiency in speeding the rate of its biochemical reaction **(Figure 4.28)**.

On either side of this pH optimum, the rate of the catalyzed reaction decreases because of the resulting alterations in charged groups. The effects on the structure and function of the active site become more extreme at pH values farther from the optimum, until the rate drops to zero. Most enzymes have a pH optimum near the pH of the cellular contents, about pH 7. Enzymes that are secreted from cells may have pH optima farther from neutrality. An example is **pepsin**, an enzyme secreted into the stomach. This enzyme's pH optimum is 1.5, close to the **acidity** of stomach contents. Similarly, trypsin has a pH optimum at about pH 8, allowing it to function well in the somewhat alkaline contents of the **intestine**, where it is secreted.

Effects of Temperature Changes. The effects of temperature changes on enzyme activity reflect two distinct processes. First, temperature has a general effect on chemical reactions of all kinds. As the temperature rises, the rate of chemical reactions typically increases. This effect reflects increases in the kinetic motion of all molecules, with more frequent and stronger collisions as the temperature rises. Second, temperature has a more specific effect on all proteins, including enzymes. As the temperature rises, the kinetic motions of the amino acid chains of an enzyme increase, along with the strength and frequency of collisions between enzymes and surrounding molecules. At some point, these disturbances become strong enough to denature the enzyme: the hydrogen bonds and other forces that maintain its three-dimensional structure break, making the enzyme unfold and lose its function (see *The Purple Pages* for a more detailed description of protein denaturation). The two effects of temperature act in opposition to each other to produce characteristic changes in the rate of enzymatic catalysis **(Figure 4.29, p. 94)**. In the range of

Effect of temperature on
enzyme activity

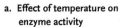
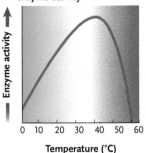

b.

Figure 4.29

Effect of temperature on enzyme activity. **(a)** As the temperature rises, the rate of the catalyzed reaction increases proportionally until the temperature reaches the point at which the enzyme begins to denature. The rate drops off steeply as denaturation progresses and becomes complete. **(b)** Visible effects of environmental temperature on enzyme activity in Siamese cats. The fur on the extremities—ears, nose, paws, and tail—contains more dark brown pigment (melanin) than the rest of the body. A heat-sensitive enzyme controlling melanin production is denatured in warmer body regions, so dark pigment is not produced, but fur colour is.

0°C to about 40°C, the reaction rate doubles for every 10°C increase in temperature. Above 40°C, the increasing kinetic motion begins to denature the enzyme, reducing the rate of increase in enzyme activity. At some point, as the temperature rises, the denaturation of the enzyme causes the reaction rate to level off at a peak. Further increases cause such extensive unfolding that the reaction rate decreases rapidly to zero.

For most enzymes, the peak in activity lies between 40°C and 50°C; the drop-off becomes steep at 55°C and falls to zero at about 60°C. Thus, the rate of an enzyme-catalyzed reaction peaks at the temperature at which kinetic motion is greatest, but no significant unfolding of the enzyme has occurred. Although most enzymes have a temperature optimum between 40°C and 50°C, some have activity peaks below or above this range. For example, the enzymes of maize (corn) pollen function best near 30°C and undergo steep reductions in activity above 32°C. As a result, environmental temperatures above 32°C can seriously inhibit the growth of corn crops. Many animals living in cold regions have enzymes with much lower temperature optima than average. For example, the enzymes of arctic snow fleas are most active at 10°C. At the other extreme are the enzymes of archaeans that live in hot springs, which are so resistant to denaturation that they remain active at temperatures of 85°C or more.

STUDY BREAK

1. Why do enzyme-catalyzed reactions reach a saturation level when substrate concentration is increased?
2. Distinguish between competitive and noncompetitive inhibition.
3. Explain why the activity of an enzyme will eventually decrease to zero as the temperature rises.

Review

To access course materials such as Aplia and other companion resources, please visit www.NELSONbrain.com.

4.1 Energy and the Laws of Thermodynamics

- Energy is the capacity to do work. Kinetic energy is the energy of motion; potential energy is energy stored in an object because of its location or chemical structure. Energy may be readily converted between potential and kinetic states, but it cannot be created or destroyed.
- The potential energy of a molecule is related to the position of electrons. The farther away an electron is from the nucleus of an atom, the greater its potential energy (Figure 4.1).
- Thermodynamics is the study of energy and how it changes during chemical and physical transformations. A system that does not exchange energy or matter with its surroundings is an isolated system. A system that exchanges energy but not matter with its surroundings is a closed system. A system that

exchanges both energy and matter with its surroundings is an open system (Figure 4.2).
- The first law of thermodynamics states that energy can be transformed from one form into another or transferred from one place to another, but it cannot be created or destroyed (Figure 4.3).
- Entropy is the tendency of energy to become dispersed or spread out. The second law of thermodynamics states that the entropy of every system and the surroundings will always increase (Figure 4.4).
- Energy spreading out as evidence of the second law of thermodynamics is exhibited by both a car and a runner (Figure 4.5).

4.2 Free Energy and Spontaneous Processes

- A process that can occur without an input of energy is referred to as spontanous.
- Reactions tend to be spontaneous if they are exothermic ($\Delta H < 0$) (Figure 4.6).
- Reactions tend to be spontaneous if entropy (S) increases (Figure 4.7).

- Entropy and enthalpy are related to reaction spontaneity by Gibbs free energy (G), where $\Delta G = \Delta H - T\Delta S$.
- Processes with a negative ΔG are referred to as spontaneous; they release free energy and are known as exergonic processes. Reactions with a positive ΔG require free energy and are known as endergonic reactions (Figure 4.8).
- Diffusion is an example of a exergonic process driven by the increase in entropy as molecules spread out (Figure 4.9).
- Reactions tend to be spontaneous if they are exothermal ($\Delta H < 0$) (Figure 4.6).
- Factors that oppose the completion of spontaneous reactions, such as the relative concentrations of reactants and products, produce an equilibrium point at which reactants are converted to products and products are converted back to reactants, at equal rates (Figure 4.10).

4.3 Thermodynamics and Life

- Living systems maintain a highly organized state because they are open systems. They bring in both energy and matter from the surroundings and use them to maintain an organized state. Because they release energy and disordered molecules into the environment, the second law of thermodynamics is upheld, as the entropy of the system and its surroundings increases (Figure 4.11).
- All biological molecules break down (entropy increases). This is why a constant supply of energy (food) is required to sustain all life (Figure 4.12).
- Energy enters the biosphere when photosynthetic organisms absorb sunlight. The remainder of the biosphere is sustained by consuming the chemical energy produced by photosynthetic organisms (Figure 4.13).

4.4 Overview of Metabolism

- Metabolism is the biochemical modification and use of energy in the synthesis and breakdown of organic molecules.
- A catabolic pathway releases the potential energy of a molecule in breaking it down to a simpler molecule. An anabolic (biosynthetic) pathway uses energy to convert a simple molecule to a more complex molecule (Figure 4.14).
- The hydrolysis of ATP releases free energy that can be used as a source of energy for the cell (Figure 4.15).
- A cell can couple the exergonic reaction of ATP breakdown (not technically a hydrolysis reaction) to make an otherwise endergonic reaction proceed spontaneously. These coupling reactions require enzymes (Figure 4.16).
- The ATP used in coupling reactions is replenished by reactions that link ATP synthesis to catabolic reactions. ATP thus cycles between reactions that release free energy and reactions that require free energy (Figure 4.17).

4.5 The Role of Enzymes in Biological Reactions

- What prevents many exergonic reactions from proceeding rapidly is that they need to overcome an energy barrier (the activation energy, E_a) to get to the transition state (Figures 4.18 and 4.19).
- Enzymes are catalysts that greatly speed the rate at which spontaneous reactions occur because they lower the activation energy (Figure 4.20).
- Enzymes are usually specific: they catalyze reactions of only a single type of molecule or a group of closely related molecules (Figure 4.21).
- Catalysis occurs at the active site, which is the site where the enzyme binds to the substrate (reactant molecule). After combining briefly with the substrate, the enzyme is released unchanged when the reaction is complete (Figure 4.22).
- Three major mechanisms contribute to enzymatic catalysis by reducing the activation energy: (1) enzymes bring reacting molecules together, (2) enzymes expose reactant molecules to altered charge environments that promote catalysis, and (3) enzymes change the shape of substrate molecules (Figure 4.23).

4.6 Factors That Affect Enzyme Activity

- When substrate is abundant, the rate of a reaction is proportional to the amount of enzyme. At a fixed enzyme concentration, the rate of a reaction increases with substrate concentration until the enzyme becomes saturated with reactants. At that point, further increases in substrate concentration do not increase the rate of the reaction (Figure 4.24).
- Many cellular enzymes are regulated by nonsubstrate molecules called inhibitors. Competitive regulation (inhibition) occurs when molecules interfere with reaction rates by combining with the active site of an enzyme (Figure 4.25).
- Noncompetitive regulation (also known as allosteric regulation) occurs when molecules influence enzyme activity by binding to the enzyme at sites other than the active site (Figure 4.25). While some molecules (allosteric activators) increase enzyme activity, others (allosteric inhibitors) result in a decrease in enzyme activity.
- An example of allosteric regulation is feedback inhibition: the product of an enzyme-catalyzed pathway acts as an allosteric inhibitor of the first enzyme in the pathway (Figure 4.27).
- Typically, an enzyme has optimal activity at a certain pH and a certain temperature; at pH and temperature values above and below the optimum, the reaction rate falls off (Figures 4.28 and 4.29).

Questions

Self-Test Questions

1. Which of the following statements about energy and thermodynamics is correct?
   a. Earth is an isolated system.
   b. Living organisms are closed systems.
   c. Energy conversions can never be 100% efficient.
   d. The total amount of energy in the universe is always decreasing.

2. Which of the following statements about entropy is correct?
   a. We eat food to maintain high entropy.
   b. The entropy of any system always increases.
   c. Entropy is a measure of the total energy content of a system.
   d. The entropy of water increases as it turns from a liquid into a gas.

3. For a reaction to be exergonic, which of the following must occur?
   a. It must also be exothermic.
   b. There must be an input of energy to proceed.
   c. The products must have less enthalpy than the reactants.
   d. The products must have less free energy than the reactants.
   e. The entropy of the products must be greater than the entropy of the reactants.

4. Which of the following statements is correct?
   a. At equilibrium, ΔG is negative.
   b. Living organisms are never at equilibrium.
   c. An isolated system will never reach equilibrium.
   d. Molecules that have high free energy are very stable.
   e. Most biochemical reactions have a ΔG far from zero.

5. Instructors often mention the "hydrolysis of ATP" as the source of energy for cellular reactions. But this statement is inaccurate. Why?
   a. A molecule can never be the source of energy.
   b. ATP actually contains very little free energy.
   c. The hydrolysis of GTP is more common than ATP in cellular reactions.
   d. Water does not enter the active site of enzymes linked to ATP breakdown.

6. Propane is thermodynamically unstable; why is it kinetically stable?
   a. It is highly electronegative.
   b. Its breakdown is exergonic ($-\Delta G$).
   c. It has a high activation energy (E_a).
   d. It contains an abundance of oxygen and little hydrogen.

7. Which of the following statements about an enzyme is correct?
   a. It decreases the ΔG of an endergonic reaction.
   b. It is a protein and therefore is encoded by a gene.

   c. It can make an endergonic reaction proceed spontaneously.
   d. One enzyme molecule can only bind a single substrate molecule at any one time.

8. Compared with competitive inhibition, which of the following statements is correct only for non-competitive inhibition of an enzyme-catalyzed reaction?
   a. It changes the conformation of the enzyme.
   b. The inhibitory molecule is similar to the normal substrate.
   c. Inhibition decreases the rate at which the product is made.
   d. It results in the enzyme becoming permanently inactive.

9. Which of the following statements about allosteric enzymes is correct?
   a. An allosteric activator prevents binding at the active site.
   b. Their activity can be finely controlled by metabolites within the cell.
   c. The allosteric site of the enzyme binds additional substrate molecules.
   d. An enzyme that possesses allosteric sites does not possess an active site.

10. Which of the following explains the shape of a curve that plots enzyme activity as a function of temperature?
    a. As temperature increases, the rate of all reactions slows down.
    b. At high temperatures, the structural integrity of the enzyme breaks down.
    c. At high temperatures, the rate of catalysis stays high and constant—it saturates.
    d. At low but increasing temperatures, the rate of collisions between substrate and enzyme molecules decreases.

Questions for Discussion

1. Trees become more complex as they develop spontaneously from seeds to adults. Does this process violate the second law of thermodynamics? Why or why not?

2. Trace the flow of energy through your body. What products increase the entropy of you and your surroundings?

3. You have found a molecular substance that accelerates the rate of a particular reaction. What kind of information would you need to demonstrate that this molecular substance is an enzyme?

4. The addition or removal of phosphate groups from ATP is a fully reversible reaction. In what way does this reversibility facilitate the use of ATP as a coupling agent for cellular reactions?

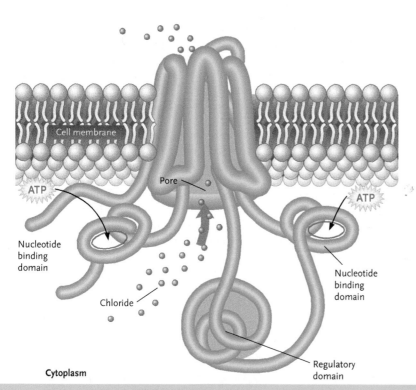

The cystic fibrosis transmembrane conductance regulator (CFTR) is a chloride pump. Mutations to the CFTR gene result in the pump being defective, causing cystic fibrosis.

Cell Membranes and Signalling

WHY IT MATTERS

Cystic fibrosis (CF) is one of the most common genetic diseases. It affects approximately 1 in 3900 children born in Canada. People with CF suffer from a progressive impairment of lung and gastrointestinal function, and although the treatment of CF patients is slowly improving, their average life span remains under 40 years. CF is caused by mutation to a gene that codes for a protein called the cystic fibrosis transmembrane conductance regulator (CFTR). In normal cells, CFTR acts as a membrane transport protein that pumps chloride ions (Cl^-) out of the cells that line the lungs and intestinal tract into the overlying mucus lining. This produces an electrical gradient across the membrane and results in the movement of positively charged sodium ions (Na^+) into the mucus lining. Because of the high ion concentration (Na^+ and Cl^-), water moves, by osmosis, out into the mucus lining, keeping it moist. Keeping the lining of the lungs and intestinal tract wet is critical to their proper functioning. In individuals with CF, the Cl^- channel CFTR does not function properly, which results in water being retained within cells, resulting in a build-up of thick, dry mucus that cannot effectively be removed by coughing. Besides obstructing airways and preventing normal breathing, the build-up of mucus in the lungs makes CF patients very susceptible to bacterial infections.

Currently, there is no cure for CF. Although treatments for CF are steadily improving, as the disease progresses in young adults, invasive procedures, including lung transplants, are often necessary. Since CF is caused by a defect to a single gene, the greatest hope is in gene therapy (see Chapter 15), which would attempt to insert normal copies of the CFTR gene into affected cells. However, many technical and ethical hurdles need to be overcome before gene therapy becomes a viable treatment option.

The structure and function of biological membranes are the focus of this chapter. We first consider the structure of membranes and then examine how membranes selectively transport substances in and out of cells and organelles. We close the chapter with a discussion of the critical role membranes play in signal transduction through the binding of molecules and the subsequent activation of intracellular signalling pathways.

5.1 An Overview of the Structure of Membranes

One of the keys to the evolution of life was the development of the cell or **plasma membrane.** By acting as a selectively permeable barrier, the plasma membrane allows for the uptake of key nutrients and elimination of waste products while maintaining a protected environment for cellular processes to occur. The subsequent development of internal membranes resulted in compartmentalization of processes and increased complexity. A good example of this is the nuclear envelope, which defines the hallmark of the eukaryotic cell—the nucleus.

5.1a A Membrane Consists of Proteins in a Fluid of Lipid Molecules

Our current view of membrane structure is based on the **fluid mosaic model (Figure 5.1).** The model proposes that membranes are not rigid with molecules

locked into place but rather consist of proteins that move around within a mixture of lipid molecules that has the consistency of olive oil.

The lipid molecules of all biological membranes exist in a double layer called a bilayer that is less than 10 nm thick. By comparison, this page is approximately 100 000 nm thick. The lipid molecules of the bilayer vibrate, flex back and forth, spin around their long axis, move sideways, and exchange places within the same bilayer half. Only rarely does a lipid molecule flip-flop between the two layers. Exchanging places within a layer occurs millions of times a second, making the lipid molecules in the membrane highly dynamic. As we will discuss later, maintaining the membrane in a fluid state is critical to membrane function.

The mosaic aspect of the fluid mosaic model refers to the fact that most membranes contain an assortment of types of proteins. This includes proteins involved in transport and attachment, signal transduction, and processes such as electron transport (Figure 5.1). Because they are larger than lipid molecules, proteins move more slowly in the fluid environment of the membrane. As well, a small number of membrane proteins anchor cytoskeleton filaments to the membrane and do not move. As also shown in Figure 5.1, a number of the lipid and protein components of some membranes have carbohydrate

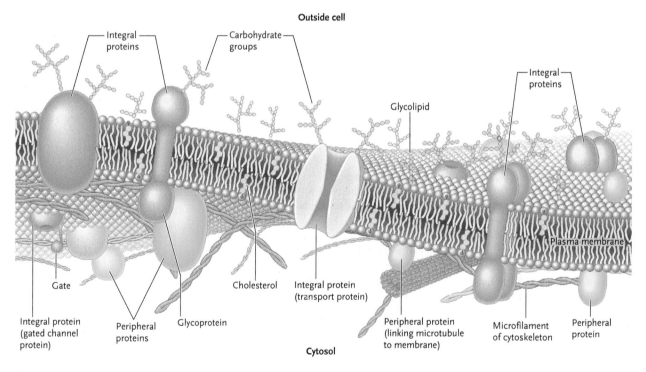

Figure 5.1
Membrane structure according to the fluid mosaic model. The model proposes that integral membrane proteins are suspended individually in a fluid lipid bilayer. Peripheral proteins are attached to integral proteins or membrane lipids mostly on the cytoplasmic side of the membrane (shown only on the inner surface in the figure). Carbohydrate groups of membrane glycoproteins and glycolipids face the cell exterior.

groups linked to them, forming glycolipids and glycoproteins.

The relative proportions of lipid and protein within a membrane vary considerably depending on the type of membrane. For example, membranes that contain protein complexes involved in electron transport, such as the inner mitochondrial membrane, contain large amounts of protein (76% protein and only 24% lipid), whereas the plasma membrane contains nearly equal amounts of protein and lipid (49% and 51%, respectively). Myelin, which is a membrane that functions to insulate nerve fibres, is composed mostly of lipids (18% protein and 82% lipid).

An important characteristic of membranes, illustrated in Figure 5.1, is that the proteins and other components of one half of the lipid bilayer are different from those that make up the other half of the bilayer. This is referred to as membrane asymmetry, and it reflects differences in the functions performed by each side of the membrane. For example, a range of glycolipids and carbohydrate groups are attached to proteins on the external side of the plasma membrane, whereas components of the cytoskeleton bind to proteins on the internal side of the plasma membrane. In addition, hormones and growth factors bind to receptor proteins that are found only on the external surface of the plasma membrane.

5.1b Experimental Evidence in Support of the Fluid Mosaic Model

The fluid mosaic model of membrane structure is supported by two major pieces of experimental evidence.

Membranes Are Fluid. In a now classic study carried out in 1970, David Frye and Michael A. Edidin grew human cells and mouse cells separately in tissue culture. They were able to tag the human or mouse membrane proteins **(Figure 5.2)** with dye molecules: the human proteins were linked to red dye molecules and the mouse proteins were linked to green. Frye and Edidin then fused the human and mouse cells. Within minutes, they found that the two distinctly coloured proteins began to mix. In less than an hour, the two colours had completely intermixed on the fused cells, indicating that the mouse and human proteins had moved around in the fused membranes.

Based on the measured rates at which molecules mix in biological membranes, the membrane bilayer appears to be about as fluid as olive oil or light machine oil.

Membrane Asymmetry. One of the key experiments revealing membrane asymmetry utilized the **freeze-fracture technique** in combination with electron microscopy **(Figure 5.3, p. 100)**. In this technique, a block of cells is rapidly frozen by dipping it in liquid nitrogen (−196°C). Then the block is fractured by hitting it with a microscopically sharp knife edge. Often

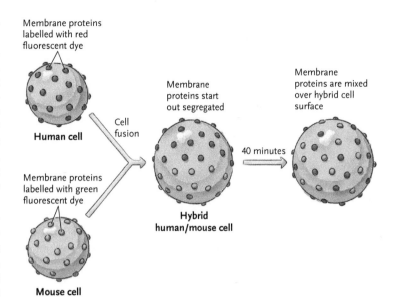

Experimental Research Figure 5.2 The Frye-Edidin experiment provided evidence that the membrane bilayer is fluid. In the experiment, membrane proteins were found to rapidly migrate over the surface of the hybrid cell.

the fracture splits bilayers into inner and outer halves, exposing the membrane interior. Using electron microscopy, the split membranes appear as smooth layers in which individual particles the size of proteins are embedded (shown in Figure 5.3c, p. 100). From these images, it is clear that the particles on either side of the membrane differ in size, number, and shape, providing evidence that the two sides are distinctly different.

STUDY BREAK

1. Describe the fluid mosaic model of membrane structure.
2. What is meant by the term *membrane asymmetry*?

5.2 The Lipid Fabric of a Membrane

The foundation or underlying fabric of all biological membranes is the lipid molecules. Collectively, the term *lipid* refers to a diverse group of water-insoluble molecules that includes **fats; phospholipids**, which are the dominant lipids in membranes; and steroids. A structural overview of these molecules is found in *The Purple Pages*. As we discuss in this section, keeping membranes in a fluid state is important to membrane function. Many organisms can adjust the types of lipids in the membranes such that membranes do not become too stiff (viscous) or too fluid (liquid).

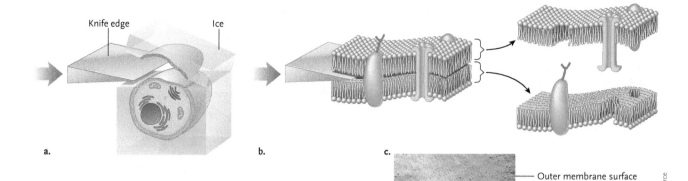

a.   b.   c.

Figure 5.3
The freeze-fracture technique allows for analysis of the membrane interior.
(a) The freeze-fracture technique. **(b)** The fracture may split the membrane bilayers into inner and outer halves. **(c)** The particles visible in the exposed membrane interior are integral membrane proteins.

Outer membrane surface

Exposed membrane interior

Don W. Fawcett/Science Source

5.2a Phospholipids Are the Dominant Lipids in Membranes

The lipid bilayer, which represents the foundation of biological membranes, is formed of **phospholipids.** As shown in **Figure 5.4a,** each phospholipid consists of a head group attached to two long chains of carbon and hydrogen (a **hydrocarbon**) called a fatty acid. The head group consists of glycerol linked to one of several types of **alcohols** or amino acids by a phosphate group (see Figure 5.4a). A property that all phospholipids possess, which is critical to the structure and function of membranes, is that they are **amphipathic**—the molecule contains a region that is *hydrophobic* (water fearing) and a region that is *hydrophilic* (water loving). Whereas the fatty acid chains of a lipid are nonpolar, the phosphate-containing head group is polar. Overall, polar molecules tend to be hydrophilic and nonpolar molecules hydrophobic. (For a review of molecular polarity, see *The Purple Pages*.) Laundry detergents are common amphipathic molecules—they are excellent at removing oil stains from clothing while also being soluble in water.

As illustrated in Figure 5.4a, phospholipids can differ in the degree of unsaturation of their fatty acids. Notice in Figure 5.4a that one of the fatty acids is fully saturated—all the carbons are bound to the maximum number of hydrogen atoms. The second fatty acid contains a carbon–carbon double bond (denoted by the arrow) and thus is **unsaturated.** As shown by the space-filling model, the presence of the C–C double bond imparts a kink or bend to the fatty acid tail (Figure 5.4b).

When added to water, phospholipids self-assemble into one of three structures—a **micelle**, a liposome, or

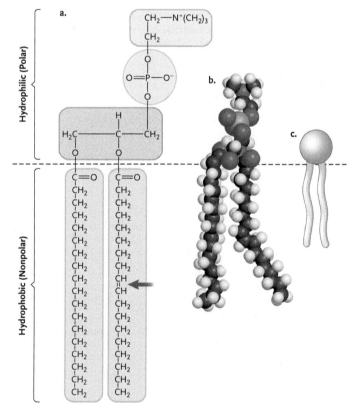

Figure 5.4
Phospholipid structure. **(a)** Chemical formula of phosphatidylcholine. The polar head group consists of glycerol (shown in pink) linked to the organic molecule choline (shown in blue) by a phosphate group (shown in yellow). In addition, the glycerol is linked to two fatty acids, each 18 carbons long. The structure of phospholipids is also often represented as space-filling models **(b)** and as an icon **(c)**. As shown in the space-filling model, the presence of a carbon–carbon double bond (denoted by the arrow in (a)) imparts a bend to one of the fatty acids.

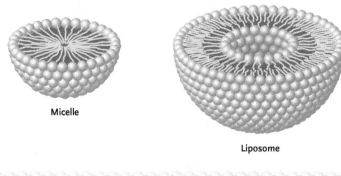

Micelle

Liposome

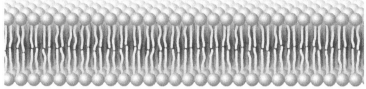

Phospholipid bilayer

Figure 5.5
In an aqueous environment, phospholipids self-assemble into micelles, liposomes, or bilayers.

a bilayer **(Figure 5.5).** Which structure forms depends mostly on the phospholipid concentration. Phospholipids spontaneously form these structures in an aqueous environment because of the *hydrophobic effect*—the tendency of polar molecules like water to exclude hydrophobic molecules such as fatty acids. This results in the aggregation of lipid molecules in structures where the fatty acid tails interact with each other and the polar head groups associate with water. These arrangements are favoured because they represent the lowest energy state and are more likely to occur over any other arrangement.

5.2b Fatty Acid Composition and Temperature Affect Membrane Fluidity

The fluidity of the lipid bilayer is primarily influenced by two factors: the type of fatty acids that make up the lipid molecules and the temperature. Fully **saturated fatty acids** are linear, which allows lipid molecules to pack tightly together **(Figure 5.6a).** In contrast, lipid molecules with one or more unsaturated fatty acids are prevented from packing closely together because the presence of double bonds introduces kinks in the fatty acid backbone (Figure 5.6b). As a result, the more unsaturated the fatty acids of the lipid molecules, the more fluid the membrane.

Besides fatty acid composition, the temperature can also dramatically affect membrane fluidity. As the temperature drops and the random molecular motion of lipid molecules slows down, a point is reached where fluidity is lost and the phospholipid molecules form a semisolid gel. This is exactly what happens when melted butter cools—at a certain temperature it

turns from a liquid into a solid. The temperature at which gelling occurs depends upon the fatty acid composition. The more unsaturated a group of lipid molecules, the lower the temperature at which gelling occurs. Likewise, at high temperatures, the increased molecular motion may result in membranes becoming too fluid, resulting in a loss of structure. For most membrane systems, the normal fluid state is achieved by a mixed population of saturated and unsaturated fatty acids.

5.2c Organisms Can Adjust Fatty Acid Composition

Keeping membranes in the optimal state of fluidity is absolutely essential to cell function. Exposure to low temperatures can be harmful because the resulting membrane gelling can decrease membrane permeability and inhibit the function of enzymes and receptors attached to, or localized within, the bilayer. Electron transport, for example, requires molecules to migrate rapidly within the membrane bilayer. If the membrane becomes less fluid due to low temperature, the rate of electron transport will decrease and eventually stop.

Problems also arise at high temperature. Membranes may become too fluid due to the increase in molecular motion, which can result in membrane leakage. Ions such as K^+, Na^+, and Ca^{2+} begin to freely diffuse across the membrane, resulting in an irreversible disruption of cellular ion balance that can rapidly lead to cell death.

Unlike with humans, the body temperature of most organisms closely matches that of the external environment. Examples of such organisms are plants, bacteria, protists, and insects. To live at a range of temperatures, these organisms are able to alter membrane fluidity by adjusting the relative proportion of unsaturated fatty acids.

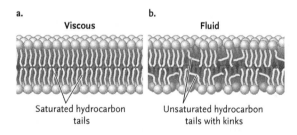

a.
Viscous

b.
Fluid

Saturated hydrocarbon tails

Unsaturated hydrocarbon tails with kinks

Figure 5.6
Lipid molecule composition affects how closely the molecules interact. Lipid molecules that contain saturated hydrocarbon tails are closely packed **(a)**, whereas unsaturated hydrocarbon tails have kinks that prevent lipid molecules from packing closely together **(b)**.

Unsaturated fatty acids are produced during fatty acid biosynthesis through the action of a group of enzymes called desaturases **(Figure 5.7a)**. All fatty acids are initially synthesized as fully saturated molecules without any double bonds. Desaturases act on these saturated fatty acids by catalyzing a reaction that removes two hydrogen atoms from neighbouring carbon atoms and introducing a double bond. There are many different desaturase enzymes, each one introducing a double bond at a specific point along the fatty acid chain. Whereas some unsaturated fatty acids contain only one carbon–carbon double bond, others may contain two or more, which indicates the action of more than one desaturase.

Like many proteins, desaturase abundance is regulated at the level of gene transcription, which results in changes to desaturase transcript (mRNA) abundance.

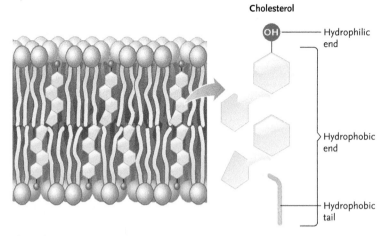

Figure 5.8

The position taken by cholesterol within a membrane. The hydrophilic–OH group at one end of the molecule extends into the hydrophilic region of the bilayer; the ring structure extends into the hydrophobic membrane interior.

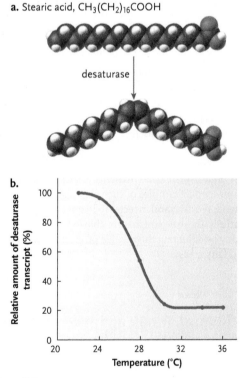

a. Stearic acid, CH₃(CH₂)₁₆COOH

desaturase

Figure 5.7

Organisms can regulate the degree of fatty acid unsaturation. **(a)** Desaturases are a class of enzymes that introduce double bonds into fatty acids, thereby altering the degree of unsaturation. **(b)** Graph showing relative amounts of desaturase transcript amounts (mRNA abundance) in relation to growth temperature in a cyanobacterium.

Figure 5.7b shows how the abundance of a specific desaturase transcript changes with growth temperature in a cyanobacterium. As growth temperature decreases, desaturase transcript abundance goes up, which results in an increase in synthesis of the desaturase enzyme. Higher amounts of desaturases, in turn, result in an increase in the abundance of unsaturated fatty acids. By regulating desaturase abundance, many organisms can closely regulate the amount of unsaturated fatty acids that get incorporated into membranes and thereby maintain proper membrane fluidity.

Besides lipids, a group of compounds called **sterols** also influence membrane fluidity. The best example of a sterol is **cholesterol (Figure 5.8),** which is found in the membranes of animal cells but not in those of plants or prokaryotes. Sterols act as membrane buffers: at high temperatures, they help restrain the movement of lipid molecules, thus reducing the fluidity of the membrane. However, at lower temperatures, sterols disrupt fatty acids from associating by occupying space between lipid molecules, thus slowing the transition to the nonfluid gel state.

STUDY BREAK

1. Why is maintaining proper membrane fluidity important for membrane function?
2. What is the relationship between temperature and desaturase expression?

5.3 Membrane Proteins

While the lipid molecules constitute the foundation of a membrane, the unique set of proteins associated with the membrane determines its function and makes each

Trans Fats

In the food industry, the use of fats containing saturated fatty acids is more desirable than the use of oils that contain unsaturated fatty acids. The lack of double bonds means that lipids containing saturated fatty acids are more stable and less prone to the oxidation that can decrease shelf life and affect the texture and taste of the final product. Moreover, hard fats have a higher melting temperature, which makes them useful in many applications, such as in baking and deep-frying.

Because animal-based saturated fats such as butter and lard are expensive and susceptible to spoilage, the food industry has, for many decades, used saturated fats produced through the industrial process of hydrogenation. This process removes *cis* double bonds from fatty acids by heating vegetable oil in the presence of hydrogen gas and a catalyst. In the food industry, partial hydrogenation is practised, which results in a product that is still malleable and not too hard. One of the unintended consequences of partial hydrogenation is that the *cis* double bonds that do not become hydrogenated tend to be reconfigured into the *trans* orientation. Although small amounts of *trans* fats are found naturally in the milk and meat of **ruminant** animals such as cows and sheep, through partial hydrogenation, human consumption of *trans* fats has increased tremendously over the last 70 years.

There is now clear medical evidence that the consumption of *trans* fats is unhealthy. A comprehensive review of research on *trans* fat consumption and health by the *New England Journal of Medicine* in 2006 clearly demonstrated the existence of a strong connection between *trans* fat consumption and elevated risk of coronary heart disease, a leading cause of death in North America. *Trans* fats have also been linked to increased incidence of other health problems as well. The physiological basis for the increased risk to health by increased *trans* fat consumption is not fully understood and remains a very active area of research. The increased risk may be due, in part, to the fact that a major group of enzymes called lipases, which aid in the breakdown of many types of lipids, including *cis* unsaturated fats, do not recognize the *trans* configuration. This leads to *trans* fats staying in the bloodstream longer, which may lead to increased incidence of arterial deposition, which may lead to coronary heart disease.

In response to the overwhelming medical evidence that *trans* fats are harmful, governments around the world are implementing restrictions on the amount of *trans* fats foods can contain. In Canada, the *trans* fat content of vegetable oils and soft margarines is now limited to 2% of the total fat content, whereas the *trans* fat content for all other foods is 5% of the total fat content, including ingredients sold to restaurants. Similar guidelines are in place in many European countries, as well as being implemented in the United States.

In response to these new guidelines, food manufacturers and restaurant chains have reformulated their products to be *trans* fat free. This has primarily been achieved by simply replacing hydrogenated fats with naturally saturated fats. Many nutritionists argue that these fully saturated alternatives may not offer any health benefit.

---

membrane unique. As we will discuss in this section, two major types of proteins are associated with membranes: integral and peripheral membrane proteins.

5.3a The Key Functions of Membrane Proteins

Membrane proteins can be separated into four major functional categories, as shown in **Figure 5.9, p. 104.** It should be noted that all of these functions may exist in a single membrane and that one protein or protein complex may serve more than one of these functions:

1. **Transport.** Many substances cannot freely diffuse through the membrane. Instead, a protein may provide a hydrophilic channel that allows movement of a specific molecule. Alternatively, a membrane protein may change its shape and in so doing shuttle specific molecules from one side of a membrane to the other.
2. **Enzymatic activity.** A number of enzymes are membrane proteins. The best example of this is the enzymes associated with the respiratory and photosynthetic electron transport chains (ETCs).
3. **Signal transduction.** Membranes often contain receptor proteins on their outer surface that bind to specific chemicals such as hormones. On binding, these receptors trigger changes on the inside surface of the membrane that lead to transduction of the signal through the cell.
4. **Attachment/recognition.** Proteins exposed to both the internal and external membrane surfaces act as attachment points for a range of cytoskeleton elements, as well as components involved in cell–cell recognition.

5.3b Integral Membrane Proteins Interact with the Membrane Hydrophobic Core

Proteins that are embedded in the phospholipid bilayer are called **integral membrane proteins.** Many of these traverse the entire lipid bilayer at least once and are referred to as *transmembrane proteins*. Because they

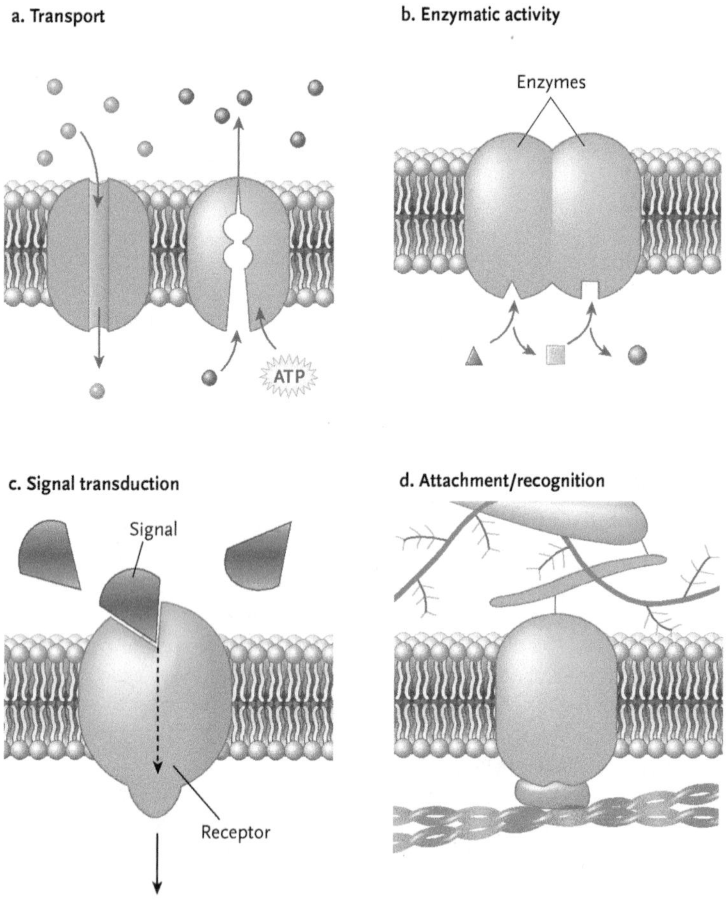

a. Transport

b. Enzymatic activity

Enzymes

ATP

c. Signal transduction

Signal

Receptor

d. Attachment/recognition

Figure 5.9
The major functions of membrane proteins.

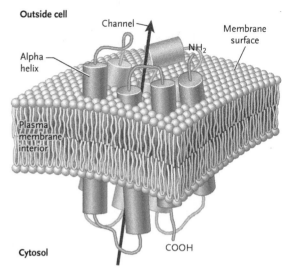

Outside cell

Channel

Alpha helix

Membrane surface

NH₂

Plasma membrane interior

Cytosol

COOH

Figure 5.10
The structure of membrane proteins. A typical integral membrane protein showing the membrane-spanning alpha-helical segments (red cylinders), connected by flexible loops of the amino acid chain at the membrane surfaces.

distinct regions of predominantly nonpolar amino acids linked by regions that are dominated by polar and charged amino acids. These polar amino acids are found in the portions of the protein that are exposed to the aqueous environment on either side of the membrane (see Figure 5.11).

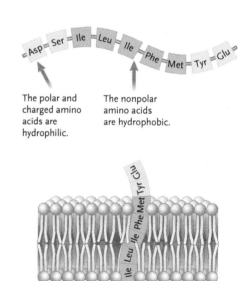

Asp — Ser — Ile — Leu — Ile — Phe — Met — Tyr — Glu

The polar and charged amino acids are hydrophilic.

The nonpolar amino acids are hydrophobic.

Asp Ser Ile Leu Ile Phe Met Tyr Glu

Figure 5.11
Transmembrane proteins can be identified by the presence of stretches of amino acids that are primarily nonpolar. These regions of the protein interact with the hydrophobic regions of the membrane. Usually between 17 and 20 amino acids are needed to span the membrane once. For clarity this model shows only five nonpolar amino acids spanning the membrane.

have to interact with both the aqueous environment on both sides of the membrane and the hydrophobic core, transmembrane proteins have distinct regions (called **domains**) that differ markedly in polarity. The domain that interacts with the lipid bilayer consists predominantly of nonpolar amino acids that collectively form a type of **secondary structure** termed an *alpha helix* **(Figure 5.10)** (see *The Purple Pages* for an overview of protein structure). By contrast, the portions of a transmembrane protein that are exposed on either side of the membrane are composed of primarily polar amino acids. (The different classes of amino acids are presented in *The Purple Pages*).

Given the amino acid sequence (**primary structure**) of a protein, it is usually quite simple to determine if it is likely a transmembrane protein. What one looks for, usually with the aid of a computer program, are stretches of primarily nonpolar amino acids. These stretches are about 17 to 20 amino acids in length, which matches the peptide length needed to span the lipid bilayer **(Figure 5.11)**. Most transmembrane proteins span the membrane more than once. So, for example, if a protein has three membrane-spanning domains, the primary sequence would show three

5.3c Peripheral Membrane Proteins Interact with the Membrane Hydrophilic Surface

The second major group of membrane proteins are **peripheral membrane proteins**, so called because they are positioned on the surface of a membrane and do not interact with the hydrophobic core of the membrane. Peripheral proteins are held to membrane surfaces by noncovalent bonds—hydrogen bonds and **ionic bonds**—usually by interacting with the exposed portions of integral proteins as well as directly with membrane lipid molecules. Many peripheral proteins are found on the cytoplasmic side of the plasma membrane and form part of the cytoskeleton (look back at Figure 5.1). In addition, as we will see in later chapters, key enzymes involved in both respiratory and photosynthetic electron transport are peripheral membrane proteins. Because peripheral membrane proteins do not interact with the hydrophobic core of the membrane, they are made up of a mixture of polar and nonpolar amino acids.

STUDY BREAK

1. What roles are served by membrane proteins?
2. What are the two major classes of membrane proteins?

5.4 Passive Membrane Transport

The hydrophobic nature of membranes severely restricts the free movement of many molecules into and out of cells and from one compartment to another. Molecules such as O_2 diffuse very rapidly across membranes, which is important considering the vital role O_2 plays in cellular respiration. However, a range of other molecules, including ions, charged molecules, and macromolecules, do not readily move across membranes. In this section, we consider the diffusion of molecules from one compartment to the other and the factors that influence the rate of that diffusion.

5.4a Passive Transport Is Based on Diffusion

Passive transport is defined as the movement of a substance across a membrane without the need to expend chemical energy such as ATP. What drives passive transport is **diffusion**, the net movement of a substance from a region of higher concentration to a region of lower concentration. Above absolute zero (–273°C), molecules are in constant motion, which results in molecules becoming uniformly distributed in space. Diffusion is the primary mechanism of **solute** movement within a cell.

The driving force behind diffusion is an increase in entropy (see Chapter 4). In the initial state, when molecules are more concentrated in one region or on one side of a membrane, the energy associated with the molecules is more localized. As diffusion occurs, the entropy increases as the energy spreads out until the molecules are evenly distributed and the entropy is highest **(Figure 5.12)**. As the distribution proceeds to the state of maximum disorder, the molecules release free energy, which can accomplish work (see Section 4.2 for a discussion of entropy and free energy).

The rate of diffusion depends on the concentration difference (**concentration gradient**) between two areas or across a membrane. The larger the gradient, the faster the rate of diffusion. Similar to chemical equilibrium (see Chapter 4), when diffusing molecules reach equilibrium, there is still movement of molecules from one space to another, but no net change in concentration (see Figure 5.12).

5.4b There Are Two Types of Passive Transport: Simple and Facilitated

There are two types of passive transport: simple diffusion and facilitated diffusion. **Simple diffusion** is the movement of molecules directly across a membrane without the involvement of a transporter. The rate of simple diffusion of a molecule depends upon two factors: molecular size and lipid solubility. As shown in **Figure 5.13, p. 106**, some molecules diffuse very rapidly across the membrane, while other molecules are essentially unable to transit the membrane.

Small nonpolar molecules such as O_2 and CO_2 are readily soluble in the hydrophobic interior of a membrane and move very rapidly from one side to the other. As well, steroid hormones and many drugs that tend to be amphipathic can readily transit the lipid bilayer. Small uncharged molecules such as water and glycerol, even though they are polar, are still able to move quite rapidly across the membrane (see Figure 5.13). In contrast, the membrane is practically impermeable to charged molecules, including ions such as Cl^-, Na^+, and phosphate (PO_4^{3-}). Transport of small ions is about a billionth (10^{-9}) the rate of the transport of water. Their charge and associated hydration shell contribute to

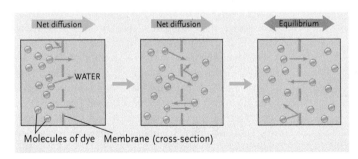

Molecules of dye   Membrane (cross-section)

Figure 5.12
Diffusion is the movement of molecules from regions of high concentration to areas of low concentration. It is driven by the increase in entropy associated with energy becoming more dispersed.

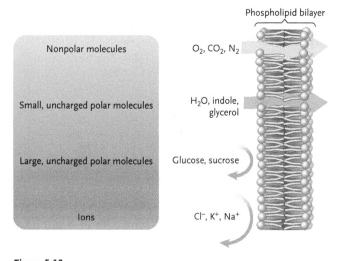

Nonpolar molecules	O_2, CO_2, N_2
Small, uncharged polar molecules	H_2O, indole, glycerol
Large, uncharged polar molecules	Glucose, sucrose
Ions	Cl^-, K^+, Na^+

Phospholipid bilayer

Figure 5.13

The size and charge of a molecule affect the rate of diffusion across a membrane.

ions being prevented from entering the hydrophobic core of the membrane.

The diffusion of molecules across a membrane through the aid of a transporter is called **facilitated diffusion**. The diffusion of many polar and charged molecules, such as water, amino acids, sugars, and ions, relies on specific transport complexes for their rapid movement from one compartment to another. Although facilitated diffusion involves specific transporters, just like simple diffusion, transport depends upon a concentration gradient across the membrane—when the gradient falls to zero, facilitated diffusion stops.

5.4c Two Groups of Transport Proteins Carry Out Facilitated Diffusion

Facilitated diffusion is carried out by two types of transport proteins: channel proteins and carrier proteins, both of which are transmembrane proteins **(Figure 5.14)**. **Channel proteins** form hydrophilic pathways in the membrane through which molecules can pass. The channel aids the diffusion of molecules by providing an avenue that is shielded from the hydrophobic core of the bilayer. Specific channel proteins are involved in the transport of certain ions and, most interestingly, the transport of water.

The diffusion of water is facilitated by water-specific transport proteins called aquaporins (Figure 5.14a). Aquaporins have been found in organisms as diverse as bacteria, plants, and humans. The aquaporin channel is very narrow and allows for the single-file movement of about a billion water molecules every second. Remarkably, the channel is very specific for water and does not allow for the diffusion of ions including protons. Recent three-dimensional models of aquaporin show the presence of positive charges in the centre of the channel that are thought to specifically

repel the transport of protons. For his discovery of aquaporins, Peter Agre at Johns Hopkins University received the Nobel Prize for chemistry in 2003.

Another type of channel protein that is found in all eukaryotes is the **gated channel** (Figure 5.14b). These transporters can switch between open, closed, and intermediate states and are critical to the movement of most ions, for example, sodium (Na^+), potassium (K^+), calcium (Ca^{2+}), and chlorine (Cl^-). The gates may be opened or closed by changes in voltage across the membrane, for instance, or by binding signal molecules. The opening or closing involves changes in the protein's three-dimensional shape. In animals, voltage-gated ion channels are used in nerve conduction and the control of muscle contraction (see Chapters 44 and 46). As well, CFTR, the Cl^- channel that is defective in individuals with cystic fibrosis, is a gated channel (see "Why It Matters").

The second class of transport proteins that form passageways through the lipid bilayer are **carrier proteins** (Figure 5.14). Each carrier protein binds a single specific solute, such as a sugar molecule or an amino acid, and transports it across the lipid bilayer. Because a single solute is transferred in this carrier-mediated fashion, the transfer is called *uniport transport*. In performing the transport step, the carrier protein undergoes conformational changes that progressively move the solute binding site from one side of the membrane to the other, thereby transporting the solute. This property distinguishes carrier protein function from channel protein function.

Most transport proteins display a high degree of substrate specificity, in a way similar to an enzyme. For example, transporters that carry glucose are unable to transport fructose, which is structurally similar. This specificity allows various cells and cellular compartments to tightly control what gets in and out. The kinds of transport proteins present in the plasma membrane or, for example, on the inner membrane of the mitochondrion depend ultimately on the type of cell and growth conditions.

How can you experimentally determine if a molecule is transported by facilitated diffusion and not just simple diffusion? First, with facilitated diffusion, the rate of movement across the membrane is much faster than one would predict based just on the chemical structure of the molecule being transported **(Figure 5.15, p. 108)**. Second, facilitated diffusion can be saturated in the same way as an enzyme can be saturated, by substrate. A membrane has a limited number of transporters for a particular molecule. If you measure the rate of transport at increasing concentration differences across a membrane, the rate of transport of a particular molecule (the substrate) reaches a plateau that represents a state when essentially all of the transporters are occupied all the time by substrate (they are saturated). Increasing the concentration further has no effect on the rate of transport (see Figure 5.15). By comparison, in simple diffusion, the whole membrane surface is effectively the transporter; thus, the rate of transport, although usually slower, never reaches a plateau.

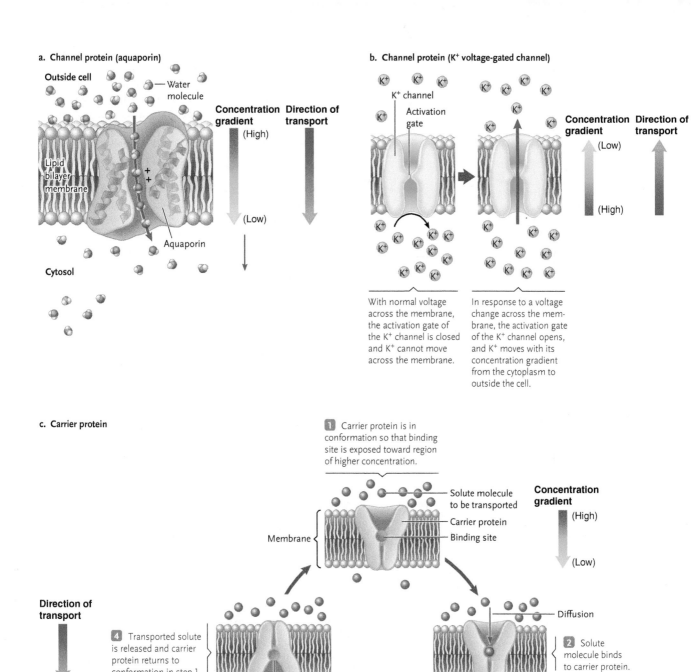

a. Channel protein (aquaporin)

Outside cell

Water molecule

Concentration gradient

(High)

Direction of transport

Lipid bilayer membrane

++

Aquaporin

(Low)

Cytosol

b. Channel protein (K+ voltage-gated channel)

K^+

K^+ channel

Activation gate

Concentration gradient

(Low)

Direction of transport

(High)

With normal voltage across the membrane, the activation gate of the K^+ channel is closed and K^+ cannot move across the membrane.

In response to a voltage change across the membrane, the activation gate of the K^+ channel opens, and K^+ moves with its concentration gradient from the cytoplasm to outside the cell.

c. Carrier protein

1 Carrier protein is in conformation so that binding site is exposed toward region of higher concentration.

Solute molecule to be transported

Concentration gradient

(High)

Carrier protein

Membrane

Binding site

(Low)

Diffusion

Direction of transport

4 Transported solute is released and carrier protein returns to conformation in step 1.

2 Solute molecule binds to carrier protein.

3 In response to binding, carrier protein changes conformation so that binding site is exposed to region of lower concentration.

Figure 5.14
Transport proteins for facilitated diffusion. **(a)** Channel protein: aquaporin. **(b)** Channel protein: K+ voltage-gated channel. **(c)** Carrier proteins: a model for how these proteins transport solutes such as glucose.

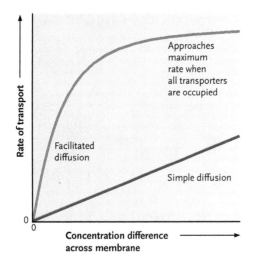

Figure 5.15
Simple diffusion and facilitated diffusion display different transport kinetics. Compared with simple diffusion, facilitated diffusion leads to higher rates of transport and displays saturation kinetics.

5.4d Osmosis Is the Passive Diffusion of Water

Like solutes, water can also move passively across membranes in a process called osmosis. The passive transport of water occurs constantly in living cells.

Inward or outward movement of water by osmosis develops forces that can cause cells to swell or shrink. Formally, **osmosis** is defined as the diffusion of water molecules across a selectively permeable membrane from a solution of lower solute concentration to a solution of higher solute concentration. For osmosis to take place, the selectively permeable membrane must allow water molecules to pass but not molecules of the solute. Osmosis occurs in cells because they contain a solution of proteins and other molecules that are retained in the cytoplasm by a membrane impermeable to them but permeable to water. Osmosis can occur by simple diffusion through the lipid bilayer or it can be facilitated by aquaporins (see Section 5.4c).

The movement of water by osmosis is dictated by solute concentration. If the solution surrounding a cell contains dissolved substances at lower concentrations than in the cell, the solution is said to be **hypotonic** to the cell (*hypo* = under or below; *tonos* = tension or tone). When a cell is in a hypotonic solution, water enters by osmosis, and the cell tends to swell **(Figure 5.16a).** Animal cells, such as red blood cells, in a hypotonic solution may actually swell to the point of bursting. This is in contrast to plant cells, where the

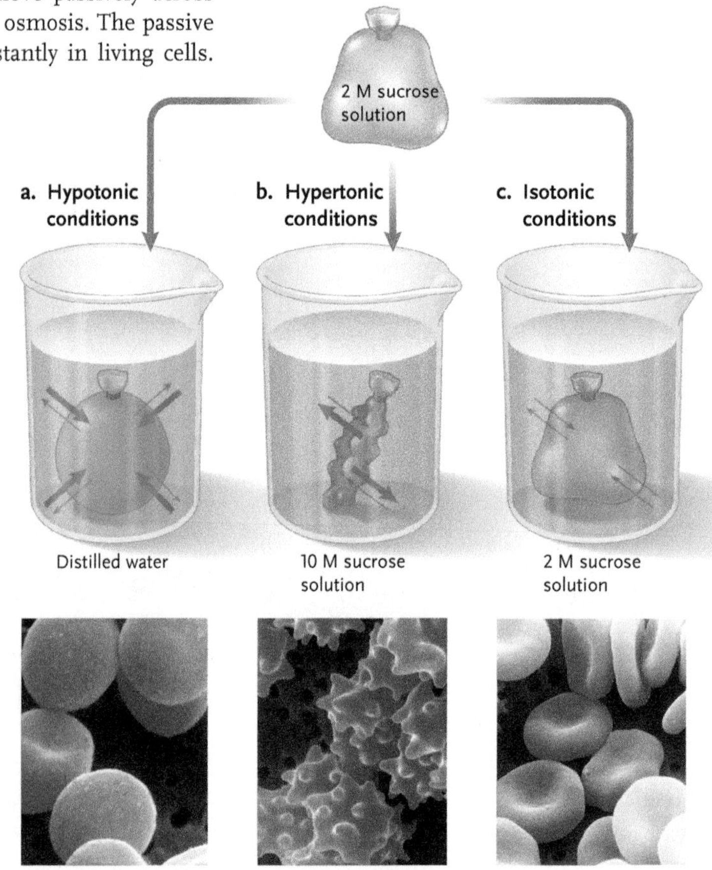

Figure 5.16
Osmotic water movement. The diagrams show what happens when a cellophane bag filled with a 2 M sucrose solution is placed in **(a)** a hypotonic, **(b)** a hypertonic, or **(c)** an isotonic solution. The cellophane is permeable to water but not to sucrose molecules. The width of the arrows shows the amount of water movement. In the first beaker, the distilled water is hypotonic to the solution in the bag; net movement of water is into the bag. In the second beaker, the 10 M solution is hypertonic to the solution in the bag; net movement of water is out of the bag. In the third beaker, the solutions inside and outside the bag are isotonic; there is no net movement of water into or out of the bag. The animal cell micrographs show the corresponding effects on red blood cells placed in hypotonic, hypertonic, or isotonic solutions. (Micrographs, M. Sheetz, R. Painter, and S. Singer. *Journal of Cell Biology*, 70:493, 1976. By permission of Rockefeller University Press.)

a. Hypotonic conditions

Distilled water

Water diffuses inward; cells swell.

b. Hypertonic conditions

10 M sucrose solution

Water diffuses outward; cells shrink.

c. Isotonic conditions

2 M sucrose solution

No net movement of water; cells do not change in size or shape.

© 1976 The Rockefeller University Press. *The Journal of Cell Biology*, 1976, 70:193–203. doi: 10.1083/jcb.70.1.193.

presence of the cell wall prevents the cells from bursting in a hypotonic solution. Instead the cell pushes against the cell wall, resulting in what is called turgor pressure. This is discussed in more detail in Chapter 35.

If the solution that surrounds a cell contains solutes at higher concentrations than in the cell, then the outside solution is said to be **hypertonic** to the cell (*hyper* = over or above) (Figure 5.16b). When a cell is in a hypertonic solution, water leaves by osmosis. If the outward osmotic movement exceeds the capacity of cells to replace the lost water, both animal and plant cells will shrink (Figure 5.16b).

In animals, ions, proteins, and other molecules are concentrated in extracellular fluids, as well as inside cells so that the concentration of water inside and outside cells is usually equal or **isotonic** (*iso* = the same), as shown in Figure 5.16c. However, this comes at an energetic cost of constantly having to pump ions from one side to the other. For example, the ATP-dependent transport of Na^+ from inside to outside the cell is essential; otherwise water would move inward by osmosis and cause the cells to burst. Osmotic movement in plant cells is discussed more in depth in Chapter 35, whereas the mechanisms by which animals balance their water content are discussed in Chapter 50.

STUDY BREAK

1. How do the size and charge of a molecule influence its transport across a membrane?
2. Explain how aquaporin functions to transport water.
3. What is the difference between passive transport and active transport?

5.5 Active Membrane Transport

As shown in Figure 5.15, compared to simple diffusion, facilitated diffusion increases the rate of movement of molecules across membranes. However, this type of transport is limited to movement down a concentration gradient. Many cellular processes require molecules to be maintained in various cell compartments at very high concentrations. This is achieved by energy-dependent transport that moves molecules against a concentration gradient—from a region of lower concentration to a region of higher concentration.

5.5a Active Transport Requires Energy

The transport of molecules across a membrane against a concentration gradient requires the expenditure of energy and is referred to as **active transport**. The energy is usually in the form of ATP, and it is estimated that about 25% of a cell's ATP requirements are for the active transport of molecules. Active transport concentrates molecules such as sugars and amino acids inside cells and pushes ions in or out of cells.

The three main functions of active transport in cells and organelles are (1) uptake of essential nutrients from the fluid surrounding cells even when their concentrations are lower than in cells, (2) removal of secretory or waste materials from cells or organelles even when the concentration of those materials is higher outside the cells or organelles, and (3) maintenance of essentially constant intracellular concentrations of H^+, Na^+, K^+, and Ca^{2+}. Because ions are charged molecules, active transport of ions may contribute to voltage—an electrical potential difference—across the plasma membrane, called a membrane potential. This electrical difference across the plasma membrane is important in neurons and muscle cells and is discussed in more detail in Chapters 44 and 46, respectively.

There are two classes of active transport: primary and secondary. In **primary active transport**, the same protein that transports the molecules also hydrolyzes ATP to power the transport directly. In **secondary active transport**, the transport is indirectly driven by ATP. That is, the transport proteins use a favourable concentration gradient of ions built up by primary active transport as the energy source to drive the transport of a different molecule.

Other features of active transport (listed in **Table 5.1, p. 110**) resemble facilitated diffusion. Both processes depend on membrane transport proteins, both are specific, and the rate of both processes can plateau at high substrate concentrations.

5.5b Primary Active Transport Moves Positively Charged Ions

All primary active transport pumps move positively charged ions—H^+, Ca^{2+}, Na^+, and K^+—across membranes **(Figure 5.17, p. 110)**. The gradients of positive ions established by primary active transport pumps underlie functions that are absolutely essential for life. For example, the **proton pumps (H^+ pumps)** in plasma membranes push hydrogen ions from the cytoplasm to the cell exterior. These pumps (as in Figure 5.17) temporarily bind a phosphate group removed from ATP during the pumping cycle. Proton pumps have various functions. For example, in bacteria, archaea, and plants and fungi, proton pumps in the plasma membrane generate membrane potential. Proton pumps in lysosomes of animals and vacuoles of plants and fungi keep the pH within the organelle low, serving to activate the enzymes contained within them.

Another active transport system is the **calcium pump (Ca^{2+} pump)**, which is widely distributed among eukaryotes. It pushes Ca^{2+} from the cytoplasm to the cell exterior and from the cytosol into the vesicles of the endoplasmic reticulum (ER). As a result, Ca^{2+} concentration is typically high outside cells and inside

Table 5.1	Characteristics of Transport Mechanisms		
	Passive Transport		
Characteristic	Simple Diffusion	Facilitated Diffusion	Active Transport
Membrane component responsible for transport	Lipids	Proteins	Proteins
Binding of transported substance	No	Yes	Yes
Energy source	Concentration gradients	Concentration gradients	ATP hydrolysis or concentration gradients
Direction of transport	With gradient of transported substance	With gradient of transported substance	Against gradient of transported substance
Specificity for molecules or molecular classes	Nonspecific	Specific	Specific
Saturation at high concentrations of transported molecules	No	Yes	Yes

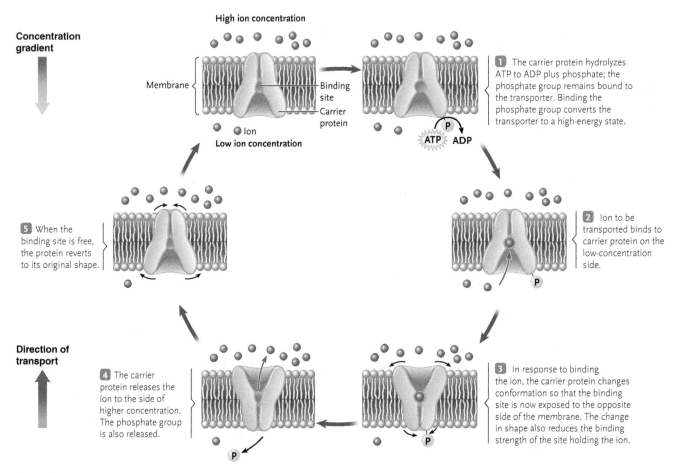

Figure 5.17

Model for how a primary active transport pump operates.

ER vesicles and low in the cytoplasmic solution. This Ca^{2+} gradient is used universally among eukaryotes as a regulatory control of cellular activities as diverse as secretion, microtubule assembly, and muscle contraction. The latter is discussed further in Chapter 46.

The **sodium–potassium pump** (or **Na⁺/K⁺ pump**), located in the plasma membrane of all animal cells, pushes three Na^+ ions out of the cell and two K^+ ions into the cell in the same pumping cycle **(Figure 5.18)**. As a result, positive charges accumulate in excess

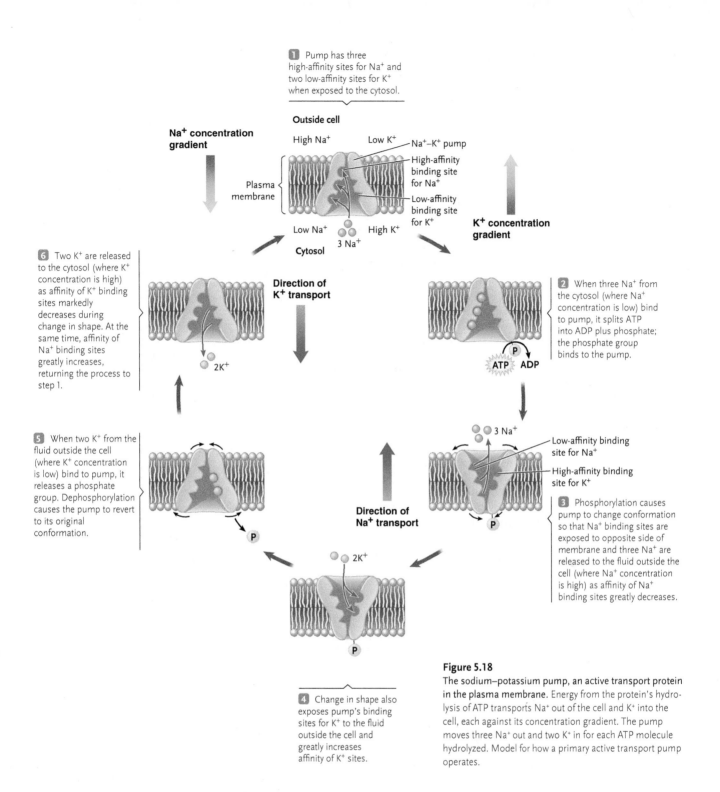

1 Pump has three high-affinity sites for Na⁺ and two low-affinity sites for K⁺ when exposed to the cytosol.

Na⁺ concentration gradient

Outside cell

High Na⁺   Low K⁺   Na⁺–K⁺ pump

High-affinity binding site for Na⁺

Low-affinity binding site for K⁺

Plasma membrane

Low Na⁺   High K⁺

K⁺ concentration gradient

3 Na⁺

Cytosol

6 Two K⁺ are released to the cytosol (where K⁺ concentration is high) as affinity of K⁺ binding sites markedly decreases during change in shape. At the same time, affinity of Na⁺ binding sites greatly increases, returning the process to step 1.

Direction of K⁺ transport

2K⁺

2 When three Na⁺ from the cytosol (where Na⁺ concentration is low) bind to pump, it splits ATP into ADP plus phosphate; the phosphate group binds to the pump.

ATP   ADP

P

3 Na⁺

5 When two K⁺ from the fluid outside the cell (where K⁺ concentration is low) bind to pump, it releases a phosphate group. Dephosphorylation causes the pump to revert to its original conformation.

Low-affinity binding site for Na⁺

High-affinity binding site for K⁺

3 Phosphorylation causes pump to change conformation so that Na⁺ binding sites are exposed to opposite side of membrane and three Na⁺ are released to the fluid outside the cell (where Na⁺ concentration is high) as affinity of Na⁺ binding sites greatly decreases.

P

Direction of Na⁺ transport

P

2K⁺

4 Change in shape also exposes pump's binding sites for K⁺ to the fluid outside the cell and greatly increases affinity of K⁺ sites.

Figure 5.18

The sodium–potassium pump, an active transport protein in the plasma membrane. Energy from the protein's hydrolysis of ATP transports Na⁺ out of the cell and K⁺ into the cell, each against its concentration gradient. The pump moves three Na⁺ out and two K⁺ in for each ATP molecule hydrolyzed. Model for how a primary active transport pump operates.

outside the membrane, and the inside of the cell becomes negatively charged with respect to the outside. Voltage—an electrical potential difference—across the plasma membrane results from this difference in charge as well as from the unequal distribution of ions across the membrane created by passive transport. The voltage across a membrane, called a **membrane potential**, measures from about −50 to −200 millivolts (mV), with the minus sign indicating that the charge inside the cell is negative versus the outside. In sum, we have both a concentration difference (of the ions) and an electrical charge difference on the two sides of the membrane, constituting what is called an **electrochemical gradient**. Electrochemical gradients store energy that is used for other transport mechanisms. For instance, the electrochemical gradient across the membrane is involved with the movement of ions associated with nerve impulse transmission (described in Chapter 44). A membrane potential derived from a proton gradient across a membrane is the basis for ATP synthesis in mitochondria and chloroplasts, which will be discussed in Chapters 6 and 7, respectively.

5.5c Secondary Active Transport Moves Both Ions and Organic Molecules

As already noted, secondary active transport pumps use the concentration gradient of an ion established by a primary pump as their energy source. For example, the driving force for most secondary active transport in animal cells is the high outside/low inside Na$^+$ gradient set up by the sodium–potassium pump. In secondary active transport, the transfer of the solute across the membrane is always coupled with the transfer of the ion supplying the driving force.

Secondary active transport occurs by two mechanisms, known as *symport* and *antiport* **(Figure 5.19)**. In **symport**, the cotransported solute moves through the membrane channel in the same direction as the driving ion, a phenomenon known as **cotransport**. Sugars such as glucose and amino acids are examples of molecules actively transported into cells by symport. In **antiport**, the driving ion moves through the membrane channel in one direction, providing the energy for the active transport of another molecule in the opposite direction, a phenomenon known as **exchange diffusion**. In many cases, ions are exchanged by antiport. For example, antiport is the mechanism used in red blood cells for the coupled movement of chloride ions and bicarbonate ions through a membrane channel.

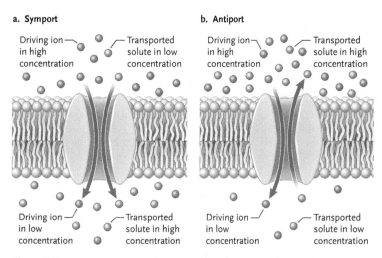

a. Symport

Driving ion in high concentration — Transported solute in low concentration

Driving ion in low concentration — Transported solute in high concentration

b. Antiport

Driving ion in high concentration — Transported solute in high concentration

Driving ion in low concentration — Transported solute in low concentration

Figure 5.19
Secondary active transport, in which a concentration gradient of an ion is used as the energy source for active transport of a solute. **(a)** In symport, the transported solute moves in the same direction as the gradient of the driving ion. **(b)** In antiport, the transported solute moves in the direction opposite to the gradient of the driving ion.

5.6 Exocytosis and Endocytosis

The largest molecules transported through cellular membranes by passive and active transport are about the size of amino acids or monosaccharides such as glucose. Eukaryotic cells import and export larger molecules by endocytosis and exocytosis. The export of materials by exocytosis primarily carries secretory proteins and some waste materials from the cytoplasm to the cell exterior. Import by endocytosis may carry proteins, larger aggregates of molecules, or even whole cells from the outside into the cytoplasm. Exocytosis and endocytosis also contribute to the back-and-forth flow of membranes between the endomembrane system and the plasma membrane. Both exocytosis and endocytosis require energy; thus, both processes stop if a cell's ability to make ATP is inhibited.

5.6a Exocytosis Releases Molecules to the Outside by Means of Secretory Vesicles

In exocytosis, secretory vesicles move through the cytoplasm and contact the plasma membrane **(Figure 5.20a)**. The vesicle membrane fuses with the plasma membrane, releasing the vesicle's contents to the cell exterior.

All eukaryotic cells secrete materials to the outside through exocytosis. For example, in animals, glandular cells secrete peptide hormones or milk proteins, and cells lining the digestive tract secrete mucus and digestive enzymes. Plant cells secrete carbohydrates by exocytosis to build a strong cell wall.

5.6b Endocytosis Brings Materials into Cells in Endocytic Vesicles

In endocytosis, proteins and other substances are trapped in pitlike depressions that bulge inward from the plasma membrane. The depression then pinches off as an endocytic vesicle. Endocytosis takes place in most eukaryotic cells by one of two distinct but related pathways. In the simpler of these mechanisms, **bulk-phase endocytosis** (sometimes called **pinocytosis**, meaning "cell drinking"), extracellular water is taken in along with any molecules that happen to be in solution in the water (Figure 5.20b). No binding by surface receptors takes place.

In the second endocytic pathway, **receptor-mediated endocytosis**, the molecules to be taken in are bound to the outer cell surface by receptor proteins

a. Exocytosis: vesicle joins plasma membrane, releases contents

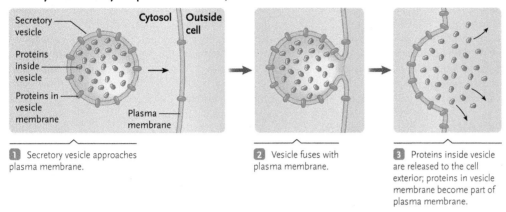

Secretory vesicle

Proteins inside vesicle

Proteins in vesicle membrane

Cytosol | Outside cell

Plasma membrane

1 Secretory vesicle approaches plasma membrane.

2 Vesicle fuses with plasma membrane.

3 Proteins inside vesicle are released to the cell exterior; proteins in vesicle membrane become part of plasma membrane.

b. Bulk-phase endocytosis (pinocytosis): vesicle imports water and other substances from outside cell

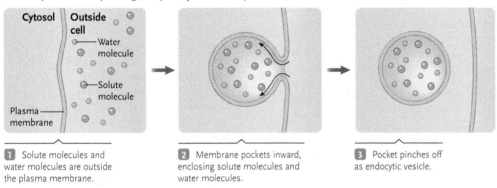

Cytosol | Outside cell

Water molecule

Solute molecule

Plasma membrane

1 Solute molecules and water molecules are outside the plasma membrane.

2 Membrane pockets inward, enclosing solute molecules and water molecules.

3 Pocket pinches off as endocytic vesicle.

c. Receptor-mediated endocytosis: vesicle imports specific molecules

Cytosol | Outside cell

Clathrin

Target molecule
Receptor

Plasma membrane

1 Substances attach to membrane receptors.

2 Membrane pockets inward.

3 Pocket pinches off as endocytic vesicle.

d. Micrographs of stages of receptor-mediated endocytosis shown in (c)

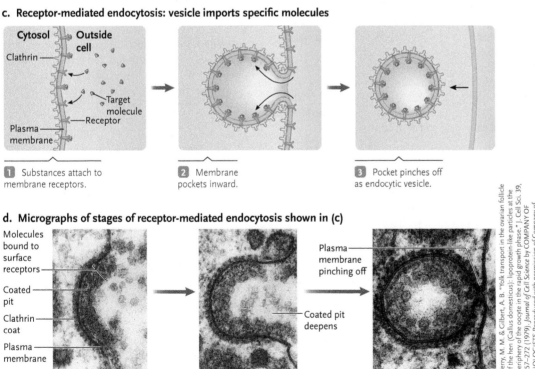

Molecules bound to surface receptors

Coated pit

Clathrin coat

Plasma membrane

Plasma membrane pinching off

Coated pit deepens

0.25 μm

Perry, M. M. & Gilbert, A. B. "Yolk transport in the ovarian follicle of the hen (Gallus domesticus): lipoprotein-like particles at the periphery of the oocyte in the rapid growth phase." J. Cell Sci. 39, 257–272 (1979). Journal of Cell Science by COMPANY OF BIOLOGISTS Reproduced with permission of Company of Biologists Ltd. in the format Republish in a book via Copyright Clearance Center.

Figure 5.20 Exocytosis and endocytosis.

(Figure 5.20c). The receptors, which are integral proteins of the plasma membrane, recognize and bind only certain molecules—primarily proteins, or other molecules carried by proteins—from the solution surrounding the cell. After binding their target molecules, the receptors collect into a depression in the plasma membrane called a **coated pit** because of the network of proteins (called **clathrin**) that coat and reinforce the cytoplasmic side. With the target molecules attached, the pits deepen and pinch free of the plasma membrane to form endocytic vesicles. Once in the cytoplasm, an endocytic vesicle rapidly loses its clathrin coat and may fuse with a lysosome. The enzymes within the lysosome then digest the contents of the vesicle, breaking them down into smaller molecules useful to the cell. These molecular products—for example, amino acids and monosaccharides—enter the cytoplasm by crossing the vesicle membrane via transport proteins. The membrane proteins are recycled to the plasma membrane.

Some cells, such as certain white blood cells (*phagocytes*) in the bloodstream or protists such as *Amoeba proteus,* can take in large aggregates of molecules, cell parts, or even whole cells by a process related to receptor-mediated endocytosis. The process, called **phagocytosis** (meaning "cell eating"), begins when surface receptors bind molecules on the substances to be taken in **(Figure 5.21)**. Cytoplasmic lobes then extend, surround, and engulf the materials, forming a pit that pinches off and sinks into the cytoplasm as a large endocytic vesicle. The materials are then digested within the cell as in receptor-mediated endocytosis, and any remaining residues are sequestered permanently into storage vesicles or are expelled from cells as waste by exocytosis.

The combined workings of exocytosis and endocytosis constantly cycle membrane segments between the internal cytoplasm and the cell surface. The balance of the two mechanisms maintains the surface area of the plasma membrane at controlled levels.

STUDY BREAK

1. What is the mechanism of exocytosis?
2. What is the difference between bulk-phase endocytosis and receptor-mediated endocytosis?

5.7 Role of Membranes in Cell Signalling

Recall from Chapter 3 that one of the key attributes of all living things is the ability to sense and respond to changes to the environment. At the cellular level this is accomplished by the perception of signals. In multicellular organisms, signals may be derived from other cell types and tissues as well as factors external to the organism. These signals may be physical, such as changes in light and temperature, or they may be chemical, such as a hormone or growth regulator. In this section, we discuss the crucial role that membranes play in the perception of signals and the transduction of the signal to bring about changes in cell function. The ability of cells to sense and respond appropriately to changes in their growth environment is critical for the maintenance of organismal homeostasis, another hallmark of living systems.

5.7a Signal Transduction Links Signals with Downstream Cellular Responses

The steps that link the initial perception of a signal with its ultimate downstream effects is termed a signal transduction pathway or cascade. Most signal pathways involve the following three steps **(Figure 5.22):**

1. **Reception.** The binding of a signal molecule with a specific receptor of target cells is termed reception (see Figure 5.22). Target cells have receptors that are specific for the signal molecule, which distinguishes them from cells that do not respond to the signal molecule. Most receptors are found on the plasma membrane, but some are found on internal membranes such as the ER. In addition, other receptors are soluble proteins that are found in the cytoplasm.
2. **Transduction.** The process whereby signal reception triggers other changes within the cell necessary to cause the cellular response is transduction (see Figure 5.22). Transduction typically involves a cascade of reactions that include several different molecules, referred to as a *signalling cascade.*
3. **Response.** In the third and last stage, the transduced signal causes a specific cellular response (see Figure 5.22). Different signalling pathways lead to different downstream responses. For example, some signal transduction pathways lead to the direct activation of a specific enzyme, while others often trigger changes in gene expression.

5.7b Membrane Surface Receptors

The membrane receptors that recognize and bind signal molecules are integral membrane proteins that extend through the entire membrane **(Figure 5.23a).** Typically, the signal-binding site of the receptor is the part of the protein that extends from the outer membrane surface and is folded in a way that closely fits the signal molecule. The fit, which is similar to an enzyme–substrate interaction, is specific so that a particular receptor binds only one type of signal. When a signal molecule binds, for example, to a surface receptor associated with the plasma membrane, the molecular structure of that receptor changes so that it transmits the signal through the plasma membrane, activating the cytoplasmic end of the receptor protein.

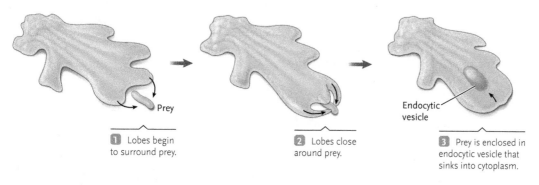

1 Lobes begin to surround prey.

2 Lobes close around prey.

3 Prey is enclosed in endocytic vesicle that sinks into cytoplasm.

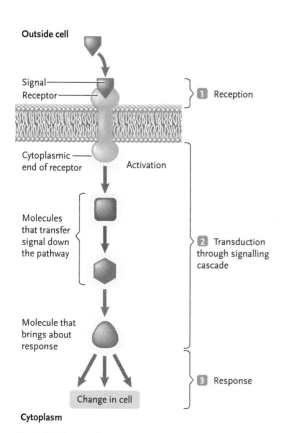

Michael Abbey/Visuals Unlimited, Inc.

Figure 5.21
Phagocytosis, in which lobes of the cytoplasm extend outward and surround a cell targeted as prey. The micrograph shows the protistan *Chaos carolinense* preparing to engulf a single-celled alga (*Pandorina*) by phagocytosis; white blood cells called phagocytes carry out a similar process in mammals.

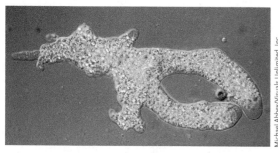

Outside cell

Signal
Receptor
1 Reception

Cytoplasmic end of receptor
Activation

Molecules that transfer signal down the pathway
2 Transduction through signalling cascade

Molecule that brings about response

Change in cell
3 Response

Cytoplasm

Figure 5.22
The three stages of signal transduction: reception, transduction, and response (shown for a system using a surface receptor).

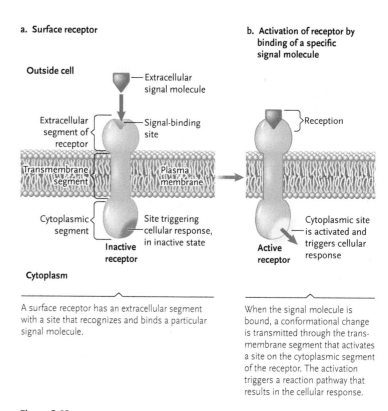

a. Surface receptor

b. Activation of receptor by binding of a specific signal molecule

Outside cell

Extracellular signal molecule

Extracellular segment of receptor
Signal-binding site

Transmembrane segment
Plasma membrane

Cytoplasmic segment
Site triggering cellular response, in inactive state

Inactive receptor

Cytoplasm

Reception

Cytoplasmic site is activated and triggers cellular response

Active receptor

A surface receptor has an extracellular segment with a site that recognizes and binds a particular signal molecule.

When the signal molecule is bound, a conformational change is transmitted through the transmembrane segment that activates a site on the cytoplasmic segment of the receptor. The activation triggers a reaction pathway that results in the cellular response.

Figure 5.23
The mechanism by which a surface receptor responds when it binds a signal molecule.

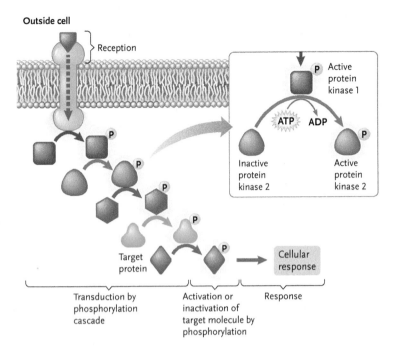

Outside cell

Reception

Active protein kinase 1

ATP → ADP

Inactive protein kinase 2

Active protein kinase 2

P

Target protein

Cellular response

Transduction by phosphorylation cascade

Activation or inactivation of target molecule by phosphorylation

Response

Cytoplasm

Figure 5.24
Phosphorylation, a key reaction in many signalling pathways.

The activated receptor then initiates the first step in a cascade of molecular events—the signalling cascade—that triggers the cellular response (Figure 5.23b, p. 115). The cells of most organisms typically have hundreds of membrane receptors that represent many receptor types. Receptors for a specific animal peptide hormone, for example, may number from 500 to as many as 100 000 or more per cell. Different cell types

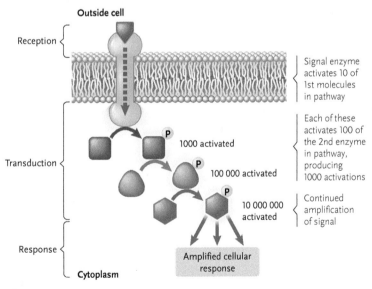

Outside cell

Reception

Transduction

Response

Cytoplasm

1000 activated

100 000 activated

10 000 000 activated

Signal enzyme activates 10 of 1st molecules in pathway

Each of these activates 100 of the 2nd enzyme in pathway, producing 1000 activations

Continued amplification of signal

Amplified cellular response

Figure 5.25
Amplification in signal transduction.

contain distinct combinations of receptors, allowing them to react individually to a diversity of signal molecules.

5.7c Signal Reception Triggers Response Pathways within the Cell

The binding of a signal molecule to a plasma membrane receptor, for example, is sufficient to trigger the activation of the signalling cascade. The signal molecule does not enter the cell. For example, experiments have shown that (1) a signal molecule produces no response if it is injected directly into the cytoplasm and (2) unrelated molecules that mimic the structure of the normal extracellular signal molecule can trigger or block a full cellular response as long as they can bind to the recognition site of the receptor. In fact, many medical conditions are treated with drugs that are signal molecule mimics.

A common characteristic of signalling mechanisms is that the signal is relayed inside the cell by **protein kinases**, enzymes that transfer a phosphate group from ATP to one or more sites on particular proteins. As shown in **Figure 5.24**, protein kinases often act in a chain, catalyzing a series of phosphorylation reactions called a *phosphorylation cascade,* to pass along a signal. The first kinase catalyzes phosphorylation of the second, which then becomes active and phosphorylates the third kinase, which then becomes active, and so on. The last protein in the cascade is the *target protein.* Phosphorylation of a target protein stimulates or inhibits its activity depending on the particular protein. This change in activity brings about the cellular response. For example, phosphorylating a target protein may alter the activity of a transcription factor that regulates the expression of a suite of genes.

The effects of protein kinases in the signal transduction pathways are balanced or reversed by another group of enzymes called **protein phosphatases**, which remove phosphate groups from target proteins. Unlike the protein kinases, which are active only when a surface receptor binds a signal molecule, most of the protein phosphatases are continuously active in cells. By continually removing phosphate groups from target proteins, the protein phosphatases quickly shut off a signal transduction pathway if its signal molecule is no longer bound at the cell surface.

Another characteristic of signal transduction pathways is **amplification**—an increase in the magnitude of each step as a signal transduction pathway proceeds **(Figure 5.25)**. Amplification occurs because many of the proteins that carry out individual steps in the pathways, including the protein kinases, are enzymes. Once activated, each enzyme can activate hundreds of proteins, including other enzymes that enter the next step in the pathway. Generally, the more enzyme-catalyzed steps in a response pathway, the greater the amplification. As a

PEOPLE BEHIND BIOLOGY 5.2

Lap-Chee Tsui, *University of Hong Kong*

Identifying the gene that is defective in patients with cystic fibrosis (CF) (see "Why It Matters," p. 97) was a breakthrough in human genetics and was achieved by a research team headed by Lap-Chee Tsui (1950–) of the Department of Genetics at the Hospital for Sick Children in Toronto.

Born in Shanghai, Tsui studied biology at the Chinese University of Hong Kong and was awarded a bachelor of science degree in 1972, which was followed by a master of philosophy degree in 1974. He undertook doctoral research in the United States, completing his Ph.D. at the University of Pittsburgh in 1979. He followed this with postdoctoral training at Oak Ridge National Laboratory in Tennessee before moving in 1981 to the Department of Genetics at the Hospital for Sick Children, where he became a staff member investigating the underlying genetic cause of CF.

Although today reports of gene discovery are common, in the 1980s,

the discovery of the gene that is mutated in patients with CF was particularly noteworthy for two major reasons. First, researchers relied on DNA isolated from people with CF to identify genetic markers of the disease. Using these, researchers used the novel method of positional cloning to identify the CF gene without any knowledge of the gene itself or what it did. Second, CF is the most common single-gene disease among Caucasians; thus, much anticipation awaited this particular discovery, with many research teams worldwide trying to be the first to identify the gene.

In 1985, Tsui and his team identified the first DNA marker linked to CF, on chromosome 7. Four years later, Tsui's team, along with collaborators at the University of Michigan, finally identified the defective gene responsible for CF, defining the principal mutation (Δ*F508). This mutation is the result of a three-nucleotide deletion that results in the

loss of the amino acid phenylalanine (F) at the 508th position of the protein. As a result, the protein does not fold normally and is more quickly degraded.

The research was described in three seminal papers in the September 8, 1989, issue of *Science*. The gene was called the cystic fibrosis transmembrane conductance regulator (CFTR). *Science* named Tsui's achievement "the most refreshing scientific development of 1989," and *Maclean's* Honour Roll hailed it as one of the "discoveries of hope at the heart of human life" in the same year.

Tsui has received many honours, including fellow of the Royal Society of Canada, several honorary doctoral degrees, and the Order of Canada. Tsui is currently the vice-chancellor of the University of Hong Kong, but he remains an active researcher and is still affiliated with the Hospital for Sick Children's Program in Genetics and Genomic Biology.

---

result, just a few extracellular signal molecules binding to their receptors can produce a full internal response.

This chapter has introduced you to the fundamentals of membrane structure and the role membranes serve in an array of functions, from transport

through cellular signalling. Membranes and the compartments they define play a fundamental role in energy metabolism, which is the central theme of the next two chapters, on respiration and photosynthesis.

Review

To access course materials such as Aplia and other companion resources, please visit www.NELSONbrain.com.

5.1 An Overview of the Structure of Membranes

- The fluid mosaic model proposes that the membrane consists of a fluid lipid bilayer in which proteins are embedded and float freely (Figure 5.1).
- Membranes are asymmetrical. The two halves of a membrane are not the same. The membrane proteins found on one half of the bilayer are structurally and functionally distinct from those of the other half.

5.2 The Lipid Fabric of a Membrane

- The lipid bilayer forms the structural framework of membranes and serves as a barrier preventing the passage of most water-soluble molecules.
- The structural basis of a membrane is a fluid phospholipid bilayer in which the polar regions of phospholipid molecules lie at the surfaces of the bilayer and their nonpolar tails associate in the interior (Figures 5.4 and 5.5).
- Saturated fatty acids contain the maximum number of hydrogen atoms and are linear molecules. Unsaturated fatty acids contain one or more double bonds, which cause the fatty acid to kink (Figure 5.6).

- Organisms can adjust the fatty acid composition of membrane lipids to maintain proper fluidity through the action of a group of enzymes called desaturases (Figure 5.7).

5.3 Membrane Proteins

- Proteins embedded in the phospholipid bilayer carry out most membrane functions, including transport of selected hydrophilic substances, enzymatic activity, recognition, and signal reception (Figure 5.9).
- Integral membrane proteins interact with the hydrophobic core of the membrane bilayer. Most integral membrane proteins, called transmembrane proteins, have domains that span the membrane numerous times. These domains are dominated by nonpolar amino acids (Figures 5.10 and 5.11).
- Peripheral membrane proteins associate with membrane surfaces.

5.4 Passive Membrane Transport

- Passive transport depends on diffusion, the net movement of molecules from a region of higher concentration to a region of lower concentration. Passive transport does not require cells to expend energy (Figure 5.12).
- Simple diffusion is the passive transport of substances across a membrane through the lipid molecules. Small uncharged molecules can move rapidly across membranes, whereas large or charged molecules may be strongly impeded from transiting a membrane (Figure 5.13).
- Facilitated diffusion is the diffusion of molecules across membranes by the use of specific membrane proteins—channel proteins and carrier proteins. Both channel proteins and carrier proteins are specific for certain substances. For many molecules, facilitated diffusion results in higher rates of transport than simple diffusion (Figures 5.14 and 5.15).
- Osmosis is the net diffusion of water molecules across a selectively permeable membrane in response to differences in the concentration of solute molecules.
- Water moves from hypotonic solutions (lower concentrations of solute molecules) to hypertonic solutions (higher concentrations of solute molecules). When the solutions on each side are isotonic, there is no osmotic movement of water in either direction (Figure 5.16).

5.5 Active Membrane Transport

- Active transport moves substances against their concentration gradients and requires cells to expend energy. Active transport depends on membrane proteins, is specific for certain substances, and becomes saturated at high concentrations of the transported substance.
- Active transport proteins are either primary transport pumps, which directly use ATP as their energy

source, or secondary transport pumps, which use favourable concentration gradients of positively charged ions, set up by primary transport pumps, as their energy source for transport (Figure 5.17).
- Secondary active transport may occur by symport, in which the transported substance moves in the same direction as the concentration gradient used as the energy source, or by antiport, in which the transported substance moves in the direction opposite to the concentration gradient used as the energy source (Figure 5.19).

5.6 Exocytosis and Endocytosis

- Large molecules and particles are moved out of and into cells by exocytosis and endocytosis. The mechanisms allow substances to leave and enter cells without directly passing through the plasma membrane (Figure 5.20).
- In exocytosis, a vesicle carrying secreted materials contacts and fuses with the plasma membrane on its cytoplasmic side. The fusion introduces the vesicle membrane into the plasma membrane and releases the vesicle contents to the cell exterior.
- In endocytosis, materials on the cell exterior are enclosed in a segment of the plasma membrane that pockets inward and pinches off on the cytoplasmic side as an endocytic vesicle. Endocytosis occurs in two overall forms, bulk-phase endocytosis (pinocytosis) and receptor-mediated endocytosis. Most of the materials entering cells are digested into molecular subunits small enough to be transported across the vesicle membranes (Figure 5.20b, c).

5.7 Role of Membranes in Cell Signalling

- Cell communication systems based on surface receptors have three components: (1) extracellular signal molecules, (2) surface receptors that receive the signals, and (3) internal response pathways triggered when receptors bind a signal (Figure 5.22).
- Surface receptors are integral membrane proteins that extend through the plasma membrane. Binding a signal molecule induces a molecular change in the receptor that activates its cytoplasmic end (Figure 5.23).
- Many cellular response pathways operate by activating protein kinases, which add phosphate groups that stimulate or inhibit the activities of the target proteins, bringing about the cellular response (Figure 5.24). Protein phosphatases that remove phosphate groups from target proteins reverse the response. In addition, receptors are removed by endocytosis when signal transduction has run its course.
- Each step of a response pathway catalyzed by an enzyme is amplified, because each enzyme can activate hundreds or thousands of proteins that enter the next step in the pathway. Through amplification, a few signal molecules can bring about a full cellular response (Figure 5.25).

Questions

Self-Test Questions

1. Which of the following statements about the fluid mosaic model is correct?
   a. The fluid refers to the phospholipid bilayer.
   b. Plasma membrane proteins orient their hydrophilic sides toward the internal bilayer.
   c. Phospholipids often flip-flop between the inner and outer layers.
   d. The mosaic refers to proteins attached to the underlying cytoskeleton.
   e. The mosaic refers to the symmetry of the internal membrane proteins and sterols.

2. What was demonstrated by the freeze-fracture technique?
   a. The plasma membrane is fluid.
   b. Membranes remain fluid at freezing temperatures.
   c. The arrangement of membrane lipids and proteins is symmetric.
   d. The plasma membrane is a bilayer with individual proteins suspended in it.
   e. Proteins are bound to the cytoplasmic side but not embedded in the lipid bilayer.

3. Which statement is correct regarding temperature and membrane fluidity?
   a. Membrane fluidity increases with decreasing temperature.
   b. Membrane fluidity remains constant over the temperature range of 0 to 100°C.
   c. At any given temperature, membrane fluidity increases as desaturase activity increases.
   d. At any given temperature, membrane fluidity decreases as the abundance of unsaturated fatty acids increases.

4. The integral membrane protein rhodopsin, which is used in light perception, is a protein that spans the membrane seven times. Which statement about rhodopsin is correct?
   a. It contains seven hydrophobic amino acids.
   b. It is composed only of hydrophobic amino acids.
   c. It contains both hydrophobic and hydrophilic domains.
   d. It contains one long stretch of hydrophobic amino acids.
   e. It has a random assortment of both polar and nonpolar amino acids.

5. Which one of the following molecules shows the slowest rate of membrane diffusion and why?
   a. Na+, because it is small
   b. K+, because it is charged
   c. glucose, because it is large
   d. CO_2, because it contains three atoms
   e. H_2O, because water is the main component of the cytosol

6. Compared to simple diffusion, which of the following statements is correct for only facilitated diffusion?
   a. It can only transport hydrophobic molecules.
   b. It can be saturated by high substrate concentrations.
   c. It requires a source of chemical energy, such as ATP.
   d. It can transport molecules against a concentration gradient.

7. In the following diagram, assume that the setup was left unattended. Which statement is correct?

Selectively Permeable Membrane			
Inside a Cell		Extracellular Fluid	
Solvent	95%	Solvent	98%
Solute	5%	Solute	2%

   a. The cell will soon shrink.
   b. The net flow of solvent is into the cell.
   c. The cell is in a hypertonic environment.
   d. Diffusion can occur here but not osmosis.
   e. The relation of the cell to its environment is isotonic.

8. An ion moving through a membrane channel in one direction gives energy to actively transport another molecule in the opposite direction. What process does this describe?
   a. cotransport
   b. symport transport
   c. exchange diffusion
   d. facilitated diffusion
   e. primary active transport pump

9. Phagocytosis illustrates which of the following?
   a. exocytosis
   b. pinocytosis
   c. cotransport
   d. bulk-phase endocytosis
   e. receptor-mediated endocytosis

10. Many signal transduction pathways are initiated by a signal binding to a membrane receptor. Which statement about this type of signalling mechanism is correct?
   a. Signal binding may activate a protein kinase.
   b. A signal molecule injected into the cytoplasm will activate the pathway.
   c. A mutation in a single gene can disrupt an entire signalling pathway.
   d. Signal transduction pathways never include components within the nucleus.
   e. Both a and c are correct.

Questions for Discussion

1. In Chapter 4, we discussed thermodynamics. What role does thermodynamics play in membrane transport?

2. The bacterium *Vibrio cholerae* causes cholera, a disease characterized by severe diarrhea that may cause infected people to lose up to 20 L of fluid in a day. The bacterium enters the body when a person drinks contaminated water. It adheres to the intestinal lining, where it causes cells of the lining to release sodium and chloride ions. Explain how this release is related to the massive fluid loss.

6

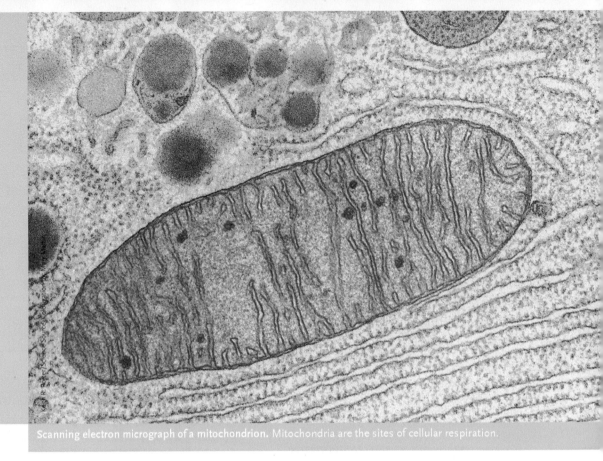

Scanning electron micrograph of a mitochondrion. Mitochondria are the sites of cellular respiration.

Cellular Respiration

WHY IT MATTERS

In the early 1960s, Swedish physician Rolf Luft mulled over some odd symptoms of a patient. The young woman was hot all the time. Even on the coldest winter days, she never stopped perspiring and her skin was always flushed. She also felt weak and was thin, despite a huge appetite.

Luft inferred that his patient's symptoms pointed to a metabolic disorder. Her cells seemed to be active, but much of their activity was being dissipated as metabolic heat. He decided to order tests to measure her metabolic rates. The patient's oxygen consumption was the highest ever recorded!

Luft also examined a tissue sample from the patient's skeletal muscles. Using a microscope, he found that her muscle cells contained many more mitochondria— the ATP-producing organelles of the cell—than normal; also, her mitochondria were abnormally shaped. Other studies showed that the mitochondria were engaged in cellular respiration—their prime function—but little ATP was being generated.

The disorder, now called *Luft syndrome,* was the first disorder to be linked directly to a defective cellular organelle. This syndrome is extremely rare and has now been shown to be due to a defect in one of the complexes of cellular respiration that links electron transport to proton pumping and subsequent ATP generation. With such a disorder, skeletal and heart muscles and the brain, the tissues with the highest energy demands, are affected the most. More than 100 mitochondrial disorders are now known. Defective mitochondria are now linked to a range of diseases and disorders including amyotrophic lateral sclerosis (ALS, also called Lou Gehrig's disease), as well as Parkinson's, Alzheimer's, and Huntington diseases.

Clearly, human health depends on mitochondria that are structurally sound and functioning properly. But of course there is nothing unique to humans here—every animal, plant, and fungus requires correctly functioning mitochondria to live. In eukaryotes, this organelle is the site of key reactions of cellular respiration—the process whereby the energy present in food molecules is extracted and converted into a form usable by the cell. In this chapter, we explore the fundamentals of cellular respiration, starting by addressing what makes a good fuel molecule.

6.1 The Chemical Basis of Cellular Respiration

We can define **cellular respiration** as the collection of metabolic reactions within cells that breaks down food molecules (e.g., carbohydrates, fats, proteins) and uses the liberated free energy to synthesize ATP. As described in detail in Chapter 4, it is ATP that is the form of chemical energy required for the thousands of biosynthetic reactions (**anabolic reactions**) that take place within a cell.

The ultimate source of the energy-rich carbon compounds found in carbohydrates, fats, and proteins is *photosynthesis,* which is the focus of the next chapter. In photosynthesis, light energy is used to extract electrons from water; the electrons then combine with hydrogen to reduce carbon dioxide into glucose, a carbohydrate. Additional biosynthetic pathways can utilize carbohydrates in the synthesis of both proteins and fats. A major by-product of photosynthesis is oxygen, a molecule needed for the most common type of cellular respiration. Thus, life and its systems are driven by a cycle of electron flow that is powered by light in photosynthesis and oxidation in cellular respiration **(Figure 6.1)**.

6.1a Food Is Fuel

Looking at **Figure 6.2, p. 122,** we can ask the following question: what is it about glucose that makes it a source of chemical energy? We could ask the same question of gasoline: what makes it good at powering a car? Both glucose and gasoline are good fuel molecules because they contain an abundance of C—H bonds. Recall from Chapter 4 that for any atom, an electron that is farther away from the nucleus contains more energy than an electron that is more closely held by the nucleus. As well, recall that as an electron moves closer to the nucleus of an atom it loses energy; as it moves away it gains energy. The electrons that form the covalent C—H bond are equidistant from both **atomic nuclei**—not strongly held by either. Because of this, the electrons can be easily removed and used to perform work. In contrast to glucose and gasoline, molecules that contain more oxygen, for example, carbon dioxide, contain less potential energy because oxygen is strongly electronegative. The more electronegative an atom, the greater the force that holds the electrons to that atom and, therefore, the greater the energy required to remove the electrons. To review the basics of electronegativity, see *The Purple Pages.* In the case of a C—H bond, neither carbon nor hydrogen is strongly electronegative. This fundamental principle of chemistry has an everyday relevance: it explains why, for example, compared to proteins and carbohydrates, fats contain more calories (energy) per unit of weight. A fat is almost entirely C—H bonds, while both proteins and carbohydrates contain varying amounts of other atoms, including oxygen. (To review the structure of these molecules, see *The Purple Pages.*)

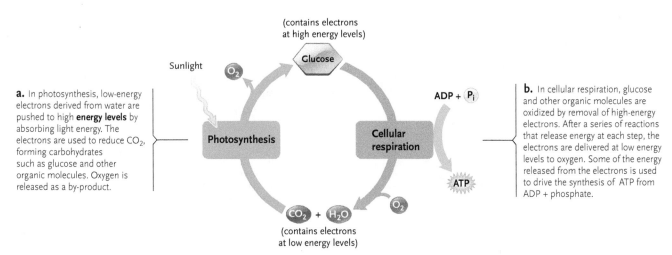

a. In photosynthesis, low-energy electrons derived from water are pushed to high **energy levels** by absorbing light energy. The electrons are used to reduce CO_2, forming carbohydrates such as glucose and other organic molecules. Oxygen is released as a by-product.

b. In cellular respiration, glucose and other organic molecules are oxidized by removal of high-energy electrons. After a series of reactions that release energy at each step, the electrons are delivered at low energy levels to oxygen. Some of the energy released from the electrons is used to drive the synthesis of ATP from ADP + phosphate.

(contains electrons at high energy levels)

Sunlight

Glucose

ADP + P_i

Photosynthesis

Cellular respiration

ATP

CO_2 + H_2O

O_2

(contains electrons at low energy levels)

Figure 6.1

Flow of energy linking photosynthesis and respiration. Photosynthesis uses light energy to convert carbon dioxide and water into energy-rich organic molecules such as glucose, which, in turn, are oxidized by cellular respiration.

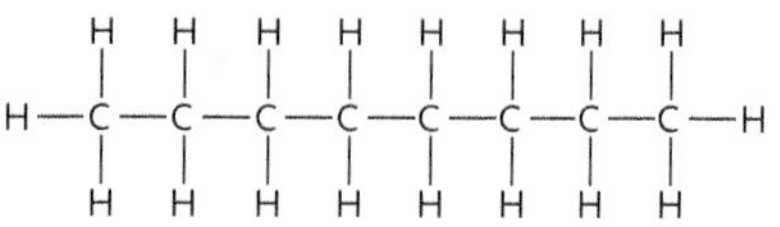

a. Gasoline

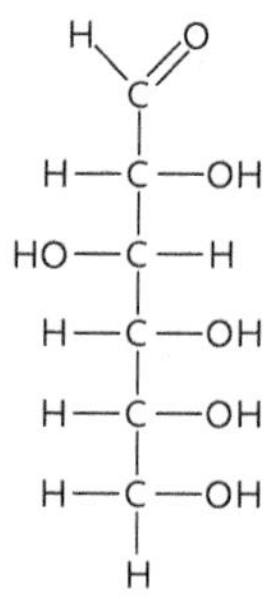

$$H-\underset{\underset{H}{|}}{\overset{\overset{H}{|}}{C}}-\underset{\underset{H}{|}}{\overset{\overset{H}{|}}{C}}-\underset{\underset{H}{|}}{\overset{\overset{H}{|}}{C}}-\underset{\underset{H}{|}}{\overset{\overset{H}{|}}{C}}-\underset{\underset{H}{|}}{\overset{\overset{H}{|}}{C}}-\underset{\underset{H}{|}}{\overset{\overset{H}{|}}{C}}-\underset{\underset{H}{|}}{\overset{\overset{H}{|}}{C}}-\underset{\underset{H}{|}}{\overset{\overset{H}{|}}{C}}-H$$

b. Glucose

Figure 6.2

Fuel molecules. Both gasoline (e.g., octane) and glucose are excellent fuels because electrons of C—H bonds can be easily removed.

6.1b Coupled Oxidation–Reduction Reactions Are Central to Energy Metabolism

The potential energy contained in fuel molecules is released when the molecules lose electrons, becoming **oxidized.** The electrons released from a molecule that is oxidized are gained by another molecule that becomes **reduced.** Oxidation and reduction reactions are coupled processes—one cannot happen without the other. A simple mnemonic to remember the direction of electron transport is OIL RIG—Oxidation Is Loss (of electrons), **Reduction** Is Gain (of electrons). For short, oxidation–reduction reactions are called **redox reactions.** A generalized redox reaction can be written like this:

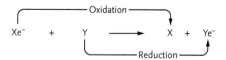

The redox reaction describing the respiratory breakdown of glucose is as follows:

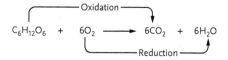

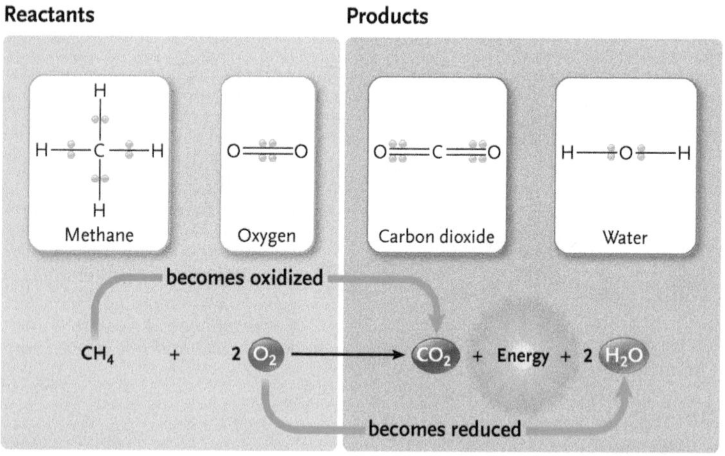

Reactants **Products**

Methane   Oxygen   Carbon dioxide   Water

becomes oxidized

CH_4 + 2 O_2 ⟶ CO_2 + Energy + 2 H_2O

becomes reduced

Figure 6.3

A redox reaction: the burning of methane in oxygen. Compare the positions of the electrons in the covalent bonds of reactants and products. In this redox reaction, methane is oxidized and oxygen is reduced.

The term *oxidation* comes from that fact that many reactions in which electrons are removed from fuel molecules involve oxygen as the atom that accepts the electrons and gets reduced. The involvement of oxygen is essential for many common oxidation reactions: a car engine requires large amounts of air (21% oxygen) to be delivered to each piston for combustion to take place; an oil fire in a pot on a stove can be rapidly extinguished by putting a lid on the pot, restricting the air supply. As we will see later in this chapter, the high affinity of O_2 for electrons (its high electronegativity) makes it ideal as the terminal electron acceptor of cellular respiration.

The concept of redox is made a little more challenging to understand by two facts. First, although many oxidation reactions involve oxygen, others, including a number involved in cellular respiration, do not. Second, the gain or loss of an electron in a redox reaction is not always complete. That is, whereas in some redox reactions electrons are transferred completely from one atom to another, in other redox reactions, what changes is the degree to which electrons are shared between two atoms. The reaction between methane and oxygen (the burning of natural gas in air) illustrates a redox reaction in which only the degree of electron sharing changes **(Figure 6.3).** The blue dots (see Figure 6.3) indicate the positions of the electrons involved in the covalent bonds of the reactants and products. Compare the reactant methane with the product carbon dioxide—in methane, the electrons are shared equally between the carbon and hydrogen atoms. In the product, carbon dioxide, electrons are closer to the oxygen than to the carbon because oxygen atoms are more electronegative. Overall, this means that the carbon atom has partially lost its shared electrons in the reaction: methane has been oxidized. Now compare the oxygen reactant with the product, water. In the oxygen molecule, the two oxygen atoms share their electrons equally. The oxygen reacts with the hydrogen from methane, producing water, in which the electrons are closer to the oxygen atom than to the hydrogen atoms. This means that each oxygen atom has partially gained electrons: oxygen has been reduced. Because of this, the reaction between methane and oxygen releases heat. The energy is released as the electrons in the C—H bonds of methane move closer to the electronegative oxygen atoms that form carbon dioxide.

6.1c Cellular Respiration Is Controlled Combustion

Like gasoline and methane, glucose can also undergo combustion and burn. The combustion of glucose releases energy as electrons are transferred to oxygen, reducing it to water, and the carbon in glucose is oxidized to carbon dioxide.

Recall from Chapter 4 that for a spontaneous reaction to proceed, the substrate molecules need to reach the transition state, which requires an energy input

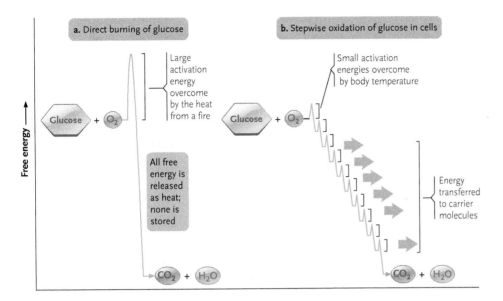

a. Direct burning of glucose

Large activation energy overcome by the heat from a fire

All free energy is released as heat; none is stored

Glucose + O_2

CO_2 + H_2O

b. Stepwise oxidation of glucose in cells

Small activation energies overcome by body temperature

Energy transferred to carrier molecules

Glucose + O_2

CO_2 + H_2O

Free energy

Figure 6.4

A comparison of the oxidation of glucose by combustion and cellular respiration.

referred to as the activation energy. To get glucose to ignite, we can use a flame to provide the high activation energy **(Figure 6.4a)**. In contrast, within a cell, the oxidation of glucose occurs through a series of enzyme-catalyzed reactions (Figure 6.4b), each with a small activation energy. Thermodynamically, the two processes are identical: they are both exergonic, having the same change in free energy (ΔG) of −686 kcal/mol. The big difference is that if you simply burn glucose, the energy is released as heat and therefore not available to drive metabolic reactions. So a good way to think of the process of cellular respiration is controlled combustion—where the energy of the C—H bonds is not liberated suddenly, producing heat, but is slowly released in a stepwise fashion, with the energy being transferred to other molecules.

In cellular respiration, the oxidation of food molecules occurs in the presence of a group of enzymes called *dehydrogenases*, which facilitate the transfer of electrons from food to a molecule that acts as an energy carrier or shuttle. The most common energy carrier is the coenzyme nicotinamide adenine dinucleotide (NAD+, oxidized; NADH, reduced) **(Figure 6.5)**. During respiration, the dehydrogenases remove two hydrogen atoms from a substrate molecule and transfer the two electrons—but only one of the protons—to NAD+, reducing it to NADH. The efficiency of the enzyme-catalyzed transfer of energy between food molecules and NAD+ is very high. As we will see later in the chapter, the potential energy carried in NADH is used to synthesize ATP.

STUDY BREAK

1. What is it about the structure of gasoline and glucose that makes them both good fuels?
2. In the respiratory breakdown of glucose, what gets oxidized and what gets reduced?

6.2 Cellular Respiration: An Overview

At this point, let's step back and remind ourselves of the primary goal of cellular respiration: it is to transform the potential energy found in food molecules into a form that can be used for metabolic processes, ATP. We will see later in the chapter that both proteins and lipids can be oxidized by the respiratory pathway and

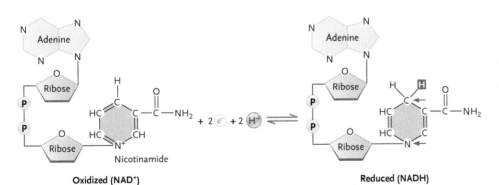

Oxidized (NAD+)

Adenine · Ribose · Nicotinamide · Ribose

Reduced (NADH)

Adenine · Ribose · Ribose

$+ 2\,e^- + 2\,H^+$

Figure 6.5

Electron carrier NAD+. As the carrier is reduced to NADH, an electron is added at each of the two positions marked by a red arrow; a proton is also added at the position boxed in red. The nitrogenous base (blue) that adds and releases electrons and protons is nicotinamide, which is derived from the vitamin niacin (nicotinic acid).

their potential energy harnessed; however, because the oxidation of glucose utilizes the entire respiratory pathway, it is the main focus of our discussion.

6.2a Cellular Respiration Can Be Divided into Three Phases

Cellular respiration can be divided into three phases **(Figure 6.6)**:

1. *Glycolysis.* Enzymes break down a molecule of glucose into two molecules of pyruvate. Some ATP and NADH is synthesized.
2. *Pyruvate oxidation and the citric acid cycle.* Acetyl coenzyme A (acetyl-CoA), which is formed from the oxidation of pyruvate, enters a metabolic cycle, where it is completely oxidized to carbon dioxide. Some ATP and NADH is synthesized.
3. *Oxidative phosphorylation.* The NADH synthesized by both glycolysis and the citric acid cycle is oxidized, with the liberated electrons being passed along an electron transport chain (ETC) until they are transferred to oxygen, producing water. The free energy released during electron transport is used to generate a proton gradient across a membrane, which, in turn, is used to synthesize ATP.

All three stages are required to extract the maximum amount of energy that is biologically possible from a molecule of glucose; however, not all organisms undergo all three stages.

6.2b The Mitochondrion Is the Site of Cellular Respiration in Eukaryotes

In archaea and bacteria, glycolysis and the citric acid cycle occur in the cytosol, whereas oxidative phosphorylation occurs on internal membranes. By comparison, in eukaryotic cells, the citric acid cycle and oxidative phosphorylation occur in a specialized membrane-bound organelle called the mitochondrion (plural, *mitochondria*) **(Figure 6.7)**. This membrane-bound organelle is often referred to as the powerhouse of the cell because, as the location of both the citric acid cycle and oxidative phosphorylation, it is the largest generator of ATP in the cell.

The mitochondrion is composed of two membranes, the outer membrane and the inner membrane, which together define two compartments (see Figure 6.7): the intermembrane space, which is found between the outer and inner membranes, and the matrix, which is the interior aqueous environment.

In the description of cellular respiration that follows, we often refer specifically to mitochondria and their various compartments, but

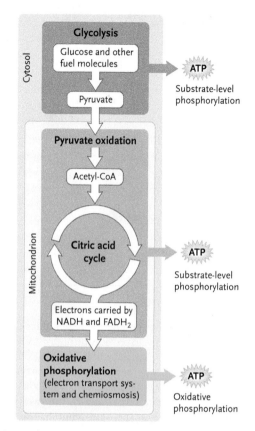

Figure 6.6
The three stages of cellular respiration: glycolysis, pyruvate oxidation and the citric acid cycle, and oxidative phosphorylation.

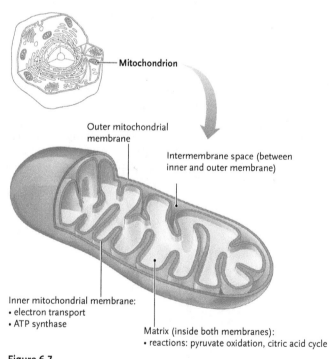

Figure 6.7
Membranes and compartments of mitochondria. Label lines that end in a dot indicate a compartment enclosed by the membranes.

it is important to remember that there is nothing uniquely eukaryotic about cellular respiration. Neither archaea nor bacteria have mitochondria, but many species of both possess the entire complement of reactions that make up cellular respiration—from glycolysis through oxidative phosphorylation.

STUDY BREAK

1. What are the three stages of cellular respiration?
2. Outline the membranes and compartments of the mitochondrion.

6.3 Glycolysis: The Splitting of Glucose

Glycolysis (*glykys* = sweet; *lysis* = breakdown) consists of 10 sequential enzyme-catalyzed reactions that lead to the oxidation of the six-carbon sugar glucose, producing two molecules of the three-carbon compound pyruvate. The potential energy released in the oxidation leads to the synthesis of both NADH and ATP.

6.3a Glycolysis Is a Universal and Ancient Metabolic Process

Glycolysis was one of the first metabolic pathways studied and is one of the best understood in terms of the enzymes involved, their mechanisms of action, and how the pathway is regulated to meet the energy needs of the cell. The first experiments investigating glycolysis took place over 100 years ago and were some of the first to show, using the extracts from yeast cells, that one could study biological reactions in an isolated, cell-free system. These experiments became the foundation of modern biochemistry.

Glycolysis is the most fundamental and probably most ancient of all metabolic pathways. This is supported by the following facts: (1) Glycolysis is universal, being found in all three domains of life—Archaea, Bacteria, and Eukarya. (2) Glycolysis does not depend upon the presence of O_2, which became abundant in Earth's atmosphere only about 2.5 billion years ago—about 1.5 billion years after scientists think life first evolved (see Chapter 3). (3) Glycolysis occurs in the cytosol of all cells using soluble enzymes and therefore does not require more sophisticated ETCs and internal membrane systems to function.

6.3b Glycolysis Includes Energy-Requiring and Energy-Releasing Steps

The key features of glycolysis are summarized in **Figure 6.8**, while **Figure 6.9, p. 126,** provides a detailed look at each reaction of the glycolytic pathway. From both figures, there are three major concepts to come away with:

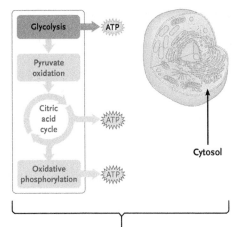

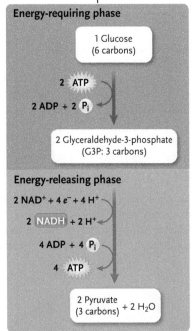

Figure 6.8
Overall reactions of glycolysis. Glycolysis, which occurs in the cytosol of all cells, splits glucose (six carbons) into pyruvate (three carbons) and yields ATP and NADH.

1. *Energy investment followed by payoff.* Glycolysis can be looked at as consisting of two distinct phases: an initial five-step energy-requiring phase followed by a five-step energy-releasing phase. Initially, two molecules of ATP are consumed as glucose and fructose- 6-phosphate become phosphorylated. The investment of two ATP for each glucose molecule leads to an energy reward, as four ATP and two NADH molecules are produced during the energy-releasing phase.
2. *No carbon is lost.* The reactions of glycolysis convert glucose (a six-carbon molecule) into two molecules of the three-carbon compound pyruvate. Thus, no carbon is lost. However, since glucose

has been oxidized, the potential energy in two molecules of pyruvate is less than that of one molecule of glucose.

3. *ATP is generated by substrate-level phosphorylation.* During glycolysis, ATP is generated by the process of **substrate-level phosphorylation**. This mode of ATP synthesis, shown in **Figure 6.10**, involves the transfer of a phosphate group from a high-energy substrate molecule to ADP, producing ATP. Substrate-level phosphorylation, which is mediated by a specific enzyme, is also the mode of ATP synthesis used in the citric acid cycle.

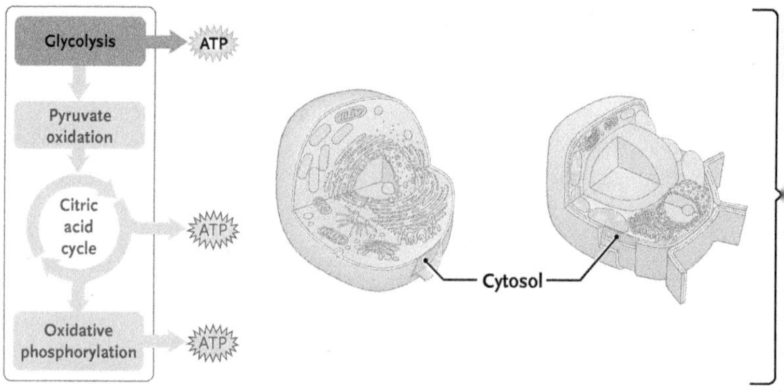

STUDY BREAK

1. What evidence suggests that glycolysis is an ancient metabolic pathway?
2. What accounts for the fact that two molecules of pyruvate have less free energy than one molecule of glucose?

6.4 Pyruvate Oxidation and the Citric Acid Cycle

The two molecules of pyruvate synthesized by glycolysis still contain usable free energy. The extraction of the remaining free energy in pyruvate and the trapping of this energy in the form of ATP and electron carriers

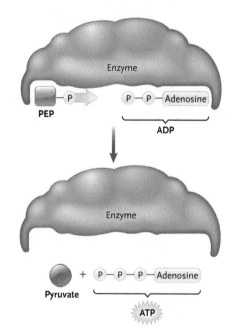

Figure 6.10
Mechanism that synthesizes ATP by substrate-level phosphorylation. A phosphate group is transferred from a high-energy donor directly to ADP, forming ATP.

Figure 6.9
Reactions of glycolysis. Because two molecules of G3P are produced in reaction 5, all the reactions from 6 to 10 are doubled (not shown). The name of the enzyme that catalyzes each reaction is in red.

such as NADH are the overarching goals of the series of reactions described in this section.

6.4a Pyruvate Oxidation Links Glycolysis and the Citric Acid Cycle

Because the reactions of the citric acid cycle are localized to the mitochondrial matrix, the pyruvate synthesized during glycolysis must pass through both the outer and inner mitochondrial membranes **(Figure 6.11, p. 128).** Large pores in the outer membrane allow pyruvate to simply diffuse through, but crossing the inner membrane requires a pyruvate-specific membrane carrier.

Once it gets into the matrix, pyruvate is converted into acetyl-CoA through a multistep process that is referred to as *pyruvate oxidation* (see Figure 6.11). The conversion of pyruvate to acetyl-CoA starts with a decarboxylation reaction whereby the carboxyl (— COO^-) group of pyruvate is lost as carbon dioxide. This reaction is understandable given that the carboxyl group itself contains no usable energy. The decarboxylation reaction is followed by oxidation of the remaining two-carbon molecule, producing acetate. This dehydrogenation reaction leads to the transfer of two electrons and a proton to NAD^+, forming NADH. Last, the acetyl group reacts with coenzyme A (CoA), forming the high-energy intermediate acetyl-CoA. Notice in Figure 6.11 that acetyl-CoA still contains three C—H bonds. Liberating the electrons in those bonds as a source of chemical energy is the goal of the reactions that make up the citric acid cycle.

6.4b The Citric Acid Cycle Oxidizes Acetyl Groups to Carbon Dioxide

The **citric acid cycle** consists of eight enzyme-catalyzed reactions: seven are soluble enzymes located in the mitochondrial matrix, and one enzyme is bound to the

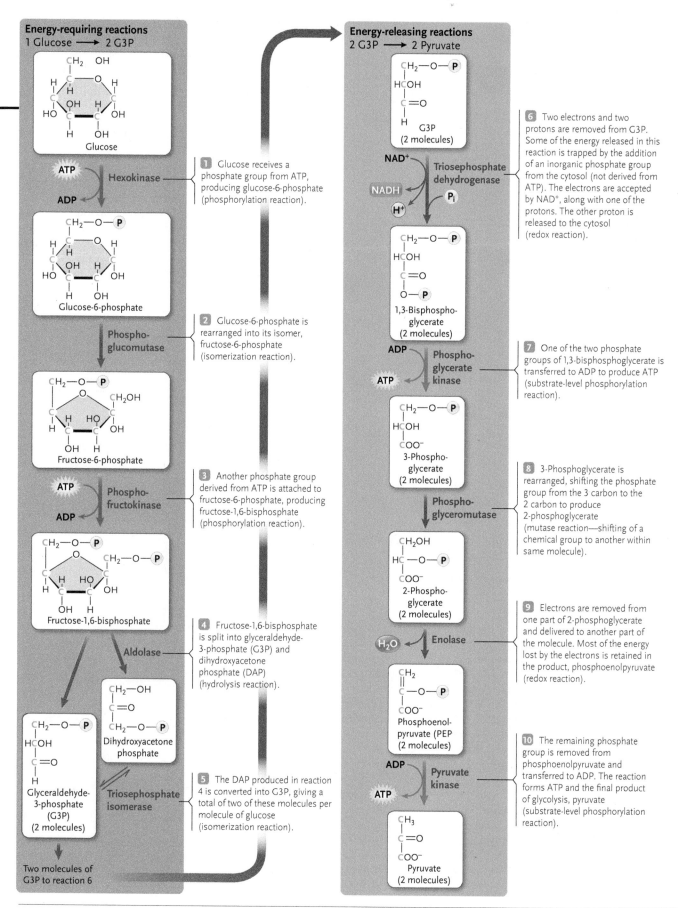

Energy-requiring reactions
1 Glucose → 2 G3P

Glucose

1 Glucose receives a phosphate group from ATP, producing glucose-6-phosphate (phosphorylation reaction).

ATP
Hexokinase
ADP

Glucose-6-phosphate

2 Glucose-6-phosphate is rearranged into its isomer, fructose-6-phosphate (isomerization reaction).

Phospho-glucomutase

Fructose-6-phosphate

3 Another phosphate group derived from ATP is attached to fructose-6-phosphate, producing fructose-1,6-bisphosphate (phosphorylation reaction).

ATP
Phospho-fructokinase
ADP

Fructose-1,6-bisphosphate

Aldolase

4 Fructose-1,6-bisphosphate is split into glyceraldehyde-3-phosphate (G3P) and dihydroxyacetone phosphate (DAP) (hydrolysis reaction).

Dihydroxyacetone phosphate

Glyceraldehyde-3-phosphate (G3P) (2 molecules)

Triosephosphate isomerase

5 The DAP produced in reaction 4 is converted into G3P, giving a total of two of these molecules per molecule of glucose (isomerization reaction).

Two molecules of G3P to reaction 6

Energy-releasing reactions
2 G3P → 2 Pyruvate

G3P (2 molecules)

NAD^+
Triosephosphate dehydrogenase
NADH
H^+
P_i

6 Two electrons and two protons are removed from G3P. Some of the energy released in this reaction is trapped by the addition of an inorganic phosphate group from the cytosol (not derived from ATP). The electrons are accepted by NAD^+, along with one of the protons. The other proton is released to the cytosol (redox reaction).

1,3-Bisphospho-glycerate (2 molecules)

ADP
Phospho-glycerate kinase
ATP

7 One of the two phosphate groups of 1,3-bisphosphoglycerate is transferred to ADP to produce ATP (substrate-level phosphorylation reaction).

3-Phospho-glycerate (2 molecules)

Phospho-glyceromutase

8 3-Phosphoglycerate is rearranged, shifting the phosphate group from the 3 carbon to the 2 carbon to produce 2-phosphoglycerate (mutase reaction—shifting of a chemical group to another within same molecule).

2-Phospho-glycerate (2 molecules)

H_2O
Enolase

9 Electrons are removed from one part of 2-phosphoglycerate and delivered to another part of the molecule. Most of the energy lost by the electrons is retained in the product, phosphoenolpyruvate (redox reaction).

Phosphoenol-pyruvate (PEP) (2 molecules)

ADP
Pyruvate kinase
ATP

10 The remaining phosphate group is removed from phosphoenolpyruvate and transferred to ADP. The reaction forms ATP and the final product of glycolysis, pyruvate (substrate-level phosphorylation reaction).

Pyruvate (2 molecules)

Figure 6.11

Reactions of pyruvate oxidation. Pyruvate (three carbons) is oxidized to an acetyl group (two carbons), which is carried to the citric acid cycle by CoA. The third carbon is released as CO_2. NAD^+ accepts two electrons and one proton removed in the oxidation. The acetyl group carried from the reaction by CoA is the fuel for the citric acid cycle.

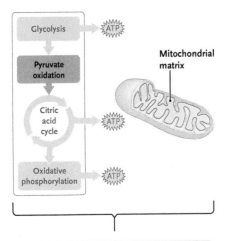

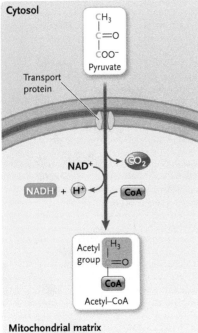

dioxide. The CoA molecule that carried the acetyl group to the site of the citric acid cycle is released and participates again in pyruvate oxidation. The net reactants and products of one turn of the citric acid cycle are

$$1 \text{ acetyl-CoA} + 3 \text{ NAD}^+ + 1 \text{ FAD} + 1 \text{ ADP} + 1 \text{ P}_i + 2 \text{ H}_2\text{O} \rightarrow$$

$$2\text{CO}_2 + 3 \text{ NADH} + 1 \text{ FADH}_2 + 1 \text{ ATP} + 3 \text{ H}^+ + 1 \text{ CoA}$$

Because one molecule of glucose is converted to two molecules of pyruvate by glycolysis and each molecule of pyruvate is converted to one acetyl group, all the reactants and products in this equation should be doubled when the citric acid cycle is considered as a continuation of glycolysis and pyruvate oxidation. **Figure 6.13,** presents a detailed view of the individual reactions of the citric acid cycle.

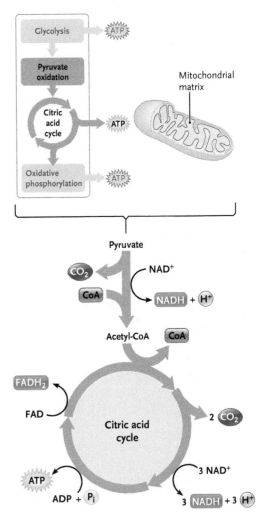

Figure 6.12

The reactions of pyruvate oxidation and the citric acid cycle. Each turn of the cycle oxidizes an acetyl group of acetyl-CoA to 2CO_2. Acetyl-CoA, NAD^+, FAD, and ADP enter the cycle; CoA, NADH, $FADH_2$, ATP, and CO_2 are released as products.

matrix side of the inner mitochondrial membrane. Combined, the reactions result in the oxidation of acetyl groups to carbon dioxide accompanied by the synthesis of ATP; NADH; and another nucleotide-based molecule, flavin adenine dinucleotide (FAD; the reduced form is $FADH_2$). A summary of the inputs and outputs of the citric acid cycle is shown in **Figure 6.12.** To put the cycle in context, the summary also includes the conversion of pyruvate to acetyl-CoA.

Looking at the stoichiometry (Figure 6.12), for one turn of the citric acid cycle, three NADH, one $FADH_2$, and a single molecule of ATP are synthesized. The energy for the synthesis of these molecules comes from the complete oxidation of one acetyl unit, resulting in the release of two molecules of carbon dioxide. The citric acid cycle is the stage of respiration where the remaining carbon atoms that were originally in glucose at the start of glycolysis are converted into carbon

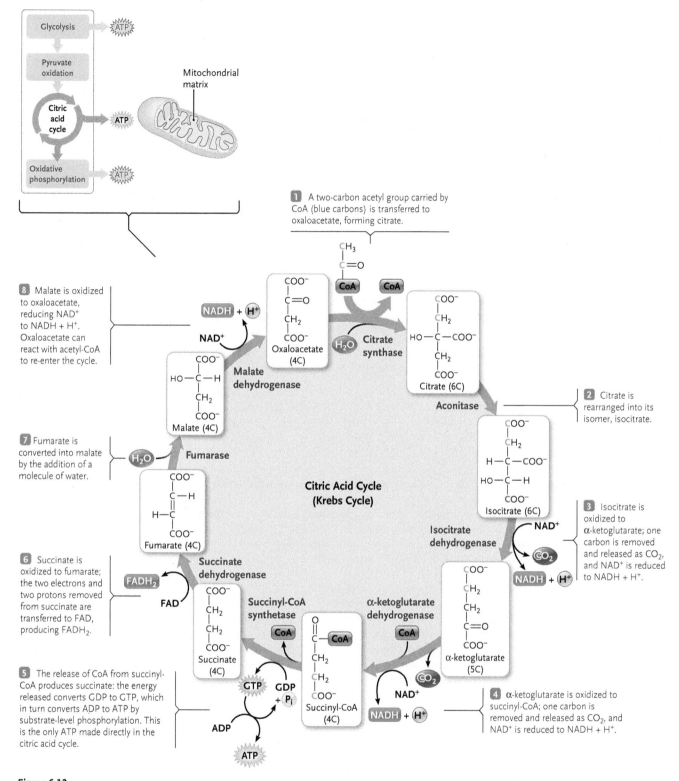

1 A two-carbon acetyl group carried by CoA (blue carbons) is transferred to oxaloacetate, forming citrate.

8 Malate is oxidized to oxaloacetate, reducing NAD^+ to $NADH + H^+$. Oxaloacetate can react with acetyl-CoA to re-enter the cycle.

7 Fumarate is converted into malate by the addition of a molecule of water.

6 Succinate is oxidized to fumarate; the two electrons and two protons removed from succinate are transferred to FAD, producing $FADH_2$.

5 The release of CoA from succinyl-CoA produces succinate: the energy released converts GDP to GTP, which in turn converts ADP to ATP by substrate-level phosphorylation. This is the only ATP made directly in the citric acid cycle.

2 Citrate is rearranged into its isomer, isocitrate.

3 Isocitrate is oxidized to α-ketoglutarate; one carbon is removed and released as CO_2, and NAD^+ is reduced to $NADH + H^+$.

4 α-ketoglutarate is oxidized to succinyl-CoA; one carbon is removed and released as CO_2, and NAD^+ is reduced to $NADH + H^+$.

Citric Acid Cycle (Krebs Cycle)

Figure 6.13

Reactions of the citric acid cycle. Acetyl-CoA, NAD^+, FAD, and ADP enter the cycle; CoA, NADH, $FADH_2$, ATP, and CO_2 are released as products. The CoA released in reaction 1 can cycle back for another turn of pyruvate oxidation. Enzyme names are in red.

STUDY BREAK

1. What are the steps involved in converting pyruvate into acetyl-CoA?
2. What purpose is served by the citric acid cycle?

6.5 Oxidative Phosphorylation: Electron Transport and Chemiosmosis

Following the citric acid cycle, all the carbon atoms originally present in glucose have been completely oxidized and released as carbon dioxide. Besides ATP formed by substrate-level phosphorylation, the potential energy originally present in glucose now exists in molecules of NADH and $FADH_2$. It is the role of the ETC coupled with the process of chemiosmosis to extract the potential energy in these molecules and synthesize additional ATP.

6.5a The Electron Transport Chain Converts the Potential Energy in NADH and $FADH_2$ into a Proton-Motive Force

The respiratory ETC (Figure 6.14) comprises a system of components that in eukaryotes is found on the inner mitochondrial membrane. The chain facilitates the transfer of electrons from $NADH_2$ and $FADH_2$ to oxygen. The chain consists of four protein complexes: complex I, NADH dehydrogenase; complex II, succinate dehydrogenase; complex III, cytochrome complex; and complex IV, cytochrome oxidase. Whereas complex II is a single peripheral membrane protein, the remaining complexes are composed of multiple proteins. For example, about 40 individual proteins make up complex I.

Electron flow between the complexes is facilitated by two mobile electron shuttles. Ubiquinone, which is a hydrophobic molecule found in the core of the membrane, shuttles electrons from complexes I and II to complex III. A second shuttle, cytochrome c, is located on the intermembrane space side of the membrane and transfers electrons from complex III to complex IV, cytochrome oxidase.

6.5b Electrons Move Spontaneously along the Electron Transport Chain

In an ETC it is not the proteins themselves that transfer the electrons, but rather electron transport is facilitated by nonprotein molecules called prosthetic groups. Protein subunits of each of complexes I, III, and IV bind a number of prosthetic groups very precisely to allow for electron transport (Figure 6.15, p. 132). Prosthetic groups are redox-active cofactors that alternate between reduced and oxidized states as they accept electrons

from upstream molecules and subsequently donate electrons to downstream molecules. A common prosthetic group is the molecule heme, which is a component of the cytochromes, including cytochrome c. Heme is a component of many biologically important compounds, including hemoglobin, where it is critical to the molecule's ability to carry oxygen. Central to its function, a heme group contains a central redox-active iron atom that alternates between Fe^{2+} and Fe^{3+}.

During electron transport (see Figure 6.15), one of the prosthetic groups of complex I, flavin mononucleotide (FMN), is reduced by electron donation from NADH on the matrix side of the inner membrane. FMN then donates the electron to the Fe/S (iron–sulfur) prosthetic group, which, in turn, donates the electron to ubiquinone. This process of reduction followed by oxidation of each carrier continues along the entire chain until, finally, the electrons are donated to oxygen (O_2), reducing it to water. The protons used in the formation of water are abundant in the aqueous environment of the cell.

A question concerning mechanism that we can ask at this stage is: what is the driving force for electron transport—why do electrons move from one complex to the next? why do electrons move down the chain? As shown in Figure 6.16, p. 132, the prosthetic groups and other electron carriers are organized in a very specific way—from high to low free energy. NADH has high potential energy because it contains high-energy electrons and thus can be readily oxidized. By contrast, O_2, the terminal electron acceptor of the chain, is strongly electronegative and can be easily reduced. As a consequence of this organization, electron movement along the chain is thermodynamically spontaneous, down a free energy gradient.

6.5c Chemiosmosis Powers ATP Synthesis by a Proton Gradient

Although the goal of cellular respiration is the synthesis of ATP, electron transport from NADH (or $FADH_2$) to O_2 does not actually produce any ATP. Electrons are simply passed along a chain of electron carriers until they are donated to oxygen, producing water. To understand how ATP is formed let's go back and take another look at Figure 6.14. As we have already mentioned, NADH has more potential energy than O_2, so one can ask the question: where does this energy go during electron transport? The energy that is released during electron transport is used to do work, specifically the work of transporting protons across the inner mitochondrial membrane from the matrix to the intermembrane space. As a consequence of this proton pumping across the inner membrane, which is essentially impermeable to protons, the H^+ concentration becomes much higher (and the pH lower) in the intermembrane space than in the matrix.

Proton translocation occurs at distinct sites along the ETC (see Figure 6.14). Within complexes I and IV,

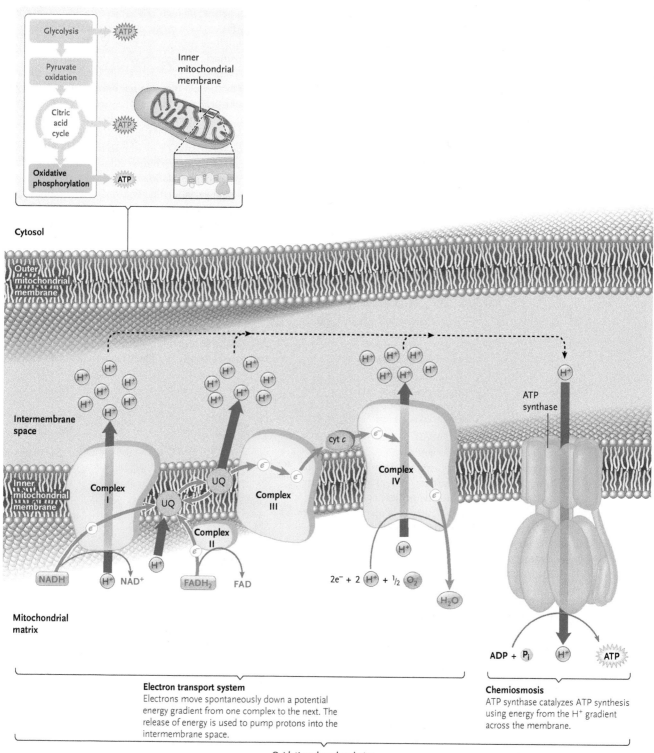

Figure 6.14

Oxidative phosphorylation: the mitochondrial ETC and ATP synthase complex. The electron transport system includes three major complexes, I, III, and IV. Two smaller electron carriers, ubiquinone (UQ) and cytochrome *c* (cyt *c*), act as shuttles between the major complexes, and succinate dehydrogenase (complex II) passes electrons to ubiquinone, bypassing complex I. Blue arrows indicate electron flow; red arrows indicate H⁺ movement. H⁺ is pumped from the matrix into the intermembrane space as electrons pass through complexes I and IV. H⁺ is also moved into the intermembrane space by the cyclic reduction/oxidation of ubiquinone. Chemiosmotic synthesis of ATP involves the ATP synthase complex that uses the energy of the proton gradient to catalyze the synthesis of ATP.

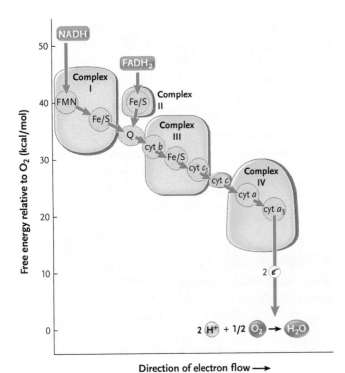

Figure 6.15
Redox components of the ETC are organized from high to low potential energy. Electron flow is spontaneous from high to low potential energy as electrons are passed from one redox molecule to the next.

"People behind Biology"). Whereas in mitochondria, the energy for chemiosmosis comes from the oxidation of energy-rich molecules such as NADH by the ETC, chemiosmosis also applies to the generation of ATP by photosynthesis energy. The utility of chemiosmosis is shown by the fact that it is not only used for ATP synthesis, the proton-motive force is also used, for example, to pump substances across membranes (see Chapter 5) and drive the rotation of flagella in bacteria.

The mode of ATP synthesis that is linked to the oxidation of energy-rich molecules by an ETC is called **oxidative phosphorylation**. Compared to the substrate-level phosphorylation that occurs during glycolysis and the citric acid cycle, oxidative phosphorylation relies on the action of a large multiprotein complex that spans the inner mitochondrial membrane called **ATP synthase** (Figure 6.16).

6.5d ATP Synthase Is a Molecular Motor

ATP synthase is a lollipop-shaped complex consisting of a basal unit, which is embedded in the inner mitochondrial membrane, connected to a headpiece by a stalk (see Figure 6.16). The headpiece extends into the mitochondrial matrix. The basal unit forms a channel through which H^+ can pass freely. The proton-motive

specific protein components use the energy released from electron transport for proton pumping. In addition, as ubiquinone molecules accept electrons from complexes I and II, they pick up protons from the matrix. After migrating through the membrane and donating electrons to complex III, ubiquinone retains a neutral charge by releasing protons into the intermembrane space.

The situation in which one side of the inner mitochondrial membrane has a higher concentration of protons than the other side represents potential energy that can be harnessed to do work. The situation is somewhat analogous to water behind a dam. The potential energy possessed by a proton gradient is derived from two factors. First, a chemical gradient exists across the membrane because the concentration of protons is not equal on both sides. Second, because protons are charged, there is an electrical difference, with the intermembrane space more positively charged than the matrix. The combination of a concentration gradient and a voltage difference across the membrane produces stored energy known as the **proton-motive force.**

Harnessing the proton-motive force to do work is referred to as **chemiosmosis**. It was first proposed as a mechanism to generate ATP by the British biochemist Peter Mitchell, who was later awarded a Nobel Prize in Chemistry for his work in this area (see

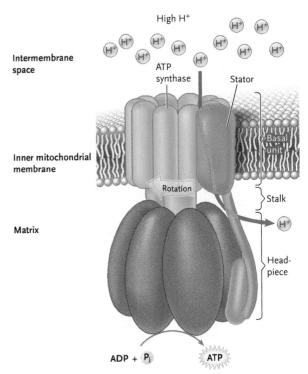

Figure 6.16
Detailed structure of ATP synthase—a molecular motor. The enzyme consists of a *basal unit*, which is embedded in the inner mitochondrial membrane, connected to a *headpiece* by a *stalk*, with the *stator* bridging the basal unit and headpiece. Protons move through a channel between the basal unit and the stator, making the stalk and headpiece spin. This results in ATP synthesis.

Peter Mitchell was a British biochemist who in 1978 was awarded the Nobel Prize in Chemistry for what the Royal Swedish Academy of Sciences committee stated was "his contribution to the understanding of biological energy transfer through the formulation of the chemiosmotic theory."

Mitchell completed an undergraduate degree and a Ph.D. at Cambridge University, graduating with the latter in 1951. In 1955, he was invited to set up and direct a biochemical research unit in the Department of Zoology, Edinburgh University, where he was a faculty member until 1964. From 1964 onward, he was director of the Glynn Research Institute. Glynn is a mansion that Mitchell renovated and turned into a personal research institute, located near Bodmin in Cornwall, England.

By the 1950s, it was known that both the chloroplast and the mitochondrion contained electron ETCs and made ATP, but a solid theory on how the two were linked was elusive. The dominant theories were based on substrate-level phosphorylation, which was already well understood. It was thought that ETCs passed energy to a high-energy chemical intermediate, which, in turn, passed it on to ATP through an ATP synthase that was known to exist in both the chloroplast and the mitochondrion. But the problem was that no one could find this chemical intermediate. Moreover, the substrate-level phosphorylation idea could not explain troubling findings: Why did so many different reagents act as uncouplers? Why were the enzymes of oxidative phosphorylation associated with the mitochondrial membrane? Why did coupling seem so dependent on the maintenance of membrane structure?

Mitchell proposed the chemiosmotic theory in 1961 in an elegant paper published in *Nature*. It is hard to imagine now how revolutionary the paper was at the time. It contained very little experimental evidence and was opposed by almost the entire biochemical community, which was stuck believing in the high-energy intermediate concept. The paper was based on Mitchell's realization that the movement of ions across an electrochemical membrane potential could provide the energy needed to produce ATP. The basis of chemiosmosis is that the components of the ETC are inserted into a membrane in only one way, which allows for protons to be transported in one direction during electron transport. The protons would flow back through the ATP synthase, causing synthesis of ATP. In Mitchell's model, the proton gradient across the membrane served as the high-energy intermediate—the elusive chemical intermediate could not be found because it did not exist.

---

force is what propels protons in the intermembrane space through the channel in the enzyme's basal unit, down their concentration gradient, and into the matrix. Evidence indicates that the binding of individual protons to sites in the headpiece causes it to rotate in a way that catalyzes the formation of ATP from ADP and P_i. The spinning of the headpiece of ATP synthase represents the smallest molecular rotary motor known in nature.

In Chapter 5, we described active transport pumps that use energy from ATP to transport ions across membranes against their concentration gradients (see Figure 5.18, p. 111). An active transport pump is, in fact, an ATP synthase that is operating in reverse. It doesn't synthesize ATP but rather uses the free energy from the hydrolysis of ATP to provide the energy necessary to pump ions (such as protons) across a membrane.

Harnessing the potential energy that is present in a proton gradient to synthesize ATP is fundamental to almost all forms of life and developed early in the evolution of life. This is shown by the fact that the ATP synthase complex found in mitochondria is structurally very similar to the ATP synthase complexes found in the thylakoid membrane of the chloroplast and the plasma membrane of many bacteria and archaea.

6.5e Electron Transport and Chemiosmosis Can Be Uncoupled

CONCEPT FIX Coming out of high school, many students think that ATP is a product of the respiratory ETC. This is a misconception that we need to fix. The generation of ATP by the ATP synthase complex is linked, or coupled, to electron transport by the proton gradient established across the inner mitochondrial membrane. But electron transport and the chemiosmotic generation of ATP are separate and distinct processes and are not always completely coupled **(Figure 6.17, p. 134).** For example, it is possible to have high rates of electron transport (and thus high rates of oxygen consumption) and yet no ATP generated by chemiosmosis. This uncoupling of the two processes occurs when mechanisms prevent the formation of a proton-motive force. ⬡

A class of chemicals called ionophores form channels across membranes through which ions, including

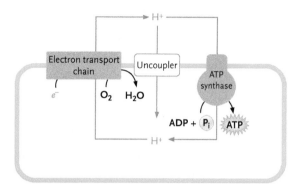

Figure 6.17

Uncoupling of electron transport and ATP synthesis. Respiratory electron transport results in the formation of a proton gradient across the membrane. Usually, this gradient is dissipated by protons flowing back to the matrix through the ATP synthase. Uncouplers, which may be specific chemicals or proteins, provide an alternative route for protons to flow back across the membrane. By circumventing the ATP synthase, no ATP is generated.

protons, can freely pass. As a consequence, in the presence of ionophores, proton pumping during electron transport is followed by the protons simply flowing back into the matrix through the ionophore channels. A proton gradient is prevented from becoming established. Often referred to as uncouplers, ionophores are very toxic because of their ability to inhibit oxidative phosphorylation. It is interesting to note that in the 1930s, low concentrations of chemical uncouplers were commonly used as diet drugs. Although people did lose weight, overdoses resulting in death were not uncommon.

When electron transport is uncoupled from the chemiosmotic synthesis of ATP, the free energy released during electron transport is not conserved by the establishment of a proton-motive force but instead is lost as heat. Many organisms take advantage of this as a means of regulating body temperature by altering the expression of a group of transmembrane proteins. These *uncoupling proteins* are localized to the inner mitochondrial membrane and, similar to chemical uncouplers, form channels through which protons can freely flow. This mechanism of regulating body temperature is especially important in animals. For example, in hibernating mammals and in newborn infants, the activity of uncoupling proteins within mitochondria of brown adipose fat is an important mechanism of heat generation.

STUDY BREAK

1. Differentiate the terms proton-motive force, chemiosmosis, and oxidative phosphorylation.
2. What does it mean that electron transport and oxidative phosphorylation are coupled processes?

6.6 The Efficiency and Regulation of Cellular Respiration

In this section, we calculate the efficiency with which cellular respiration extracts the energy from glucose. As well, we discuss how this entire multi-enzyme pathway is regulated so that it remains flexible in the face of changing cellular demands for ATP and changes in food supply.

6.6a What Are the ATP Yield and Efficiency of Cellular Respiration?

Determining the total number of ATP molecules synthesized for each molecule of glucose oxidized during cellular respiration is an important exercise that forces us to integrate all parts of the respiratory pathway. But before we look at the whole pathway, we first consider a question concerning oxidative phosphorylation: how many ATP molecules are produced by oxidative phosphorylation? Recent research suggests that for each NADH that is oxidized, and thus for each pair of electrons that travels down the ETC, 10 H^+ are pumped into the inner membrane space. (Note: Don't try to figure out how you get 10 protons pumped from 2 electrons—it is not straightforward—wait until you take an advanced biochemistry course.) We also know that somewhere between three and four H^+ are needed to flow back through the ATP synthase for the synthesis of one molecule of ATP. So that gives between 2.5 and 3.3 molecules of ATP synthesized for every NADH oxidized by the ETC. To make life easier, let's round off and say that for each NADH oxidized three ATP are synthesized. Because the oxidation of $FADH_2$ skips the proton-pumping complex I (look back at Figure 6.14, p. 131), only about two molecules of ATP are synthesized for each $FADH_2$ oxidized.

A detailed accounting of the ATP yield for each molecule of glucose oxidized is provided in **Figure 6.18.** Recall that the products of glycolysis include two molecules of ATP and two molecules of NADH. Next, the oxidation of the two molecules of pyruvate generated by glycolysis results in the synthesis of two NADH. During the citric acid cycle, the two molecules of acetyl-CoA that are oxidized result in the synthesis of two ATP, along with six NADH and two $FADH_2$. That gives us a total of ten NADH and two $FADH_2$ that can be oxidized by the ETC. Recall that about three ATP are produced by oxidative phosphorylation for each NADH oxidized by the ETC, while $FADH_2$ oxidation yields two ATP. So that gives a total of 34 ATP generated by oxidative phosphorylation as a result of the oxidation of 10 NADH and 2 $FADH_2$. So, adding up, we have 2 ATP from glycolysis, 2 ATP directly from the citric acid cycle, and 34 ATP from oxidative phosphorylation, yielding 38 molecules of ATP synthesized for each glucose oxidized!

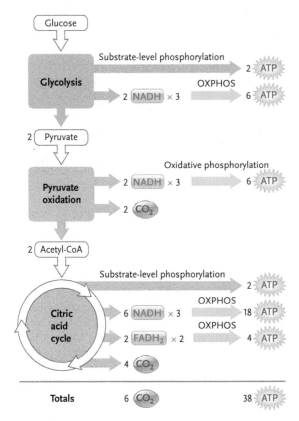

Figure 6.18

ATP yield from the oxidation of glucose. The maximum possible ATP yield from the oxidation of 1 molecule of glucose is 38. However, this yield is rarely achieved. (OXPHOS = oxidative phosphorylation)

The 38 ATP for each glucose oxidized is the maximum theoretical yield. There are three reasons, however, that this maximum is rarely achieved. First, while the maximum of 38 is true in bacteria, this is not the case in eukaryotic cells, where the theoretical maximum is only 36 ATP. This difference is due to the energy costs of transporting the NADH generated by glycolysis into the mitochondrion. The active transport system needed to move the electrons associated with NADH into the mitochondrion consumes one ATP for each molecule of NADH transported. Since two NADH are transported, the yield of ATP drops by two. The second reason the yield is less than 38 ATP is that electron transport and oxidative phosphorylation are rarely completely coupled to each other. Even under normal metabolic conditions, the inner mitochondrial membrane is somewhat leaky to protons, and thus not all the protons pumped across during electron transport pass back into the matrix through the ATP synthase. Some re-enter the matrix by slowly diffusing directly through the inner mitochondrial membrane. The third reason the theoretical maximum is not attained is that the proton-motive force generated by electron transport is used for other things besides simply generating

ATP. As a source of potential energy, the proton-motive force is used, for example, to transport the pyruvate synthesized by glycolysis into the matrix.

So how efficient is cellular respiration at extracting the energy from glucose and converting it into ATP? The phosphorylation of ADP to ATP requires about 7.3 kcal/mol. In eukaryotes, the theoretical maximum yield from that complete oxidation of a mole of glucose is 36 moles of ATP, so 36×7.3 gives a total of 263 kcal of energy. The complete oxidation of a mole of glucose releases exactly 686 kcal of energy. From these two numbers we can calculate the efficiency to be $263/686 \times 100 = 38\%$. In other words, 38% of the energy in glucose is converted into ATP. While this value of efficiency doesn't seem very high, it is greater than the energy transformations associated with most machines engineers have developed. For example, an automobile extracts only about 25% of the energy in the fuel it burns. Recall from Chapter 4 that the second law of thermodynamics states that energy transformations can never be 100% efficient, as some of the energy is used to increase the entropy of the surroundings. We cannot forget that entropy plays a role in the energy transformations that occur during cellular respiration as well.

6.6b Fats, Proteins, and Carbohydrates Can Be Oxidized by Cellular Respiration

In addition to glucose and other six-carbon sugars, reactions leading from glycolysis through pyruvate oxidation also oxidize a range of other carbohydrates, as well as lipids and proteins, which enter the respiratory pathway at various points **(Figure 6.19, p. 136)**.

Carbohydrates such as sucrose and other disaccharides are easily broken down into monosaccharides such as glucose and fructose, which enter glycolysis at early steps. Starch is hydrolyzed by digestive enzymes into individual glucose molecules, whereas **glycogen**, a more complex carbohydrate, is broken down and converted by enzymes into glucose-6-phosphate, an early substrate molecule in glycolysis.

Among the fats, the **triglycerides** are major sources of electrons for ATP synthesis. Before entering the oxidative reactions, they are hydrolyzed into glycerol and individual fatty acids. The glycerol is converted to glyceraldehyde-3-phosphate before entering glycolysis. The fatty acids—and many other types of lipids—are split into two-carbon fragments, which enter the citric acid cycle as acetyl-CoA.

Proteins are hydrolyzed to amino acids before oxidation. The amino group ($2NH_2$) is removed, and the remainder of the molecule enters the respiratory pathway as pyruvate, acetyl units carried by coenzyme A, or intermediates of the citric acid cycle (see Figure 6.19). For example, the amino acid alanine is converted into pyruvate; leucine, into acetyl units; and phenylalanine, into fumarate, which enters the citric acid cycle.

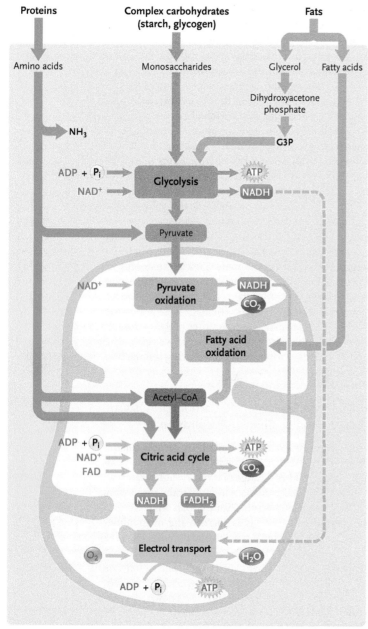

Figure 6.19

Major pathways that oxidize carbohydrates, fats, and proteins. Reactions that occur in the cytosol are shown against a tan background; reactions that occur in mitochondria are shown inside the organelle. CoA funnels the products of many oxidative pathways into the citric acid cycle.

6.6c Respiratory Intermediates Are Utilized for Anabolic Reactions

Organic molecules (carbohydrates, fats, proteins) are oxidized by cellular respiration, which is linked to the generation of ATP. Interestingly, these molecules are also the source of the carbon atoms found in a wide range of essential molecules. For example, the intermediates of glycolysis and the citric acid cycle are routinely diverted and used as the starting

substrates required to synthesize amino acids, fats, and the pyrimidine and purine bases needed for nucleic acid synthesis. As well, respiratory intermediates supply the carbon backbones for the array of hormones, growth factors, prosthetic groups, and cofactors that are essential to cell function.

The metabolic flexibility of cellular respiration allows for reactions to be adjusted rapidly. For example, whereas fatty acids can be used as a source of energy by being oxidized to acetyl-CoA, excess acetyl-CoA can be removed from the respiration and used to synthesize the fatty acids needed for a range of cellular processes.

6.6d Cellular Respiration Is Controlled by Supply and Demand

The rate at which food molecules (see Figure 6.19) are oxidized by cellular respiration is tightly controlled such that the rate of ATP generation matches the requirements of the cell for chemical energy. This illustrates the concept of supply and demand—the cell does not waste resources synthesizing molecules it already has in excess. Most metabolic pathways are regulated by supply and demand through the process of feedback inhibition: the end-products of the pathway inhibit an enzyme early in the pathway (look back at Chapter 4, Figure 4.10).

The rate of glucose oxidation by glycolysis for example, is closely regulated by several mechanisms to match the cellular demands for ATP. A key enzyme of glycolysis that is tightly regulated is phosphofructokinase, which catalyses the conversion of fructose 6-phosphate to fructose 1,6-bisphosphate **(Figure 6.20)**. Because it is an allosteric enzyme (see Chapter 4), the activity of phosphofructokinase can be adjusted by the binding of certain metabolic activators and inhibitors. Two of the key regulators of phosphofructokinase are ATP and ADP.

ATP is an allosteric inhibitor of phosphofructokinase: if excess ATP is present in the cytosol it binds to phosphofructokinase, inhibiting its activity. The resulting decrease in the concentration of fructose 1,6-bisphosphate slows or stops the subsequent reactions of glycolysis. The enzyme becomes active again when metabolic demands consume the excess ATP and the inhibition of phosphofructokinase is released. The increase in phosphofructokinase activity is not due solely to the release of ATP inhibition, however ADP, which accumulates when ATP is hydrolyzed during metabolism, is an allosteric activator of the enzyme (see Figure 6.20). Besides ATP and ADP, phosphofructokinase activity is also sensitive to the levels of citrate, which is the first product of the citric acid cycle. If the products of the citric acid cycle are in high demand, then citrate should not accumulate in the cell. Increased citrate concentrations suggest that the demand for ATP is low, which may occur, for example, under conditions of limited oxygen when the rate of oxidative phosphorylation

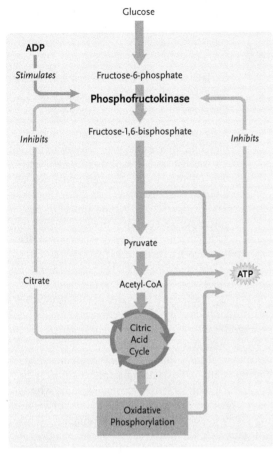

Figure 6.20
The control of cellular respiration. A major mechanism is allosteric control of the activity of the enzyme phospho-fructokinase, which is found early in glycolysis. High levels of ATP and the citric acid cycle intermediate citrate allosterically inhibit phosphofructokinase. Alternatively, when ATP concentrations are low, the levels of ADP increase. ADP is an allosteric activator of the enzyme.

is restricted. Alternatively, it may indicate that citrate is not required as a carbon backbone for the products of biosynthetic reactions. Overall, through various metabolic activators and inhibitors altering phosphofructokinase activity, the functional state of glycolysis and the citric acid cycle can be kept balanced.

STUDY BREAK

1. Give an accounting of the total ATP yield from the oxidation of a molecule of glucose.
2. Explain how the activity of the enzyme phospho-fructokinase is controlled.

6.7 Oxygen and Cellular Respiration

A constant supply of oxygen is required to maintain the high rates of oxidative phosphorylation necessary to supply cells with sufficient ATP. Although humans need

an almost constant supply of oxygen, other organisms can survive and even thrive in the absence of oxygen.

There are two general mechanisms where cellular respiration can occur in the absence of oxygen: fermentation and anaerobic respiration. The distinction between these two processes is that fermentation does not involve the citric acid cycle or electron transport, whereas anaerobic respiration uses a molecule other than oxygen as the terminal electron acceptor of electron transport.

6.7a In Eukaryotic Cells, Low Oxygen Levels Result in Fermentation

Following glycolysis, in eukaryotic cells cellular respiration can continue along one of two distinct pathways depending on whether or not oxygen is present **(Figure 6.21, p. 138)**. When oxygen is plentiful, the pyruvate and NADH produced by glycolysis are transported into mitochondria, where they are oxidized using the citric acid cycle and the ETC. If, instead, oxygen is absent or in short supply, the pyruvate remains in the cytosol, where it is reduced, consuming the NADH generated by glycolysis by a metabolic process called **fermentation.**

Two types of fermentation exist: lactate fermentation and alcohol fermentation. In **lactate fermentation,** which is found in many bacteria and some plant and animal tissues, pyruvate is converted into the three-carbon molecule lactate **(Figure 6.22a, p. 138).** Lactate fermentation occurs, for example, when vigorous contraction of muscle cells calls for more oxygen than the circulating blood can supply. When the oxygen content of the muscle cells returns to normal levels, the reverse of the reaction in Figure 6.22a regenerates pyruvate and NADH. Lactate is also the fermentation product of some bacteria; the sour taste of buttermilk, yogurt, and dill pickles is a sign of their activity.

Alcohol fermentation (Figure 6.22b) occurs in microorganisms such as yeasts, which are single-celled fungi. In this reaction, pyruvate is reduced to ethyl alcohol as CO_2 is released and NADH is oxidized to NAD^+. Alcoholic fermentation by yeasts has widespread commercial applications. Bakers use the yeast *Saccharomyces cerevisiae* to make bread dough rise. They mix the yeast with a small amount of sugar and blend the mixture into the dough, where oxygen levels are low. As the yeast cells convert the sugar into ethyl alcohol and CO_2, the gaseous CO_2 expands and creates bubbles that cause the dough to rise. Oven heat evaporates the alcohol and causes further expansion of the bubbles, producing a light-textured product. Alcoholic fermentation is also the mainstay of beer and wine brewing. Fruits are a natural home to wild yeasts **(Figure 6.23, p. 139)**; for example, winemakers rely on a mixture of wild and cultivated yeasts to produce wine. Alcoholic fermentation also occurs naturally in the environment; for example, overripe or rotting fruit will

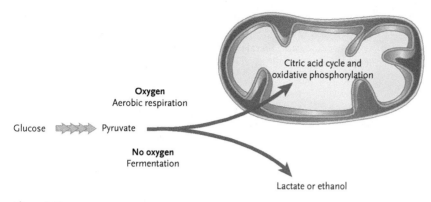

Figure 6.21

The metabolic pathway of pyruvate oxidation depends upon the presence of oxygen.

frequently start to ferment, and birds that eat the fruit may become too drunk to fly.

Overall, the reactions of fermentation play a critical role whenever organisms are exposed to conditions in which the oxygen concentration is too low to support oxidative phosphorylation. By consuming the NADH generated by glycolysis, fermentation reactions keep cytosolic NAD$^+$ levels high. This is of critical metabolic importance because NAD$^+$ is required for glycolysis (look back at Figure 6.9, step 6, p. 127). As long as there is sufficient NAD$^+$, glycolysis will continue to operate and generate ATP. Of course, the amount of ATP generated is small compared to oxidative phosphorylation,

and thus fermentation is not sufficient to support the high ATP requirement of brain cells, for example.

6.7b In Anaerobic Respiration, the Terminal Electron Acceptor Is Not Oxygen

Although they lack mitochondria, many bacteria and archaea have respiratory ETCs that are located on internal membrane systems derived from the plasma membrane. Some of these electron transport systems are very similar to those found in the mitochondria of eukaryotes and use O_2 as the terminal electron acceptor. Other bacteria and archaea, however, have respiratory chains that use a molecule other than O_2 as the electron acceptor and are said to possess anaerobic (*an* = without; *aero* = air) respiration. Instead of O_2, sulfate (SO_4^{2-}), nitrate (NO_3^-), and the ferric ion (Fe^{3+}) are commonly used terminal electron acceptors. There is a huge diversity of molecules that have a high affinity for electrons that are used as electron acceptors for electron transport and support ATP generation by oxidative phosphorylation. If oxidative phosphorylation can proceed in anaerobic organisms, what explains why aerobic respiration evolved to be the dominant form of respiratory metabolism? Simply by being highly electronegative, O_2 has greater affinity for oxygen than any

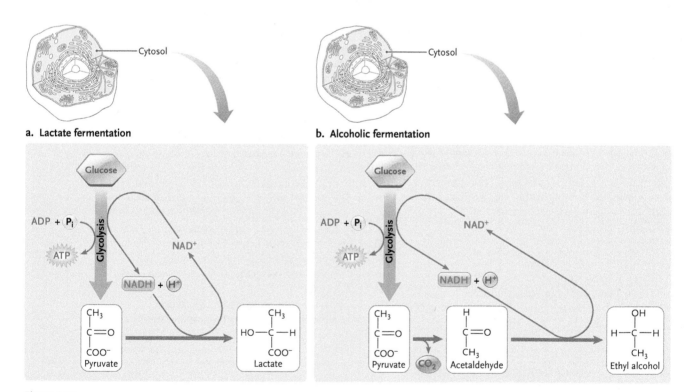

a. Lactate fermentation

b. Alcoholic fermentation

Figure 6.22

Fermentation reactions that produce **(a)** lactate and **(b)** ethyl alcohol. The fermentations, which occur in the cytosol, convert NADH to NAD$^+$, allowing the electron carrier to cycle back to glycolysis. This process keeps glycolysis running, with continued production of ATP.

Figure 6.23
Alcoholic fermentation in nature: wild yeast cells, visible as a dustlike coating on grapes.

other electron acceptor. This enables ETCs that employ O_2 to extract a greater amount of potential energy out of substrate molecules (e.g., NADH, FADH$_2$).

6.7c Organisms Differ with Respect to Their Ability to Use Oxygen

We can differentiate three lifestyles depending on the requirements of an organism for oxygen. Many archaea and bacteria and most eukaryotes are **strict aerobes**—they have an absolute requirement for oxygen for survival and are unable to live solely by fermentation. To understand why this is, look back at Figure 6.18, p. 135. In the absence of oxygen, ATP is generated solely by substrate-level phosphorylation during glycolysis: 2 ATP generated for every glucose oxidized. By comparison, in the presence of oxygen, up to 38 ATP can be generated—that's 19 times as much ATP for each glucose oxidized. As shown in Figure 6.19, the difference is explained by the huge ATP yield of oxidative phosphorylation. Humans and other animals are especially sensitive to low-oxygen environments because certain tissues, such as brain cells, have requirements for ATP that can only be met by constant and high rates of oxidative phosphorylation.

Other organisms, called **facultative anaerobes**, can switch between fermentation and aerobic respiration, depending on the oxygen supply. Facultative anaerobes include *Escherichia coli,* the bacterium that inhabits the digestive tract of humans; the *Lactobacillus* bacteria used to produce buttermilk and yogurt; and *S. cerevisiae,* the yeast used in brewing and baking. Many cell types in higher organisms, including vertebrate muscle cells, are also facultatively anaerobic. Lastly, some bacteria, some archaea, and a few fungi are classified as **strict anaerobes** because they require an oxygen-free environment to survive. Strict anaerobes gain ATP from either fermentation or anaerobic respiration. Among these organisms are the bacteria that cause botulism, tetanus, and some other serious diseases. For example, the bacterium that causes botulism thrives in the oxygen-free environment of

canned foods that prevents the growth of most other microorganisms.

6.7d The Paradox of Aerobic Life Is That Oxygen Is Essential and Toxic

As we mentioned above, some microbes are strict anaerobes—they cannot live in an oxygen environment. But why can't they? Lacking the ability to use O_2 as an electron acceptor is one thing, but actually dying in the presence of O_2? The reason that strict anaerobes die in an oxygen environment is related to what is often called the *paradox of aerobic life:* although oxygen is absolutely essential to the survival of many organisms, oxygen is also potentially toxic.

It takes four electrons to completely reduce a molecule of O_2 to water **(Figure 6.24).** Partially reduced forms of O_2 are formed when O_2 accepts fewer electrons, producing what are called *reactive oxygen species* (ROS). These molecules, which include the compounds superoxide and hydrogen peroxide (see Figure 6.24), are powerful oxidizing molecules and readily remove electrons from proteins, lipids, and DNA, resulting in oxidative damage. If ROS levels within a cell are excessive, their strong oxidizing nature can result in the destruction of many biological molecules and can be lethal. Because most cells contain an abundance of both O_2 and electron-rich molecules (e.g., proteins, lipids, nucleic acids) the formation of ROS is a consequence of aerobic life that cannot be avoided.

To survive in an oxygen-rich environment, aerobic organisms have evolved an antioxidant defence system that includes both enzymes and nonenzyme molecules that have the role of intercepting and inactivating reactive oxygen molecules as they are produced within cells. Two of the major ROS-scavenging enzymes are superoxide dismutase and catalase (see Figure 6.24). Working in concert, superoxide dismutase converts the superoxide anion to hydrogen peroxide, which in turn is reduced to water by the action of catalase. In addition to enzymes, many cells have a range of antioxidants,

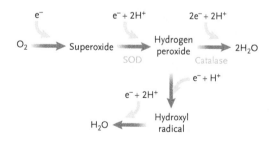

Figure 6.24
The conversion of O_2 to water is a four-electron reduction. If this occurs stepwise, it results in the formation of the intermediate ROS, which are potentially harmful. Aerobic cells contain the enzymes superoxide dismutase (SOD) and catalase, which together quickly convert superoxide and hydrogen peroxide to water.

Cyanide

Cyanide is an ion that consists of a carbon atom triple-bonded to an atom of nitrogen (C — N⁻). It is a very toxic metabolic poison acting as an irreversible inhibitor of the terminal enzyme of respiratory electron transport, cytochrome oxidase. By binding to the iron atom of the heme prosthetic groups in the enzyme, cyanide prevents electron flow to O_2, essentially inhibiting electron transport and subsequent chemiosmosis. Acute cyanide poisoning can result in death within minutes of exposure.

Cyanide is produced in small amounts by a range of microorganisms and is found in small amounts in apple seeds, almonds, and the pits of fruits such as peaches. In some plants, the production of cyanide in a form bound to sugars is thought to be a deterrent to herbivory. The presence of cyanide in the potato-like root of the cassava plant is of concern because it is a staple food in a number of tropical countries. The presence of cyanide

glycosides is diminished by extensive soaking and cooking of the cassava root, but health problems associated with chronic cyanide poisoning remain quite common.

Cyanide has clear applications in a range of industries but especially in electroplating, metallurgy, and mining owing to the high solubility of gold $[Au(CN)_2]^-$ and silver $[Ag(CN)_2]^-$ cyanides in water. For these purposes, approximately 500 thousand tonnes of highly toxic sodium cyanide are produced each year. In gold mining, the addition of a solution of sodium cyanide to ore containing low amounts of gold is effective at extracting the gold by bringing the gold into solution. The resulting formation of huge amounts of cyanide-contaminated water makes this form of gold mining highly controversial, yet it remains a very effective and cheap method of extraction.

In addition to a respiratory ETC that is inhibited by cyanide, plants

contain a pathway of electron transport that is resistant to cyanide. Instead of using cytochrome oxidase, this second pathway of respiration uses a terminal oxidase called the alternative oxidase. This alternative pathway of respiration is not linked to proton pumping like the normal respiratory chain; instead, electron flow simply generates heat. Intestinally, high levels of alternative oxidase in the flowers of some plant species are used to volatilize attractants for pollinators. This includes the aptly named skunk cabbage, which tells you that the attractants for pollinators are not necessarily pleasant.

In addition to being found in all plants, the alternative oxidase has been found in algae, some fungi, and, recently, some animal phyla. The physiological role of cyanide-resistant respiration in these species is being actively investigated by a number of research groups.

---

including vitamin C and vitamin E, which act as reducing agents, safely and rapidly reducing reactive oxygen compounds to water. In recent years, excessive ROS formation has been implicated in a wide variety of degenerative diseases, including Parkinson's disease and Alzheimer dementia. In fact, it is thought that the progressive build-up of oxidative damage may underlie the aging process itself. This, in part, explains the huge interest in the possible protective value of a wide variety of antioxidant compounds, particularly those from certain fruits and vegetables.

So why do strict anaerobes die in the presence of oxygen? For one group, their inability to live in an oxygen environment is because they lack one or both of the enzymes superoxide dismutase and catalase, which results in a build-up of toxic ROS within their cells if they are exposed to oxygen. Interestingly, some strict anaerobes do contain these enzymes, which are highly expressed when cells are placed in an oxygen environment. The inability of this second group of anaerobes to survive in an oxygen environment seems to be linked to oxygen itself inhibiting key metabolic enzymes.

As discussed in the last section, oxidative phosphorylation generates much more ATP than the substrate-level phosphorylation that takes place during glycolysis and the citric acid cycle. From this it is clear that the evolution of the electron transport system with oxygen as the terminal electron acceptor enabled cells to extract far more energy from food molecules than other modes of metabolism. However, the evolution of the aerobic lifestyle required the development of antioxidants and enzymes such as catalase and superoxide dismutase to combat the harmful effects of oxygen, which include the inevitable formation of ROS. In addition, it required that cytochrome oxidase, the last enzyme of the mitochondrial ETC, develop a remarkable mode of catalysis. Looking back at Figure 6.14, p. 131, notice that the cytochrome oxidase complex donates electrons from the electron carrier cytochrome c to O_2. However, it does so in a way that, remarkably, leads to essentially no reactive oxygen generation. The enzyme is structurally quite complex, containing four redox centres (two hemes and two copper ions), each of which can store a single electron. When all centres are reduced, the enzyme simultaneously transfers all four electrons to O_2, producing two molecules of water. That cytochrome oxidase is the only enzyme that aerobic organisms, from bacterial to human, use as the terminal complex of electron transport indicates the chemical difficulty of carrying out the transfer of electrons to O_2 in a safe and controlled manner. Given that this single enzyme handles approximately 98% of the oxygen we metabolize, if the reaction resulted in significant amounts of partially reduced forms of oxygen (e.g., superoxide, hydrogen peroxide), aerobic life as we know it would have probably never evolved.

Review

To access course materials such as Aplia and other companion resources, please visit www.NELSONbrain.com.

6.1 The Chemical Basis of Cellular Respiration

- Glucose, like gasoline, is a good fuel because of the presence of C—H bonds, which contain electrons that can be easily removed and used to do work (see Figure 6.2).
- Oxidation–reduction reactions, called redox reactions, partially or completely transfer electrons from donor to acceptor atoms; the donor is oxidized as it releases electrons, and the acceptor is reduced (see Figure 6.3).
- Almost all organisms obtain energy for cellular activities through cellular respiration, the process of transferring electrons from donor organic molecules to a final acceptor molecule such as oxygen; the energy that is released drives ATP synthesis.

6.2 Cellular Respiration: An Overview

- Cellular respiration occurs in three stages: (1) in glycolysis, glucose is converted to two molecules of pyruvate; (2) in pyruvate oxidation and the citric acid cycle, pyruvate is converted to an acetyl compound that is oxidized completely to CO_2; and (3) in oxidative phosphorylation, high-energy electrons produced from the first two stages pass along an electron transport chain (ETC), with the energy released being used to establish a proton gradient across the membrane. This gradient is used to synthesize ATP (see Figure 6.6).
- Both eukaryotes and prokaryotes may undergo cellular respiration. In eukaryotes, however, most of the reactions of cellular respiration occur in mitochondria (see Figure 6.7).

6.3 Glycolysis: The Splitting of Glucose

- In glycolysis, which occurs in the cytosol, glucose (six carbons) is oxidized into two molecules of pyruvate (three carbons each). Electrons removed in the oxidation are delivered to NAD^+, producing NADH. The reaction sequence produces a net gain of two ATP, two NADH, and two pyruvate molecules for each molecule of glucose oxidized (see Figures 6.8 and 6.9).
- ATP molecules produced in the energy-releasing steps of glycolysis result from substrate-level phosphorylation, an enzyme-catalyzed reaction that transfers a phosphate group from a substrate to ADP (see Figure 6.10).

6.4 Pyruvate Oxidation and the Citric Acid Cycle

- In pyruvate oxidation, which occurs inside mitochondria, one pyruvate (three carbons) is oxidized to one acetyl group (two carbons) and one CO_2. Electrons removed in the oxidation are accepted by one NAD^+ to produce one NADH. The acetyl group is transferred to coenzyme A (CoA), which carries it to the citric acid cycle (see Figure 6.11).
- In the citric acid cycle, which occurs in the matrix of the mitochondrion, acetyl groups are oxidized completely to CO_2. Electrons removed in the oxidation are accepted by NAD^+ or FAD, and substrate-level phosphorylation produces ATP. For each acetyl group oxidized by the cycle, two CO_2, one ATP, three NADH, and one $FADH_2$ are produced (see Figures 6.12 and 6.13).

6.5 Oxidative Phosphorylation: Electron Transport and Chemiosmosis

- Electrons are passed from NADH and $FADH_2$ to the ETC, which consists of four major protein complexes and two smaller shuttle carriers. As the electrons flow from one carrier to the next through the system, some of their energy is used by the complexes to pump protons across the inner mitochondrial membrane (see Figure 6.14).
- Two major protein complexes (I and IV) and the reduction/-oxidation of ubiquinone contribute to the pumping of protons from the matrix to the intermembrane space, generating a proton gradient.
- The proton gradient produced by the electron transport system is used by ATP synthase as an energy source for synthesis of ATP from ADP and P_i. The ATP synthase is embedded in the inner mitochondrial membrane together with the ETC (see Figure 6.16).
- Electron transport and the chemiosmotic synthesis of ATP are distinct and separate processes that are usually linked, or coupled, by the proton gradient. The uncoupling of the two results in high rates of electron transport (and oxygen consumption), without chemiosmotic ATP synthesis. Uncoupling results in heat generation (see Figure 6.17).

6.6 The Efficiency and Regulation of Cellular Respiration

- An estimated three ATP are synthesized as each electron pair travels from NADH to oxygen through the mitochondrial ETC; about two ATP are synthesized as each electron pair travels through the system from $FADH_2$ to oxygen.

- In glycolysis, two ATP and two NADH are synthesized; during the oxidation of pyruvate and the citric acid cycle, two ATP, eight NADH, and two $FADH_2$ are produced. That gives a total of 10 NADH and 2 $FADH_2$ that are oxidized by the ETC, leading to the synthesis of about 34 ATP. This gives a total theoretical maximum ATP yield for each glucose oxidized of 38. For a number of reasons this maximum yield is rarely reached.
- The efficiency with which the energy in glucose is conserved in the synthesis of ATP is about 30% (see Figure 6.18).
- Besides simple sugars, energy can be extracted from fats, proteins, and carbohydrates that enter the respiratory chain at different points (see Figure 6.19).
- A number of different molecules can activate and repress key steps of the respiratory pathway so that it can be controlled by supply and demand (see Figure 6.20).

6.7 Oxygen and Cellular Respiration

- Fermentation is a pathway of respiration that oxidizes fuel molecules in the absence of oxygen and does not involve oxidative phosphorylation (see Figure 6.21).

- During fermentation, pyruvate reduction in the cytosol consumes NADH. In so doing, NAD^+ is produced, which is required as a substrate for glycolysis. This allows glycolysis to continue to run, producing ATP by substrate-level phosphorylation (see Figure 6.22).
- In organisms with anaerobic respiratory pathways, the terminal electron acceptor of electron transport is a molecule other than oxygen. Anaerobic respiratory pathways are found only in archaea and bacteria.
- Many archaea, bacteria, and eukaryotes are strict aerobes. They have an absolute requirement for oxygen because they require the high-ATP yield of oxidative phosphorylation.
- Facultative anaerobes can grow in the presence of oxygen and can grow in the absence of oxygen using fermentative pathways.
- Strict anaerobes cannot grow in the presence of oxygen.
- Although oxygen is required for aerobic life, paradoxically, oxygen is toxic to cells. Reactive oxygen species (ROS) are partially reduced forms of oxygen that can damage cells. The formation of ROS by the respiratory pathway is unavoidable (see Figure 6.24).
- Cells are protected from the toxicity of oxygen by both enzymatic and nonenzymatic antioxidants that detoxify ROS.

Questions

Self-Test Questions

1. Which of the following is found in organic molecules that are good fuels?
   a. many C—H bonds
   b. many C=C double bonds
   c. an abundance of oxygen
   d. a high molecular weight

2. Which of the following general statements about cellular respiration is correct?
   a. In cellular respiration oxygen is used as an electron donor.
   b. Since bacteria lack mitochondria, they do not perform cellular respiration.
   c. Cellular respiration represents a series of reactions in which a carbon substrate is oxidized.
   d. The carbon dioxide produced during cellular respiration can be used as an energy source for metabolism.

3. Which of the following processes occurs during glycolysis?
   a. the oxidation of pyruvate
   b. the reduction of glucose
   c. oxidative phosphorylation
   d. substrate-level phosphorylation

4. Which of the following is an accurate statement about the proton-motive force?
   a. It needs to be high to synthesize ATP during the citric acid cycle.
   b. If protons were uncharged, the proton-motive force would be zero.
   c. Along with multicellularity, it was a key development in eukaryotic cells.
   d. It represents the energy associated with a proton gradient across a membrane.

5. You are reading this text while breathing in oxygen and breathing out carbon dioxide. Which two processes are the sources of the carbon dioxide?
   a. glycolysis and pyruvate oxidation
   b. glycolysis and oxidative phosphorylation
   c. pyruvate oxidation and the citric acid cycle
   d. the citric acid cycle and oxidative phosphorylation

6. Under conditions of low oxygen, what key role is played by fermentation in overall metabolism?
   a. It regenerates the NAD^+ required for glycolysis.
   b. It synthesizes additional NADH for the citric acid cycle.
   c. It allows for pyruvate to be oxidized in mitochondria.
   d. By activating oxidative phosphorylation, it allows for the synthesis of extra ATP.

7. In cellular respiration, what does the term *uncoupled* specifically refer to?
   a. when the two parts of glycolysis are running independently of each other
   b. when respiratory electron transport is operating, but chemiosmosis is inhibited
   c. when respiratory electron transport is operating, but proton pumping is inhibited
   d. when oxidative phosphorylation is occurring, but the proton-motive force remains high

8. Phosphofructokinase (PFK) is regulated by a number of metabolites. Besides the ones mentioned in the text, which one of the following would also make sense?
   a. Pyruvate could function as an activator of PFK.
   b. Glucose could function as an inhibitor of PFK.
   c. ADP could function as an activator of PFK.
   d. Acetyl-CoA could act as an activator of PFK.

7

Bioreactors of algae being grown at the University of Arizona. Through the process of photosynthesis atmospheric CO_2 is being converted by these algae into a wide range of organic compounds. Some of these compounds are being studied for their feasibility as alternative energy sources (so-called biofuels).

Photosynthesis

WHY IT MATTERS

Renewable sources of energy, including solar and wind power, are meeting an ever-increasing proportion of global energy demands. Although this is good news, well over 90% of the world's energy still comes from the burning of nonrenewable reserves of coal, oil, and natural gas. The combustion of these sources of energy has been shown to be the major contributing factor to increasing atmospheric CO_2 concentrations and the acceleration of global climate change over the past 100 years.

Coal, oil, and natural gas are referred to as "fossil fuels" because they are in fact the remnants of ancient forests—formed by geological processes over millions of years. The organic carbon compounds that are burned were formed in these ancient plants through the process of photosynthesis.

In recent years, harnessing photosynthesis to generate renewable fuels has been a major aspect of the biofuel industry. Unlike coal and oil, biofuels are produced by living organisms through processes such as fermentation and photosynthesis. Biofuels include ethanol and a variety of oils that can be used, for example, to generate jet fuel.

One source of photosynthetically generated biofuels that is being intensively studied is single-celled algae grown in artificial lakes or bioreactors (small bioreactors are shown above). Culturing algae offers numerous advantages over crop plants, the traditional source of most oils. Algae grow very rapidly, and the extraction of oils is often easier than it is from plants. In addition, cultivating algae would preserve precious arable land that could be dedicated to growing food crops.

There remain a number of issues surrounding the wide implementation of algae and biofuel production. The costs associated with growing algae on a large scale are high, while the yield of oil needs to increase for it to be economically feasible. Such issues need to be addressed if biofuels are to make a serious dent in our current dependence on fossil fuels.

The focus of this chapter is photosynthesis—the process by which light energy is used to convert carbon dioxide into organic molecules. The chapter starts by laying out the basic chemistry of photosynthesis focusing on the photophysical nature of light and light absorption. This adds to the more cursory treatment of light that is found in Chapter 1. Details of the two stages of photosynthesis—the light reactions and the Calvin cycle—follow, as does a discussion of how various photosynthetic organisms have evolved mechanisms to cope with a surprising attribute of the carbon-fixing enzyme rubisco. The chapter ends with an important section on comparing photosynthesis with the topic of the previous chapter, cellular respiration.

Figure 7.1
Examples of photoautotrophs.

7.1 Photosynthesis: An Overview

Photosynthesis is the use of light energy to convert carbon dioxide into organic compounds such as carbohydrates. We define an organic compound as one that contains one or more C—H bonds. Because they do not need to import already-formed organic compounds from the environment, photosynthetic organisms are called **autotrophs** (*auto* = self, *trophos* = feeding). They are more narrowly defined as **photoautotrophs** because the energy to drive the conversion of carbon dioxide into an organic form comes from light. Some organisms are autotrophic but don't use light as the energy source; instead they use compounds such as hydrogen sulfide (H_2S) and ferrous iron (Fe^{2+}). This type of metabolism is found only in some bacteria and archaeans and is termed chemoautotrophy.

Photoautotrophic organisms are known as Earth's **primary producers (Figure 7.1)**. This is because they represent the major group of organisms that generate the organic compounds that are used by other organisms—the consumers, the organisms that that live by eating plants or other animals. Eventually, the bodies of both primary producers and consumers provide the organic energy-rich molecules to support a range of **decomposers**, such as a range of bacteria and all fungi. Recall from Chapter 3 that consumers and decomposers are classified as heterotrophs because they require an already-synthesized source of organic molecules to live.

As mentioned in Chapter 3, photosynthesis is an ancient process that evolved in bacteria perhaps as early as 2.5 billion years ago. Interestingly, today photosynthesis is found in the domains Bacteria and Eukarya but is not present in the Archaea. Some archaeans, such as the Halobacteria (see Chapter 1),

do harvest light energy and convert it into chemical energy, but since this light energy is not used to convert carbon dioxide into an organic form, Halobacteria are not considered to be photosynthetic.

7.1a Photosynthesis Is an Oxidation–Reduction Process

If you studied photosynthesis in high school biology, one thing you probably memorized was the balanced chemical equation for the overall process, which is

$$6CO_2 + 12H_2O \rightarrow C_6H_{12}O_6 + 6O_2 + 6H_2O \quad (7.1)$$

As chemical equations go this seems pretty straightforward, but let's deconstruct it to see what's really going on. Taking the reaction as written, you could say that water is reacting with CO_2 (it's hydrating the carbon) to produce a six-carbon carbohydrate glucose, with O_2 and H_2O produced as by-products. As we will discuss later in the chapter, glucose is technically not the direct product of the Calvin cycle but is made soon after and so is used here for convenience. Notice from equation (7.1) that equal molar amounts of the gases CO_2 and O_2 are consumed and produced, respectively. This means that one can measure the rate of photosynthesis as either the rate at which CO_2 is consumed or the rate at which O_2 is produced or evolved.

What may not be clear to you yet is that equation 7.1 is a classic example of a oxidation–reduction or redox reaction. This type of reaction was introduced in Chapter 6, Section 6.1. To make it easy to see its redox nature let's put the equation in its simplest form by dividing through by six, giving

$$CO_2 + 2H_2O \rightarrow (CH_2O) + O_2 + H_2O \quad (7.2)$$

where the term (CH_2O) is the basic unit of a carbohydrate consisting of carbon, hydrogen, and oxygen atoms in the ratio 1C:2H:1O. A molecule of glucose is therefore six units, $(CH_2O)_6$.

Like all redox reactions, equation 7.2 is actually two half-reactions: one oxidation reaction is coupled to a reduction reaction. In equation (7.2) it is the water that is being oxidized to O_2. Removing electrons from water is not easy, and in photosynthesis it involves energy that comes from light:

$$2H_2O + \text{light energy} \rightarrow O_2 + 4H^+ + 4e^-$$

In equation (7.2), it is the CO_2 that is being reduced to carbohydrate:

$$CO_2 + 4H^+ + 4e^- \rightarrow (CH_2O) + H_2O$$

Looking back at equation (7.1), you could easily assume that the water is reacting directly with the carbon dioxide to produce the carbohydrate and cause O_2 release. As we will see in the next section, the oxidation of H_2O and the reduction of carbon dioxide are associated with distinctly different processes that are spatially separated within the chloroplast.

7.1b Photosynthesis Can Be Divided into the Light Reactions and the Calvin Cycle

The conversion of carbon dioxide into carbohydrates that defines photosynthesis requires the integration of two distinct processes **(Figure 7.2)**: the light reactions and the Calvin cycle. The light reactions involve the capture of light energy by pigment molecules and the utilization of that energy to synthesize both NADPH (nicotinamide adenine dinucleotide phosphate) and ATP. The electrons needed to reduce NADP$^+$ to NADPH come from the oxidation of H_2O, resulting in the release of O_2 (Figure 7.2). In the Calvin cycle, the electrons and protons carried by NADPH and the energy of ATP hydrolysis are used to convert

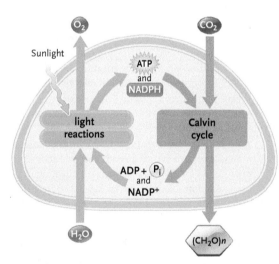

Figure 7.2

The light reactions and the Calvin cycle are the two stages of photosynthesis. The two are linked by reactants and products. Both processes occur in the chloroplasts of photoautotrophic eukaryotes (plants and algae) as well as in photosynthetic bacteria.

CO_2 into carbohydrate. This reduction reaction, referred to as *carbon fixation* or *CO_2 fixation*, is a reduction reaction with electrons (and protons) being added to CO_2.

It is important to realize that the carbohydrate synthesized by the Calvin cycle ends up being used for a huge range of processes. Besides sugars like glucose being a useful source of energy for cellular respiration, the carbohydrates also represent the source of the carbon skeletons used in the biosynthesis of a huge range of other molecules including lipids, amino acids, and nucleotides. In fact, one can consider all the organic molecules present in organisms as direct or indirect products of photosynthesis.

7.1c In Eukaryotes, Photosynthesis Takes Place in Chloroplasts

In photosynthetic eukaryotes, both the light reactions and the Calvin cycle take place within the chloroplast, an organelle that is comprised of three membranes that define three distinct compartments **(Figure 7.3)**. An *outer membrane* covers the entire surface of the organelle, whereas an *inner membrane* lies just inside the outer membrane. Between the outer and inner membranes is the *intermembrane space*. The aqueous environment within the inner membrane is the *stroma* of the chloroplast. Within the stroma is the third membrane system, the *thylakoid membranes*, or thylakoids, which often form flattened, closed sacs. The space enclosed by a thylakoid is called the *thylakoid lumen*.

Embedded within the thylakoid membrane are the components that carry out the light reactions of photosynthesis: proteins, pigments, electron transport carriers, and ATP synthase. The enzymes that catalyze the reactions of the Calvin cycle are found in the stroma of the chloroplast.

A number of phyla of bacteria, including the cyanobacteria, have thylakoid membranes that are formed from infoldings of the plasma membrane and carry out carbon fixation in the cytosol of the cell. In most ways, photosynthesis carried out in cyanobacteria is biochemically identical to that found in the chloroplasts of plant leaves and is part of the evidence that indicates that chloroplasts are descended from free-living cyanobacteria (see Chapter 3).

7.1d Photosynthesis from a Global Perspective

The importance of photosynthesis to life on Earth is perhaps best appreciated by getting a global perspective. A sensor onboard the OrbView-2 satellite can detect visible light at Earth's surface, including the green wavelengths that are reflected by chlorophyll, the primary photosynthetic pigment. This gives an unprecedented global estimate of both the abundance and distribution of photosynthetic organisms **(Figure 7.4, p. 148)**. Along with other information, scientists have used the satellite data to estimate that a staggering 11×10^{13} kg of CO_2 is fixed through photosynthesis each year.

While we often think about photosynthesis in terms of plants and trees, about half of the carbon is fixed by unicellular photosynthetic algae called phytoplankton that inhabit marine environments. Looking carefully at the global distribution in the oceans (Figure 7.4, p. 148), notice that phytoplankton are more abundant around the poles than they are nearer the equator. This may seem odd because the oceans near the equator receive more sunlight and are warmer. In fact, the distribution of phytoplankton is explained by the abundance of nutrients: the oceans around the equator tend to be nutrient poor, while the cold waters around the Arctic and Antarctic are nutrient rich and thus can support large phytoplankton communities.

The nutrient that limits phytoplankton growth in temperate regions of the oceans is iron. As a cofactor of many enzymes and a redox component of electron transport chains (ETCs), iron is required by most organisms in relatively high amounts. The realization that primary productivity in much of the ocean is limited by iron has spurred experiments that have seen small areas of the Pacific Ocean being fertilized with iron. These fertilized regions have seen rapid increases in phytoplankton growth. The widespread addition of iron to marine environments is seen by some as one way to combat climate change. Because climate change is associated, in part, with increased atmospheric CO_2 concentrations, increased photosynthesis in the ocean could help draw down this CO_2.

STUDY BREAK

1. Differentiate between autotroph and heterotroph; photoautotroph and chemoautotroph.
2. Define *carbon fixation*.
3. What explains the low chlorophyll concentration in the warm waters of the Pacific Ocean?

7.2 The Photosynthetic Apparatus

The photosynthetic apparatus is a series of large protein complexes found in the thylakoid membrane that are responsible for the light reactions. Central to these are two complexes built around proteins that bind pigment molecules that result in light absorption. These **photosystems** lead to the conversion of light energy into chemical energy in the initial reactions of photosynthesis.

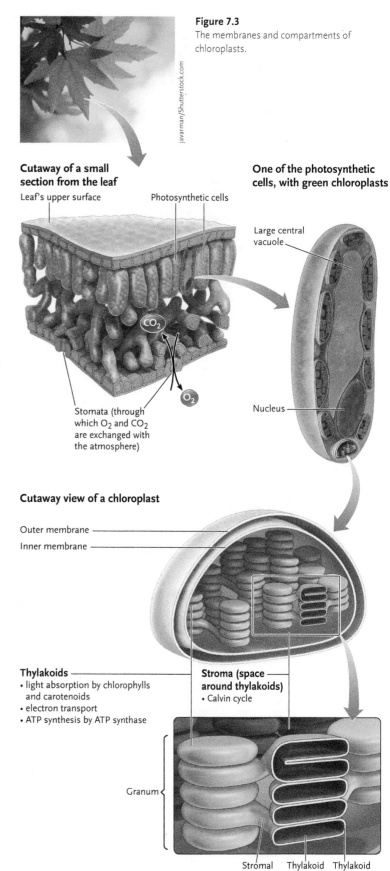

Figure 7.3
The membranes and compartments of chloroplasts.

javarman/Shutterstock.com

Cutaway of a small section from the leaf
Leaf's upper surface
Photosynthetic cells
CO_2
O_2
Stomata (through which O_2 and CO_2 are exchanged with the atmosphere)

One of the photosynthetic cells, with green chloroplasts
Large central vacuole
Nucleus

Cutaway view of a chloroplast
Outer membrane
Inner membrane

Thylakoids
• light absorption by chlorophylls and carotenoids
• electron transport
• ATP synthesis by ATP synthase

Stroma (space around thylakoids)
• Calvin cycle

Granum

Stromal lamella
Thylakoid lumen
Thylakoid membrane

Figure 7.4
Global oceanic and terrestrial photoautotroph abundance can be estimated by the satellite detection of chlorophyll at the Earth's surface. Data collected by NASA's SeaWiFS sensor onboard the OrbView-2 satellite.

7.2a Electrons in Pigment Molecules Absorb Light Energy

Photosynthesis requires the capture and utilization of light energy. As we did in Chapter 1, we can define light as that portion of the electromagnetic spectrum that humans can detect with their eyes **(Figure 7.5)**. The various forms of radiation that make up the electromagnetic spectrum differ in wavelength, ranging from very long radio waves, which have wavelengths in the

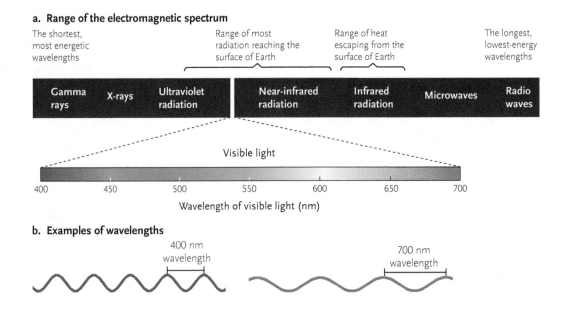

Figure 7.5
The electromagnetic spectrum. **(a)** The electromagnetic spectrum ranges from gamma rays to radio waves; visible light, which includes the wavelengths used for photosynthesis, occupies only a narrow band of the spectrum. **(b)** Examples of wavelengths, showing the difference between the longest and shortest wavelengths of visible light.

range of 10 m to hundreds of kilometres, to gamma rays, which have wavelengths in the range of one hundredth to one millionth of a nanometre. The electromagnetic radiation that humans can detect (light or visible light) has wavelengths between about 400 nm, seen as blue light, and 700 nm, seen as red light (see Figure 7.5).

Although light can be described using the concept of a wave moving through space, the interaction of light with matter is best understood in terms of discrete packets of energy called photons (also called *quanta*). A photon of light contains a fixed amount of energy that is inversely related to its wavelength: the shorter the wavelength, the greater the amount of energy that photons of that wavelength contain. So, for example, the energy of a photon of blue light is greater than the energy found in a red photon of light.

To be used as a source of energy, photons of light must be absorbed by a molecule **(Figure 7.6a)**. Absorption occurs when the energy of a photon is transferred to an electron within a molecule, moving the electron from the ground state to an excited state. In the excited state, the electron is farther away from the nucleus and thus it contains more energy. A major class of molecules that are very efficient at absorbing visible light are pigments because their structure results in a number of excitable electrons. The structures of a diversity of pigments are presented in Chapter 1, Figure 1.5.

After a pigment molecule absorbs a photon of light, one of three possible events can occur (Figure 7.6).

1. The excited electron from the pigment molecule returns to its ground state, releasing its energy either as heat or as an emission of light of a longer wavelength—a process called *fluorescence*.
2. The energy of the excited electron (but not the electron itself) is transferred to a neighbouring pigment molecule. This transfer of energy excites an electron in the second molecule, while the electron in the first pigment molecule returns to its ground state. Very little energy is lost in this energy transfer.
3. The excited electron is transferred from the pigment molecule to a nearby electron-accepting molecule.

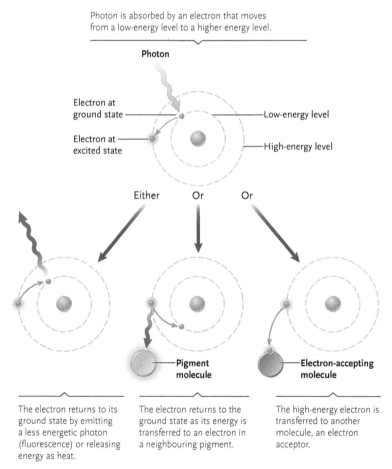

Photon is absorbed by an electron that moves from a low-energy level to a higher energy level.

Photon

Electron at ground state — Low-energy level

Electron at excited state — High-energy level

Either   Or   Or

Pigment molecule   Electron-accepting molecule

The electron returns to its ground state by emitting a less energetic photon (fluorescence) or releasing energy as heat.

The electron returns to the ground state as its energy is transferred to an electron in a neighbouring pigment.

The high-energy electron is transferred to another molecule, an electron acceptor.

Figure 7.6
Three possible fates of an excited-state electron within a pigment molecule.

7.2b Chlorophylls and Carotenoids Cooperate in Light Absorption

In photosynthesis, light is absorbed by molecules of green pigments called chlorophylls and yellow-orange pigments called carotenoids. Chlorophylls are the major photosynthetic pigments in plants, green algae, and cyanobacteria. Of the chlorophylls, the most dominant types are chlorophyll *a* and *b*, which are structurally only slightly different **(Figure 7.7, p. 150)**.

One can precisely determine the wavelengths of light absorbed by a pigment such as chlorophyll *a* by producing an absorption spectrum for that pigment using an instrument called a spectrophotometer and a pure sample of the pigment. An **absorption spectrum** is a plot of the absorption of light as a function of wavelength. **Figure 7.8a, p. 150,** shows that chlorophyll *a* strongly absorbs blue and red light but does not absorb green or yellow light. Why doesn't chlorophyll absorb green or yellow light? Recall from Chapter 1 that for a photon of light to be

a. Chlorophyll structure

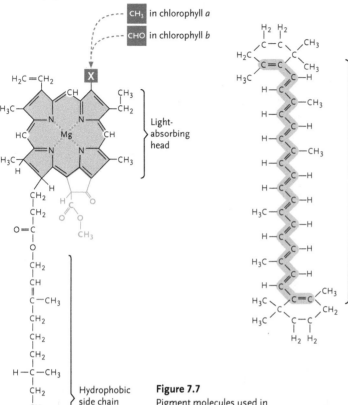

CH₃ in chlorophyll *a*

CHO in chlorophyll *b*

Light-absorbing head

Hydrophobic side chain

b. Carotenoid structure

Light-absorbing region

Figure 7.7

Pigment molecules used in photosynthesis. **(a)** Chlorophylls *a* and *b*, which differ only in the side group attached at the X. **(b)** An example of a carotenoid. In both (a) and (b), the light-absorbing electrons are distributed among the bonds shaded in orange.

effectiveness of light of particular wavelengths in driving a process (Figure 7.8b). An action spectrum for photosynthesis is usually determined by using a suspension of chloroplasts or algal cells and measuring the amount of O_2 released by photosynthesis at different wavelengths of visible light.

One of the earliest action spectra was produced in 1883 by Theodor Engelmann, who used only a light microscope and a glass prism to determine which wavelengths of light were most effective for photosynthesis **(Figure 7.9)**. Engelmann placed a strand of a green alga, *Spirogyra*, on a glass microscope slide, along with water containing aerobic bacteria. He adjusted the prism so that it split a beam of light into its separate colours, which spread like a rainbow across the strand (see Figure 7.9).

a. The absorption spectra of chlorophylls *a* and *b* and carotenoids

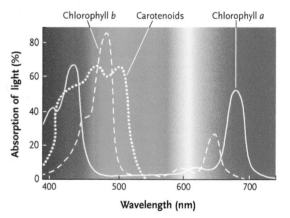

b. The action spectrum in higher plants, representing the combined effects of chlorophylls and carotenoids

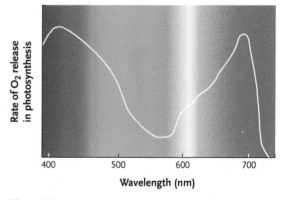

Figure 7.8

The absorption spectra of three photosynthetic pigments **(a)** and the action spectrum of photosynthesis **(b)** in plants. The absorption spectra in (a) were made from pigments that were extracted from cells and purified.

absorbed, the energy of that photon needs to match the amount of energy required to raise a pigment electron from the ground state to an excited state. If the energies do not match, then the photon is not absorbed. Chlorophyll has really only two excited states: one that matches the energy of a blue photon and one that matches that of a red photon.

The absorption spectra of the accessory pigments (chlorophyll *b* and carotenoids; see Figure 7.8a) illustrate that these pigments expand the wavelengths of light that can be effectively captured and used for photosynthesis. Figure 7.8a illustrates that the slight differences in structure between chlorophyll *a* and chlorophyll *b* are reflected in differences in their absorption spectra.

Photosynthesis depends on the absorption of light by chlorophylls and carotenoids, acting in combination. This is supported by the **action spectrum** for photosynthesis. An action spectrum is a plot of the

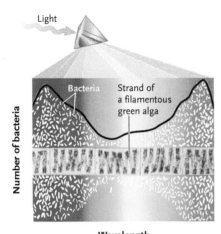

Figure 7.9
Engelmann's experiment revealed the action spectrum of light used in photosynthesis by *Spirogyra*, a green alga. The aerobic bacteria clustered along the algal strand in the regions where oxygen was released in greatest quantity—the regions in which photosynthesis proceeded at the greatest rate. Those regions corresponded to the colours (wavelengths) of light being absorbed most effectively by the alga—in this case, blue and red.

After a short time, he noticed that the bacteria had begun to cluster around the algal strand in different locations. The largest clusters were under the blue and violet light at one end of the strand and the red light at the other end. Very few bacteria were found in the green light.

7.2c Photosynthetic Pigments Are Organized into Photosystems

Photosynthetic pigments are required not only to absorb photons of light but also to transfer the energy to neighbouring molecules. To do this efficiently, pigment molecules do not float freely within the thylakoid membrane but rather are bound very precisely to specific proteins. These pigment-proteins are organized within the thylakoid membrane into complexes called photosystems **(Figure 7.10)**. Each photosystem is composed of a large **antenna complex** (also called a *light-harvesting complex*) of pigment-proteins that surrounds a central *reaction centre*. The reaction centre of a photosystem comprises a small number of proteins that bind a special chlorophyll *a* molecule and an electron-accepting molecule called the *primary electron acceptor* (Figure 7.10).

The function of a photosystem is to trap photons of light and use the energy to oxidize a reaction centre chlorophyll, with the electron being transferred to the primary electron acceptor. High rates of this oxidation–reduction reaction within the reaction centre are achieved by the large antenna complex

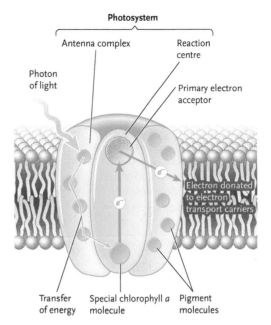

Figure 7.10
Major components of a photosystem. A group of pigment proteins form an antenna complex that surrounds a reaction centre. Light energy absorbed anywhere in the antenna complex is transferred to a special chlorophyll *a* molecule in the reaction centre. The absorbed light is converted to chemical energy when an excited electron from the chlorophyll *a* is transferred to a primary acceptor, also in the reaction centre. High-energy electrons are passed out of the photosystem to the electron transport system. The yellow arrow shows the migration of energy from one pigment to the other, while the blue arrows show movement of electrons.

of pigments absorbing light of a range of wavelengths and efficiently transferring the energy to the **reaction centre.**

There are two different types of photosystems: photosystem I and photosystem II. The specialized chlorophyll *a* in the reaction centre of **photosystem I** is called P700 (P = pigment) because its absorption maximum is at a wavelength of 700 nm. The reaction centre of **photosystem II** contains a specialized chlorophyll *a*, P680, which absorbs light maximally at 680 nm. Within a single leaf chloroplast there are thousands of photosystems (both I and II) each containing about 500 chlorophyll molecules.

STUDY BREAK

1. What contains more energy, a photon of green light or a photon of orange light?
2. What are the three possible fates of an excited-state electron?
3. How is an absorption spectrum different from an action spectrum?

The D1 Protein Keeps Photosystem II Operating

Photosystem II can be considered the most important development in the evolution of life on Earth. Unlike anything that came before it, photosystem II meant that organisms that had it could harvest the energy of the Sun and use it to extract electrons from water. These electrons were used to convert CO_2 from the atmosphere into the organic building blocks of the cell. This ability to use water meant that life could thrive almost anywhere on the planet and led to an explosion in the conversion of CO_2 into organic molecules. By splitting water, photosystem II also produced O_2, which gradually accumulated in the atmosphere and led to the development of aerobic respiration. The process of aerobic respiration extracts 18 times as much energy from sugar as the anaerobic pathway that came before it, resulting in an energy bounty that allowed the emergence of complex,

multicellular eukaryotic organisms. Because of this, photosystem II is known as the engine of life.

The splitting of water by photosystem II is the most energetically demanding reaction in all of biology. The reaction is carried out by a molecule, P680, that is found in the core of photosystem II, bound to a protein called D1. When photosystem II absorbs light, P680 is converted into the strongest known biological oxidant, $P680^+$, and this molecule is able to break apart H_2O, releasing electrons, protons, and O_2.

As a consequence of absorbing the energy of about 10 thousand photons every second and generating powerful oxidants, photosystem II is constantly being damaged, which results in its inactivation. The major site of damage is the D1 protein, which is found in the core of the complex and binds P680. Over the course of 2 billion years of

evolution, organisms that have photosystem II have been unable to prevent the damage from occurring—but they have developed a highly specialized mechanism to repair it.

It takes only 20 minutes for a newly synthesized photosystem II complex to stop working because of damage to D1. However, damaged complexes are rapidly disassembled, the damaged D1 protein is removed and degraded, a newly synthesized D1 protein is inserted, and a functional photosystem is reassembled. This repair cycle is very efficient and depends on a high rate of D1 protein synthesis. It has been estimated that in the absence of this repair system, damage to photosystem II would lower the photosynthetic productivity of the planet by 95%. Thus, life on Earth could not have evolved to present-day levels of both abundance and complexity in the absence of a D1 repair mechanism.

7.3 The Light Reactions

Photosystem I and photosystem II are the two light-trapping components involved in photosynthetic electron transport. In this section, we look in detail at how this particular electron transport chain operates and draw some analogies to respiratory electron transport.

7.3a Photosynthetic Electron Transport Synthesizes NADPH and Generates a Proton Gradient

Figure 7.11, p. 153, shows the components of photosynthetic electron transport and the ATP synthase complex within the thylakoid membrane. As in all electron transport systems, the electron carriers of the photosynthetic system consist of nonprotein cofactors that alternate between being oxidized and being reduced as electrons move through the system (see Chapter 6). The carriers, many of which are bound precisely to proteins, include the same types that act in mitochondrial electron transfer—cytochromes, quinones, and iron–sulfur centres.

Most of the electron carriers are organized into three large complexes embedded in the thylakoid membrane: photosystem II, the cytochrome complex, and photosystem I. Electron flow between photosystem II

and the cytochrome complex is facilitated by a pool of plastoquinone (PQ) molecules, which are similar in structure and function to the ubiquinone of respiratory electron transport. Electron flow from the cytochrome complex to photosystem I is linked by the mobile copper-containing protein plastocyanin.

From photosystem I, electrons are donated to an iron–sulfur protein called ferredoxin, which in turn donates electrons to the enzyme $NADP^+$ reductase found on the stromal side of the thylakoid membrane. The enzyme reduces $NADP^+$ to NADPH by using two electrons from electron transport and a proton from the surrounding aqueous environment.

7.3b Light Is Used Specifically to Oxidize Chlorophyll

Just like respiratory electron transport (Chapter 6), photosynthetic electron transport operates with electrons flowing spontaneously from molecules that are easily oxidized to molecules that are progressively more easily reduced. In the case of mitochondrial electron transport, recall that flow is from NADH, which is a source of electrons, to O_2, which has a very high affinity for electrons. In photosynthesis, electron transport occurs by the same principle; however, unlike NADH, the chlorophyll molecules in the

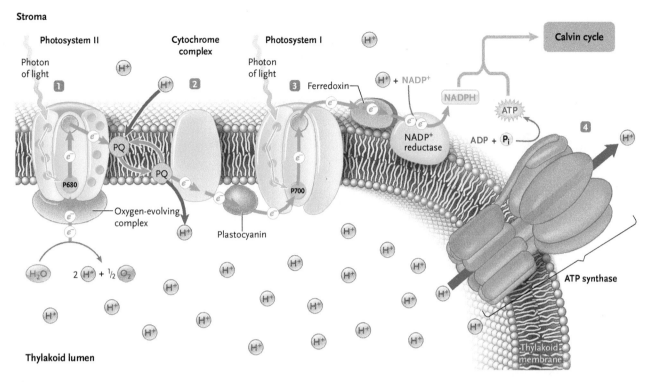

Stroma

Photosystem II · Cytochrome complex · Photosystem I · Calvin cycle

Photon of light · **1**

H^+ · **2**

Photon of light · **3** · Ferredoxin

H^+ + NADP$^+$

NADPH · ATP

NADP$^+$ reductase

ADP + P$_i$ · **4**

H^+

PQ · PQ · P680 · P700

Oxygen-evolving complex · Plastocyanin

H_2O · 2 H^+ + ¹/₂ O_2

ATP synthase

Thylakoid lumen · Thylakoid membrane

Figure 7.11
A model of the eukaryotic thylakoid membrane illustrating the major protein and redox cofactors required for photosynthetic electron transport and ATP synthesis.

1 Absorption of light energy by photosystem II results in the oxidation of P680. The released electron reduces the primary acceptor molecule. P680$^+$ is returned to the reduced state (P680) by donation of an electron from water, a process mediated by the oxygen-evolving complex.

2 From the primary acceptor, the electron is passed to the mobile carrier molecule plastoquinone (PQ). As it accepts an electron from photosystem II, PQ picks up a proton from the stroma. PQ diffuses through the membrane before binding to the cytochrome complex, at which point it donates an electron and releases a proton into the thylakoid lumen. From the cytochrome complex the electron is donated to plastocyanin.

3 Absorption of light energy by photosystem I results in the oxidation of P700. The liberated electron is used to reduce the primary acceptor before being passed to ferredoxin. This single electron is then held by the NADP$^+$ reductase complex. P700$^+$ is reduced back to P700 by the electron that is coming from plastocyanin. Once a second electron travels along the chain and reaches NADP$^+$ reductase complex, NADP$^+$ is reduced to NADPH.

4 Proton movement by the reduction–oxidation of plastoquinone (red arrows) creates a concentration gradient of H$^+$ (a proton-motive force) across the thylakoid membrane. The gradient is dissipated as H$^+$ diffuses back into the stroma through the ATP synthase complex, which drives the synthesis of ATP from ADP and P$_i$.

reaction centres of photosystem II and photosystem I are not easily oxidized. So what process gets a chlorophyll molecule into a state in which it readily gives up an electron? The absorption of a photon of light within photosystem II and photosystem I and the funnelling of this high energy to the reaction centre is used to excite an electron within P680 or P700 **(Figure 7.12, p. 154)**. By raising an electron in P680 to a higher excited state (denoted as P680*), the absorption of light energy produces a molecule that is easily oxidized by the ETC, and electron flow is a spontaneous process from P680* to photosystem I. A second photon of light absorbed by photosystem I results in the formation of P700*, which is easily oxidized by the primary electron acceptor of photosystem I, and in turn ferredoxin, before the electron finally being donated to NADP$^+$

(see Figure 7.12). Oxidized P680 (P680$^+$) is reduced by electrons donated from water (Figure 7.11), while P700$^+$ is reduced back to P700 by electrons coming from PSII.

7.3c In the Light Reactions, ATP Is Generated by Chemiosmosis

In a way analogous to respiratory electron transport, the flow of electrons along the photosynthetic ETC is coupled to ATP synthesis by the build-up of a proton gradient. In photosynthetic electron transport, the proton gradient across the thylakoid membrane is derived from three processes (see Figure 7.11). First, protons are translocated into the lumen by the cyclic reduction and oxidation of plastoquinone as it migrates

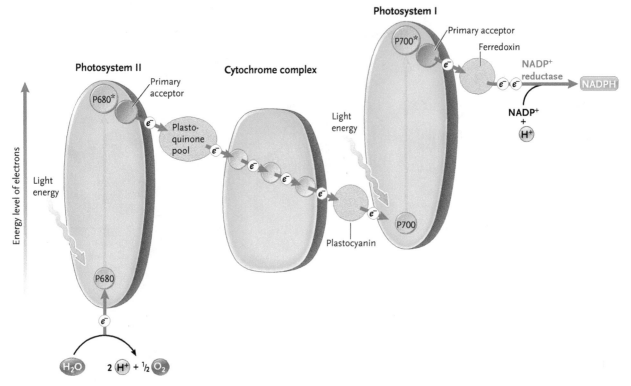

Figure 7.12

The components of the thylakoid membrane organized according to their energy level. This is also referred to as the Z scheme. When photosystem II absorbs a photon of light, an electron within the reaction centre chlorophyll of P680 gets excited to a higher energy level (P680*). This results in spontaneous electron transport to photosystem I. However, the energy level of $NADP^+$ is greater than that of P700. This energy difference is overcome by photosystem I absorbing a photon of light, producing P700*. Thus, two photons of light, one absorbed by photosystem II and another absorbed by photosystem I, are required to overcome the energy difference between H_2O and $NADP^+$.

from photosystem II to the cytochrome complex and back again. Second, the gradient is enhanced by the addition of two protons to the lumen from the oxidation of water, which occurs on the luminal side of photosystem II. Third, the removal of one proton from the stroma for each NADPH molecule synthesized further decreases the H^+ concentration in the stroma, thereby enhancing the gradient across the thylakoid membrane. The proton-motive force (see Section 6.5) established across the thylakoid membrane is used to synthesize ATP by chemiosmosis using the chloroplast ATP synthase. This multiprotein complex is structurally and functionally analogous to the ATP synthase used in oxidative phosphorylation in cellular respiration (see Figure 6.16, Chapter 6). Distinct from oxidative phosphorylation in cellular respiration, the process of using light to generate ATP is often referred to as **photophosphorylation**.

7.3d The Stoichiometry of Linear Electron Transport

We have described in detail the structure and function of the photosynthetic apparatus. Now it's time to go over the stoichiometry of the light reactions. To get a

single electron down the ETC from photosystem II (or water; it doesn't matter) to $NADP^+$ takes two photons of light, one photon absorbed by photosystem II and a second by photosystem I. Figure 7.12 shows this. But how many photons need to be absorbed by the photosynthetic apparatus to produce a single molecule of O_2? For all of these types of questions, we start by writing out a balanced chemical reaction, such as

$$2H_2O \rightarrow 4H^+ + 4e^- + O_2$$

The reaction shows that to produce one molecule of O_2 you need to oxidize two molecules of water, which results in the release of four electrons. Now to move a single electron down the ETC requires the absorption of two photons. It follows then that to get four electrons from photosystem II to $NADP^+$, the photosynthetic apparatus needs to absorb a total of eight photons of light, four by each photosystem.

7.3e Cyclic Electron Transport Generates ATP in the Absence of NADPH

The pathway of electron flow from photosystem II through photosystem I to synthesize NADPH is referred to as linear electron transport. Although this

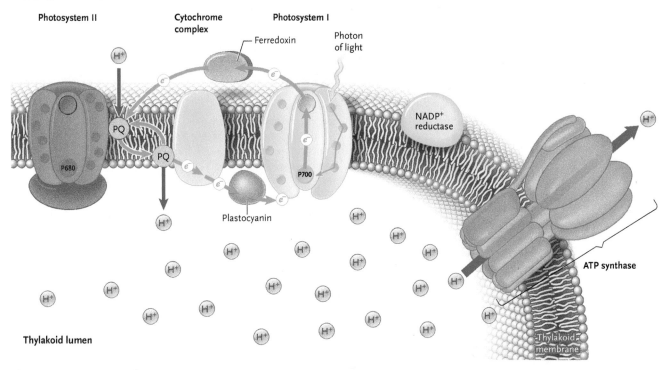

Stroma

Photosystem II

Cytochrome complex

Photosystem I

Ferredoxin

Photon of light

$NADP^+$ reductase

PQ

P680

PQ

Plastocyanin

P700

ATP synthase

Thylakoid membrane

Thylakoid lumen

Figure 7.13
Cyclic electron transport. Electrons move in a circular pathway from photosystem I through ferredoxin back to the plastoquinone pool, through the cytochrome complex and plastocyanin and then back to photosystem I. In cyclic electron transport, photosystem II does not operate. The pathway generates proton pumping and thus leads to ATP production but does not result in the synthesis of NADPH.

is the pathway of electron flow that occurs most often, photosystem I can function independently of photosystem II in what is called **cyclic electron transport (Figure 7.13).** In this process, electron flow from photosystem I to ferredoxin is not followed by electron donation to the $NADP^+$ reductase complex. Instead, reduced ferredoxin donates electrons back to the plastoquinone pool. In this manner, the plastoquinone pool gets continually reduced and oxidized and keeps moving protons across the thylakoid membrane without the involvement of electrons coming from photosystem II. Overall, cyclic electron transport only involves light absorption by photosystem I, with the energy being used to establish a proton-motive force and generate ATP. Unlike linear electron transport, NADPH is not formed during cyclic electron transport.

Cyclic electron transport plays an important role in overall photosynthesis. The reduction of carbon dioxide by the Calvin cycle requires more ATP than NADPH, and the additional ATP molecules are provided by cyclic electron transport. Other energy-requiring reactions in the chloroplast also depend on ATP produced by the cyclic pathway.

STUDY BREAK

1. In which compartment of the chloroplast is NADPH generated?
2. How is the proton gradient across the thylakoid membrane established during electron transport?
3. How many photons of light are required to generate one molecule of NADPH by linear electron transport?

7.4 The Calvin Cycle

Recall from Chapter 6 that carbon dioxide is a fully oxidized carbon molecule and contains no usable energy. On the other hand, carbohydrate molecules such as glucose and sucrose are an abundant source of energy because they contain many C—H bonds (see Chapter 6). In the cytosol of photosynthetic bacteria and in the stroma of the chloroplast, a series of 11 enzyme-catalyzed reactions use NADPH to reduce CO_2 into sugar. The overall process is endergonic, requiring energy supplied by ATP. These 11 enzyme-catalyzed

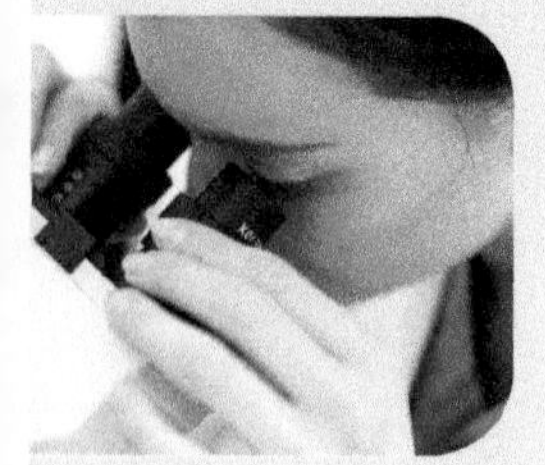

PEOPLE BEHIND BIOLOGY 7.2

Norm Hüner, *Western University*

A number of advances to our understanding of the regulation of photosynthesis have been elucidated by the research group of Norm Hüner, who holds a Tier 1 Canada Research Chair in Environmental Stress Biology at the Western University in London, Ontario.

Hüner's research has established that the photosynthetic apparatus has a dual role: not only does it function as the primary energy transformer of the biosphere, but it also acts as a sensor of environmental change in all photoautotrophs. Using a range of organisms, including plants, green algae, and cyanobacteria, Hüner's group has discovered that the relative redox state of photosynthetic electron transport acts as a natural sensor of the balance between energy input from the Sun and the demands for that energy by the metabolic processes of the organism. The redox state of the photosynthetic apparatus can be readily assessed by measuring the *excitation pressure* on photosystem II using a fluorescence-based technique. Hüner's group has shown that changes in excitation pressure are a key trigger that initiates changes in a number of cellular processes, including gene expression, which enable photoautotrophs to readily acclimate to changes in light, temperature, and nutrient availability.

Hüner is the coauthor of an internationally acclaimed textbook entitled *Introduction to Plant Physiology*, which is currently in its fourth edition. As well, he has received more than 25 national and international awards and honours for his research, which include election as a fellow of the Academy of Science, Royal Society of Canada, and president of the Canadian Society of Plant Physiologists; an honorary degree from the University of Umea, Sweden; and an honorary professorship from Xinjiang University, China.

In recent years, Hüner has been the lead investigator in the establishment of the Biotron Experimental Climate Change Research Centre, an international research facility on the campus of Western University. The research focus of this $30 million facility is the elucidation of the mechanisms by which plants, microbes, and insects sense and adjust to climate change. One of the unique aspects of the Biotron is that it gives researchers the ability to conduct control experiments on a much larger scale than possible in a conventional laboratory. This allows for the study of how changes in temperature, light, nutrients, and carbon dioxide concentrations may affect the growth of not only individual species but also entire ecosystems.

reactions are collectively known as the Calvin cycle (or **light-independent reactions**), which is the most common pathway on Earth by which carbon dioxide is transformed into carbohydrates.

7.4a The Calvin Cycle Reduces Carbon Dioxide to a Carbohydrate

Like other metabolic cycles, including the citric acid cycle, the Calvin cycle generates products that are removed but it also requires that molecules be regenerated so that cycling can continue.

During each turn of the Calvin cycle, one molecule of CO_2 is converted into one reduced carbon—essentially one (CH_2O) unit of carbohydrate. To help you better understand the Calvin cycle, **Figure 7.14,** represents a summary of what occurs following three turns of the cycle. It is only after three carbon dioxide molecules get reduced that one actually generates a separate molecule—a three-carbon sugar glyceraldehyde-3-phosphate (G3P). By a reaction that is not part of the Calvin cycle, two molecules of G3P can synthesize one molecule of the six-carbon sugar glucose.

As shown in Figure 7.14, the Calvin cycle can be subdivided into three distinct phases: fixation, reduction, and regeneration. The events that take place in each of these phases during *one* turn of the cycle are as follows:

Phase 1: Fixation. This phase involves the incorporation (i.e., fixing) of a carbon atom from CO_2 (one per turn) into one molecule of the five-carbon sugar ribulose-1,5-bisphosphate (RuBP) to produce two molecules of the three-carbon compound 3-phosphoglycerate.

Phase 2: Reduction. In this phase, each molecule of 3-phosphoglycerate gets an additional phosphate added from the breakdown of ATP. This produces a total of two molecules of 1,3-bisphosphoglycerate. Each of these molecules is subsequently reduced by electrons from NADPH, producing a molecule of G3P.

Phase 3: Regeneration. For each turn of the Calvin cycle, two molecules of G3P are produced—a total of six carbon atoms. In a multistep process, five of these carbons are rearranged to regenerate the single molecule of RuBP required for the next round of carbon fixation.

Let's work through Figure 7.14 (the key is to keep track of the carbons). In three turns of the Calvin cycle, $3CO_2$ (3 carbons) are incorporated into 3 molecules of RuBP (15 carbons), which produces 6 molecules of 3-phosphoglycerate (18 carbons). Each of these molecules is phosphorylated by a phosphate donated by ATP. In total, six ATP are consumed to phosphorylate the six molecules

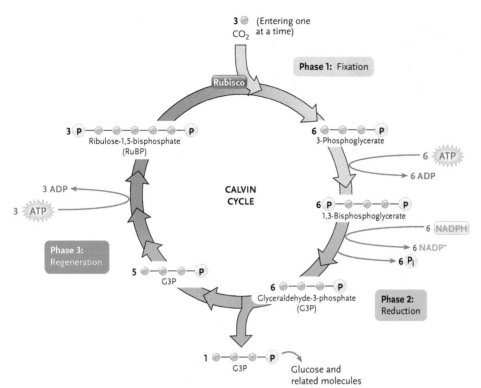

3 ⊙ (Entering one
CO₂   at a time)

Phase 1: Fixation

Rubisco

3 (P)─⊙─⊙─⊙─⊙─(P)   6 (P)─⊙─⊙─(P)
Ribulose-1,5-bisphosphate   3-Phosphoglycerate
(RuBP)

     6 ATP
     → 6 ADP

**CALVIN
CYCLE**

3 ADP ←
     6 (P)─⊙─⊙─(P)
3 ATP   1,3-Bisphosphoglycerate

     6 NADPH
     → 6 NADP⁺
     → 6 Pᵢ

Phase 3:
Regeneration

5 ⊙─⊙─(P)
G3P

     6 ⊙─⊙─(P)
     Glyceraldehyde-3-phosphate
     (G3P)

Phase 2:
Reduction

1 ⊙─⊙─(P)
G3P
     Glucose and
     related molecules

Figure 7.14

The Calvin cycle. An overview of the three phases of the Calvin cycle. The figure tracks the carbon atoms (red balls) during three turns of the cycle. For every three molecules of CO_2 that are fixed, one molecule of the three-carbon sugar G3P is synthesized.

of 3-phosphoglycerate, generating six molecules of 1,3-bisphosphoglycerate. Six molecules of NADPH are consumed in converting the 6 molecules of 1,3-bisphosphoglycerate into 6 molecules of G3P (18 carbons). Five molecules of G3P (totalling 15 carbons) are used to regenerate 3 RuBP molecules (15 carbons), which requires 3 molecules of ATP. Thus, the cycle generates one surplus molecule of G3P (three carbons) after every three turns. For the synthesis of this one extra G3P, the Calvin cycle requires a total of nine molecules of ATP and six molecules of NADPH. Both ATP and NADPH are regenerated from ADP and NADP⁺, respectively, by the light reactions.

7.4b G3P Is the Starting Point for the Synthesis of Many Other Organic Molecules

The G3P molecule formed by three turns of the Calvin cycle is the starting point for the production of a wide variety of organic molecules. Carbohydrates, such as glucose and other monosaccharides, are made from G3P by reactions that, in effect, reverse the first half of glycolysis. Once produced, the monosaccharides may enter biochemical pathways that make disaccharides such as sucrose, polysaccharides such as starches and cellulose, and other complex carbohydrates. Other pathways that consume G3P manufacture a diverse array of other molecules, including amino acids, fatty acids, and lipids. The reactions forming these products occur both within chloroplasts and in the surrounding cytosol.

Sucrose, a disaccharide consisting of glucose linked to fructose, is the main form in which the products of photosynthesis circulate from cell to cell in plants. Organic

nutrients are stored in most plants as sucrose, starch, or a combination of the two in proportions that depend on the plant species. For example, sugar cane and sugar beets, which contain stored sucrose in high concentrations, are the main sources of the sucrose we use as table sugar.

7.4c Rubisco Is the Most Abundant Protein on Earth

Ribulose-1,5-bisphosphate (RuBP) carboxylase oxygenase, or **Rubisco**, is the enzyme of the Calvin cycle that catalyzes the fixation of CO_2 into organic form:

$$\text{Ribulose-1,5-bisphosphate (RuBP)} + CO_2 \rightarrow$$
$$2 \text{ 3-phosphoglycerate}$$

Rubisco is considered the most important enzyme of the biosphere because by catalyzing CO_2 fixation in all photoautotrophs, it provides the source of organic carbon for most of the world's organisms. The enzyme converts a staggering 100 billion tonnes of CO_2 into carbohydrates annually. There are so many Rubisco molecules in chloroplasts that this one enzyme accounts for about 50% of the total protein content of plant leaves. This makes Rubisco easily the planet's most abundant protein, estimated to total some 40 million tonnes worldwide. Interestingly, the high abundance of Rubisco in photosynthetic cells is explained by the fact that this very important enzyme is catalytically very slow. For most enzymes, one molecule of enzyme can react with hundreds to many thousands of molecules of substrate per second. Rubisco only processes about 3 to 10 molecules of carbon dioxide per second.

Figure 7.15

Model of Rubisco. **(a)** The functional enzyme is composed of a total of 16 subunits: 8 large subunits (LSU) (shown in white and grey) and 8 small subunits (SSU) (shown in orange and blue). The synthesis of Rubsico **(b)** requires coordinated gene expression of two genomes. Each LSU is synthesized in the stroma of the chloroplast following the transcription of a gene coded by the chloroplast chromosome. The gene that encodes the SSU is found in the nucleus, with SSU monomers being synthesized by cytosolic ribosomes before being imported into the chloroplast.

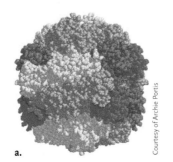

a.

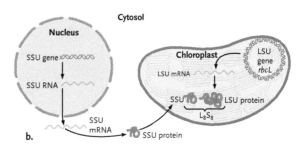

b.

Isolation and purification of Rubisco from the chloroplast stroma has led to the elucidation of its three-dimensional structure. The molecule is cube shaped and contains eight small subunits and eight large subunits **(Figure 7.15a)**. Each of the large subunits contains an active site, which has defined binding sites for both CO_2 and RuBP. The small subunits do not have a role in catalysis but do serve an important regulatory role, although their exact function remains unknown.

The synthesis of Rubisco is quite remarkable as it requires the coordinated expression of genes of two different genomes (Figure 7.15b). While the large subunit is encoded by a gene of the chloroplast genome, the small subunit is encoded by a gene that is found in the nucleus. After the small subunit polypeptide is synthesized in the cytosol, it is imported into the chloroplast, where it associates with large subunit monomers to make the functional enzyme.

Interestingly, the vast majority of the proteins found in chloroplasts (and mitochondria) are, in fact, encoded by the nuclear genome and thus are synthesized on ribosomes in the cytosol (see Chapter 3 for further discussion on this).

STUDY BREAK

1. Glucose is not the actual product of the Calvin cycle. What is?
2. For the Calvin cycle to keep going, what compound needs to be constantly regenerated?
3. What role does the chloroplast genome play in the synthesis of Rubisco?

7.5 Photorespiration and CO_2-Concentrating Mechanisms

For being arguably the most important enzyme on the planet, Rubsico is surprisingly inefficient at fixing CO_2. The cause of this inefficiency is that the active site of Rubisco is not specific to CO_2—a molecule of O_2 can also bind to the active site and react with RuBP. When this occurs, one of the products is a two-carbon compound that is exported from the chloroplast and actually requires the cell to consume ATP to convert it into carbon dioxide, which is simply lost. This wasteful process is called **photorespiration** because it occurs in the light and is similar to cellular respiration in that it consumes O_2 and releases CO_2. In this section, we present details on the biochemistry of the reactions that Rubsico catalyzes with O_2 and CO_2. As well, we discuss how photorespiration is exacerbated by certain environmental conditions and the key adaptations some plants and algae have evolved to minimize photorespiration.

7.5a Rubisco Is an Ancient Enzyme That Is Inhibited by Oxygen

Before we discuss the biochemistry of photorespiration, a key question we could ask is: why would natural selection have led to the evolution of an enzyme that accepts a second substrate molecule that produces a wasteful product? Rubisco and Rubisco-like proteins evolved at least 3 billion years ago as the primary enzyme in the biosphere for reducing carbon dioxide into organic form. Support for this comes, in part, from Rubisco being found in a huge diversity of organisms, including many bacteria and archaea (while they don't carry out photosynthesis, some archaea do have Rubisco). As discussed in Chapter 3, the atmosphere 3 billion years ago contained only trace amounts of O_2 and much higher levels of CO_2 than today. Under such conditions, an early form of Rubisco that could bind O_2 as well as CO_2 would not have been detrimental to an organism. Photorespiration became a problem only as the levels of oxygen in the atmosphere increased. There is evidence that over time Rubisco has slowly evolved to be more specific for CO_2, but the inhibition by O_2 remains.

O_2 can directly compete with CO_2 for the active site of Rubisco, and as such is an excellent example of a

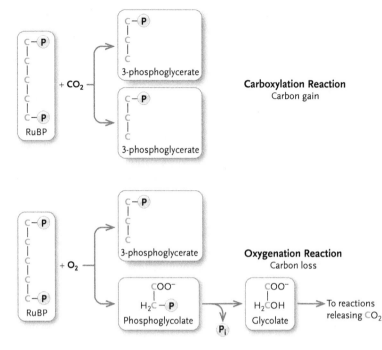

Figure 7.16
The enzyme Rubisco possesses both a carboxylase and an oxygenase activity. Compared with the usual carboxylase activity of the Calvin cycle, the oxygenase activity results in a net loss of carbon by the plant. Because oxygenase activity consumes O_2 and releases CO_2, it is also called photorespiration.

competitive inhibitor of enzyme function (see Chapter 4). When oxygen binds to the active site of Rubisco, the enzyme acts as an *oxygenase* instead of a *carboxylase*. A comparison of the products of the carboxylation reaction and the oxygenation reaction of Rubisco is shown in **Figure 7.16.** The incorporation of a CO_2 molecule into the five-carbon compound RuBP leads to a net increase in carbon by producing two molecules of the three-carbon compound 3-phosphoglycerate. By comparison, the incorporation of O_2 into RuBP in the oxygenation reaction produces a single molecule of 3-phosphoglycerate and one molecule of the two-carbon compound phosphoglycolate. There is no carbon gain—five carbons in and five carbons out. However, what makes photorespiration perhaps even more detrimental is that photoautotrophs cannot use phosphoglycolate. In the process of breaking it down to salvage the carbon, a toxic compound called glycolate is produced. The elimination of glycolate through its oxidation results in the release of carbon dioxide. Thus, whereas the carboxylation reaction leads to carbon gain, the oxygenation reaction actually results in the plant losing carbon.

If we compare the carboxylation and oxygenation reactions of Rubisco under laboratory conditions, where we can keep the concentrations of both O_2 and CO_2 equal, then the carboxylation reaction will dominate because the active site of Rubisco has a greater affinity for CO_2 than O_2. In fact, the carboxylation reaction will occur about 80 times as fast as the oxygenation reaction. However, unlike in the laboratory, the atmosphere does not contain equal amounts of the two gases—it contains approximately 21% O_2 and only about 0.04% CO_2. Because of this, under normal atmospheric concentrations and at moderate temperatures,

the oxygenation reaction can occur about once for every three times the carboxylation reaction occurs. This means that 25% of the time, the wasteful oxygenation reaction occurs, which results in net carbon loss. To counter the extent to which the oxygenation reaction occurs, many species have evolved mechanisms to try to decrease the prevalence of the oxygenation reaction. The strategies involve using mechanisms that increase the CO_2/O_2 ratio at the site of Rubisco.

7.5b Algae Pump Carbon Dioxide into Their Cells

In aquatic environments, the concentration of CO_2 dissolved in the water is usually low, well below what is needed to saturate the active site of Rubisco. Yet, interestingly, bubbling additional CO_2 into a culture of algae does not usually lead to an increase in the rate of photosynthesis, which is what you would expect. The lack of response to additional CO_2 is explained by the presence of a *carbon-concentrating mechanism* that pumps inorganic carbon into algal cells. This means that even when the concentration of CO_2 in the water is low, the amount that is actually within the cells is kept very high by this active pumping mechanism.

A model for one type of carbon-concentrating mechanism is presented in **Figure 7.17, p. 160.** In most aquatic environments, the dominant form of inorganic carbon is not CO_2 but rather the bicarbonate anion (HCO_3^-). Bicarbonate gets pumped into cells by the action of an ATP-dependent transporter on the plasma membrane. Within the cytosol, the bicarbonate is rapidly converted into CO_2 by the enzyme carbonic anhydrase. The CO_2 then diffuses into the chloroplast to the

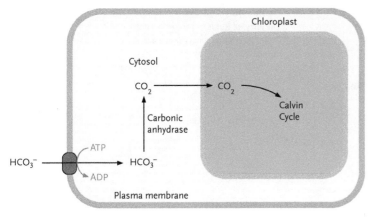

Figure 7.17

CO_2 concentration mechanism. Many aquatic photoautotrophs (e.g., algae) can increase their intracellular carbon dioxide concentrations through a mechanism that involves an ATP-dependent bicarbonate (HCO_3^-) pump on the plasma membrane. The bicarbonate is rapidly converted in the cytosol to CO_2 by the enzyme carbonic anhydrase.

site of Rubisco. This system results in a concentration of CO_2 at the site of Rubisco that is sufficiently high to essentially out-compete the O_2 that is present for the active site of Rubisco.

7.5c High Temperatures Increase Photorespiration

Like algae, land plants also face the problem of photorespiration. However, many land plants face the additional problem of trying to conserve water. Interestingly, these two problems are linked.

The surface of a plant leaf consists of a waxy cuticle that prevents evaporation of water into the air. Because this waxy cuticle also inhibits the flow of carbon dioxide, the leaf surface is covered by small pores called stomata (singular, *stoma*) that facilitate the movement of gases into and out of the leaf **(Figure 7.18)**. What direction a gas moves through the stomata is governed by diffusion—movement from high to low concentration. As shown in Figure 7.18b, carbon dioxide diffuses into plant leaves. Its concentration is higher outside the leaf than it is inside because CO_2 is being consumed within the leaf by photosynthesis. Both O_2 and H_2O (water vapour) diffuse out of the leaf because their concentrations are higher in the leaf than in the outside air; O_2 is being made during photosynthesis by photosystem II, and water is moving through the plant following uptake by the roots.

Plants can regulate the size of their stomata from fully closed (to minimize water loss) to fully open (to maximize CO_2 uptake). This then illustrates the balancing act performed by plants, especially those living in dry **climates**; they need to open their stomata to let CO_2 in for photosynthesis, but to conserve water they need to keep their stomata closed. This balancing act is made more difficult in environments that are not only dry but hot as well. This is because

photorespiration becomes a bigger problem the warmer the climate. The reason for this relates to the effect of temperature on the solubility of gases in solution. As shown in **Table 7.1**, the solubility of O_2 and CO_2 (in fact all gases) *decreases* as the temperature *increases*. However, the solubility of CO_2 decreases more rapidly than that of O_2 as the temperature rises. This means that in the aqueous environment of the chloroplast stoma, the CO_2/O_2 ratio decreases as the temperature increases, and as a consequence the oxygenation reaction of Rubisco (photorespiration) becomes more common.

7.5d C$_4$ Plants Spatially Separate the C$_4$ Pathway and the Calvin Cycle

Some plant species that are adapted to hot, dry climates have evolved a mode of carbon fixation that minimizes photorespiration. In addition to the Calvin cycle, these plants have a second carbon fixation pathway called the C_4 cycle **(Figure 7.19, p. 162)**. In this cycle, CO_2 initially combines with a three-carbon molecule, phosphoenolpyruvate (PEP), producing oxaloacetate, which in turn is reduced to malate. After being transported to the site of the Calvin cycle, the malate gets oxidized to pyruvate, releasing CO_2. To complete the cycle, pyruvate is converted back into PEP (for details see Figure 7.19). Because CO_2 is generated by the enzymatic conversion of malate to pyruvate, the levels of carbon dioxide at the site of the Calvin cycle are high, effectively inhibiting the oxygenation reaction of Rubisco, thereby minimizing photorespiration.

The C_4 cycle gets its name because its first product, oxaloacetate, is a four-carbon molecule rather than the three-carbon phosphoglycerate, the first product of the Calvin cycle. One often talks in terms of the C_4 pathway and the C_3 pathway when distinguishing between plants that have the C_4 cycle and those that possess only the Calvin cycle. A key distinction between C_4 and C_3 metabolism concerns the carboxylation reactions. In the C_4 cycle, the initial carboxylation reaction that incorporates CO_2 into PEP is catalyzed by the enzyme *PEP carboxylase* (Figure 7.19). Compared to Rubisco, PEP carboxylase has a rate of catalysis that is much faster, and, more importantly, O_2 cannot compete with CO_2 for its active site. It can efficiently catalyze the carboxylation of PEP regardless of the O_2 concentration near the enzyme.

C_4 metabolism is found in many tropical plants and several temperate crop species, including corn and sugar cane. In these species, the C_4 cycle occurs in mesophyll cells, which lie close to the surface of leaves and stems, where O_2 from the air is abundant (see **Figure 7.20, p. 163**). The malate intermediate of the C_4 cycle diffuses from the mesophyll cells to *bundle sheath cells*, located in deeper tissues, where O_2 concentrations are lower. In these cells, in which the Calvin cycle operates, the malate enters chloroplasts and is converted to pyruvate and CO_2.

Table 7.1	Effect of Temperature on the Solubility of O_2 and CO_2		
Temperature (°C)	[CO_2] (µM in solution)	[O_2] (µM in solution)	$\frac{[CO_2]}{[O_2]}$
5	21.93	401.2	0.0547
15	15.69	319.8	0.0491
25	11.68	264.6	0.0441
35	9.11	228.2	0.0399

You may ask: if C_4 metabolism is so good at preventing photorespiration, why don't all plants use it? Looking at Figure 7.19, notice that the C_4 pathway has an additional energy requirement. For each turn of the C_4 cycle, one molecule of ATP is required to regenerate PEP. In hot climates, photorespiration can decrease carbon fixation efficiency by over 50%, so the additional ATP requirement is worthwhile. As well, hot climates tend to receive a lot of sunlight, so the requirement for more ATP is easily met by absorbing more light energy and increasing the output of the light reactions.

In temperate climates (like in Canada), the lower ambient temperatures mean that photorespiration is not as big of a problem (look at Table), and the additional ATP requirement is often harder to meet given that these regions, on average, receive less sunlight. These differences in temperature and sunlight are the underlying reasons why, for example, in Florida, 70% of all native species are C_4 plants, while in Manitoba all native species are C_3 plants.

Not only do C_4 plants perform better than C_3 plants where it is hot, but they also perform better where it is dry. Because of the competing oxygenation reaction, C_3 plants need to keep their stomata open longer to fix the same number of CO_2 molecules as C_4 plants. This means that C_4 plants lose less water and are thus much better suited to arid conditions.

7.5e CAM Plants Temporally Separate the C_4 Pathway and the Calvin Cycle

Instead of running the Calvin and C_4 cycles simultaneously in different locations (spatial separation) as is the case with C4 plants, some plants, such as pineapple, run the cycles at different times (temporal separation). These plants are known as **CAM plants**, named for **crassulacean acid metabolism**, from the Crassulaceae family in which the adaptation was first observed. The plants in this group include many with thick, succulent leaves or stems, such cactus. A comparison of C_4 and CAM metabolism is illustrated in Figure 7.20.

CAM plants typically live in regions that are hot and dry during the day and cool at night. Their fleshy leaves or stems have a low surface-to-volume ratio, and their stomata are reduced in number. Further, the stomata open only at night, when they release O_2 that accumulates

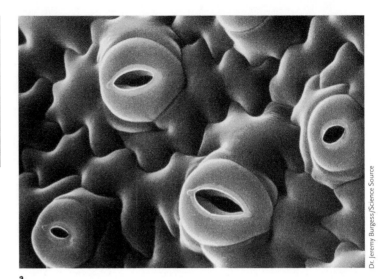

a.

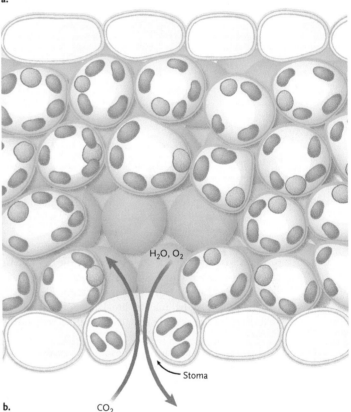

H₂O, O₂

Stoma

b. CO_2

Figure 7.18

Stomata. a. Micrograph of a leaf surface showing the presence of pores called stomata (sing. stoma). b. Each stoma is formed from two guard cells that control the opening and closing of the pore. This controls the movement of gases into and out of the plant and water loss.

from photosynthesis during the day and allow CO_2 to enter the leaves. The entering CO_2 is fixed by the C_4 pathway into malate, which accumulates throughout the night and is stored in large cell vacuoles.

Daylight initiates the second phase of the strategy. As the Sun comes up and the temperature rises, the

Figure 7.19

The C$_4$ cycle and its integration with the Calvin cycle. Each turn of the cycle delivers one molecule of CO$_2$ to the Calvin cycle. This process is energy dependent, consuming ATP.

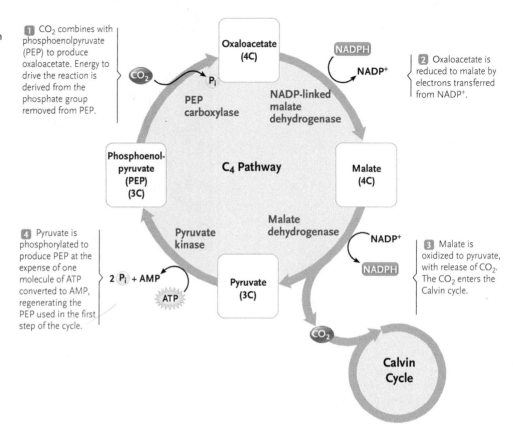

1 CO$_2$ combines with phosphoenolpyruvate (PEP) to produce oxaloacetate. Energy to drive the reaction is derived from the phosphate group removed from PEP.

2 Oxaloacetate is reduced to malate by electrons transferred from NADP$^+$.

3 Malate is oxidized to pyruvate, with release of CO$_2$. The CO$_2$ enters the Calvin cycle.

4 Pyruvate is phosphorylated to produce PEP at the expense of one molecule of ATP converted to AMP, regenerating the PEP used in the first step of the cycle.

stomata close, reducing water loss and cutting off the exchange of gases with the atmosphere. Malate diffuses from cell vacuoles into the cytosol, where it is oxidized to pyruvate, and CO$_2$ is released in high concentration. The high CO$_2$ concentration favours the carboxylase activity of Rubisco, allowing the Calvin cycle to proceed at maximum efficiency with little loss of organic carbon from photorespiration. The pyruvate produced by malate breakdown accumulates during the day; as night falls, it enters the C$_4$ reactions, converting it back to malate. During the night, oxygen is released by the plants, and more CO$_2$ enters.

Reduction of water loss by closure of the stomata during the hot daylight hours has the added benefit of making CAM plants highly resistant to dehydration. As a result, CAM species can tolerate extreme daytime heat and dryness.

STUDY BREAK

1. Explain how oxygenase activity suggests that Rubisco is an ancient enzyme.
2. Why is photorespiration thought to be a wasteful process?
3. What happens to the solubility of O$_2$ and CO$_2$ as the temperature is increased?

7.6 Photosynthesis and Cellular Respiration Compared

A popular misconception is that photosynthesis occurs in plants, and cellular respiration occurs only in animals. In fact, both processes occur in plants, with photosynthesis confined to tissues containing chloroplasts and cellular respiration taking place in all cells. **Figure 7.21, p. 164,** presents side-by-side schematics of photosynthesis and cellular respiration to highlight their similarities and points of connection. Note that their overall reactions are basically the reverse of each other. That is, the reactants of photosynthesis—CO$_2$ and H$_2$O—are the products of cellular respiration, and the reactants of cellular respiration—glucose and O$_2$— are the products of photosynthesis. Both processes have key phosphorylation reactions involving an **electron transfer system**—photophosphorylation in photosynthesis and oxidative phosphorylation in cellular respiration—followed by the chemiosmotic synthesis of ATP. Further, G3P is found in the pathways of both processes. In photosynthesis, it is a product of the Calvin cycle and is used for the synthesis of sugars and other organic fuel molecules. In cellular respiration, it is an intermediate generated in glycolysis in the conversion of glucose to pyruvate. Thus, G3P is used by anabolic pathways when it is generated

a. C₄—Spatial separation

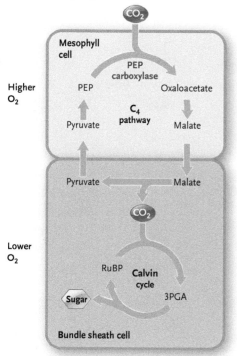

a. C$_4$—Spatial separation

Higher O$_2$

Mesophyll cell

CO$_2$

PEP → [PEP carboxylase] → Oxaloacetate

PEP ← Pyruvate

C$_4$ pathway

Oxaloacetate → Malate

Lower O$_2$

Pyruvate ← Malate

CO$_2$

RuBP **Calvin cycle** 3PGA

Sugar

Bundle sheath cell

b. CAM—Temporal separation

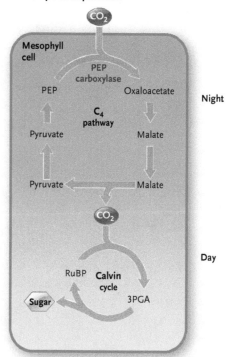

b. CAM—Temporal separation

CO$_2$

Mesophyll cell

PEP → [PEP carboxylase] → Oxaloacetate

Night

PEP ← Pyruvate

C$_4$ pathway

Oxaloacetate → Malate

Pyruvate ← Malate

Day

CO$_2$

RuBP **Calvin cycle** 3PGA

Sugar

Zea mays (corn)

Photodisk/Getty Images

Opuntia basilaris (beavertail cactus)

Steve Bower/Shutterstock.com

Figure 7.20

Two alternative processes of carbon fixation to minimize photorespiration. In each case, carbon fixation produces the four-carbon oxaloacetate, which is processed to generate the CO$_2$ that feeds into the Calvin (C$_3$) cycle. **(a)** In C$_4$ plants, carbon fixation and the Calvin cycle occur in different cell types: carbon fixation by the C$_4$ pathway takes place in mesophyll cells, while the Calvin cycle takes place in bundle sheath cells. **(b)** In CAM plants, carbon fixation and the Calvin cycle occur at different times in mesophyll cells: carbon fixation by the C$_4$ pathway takes place at night, while the Calvin cycle takes place during the day.

by photosynthesis, and it is a product of a catabolic pathway in cellular respiration.

In this chapter, you have seen how photosynthesis supplies the organic molecules used as fuels by almost all the organisms of the world. It is a story of electron flow: electrons, pushed to high energy levels by the absorption of light energy, are added to CO$_2$, which is fixed into carbohydrates and other fuel molecules. The high-energy electrons are then removed from the fuel molecules by the oxidative reactions of cellular respiration, which use the released energy to power the activities of life. Among the most significant of these activities are cell growth and division, the subjects of the next chapter.

Figure 7.21
Schematic diagrams of the process of photosynthesis (left) and cellular respiration (right). Cellular respiration is shown upside down with respect to the direction of reactions to help illustrate the similarities of the process with photosynthesis.

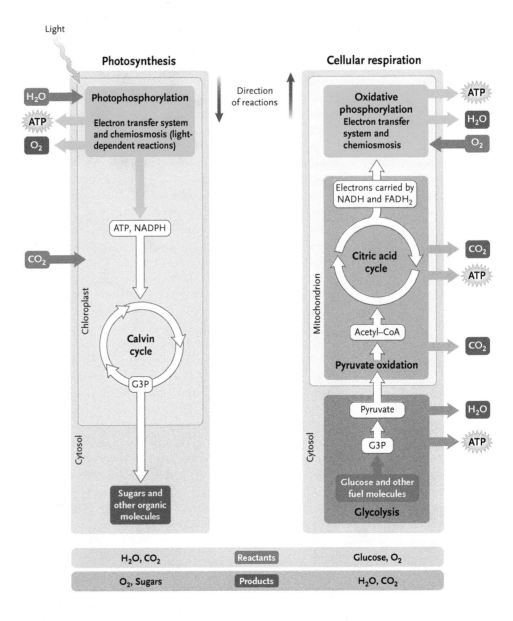

Review

To access course materials such as Aplia and other companion resources, please visit www.NELSONbrain.com.

7.1 Photosynthesis: An Overview

- Photosynthesis is the use of light energy to convert carbon dioxide into an organic form.
- Photoautotrophs are the primary producers of the planet as they use the energy of sunlight to drive synthesis of organic molecules from simple inorganic molecules such as CO_2. The organic molecules are used by the photosynthetic organisms

themselves as fuels; they also form the primary energy source for animals, fungi, and other heterotrophs.

- Photosynthesis can be divided into the light reactions and the Calvin cycle. In eukaryotes, both stages take place inside chloroplasts. The light reactions, which occur on the thylakoid membrane of chloroplasts (in eukaryotes), use the energy of light to drive the synthesis of NADPH and ATP. These are consumed by the Calvin cycle, which fixes CO_2 into carbohydrates (see Figure 7.2).

7.2 The Photosynthetic Apparatus

- Visible light occurs between 400 nm (blue light) and 700 nm (red light). The energy of a photon of light is inversely related to its wavelength (see Figure 7.5).
- The absorption of light energy by pigment molecules results in electrons within the pigment being raised to a higher-energy (excited) state. There are three fates of this excited state: energy loss, transport of the energy, or oxidation of the pigment (loss of the electron) (see Figure 7.6).
- Chlorophylls and carotenoids, the photon-absorbing pigments in eukaryotes and cyanobacteria, together absorb light energy at a range of wavelengths, enabling a wide spectrum of light to be used (see Figures 7.7 and 7.8)
- Photosynthetic pigments are organized into two types of photosystems: photosystem II and photosystem I. Each photosystem consists of a reaction centre surrounded by an antenna complex. Energy trapped by pigments in the antenna is funnelled to the reaction centre, where it is used to oxidize a special reaction centre chlorophyll (denoted by P680 for photosystem II and P700 for photosystem I). The oxidation of reaction center chlorophyll is coupled to the reduction of the primary electron acceptors within each reaction centre (see Figure 7.10).

7.3 The Light Reactions

- The photosynthetic electron transport chain (ETC; the light reactions) uses the energy of light absorbed by photosystem II and photosystem I to generate reducing power in the form of NADPH. Electrons released by the oxidation of the reaction centre chlorophyll of photosystem II are passed along an ETC. To get all the way down the chain, electrons become excited again at photosystem I, and then they are delivered to $NADP^+$ as final electron acceptor. $NADP^+$ is reduced to NADPH (see Figure 7.11).
- In a way similar to respiratory electron transport, the process of photosynthetic electron transport results in the establishment of a proton gradient, in this case, across the thylakoid membrane. The proton gradient is used to generate ATP through chemiosmosis using the ATP synthase complex embedded in the thylakoid membrane (see Figure 7.11).
- Besides linear electron transport from photosystem II through photosystem I, electrons can also flow in a cycle around photosystem I, building the H^+ concentration and allowing extra ATP to be produced, but no NADPH (see Figure 7.13).

7.4 The Calvin Cycle

- In the Calvin cycle, CO_2 is reduced and converted into carbohydrate by the addition of electrons and hydrogen carried by the NADPH produced in the light-dependent reactions. ATP, also derived from the light-dependent reactions, provides energy.

The key enzyme of the light-independent reactions is Rubisco (RuBP carboxylase/oxygenase), which catalyzes the reaction that combines CO_2 with a molecule of ribulose-1,5-bisphosphate (RuBP), producing two molecules of the three-carbon compound 3-phosphoglycerate (see Figure 7.14).
- For three turns of the Calvin cycle, one molecule of the three-carbon sugar glyceraldehyde-3-phosphate (G3P) is synthesized. G3P is the starting point for synthesis of glucose (requires two G3P molecules), sucrose, starch, and other organic molecules.

7.5 Photorespiration and CO_2-Concentrating Mechanisms

- Oxygen is a competitive inhibitor of Rubisco—it can compete with CO_2 for the active site. As an oxygenase, Rubisco catalyzes the combination of RuBP with O_2 rather than CO_2, forming toxic products that cannot be used in photosynthesis. The toxic products are eliminated by reactions that release carbon in inorganic form as CO_2, greatly reducing the efficiency of photosynthesis. The entire process is called photorespiration because it uses oxygen and releases CO_2 (see Figure 7.16).
- To avoid photorespiration, a range of plants and algae have evolved mechanisms to decrease the amount of O_2 that is present at the site of Rubisco and carbon fixation.
- In aquatic photoautotrophs, an ATP-dependent process pumps bicarbonate (HCO_3^-) into the cell, which is converted to CO_2 through the action of the enzyme carbonic anhydrase. This makes the CO_2/O_2 ratio greater at the site of Rubisco (Figure 7.17).
- Some plants have evolved C_4 metabolism whereby CO_2 from the air is first fixed by a carboxylase that does not have oxygenase activity into the four-carbon compound that occurs in mesophyll cells (the site of the Calvin cycle in C_3 plants). Following transport into bundle sheath cells, decarboxylation of a related four-carbon compound releases CO_2 at the site of Rubisco. This results in the CO_2/O_2 ratio being very high (see Figures 7.19 and 7.20).
- CAM plants also first fix CO_2 into oxaloacetate and then generate CO_2 for the Calvin cycle. Here both the carbon fixation and the Calvin cycle occur in mesophyll cells, but they are separated by time; initial carbon fixation occurs at night and the Calvin cycle occurs during the day (see Figure 7.20).

7.6 Photosynthesis and Cellular Respiration Compared

- Photosynthesis occurs in the cells of plants that contain chloroplasts, whereas cellular respiration occurs in all cells. The overall reactions of the two processes are essentially the reverse of each other, with the reactants of one being the products of the other (see Figure 7.21).

Questions

Self-Test Questions

1. What is the correct definition of the term *autotroph*?
   a. an organism that uses light energy to live
   b. an organism that can synthesize carbohydrates
   c. an organism that consumes the molecules found in other organisms
   d. an organism that synthesizes organic molecules using inorganic carbon

2. Why is chlorophyll green in colour?
   a. Chlorophyll only absorbs green photons of light.
   b. Green photons of light excite electrons within chlorophyll.
   c. Chlorophyll lacks an excited state that matches the energy of green photons.
   d. Green photons of light are not of high enough energy to excite electrons in chlorophyll.

3. Which statement about light reactions is correct?
   a. They result in an increase in the pH of the thylakoid lumen.
   b. Ferredoxin shuttles electrons from the cytochrome complex to photosystem I.
   c. $P680^*$ is easier to oxidize than P680.
   d. Energy transfer from the antenna to the reaction centre of a photosystem is through electron transport.

4. What is the minimum number of photons that need to be absorbed by the photosystems to reduce three molecules of $NADP^+$ to NADPH by the photosynthetic ETC?
   a. 3   c. 12
   b. 6   d. 18

5. Which of the following statements correctly distinguishes between linear electron transport and cyclic electron transport?
   a. NADH is generated only during linear electron transport.
   b. Photosystem I is used only during linear electron transport.
   c. Photosystem II is required only during cyclic electron transport.
   d. A proton-motive force is generated only during cyclic electron transport.

6. The Calvin cycle is sometimes called the light-independent reactions. This is misleading since the Calvin cycle will stop operating after a plant is placed in the dark. Why will it stop?
   a. Rubisco is rapidly degraded in the dark.
   b. NAD^+ generated by the light reactions is needed to activate 3-phosphoglycerate.
   c. In the dark, oxygen builds up in the chloroplast and inhibits Rubisco activity.
   d. The Calvin cycle requires a constant supply of ATP generation by the light reactions.

7. Which of the following statements about the Calvin cycle is correct?
   a. The cycle stops if the regeneration of RuBP is prevented.
   b. After three turns, one molecule of glucose is synthesized.
   c. It takes three turns of the cycle to fix one molecule of CO_2.
   d. It takes nine molecules of ATP to fix one molecule of CO_2.

8. Why don't C_4 plants photorespire?
   a. They lack mitochondria.
   b. They express high levels of carbonic anhydrase.
   c. The CO_2/O_2 ratio in their chloroplasts is very high.
   d. The Rubisco in their chloroplasts only has affinity for CO_2.

9. Compared to C_3 plants, one often find C_4 plants in drier habitats. Why is that?
   a. They have a larger root system.
   b. They can keep their stomata closed at all times.
   c. They don't have to keep their stomata open as long.
   d. Unlike C_3 plants, the leaves of C_4 plants are covered by a waxy cuticle.

10. In what way are the light reactions of photosynthesis similar to aerobic respiration?
    a. Both processes synthesize NADPH.
    b. Both processes use substrate phosphorylation to synthesize ATP.
    c. Chemiosmosis using the proton-motive force occurs in both.
    d. Both require oxygen as the final electron acceptor of electron transport.

Questions for Discussion

1. Like other accessory pigments, the carotenoids extend the range of wavelengths absorbed in photosynthesis. They also protect plants from a potentially lethal process known as *photooxidation*. This process begins when excitation energy in chlorophylls drives the conversion of oxygen into reactive oxygen species (ROS) (see Chapter 6), substances that can damage organic compounds and kill cells. When plants that cannot produce carotenoids are grown in light, they bleach white and die. Given this observation, what molecules in the plants are likely to be destroyed by photooxidation?

2. Exposing plants to light at low temperatures increases the damage to photosystem II. Why do you think this is the case?

3. If global warming raises the temperature of our climate significantly, will C_3 plants or C_4 plants be favoured by natural selection? How will global warming change the geographical distributions of plants?

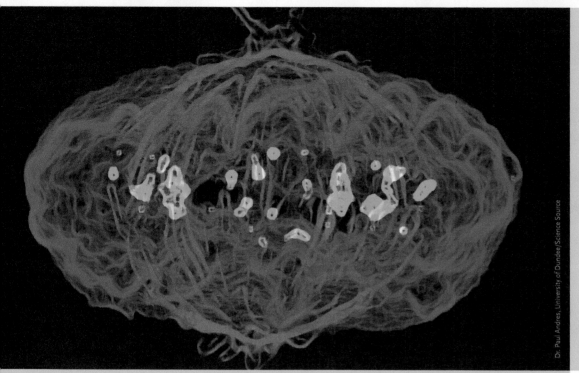

A cell in mitosis (fluorescence micrograph). The spindle (red) is separating copies of the cell's chromosomes (green) before cell division.

Cell Cycles

WHY IT MATTERS

As the rainy season recedes in Northern India, rice paddies and other flooded areas begin to dry. These shallow seasonal pools have provided an environment of slow-moving warm water for zebrafish (*Danio rerio*) to spawn **(Figure 8.1, p. 168).** Over the past few months, many millions of cell divisions have fuelled the growth and development of single fertilized eggs into the complex multicellular tissues and organs of these small, boldly striped fish. Most cells in the adults have now stopped dividing and are dedicated to particular functions.

Moving into the fast-running streams that feed the Ganges River, the young zebrafish encounter larger predators, such as knifefish (*Notopterus notopterus*). Imagine for a moment that a zebrafish is attacked by a knifefish; the prey narrowly escapes but not without leaving one of its fins behind in the mouth of the predator. In an amazing feat of cell cycle regulation, the entire zebrafish fin will be regenerated—skin, nerves, muscles, bones, and all—within a week!

As a model system for vertebrate development, the zebrafish has provided a popular tool for researchers to identify the stages of regeneration at the molecular level. (See *The Purple Pages* for more information about zebrafish as model organisms.) In the first step, existing skin cells migrate to close the wound and prevent bleeding. Then cells under the new skin form a temporary tissue called a blastema. Blastema cells divide up to 50 times as fast as usual, providing large numbers of daughter cells capable of maturing into new bone, nerve, muscle, and blood vessel cells in response to signal proteins produced by the skin. Once the regenerated fin has reached its normal size and shape, the new cells stop growing and dividing.

Figure 8.1
Zebrafish (*Danio rerio*).

replication, and cell division in the face of a changing environment.

Although this chapter highlights the characteristics of dividing cells, it is important for you to realize that most cells in the body of a multicellular organism are *not* destined to divide any time soon, if

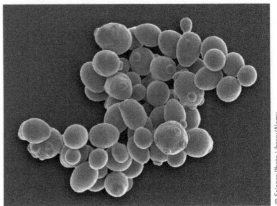

a.

The remarkable ability of eukaryotic cells to coordinate their growth and division, always yielding daughter cells in a timely fashion with a complete set of genetic material, is the focus of this chapter. In particular, we intend for you to appreciate how this coordination is achieved through the interplay of three cellular processes: (1) DNA replication, (2) a dynamically changing cytoskeleton, and (3) cell cycle "checkpoints." To provide a hint of what the ancestral cell division process may have been like, the chapter opens with a look at cell division in prokaryotic organisms and the simpler eukaryotes.

8.1 The Cycle of Cell Growth and Division: An Overview

While regenerating a lost body part is certainly dramatic at the scale of an individual organism, we invite you now to consider the wider, grander, view of the relevance of the cell division cycle. Scientists have known since the early nineteenth century that all life on Earth is composed of cells and their products. All cells, in all organisms that have ever lived, are descended from previous cells in an unbroken chain of cell division stretching billions of years into the past. New progeny cells are needed for expanding population size (single-celled organisms), multicellular tissue growth (new leaves), asexual reproduction, and replacement of cells lost to wear (shedding skin and gut lining) and tear (wound repair, virus infection) **(Figure 8.2)**. Although the cell division cycle is conceptually simple—grow, divide, grow, divide—repeat for billions of years—regulation of this process must be precise and complex. If cells divide too quickly, daughter cells may be too small or lacking essential cytoplasm or genetic material. If cells divide too slowly, they may grow inefficiently large or accumulate extra chromosomes. All dividing cells must meet the challenge of closely coordinating their growth, DNA

b.

c.

Figure 8.2
Actively dividing cells provide for increased population size of yeast **(a)**, growth of skin **(b)**, and expansion of conifer needles **(c)**.

ever. In fact, some cells may even be programmed to die immediately!

8.2 The Cell Cycle in Prokaryotic Organisms

A newly formed prokaryotic cell, such as the bacterium *Escherichia coli*, must double in size, replicate its circular chromosome, and then move each of the resulting two daughter chromosomes into its own progeny cell during cell division. The entire mechanism of prokaryotic cell division, called **binary fission**, that is, splitting or dividing into two parts, can be thought of in three periods, as shown in **Figure 8.3**. Following birth, cells may grow for some time before initiating DNA synthesis (B period). Once the chromosomes are replicated and separated to opposite ends of the cell (C period), the membrane pinches together between them and two daughter cells are formed (D period).

8.2a Replication Occupies Most of the Cell Cycle in Rapidly Dividing Prokaryotic Cells

All bacteria and archaea use DNA as their hereditary information, and the vast majority of species package it all in a single, circular chromosome of double-stranded DNA (Figure 8.3, step 1). Although the chromosome is shown extended in Figure 8.3 for the purposes of illustration, it is actually compacted in a central region called the **nucleoid** throughout the cell cycle (see Figure 2.7, Chapter 2). When nutrients are abundant, prokaryotic cells have no need for a B period since they can grow quickly enough to divide their cytoplasm as soon as DNA replication is complete and chromosomes are separated. Under such optimal conditions, populations of *E. coli* cells can double every 20 minutes.

8.2b Replicated Chromosomes Are Distributed Actively to the Halves of the Prokaryotic Cell

In the 1860s, François Jacob of The Pasteur Institute in Paris, France, proposed a model for the **segregation** of bacterial chromosomes to the daughter cells in which the two chromosomes attach to the plasma membrane near the middle of the cell and separate as a new plasma membrane is added between the two sites during cell elongation. The essence of this model is that chromosome separation is passive. However, current research indicates that bacterial chromosomes rapidly separate in an active way that is linked to DNA replication events and is independent of cell elongation. The new model is summarized in the C period of Figure 8.3.

Replication of the bacterial chromosome commences at a specific region called the **origin of replication**

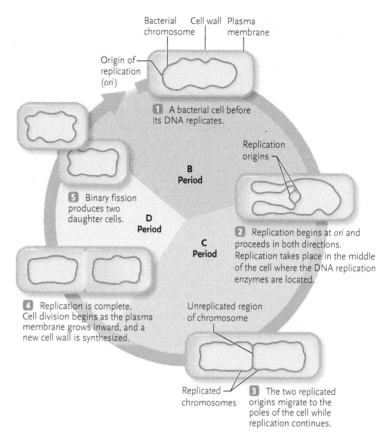

Figure 8.3

The bacterial cell cycle. During the B period, from birth to the initiation of DNA replication, the cell grows in size. The chromosome is replicated and the resulting daughter chromosomes move to opposite ends during the C period. Then the cell divides by binary fission during the D period. In very fast growing cultures, the B period may be nonexistent; cells may be born with chromosomes that are already partly replicated!

(*ori*). The *ori* is in the middle of the cell, where the enzymes for DNA replication are located. Once the *ori* has been duplicated, the two new origins migrate toward the two opposite ends (poles) of the cell as replication continues for the rest of the chromosome (see Figure 8.3, step 3). The mechanism that propels the two replicated chromosomes to their respective ends of the cell is still unknown. Next, cytoplasmic division is associated with an inward constriction of a cytokinetic ring of cytoskeletal proteins. New plasma membrane and cell wall material is assembled to divide the cell into two equal parts (see Figure 8.3, step 5).

8.2c Mitosis Has Evolved from an Early Form of Binary Fission

The prokaryotic mechanism works effectively because most prokaryotic organisms have only a single chromosome. Thus, if a daughter cell receives at least one copy of the chromosome, its genetic information is complete. By contrast, the genetic information of eukaryotes is divided among several chromosomes, with each chromosome containing a much greater length of DNA than a prokaryotic chromosome does. If a daughter cell fails to receive a copy of even one chromosome, the effects are usually lethal. It is also important to note that, during most of the cell cycle, eukaryotic chromosomes are contained within the nuclear membrane. Bacteria and archaea do not have an internal membrane around their nucleoid. Therefore, eukaryotic cellular and chromosomal architecture demands a quite different mechanism for distributing chromosomes to daughter cells. Mitosis is that different mechanism, and we will examine this process in detail later in the chapter (see **Figure 8.6, p. 172**). For now, just be aware that one of the central innovations of the evolution of mitosis is the ability to hold the two newly created molecules of double-stranded DNA (now called **chromatids**) together following DNA synthesis. This enables cells to keep track of such long replicated chromosomes and to orient them relative to the cytoskeleton at the proper time to ensure precise distribution to daughter cells. In most higher eukaryotes, the nuclear membrane disintegrates at the time when chromosomes are being distributed and then reforms around them in daughter cells.

Variations in the mitotic apparatus in modern-day organisms illuminate possible intermediates in the evolutionary pathway to mitosis from some ancestral type of binary fission. For example, in many primitive eukaryotes, such as dinoflagellates (a type of single-celled alga), the nuclear envelope remains intact during mitosis, and the chromosomes bind to the inner membrane of the nuclear membrane. When the nucleus divides, the chromosomes are segregated.

A more advanced form of the mitotic apparatus is seen in yeasts and diatoms (another type of single-celled alga). In these organisms, a **spindle** of microtubules made of polymerized tubulin protein forms and chromosomes segregate to daughter nuclei without the disassembly and reassembly of the nuclear envelope. Current evidence suggests that the type of mitosis seen in yeasts and diatoms and the type of mitosis in animals and higher plants described later in this chapter evolved separately from a common ancestral type.

STUDY BREAK

What are the three main steps in binary fission of prokaryotic organisms?

8.3 Mitosis and the Eukaryotic Cell Cycle

As long as eukaryotes require their daughter cells to be genetic copies of the **parental** cell, **mitosis** serves very well to divide the replicated DNA equally and precisely.

This is the result of three elegantly interrelated systems:

1. An elaborate master program of molecular checks and balances ensures an orderly and timely progression through the cell cycle.
2. Within the overall regulation of the cell cycle, a process of DNA synthesis replicates each DNA chromosome into two copies with almost perfect fidelity (see Section 12.3).
3. A structural and mechanical web of interwoven "cables" and "motors" of the cytoskeleton separates the replicated DNA molecules precisely into the daughter cells.

However, at a particular stage of the life cycle of sexually reproducing organisms, a cell division process called meiosis produces some cells that are genetically different from the parent cells. **Meiosis** produces daughter nuclei that are different in that they have one-half the number of chromosomes the parental nucleus had. Also, the mechanisms involved in producing the daughter nuclei produce arrangements of genes on chromosomes that are different from those in the parent cell (see Chapter 9). The cells that are the products of meiosis may function as gametes in animals (fusing with other gametes to make a zygote) and as spores in plants and many fungi (dividing by mitosis). Meiosis and its role in eukaryotic sexual reproduction are addressed in Chapter 9. We begin our discussion of mitosis with **chromosomes**, the nuclear units of genetic information divided and distributed by mitotic cell division.

8.3a Chromosomes Are the Genetic Units Divided by Mitosis

In all eukaryotes, the hereditary information of the nucleus is distributed among several linear, double-stranded DNA molecules. These DNA molecules are combined with proteins that stabilize the DNA, assist in packaging DNA during cell division, and influence the expression of individual genes. Each chromosome (*chroma* = colour, when stained with dyes used in light microscopy; *soma* = body; **Figure 8.4**) in a cell is composed of one of these DNA molecules, along with its associated proteins.

Most eukaryotes have two copies of each type of chromosome in their nuclei, and their chromosome complement is said to be **diploid**, or $2n$. For example, humans have 23 different pairs of chromosomes for a diploid number of 46 chromosomes ($2n = 46$). Other eukaryotes, mostly microorganisms, may have only one copy of each type of chromosome in their nucleus, so their chromosome complement is said to be **haploid**, or n. Baker's yeast (*Saccharomyces cerevisiae*) is an example of an organism that can grow as a diploid ($2n = 32$) and as a haploid ($n = 16$). Still others, such as many plant species, have three, four, or even more complete sets of chromosomes in each cell. The

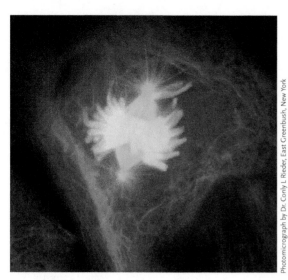

Figure 8.4
Eukaryotic chromosomes (stained blue) during mitosis.

number of chromosome sets is called the **ploidy** of a cell or species. See Chapter 19 for a look at the role of ploidy in the formation of new species.

Before a cell divides in mitosis, duplication of each chromosome produces two identical copies of each chromosome called **sister chromatids.** Duplication of a chromosome involves replicating the DNA molecule it contains, plus doubling the proteins that are bound to the DNA to stabilize it. Newly formed sister chromatids are held together tightly by sister chromatid cohesion, in which proteins called cohesins encircle the sister chromatids along their length. During mitosis, the cohesins are removed and the sister chromatids are separated, with one of each pair going to each of the two daughter nuclei. As a result of this precise division, each daughter nucleus receives exactly the same number and types of chromosomes and contains the same genetic information as the parent cell that entered the division. The equal distribution of daughter chromosomes into each of the two daughter cells that result from cell division is called **chromosome segregation.**

CONCEPT FIX The double-strandedness of DNA, the mechanism of cell division, and new vocabulary can lead to confusion about just how many chromosomes are in a particular cell at a particular time. Let's pick the fruit fly *Drosophila melanogaster* as an example organism because all of its genes are contained in only four different chromosomes. Every body cell in a fruit fly is diploid (2n) and therefore contains two of each of the four distinct *Drosophila* chromosomes—for a total of eight. Each of these eight chromosomes is composed of one double-stranded DNA molecule of the type shown in Figure 12.6, Chapter 12. If the cell is preparing to divide, DNA synthesis, as shown in Figure 12.7, Chapter 12, creates two identical DNA molecules from each of the eight originals. The two new DNA molecules created

from each original chromosome remain attached to one another and are now called sister chromatids. (Someone once suggested that these two new molecules should be called twin chromatids because they are identical.) Now here comes the confusing part. Since sister chromatids remain attached to each other at their centromeres following DNA synthesis, the pair of them is still referred to as just one chromosome. Before replication, one chromosome is composed of one DNA molecule; after replication, one chromosome is composed of two DNA molecules. You should see that DNA replication increases the amount of DNA in the nucleus but it does not increase the number of chromosomes. Our *Drosophila* cell has eight DNA molecules in the nucleus before DNA synthesis and eight pairs of molecules after. There are eight chromosomes before DNA synthesis and eight replicated chromosomes after. During cell division, each of the two daughter cells receives one of the two sister chromatids from each replicated chromosome. You should therefore agree to the rather counterintuitive claim that two daughter cells can each receive eight chromosomes even though there were only eight chromosomes in the original cell. ⬡

The precision of chromosome replication and segregation in the mitotic cell cycle creates a group of cells called a **clone.** Except for rare chance mutations, all cells of a clone are genetically identical. Since all the diverse cell types of a complex multicellular organism arose by mitosis from a single zygote, they should all contain the same genetic information. Forensic scientists rely on this feature of organisms when, for instance, they match the genetic profile of a small amount of tissue (e.g., cells in dog saliva recovered from a bite victim) with that of a blood sample from the suspected animal.

STUDY BREAK

1. What are the three interrelated systems that contribute to the eukaryotic cell cycle?
2. What is a chromosome composed of?

8.3b Interphase Extends from the End of One Mitosis to the Beginning of the Next Mitosis

If we set the formation of a new daughter cell as the beginning of the mitotic cell cycle, then the first and longest stage is **interphase (Figure 8.5, p. 172).** Interphase comprises three phases of the cell cycle:

1. **G_1 phase,** in which the cell carries out its function, and in some cases grows
2. **S phase,** in which DNA replication and chromosome duplication occur
3. **G_2 phase,** a brief gap in the cell cycle during which cell growth continues and the cell prepares for mitosis (the fourth phase of the cell cycle; also called M phase) and cytokinesis.

Figure 8.5

The cell cycle. The length of G_1 varies, but for a given cell type, the timing of S phase, G_2 phase, and mitosis is usually relatively uniform. Cytokinesis (red segment) usually begins while mitosis is in progress and reaches completion as mitosis ends. Cells in a state of division arrest are considered to enter a side loop (or shunt) from G_1 phase called G_0 phase.

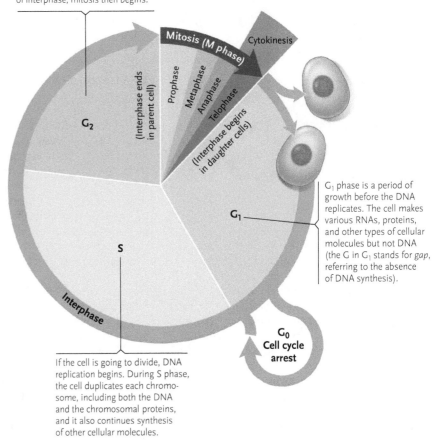

G_2 refers to the second gap in which there is no DNA synthesis. During G_2, the cell continues to synthesize RNAs and proteins, including those for mitosis, and it continues to grow. The end of G_2 marks the end of interphase; mitosis then begins.

Mitosis (M phase)

Cytokinesis

Prophase
Metaphase
Anaphase
Telophase

(Interphase ends in parent cell)

(Interphase begins in daughter cells)

G_2

G_1

G_1 phase is a period of growth before the DNA replicates. The cell makes various RNAs, proteins, and other types of cellular molecules but not DNA (the G in G_1 stands for *gap*, referring to the absence of DNA synthesis).

S

Interphase

G_0
Cell cycle arrest

If the cell is going to divide, DNA replication begins. During S phase, the cell duplicates each chromosome, including both the DNA and the chromosomal proteins, and it also continues synthesis of other cellular molecules.

Figure 8.6

Chromosomes from the muntjac deer are individually "painted" with fluorescent stain. Note that there are two cells in this picture. The metaphase cell shows two copies of each of three long, condensed chromosomes. The interphase nucleus shows the DNA of different chromosomes organized in close proximity rather than randomly distributed.

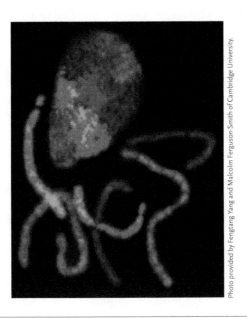

Photo provided by Fengtang Yang and Malcolm Ferguson-Smith of Cambridge University.

Usually, G_1 is the only phase of the cell cycle that varies in length. The other phases are typically uniform in length within a species. Thus, whether cells divide rapidly or slowly depends primarily on the length of G_1. Once DNA replication begins, most mammalian cells take about 10 to 12 hours to proceed through the S phase, about 4 to 6 hours to go through G_2, and about 1 hour or less to complete mitosis.

G_1 is also the stage in which many cell types stop dividing. Cells that are not destined to divide immediately enter a shunt from G_1 called the **G_0 phase.** In some cases, a cell in G_0 may start dividing again by re-entering G_1. Some cells never resume the cell cycle; for example, most cells of the human nervous system stop dividing once they are fully mature. During all the stages of interphase the chromosomes are organized, but relatively loosely packaged, within the nucleus (Figure 8.6).

Internal regulatory controls trigger each phase of the cell cycle, ensuring that the processes of one phase are

How can investigators safely test whether a particular substance is toxic to human cells or whether it can cure or cause cancer? One widely used approach is to work with **cell cultures**—living cells grown in laboratory vessels. Many types of prokaryotic and eukaryotic cells can be grown in this way.

When cell cultures are started from single cells, they form **clones**: barring mutations, all the individuals descended from the original cell are genetically identical. Clones are ideal for experiments in genetics, biochemistry, molecular biology, and medicine because the cells lack genetic differences that could affect the experimental results.

Microorganisms such as yeasts and many bacteria are easy to grow in laboratory cultures. For example, the human intestinal bacterium *E. coli* can be grown in solutions (growth media) that contain only an organic carbon source such as glucose, a nitrogen source, and inorganic salts. The cells may be grown in liquid suspensions or on the surface of a solid growth medium such as an agar gel (agar is a polysaccharide extracted from an

alga). Many thousands of bacterial strains are used in a wide variety of experimental studies.

Many types of plant cells can also be cultured as clones in specific growth media. With the addition of plant growth hormones, complete plants can often be grown from single cultured cells. Growing plants from cultured cells is particularly valuable in genetic engineering, in which genes introduced into cultured cells can be tracked in fully developed plants. Plants that have been engineered successfully can then be grown simply by planting their seeds.

Animal cells vary in what is needed to culture them. For many types, the culture medium must contain essential amino acids—that is, the amino acids that the cells cannot make for themselves. In addition, mammalian cells require specific growth factors provided by adding blood serum, the fluid part of the blood left after red and white blood cells are removed.

Even with added serum, many types of normal mammalian cells cannot be grown in long-term cultures. Eventually, the cells stop dividing and

die. By contrast, tumour cells often form cultures that grow and divide indefinitely.

The first successful culturing of cancer cells was performed in 1951 in the laboratory of George and Margaret Gey (Johns Hopkins University, Baltimore, Maryland). Gey and Gey's cultures of normal cells died after a few weeks, but the researchers achieved success with a culture of tumour cells from a cancer patient. The cells in culture continued to grow and divide; in fact, descendants of those cells are still being cultured and used for research today. The cells were given the code name *HeLa*, from the first two letters of the patient's first and last names—Henrietta Lacks. Unfortunately, the tumour cells in Lacks's body also continued to grow, and she died within two months of her cancer diagnosis.

Other types of human cells have since been grown successfully in culture, derived from either tumour cells or normal cells that have been "immortalized" by inducing genetic changes that transformed them into tumour like cells.

completed successfully before the next phase can begin. Various internal mechanisms also regulate the overall number of cycles that a cell goes through. These internal controls may be subject to various external influences, such as other cells or viruses and signal molecules, including hormones, growth factors, and death signals.

CONCEPT FIX Since the emphasis of this chapter is on the behaviour of chromosomes, your attention might get focused on the events of mitosis such that you assume nothing much happens during interphase. Cells are not just "resting up" for the next round of mitosis. During interphase, an appropriate suite of genes is actively expressed to support cell growth and metabolism. It is also during interphase that DNA is replicated. ⬡

8.3c After Interphase, Mitosis Proceeds in Five Stages

If you were to watch a cell going through mitosis **(Figures 8.7, p. 174,** and **8.8, p. 176)**, you would notice several dramatic changes that signal the progression

through different stages: prophase (*pro* = before), prometaphase (*meta* = between), metaphase, anaphase (*ana* = back), and telophase (*telo* = end).

Prophase. During **prophase**, the greatly extended chromosomes that were replicated during interphase begin to *condense* into compact, rodlike structures (see chromatin packing in Section 12.5). Each diploid human cell, although only about 40 to 50 μm in diameter, contains *2 m* of DNA distributed among 23 pairs of chromosomes. Condensation during prophase packs these long DNA molecules into units small enough to be divided successfully during mitosis. As they condense, the chromosomes appear as thin threads under the light microscope. The word *mitosis* (*mitos* = thread) is derived from this threadlike appearance.

While condensation is in progress, the nucleolus becomes smaller and eventually disappears in most species. The disappearance reflects a shutdown of all types of RNA synthesis, including the ribosomal RNA made in the nucleolus.

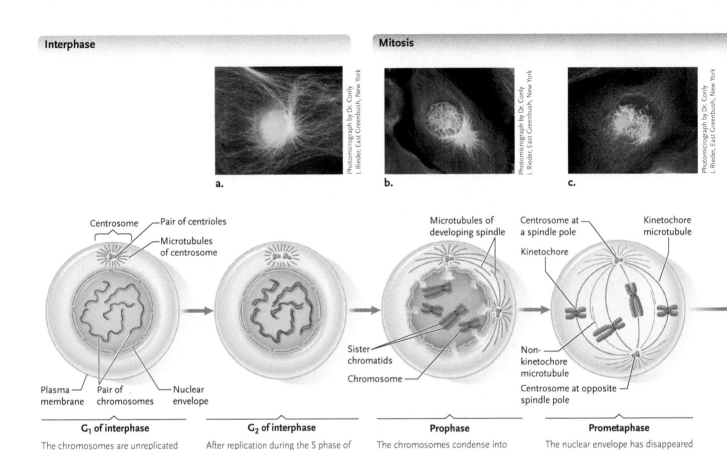

a.

b.

c.

G₁ of interphase

The chromosomes are unreplicated and extend throughout the nucleus. For simplicity we show only two pairs of chromosomes. One of each pair was inherited from one parent, and the other was inherited from the other parent.

G₂ of interphase

After replication during the S phase of interphase, each chromosome is double at all points and now consists of two sister chromatids. Cohesins encircle each pair of sister chromatids along their lengths, aligning them tightly. The centrioles within the centrosome have also doubled into pairs.

Prophase

The chromosomes condense into threads that become visible under the light microscope. Each chromosome is double as a result of replication. The centrosome has divided into two parts, which are generating the spindle as they separate.

Prometaphase

The nuclear envelope has disappeared and the spindle enters the former nuclear area. Microtubules from opposite spindle poles attach to the two kinetochores of each chromosome.

Figure 8.7

The stages of mitosis. Triple-stained immunofluorescent light micrographs show mitosis in an animal cell (salamander lung). The chromosomes are blue, the spindle and cytoplasmic microtubules are yellow-green, and the intermediate filaments are red. **(a)** Interphase. Microtubules focus on the centrosome, located adjacent to the nucleus. **(b)** Prophase. Chromosomes are well condensed, the nuclear envelope is intact, and the microtubules are organized into radial arrays. **(c)** Prometaphase. The nuclear envelope has broken down to allow the chromosomes to interact with the microtubules originating from two separate centrosomes. **(d)** Metaphase. All of the replicated chromosomes are aligned on the equator of the mature mitotic spindle. **(e)** Anaphase/telophase. Chromosomes have been equally segregated and have decondensed to form two independent daughter nuclei. This cell has just begun cytokinesis. **(f)** The end result of mitosis: two genetically identical daughter cells.

In the cytoplasm, the **mitotic spindle (Figure 8.9, p. 176;** see also **Figure 8.13, p. 178)** begins to form between the two centrosomes as they start migrating toward the opposite ends of the cell to form the **spindle poles.** The spindle develops as bundles of microtubules that radiate from the spindle poles.

Prometaphase. At the end of prophase, the nuclear envelope breaks down, heralding the beginning of **prometaphase.** Bundles of spindle microtubules grow from centrosomes at the opposing spindle poles toward the centre of the cell. Some of the developing spindle enters the former nuclear area and attaches to the chromosomes.

Although replicated chromosomes are seldom visible as a double structure at this point, it is important for you to remember that each one is made up of two identical sister chromatids held together only at their **centromeres.** By this time, a complex of several proteins, a **kinetochore,** has formed on each chromatid at the centromere. Kinetochore microtubules bind to the kinetochores. These connections determine the outcome of mitosis because they attach the sister chromatids of each chromosome to microtubules leading to the opposite spindle poles (see Figure 8.9, p. 176). Microtubules that do not attach to kinetochores overlap those from the opposite spindle pole.

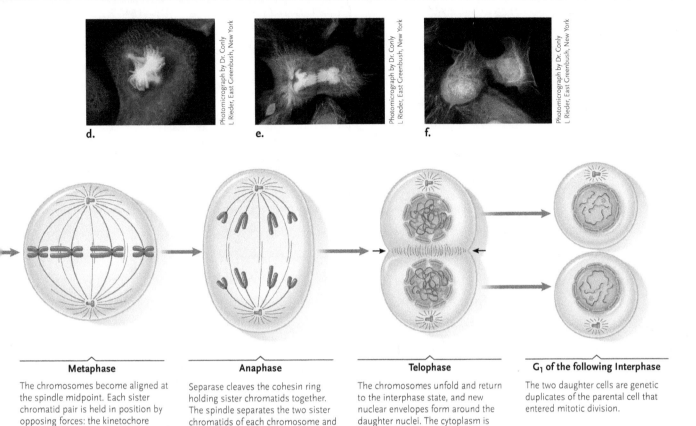

Metaphase	Anaphase	Telophase	G₁ of the following Interphase
The chromosomes become aligned at the spindle midpoint. Each sister chromatid pair is held in position by opposing forces: the kinetochore microtubules pulling to the poles and the cohesins binding the sister chromatids together.	Separase cleaves the cohesin ring holding sister chromatids together. The spindle separates the two sister chromatids of each chromosome and moves them to opposite spindle poles.	The chromosomes unfold and return to the interphase state, and new nuclear envelopes form around the daughter nuclei. The cytoplasm is beginning to divide by furrowing at the points marked by arrows.	The two daughter cells are genetic duplicates of the parental cell that entered mitotic division.

Metaphase. During **metaphase**, the spindle reaches its final form and the spindle microtubules move the chromosomes into alignment at the spindle midpoint, also called the metaphase plate. The chromosomes complete their condensation in this stage and assume their characteristic shape as determined by the location of the centromere and the length and thickness of the chromatid arms.

Only when the chromosomes are all assembled at the spindle midpoint, with the two sister chromatids of each one attached to microtubules leading to opposite spindle poles, can metaphase give way to actual separation of chromatids.

CONCEPT FIX Although you probably think of chromosomes as X shapes, it is important to realize that few chromosomes ever actually look like this. Only chromosomes with their centromere near the middle could ever appear as an X. Only during (pro)metaphase are chromosomes condensed enough to take on any shape at all. ●

The complete collection of metaphase chromosomes, arranged according to size and shape, forms the **karyotype** of a given species. In many cases, the karyotype is so distinctive that a species can be identified from this characteristic alone. **Figure 8.10, p. 176,** shows a human karyotype.

Anaphase. During **anaphase**, sister chromatids separate and move to opposite spindle poles. The first signs of chromosome movement can be seen at the centromeres as the kinetochores are the first sections to move toward opposite poles. The movement continues until the separated chromatids, now called daughter chromosomes, have reached the two poles. At this point, chromosome segregation has been completed.

Telophase. During **telophase**, the spindle disassembles and the chromosomes at each spindle pole decondense and return to the extended state typical of interphase. As decondensation proceeds, the nucleolus reappears, RNA transcription resumes, and a new nuclear envelope forms around the chromosomes at each pole, producing the two daughter nuclei. At this point, nuclear division is complete, and the cell has two nuclei.

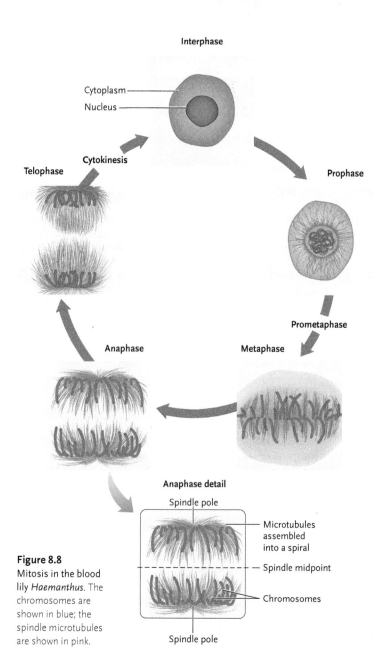

Interphase

Cytoplasm

Nucleus

Cytokinesis

Telophase

Prophase

Anaphase

Metaphase

Prometaphase

Anaphase detail

Spindle pole

Microtubules assembled into a spiral

Spindle midpoint

Chromosomes

Spindle pole

Figure 8.8
Mitosis in the blood lily *Haemanthus*. The chromosomes are shown in blue; the spindle microtubules are shown in pink.

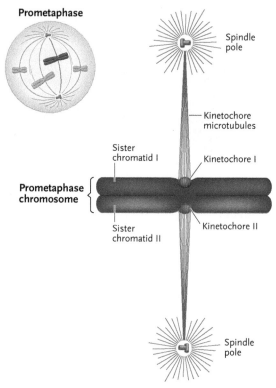

Prometaphase

Spindle pole

Kinetochore microtubules

Sister chromatid I

Kinetochore I

Prometaphase chromosome

Sister chromatid II

Kinetochore II

Spindle pole

Figure 8.9
Spindle connections made by chromosomes at mitotic metaphase in typical animal cells. The two kinetochores of the chromosome connect to opposite spindle poles, ensuring that the chromatids are separated and moved to opposite spindle poles during anaphase.

8.3d Cytokinesis Completes Cell Division by Dividing the Cytoplasm between Daughter Cells

Cytokinesis, the division of the cytoplasm, usually follows the nuclear division stage of mitosis and produces two daughter cells, each containing one of the daughter nuclei. In most cells, cytokinesis begins during telophase or even late anaphase. By the time cytokinesis is completed, the daughter nuclei have progressed to the interphase stage and entered the G_1 phase of the next cell cycle.

Cytokinesis proceeds by different pathways in the different kingdoms of eukaryotic organisms. In animals, protists, and many fungi, a groove, the **furrow,** girdles the cell and gradually deepens until it cuts the cytoplasm into two parts. In plants, a new cell wall, called the **cell plate,** forms between the daughter nuclei and grows laterally until it divides the cytoplasm. In both cases, the plane of cytoplasmic division is determined by the layer of microtubules that persist at the former spindle midpoint.

Furrowing. In furrowing, the layer of microtubules that remains at the former spindle midpoint expands laterally until it stretches entirely across the dividing

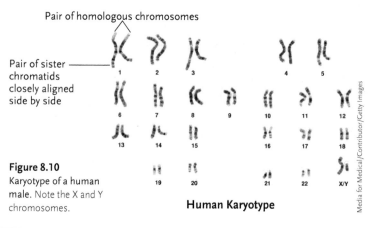

Pair of homologous chromosomes

Pair of sister chromatids closely aligned side by side

1 2 3 4 5

6 7 8 9 10 11 12

13 14 15 16 17 18

19 20 21 22 X/Y

Figure 8.10
Karyotype of a human male. Note the X and Y chromosomes.

Human Karyotype

Media for Medical/Contributor/Getty Images

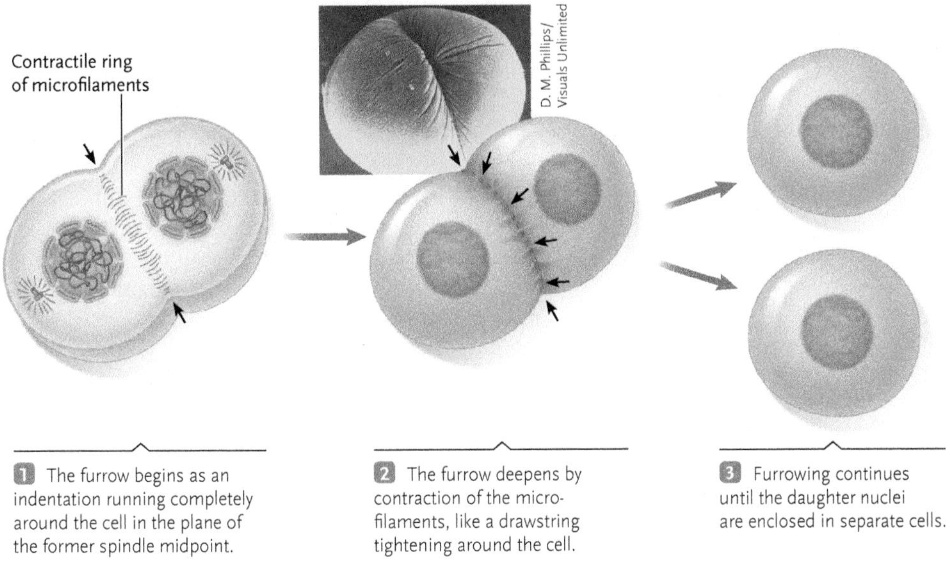

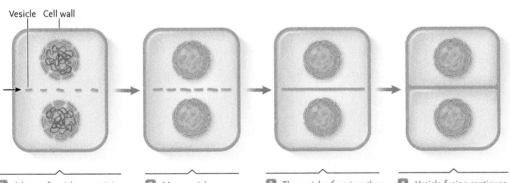

Contractile ring
of microfilaments

D. M. Phillips/
Visuals Unlimited

Figure 8.11
Cytokinesis by furrowing. The micrograph shows a furrow developing in the first division of a fertilized egg cell.

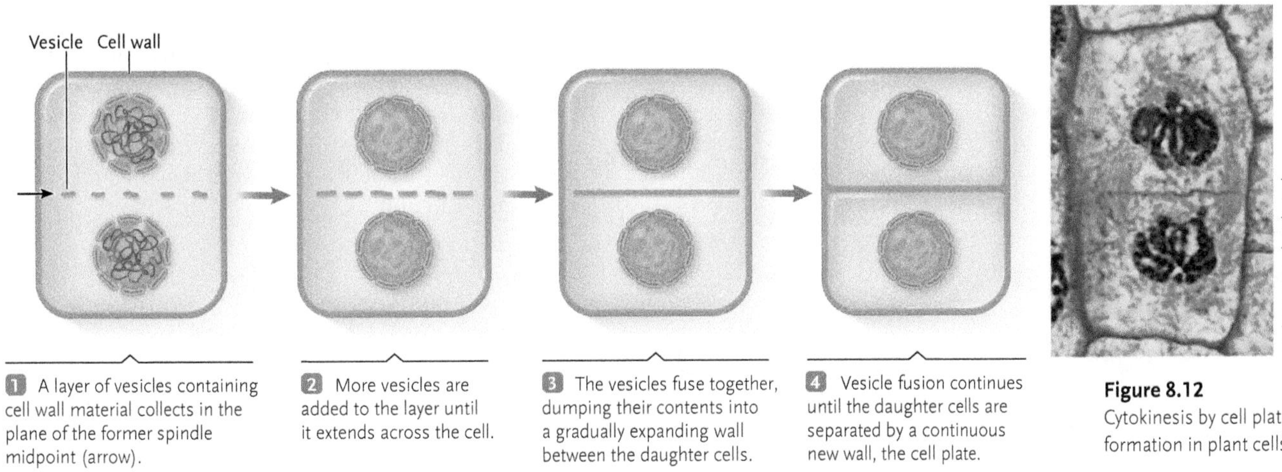

1 The furrow begins as an indentation running completely around the cell in the plane of the former spindle midpoint.

2 The furrow deepens by contraction of the microfilaments, like a drawstring tightening around the cell.

3 Furrowing continues until the daughter nuclei are enclosed in separate cells.

Vesicle Cell wall

R. Calentine/Visuals Unlimited

1 A layer of vesicles containing cell wall material collects in the plane of the former spindle midpoint (arrow).

2 More vesicles are added to the layer until it extends across the cell.

3 The vesicles fuse together, dumping their contents into a gradually expanding wall between the daughter cells.

4 Vesicle fusion continues until the daughter cells are separated by a continuous new wall, the cell plate.

Figure 8.12
Cytokinesis by cell plate formation in plant cells.

cell **(Figure 8.11)**. As the layer develops, a band of microfilaments forms just inside the plasma membrane, forming a belt that follows the inside boundary of the cell in the plane of the microtubule layer (microfilaments are discussed in Section 2.3f). Powered by motor proteins, the microfilaments slide together, tightening the band and constricting the cell. The constriction forms a groove—the furrow—in the plasma membrane. The furrow gradually deepens, much like the tightening of a drawstring, until the daughter cells are completely separated. The cytoplasmic division isolates the daughter nuclei in the two cells and, at the same time, distributes the organelles and other structures (which have also doubled) approximately equally.

Cell Plate Formation. In cell plate formation, the layer of microtubules that persists at the former spindle midpoint serves as an organizing site for vesicles produced by the endoplasmic reticulum (ER) and Golgi complex **(Figure 8.12)**. As the vesicles collect, the layer

expands until it spreads entirely across the dividing cell. During this expansion, the vesicles fuse together and their contents assemble into a new cell wall—the cell plate—stretching completely across the former spindle midpoint. The junction separates the cytoplasm and its organelles into two parts and isolates the daughter nuclei in separate cells. The plasma membranes that line the two surfaces of the cell plate are derived from the vesicle membranes.

STUDY BREAK

1. During which stage(s) of the cell cycle is a chromosome composed of two chromatids?
2. What are the conditions under which a chromosome could appear as an X shape under the microscope?
3. How does cytokinesis differ in plant and animal cells?

8.4 Formation and Action of the Mitotic Spindle

The mitotic spindle is central to both mitosis and cytokinesis. The spindle is made up of microtubules and their proteins, and its activities depend on their changing patterns of organization during the cell cycle.

Microtubules form a major part of the interphase cytoskeleton of eukaryotic cells. (Section 2.3f outlines the patterns of microtubule organization in the cytoskeleton.) As mitosis approaches, the microtubules disassemble from their interphase arrangement and reorganize into the spindle, which grows until it fills almost the entire cell. This reorganization follows one of two pathways in different organisms, depending on the presence or absence of a *centrosome* during interphase. However, once organized, the basic function of the spindle is the same, regardless of whether a centrosome is present.

8.4a Animals and Plants Form Spindles in Different Ways

Animal cells and many protists have a **centrosome**, a site near the nucleus from which microtubules radiate outward in all directions (**Figure 8.13**, step 1). The centrosome is the main **microtubule organizing centre** (**MTOC**) of the cell, anchoring the microtubule cytoskeleton during interphase and positioning many of the cytoplasmic organelles. The centrosome contains a pair of **centrioles**, usually arranged at right angles to each other. Although centrioles originally appeared to be important in the construction of the mitotic spindle, it has now been shown that they can be removed with no ill effect. The primary function of centrioles is actually to generate the microtubules needed for flagella or cilia, the whiplike extensions that provide cell motility.

When DNA replicates during the S phase of the cell cycle, the centrioles within the centrosome also duplicate, producing two pairs of centrioles (see Figure 8.13, step 2). As prophase begins in the M phase, the centrosome separates into two parts (step 3). The duplicated centrosomes, with the centrioles inside them, continue to separate until they reach opposite ends of the nucleus (step 4). As the centrosomes move apart, the microtubules between them lengthen and increase in number.

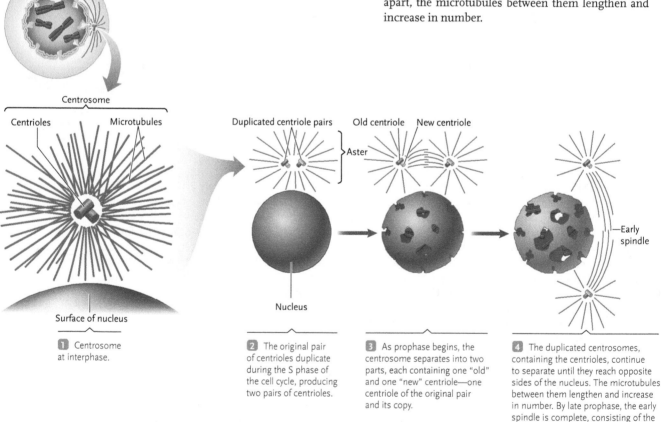

Figure 8.13
The centrosome and its role in spindle formation.

By late prophase, when the centrosomes are fully separated, the microtubules that extend between them form a large mass around one side of the nucleus called the early spindle. When the nuclear envelope subsequently breaks down at the end of prophase, the spindle moves into the region formerly occupied by the nucleus and continues growing until it fills the cytoplasm. The microtubules that extend from the centrosomes also grow in length and extent, producing radiating arrays that appear starlike under the light microscope. Initially named by early microscopists, **asters** are the centrosomes at the spindle tips, which form the poles of the spindle. By separating the duplicated centrioles, the spindle ensures that, when the cytoplasm divides during cytokinesis, the daughter cells each receive a pair of centrioles.

No centrosome or centrioles are present in angiosperms (flowering plants) or in most gymnosperms, such as conifers. Instead, the spindle forms from microtubules that assemble in all directions from multiple MTOCs surrounding the entire nucleus (see prophase in Figure 8.8). When the nuclear envelope breaks down at the end of prophase, the spindle moves into the former nuclear region, as in animals.

8.4b Mitotic Spindles May Move Chromosomes by a Combination of Two Mechanisms

When fully formed at metaphase, the spindle may contain from hundreds to many thousands of microtubules, depending on the species **(Figure 8.14)**. In almost all eukaryotes, these microtubules are divided into two groups. Some, called kinetochore microtubules, connect the chromosomes to the spindle poles **(Figure 8.15a)**. Others, called nonkinetochore microtubules, extend between the spindle poles without connecting to chromosomes; at the spindle midpoint, the microtubules from one pole overlap with the microtubules from the opposite pole (Figure 8.15b). The separation of the chromosomes at anaphase appears to result from a combination of separate but coordinated movements produced by the two types of microtubules.

The exact mechanism by which chromosomes move is still uncertain; at one time, it was believed that microtubules pulled the chromosomes toward the poles of dividing cells. However, subsequent data suggest that chromosomes "walk" themselves to the poles along stationary microtubules, using motor proteins in their kinetochores **(Figure 8.16, p. 180)**. The tubulin subunits of the kinetochore microtubules disassemble as the kinetochores pass along them; thus, the microtubules become shorter as the movement progresses (see Figure 8.15a). The movement is similar to pulling yourself, hand over hand, up a rope as it falls apart behind you.

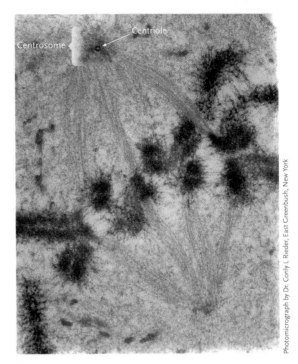

Photomicrograph by Dr. Conly L Rieder, East Greenbush, New York

Figure 8.14
A fully developed spindle in a mammalian cell. Only microtubules connected to chromosomes have been caught in the plane of this section. One of the centrioles is visible in cross-section in the centrosome at the top of the micrograph (arrow). Original magnification × 14 000.

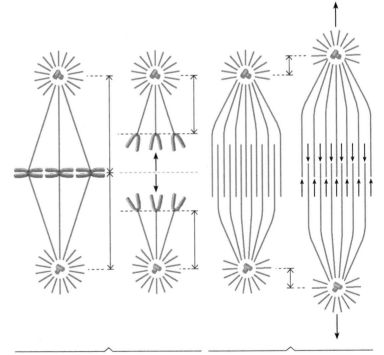

a. The kinetochore microtubules connected to the kinetochores of the chromosomes become shorter, lessening the distance from the chromosomes to the poles.

b. Sliding of the nonkinetochore microtubules in the zone of overlap at the spindle midpoint pushes poles farther apart and increases the total length of the spindle.

Figure 8.15
The two microtubule-based movements of the anaphase spindle.

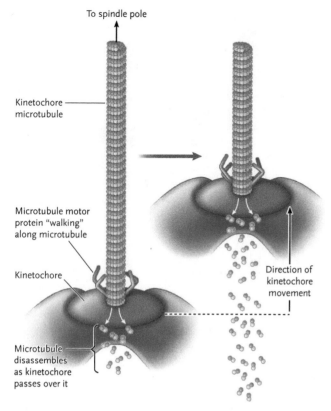

Figure 8.16
Microtubule motor proteins "walking" the kinetochore of a chromosome along a microtubule.

Chromosomes can also move toward the poles by a mechanism in which motor proteins at the spindle poles pull kinetochore microtubules poleward, disassembling those microtubules into tubulin subunits as that occurs. Both walking and pulling mechanisms are used in mitosis, although the relative contributions of the two mechanisms to chromosome movement varies among species and cell types. (The cell type in the experiment of Figure 8.16 predominantly used walking.) In nonkinetochore microtubule-based movement, the entire spindle is lengthened, elongating the cell in Metaphase and Anaphase. (see Figure 8.15b). The pushing movement is presumably produced by microtubules sliding over one another in the zone of overlap, powered by proteins acting as microtubule motors. In many species, the nonkinetochore microtubules also push the poles apart by growing in length as they slide.

STUDY BREAK

1. What is the role of the centrosome?
2. What is the role of the kinetochore?

8.5 Cell Cycle Regulation

In this section, we discuss experimental evidence for (and the operation of) regulatory mechanisms that control the mitotic cell cycle.

8.5a Cell Fusion Experiments and Studies of Yeast Mutants Identified Molecules That Control the Cell Cycle

The first insights into how the cell cycle is regulated came from experiments by Robert T. Johnson and Potu N. Rao at the University of Colorado Medical Center, Denver, published in 1970. They fused human

Evidence supporting kinetochore-based movement comes from experiments in which researchers tagged kinetochore microtubules with a microscopic beam of ultraviolet light, producing bleached sites that could be seen in the light microscope **(Figure 8.17).** As the chromosomes moved to the spindle poles, the bleached sites stayed in the same place. This result showed that the kinetochore microtubules do not move much with respect to the poles during the anaphase movement.

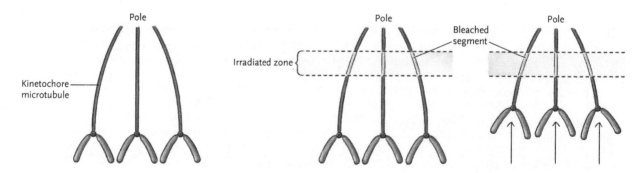

Experimental Research Figure 8.17 Experiment demonstrating that kinetochore microtubules remain stationary as chromosomes move **during anaphase.** A bleached region of spindle remained at the same distance from the pole as the chromosomes moved toward the pole. These observations support the hypothesis that chromosomes move by sliding over or along microtubules.

HeLa cells (a type of cancer cell that can be grown in cell culture) that were in different stages of the cell cycle and determined whether one nucleus could influence the other. Their results suggested that specific molecules in the cytoplasm cause the progression of cells from G_1 to S, and from G_2 into M.

Some key research using baker's yeast, *S. cerevisiae*, helped to identify these cell cycle control molecules and contributed to our general understanding of how the cell cycle is regulated. (*The Purple Pages* describe yeast and its role in research in more detail.) In particular, Leland Hartwell investigated yeast mutants that become stuck at some point in the cell cycle, but only when they are cultured at a high temperature. By growing the mutant cells initially at the standard temperature, and then shifting the cells to the higher temperature, Hartwell was able to use time-lapse photomicroscopy to see if and when growth and division were affected. In this way he isolated many cell division cycle, or *cdc*, mutants. By examining the mutants, he could identify the stage in the cell cycle where each mutant type was blocked by noting whether nuclei had divided, chromosomes had condensed, the mitotic spindle had formed, cytokinesis had occurred, and so on. Using this approach, Hartwell identified many genes that code for proteins involved in yeast's cell cycle and hypothesized where in the cycle these proteins operated. As might be expected, some of the proteins were involved in DNA replication, but a number of others were shown to function in cell cycle regulation. Hartwell received a Nobel Prize in 2001 for his discovery.

Paul Nurse of the Imperial Cancer Research Fund, London, United Kingdom, carried out similar research with the fission yeast *Schizosaccharomyces pombe*, a species that divides by fission rather than budding. He identified a gene called *cdc2* that encodes a protein needed for the cell to progress from G_2 to M. Nurse also made the breakthrough discovery that all eukaryotic cells studied have counterparts of the yeast *cdc2* gene, implying that this gene originated early during eukaryotic evolution and has played an essential role in cell cycle regulation in all eukaryotes since that time. The protein product of *cdc2* is a protein kinase, an enzyme that catalyzes the phosphorylation of a target protein. (Recall from Section 5.7c that phosphorylation of proteins by protein kinases can activate or inactivate proteins.) That discovery was pivotal in determining how cell cycle regulation occurs. Paul Nurse received a Nobel Prize in 2001 for his discovery.

8.5b The Cell Cycle Can Be Arrested at Specific Checkpoints

A cell has internal controls that monitor its progression through the cell cycle through the action of a particular set of control proteins called *cyclins*. Three key **checkpoints** prevent critical phases from beginning until the previous phases are completed correctly (**Figure 8.18, p. 182**):

1. The G_1/S *checkpoint* is the main point in the cell cycle at which the mechanisms governing the cell cycle determine whether the cell will proceed through the rest of the cell cycle and divide. Once it passes this checkpoint, the cell is committed to continue the cell cycle through to cell division in M. The cell cycle arrests (the cell stops proceeding through the cell cycle) at the G_1/S checkpoint if, for example, the DNA is damaged by radiation or chemicals. The G_1/S checkpoint is also the primary point at which cells "read" extracellular signals for cell growth and division. Therefore, if a hormone or growth factor required for stimulating cell growth is absent, the cells may arrest at this checkpoint. (Extracellular signals and their effects on the cell cycle are discussed in more detail later.)

2. The G_2/M *checkpoint* is at the junction between the G_2 and M phases. Passage through this checkpoint commits a cell to mitosis. Cells are arrested at the G_2/M checkpoint if DNA was not replicated fully in S, or if the DNA has been damaged by radiation or chemicals. Complete DNA replication is essential for producing genetically identical daughter cells, highlighting the importance of this checkpoint.

3. The *mitotic spindle checkpoint* is within the M phase before metaphase. This checkpoint assesses whether chromosomes are attached properly to the mitotic spindle so that they will align correctly at the metaphase plate. The checkpoint is essential for production of genetically identical daughter cells, which depends on separation of daughter chromosomes in anaphase, which, in turn, depends on the correct alignment of the chromosomes on the spindle in metaphase. Once the cell begins anaphase, it is irreversibly committed to completing M, underlining the importance of the mitotic spindle checkpoint.

The control systems that operate at the checkpoints are signals to stop; basically, they are brakes. This becomes evident when a checkpoint is inactivated by mutation or chemical treatment, allowing the cell cycle to proceed, even if DNA is damaged, DNA replication is incomplete, or the spindle did not assemble completely.

8.5c Cyclins and Cyclin-Dependent Kinases Are the Internal Controls That Directly Regulate Cell Division

The direct regulation of the cell cycle involves an internal control system consisting of proteins called **cyclins** and enzymes called **cyclin-dependent kinases (Cdks)** (see Figure 8.18, p. 182). A Cdk is a *protein kinase*, which phosphorylates and thereby regulates the

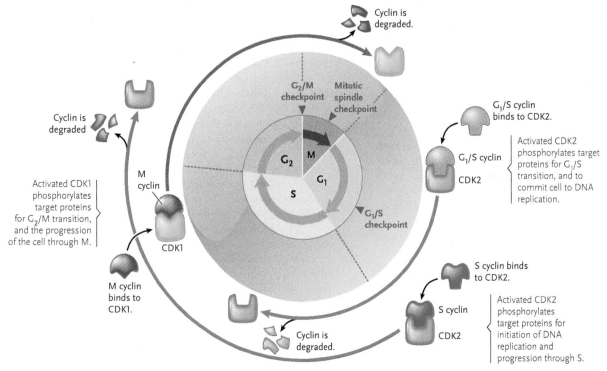

Figure 8.18

Regulation of the mitotic cell cycle by internal controls. Three key checkpoints for the G_1/S transition, for the G_2/M transition, and for the attachment of chromosomes to the mitotic spindle monitor cell cycle events to prevent crucial phases of the cell cycle from starting until previous phases are completed correctly. Complexes of cyclins and cyclin-dependent kinases (Cdks) regulate the progression of the cell through the cell cycle. The three cyclin–Cdks present in all eukaryotes are shown. The Cdks are present throughout the cell cycle, but they are active only when complexed with a cyclin (shown by the broad arrows in the figure). Each cyclin is synthesized and degraded in a regulated way so that it is present only for a particular phase of the cell cycle. During that phase, the Cdk to which it is bound phosphorylates and, thereby, regulates the activity of target proteins in the cell that are involved in initiating or regulating key events of the cell cycle.

activity of target proteins. Cdk enzymes are "cyclin dependent" because they are active *only* when bound to a cyclin molecule. Cyclins are named because their concentrations change as the cell cycle progresses. R. Timothy Hunt of the Imperial Cancer Research Fund received a Nobel Prize in 2001 for discovering cyclins. The basic control of the cell cycle by Cdks and cyclins is the same in all eukaryotes, but there are differences in the number and types of the molecules. We will focus on cell cycle regulation in vertebrates to explain how these proteins work.

The concentrations of the various Cdks remain constant throughout the cell cycle, while the concentrations of cyclins change as they are synthesized and degraded at specific stages of the cell cycle. Thus, a specific Cdk becomes active when the cell synthesizes the cyclin that binds to it and remains active until the cyclin is degraded. Each active Cdk phosphorylates particular target proteins, which play roles in initiating or regulating key events of the cell cycle. The phosphorylation regulates the activities of these proteins and keeps the cycle operating in an orderly way. These key events are DNA replication, mitosis, and cytokinesis. A succession of cyclin–Cdk complexes, each of which has specific regulatory effects, ensures that these

stages follow in sequence somewhat like a clock passing through the sequence of hours. Regulation of the activity of cyclin–Cdk complexes is integrated with the regulatory events at the cell cycle checkpoints to ensure that daughter cells do not inherit damaged DNA or abnormal numbers of chromosomes.

Three classes of cyclins, each named for the stage of the cell cycle at which they bind and activate Cdks, operate in all eukaryotes (see Figure 8.18):

1. G_1/S cyclin binds to Cdk2 near the end of G_1, forming a complex required for the cell to make the transition from G_1 to S and to commit the cell to DNA replication.
2. S cyclin binds to Cdk2 in the S phase, forming a complex required for the initiation of DNA replication and the progression of the cell through S.
3. M cyclin binds to Cdk1 in G_2, forming a complex required for the transition from G_2 and M and the progression of the cell through mitosis.

The M cyclin–Cdk1 complex is also called **M phase-promoting factor (MPF)**. In addition to initiating mitosis, the M cyclin–Cdk1 complex (MPF) also orchestrates some of its key events. When all chromosomes are correctly attached to the mitotic spindle near the end of metaphase, the M cyclin–Cdk1 complex activates another enzyme complex, the **anaphase-promoting complex (APC)**. Activated APC degrades an inhibitor of anaphase, leading to the separation of sister chromatids and the onset of daughter chromosome separation in anaphase. Later in anaphase, APC directs the degradation of the M cyclin, causing Cdk1 to lose its activity. The loss of Cdk1 activity then allows the separated chromosomes to become extended again, the nuclear envelope to reform around the two clusters of daughter chromosomes in telophase, and the cytoplasm then to divide in cytokinesis.

8.5d External Controls Coordinate the Mitotic Cell Cycle of Individual Cells with the Overall Activities of the Organism

The internal controls that regulate the cell cycle are modified by signal molecules that originate from outside the dividing cells. In animals, these signal molecules include the peptide hormones and similar proteins called growth or death factors.

Many of these external factors bind to receptors at the cell surface, which respond by triggering reactions inside the cell. These reactions often include steps that add phosphate groups to the cyclin–Cdk complexes, thereby affecting their function. The overall effect is to speed, slow, or stop the progress of cell division, depending on the particular hormone or factor and the internal pathway that is stimulated. Some growth factors are even able to break the arrest of cells shunted into the G_0 stage and return them to active division. (Hormones, growth factors, and other signal molecules are part of the cell communication system, as discussed in Chapter 5.)

Cell surface receptors in animal cells also recognize contact with other cells or with molecules of the extracellular matrix (ECM). The contact triggers internal reaction pathways that inhibit division by arresting the cell cycle, usually in the G_1 phase. The response, called **contact inhibition**, stabilizes cell growth in fully developed organs and tissues. As long as the cells of most tissues are in contact with one another or with the ECM, they are shunted into the G_0 phase and prevented from dividing. If the contacts are broken, the freed cells often enter rounds of division.

Contact inhibition is easily observed in cultured mammalian cells grown on a glass or plastic surface. In such cultures, division proceeds until all the cells are in contact with their neighbours in a continuous, unbroken, single layer. At this point, division stops. If a researcher then scrapes some of the cells from the surface, cells at the edges of the "wound" are released from inhibition and divide until they form a continuous layer and all the cells are again in contact with their neighbours.

8.5e Stem Cells Exhibit Asymmetric Cell Division

The mitotic mechanism described so far in this chapter is symmetric in that it produces two daughter cells of roughly the same size, shape, and function whose genomes are essentially identical. However, asymmetric cell division, producing daughter cells that are decidedly different in some characteristic or other, is quite common in multicellular organisms, particularly during growth and development. One of the most striking examples of asymmetric cell division is found in the populations of stem cells present in plant meristem and various animal tissues **(Figure 8.19)**.

Asymmetric cell division of stem cells provides new cells for growth and maintenance while, at the same time, maintaining the pool of stem cells. Stem cell division is asymmetric in that the two daughter cells each have a different fate. One daughter cell remains a stem cell and therefore contributes to a pool of self-renewing, relatively undifferentiated cells that are capable of multiple cell divisions. The other daughter cell, called a progenitor cell, divides a limited

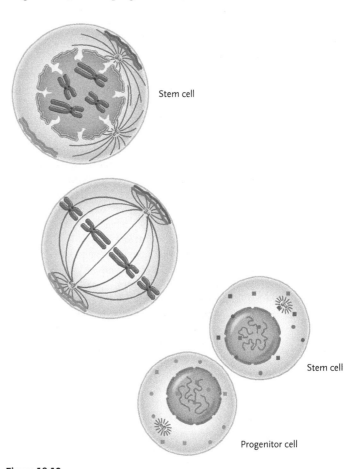

Stem cell

Stem cell

Progenitor cell

Figure 18.19
Asymmetric cell division of stem cells. The localization of different gene regulatory proteins and mRNA at the two poles during early mitosis anchors the mitotic spindle and ensures that the two daughter cells inherit a different array of regulatory elements. One cell remains a stem cell; the other becomes a differentiating progenitor cell.

number of times while undergoing subsequent differentiation into a specialized cell type needed for growth.

This asymmetry in cell fate arises from the ability of stem cells to specify the location of certain cytoplasmic components during cell division. Although mitosis divides the DNA and distributes cytoplasmic organelles relatively equally to each daughter cell, specific regulatory proteins and mRNAs (e.g., cyclins and transcription factors) are localized at only one pole or the other in the dividing cell. Therefore, the two resulting daughter cells each receive a different array of regulatory proteins that will, in turn, influence gene expression toward different cell fates.

Regulation of asymmetric division ensures the important balance between maintaining the stem cell pool and producing specialized somatic tissue. The local area where stem cells are dividing is called a niche. Signalling proteins produced by cells surrounding the niche maintain external regulation of stem cell division. Loss of this regulation is associated with cancer in brain and other tissues.

8.5f Most Cells in a Multicellular Body Cannot Divide Indefinitely

In 1961, Leonard Hayflick and Paul Moorhead reported that normal human skin cells eventually stopped dividing when grown in artificial culture. This loss of proliferative ability over time is called **cellular senescence**, and scientists have been searching for the *Hayflick factors* that are responsible for it. We consider two candidates: DNA damage and telomere shortening.

The progressive accumulation of damage to a cell's DNA sequence, or its chromosome structure, or even the genes coding for the enzyme machinery needed to repair such damage, is perhaps the most intuitive Hayflick factor. One would expect "older" cells to have diminished function if they have suffered mutations in genes controlling critical activities.

Telomeres are repetitive DNA sequences that are added to the ends of chromosomes by the enzyme telomerase. Since DNA replication machinery is unable to replicate the entire ends of linear chromosomes, telomere sequence is lost at each round of replication (see Figure 12.18, Chapter 12). Once telomeres diminish to a certain minimum length, cells stop dividing (senesce) and may die.

You might wonder why we do not just take a pill to stimulate our telomerase, rejuvenate our cells, and extend our life span. It turns out that cellular senescence is an important antitumour mechanism. Some researchers have stimulated the telomerase of cultured cells: they become "immortal" and divide out of control. Mice that have been engineered to lack telomerase, and therefore suffer faster senescence, are significantly *resistant* to cancer. It seems that by the time cells are short on telomeres, many of them are also a long way toward cancerous growth, as described below.

8.5g Cell Cycle Controls Are Lost in Cancer

Cancer occurs when cells lose the normal controls that determine when and how often they will divide. Cancer cells divide continuously and uncontrollably, producing a rapidly growing mass called a tumour **(Figure 8.20)**. Cancer cells also typically lose their adhesions to other cells and may become actively mobile. As a result, in a process called metastasis, they tend to break loose from an original tumour, spread throughout the body, and grow into new tumours in other body regions. Metastasis is promoted by changes that defeat contact inhibition and alter the cell surface molecules that link cells together or to the ECM.

Growing tumours damage surrounding normal tissues by compressing them and interfering with blood supply and nerve function. Tumours may also break through barriers such as the outer skin, internal cell layers, or the gut wall. The breakthroughs cause bleeding, open the body to infection by microorganisms, and destroy the separation of body compartments necessary for normal function. Both compression and breakthroughs can cause pain that, in advanced cases, may become extreme. As tumours increase in mass, the actively growing and dividing cancer cells may deprive normal cells of their required nutrients, leading to generally impaired body functions, muscular weakness, fatigue, and weight loss.

Cancer cells have typically accumulated mutations in a variety of genes that promote uncontrolled cell division or metastasis. Before they undergo mutation, many of these genes code for components of the cyclin–Cdk system that regulates cell division; others encode proteins that regulate gene expression, form cell surface receptors, or make up elements of the signalling pathways controlled by the receptors. When

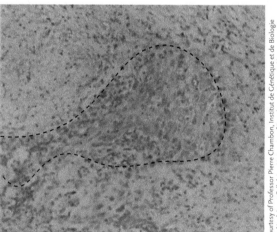

Courtesy of Professor Pierre Chambon, Institut de Génétique et de Biologie Moléculaire et Cellulaire, University of Strasbourg. Reprinted by permission from *Nature* 348:699. Copyright 1990 Macmillan Magazines, Ltd.

Figure 8.20

A mass of tumour cells (dashed line) embedded in normal tissue. As is typical, the tumour cells appear to be more densely packed because they have less cytoplasmic volume than normal cells. Original magnification × 270.

Roscovitine

Screening of a wide variety of artificially modified adenine molecules has led to the discovery of a group of compounds related to plant cytokinin hormones that selectively inhibit Cdks by competing for (and blocking) their ATP binding site. The example shown below, roscovitine, has antitumour and antiviral activity resulting from stimulation of cell death in affected cells. Note the adenine in each molecule (rectangle).

Figure 1
(a) *Roscovitine.* **(b)** *The plant cytokinin hormone zeatin.* **(c)** *ATP.*

mutated, the genes, called **oncogenes**, encode altered versions of these products.

For example, a mutation in a gene that codes for a surface receptor might result in a protein that is constantly active even without binding the intended extracellular signal molecule. As a result, the internal reaction pathways triggered by the receptor, which induce cell division, are continually stimulated. Another mutation, this time in a cyclin gene, could result in increased cyclin–Cdk binding that triggers DNA replication and the rest of the cell cycle. Cancer, oncogenes, and the alterations that convert normal genes to oncogenes are discussed in further detail in Chapter 14.

8.5h Some Cells Are Programmed to Die

Normal development of multicellular organisms is a highly regulated balance between cell proliferation and cell death. Programmed cell death, called **apoptosis**, appears to be a very ancient mechanism common to all multicellular eukaryotes studied so far. Initiation of cell death can result from either internal or external signals. The nematode *Caenorhabditis elegans* is one useful model organism to study this signalling because all adult animals have exactly the same number of cells **(Figure 8.21a)**.

In addition, the fate of each of these cells, from the zygote to the adult, can be tracked with a light microscope. Detailed studies of the 1090 cells that are generated to form an adult reveal that 131 of them not only stop dividing—they stop living.

The apoptosis machinery in *C. elegans* is available in all of its cells, waiting in an inactive state for the right trigger. The main "executioner" enzyme is one of a family of normally inactive proteases called **caspases** and is coded by the *cell death abnormal* gene, *CED-3* (Figure 8.21b). If a cell is destined to die by

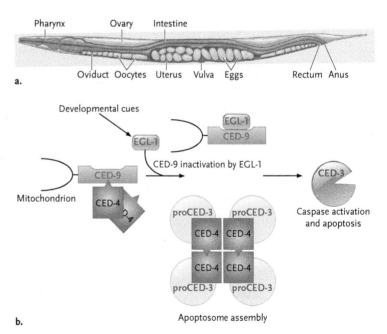

Figure 8.21
(a) The adult nematode "worm" *Caenorhabditis elegans* is about 1 mm long and is composed of 959 living cells. **(b)** The main cascade of programmed cell death in *C. elegans*. Cells destined to die express EGL-1 protein that, by binding to mitochondrial-bound CED-9, releases CED-4 protein. A complex of CED-4 then activates the main "executioner" caspase protease enzyme, CED-3.

PEOPLE BEHIND BIOLOGY 8.3
Dr. John Dick, *University of Toronto*

One of the best places to find actively cycling cells in a vertebrate body is in bone marrow. It is here that hematopoietic stem cells divide to produce progeny cells capable of proliferating and differentiating into the various specialized cells needed to maintain the liquid tissue called blood.

One of the best places to try to understand this developmental process, as well as the mechanisms underlying human blood disorders and cancer (leukemia), is the laboratory of John Dick at the University of Toronto. Dick is a professor of medical genetics and microbiology, a fellow of the Royal Society of Canada, and Canada Research Chair in Stem Cell Biology. Originally from rural Manitoba, he now heads a team of coworkers and international collaborators from his office in the MaRS Discovery District in downtown Toronto.

One of Dick's most powerful tools, one that gained him international recognition, is his system for modelling the production of blood by establishing human hematopoietic cells in mice. That is, he creates mice that make human blood instead of their usual mouse blood. Mice that make human blood also show human blood disorders, and Dick's team has been able to study the initiation and progression of human leukemia entirely in mice. This mouse model system provides an opportunity to better understand the genetic changes involved in leukemia and the effectiveness of emerging therapies.

Dick's sustained success arises from his ability to locate stem cells and understand their biology. His original discovery of the role of aberrant stem cells at the root of leukemia is now seen as the opening line of a story that is fundamentally altering the prevailing view of cancer and its treatment. If Dick is correct in his hypothesis that many cancers are initiated and fed by the progeny of relatively slow cycling, genetically aberrant stem cells (as is suggested by a growing body of research), then traditional therapies designed to indiscriminately kill rapidly cycling cancer cells are understandably "hit and miss." Dick has been able to identify and sort colon cancer cells into two fractions: those that can reproduce new tumours and those that cannot. This ability to specifically target cancer stem cells will be at the centre of the development of anticancer therapies.

apoptosis, the cascade begins when internal developmental cues stimulate expression of a gene called *egg laying -deficient, EGL-1*. EGL-1 protein then binds to CED-9 protein, resulting in the release of bound CED-4 protein and the formation of an active apoptosome. CED-3 caspase is thus activated, and cell death ensues. The causes of death are nuclear DNA degradation and disrupted mitochondrial function. The corpses of dead cells are engulfed and eaten by neighbouring cells. The 2002 Nobel Prize in Physiology or Medicine was awarded jointly to Sydney Brenner, Robert Horvitz, and John Sulston for their discoveries concerning "genetic regulation of organ development and programmed cell death" in *C. elegans*. The Model Research Organisms section *of The Purple Pages* describes *C. elegans* and its role in research in more detail.

Removing cells that are surplus for development is one function of apoptosis, but why are other cells programmed to die? We hope you will agree that it would be beneficial for an organism to provoke apoptosis in cells suffering severe DNA damage, viral infection, or mutations leading to uncontrolled division. Sometimes perfectly normal and healthy cells die by apoptosis. For instance, the cells that make up xylem elements in the vascular tissue of woody plants actually function as "skeletons." They must die to fulfill their function as hollow, water-conducting pipes.

The overview of the cell cycle and its regulation presented in this chapter only hints at the complexity of cell growth and division. The likelihood of any given cell dividing is determined by weighing a variety of internal signals in the context of external cues from the environment. If a cell is destined to divide, then the problem of accurately replicating and partitioning its DNA requires a highly regulated, intricately interrelated series of mechanisms. Although male Australian Jack Jumper ants (*Myrmecia pilosula*) have only one chromosome to deal with, think of the problems faced by the fern *Ophioglossum pycnostichum*, which has 1260 chromosomes in each cell!

STUDY BREAK

1. Explain how the *activity* of Cdks can rise and fall with each turn of the cell cycle, whereas the *concentration* of these enzymes remains constant.
2. What observation do Hayflick factors explain?
3. What is metastasis?

Review

 aplia

To access course materials such as Aplia and other companion resources, please visit www.NELSONbrain.com.

8.1 The Cycle of Cell Growth and Division: An Overview

- In mitotic cell division, DNA replication is followed by the equal separation—that is, segregation—of the replicated DNA molecules and their delivery to daughter cells. The process ensures that the two cell products of a division have the same genetic information as the parent cell entering division.

- Mitosis is the basis for growth and maintenance of body mass in multicelled eukaryotes and for the reproduction of many single-celled eukaryotes.

- The chromosomes of eukaryotic cells are individual, linear DNA molecules with associated proteins.

- DNA replication and the duplication of chromosomal proteins convert each chromosome into a structure composed of two exact copies known as sister chromatids.

8.2 The Cell Cycle in Prokaryotic Organisms

- Prokaryotic cells undergo a cycle of binary fission involving coordinated cytoplasmic growth, DNA replication, and cell division, producing two daughter cells from an original parent cell.

- Replication of the bacterial chromosome consumes most of the time in the cell cycle and begins at a single site called the origin through reactions catalyzed by enzymes located in the middle of the cell. Once the origin of replication (*ori*) is duplicated, the two origins actively migrate to the two ends of the cell. Division of the cytoplasm then occurs through a partition of cell wall material that grows inward until the cell is separated into two parts (see Figure 8.3).

8.3 Mitosis and the Eukaryotic Cell Cycle

- Mitosis and interphase constitute the mitotic cell cycle. Mitosis occurs in five stages. In prophase (stage 1), the chromosomes condense into short rods and the spindle forms in the cytoplasm (see Figures 8.7 and 8.8).

- In prometaphase (stage 2), the nuclear envelope breaks down, the spindle enters the former nuclear area, and the sister chromatids of each chromosome make connections to opposite spindle poles. Each chromatid has a kinetochore that attaches to spindle microtubules (see Figures 8.7 and 8.8).

- In metaphase (stage 3), the spindle is fully formed and the chromosomes, moved by the spindle microtubules, become aligned at the metaphase plate (see Figure 8.7).

- In anaphase (stage 4), the spindle separates the sister chromatids and moves them to opposite spindle poles. At this point, chromosome segregation is complete (see Figures 8.7 and 8.8).

- In telophase (stage 5), the chromosomes decondense and return to the extended state typical of interphase. A new nuclear envelope forms around the chromosomes (see Figures 8.7 and 8.8).

- Cytokinesis, the division of the cytoplasm, completes cell division by producing two daughter cells, each containing a daughter nucleus produced by mitosis (see Figures 8.7 and 8.8).

- Cytokinesis in animal cells proceeds by furrowing, in which a band of microfilaments just under the plasma membrane contracts, gradually separating the cytoplasm into two parts (see Figure 8.11).

- In plant cytokinesis, cell wall material is deposited along the plane of the former spindle midpoint; the deposition continues until a continuous new wall, the cell plate, separates the daughter cells (see Figure 8.12).

8.4 Formation and Action of the Mitotic Spindle

- In animal cells, the centrosome divides and the two parts move apart. As they do so, the microtubules of the spindle form between them. In plant cells with no centrosome, the spindle microtubules assemble around the nucleus (see Figure 8.13).

- In the spindle, kinetochore microtubules run from the poles to the kinetochores of the chromosomes, and nonkinetochore microtubules run from the poles to a zone of overlap at the spindle midpoint without connecting to the chromosomes (see Figure 8.15).

- During anaphase, the kinetochores move along the kinetochore microtubules, pulling the chromosomes to the poles. The nonkinetochore microtubules slide over each other, pushing the poles farther apart (see Figures 8.15 and 8.16).

8.5 Cell Cycle Regulation

- The cell cycle is controlled directly by complexes of cyclins and a cyclin-dependent protein kinase (Cdk). A Cdk is activated when combined with a cyclin and then adds phosphate groups to target proteins, activating them. The activated proteins trigger the cell to progress to the next cell cycle stage. Each major stage of the cell cycle begins with activation of one or more cyclin–Cdk complexes and ends with deactivation of the complexes by breakdown of the cyclins (see Figure 8.18).

- Important internal controls create checkpoints to ensure that the reactions of one stage are complete before the cycle proceeds to the next stage.

- External controls are based primarily on surface receptors that recognize and bind signals such as peptide hormones and growth factors, surface groups on other cells, or molecules of the extracellular matrix (ECM). The binding triggers internal reactions that speed, slow, or stop cell division.

- Stem cells divide asymmetrically to produce two daughter cells with different developmental fates. Although they inherit the same genetic material, they contain different arrays of gene regulatory proteins.

- Most cells in multicellular eukaryotes progressively lose the ability to divide over time by a process called cellular senescence. Factors that contribute to senescence include accumulating DNA damage and shortening telomeres.

- In cancer, control of cell division is lost and cells divide continuously and uncontrollably, forming a rapidly growing mass of cells that interferes with body functions. Cancer cells also break loose from their original tumour (metastasize) to form additional tumours in other parts of the body.

- Certain cells may undergo a programmed cell death called apoptosis. Such a fate is appropriate for cells that are, for instance, surplus for development, damaged, infected, or functional only after death.

Questions

Self-Test Questions

1. Which of the following situations is characteristic of cell division in bacteria?
   a. Several chromatids are separated at anaphase.
   b. Binary fission produces four daughter cells.
   c. Replication begins at the *ori*, and the two new DNA molecules separate.
   d. The daughter cells receive different genetic information from the parent cell.

2. When does the mass of DNA in an elephant cell increase during the cell cycle?
   a. M phase (mitosis)
   b. G_1 phase
   c. G_2 phase
   d. S phase

3. Honeybee eggs that are not fertilized develop into fertile, haploid males called drones. Fertilized eggs can develop into diploid females, one of which might become a queen. (Fertilized eggs might also become males, but they are taken out and killed by the drones.)

   If the queen has 32 chromosomes in her body cells, how many chromatids will be present in a G_2 drone cell?
   a. 8
   b. 16
   c. 32
   d. 64

4. Which of the following is the major microtubule-organizing centre of the animal cell?
   a. the centrosome, composed of centrioles
   b. the chromatin, composed of chromatids
   c. the chromosomes, composed of centromeres
   d. the spindle, composed of actin

5. For one given oak tree cell, which of the following are more plentiful at the end of S phase than at the beginning?
   a. nuclei
   b. chromatids
   c. chromosomes
   d. Cdk2 molecules

6. Which of the following statements about mitosis is true?
   a. In prophase, the spindle separates sister chromatids and pulls them apart.
   b. Chromosomes congregate near the centre of the cell during metaphase.
   c. Both the animal cell furrow and the plant cell plate form at their former spindle poles.
   d. Cytokinesis describes the movement of chromosomes.

7. While researching an assignment on the Internet, you come across the following passage: "The cell cycle has a DNA synthesis phase (S phase) that doubles the normal full number of chromosomes from diploid ($2n$) to tetraploid ($4n$). This is followed by a G_2 cell phase that biochemically prepares the cell for the mitotic or M phase, which includes cytokinesis."

In what way is the author of the above passage mistaken?
   a. DNA synthesis does not occur in S phase.
   b. S phase does not increase ploidy from $2n$ to $4n$.
   c. G_2 does not follow S phase.
   d. Cytokinesis is not part of mitotic cell division.

8. Which of the following statements about cell cycle regulation is true?
   a. Caspase is inactivated by cyclin binding.
   b. Cyclin binding activates Cdks to degrade target proteins.
   c. Telomere shortening promotes cell cycling.
   d. Stem cells divide more often than other somatic cells.

9. Which of the following is a characteristic of cancer cells?
   a. avoidance of metastasis
   b. avoidance of Hayflick factors
   c. contact inhibition
   d. cycle arrest at checkpoints

10. Imagine that you are in a job interview for a pharmaceutical company and are asked to suggest a good mechanism for an anticancer drug. Which of the following mechanisms would you suggest?
   a. decreased apoptosis
   b. decreased binding of cyclin to Cdk
   c. increased Cdk activity
   d. increased telomerase

Questions for Discussion

1. You have a means of measuring the amount of DNA in a single cell. You first measure the amount of DNA during G_1. At what point(s) during the remainder of the cell cycle would you expect the amount of DNA per cell to change?

2. A cell has 38 chromosomes. After mitosis and cell division, 1 daughter cell has 39 chromosomes and the other has 37. What might have caused these abnormal chromosome numbers? What effects do you suppose this might have on cell function? Why?

3. Taxol (Bristol-Myers Squibb, New York), a substance derived from the Pacific yew (*Taxus brevifolia*), is effective in the treatment of breast and ovarian cancers. It works by stabilizing microtubules, thereby preventing them from disassembling. Why would this activity slow or stop the growth of cancer cells?

4. Many chemicals in the food we eat potentially have effects on cancer cells. Chocolate, for example, contains a number of flavonoid compounds, which act as natural antioxidants. Design an experiment to determine whether any of the flavonoids in chocolate inhibit the cell cycle of breast cancer cells growing in culture.

5. The genes and proteins involved in cell cycle regulation are very different in bacteria and archaea than in eukaryotes. However, both prokaryotic and eukaryotic organisms use similar molecular regulatory reactions to coordinate DNA synthesis with cell division. What does this observation mean from an evolutionary perspective?

Mating octopuses.

Genetic Recombination

WHY IT MATTERS

A couple clearly shows mutual interest. First, he caresses her with one arm, then another—then another, and another, and another. She reciprocates. This interaction goes on for hours—a hug here, a squeeze there. At the climactic moment, the male reaches deftly under his mantle and removes a packet of sperm, which he inserts under the mantle of the female. For every one of his sperm that successfully performs its function, a fertilized egg can develop into a new octopus.

For the octopus, sex is an occasional event, preceded by a courtship ritual that involves intermingled tentacles. For another marine animal, the slipper limpet, sex is a lifelong group activity. Slipper limpets are relatives of snails. Like many other animals, a slipper limpet passes through a free-living immature stage before it becomes a sexually mature adult. When the time comes for an immature limpet to transform into an adult, it settles onto a rock or other firm surface. If the limpet settles by itself, it develops into a female. If instead it settles on top of a female, it develops into a male. If another slipper limpet settles down on that male, it, too, becomes a male. Adult slipper limpets almost always live in such piles, with the one on the bottom always being a female. All the male limpets continually contribute sperm that fertilizes eggs shed by the female. If the one female dies, the surviving male at the bottom of the pile changes into a female and reproduction continues.

The life history of these octopuses and slipper limpets illustrates a tension in biology between sameness and difference. On the one hand, the growth and repair of their multicellular tissues depend on faithful replication of DNA during mitotic cell division, as described in the previous chapter. At the level of the organism, it is important that all the individual cells in the body of a slipper limpet, for example, are genetically identical. However, on the other hand, at the level of the population, it is important that the individual limpets are genetically *different* from one another. If populations have genetic variability, they have the potential to evolve. Natural selection can act on this variability such that certain variants leave more offspring than others. Over time, the relative proportion of different variants will change. This is evolution in action.

The ultimate source of genetic diversity is mutation of the DNA sequence, often resulting from errors during DNA replication. Since mutations are relatively rare, diversity is amplified through various mechanisms that shuffle existing mutations into novel combinations. This process, of literally cutting and pasting DNA backbones into new combinations, is called **genetic recombination** and is very widespread in nature. Genetic recombination allows "jumping genes" to move, inserts some viruses into the chromosome of their hosts, underlies the spread of antibiotic resistance among bacteria and archaea, and is at the heart of meiosis in eukaryotic organisms. Genetic recombination puts the "sexual" in sexual reproduction; without genetic recombination, reproduction is asexual, and offspring are simply identical clones of their parent. We begin this chapter with a look at the basic mechanism of DNA recombination.

see Chapter 12 for a more comprehensive look at DNA structure.) Figure 9.1a shows two similar double helixes lying close together as the first step in recombination. Most of the recombination discussed in this chapter occurs between regions of DNA that are very similar, but not identical, in the sequence of bases. Such regions, which may be as short as a few base pairs or as long as an entire chromosome, are called **homologous**. Homology allows different DNA molecules to line up and recombine precisely. Once homologous regions of DNA are paired, enzymes break a covalent bond in each of the four sugar–phosphate backbones. The free ends of each backbone are then exchanged and reattached to those of the other DNA molecule, as shown in Figure 9.1b and c. The result is two recombined molecules in which the original red DNA is now covalently bound to the blue DNA, and vice versa. In this chapter, we consider all the steps shown in Figure 9.1 to make up a single recombination event. This idea is worth restating: cutting and pasting *four* DNA backbones results in *one* recombination event.

As we move through diverse examples of recombination in this chapter, from plasmids to meiotic crossing-over to transposons, the characteristics of the

9.1 Mechanism of Genetic Recombination

Biologists who study genetic recombination have developed several models to precisely explain the process in various situations. In its most general sense, genetic recombination requires the following: two DNA molecules that differ from one another, a mechanism for bringing the DNA molecules into close proximity, and a collection of enzymes to "cut," "exchange," and "paste" the DNA back together. **Figure 9.1** conveys a very simple model for recombination that, although lacking the details of more sophisticated models, highlights the basic steps involved.

The elegant double helix of DNA represented in Figure 9.1 is one of the most widely recognized biological molecules; you should be able to discern the "backbone" of the helix winding around the interior "steps" of paired bases. The sugar–phosphate backbone is held together by strong covalent bonds, whereas the bases pair with their partners through relatively weak hydrogen bonds. (If these ideas are new to you,

Figure 9.1

A simplified model of genetic recombination. **(a)** Two molecules of DNA with similar sequence are brought into close proximity. **(b)** Enzymes nick the DNA backbones, exchange the ends, and reattach them. **(c)** and **(d)** In this case, the final result is two recombined DNA molecules.

participating DNA molecules will be different, the enzymes will change, and the results of recombination will have quite different consequences for the organism in question. However, you can always return to Figure 9.1 to remind yourself of the basic underlying mechanism.

STUDY BREAK

What would happen if two circular DNA molecules were involved in a single recombination event?

9.2 Genetic Recombination in Bacteria

Genetic recombination was historically first associated with meiosis in sexually reproducing eukaryotes. Genetic and microscopic research in the early decades of the twentieth century characterized recombination and culminated in the construction of the first genetic maps of chromosomes. However, by the middle of that century, improved techniques for studying the genetics of prokaryotic organisms (and their viruses) enabled researchers to look for evidence of genetic recombination even though these organisms do not reproduce sexually by meiosis. The data showed that, for particular bacteria, there are mechanisms to bring DNA from different cells together and that this DNA recombines to create offspring that are different from either parent cell. Bacteria clearly have a type of sex in their lives. It may be surprising for you to learn that, in some types of bacterial recombination, one of the participating cells is dead. Watch for this.

Escherichia coli, the most extensively studied prokaryotic organism, is named in honour of its discoverer, a Viennese pediatrician named Theodor Escherich, who isolated it from dirty diapers during an outbreak of diarrhea in 1885. Ready availability and ease of growth in the laboratory have made *E. coli* a workhorse of bacterial genetics that has helped lay the foundations for our understanding of the role of DNA as the genetic material, as well as the molecular structure, expression, and recombination of genes. (See more information about *E. coli* as a model research organism in *The Purple Pages*.)

9.2a Genetic Recombination Occurs in *E. coli*

In 1946, two scientists at Yale University, Joshua Lederberg and Edward L. Tatum, set out to determine if genetic recombination occurs in bacteria, using *E. coli* as their experimental organism. In essence, they were testing whether bacteria have a kind of sexuality in their reproduction process. In order to understand Lederberg and Tatum's work, you first need to know how bacteria are grown in the laboratory.

Escherichia coli and many other bacteria can be grown in a **minimal medium** containing water, an organic carbon source such as glucose, and a selection of inorganic salts, including one, such as ammonium chloride, that provides nitrogen. The growth medium can be in liquid form or in the form of a gel made by adding agar to the liquid medium. (Agar is a polysaccharide material, indigestible by most bacteria, that is extracted from algae.) Since it is not practical to study a single bacterium for most experiments, researchers developed techniques for starting bacterial cultures from a single cell, generating cultures with a large number of genetically identical cells. Cultures of this type are called **clones**. To start bacterial clones, the scientist spreads a drop of a bacterial culture over a sterile agar gel in a culture dish. The culture is diluted enough to ensure that cells will be widely separated on the agar surface. Each cell divides many times to produce a clump of identical cells called a *colony*. Cells can be removed from a colony and introduced into liquid media or spread on agar and grown in essentially any quantity.

Now, for Lederberg and Tatum to detect genetic recombination, they needed some sort of detectable differences that could be shown to occur in changing combinations. The difference that proved most useful was related to nutrition. Cells require various amino acids for synthesis of proteins. Strains that are able to synthesize the necessary amino acids are called **prototrophs**. Mutant strains that are unable to synthesize amino acids are called **auxotrophs**; they can grow only if the required amino acid is provided for them in the growth medium. A strain that cannot manufacture its own arginine is represented by the genetic shorthand $argA^-$. In this shorthand, $argA$ refers to one of the genes that govern a cell's ability to synthesize arginine from simple inorganic molecules. A given strain of bacteria might carry this gene in its normal form, $argA^+$, or its mutant form, $argA^-$. These alternative forms of the gene are called alleles and might differ by as little as one base pair in their respective DNA sequences. Prokaryotic cells typically have one circular chromosome that carries one particular allele for each of their genes.

Using mutagens such as X-rays or ultraviolet light, Lederberg and Tatum isolated two different strains of *E. coli* carrying distinctive combinations of alleles for various metabolic genes. See **Figure 9.2, p. 192**, to understand how **replica plating** could isolate these auxotrophic strains. One particular strain could grow only if the vitamin biotin and the amino acid methionine were added to the culture medium. A second mutant strain did not need biotin or methionine but could grow only if the amino acids leucine and threonine were added along with the vitamin thiamine. These two multiple-mutant strains of *E. coli* were represented in genetic notation as follows:

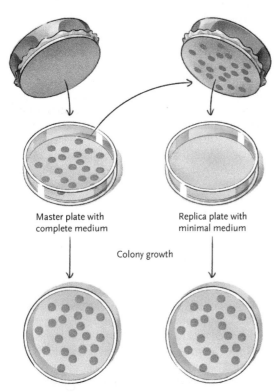

Master plate with complete medium   Replica plate with minimal medium

Colony growth

Research Method Figure 9.2 Replica plating transfers cells from complete media to minimal media where auxotrophs fail to grow.

Strain 1   bio⁻ met⁻ leu⁺ thr⁺ thi⁺

Strain 2   bio⁺ met⁺ leu⁻ thr⁻ thi⁻

Lederberg and Tatum mixed about 100 million cells of the two mutant strains together and placed

them on a minimal medium **(Figure 9.3)**. Several hundred colonies grew, even though, individually, none of the original cells carried all of the normal alleles needed for growth. You might be thinking, "They are mutants. Maybe some of the originally mutated alleles went back to normàl." This possibility was easily discounted by plating large numbers of cells from each original strain onto minimal medium separately. If mutation were responsible for the initial results with mixed cultures, then colonies should have also appeared when strains were plated separately. There were none. Some form of recombination between the DNA molecules of the two parental types must have produced the necessary combination with normal alleles for each of the five genes:

bio⁺ met⁺ leu⁺ thr⁺ thi⁺

9.2b Bacterial Conjugation Brings DNA of Two Cells into Close Proximity

How was DNA from two different bacterial cells able to recombine? We will see in Section 9.3 that genetic recombination in eukaryotes occurs in diploid cells by an exchange of segments between pairs of chromosomes. However, bacteria are haploid organisms; each cell typically has its own single, circular chromosome. So where do the "pairs" of chromosomes come from in bacteria? Although bacterial cells were first thought to bring their DNA together by fusing two cells together, it was later established that transfer of genetic information is unidirectional, from one donor cell to a recipient cell. Instead of fusing, bacterial cells *conjugate*. That is, cells contact each other by a long tubular structure called a *sex pilus* and then form a cytoplasmic

Experimental Research Figure 9.3
Experimental evidence for genetic recombination in bacteria.

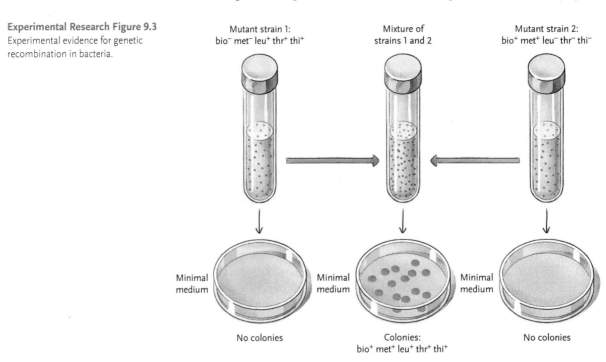

Mutant strain 1: bio⁻ met⁻ leu⁺ thr⁺ thi⁺

Mixture of strains 1 and 2

Mutant strain 2: bio⁺ met⁺ leu⁻ thr⁻ thi⁻

Minimal medium   Minimal medium   Minimal medium

No colonies   Colonies: bio⁺ met⁺ leu⁺ thr⁺ thi⁺   No colonies

a. Attachment by sex pilus

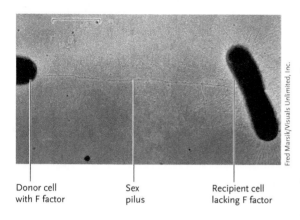

Donor cell
with F factor

Sex
pilus

Recipient cell
lacking F factor

Fred Marsik/Visuals Unlimited, Inc.

b. Cytoplasmic bridge formed

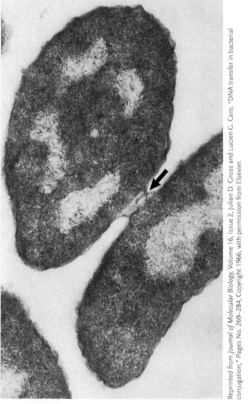

Reprinted from *Journal of Molecular Biology*, Volume 16, Issue 2, Julian D. Gross and Lucien G. Caro, "DNA transfer in bacterial conjugation," Pages No. 269–284, Copyright 1966, with permission from Elsevier.

Figure 9.4
Conjugating *E. coli* cells. **(a)** Initial attachment of two cells by the sex pilus. **(b)** A cytoplasmic bridge (arrow) has formed between the cells, through which DNA moves from one cell to the other.

bridge **(Figure 9.4a, b).** During **conjugation**, a copy of part of the DNA of one cell moves through the cytoplasmic bridge into the other cell. Once DNA from one cell enters the other, genetic recombination can occur. Through this unidirectional transfer of a part of the chromosome, conjugation facilitates a kind of sexual reproduction in prokaryotic organisms.

The F Factor and Conjugation. Conjugation is initiated by a bacterial cell that contains a small circle of DNA in addition to the main circular chromosomal DNA **(Figure 9.5** and **Figure 9.6, p. 194).** Such small circles are called plasmids, and this particular one is known as the *fertility* plasmid or the *F factor*. Like all plasmids, the F factor carries several genes as well as a **replication origin** that permits a copy to be passed on to each daughter cell during the usual process of bacterial cell division. This is an example of *vertical* inheritance from one generation to the next, which you should be familiar with. However, during conjugation, the F factor also can be copied and passed directly from the donor cell to the recipient cell. This is an example of *horizontal* inheritance.

Donor cells are called **F⁺ cells** because they contain the F factor. They are able to mate with recipient cells but not with other donor cells. Recipient cells lack the F factor and, hence, are called **F⁻ cells.** The F factor carries about 20 genes. Several of them encode proteins of the **sex pilus**, also called the **F pilus** (plural, *pili*) (see Figures 9.4 and 9.6a, step 1, p. 194).

a. Bacterial DNA released from cell

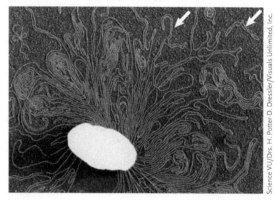

Science VU/Drs. H. Potter-D. Dressler/Visuals Unlimited, Inc.

b. Plasmid

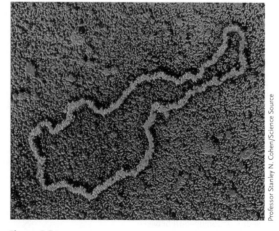

Professor Stanley N. Cohen/Science Source

Figure 9.5
Electron micrographs of DNA released from a disrupted bacterial cell. **(a)** Plasmids (arrows) near the mass of chromosomal DNA. **(b)** A single plasmid at higher magnification (colourized).

a. Transfer of the F factor

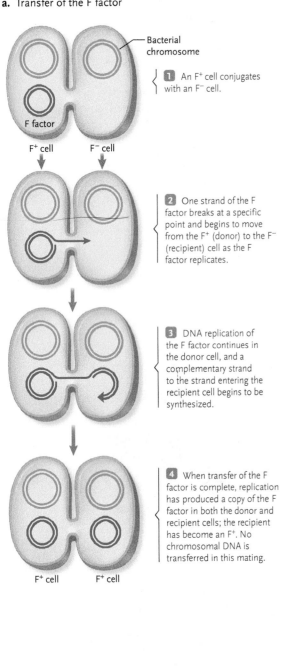

① An F⁺ cell conjugates with an F⁻ cell.

② One strand of the F factor breaks at a specific point and begins to move from the F⁺ (donor) to the F⁻ (recipient) cell as the F factor replicates.

③ DNA replication of the F factor continues in the donor cell, and a complementary strand to the strand entering the recipient cell begins to be synthesized.

④ When transfer of the F factor is complete, replication has produced a copy of the F factor in both the donor and recipient cells; the recipient has become an F⁺. No chromosomal DNA is transferred in this mating.

b. Transfer of bacterial genes

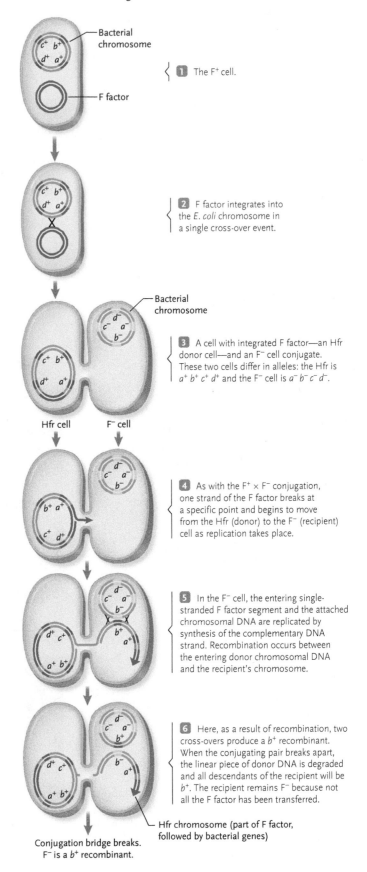

① The F⁺ cell.

② F factor integrates into the *E. coli* chromosome in a single cross-over event.

③ A cell with integrated F factor—an Hfr donor cell—and an F⁻ cell conjugate. These two cells differ in alleles: the Hfr is a^+ b^+ c^+ d^+ and the F⁻ cell is a^- b^- c^- d^-.

④ As with the F⁺ × F⁻ conjugation, one strand of the F factor breaks at a specific point and begins to move from the Hfr (donor) to the F⁻ (recipient) cell as replication takes place.

⑤ In the F⁻ cell, the entering single-stranded F factor segment and the attached chromosomal DNA are replicated by synthesis of the complementary DNA strand. Recombination occurs between the entering donor chromosomal DNA and the recipient's chromosome.

⑥ Here, as a result of recombination, two cross-overs produce a b^+ recombinant. When the conjugating pair breaks apart, the linear piece of donor DNA is degraded and all descendants of the recipient will be b^+. The recipient remains F⁻ because not all the F factor has been transferred.

Hfr chromosome (part of F factor, followed by bacterial genes)

Conjugation bridge breaks. F⁻ is a b^+ recombinant.

Figure 9.6
Transfer of genetic material during conjugation between *E. coli* cells. **(a)** Transfer of the F factor during conjugation between F⁺ and F⁻ cells. **(b)** Transfer of bacterial genes and the production of recombinants during conjugation between Hfr and F⁻ cells.

During conjugation, the F factor replicates using a special type of DNA replication called *rolling circle*. To understand this mechanism, first picture a site, called the origin of transfer, on the F factor. Then imagine a break in just one strand of the double helix at this site. Now, imagine gently pulling the free end of the single strand of DNA away from the F factor, through the cytoplasmic bridge, and into the recipient cell. As the single strand is pulled, the remaining strand—still a circle—"rolls" like the spool on a tape dispenser. DNA synthesis fills in the complementary bases to ensure that the F factor is double stranded in both the donor and the recipient cells. When the entire F factor strand has transferred and replicated, it circularizes again (see Figure 9.6a, step 4). It is important to understand that although the recipient cell becomes F⁺, no chromosomal DNA is transferred between cells in this process. *That is, no genetic recombination occurs between the DNA of two different cells in such a mating.*

So why are we including F factor conjugation in this chapter if it does not recombine DNA of different cells? The answer lies in the Hfr cells described in the next section.

Hfr Cells and Genetic Recombination. In some F⁺ cells, the F factor comes into close proximity with the main chromosome and, lining up in a short region of homology, undergoes a recombination event. When two circular DNA molecules recombine (by the mechanism shown in Figure 9.1, p. 190), they simply fuse into one larger circle. In this way, the F factor actually becomes a part of the main bacterial chromosome (see Figure 9.6b, step 2). These special donor cells are known as **Hfr cells** (Hfr = high-frequency recombination). It is important not to be confused at this point; although a recombination event integrated the F factor into the host chromosome, this is recombination within one cell, not between the chromosomes of different cells. Hfr cells are called "high-frequency recombination" because they can promote recombination between DNA of different cells by "exporting" copies of chromosomal genes to another cell, as described below.

When the F factor is integrated into the bacterial chromosome, its genes are still available for expression. Therefore, these Hfr cells make sex pili and can conjugate with an F⁻ cell. Figure 9.6b, step 3, shows an Hfr × F⁻ mating where the two cell types differ in alleles for the genes *a*, *b*, *c*, and *d*. Note that a segment of the F factor moves through the conjugation bridge into the recipient, bringing the single-stranded chromosomal DNA behind it (see Figure 9.6b, steps 4 and 5). This is, again, rolling circle replication, in which both donor and recipient cells restore the DNA to double-strandedness. In this situation, the circle that rolls is the entire Hfr donor chromosome! Although DNA transfer often continues long enough for several genes to enter the recipient cell, the fragile

conjugation bridge soon breaks. It is rare for the entire donor chromosome to be transferred.

At this point, it is important to recall that when the F factor transfers by itself, as described in the previous section, the recipient cells often become F⁺. However, in Hfr cells, the origin of transfer is near the middle of the integrated F factor. As a result, only half of the F factor DNA is transferred at the front of the chromosomal DNA. (Think of the engine of a train.) The other half of the F factor (the dining car at the end of the train) can follow only after the rest of the entire chromosome (see Figure 9.6b, steps 4 to 6). As a result, it is very unusual for a recipient cell to obtain the entire F factor and become Hfr as well. Most likely, the recipient cell will become a **partial diploid**; it will have two copies of only those genes that came through the conjugation bridge on the donor chromosomal DNA segment.

For our example, the recipient cell in Figure 9.6b, step 5, has become, for the moment, *a⁺ b⁺/a⁻ b⁻*. Although the DNA carrying + alleles for genes *a* and *b* differs slightly from that carrying – alleles, these regions are homologous and can pair for recombination. In fact, Figure 9.6 shows two recombination events, one on either side of the *b* gene, resulting in the exchange of the donor allele with that of the recipient (see Figure 9.6b, step 5). As a result, the recipient cell has become an *a⁻ b⁺* **recombinant.** Since enzymes in the recipient cell degrade the linear Hfr chromosome soon after recombination occurs, any incoming alleles that are not recombined onto the chromosome are lost. Following recombination, the bacterial DNA replicates and the cell divides normally, producing a clone of cells with the new combination of alleles.

In other pairs in the mating population, recombination events at different locations would lead to different recombinant recipients; perhaps the *a* gene could recombine with the homologous recipient gene, or both *a* and *b* genes could recombine to give *a⁺ b⁺* recipients. The various genetic recombinants observed in the Lederberg and Tatum experiment described earlier were produced in this general way.

Mapping Genes by Conjugation. The use of conjugation for genetic mapping was discovered by two scientists, François Jacob (the same scientist who proposed the operon model for the regulation of gene expression in bacteria; see Section 14.1) and Elie L. Wollman, at the Pasteur Institute in Paris. They began their experiments by mating Hfr and F⁻ cells that differed in a number of alleles. At regular intervals after conjugation commenced, they removed some of the cells and agitated them in a blender to break apart mating pairs. They then cultured the separated cells and analyzed them for recombinants. They found that the longer they allowed cells to conjugate before separation, the greater the number of donor genes that entered the recipient and produced recombinants. By noting the order and time at which genes were transferred, Jacob and Wollman were able to map and assign the relative positions of several genes in the *E. coli* chromosome.

9.2c Transformation and Transduction Provide Additional Sources of DNA for Recombination

The discovery of conjugation and genetic recombination in *E. coli* showed that genetic recombination is not restricted to eukaryotes. Further discoveries demonstrated that DNA can transfer from one bacterial cell to another by two additional mechanisms, transformation and transduction. Like conjugation, these mechanisms transfer DNA in one direction and create partial diploids in which recombination can occur between alleles in the homologous DNA regions. Unlike conjugation, in which both donor and recipient cells are living, transformation and transduction enable recipient cells to recombine with DNA obtained from dead donors.

Transformation. In **transformation**, bacteria simply take up pieces of DNA that are released into the environment as other cells disintegrate. Fred Griffith, a medical officer in the British Ministry of Health, London, discovered this phenomenon in 1928 while trying to understand how bacteria cause pneumonia in mice. Cells of the virulent strains of *Streptococcus pneumoniae* were surrounded by a polysaccharide capsule, whereas the nonvirulent strains were not. Griffith found that a mixture of heat-killed virulent cells and living nonvirulent cells still caused pneumonia. One interpretation of this observation was that the living nonvirulent cells had been transformed to virulence by something released from the dead cells. In 1944, Oswald Avery and his colleagues at New York University found that the substance derived from the killed virulent cells, the substance capable of transforming nonvirulent bacteria to the virulent form, was DNA (discussed in Section 12.1).

Subsequently, geneticists established that in the transformation of *Streptococcus*, the linear DNA fragments taken up from disrupted virulent cells recombine with the chromosomal DNA of the non-virulent cells in much the same way as genetic recombination takes place in conjugation. In this case, the recombination introduces the normal allele for capsule formation into the DNA of the nonvirulent cells; expression of that normal allele generates a capsule around the cell and its descendants, making them virulent.

Only some species of bacteria can take up DNA from the surrounding medium by natural mechanisms, and *E. coli* is not one of them. Fortunately for molecular biologists, *E. coli* cells can be induced to take up DNA in the laboratory by a variety of artificial transformation techniques involving exposure to calcium ions and/or pulses of electric current. Artificial transformation is often used to insert recombinant DNA plasmids into *E. coli* cells as part of cloning or genetic engineering techniques. (DNA cloning and genetic engineering are discussed further in Chapter 15.)

Transduction. In **transduction**, DNA is transferred from donor to recipient cells inside the head of an infecting bacterial virus. The infection cycles of viruses that infect bacteria, called **bacteriophages** (or just phages), are described in Chapter 23. The basic details of phage infection are shown in **Figure 9.7** and **Figure 9.8, p. 198**. In general, transduction begins when new phages assemble within an infected bacterial cell; they sometimes incorporate fragments of the host cell DNA along with, or instead of, the viral DNA. After the host cell is killed, the new phages that are released may then attach to another cell and inject the bacterial DNA (and the viral DNA if it is present) into that recipient cell. The introduction of this DNA, as in conjugation and transformation, makes the recipient cell a partial diploid and allows recombination to take place. Recipients are not killed because they have received bacterial DNA rather than infective viral DNA. Lederberg and his graduate student, Norton Zinder, then at the University of Wisconsin at Madison, discovered transduction in 1952 in experiments with the bacterium *Salmonella typhimurium* and phage P22. Lederberg received a Nobel Prize in 1958 for his discovery of conjugation and transduction in bacteria.

There are two different types of transduction, generalized and specialized, arising from the different infection cycles of the phage involved. **Generalized transduction**, in which all donor genes are equally likely to be transferred, is associated with some **virulent bacteriophages**, which kill their host cells during each cycle of infection (the **lytic cycle**). Notice in Figure 9.7 that, during infection by the virulent phage, the host bacterial chromosome is degraded to provide raw material for synthesis of new phage chromosomes. However, sometimes a fragment of host chromosome avoids degradation and is packed into the head of a new phage *by mistake*. This particular phage now contains a small random sample of bacterial genes *instead of* phage genes. When the host cell bursts to release the new phage, this *transducing phage* can mechanically infect a recipient cell. However, it will deliver a linear piece of DNA from the donor cell rather than an infectious phage chromosome. The newly infected (and incredibly lucky) recipient cell will survive; incoming DNA may then pair, and recombine, with homologous regions on the recipient chromosome.

One of the most extensively studied bacteriophages is phage lambda (λ), which infects *E. coli*. Again, a mistake in the infection cycle can result in the transfer of bacterial genes from a donor to a recipient cell. However, in this case, a different type of mistake, in a different infection cycle, gives rise to a different type of transduction: **specialized transduction** (shown

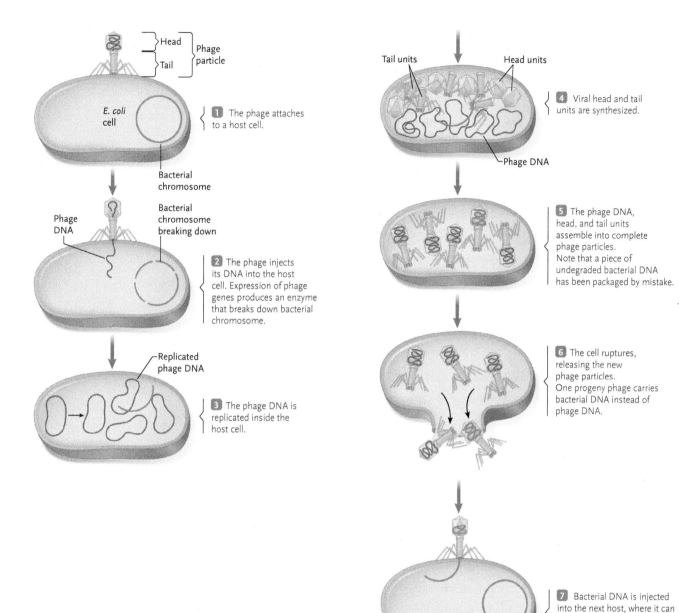

Head
Tail
Phage particle

E. coli cell

1 The phage attaches to a host cell.

Bacterial chromosome

Phage DNA

Bacterial chromosome breaking down

2 The phage injects its DNA into the host cell. Expression of phage genes produces an enzyme that breaks down bacterial chromosome.

Replicated phage DNA

3 The phage DNA is replicated inside the host cell.

Tail units   Head units

4 Viral head and tail units are synthesized.

Phage DNA

5 The phage DNA, head, and tail units assemble into complete phage particles. Note that a piece of undegraded bacterial DNA has been packaged by mistake.

6 The cell ruptures, releasing the new phage particles. One progeny phage carries bacterial DNA instead of phage DNA.

7 Bacterial DNA is injected into the next host, where it can recombine with similar regions on the host chromosome.

Figure 9.7
Generalized transduction. Movement of bacterial DNA from one cell to another inside the head of a lytic bacteriophage.

in Figure 9.8, p. 198). Lambda is a **temperate bacteriophage**. That is, when lambda first infects a new host, it determines whether this cell is likely to be a robust and long-lived host. Is it starving? Is it suffering from DNA damage? If the host cell passes this molecular health checkup, then the lambda chromosome lines up with a small region of homology on the bacterial chromosome and a phage-coded enzyme catalyzes a single recombination event. The phage is thus integrated into the host chromosomal DNA and, in this state, is called a **prophage**. (Overall, this mechanism is very similar to the integration of the F factor discussed previously.) The prophage is then replicated and passed to daughter cells along with the rest of the bacterial chromosome

as long as conditions remain favourable (the **lysogenic cycle** in Figure 9.8, p. 198).

If, however, the host cell becomes inhospitable (perhaps as a result of ultraviolet-induced DNA damage), the prophage activates several genes, releases itself from the chromosome by a recombination event, and proceeds to manufacture new phages, which are released as the cell bursts as a result of lytic growth.

In specialized transduction, the "mistake" occurs when the prophage is excised from the chromosome. Sometimes this recombination event is imprecise; bacterial DNA is removed from the host chromosome, and some prophage DNA is left behind. As a result, this bacterial DNA is packaged into new phages and carried

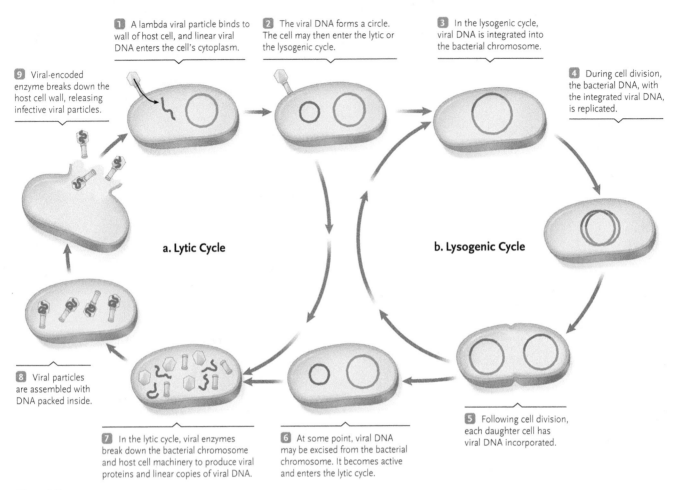

① A lambda viral particle binds to wall of host cell, and linear viral DNA enters the cell's cytoplasm.

② The viral DNA forms a circle. The cell may then enter the lytic or the lysogenic cycle.

③ In the lysogenic cycle, viral DNA is integrated into the bacterial chromosome.

④ During cell division, the bacterial DNA, with the integrated viral DNA, is replicated.

⑤ Following cell division, each daughter cell has viral DNA incorporated.

⑥ At some point, viral DNA may be excised from the bacterial chromosome. It becomes active and enters the lytic cycle.

⑦ In the lytic cycle, viral enzymes break down the bacterial chromosome and host cell machinery to produce viral proteins and linear copies of viral DNA.

⑧ Viral particles are assembled with DNA packed inside.

⑨ Viral-encoded enzyme breaks down the host cell wall, releasing infective viral particles.

a. Lytic Cycle

b. Lysogenic Cycle

Figure 9.8

The infective cycle of lambda, an example of a temperate phage, which can go through the lytic cycle **(a)** or the lysogenic cycle **(b)**.

to recipient cells. Since the transducing phage is defective, having left some of its genes behind in the host, it does not kill its new host. You should be able to see that in the case of specialized transduction only bacterial genes that are close to the integration site of the phage will likely be incorporated into the phage chromosome by the recombination mistake. Typically, only genes coding for galactose and biotin metabolism are transferred at high frequency by phage lambda.

Conjugation, transformation, and transduction are all ways in which DNA from two different bacterial cells is brought into close proximity. Homologous regions may then pair and recombine to give rise to a recipient cell that carries a different collection of alleles than it had previously. Overall, these processes create more diversity in the DNA sequence among members of a population than would arise by mutation and binary fission alone. More diversity leads to a higher likelihood that at least some individuals will be well suited to survival in a changing environment.

These basic principles also apply to single-celled and multicellular eukaryotes. The next section of this chapter introduces genetic recombination in eukaryotes as it occurs within the overall process of meiosis. Notice how DNA from two different individuals is brought close together in the same cell following fertilization. Also watch for extensive similarity of the DNA sequence (homology) that now extends the full length of large linear chromosomes. Finally, notice the genetic recombination at the centre of this process, which generates novel chromosomes with new combinations of alleles.

STUDY BREAK

1. Contrast the characteristics of F⁻, F⁺, and Hfr cells.
2. Explain why all genes have an equal likelihood of transfer by generalized transduction but not by specialized transduction.

9.3 Genetic Recombination in Eukaryotes: Meiosis

The octopuses and slipper limpets described at the opening of this chapter are engaged in forms of **sexual reproduction**, the production of offspring through the union of male and female **gametes**—for example, eggs and sperm cells in animals. Sexual reproduction depends on **meiosis**, a specialized process of cell division that recombines DNA sequences and produces cells with half the number of chromosomes present in the **somatic cells** (body cells) of a species. The derivation of the word *meiosis* (*meioun* = to diminish) reflects this reduction. At **fertilization**, the nuclei of an egg and a sperm cell fuse, producing a cell called the **zygote**, in which the chromosome number typical of the species is restored. Without the halving of chromosome number by the meiotic divisions, fertilization would double the number of chromosomes in each subsequent generation.

Both meiosis and fertilization also mix genetic information into new combinations; thus, none of the offspring of a mating pair are likely to be genetically identical to either their parents or their siblings. This genetic variability is the raw material for the process of evolution as described in Chapter 17.

The biological foundations of sexual reproduction are the mixing of genetic information into new combinations and the halving of the chromosome number, both of which occur through meiosis, as well as the restoration of the original chromosome number by fertilization. Intermingled tentacles in octopuses, communal sex among limpets, clouds of pollen in the wind, and the courting and mating rituals of humans are nothing more or less than variations of the means for achieving fertilization, thus bringing DNA together for recombination.

9.3a Meiosis Occurs in Different Places in Different Organismal Life Cycles

Although the life cycle of nearly all eukaryotes alternates between a stage with one basic set of chromosomes (haploid) and a stage with two basic sets of chromosomes (diploid), **Figure 9.9** shows that evolution has produced wide variety in the relative timing of mitosis, meiosis, and fertilization among different species.

CONCEPT FIX The life cycles of plants, algae, and fungi may be unfamiliar to you and can be better understood by focusing your attention on the function of the cells that are the immediate products of meiosis. You might assume that gametes are made by meiosis. This assumption is true—but only for yourself and other animals. In the life cycle of houseplants and some of the fungi living in the soil in the park, the haploid products of meiosis are spores, not gametes. These spores divide by mitosis

a. Animal life cycles

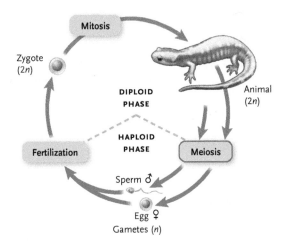

b. All land plants and some fungi and algae (fern shown; relative length of the two phases varies widely in plants)

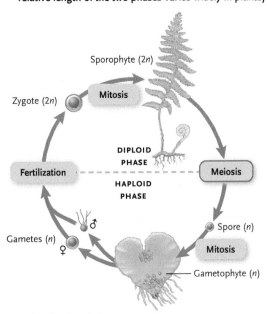

c. Other fungi and algae

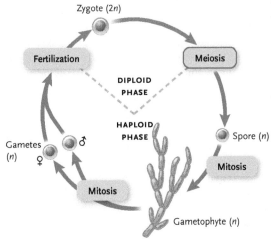

Figure 9.9
Variations in the time and place of meiosis and mitosis in the life cycle of eukaryotes. The diploid phase of the life cycles is shown in red; the haploid phase is shown in blue. *n* refers to the haploid number of chromosomes; 2*n* refers to the diploid number. **(a)** Meiosis in animal life cycles. Zygotes divide by mitosis. **(b)** Meiosis in most plants and some fungi and algae. Spores and zygotes divide by mitosis. **(c)** Meiosis in other fungi and algae. Spores divide by mitosis.

to form multicellular bodies that, in turn, make gametes by mitosis. That idea is worth repeating: many organisms make gametes by mitosis. ⬡

Animals. Animals follow the pattern in which the diploid phase dominates the life cycle (see Figure 9.9a, p. 199), the haploid phase is reduced, and meiosis is followed directly by gamete formation. (You could think of this as the "diploid life cycle" since the diploid stage is multicellular.) In male animals, each of the four nuclei produced by meiosis is enclosed in a separate cell by cytoplasmic divisions, and each of the four cells differentiates into a functional sperm cell. In female animals, only one of the four nuclei becomes functional as an egg cell nucleus.

Fertilization restores the diploid phase of the life cycle. Thus, animals are haploids only as sperm or eggs, and no mitotic divisions occur during the haploid phase of the life cycle.

Most Plants and Some Fungi. Most plants and some algae and fungi follow the life cycle pattern shown in Figure 9.9b. These organisms alternate between haploid and diploid generations in which, depending on the organism, either generation may dominate the life cycle, and mitotic divisions occur in both phases. (You could think of this as the "alternating-generations life cycle" since both the diploid and the haploid stages can be multicellular.) In these organisms, fertilization produces the diploid generation, in which the individuals are called **sporophytes** (*spora* = seed; *phyta* = plant). After the sporophytes grow to maturity by mitotic divisions, some of their cells undergo meiosis, producing haploid, genetically different, reproductive cells called **spores.** The spores are not gametes; they germinate and grow directly by mitotic divisions into a generation of haploid individuals called **gametophytes** (*gameta* = gamete). At maturity, the nuclei of some cells in gametophytes develop into egg or sperm nuclei. All the egg or sperm nuclei produced by a particular gametophyte are genetically identical because they arise through mitosis; meiosis does not occur in gametophytes. Fusion of a haploid egg and sperm nucleus produces a diploid zygote nucleus that divides by mitosis to produce the diploid sporophyte generation again.

In all plants (except bryophytes), the diploid sporophyte generation is the most visible part of the plant. The gametophyte generation is reduced to an almost microscopic stage that develops in the reproductive parts of the sporophytes—in flowering plants, in the structures of the flower. The female gametophyte remains in the flower; the male gametophyte is released from flowers as microscopic pollen grains. When pollen contacts a flower of the same species, it releases a haploid nucleus that fertilizes a haploid egg cell of a female gametophyte in the flower. The resulting cell, the zygote, reproduces by mitosis to form a sporophyte.

Sphagnum moss (commonly known as peat moss) is a good example of a plant in which the gametophyte is the most visible and familiar stage of the life cycle. In this case, the sporophyte is reduced and develops from a zygote within the body of the gametophyte. Vast peatlands of *Sphagnum* gametophytes are industrially harvested in many parts of the world for fuel and horticultural use.

Most Fungi. The life cycle of most fungi and algae follows the third life cycle pattern (see Figure 9.9c). In these organisms, the diploid phase is limited to a single cell, the zygote, produced by fertilization. Immediately after fertilization, the diploid zygote undergoes meiosis to produce the haploid phase. Mitotic divisions occur only in the haploid phase. (You could think of this as the "haploid life cycle" since the haploid stage is multicellular.)

During fertilization, two haploid gametes, usually designated simply as positive (+) and negative (−) because they are similar in structure, fuse to form a diploid nucleus. This nucleus immediately enters meiosis, producing four haploid cells. These cells develop directly or after one or more mitotic divisions into haploid spores. These spores germinate to produce haploid individuals, which grow or increase in number by mitotic divisions. Eventually, positive and negative gametes are formed in these individuals by differentiation of some of the cells produced by the mitotic divisions. Because the gametes are produced by mitosis, all the gametes of an individual are genetically identical.

⬤CONCEPT FIX We are emphasizing that zygotes arising from fertilization contain DNA from two different parents in close proximity so that recombination may occur. However, note carefully that in the life cycles of the animals and plants you are likely familiar with, it is not this single-celled fertilized zygote that undergoes recombination. It is only after many rounds of replication by mitosis that certain cells in the resulting multicellular body are destined to divide by meiosis. That is when and where recombination occurs. ⬡

9.3b Meiosis Changes Both Chromosome Number and DNA Sequence

In order to understand the mechanism of meiosis, it is helpful to keep the big picture in mind. Chapter 8 made the point that the essence of mitotic cell division is *sameness*. That is, chromosomes are replicated and partitioned to ensure that cells produced by the process have the same number of chromosomes, with the same DNA sequence, as the cell that began the process. In this way, somatic cells are produced for most of the requirements of haploid or diploid multicellular organisms. However, the essence of meiosis is *difference*—actually two kinds of difference: halved chromosome number and recombined chromosomal DNA sequence. The products of meiosis are not intended to contribute to the body of the organisms that make them. In multicellular animals and plants, you would find that meiosis occurs only in specialized tissues that produce gametes and spores, respectively.

Both types of difference mentioned above arise from the very different behaviour of chromosomes in meiosis relative to mitosis. If you understand the significance of the chromosome pairs in diploid organisms as described below, then the differences in chromosome behaviour in meiosis and mitosis will make sense more easily.

As discussed in Section 9.1, the two representatives of each chromosome in a diploid cell constitute a *homologous pair* (*homo* = same; *logos* = information)—they have the same genes, arranged in the same order, in the DNA of the chromosomes. One chromosome of each homologous pair, the **paternal chromosome**, is derived from the male parent of the organism, and the other chromosome, the **maternal chromosome**, is derived from its female parent. Although two homologous chromosomes carry the same genes arranged in the same order, different *versions* of these genes, **alleles**, may be present on either chromosome. Recall from the bacterial conjugation material at the beginning of this chapter that different alleles of a given gene have similar, but distinct, DNA sequences. They therefore likely encode variations of the given RNA or protein gene product, which may then have a different structure, different biochemistry, or both.

For example, all the different breeds of dogs normally have 78 chromosomes in their cells, made up of 39 homologous pairs. However, each individual has a unique combination of the alleles carried by the two chromosomes of each homologous pair. The distinct set of alleles, arising from the mixing mechanisms of meiosis and fertilization in the parents, gives each individual offspring its own unique combination of inherited traits, including attributes such as size, coat colour, susceptibility to certain diseases and disorders, and aspects of behaviour and intelligence.

One of the more dramatic accomplishments of meiosis in an organism like a dog is the separation of the members of each homologous pair into different cells, thereby reducing the diploid or 2*n* number of chromosomes to the haploid or *n* number. Each cell produced by meiosis carries only one member of each homologous pair. An egg or sperm cell contains 39 chromosomes, one of each pair. When the egg and sperm combine in sexual reproduction to produce the zygote—the first cell of the new puppy—the diploid number of 78 chromosomes (39 pairs) is regenerated. The processes of DNA replication and mitotic cell division ensure that this diploid number is maintained in the body cells as the zygote divides and develops (see Chapter 8).

The second significant consequence of meiotic cell division is, of course, genetic recombination of the actual DNA sequence on chromosomes. Referring back to Figure 9.1, p. 190, recall that recombination involves the precise breaking of covalently bonded DNA backbones, exchanging the "ends" with those of the other homologue and reforming the bonds. As a result, each chromosome passed on to offspring is composed of a novel mixture of both maternal and paternal DNA sequence.

The following sections describe how the ability of homologues to find their respective partners, and pair intimately along their length, allows both the partitioning of homologues into separate cells and the process of recombination to occur during the first part of the two-step process of meiosis.

9.3c Meiosis Produces Four Genetically Different Daughter Cells

Cells that are destined to divide by meiosis (called **meiocytes**) move through their last turn of the cell cycle as usual, replicating DNA and making more chromosomal proteins during S phase. (See Chapter 12 for details of DNA replication.) The resulting G2 cells carry replicated chromosomes, each composed of two identical sister chromatids **(Figure 9.10, p. 202)**. Following this premeiotic interphase, cells enter the first of the two meiotic divisions: meiosis I and meiosis II. During **meiosis I**, chromosomes behave dramatically differently than they do during mitosis. That is, early in meiosis I, homologous chromosomes find their partners and pair lengthwise, gene for gene, in a process called synapsis. During this intimate pairing, recombination occurs, and chromosomal segments are exchanged. As the meiocyte continues through to the end of the first division, the members of each homologous pair are moved into one or the other of the two daughter cells. These daughter cells still contain replicated chromosomes (composed of two chromatids each); however, the number of such chromosomes is only half that of the original meiocyte. That is, the cells now have the haploid number of chromosomes but each chromosome still has two chromatids.

During the second meiotic division, **meiosis II**, the sister chromatids are separated into different cells, further reducing the amount of DNA in each product of meiosis. A total of four cells, each with the haploid number of chromosomes and a novel collection of alleles, is the final result of the two meiotic divisions.

CONCEPT FIX Notice that the chromosome in the cells at the bottom of Figure 9.10 is an unreplicated, single structure. Since these cells are haploid, sometimes people come to believe that all chromosomes in haploid cells are unreplicated, single structures, while all chromosomes in diploid cells are double structures with two chromatids each. However, Figure 9.10 clearly shows that the top cell is diploid, even though its two chromosomes are unreplicated. Following meiosis I, the cells are haploid, even though their single

Figure 9.10

Production of four haploid nuclei by the two meiotic divisions. For simplicity, just one pair of homologous chromosomes is followed through the divisions.

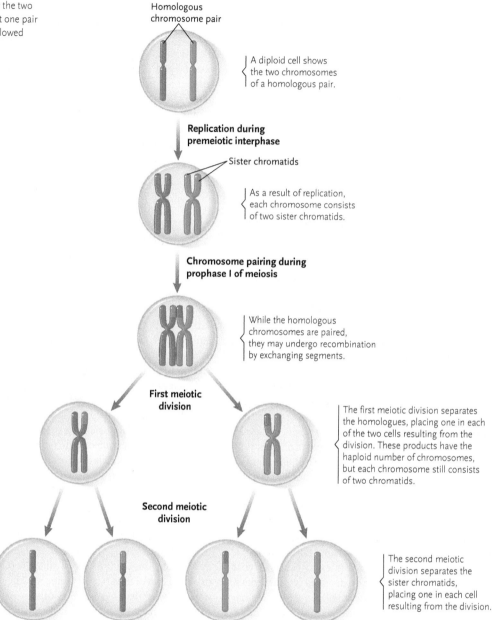

Homologous chromosome pair

A diploid cell shows the two chromosomes of a homologous pair.

Replication during premeiotic interphase

Sister chromatids

As a result of replication, each chromosome consists of two sister chromatids.

Chromosome pairing during prophase I of meiosis

While the homologous chromosomes are paired, they may undergo recombination by exchanging segments.

First meiotic division

The first meiotic division separates the homologues, placing one in each of the two cells resulting from the division. These products have the haploid number of chromosomes, but each chromosome still consists of two chromatids.

Second meiotic division

The second meiotic division separates the sister chromatids, placing one in each cell resulting from the division.

chromosome is replicated. Ploidy is determined only by the number of chromosomes; it is not influenced by whether the chromosomes are replicated or not. ⬡

For convenience, biologists separate each meiotic division into the same key stages as mitosis: prophase, prometaphase, metaphase, anaphase, and telophase. The stages are identified as belonging to the two divisions, meiosis I and meiosis II, by a I or a II, as in prophase I and prophase II. A brief interphase called **interkinesis** separates the two meiotic divisions, *but no DNA replication occurs during interkinesis.*

Prophase I. At the beginning of prophase I, the replicated chromosomes, each consisting of two sister chromatids, begin to fold and condense into threadlike structures in the nucleus (**Figure 9.11, p. 204,** step 1). The two chromosomes of each homologous pair then come together and line up side by side in a zipperlike way; this process is called **pairing** or **synapsis** (step 2). The fully paired homologues are called **tetrads**, referring to the fact that each homologous pair consists of four chromatids. *Note that chromosomes do not behave like this in mitosis.*

While they are paired, the chromatids of homologous chromosomes physically exchange segments (step 3). This physical exchange, genetic recombination, is the step that mixes the alleles of the homologous chromosomes into new combinations and contributes to the generation of variability in sexual reproduction. (This is the process, described in Chapter 11, that underlies **recombination frequency** mapping.) As prophase I finishes, a spindle forms in the cytoplasm by the same basic mechanisms described in Chapter 8.

Prometaphase I. In prometaphase I, the nuclear envelope breaks down and the spindle enters the former nuclear area (see Figure 9.11, p. 204, step 4). The two chromosomes of each pair attach to kinetochore microtubules that are anchored to opposite spindle poles. That is, both sister chromatids of one homologue attach to microtubules leading to one spindle pole, whereas both sister chromatids of the other homologue attach to microtubules leading to the opposite pole. *Notice, again, how this is different from the spindle attachments during mitosis.*

Metaphase I and Anaphase I. At metaphase I, movements of the spindle microtubules have aligned the recombined tetrads on the equatorial plane—the *metaphase plate*—between the two spindle poles (see Figure 9.11, p. 205, step 5). Then the two chromosomes of each homologous pair separate and move to opposite spindle poles during anaphase I (step 6). The movement segregates homologous pairs, delivering a haploid set of chromosomes to each pole of the spindle. However, all the chromosomes at the poles are still double structures composed of two sister chromatids joined at their centromeres.

Telophase I and Interkinesis. Telophase I is a brief, transitory stage in which there is little or no change in the chromosomes (see Figure 9.11, p. 205, step 7). New nuclear envelopes form in some species but not in others. Telophase I is followed by an interkinesis in which the single spindle of the first meiotic division disassembles and the microtubules reassemble into two new spindles for the second division. Recall that there is no DNA replication between the first and the second division.

Prophase II, Prometaphase II, and Metaphase II. During prophase of meiosis II, the chromosomes condense (see Figure 9.11, p. 204, step 8). During prometaphase II, the nuclear envelope breaks down, the spindle enters the former nuclear area, and spindle microtubules leading to opposite spindle poles attach to the two kinetochores of each chromosome. At metaphase II, movements of the chromosomes within the spindle bring them to rest at the metaphase plate (step 9).

🔴 CONCEPT FIX Although the separation of chromatids during meiosis II is superficially similar to that in a mitotic division, it is important to remember that these two processes are quite distinct. Meiosis II is not "just like mitosis." Meiosis II occurs only in reproductive tissue, there is no immediately preceding DNA replication phase, and the resulting daughter cells are not genetically identical (see Figure 9.16, p. 210). ⬡

Anaphase II and Telophase II. Anaphase II begins as the sister chromatids of each chromosome separate from each other and move to opposite spindle poles (see **Figure 9.11, p. 205,** step 10). At the completion of anaphase II, the separated chromatids—now called chromosomes—have been segregated to the two poles. During telophase II, the chromatids decondense to the extended interphase state, the spindles disassemble, and new nuclear envelopes form around the masses of chromatin (step 11). The result is four haploid cells, each with a nucleus containing half the number of chromosomes present in the cell at the beginning of meiosis. These chromosomes all carry various new combinations of maternal and paternal alleles.

Failure in Chromosome Segregation. Rarely, chromosome segregation fails at either meiosis I or II. For example, during meiosis I, both chromosomes of a homologous pair may connect to the same spindle pole in anaphase I. In the resulting nondisjunction, as it is called, the spindle fails to separate the homologous chromosomes of the tetrad. As a result, one pole receives both chromosomes of the homologous pair, whereas the other pole has no copies of that chromosome. Meiosis II will proceed to separate the chromatids of the extra chromosome as usual, with the result that gametes will have two copies of this chromosome (instead of one). A failure at meiosis II, in which chromatids do not separate to opposite poles, also results in gametes with abnormal numbers of chromosomes. Zygotes that receive an extra chromosome from an abnormal gamete therefore have three copies of a given chromosome instead of two. In humans, most zygotes of this kind do not result in live births. One exception is Down syndrome, which can result from three copies of chromosome 21. Down syndrome involves characteristic alterations in body and facial structure, developmental delays, and significantly reduced fertility due to extra genetic information (see Chapter 11 for a more detailed discussion of Down syndrome).

Sex Chromosomes. In many eukaryotes, including most animals, one or more pairs of chromosomes, called the **sex chromosomes**, are different in male and female individuals of the same species. For example, in fruit flies, the cells of females contain a pair of sex chromosomes called the *XX pair*. Male flies contain a pair of sex chromosomes that consist of one X chromosome and a smaller chromosome called the **Y chromosome**. The two X chromosomes in females are fully homologous, whereas the male X and Y chromosomes are

Prophase I

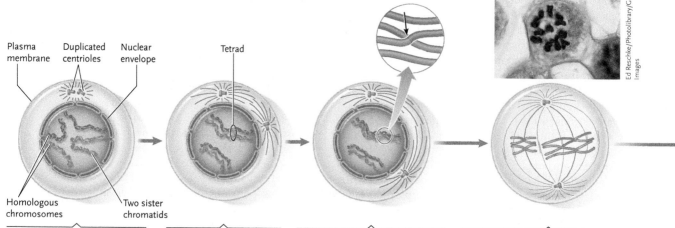

Plasma membrane | Duplicated centrioles | Nuclear envelope

Tetrad

Homologous chromosomes | Two sister chromatids

Condensation of chromosomes

1 At the beginning of prophase I, the chromosomes begin to condense into threadlike structures. Each consists of two sister chromatids, as a result of DNA replication during premeiotic interphase. The chromosomes of two homologous pairs, one long and one short, are shown.

Synapsis

2 Homologous chromosomes come together and pair.

Recombination

3 While they are paired, the chromatids of homologous chromosomes undergo recombination by exchanging segments. The enlarged circle shows a site undergoing recombination (arrow).

Prometaphase I

4 In prometaphase I, the nuclear envelope breaks down, and the spindle moves into the former nuclear area. Kinetochore microtubules connect to the chromosomes—kinetochore microtubules from one pole attach to both sister kinetochores of one duplicated chromosome, and kinetochore microtubules from the other pole attach to both sister kinetochores of the other duplicated chromosome.

Second meiotic division

Prophase II

8 The chromosomes condense and a spindle forms.

Figure 9.11
The meiotic divisions. The artwork summarizes the behaviour of chromosomes in a hypothetical animal cell having two homologous pairs of chromosomes ($2n = 4$). Photomicrographs show comparable stages in the anther cells of a lily plant.

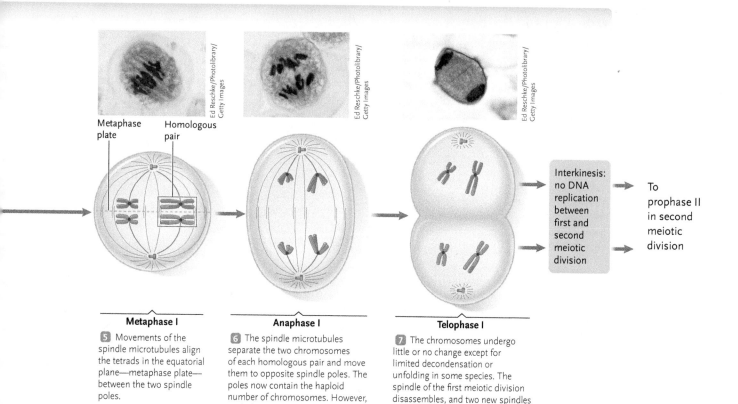

Metaphase I

5 Movements of the spindle microtubules align the tetrads in the equatorial plane—metaphase plate—between the two spindle poles.

Anaphase I

6 The spindle microtubules separate the two chromosomes of each homologous pair and move them to opposite spindle poles. The poles now contain the haploid number of chromosomes. However, each chromosome at the poles still contains two chromatids.

Telophase I

7 The chromosomes undergo little or no change except for limited decondensation or unfolding in some species. The spindle of the first meiotic division disassembles, and two new spindles form for the second division.

Interkinesis: no DNA replication between first and second meiotic division

To prophase II in second meiotic division

Metaphase plate

Homologous pair

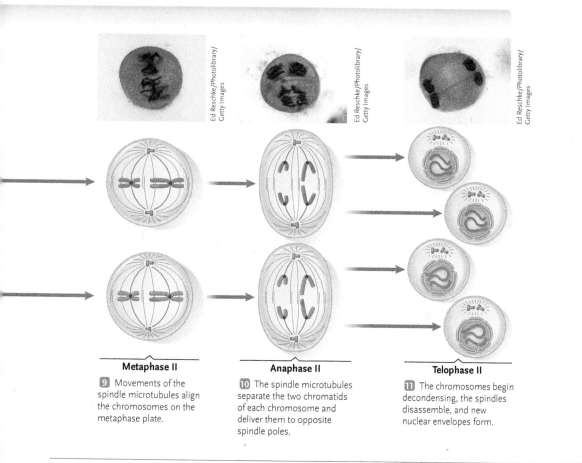

Metaphase II

9 Movements of the spindle microtubules align the chromosomes on the metaphase plate.

Anaphase II

10 The spindle microtubules separate the two chromatids of each chromosome and deliver them to opposite spindle poles.

Telophase II

11 The chromosomes begin decondensing, the spindles disassemble, and new nuclear envelopes form.

Bisphenol A and the Grandmother Effect

Although this chapter documents the role of meiosis in generating genetically diverse offspring, one type of diversity that must be avoided is differences in chromosome number. Cells (or organisms) that have more, or fewer, than the normal number of chromosomes are called *aneuploid*; agents that promote this problem are known as *aneugens*. The formation of gametes by meiosis is under hormonal control in mammals, and it is not surprising to learn that synthetic chemicals influencing the action of reproductive hormones can be aneugenic. Bisphenol A, a chemical monomer used in the manufacture of polycarbonate plastics and resins, binds to estrogen receptors in mice. Exposure to relatively high concentrations has been shown to elevate the incidence of aneuploid gametes and offspring. Since meiosis is active in females before they are born, exposure of pregnant mouse mothers resulted in aneuploid gametes produced by their daughters, which, in turn, gave rise to aneuploid grandchildren.

Canada has declared BPA a toxic substance and banned its use in baby bottles.

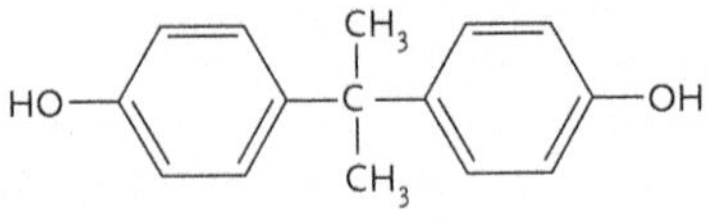

Figure 1
Bisphenol A.

homologous only through a short region. The X and Y chromosomes behave as homologues (i.e., they pair where homologous, recombine, and move together to the metaphase plate) during meiosis in males. As a result of meiosis, a gamete formed by females may receive either member of the XX pair. A gamete formed by males receives either an X or a Y chromosome. (See Chapter 11 for a discussion of the inheritance of genes on sex chromosomes.)

The sequence of steps in the two meiotic divisions accomplishes the major outcomes of meiosis: the generation of genetic variability and the reduction in chromosome number. (Figure 9.16, p. 210, reviews the two meiotic divisions and compares them with the single division of mitosis.)

9.3d Several Mechanisms Contribute to Genetic Diversity

The generation of genetic variability by meiosis is a prime evolutionary advantage of sexual reproduction **(Figure 9.12).** Such variability increases the chance that at least some offspring will have combinations of alleles that will be successful in surviving and reproducing in

Figure 9.12
Genetic variability as shown in the appearance of domestic cats.

Marc Henrie/Dorling Kindersley/Getty Images

Dave King/Dorling Kindersley/Getty Images

Elena Butinova/Shutterstock.com

Maksim Shmeljov/Shutterstock.com

Lexx/Shutterstock.com

GlobalP/iStock/Thinkstock

Dr. Aurora Nedelcu, *University of New Brunswick*

Whereas the octopuses and limpets mentioned at the opening of this chapter have no choice but to undergo meiosis and follow the remaining steps of their sexual life cycle, bacteria, archaea, and many lower eukaryotes become sexual only in response to suboptimal environmental conditions, such as elevated temperature or nutrient deficiency. This observation led Aurora Nedelcu and her colleagues in The Green Lab at the University of New Brunswick to gather evidence to test the hypothesis that sex originally evolved as one of several responses available to cells dealing with stress.

A variety of external stresses all eventually cause internal oxidative stress resulting from increased concentration of damaging reactive oxygen species (ROS). Using her multicellular algal model system (*Volvox carteri*), Nedelcu has shown that stress-induced increase in ROS does indeed stimulate the expression of sex-related genes **(Figure 1)**. She believes that the cells experiencing oxidative stress "turn on" their sex genes in order to benefit from the possibility that meiotic recombination will repair DNA damage caused by ROS.

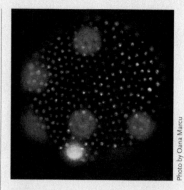

Photo by Oana Marcu

Figure 1
Volvox carteri *under heat stress. ROS indicated by green fluorescence.*

changing environments. In fact, some scientists argue that meiosis exists not to create just any variability but to generate "repaired" chromosomes to be passed on to the next generation (see "People behind Biology"). As you work through the ideas in this section, try to envision how you could pass a "perfect" copy of chromosome 6 to your children even if both copies of chromosome 6 you inherited from your parents are damaged.

The variability produced by sexual reproduction is apparent all around us, particularly in the human population. Except for identical twins, no two humans look alike, act alike, or have identical biochemical and physiological characteristics, even if they are members of the same immediate family. Other species that reproduce sexually show equivalent variability arising from meiosis.

During meiosis and fertilization, genetic variability arises from four sources: (1) genetic recombination of homologous chromosomes, (2) the differing combinations of maternal and paternal chromosomes segregated to the poles during anaphase I, (3) the differing combinations of recombinant chromatids segregated to the poles during anaphase II, and (4) the particular sets of male and female gametes that unite in fertilization. The four mechanisms, working together, produce so much total variability that no two products of meiosis produced by the same or different individuals and no two zygotes produced by union of the gametes are likely to have the same genetic makeup. Each of these sources of variability is discussed in further detail in the following sections. **Figure 9.13, p. 208,** contrasts the genetically identical daughter cells

arising from mitosis with the diverse daughter cells produced by meiosis.

Genetic Recombination. Recombination, the key genetic event of prophase I, starts when homologous chromosomes pair **(Figure 9.14, p. 209,** step 1). Recall that although homologous chromosomes have the same genes in the same order, they likely carry different versions of those genes (alleles). This means that the underlying DNA sequence is similar enough to form the basis of meiotic pairing, yet different enough to generate novel combinations after recombination. (Recall Lederberg's multiple auxotrophic *E. coli* mutants here; the idea is the same.) As the homologous chromosomes pair, they are held together tightly by a protein framework called the synaptonemal complex **(Figure 9.15, p. 209).** Supported by this framework, regions of homologous chromatids exchange segments, producing new combinations of alleles (see Figure 9.14, step 2). Recall that the exchange process is very precise and involves the breakage and rejoining of DNA molecules by enzymes (Figure 9.1, p. 190). When the exchange is complete toward the end of prophase I, the synaptonemal complex disassembles and disappears. If you now follow meiosis I and II through to the end in your mind, notice that each of the four resulting nuclei receives one of these four chromatids (see Figure 9.14, p. 209, step 3); two receive unchanged "parental" chromatids, and two receive chromatids that have new combinations of alleles due to recombination; these are called *recombinants*.

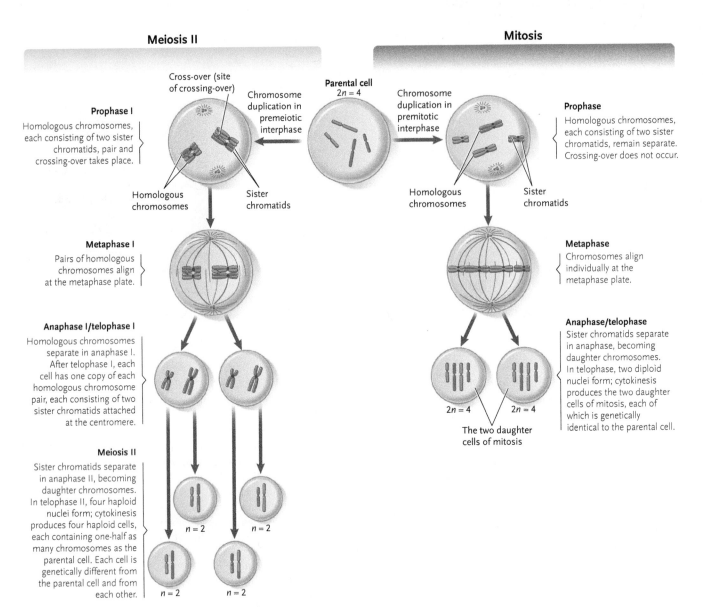

Figure 9.13

Comparison of key steps in meiosis and mitosis. Both diagrams use an animal cell as an example. Maternal chromosomes are shown in red; paternal chromosomes are shown in blue.

The physical effect of recombination can be seen later in prophase I, when increased condensation of the chromosomes thickens the chromosomes enough to make them visible under the light microscope (see Figure 9.11, p. 204, steps 3 and 4). Regions in which nonsister chromatids cross one another, called **cross-overs** or **chiasmata** (singular, *chiasma* = cross-piece), clearly show that two of the four chromatids have exchanged segments. Because of the shape produced, the recombination process is also called **crossing-over.**

Note that illustrations of recombination usually show chromosomes "paired" side by side, with only the closest chromatids participating in recombination (see Figure 9.14); however, chromosomes actually pair "one on top of the other" such that any two of the four chromatids can participate in a given recombination event. Recombination takes place largely at random, at almost any position along the chromosome arms. Several events likely occur at various locations along all chromatids.

CONCEPT FIX Notice in Figure 9.14 that a recombination event does not just "switch" the alleles of a given gene in a localized area. Rather, all of the DNA sequence stretching from the site of recombination to the ends of the participating chromatids is exchanged. ⬡

Random Segregation. Random segregation of chromosomes of maternal and paternal origin accounts for the second major source of genetic variability in meiosis.

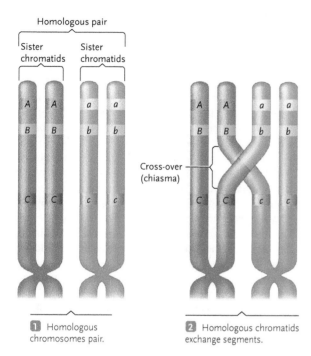

Homologous pair

Sister chromatids | Sister chromatids

A A	a a
B B	b b
C C	c c

1 Homologous chromosomes pair.

A A	a a
B B	b b
C C	c c

Cross-over (chiasma)

2 Homologous chromatids exchange segments.

A a	A a
B b	B b
C C	c c

3 Homologous chromosomes separate at first meiotic division.

Figure 9.14
Effects of the exchange between chromatids that accomplishes genetic recombination. Although the closest chromatids are shown crossing over, any pair of nonsister chromatids may recombine. The letters indicate two alleles (e.g., *A* and *a*) for each of three genes. In the meiocyte, the alleles are in the combination of *A–B–C* and *a–b–c* on their respective homologues. As a result of this recombination event, two of the chromatids, the recombinants, have a new combination: *a–b–C* and *A–B–c*.

Recall that the maternal and paternal members of each homologous pair are different in that they typically carry different alleles of many of the genes on that chromosome. During prometaphase I, spindle microtubules make connections to kinetochores. For each homologous pair, one chromosome makes spindle connections leading to one pole and the other chromosome connects to the opposite pole in a random choice. In making these connections, all the maternal chromosomes may connect to one pole and all the paternal chromosomes may connect to the opposite pole. Or, as is much more likely, a random combination of maternal and paternal chromosomes will be segregated to a given spindle pole **(Figure 9.16, p. 210)**.

The number of possible random combinations depends on the number of chromosome pairs in a species. For example, the 39 chromosome pairs in dogs allow 2^{39} different combinations of maternal and paternal chromosomes to be delivered to the poles, producing potentially 550 billion genetically different gametes from this source of variability alone. Note that this random partitioning of maternal and paternal chromosomes is responsible for the independent assortment of the alleles of two genes in Mendel's experiments with garden peas described in Chapter 10.

Alternative Combinations at Meiosis II. If you look carefully at the cells drawn in metaphase II in Figure 9.14, you will see that the chromosomes are still replicated, and, as a result of recombination in prophase I, each chromosome carries one recombinant chromatid and one nonrecombinant chromatid. Notice that, in this case, the chromosomes have aligned at metaphase II with both recombinant chromatids attached to the

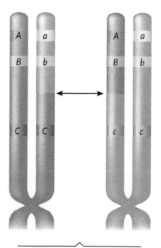

Sister chromatids of one of a homologous pair of chromosomes

Sister chromatids of the other of a homologous pair of chromosomes

Synaptonemal complex

Figure 9.15
The synaptonemal complex as seen in a meiotic cell of the fungus *Neotiella*.

same spindle pole. However, since the attachment of spindles to kinetochores is random at this stage, you should be able to see that it is just as likely that these chromosomes *could* have lined up, with the smaller chromosome sending its recombinant chromatid to one pole and the larger chromosome sending its recombinant chromatid to the opposite pole. The resulting daughter cells will be genetically different, depending on how the chromosomes align in metaphase II.

Random Fertilization. The haploid products of meiosis are genetically diverse. The random combination of these cells (or their descendants) during fertilization is a matter of chance that amplifies the variability of sexual reproduction. For example, if we consider only the variability available from random separation of

CHAPTER 9 GENETIC RECOMBINATION | 209

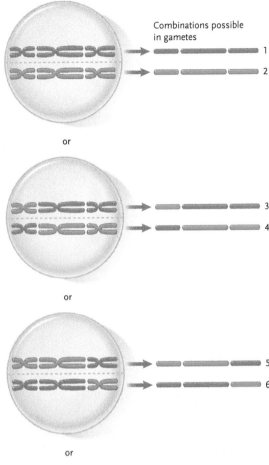

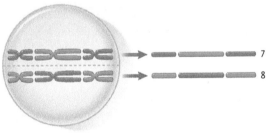

Figure 9.16

Independent assortment. Possible outcomes of the random spindle connections of three pairs of chromosomes at metaphase I of meiosis. Maternal chromosomes are red; paternal chromosomes are blue. There are four possible patterns of connections, giving eight possible combinations of maternal and paternal chromosomes in gametes (labelled 1–8).

Combinations possible in gametes

1
2

3
4

5
6

7
8

or

or

or

homologous chromosomes at meiosis I along with that from random fertilization, the possibility that two children of the same human parents could receive the same combination of maternal and paternal chromosomes is 1 chance out of $(2^{23})^2$ or 1 in about 70 trillion, a number that far exceeds the number of humans who have ever lived. The further variability introduced by recombination and shuffling at meiosis II makes it practically impossible for humans and most other

sexually reproducing organisms to produce genetically identical gametes or offspring. The only exception is identical twins (or identical triplets, identical quadruplets, and so forth), which arise not from the combination of identical gametes during fertilization but from mitotic division of a single fertilized egg into separate cells that give rise to genetically identical individuals.

We have just seen that meiosis has three outcomes that are vital to sexual reproduction. This process reduces the chromosomes to the haploid number so that they can be brought together with those of another individual without doubling the usual chromosome number during fertilization. Through genetic recombination and random separation of maternal and paternal chromosomes, meiosis produces genetic variability in gametes; further variability is provided by the random combination of gametes in fertilization. These ideas form the "mechanics" that underlie the patterns of inheritance of traits in sexually reproducing organisms discovered by Mendel and described in Chapter 10.

STUDY BREAK

1. Which phase (diploid or haploid) dominates the respective life cycles of animals, plants, and fungi?
2. What are the two functions of meiosis?
3. What are the four sources of genetic variability in sexually reproducing organisms?
4. What is nondisjunction, and how does it occur?

9.4 Mobile Elements

Our examples have so far involved two participating DNA molecules that have always been at least partially homologous and that have always originated from two different individuals. However, one of the most interesting examples of genetic recombination in nature shows neither of these characteristics. All organisms appear to contain particular segments of DNA, called **mobile elements**, that can move from one place to another; they cut and paste sections of DNA using a type of recombination that does *not necessarily require homology*. Sometimes called *jumping genes,* these elements normally move from place to place *within the genome of a given cell*. The following section describes these fascinating elements in more detail.

9.4a Insertion Sequence Elements and Transposons Are the Two Major Types of Prokaryotic Mobile Elements

Mobile elements are also known by the more specific term **transposable elements (TEs)**, and their mechanism of movement, involving nonhomologous recombination, is called **transposition.** Transposition usually

a. Cut-and-paste transposition

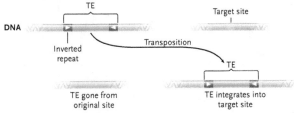

b. Copy-and-paste transposition

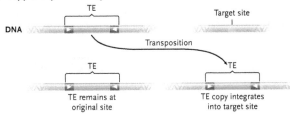

Figure 9.17

Two transposition processes for transposable elements. **(a)** Cut-and-paste transposition, in which the TE leaves one location in the DNA and moves to a new location. **(b)** Copy-and-paste transposition, in which a copy of the TE moves to a new location, leaving the original TE behind.

occurs at a low frequency in either of two ways, depending on the type of element: (1) a cut-and-paste process, in which the TE leaves its original location and transposes to a new location **(Figure 9.17a)**, and (2) a copy-and-paste process, in which a copy of a TE transposes to a new location, leaving the original TE behind (Figure 9.17b). For most TEs, transposition starts with contact between the TE and the target site. This also means that TEs do not exist free of the DNA in which they are integrated; hence, the popular name *jumping genes* is actually inaccurate. TEs are never "in the air" between one location and another. TEs are important because of the genetic changes they cause. For example, they produce mutations by transposing into genes and knocking out their functions, and they increase or decrease gene expression by transposing into regulatory sequences of genes. As such, TEs are biological mutagens that increase genetic variability.

Bacterial TEs were discovered in the 1960s. They have been shown to move from site to site within the bacterial chromosome, between the bacterial chromosome and plasmids, and between plasmids. The frequency of transposition is low but constant for a given TE. Some bacterial TEs insert randomly, at any point in the DNA, whereas others recognize certain sequences as "hot spots" for insertion and insert preferentially at these locations.

The two major types of bacterial TEs are **insertion sequences (ISs)** and **transposons**. Insertion sequences are the simplest TEs. They are relatively small and contain only genes for their transposition, notably the gene for **transposase**, an enzyme that catalyzes some of the recombination reactions for inserting or removing

the TE from the DNA **(Figure 9.18)**. At each of the two ends of an IS is a short **inverted repeat** sequence—the same DNA sequence running in opposite directions (shown by directional arrows in the figure). The inverted repeat sequences enable the transposase enzyme to identify the ends of the TE when it catalyzes transposition. The inverted repeat sequence is an IS element on both the F factor and the bacterial chromosome that provides the homology needed for the creation of the Hfr strains described in Section 9.2.

The second type of bacterial TE, called a transposon, has an inverted repeat sequence at each end enclosing a central region with one or more genes. In a number of bacterial transposons, the inverted repeat sequences are insertion sequences, which provide the transposase for movement of the element (see Figure 9.18). Additional genes in the central region typically code for antibiotic resistance; they can originate from the main bacterial chromosome or from plasmids. These non-IS genes included in transposons are carried along as the TEs move from place to place.

Many antibiotics, such as penicillin, erythromycin, tetracycline, ampicillin, and streptomycin, which were once successful in curing bacterial infections, have lost much of their effectiveness because of resistance genes carried in transposons. Movements of the transposons, particularly to plasmids that can be transferred by conjugation within and between bacterial species, greatly increase the spread of genes, providing antibiotic resistance to infecting cells. Resistance genes have made many bacterial diseases difficult or impossible to treat with standard antibiotics.

9.4b Transposable Elements Were First Discovered in Eukaryotes

TEs were first discovered in a eukaryote, maize (corn), in the 1940s by Barbara McClintock, a geneticist working at the Cold Spring Harbor Laboratory in New York. McClintock noted that some mutations affecting kernel and leaf colour appeared and disappeared rapidly

a. IS element

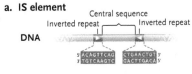

b. Transposon

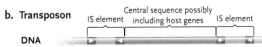

Figure 9.18

Types of bacterial TEs. **(a)** IS element. **(b)** Transposon in which the central sequence is transposed by flanking IS elements.

Figure 9.19

Barbara McClintock and corn kernels showing different colour patterns due to the movement of transposable elements. As TEs move into or out of genes, controlling pigment production in developing kernels, the ability of cells and their descendants to produce the dark pigment is destroyed or restored. The result is random patterns of pigmented and colourless (yellow) segments in individual kernels.

Nik Kleinberg

under certain conditions. Mapping the alleles by linkage studies produced a surprising result: the map positions changed frequently, indicating that the alleles could move from place to place in the corn chromosomes. Some of the movements were so frequent that changes in their effects could be noticed at different times in a single developing kernel **(Figure 9.19).**

When McClintock first reported her results, her findings were regarded as an isolated curiosity, possibly applying only to corn. This was because the then-prevailing opinion among geneticists was that genes are fixed in the chromosomes and do not move to other locations. Her conclusions were widely accepted only after TEs were detected and characterized in bacteria in the 1960s. By the 1970s, further examples of TEs were discovered in other eukaryotes, including yeast and mammals. McClintock was awarded a Nobel Prize in 1983 for her pioneering work, after these discoveries confirmed her early findings that TEs are probably universally distributed among both prokaryotic and eukaryotic organisms.

9.4c Eukaryotic Transposable Elements Are Classified as Transposons or Retrotransposons

Eukaryotic TEs fall into two major classes: transposons and retrotransposons. They are distinguished by the way the TE sequence moves from place to place in the DNA. Eukaryotic transposons are similar to bacterial transposons in their general structure and in the ways they transpose. However, members of the other class of eukaryotic TEs, the **retrotransposons**, transpose by a copy-and-paste mechanism that is unlike any of the other TEs we have discussed. Retrotransposons have this name because transposition occurs via an intermediate RNA copy of the TE **(Figure 9.20).** First, the retrotransposon, which is a DNA element

integrated into the chromosomal DNA, is transcribed into a complementary RNA copy. Next, an enzyme called **reverse transcriptase**, which is encoded by one of the genes of the retrotransposon, uses the RNA as a **template** to make a DNA copy of the retrotransposon.

The DNA copy is then inserted into the DNA at a new location, leaving the original in place. This insertion step involves breaking and rejoining DNA backbones, as we have seen several times in this chapter.

Once TEs are inserted into chromosomes, they become more or less permanent residents, duplicated and passed on during cell division along with the rest of the DNA. TEs inserted into the DNA of reproductive cells may be inherited, thereby becoming a permanent part of the genetic material of a species. Long-standing TEs are subject to mutation along with other sequences in the DNA. Such mutations may accumulate in a TE, gradually altering it into a nonmobile, residual sequence in the DNA. The DNA of many eukaryotes, including humans, contains a surprising amount of nonfunctional TE sequence likely created in this way.

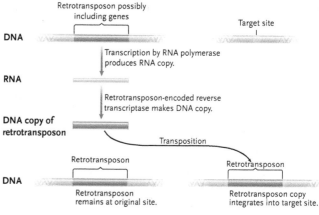

Figure 9.20

Transposition of a eukaryotic retrotransposon to a new location by means of an intermediate RNA copy.

9.4d Retrotransposons Are Similar to Retroviruses

The RNA to DNA reverse transcription associated with retrotransposon movement is strikingly similar to that employed by a class of eukaryotic viruses called **retroviruses.** When a retrovirus infects a host cell, a reverse transcriptase carried in the virus particle is released and copies the single-stranded RNA genome into a double-stranded DNA copy. The viral DNA is then inserted into the host DNA (by genetic recombination), where it is replicated and passed to progeny cells during cell division. Similar to the prophage of bacteria, the inserted viral DNA is known as a **provirus (Figure 9.21).**

Retroviruses are found in a wide range of organisms, with most so far identified in vertebrates. You, as well as other humans and mammals, contain several retroviruses in your genome as proviruses. In total, retrotransposons and retroviruses of all types occupy some 40% of the human genome!

Although many of the retroviruses do not produce infectious virus particles, they sometimes cause DNA rearrangements such as deletions and translocations. Such changes may alter the relative position of DNA sequences on the chromosome and, in turn, disturb the normal regulation of gene expression. Given your knowledge of transduction by bacterial viruses described earlier in this chapter, you will not be surprised to hear that retroviruses sometimes pick up host eukaryotic genes and move them to recipients. Such genes may become abnormally active through the effects of regulatory sequences located in the TE itself or the DNA nearby. Certain forms of cancer have been linked to this type of abnormal activation of genes that are important in regulating cell division (see Section 14.4). In one of the most dramatic examples, a cellular gene is transported to an infected cell by the avian sarcoma retrovirus. The cellular gene is overexpressed in the new environment, resulting in uncontrolled growth of infected cells, leading to tumours in infected birds.

STUDY BREAK

Among eukaryotic mobile elements, how do transposons, retrotransposons, and retroviruses differ?

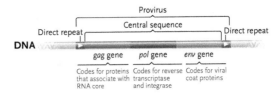

Figure 9.21

A mammalian retrovirus in the provirus form in which it is inserted into chromosomal DNA. The direct repeat at either end contains sequences capable of acting as enhancer, promoter, and termination signals for transcription. The central sequence contains genes coding for proteins, concentrated in the *gag*, *pol*, and *env* regions. The provirus of **human immunodeficiency virus (HIV),** the virus that causes **acquired immune deficiency syndrome (AIDS),** takes this form.

This has been a long chapter. We hope that, taken together, all of these ideas will help you understand the balance that life must strike between the stability and the plasticity of its genetic material. On the one hand, DNA must be faithfully replicated and passed to the next generation. Lack of quality control at this step would allow widespread random mutations to undermine the selection and preservation of good combinations of alleles. On the other hand, any system that made only perfectly "photocopied" DNA available for the next generation would be doomed as well; a wide variety of diverse genetic "solutions" are needed for a population to survive in constantly changing environments that are impossible to anticipate.

Genetic recombination is central to many processes that contribute changes to the sequence of DNA in all forms of life. (And we did not even discuss interesting examples of developmental genetic recombination in infecting parasites or the cells of the developing immune system, or foreign DNA taken up by rotifers.) The genetic elements discussed in this chapter, particularly plasmids and retroviruses, often act as natural genetic engineers by moving genes between species. Chapter 15 describes how human genetic engineers manipulate and clone DNA.

Review

To access course materials such as Aplia and other companion resources, please visit www.NELSONbrain.com.

9.1 Mechanism of Genetic Recombination

- Genetic recombination requires two DNA molecules that differ from one another; a mechanism for bringing the DNA molecules into close proximity; and a collection of enzymes to cut, exchange, and paste the DNA back together.

- Homology allows DNA on different molecules to line up and recombine precisely.

- Enzymatic cutting and pasting of both DNA backbones from each of the two DNA molecules is required for each recombination event (see Figure 9.1).

9.2 Genetic Recombination in Bacteria

- Study of bacterial recombination requires strains carrying different alleles.

- Lederberg and Tatum mutated bacteria to create strains that were different in their ability to manufacture certain amino acids and vitamins.

- In bacteria, the DNA of the bacterial chromosome may recombine with DNA brought into close proximity from another cell.

- Three primary mechanisms bring DNA into bacterial cells from the outside: conjugation, transformation, and transduction.

- In conjugation, two bacterial cells form a cytoplasmic bridge allowing at least some of the DNA of one cell to move into the other cell. The donated DNA can then recombine with homologous sequences of the recipient cell's DNA.

- *Escherichia coli* bacteria that are able to act as DNA donors in conjugation have an F factor, making them F+; recipients have no F factor and are F−. In Hfr strains of *E. coli*, the F factor is a part of the main chromosome. As a result, genes from the main chromosome can be transferred into F− cells along with a portion of the F factor DNA (see Figure 9.6).

- In transformation, intact cells of some species absorb pieces of DNA released from cells that have disintegrated. The entering DNA fragments can recombine with the recipient cell's DNA.

- In transduction, DNA is transferred from one cell to another "by mistake" inside the head of an infecting virus (see Figure 9.7).

- Since generalized transduction transfers random fragments of the host chromosome, all host genes are transferred at equal frequency. Specialized transduction only transfers genes lying close to the point of insertion of the prophage (see Figure 9.8).

9.3 Genetic Recombination in Eukaryotes: Meiosis

- The time and place of meiosis follow one of three major pathways in the life cycles of eukaryotes, which reflect the portions of the life cycle spent in the haploid and diploid phases and whether mitotic divisions intervene between meiosis and the formation of gametes (see Figure 9.9).

- Animals have a diploid life cycle in which the diploid phase is multicellular and the haploid phase is unicellular. Meiosis is followed by gamete formation.

- Plants and some fungi have an alternating-generations life cycle in which either haploid or diploid phases are multicellular and both of which divide by mitosis. The diploid sporophytes are produced by fertilization, and the haploid gametophytes are produced by mitotic divisions of the spores formed by meiosis.

- Most fungi exhibit a haploid life cycle in which the haploid phase is multicellular and the diploid phase is limited to a single cell produced by fertilization, which then immediately undergoes meiosis.

- In animals, the products of meiosis are haploid gametes. The diploid phase of the life cycle is then restored when one gamete fuses with another at fertilization. In plants, meiosis occurs in some of the cells of the diploid sporophytes and produces a generation of haploid spores. These spores then divide by mitosis to produce multicellular gametophytes. Gametes are formed from mitotic division of specific sporophyte tissues.

- The functions of meiosis are to reduce the chromosome number (from diploid to haploid) and to generate genetic diversity in sexually reproducing organisms (see Figure 9.10).

- Meiosis occurs only in eukaryotes that reproduce sexually and only in organisms that are at least diploid—that is, organisms that have at least two representatives of each chromosome (see Figure 9.11).

- DNA replicates and the chromosomal proteins are duplicated during the premeiotic interphase, producing two copies, the sister chromatids, of each chromosome.

- During prophase I of the first meiotic division (meiosis I), the replicated chromosomes condense and come together and pair as the spindle forms in the cytoplasm.

- While they are paired, the chromatids of homologous chromosomes undergo recombination by breaking the covalent bonds of the DNA backbones, matching complementary sequences on nonsister chromatids, exchanging the ends, and restoring the bonds.

- During prometaphase I, the nuclear envelope breaks down, the spindle enters the area of the former nucleus, and kinetochore microtubules leading to opposite spindle poles attach to one kinetochore of each pair of sister chromatids of homologous chromosomes.

- At metaphase I, spindle microtubule movements have aligned the tetrads on the metaphase plate, the equatorial plane between the two spindle poles. The connections of kinetochore microtubules to opposite poles ensure that the homologous pairs separate and move to opposite spindle poles during anaphase I, reducing the chromosome number to the haploid value. Each chromosome at the poles still contains two chromatids.

- Telophase I and interkinesis are brief and transitory stages; no DNA replication occurs during interkinesis.

During these stages, the remaining single spindle of the first meiotic division disassembles and the microtubule subunits are available to reassemble into two new spindles for the second division.

- During prophase II, the chromosomes condense and the spindle reorganizes. During prometaphase II, the nuclear envelope breaks down, the spindle enters the former nuclear area, and spindle microtubules leading to opposite spindle poles attach to the two kinetochores of each chromosome. At metaphase II, the chromosomes become aligned on the metaphase plate. The connections of kinetochore microtubules to opposite spindle poles ensure that during anaphase II, the chromatids of each chromosome are separated and segregate to those opposite spindle poles.

- During telophase II, the chromosomes decondense to their extended interphase state, the spindles disassemble, and new nuclear envelopes form. The result is four haploid cells, each containing half the number of chromosomes present in a G1 nucleus of the same species. In animals, these products of meiosis function as gametes that fuse in fertilization; in plants, these products function as spores that divide by mitosis to form gametophytes.

- Meiosis II differs from mitosis in that meiosis II occurs only in reproductive tissue, is not preceded by an S phase, and results in genetically different daughter cells (see Figure 9.13).

- Nondisjunction occurs when both members of a pair of homologous chromosomes connect to spindles from the same pole. Following anaphase, one pole then receives both copies of the pair, and the other pole receives none. The overall results (following normal meiosis II) are haploid products of meiosis that have two copies of the given chromosome. After fertilization, the resulting zygote will therefore have three copies of the chromosome instead of two.

- In many eukaryotes, including most animals, one or more pairs of chromosomes, called the sex chromosomes, are different in male and female individuals of the same species.

- Recombination is the first source of the genetic variability produced by meiosis. During recombination, chromatids generate new combinations of alleles by physically exchanging segments. The exchange process involves precise breakage and joining of DNA molecules. It is catalyzed by enzymes and occurs

while the homologous chromosomes are held together tightly by the synaptonemal complex. The cross-overs visible between the chromosomes at late prophase I reflect the exchange of chromatid segments that occurred during the molecular steps of genetic recombination (see Figures 9.13 and 9.14).

- The random segregation of homologous chromosomes is the second source of genetic variability produced by meiosis. The homologous pairs separate at anaphase I of meiosis, creating random combinations of maternal and paternal chromosomes travelling to each of the two spindle poles (see Figure 9.15).

- Random segregation of the chromatids of replicated chromosomes at meiosis II is a third mechanism for generating diversity.

- Random joining of male and female gametes in fertilization is the fourth source of genetic variability.

9.4 Mobile Elements

- Both prokaryotic and eukaryotic organisms contain transposable elements (TEs)—DNA sequences that can move from place to place in the DNA. The TEs may move from one location in the DNA to another or generate duplicated copies that insert at new locations while leaving the parent copy in its original location (see Figure 9.17).

- Genes of the host cell DNA may become incorporated into a TE and may be carried with it to a new location. There the genes may become abnormally active when placed near sequences that control the activity of genes within the TE or near the control elements of active host genes (see Figure 9.18).

- Eukaryotic TEs occur as transposons, which release from one location in the DNA and insert at a different site, or as retrotransposons, which move by making an RNA copy, which is then used to assemble a DNA copy that is inserted at a new location. The parent copy remains at the original location. Like retrotransposons, retroviruses make a DNA copy of their RNA genome and insert this into the host's chromosome. Retroviruses may have evolved from retrotransposons (see Figure 9.20).

- TE-instigated abnormal activation of genes regulating cell division has been linked to the development of some forms of cancer in humans and other complex animals.

Questions

Self-Test Questions

1. If recombination occurred in a bacterium undergoing transformation as shown in the figure, what would be the final genotype of the bacterial chromosome?

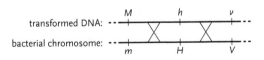

transformed DNA:

bacterial chromosome:

a. *MHv*
b. *MHv*
c. *mHV*
d. *mhV*

2. Which of the following events turns F+ cells into Hfr cells?
   a. replication of the F factor by rolling circle replication
   b. recombination between the F factor and the recipient chromosome
   c. transfer of the F factor to a recipient cell
   d. integration of the F factor into the host chromosome

3. Which of the following describes an aspect of bacterial conjugation?
   a. Recipient cells incorporate single-stranded DNA from donors into their chromosome.
   b. DNA from dead donor bacteria is transferred to live recipient cells.

c. Genes are transferred in a particular order from donors to recipients.

d. A virus is required for the transfer of DNA from donors to recipient cells.

4. If a virus is in the lysogenic phase of its life cycle, what is it doing?
   a. bursting the host cell
   b. transducing genes into a bacterial cell
   c. assembling viral particles for cell rupture
   d. being expressed and/or copied as a part of the host DNA

5. If the diploid number of an organism is 6, which stage of cell division does the figure below represent?

   a. mitotic metaphase
   b. meiotic metaphase I
   c. meiotic metaphase II
   d. could be either mitotic metaphase or meiotic metaphase II

6. Imagine that you are helping your younger brother with his biology homework. You notice that he has written down in his notes that "Plants are haploid and make gametes by mitosis. Animals are diploid and make gametes by meiosis." What should your response be?
   a. Yes, plants make gametes by mitosis and most animals make gametes by meiosis. However, animals and plants both have a haploid and a diploid stage of their life cycle.
   b. Yes, both plants and animals make gametes. The difference is that plant gametes divide by mitosis but animal gametes do not.
   c. Yes, plants are simpler organisms than animals and have fewer chromosomes in their cells.
   d. Yes, plants and animals use meiosis for different purposes. Animals make gametes by meiosis while plants make zygotes.

7. As a result of genetic recombination, each of the chromosomes of your family dog contains a different combination of alleles compared to those of its brothers and sisters. When did this recombination occur?
   a. when your dog's parents made gametes
   b. when your dog was a newly fertilized, single-celled zygote
   c. when your dog grew from a zygote to a multicellular organism
   d. when your dog reached sexual maturity

8. The number of human chromosomes in a cell in prophase I of meiosis is ___ and in telophase II is ___.
   a. 92; 46
   b. 46; 23
   c. 23; 23
   d. 23; 16

9. Consider a penguin gamete. The amount of DNA (pg) in this gamete is defined as $1C$. The number of chromosomes in this gamete is defined as $1n$.

That is, the value of C and the value of n are equal in a penguin gamete. During which other stage of penguin cell division would the value of C and the value of n also be equal?
   a. during G1; both n and C equal 2
   b. during G2; both n and C equal 4
   c. during metaphase of meiosis II; both n and C equal 1
   d. during metaphase of mitosis; both n and C equal 2

10. Which of the following is a feature of mobile elements?
   a. They have no negative impact on host cells.
   b. They have inverted repeat sequences at their centre.
   c. They make use of recombination that does not require extensive homology.
   d. They are a kind of virus.

Questions for Discussion

1. You set up an experiment like the one carried out by Lederberg and Tatum, mixing millions of *E. coli* of two strains with the following genetic constitutions.

Strain 1: bio^- met^- thr^+ leu^+

Strain 2: bio^+ met^+ thr^- leu^-

Among the bacteria obtained after mixing, you find some cells that do not require threonine, leucine, or biotin to grow but still need methionine. How might you explain this result?

2. You have a technique that allows you to measure the amount of DNA in a cell nucleus. You establish the amount of DNA in a sperm cell of an organism as your baseline. Which multiple of this amount would you expect to find in a nucleus of this organism at G2 of premeiotic interphase? At telophase I of meiosis? During interkinesis? At telophase II of meiosis?

3. Mutations are changes in DNA sequences that can create new alleles. In which cells of an individual, somatic or meiotic cells, would mutations be of greatest significance to that individual? What about to the species to which the individual belongs?

4. Sometimes pieces of chromosomes can be exchanged in a kind of rearrangement called a reciprocal translocation. Imagine the case in a diploid organism where the end of one chromosome 4 was exchanged for the end of a chromosome 12. The other chromosomes 4 and 12 remained uninvolved and normal in structure. What shape might these four chromosomes take as they tried to pair during meiosis I?

5. Experimental systems have been developed in which TEs can be induced to move under the control of a researcher. Following the induced transposition of a yeast TE, two mutants were identified with altered activities of enzyme X. One of the mutants lacked enzyme activity completely, whereas the other had five times the enzyme activity of normal cells. Both mutants were found to have the TE inserted into the gene for enzyme X. Propose hypotheses for how the two different mutant phenotypes were produced.

Rabbits, showing genetic variation in coat colour.

Mendel, Genes, and Inheritance

WHY IT MATTERS

Parties and champagne were among the last things on Ernest Irons's mind on New Year's Eve, 1904. Irons, a medical intern, was examining a blood specimen from a new patient and was sketching what he saw through his microscope—peculiarly elongated red blood cells **(Figure 10.1, p. 218).** He and his supervisor, James Herrick, had never seen anything like them. The shape of the cells was reminiscent of a sickle, a cutting tool with a crescent-shaped blade.

The patient had complained of weakness, dizziness, shortness of breath, and pain. His father and two sisters had died from mysterious ailments that had damaged their lungs or kidneys. Did those deceased family members also have sickle-shaped red cells in their blood? Was there a connection between the abnormal cells and the ailments? How did the cells become sickled?

The medical problems that baffled Irons and Herrick killed their patient when he was only 32 years old. The patient's symptoms were characteristic of a genetic disorder now called *sickle cell disease*. This disease develops when a person has received two copies of a gene (one from each parent) that codes for an altered subunit of hemoglobin, the oxygen-transporting protein in red blood cells. When oxygen supplies are low, the altered hemoglobin forms long, fibrous, crystal-like structures that push red blood cells into the sickle shape. The altered protein differs from the normal protein by just a single amino acid.

The sickled red blood cells are too elongated and inflexible to pass through the capillaries, the smallest vessels in the circulatory system. As a result, the cells block the capillaries. The surrounding tissues become starved for oxygen and saturated

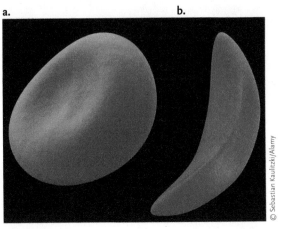

a. **b.**

Figure 10.1
Red blood cell shape in sickle cell disease.

Figure 10.2
Gregor Mendel (1822–1884), the founder of genetics.

with metabolic wastes, causing the symptoms experienced by Irons and Herrick's patient. The problem worsens as oxygen concentration falls in tissues and more red blood cells are pushed into the sickled form. (You will learn more about sickle cell disease in this chapter and in Chapter 11.)

Researchers have studied sickle cell disease in great detail at both the molecular and the clinical level. You may find it curious, however, that our understanding of sickle cell disease—and all other heritable traits—actually began with studies of pea plants in a monastery garden.

Fifty years before Ernest Irons sketched sickled red blood cells, a scholarly monk named Gregor Mendel **(Figure 10.2)** used garden peas to study patterns of inheritance. To test his hypotheses about inheritance, Mendel bred generation after generation of pea plants and carefully observed the patterns by which parents transmit traits to their offspring. Through his experiments and observations, Mendel discovered the fundamental rules that govern inheritance. His discoveries and conclusions founded the science of genetics and still have the power to explain many of the puzzling and sometimes devastating aspects of inheritance that continue to occupy our attention.

10.1 The Beginnings of Genetics: Mendel's Garden Peas

Until about 1900, scientists and the general public believed in the **blending theory of inheritance**, which suggested that hereditary traits blend evenly in offspring through mixing of the parents' blood, much like the effect of mixing coffee and cream. Even today, many people assume that parental characteristics such as skin colour, body size, and facial features blend evenly in their offspring, with the traits of the children appearing

about halfway between those of their parents. Yet if blending takes place, why don't extremes, such as very tall and very short individuals, gradually disappear over generations as repeated blending takes place? Also, why do children with blue eyes keep turning up among the offspring of brown-eyed parents?

Gregor Mendel's experiments with garden peas, performed in the 1860s, provided the first answers to these questions and many more. Mendel was an Augustinian monk who lived in a monastery in Brünn, now part of the Czech Republic. But he had an unusual education for a monk in the mid-nineteenth century. He had studied mathematics, chemistry, zoology, and botany at the University of Vienna under some of the foremost scientists of his day. He grew up on a farm and was well aware of agricultural principles and their application. He kept abreast of breeding experiments published in scientific journals. Mendel also won several awards for developing improved varieties of fruits and vegetables.

In his work with peas, Mendel studied a variety of heritable characteristics called **characters**, such as flower colour or seed shape. A variation in a character, such as purple or white flower colour, is called a **trait**. Mendel established that characters are passed to offspring in the form of discrete hereditary factors, which are now known as genes. Mendel observed that rather than blending evenly, many parental traits appear unchanged in offspring, whereas others disappear in one generation to reappear unchanged in the next. Although Mendel did not know it, the inheritance patterns he observed are the result of the segregation of chromosomes, on which the genes are located, to gametes in meiosis (see Chapter 9). Mendel's methods illustrate, perhaps as well as any experiments in the history of science, how rigorous scientific work is conducted: through observation, making hypotheses, and testing the hypotheses with experiments. Although others had studied inheritance patterns before him, Mendel's most important innovation was his quantitative approach to science, specifically his rigour and statistical analysis in an era when qualitative, purely descriptive science was the accepted practice. In this chapter, we will pay particular attention to the experimental aspect of Mendel's approach to explaining inheritance.

10.1a Mendel Chose True-Breeding Garden Peas for His Experiments

Mendel chose the garden pea (*Pisum sativum*) for his research because the plant could be grown easily in the monastery garden, without elaborate equipment. As in other flowering plants, gametes are produced in structures of the flowers **(Figure 10.3)**. The male gametes are sperm nuclei contained in the pollen, which is produced in the *anthers* of the flower. The female gametes are egg cells, produced in the *carpel* of the flowers. Normally, pea plants **self-fertilize** (also known as **self-pollinate** or, more simply, *self*): sperm nuclei in pollen produced by anthers fertilize egg cells housed in the carpel of the same flower. However, for his experiments, Mendel prevented self-fertilization by cutting off the anthers. Pollen to fertilize these flowers then had to come from a different plant. This technique is called **cross-pollination** or, more simply, a *cross*. This technique allowed Mendel to test the effects of mating pea plants of different parental types.

To begin his experiments, Mendel chose pea plants that were known to be **true-breeding** (also called *pure-breeding*); that is, when self-fertilized or, more simply, *selfed*, they passed traits without change from one generation to the next.

10.1b Mendel First Worked with Single-Character Crosses

Flower colour was among the seven characters Mendel selected for study; one true-breeding variety of peas had purple flowers, and the other true-breeding variety had white flowers (see Figure 10.3). Would these traits blend evenly if plants with purple flowers were cross-pollinated with plants with white flowers?

To answer this question, Mendel took pollen from the anthers of plants with purple flowers and placed it in the flowers of white-flowered plants. He placed the pollen on the *stigma*, the part of the carpel that receives pollen in flowers (see Figure 10.3). He also performed the reciprocal experiment by placing pollen from white-flowered plants on the stigmas of purple-flowered

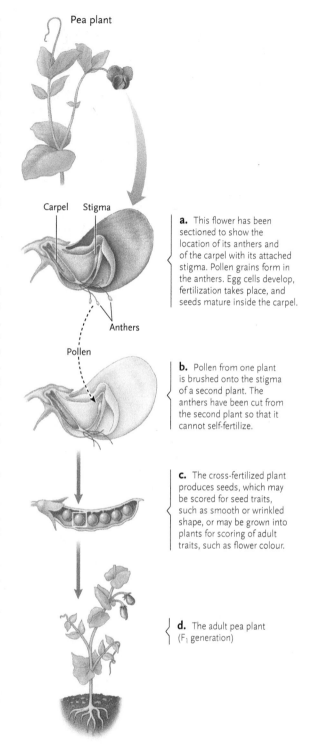

a. This flower has been sectioned to show the location of its anthers and of the carpel with its attached stigma. Pollen grains form in the anthers. Egg cells develop, fertilization takes place, and seeds mature inside the carpel.

b. Pollen from one plant is brushed onto the stigma of a second plant. The anthers have been cut from the second plant so that it cannot self-fertilize.

c. The cross-fertilized plant produces seeds, which may be scored for seed traits, such as smooth or wrinkled shape, or may be grown into plants for scoring of adult traits, such as flower colour.

d. The adult pea plant (F_1 generation)

Research Method Figure 10.3 The garden pea (*Pisum sativum*), the focus of Mendel's experiments.

plants. Seeds were the result of the crosses; each seed contains a zygote, or embryo, that will develop into a new pea plant. The plants that develop from the seeds produced by the cross—the first generation of offspring from the cross—are the F_1 **generation** (F stands for *filial; filius* = son). The plants used in the initial cross are called the parental or **P generation**. The plants that grew from the F_1 seeds all formed purple flowers, as if the trait for white flowers had disappeared. The flowers showed no evidence of blending.

Mendel then allowed the purple-flowered F_1 plants to self, producing seeds that represented the **F_2 generation**. When he planted the F_2 seeds produced by this cross, the white-flowered trait reappeared; both purple-flowered and white-flowered plants were produced. Mendel counted 705 plants with purple flowers and 224 with white flowers, in a ratio that he noted was close to 3:1, or about 75% purple-flowered plants and 25% white-flowered plants.

Mendel made similar crosses that involved six other characters, each with pairs of traits **(Figure 10.4)**; for example, the character of seed colour has the traits yellow and green. In all cases, he observed a uniform F_1 generation, in which only one of the two traits was present. In the F_2 generation, the missing trait reappeared, and both traits were present among the offspring. Moreover, the trait present in the F_1 generation was present in a definite, predictable proportion among the F_2 offspring.

10.1c Mendel's Single-Character Crosses Led Him to Propose the Principle of Segregation

Using his knowledge of mathematics, Mendel developed a set of hypotheses to explain the results of his crosses. His first hypothesis was that *the adult plants carry a pair of factors that govern the inheritance of each character*. He correctly deduced that for each character, an organism inherits one factor from each parent.

In modern terminology, Mendel's factors are called *genes*, which are located on chromosomes. The different versions of a gene that produce different traits of a character are called **alleles**. Thus, there are two alleles of the gene that govern flower colour in garden peas: one allele for purple flowers and the other allele for white flowers. Organisms with two copies of each gene are now known as diploids; the two alleles of a gene in a diploid individual may be identical or different.

How can the disappearance of one of the traits, such as white flowers, in the F_1 generation and its reappearance in the F_2 generation be explained? Mendel

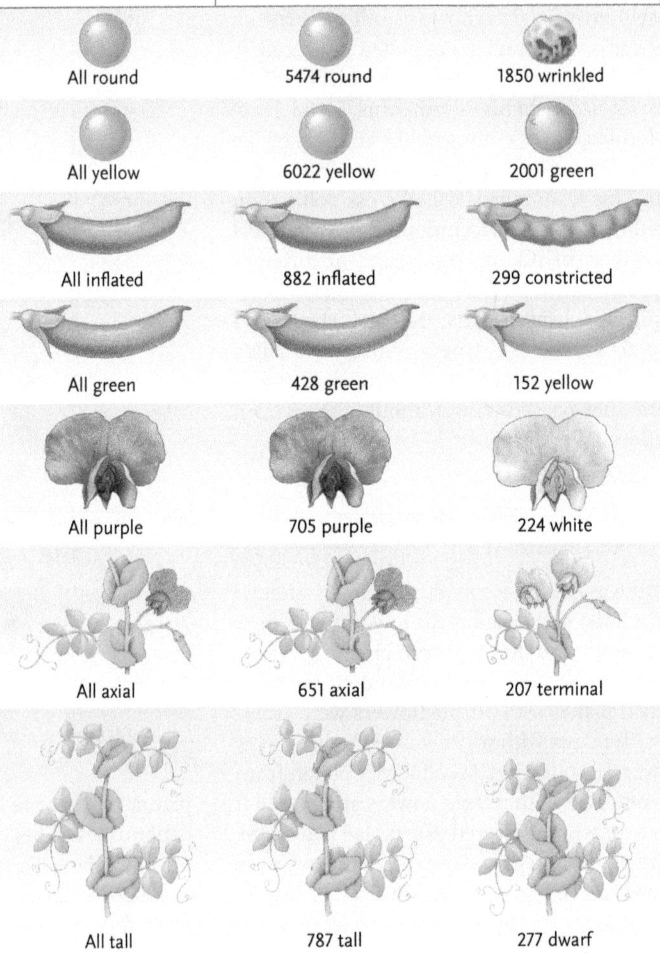

Figure 10.4
Mendel's crosses with seven different characters in peas, including his results and the calculated ratios of offspring.

Character	Traits crossed	F_1	F_2		Ratio
Seed shape	round × wrinkled	All round	5474 round	1850 wrinkled	2.96:1
Seed colour	yellow × green	All yellow	6022 yellow	2001 green	3.01:1
Pod shape	inflated × constricted	All inflated	882 inflated	299 constricted	2.95:1
Pod colour	green × yellow	All green	428 green	152 yellow	2.82:1
Flower colour	purple × white	All purple	705 purple	224 white	3.15:1
Flower position	axial (along stems) × terminal (at tips)	All axial	651 axial	207 terminal	3.14:1
Stem length	tall × dwarf	All tall	787 tall	277 dwarf	2.84:1

deduced that the trait that had seemed to disappear in the F_1 generation was actually present but was masked in some way by the "stronger" allele. Mendel called the masking effect **dominance**. Accordingly, Mendel's second hypothesis stated that *if an individual's pair of genes consists of different alleles, one allele is dominant over the other, **recessive**, allele.*

CONCEPT FIX What makes an allele **dominant?** In the case of flower colour in Mendel's peas, the purple allele is declared to be dominant simply because, when both alleles are present, the flowers are purple rather than white. More generally, when an organism carries two different alleles, the dominant allele is simply the one that determines the appearance of the organism. In the years since Mendel's work, the underlying mechanisms of dominance have been discovered. For example, notice the round versus wrinkled pea seed shape character shown in Figure 10.4. We now know that round seeds contain a branched form of starch called amylopectin, while wrinkled seeds do not. In the DNA of pea plants there is a gene that codes for an enzyme that produces amylopectin. At some time in the past, a mutation in this gene created an alternative, mutant, version. This mutant allele codes for an enzyme that is nonfunctional and produces no amylopectin. Therefore, plants that contain both of these alleles produce both the functional and the nonfunctional enzymes. The functional enzyme creates amylopectin, resulting in round seeds. Since the allele coding the functional enzyme determines the appearance of the seeds in such plants, it is called the dominant allele. *Notice that dominant alleles do not directly inhibit recessive alleles.* ◉

As a third hypothesis, Mendel proposed the following: the pairs of alleles that control a character **segregate** (separate) as gametes are formed; half the gametes carry one allele, and the other half carry the other allele. This hypothesis is now known as Mendel's **principle of segregation**. During fertilization, fusion of the haploid maternal and paternal gametes produces a diploid nucleus called the zygote nucleus. The zygote nucleus receives one allele for the character from the male gamete and one allele for the same character from the female gamete, reuniting the pairs.

Mendel's three hypotheses explained the results of the crosses, as summarized in **Figure 10.5, p. 222**. Both alleles of the flower colour gene in the true-breeding parent plant with purple flowers are the same. The symbol P is used here to designate this allele, with the capital letter indicating that it is dominant, which gives this true-breeding parent the PP combination of alleles. Such an individual is called a **homozygote** (*homo* = same) and is said to be **homozygous** for the P allele. Therefore, when the individual produces gametes and the paired alleles separate during meiosis, all the gametes from this individual will receive a P allele (steps 1 and 2 in Figure 10.5).

In the original true-breeding parent with white flowers, both alleles of the flower colour gene are also the same. Here the symbol p is used to designate this allele, with the lowercase letter indicating that it is recessive, which gives this true-breeding plant the homozygous pp combination of alleles. These alleles also separate during meiosis, leading to gametes that all contain one p allele.

All the F_1 plants produced by crossing purple-flowered and white-flowered plants—the cross $PP \times pp$—received the same combination of alleles: P from one parent and p from the other (step 3 in Figure 10.5, p. 222). An individual of this type, with two different alleles of a gene, is called a **heterozygote** (*hetero* = different) and is said to be **heterozygous** for the trait. Because P is dominant over p, all the Pp plants have purple flowers, even though they also carry the allele for white flowers. An F_1 heterozygote produced from a cross that involves a single character is called a **monohybrid** (*mono* = one; *hybrid* = an offspring of parents with different traits).

According to Mendel's hypotheses, all the Pp plants in the F_1 generation produce two kinds of gametes. Because the heterozygous Pp pair separates during meiosis I, half of the gametes receive the P allele and half receive the p allele (steps 4 and 5 of Figure 10.5, p. 222). Step 5 of Figure 10.5 shows how these gametes can combine during selfing of F_1 plants. Generally, a cross between two individuals that are each heterozygous for the same pair of alleles—$Pp \times Pp$ here—is called a **monohybrid cross**. The gametes are entered in both the rows and columns in Figure 10.5; the cells show the possible combinations. Combining two gametes that both carry the P allele produces a PP F_2 plant; combining P from one parent and p from the other produces a Pp plant; and combining p from both F_1 parents produces a pp F_2 plant. The homozygous PP and heterozygous Pp plants in the F_2 generation have purple flowers, the dominant trait; the homozygous pp offspring have white flowers, the recessive trait.

Mendel's hypotheses explain how individuals may differ genetically but still look the same. The PP and Pp plants, although genetically different, both have purple flowers. In modern terminology, **genotype** refers to the *genetic constitution of an organism,* and **phenotype** (Greek *phainein* = to show) refers to its *outward appearance.* In this case, the two different genotypes PP and Pp produce the same purple-flower phenotype.

Thus, the results of Mendel's crosses support his three hypotheses:

1. The genes that govern genetic characters are present in two copies in individuals.
2. If different alleles are present in an individual's pair of genes, one allele is dominant over the other.
3. The two alleles of a gene segregate and enter gametes singly.

Experimental Research Figure 10.5 Mendel's experiment illustrating the principle of segregation for flower colour in peas.

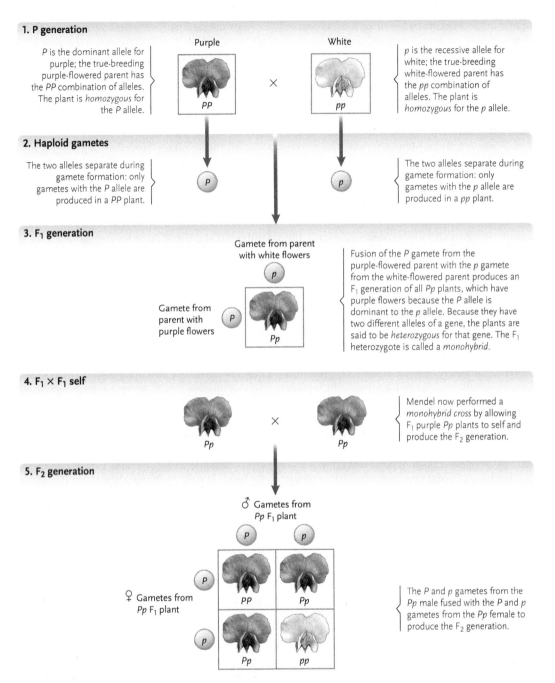

1. P generation

P is the dominant allele for purple; the true-breeding purple-flowered parent has the *PP* combination of alleles. The plant is *homozygous* for the *P* allele.

Purple

×

White

p is the recessive allele for white; the true-breeding white-flowered parent has the *pp* combination of alleles. The plant is *homozygous* for the *p* allele.

PP

pp

2. Haploid gametes

The two alleles separate during gamete formation: only gametes with the *P* allele are produced in a *PP* plant.

P

p

The two alleles separate during gamete formation: only gametes with the *p* allele are produced in a *pp* plant.

3. F₁ generation

Gamete from parent with white flowers

p

Gamete from parent with purple flowers

P

Pp

Fusion of the *P* gamete from the purple-flowered parent with the *p* gamete from the white-flowered parent produces an F₁ generation of all *Pp* plants, which have purple flowers because the *P* allele is dominant to the *p* allele. Because they have two different alleles of a gene, the plants are said to be *heterozygous* for that gene. The F₁ heterozygote is called a *monohybrid*.

4. F₁ × F₁ self

Pp

×

Pp

Mendel now performed a *monohybrid cross* by allowing F₁ purple *Pp* plants to self and produce the F₂ generation.

5. F₂ generation

♂ Gametes from *Pp* F₁ plant

P   *p*

♀ Gametes from *Pp* F₁ plant

P

PP   *Pp*

p

Pp   *pp*

The *P* and *p* gametes from the *Pp* male fused with the *P* and *p* gametes from the *Pp* female to produce the F₂ generation.

10.1d Mendel Could Predict Both Classes and Proportions of Offspring from His Hypotheses

Mendel could predict both classes and proportions of offspring from his hypotheses. To understand how Mendel's hypotheses allowed him to predict the proportions of offspring resulting from a genetic cross, let's review the mathematical rules that govern **probability**— that is, the possibility that an outcome will occur if it is a matter of chance, as in the random fertilization of an egg by a sperm cell that contains one allele or another.

In the mathematics of probability, the likelihood of an outcome is predicted on a scale of 0 to 1. An outcome that is certain to occur has a probability of 1, and an outcome that cannot possibly happen has a probability of 0. The standard game die, a cube with one of the numbers 1 through 6 on each face, is a familiar model to demonstrate working with probability. In general, we determine the probability of any given outcome (rolling a 4) by dividing that outcome by the total number of possible outcomes. For obtaining 4 in rolling a die, the probability is 1 divided by 6, or 1/6. The likelihood of rolling an even number (2 or 4 or 6) is 3/6 = 1/2. The probabilities of all the possible outcomes, when added together, must equal 1.

The Product Rule in Probability. If you roll two dice together, what is the chance of rolling double fours? Because the outcome of one die has no effect on the outcome of the other one, the two rolls are independent. When two or more events are independent, the probability that they will both occur is calculated using the **product rule**—their individual probabilities are multiplied. That is, the probability that events A and B *both* will occur equals the probability of event A *multiplied* by the probability of event B. For example, the probability of getting a 4 on the first die is 1/6; the probability of a 4 on the second die is also 1/6 **(Figure 10.6)**. Because the events are independent, the probability of getting a 4 on both dice is 1/6 × 1/6 = 1/36. Applying this principle to human families, the sex of one child has no effect on the sex of the next child; therefore, the probability of having four girls in a row is the product of their individual probabilities (very close to 1/2 for each birth): 1/2 × 1/2 × 1/2 × 1/2 = 1/16.

The Sum Rule in Probability. Another relationship, the **sum rule**, applies when several different events all give the same outcome; that is, the probability that *either* event A *or* event B *or* event C will occur equals the probability of event A *plus* the probability of event B *plus* the probability of event C. Returning to the two dice example, what is the probability of rolling a 7? Several

different events all give the same total. One could make a total of 7 from a 1 on the first die and a 6 on the second, or a 5 on the first and a 2 on the second, or a 4 on the first and a 3 on the second. Each of these three combinations would be expected to occur at a frequency of 1/6 × 1/6 = 1/36. You should be able to see three more possible combinations that are just the opposite of the first three, that is, 6 on the first die and 1 on the second, and so on, for a total of six different ways to roll a 7. That is, there are six ways of obtaining the same outcome. Therefore, for the probability of rolling a 7, we sum the individual probabilities to get the final probability: 1/36 + 1/36 + 1/36 + 1/36 + 1/36 + 1/36 = 6/36 = 1/6. On average, you could expect to roll a combination of numbers totalling 7 once in every six attempts.

Probability in Mendel's Crosses. Since the randomness inherent in meiosis is comparable to the randomness inherent in rolling dice, the same rules of probability just discussed apply to genes carried on chromosomes in Mendel's crosses. For example, in the crosses that involve the purple-flowered and white-flowered traits, half of the gametes of the F_1 generation contain the *P* allele of the gene and half contain the *p* allele (see Figure 10.5, p. 222). To produce a *PP* zygote, two *P* gametes must combine. The probability of selecting a *P* gamete from one F_1 parent is 1/2, and the probability of selecting a *P* gamete from the other F_1 parent is also 1/2. Therefore, the probability of producing a *PP* zygote from this monohybrid cross is 1/2 × 1/2 = 1/4. That is, by the product rule, one-fourth of the offspring of the F_1 cross *Pp* × *Pp* are expected to be *PP*, which have purple flowers **(Figure 10.7a, p. 224)**. By the same line of reasoning, one-fourth of the F_2 offspring are expected to be *pp*, which have white flowers (Figure 10.7b).

What about the production of *Pp* offspring? The cross *Pp* × *Pp* can produce *Pp* in two different ways. A *P* gamete from the first parent can combine with a *p* gamete from the second parent (*Pp*), or a *p* gamete from the first parent can combine with a *P* gamete from the second parent (*pP*) (Figure 10.7c). Because there are two different ways to get the same outcome, we apply the sum rule to obtain the combined probability. Each of the ways to get *Pp* has an individual probability of 1/4; when we add these individual probabilities, we have 1/4 + 1/4 = 1/2. Therefore, half of the offspring are expected to be *Pp*, which have purple flowers. We could get the same result from the requirement that all of the individual probabilities must add up to 1. If the probability of *PP* is 1/4 and the probability of *pp* is 1/4, then the probability of the remaining possibility, *Pp*, must be 1/2, because the total of the individual probabilities must add up to 1: 1/4 + 1/4 + 1/2 = 1.

What if we want to know the probability of obtaining purple flowers in the cross *Pp* × *Pp*? In

a. Likelihood of rolling a double four.

$$\frac{1}{6} \times \frac{1}{6} = \frac{1}{36}$$
Likelihood of rolling a double 4

b. Likelihood of rolling a seven in any combination.

Figure 10.6

Rules of probability. **(a)** For each die, the probability of a 4 is 1/6. Because the outcome of one die is independent of that of the other, the combined probability of rolling a 4 on both dice at the same time is calculated by multiplying the individual probabilities (product rule). **(b)** Since there are six different outcomes, each of which adds up to 7, the total likelihood of rolling a 7 is calculated by adding the individual probabilities (sum rule).

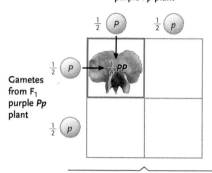

Gametes from F₁ purple *Pp* plant

a. To produce an F₂ plant with the *PP* genotype, two *P* gametes must combine. The probability of selecting a *P* gamete from one F₁ parent is $\frac{1}{2}$, and the probability of selecting a *P* gamete from the other F₁ parent is also $\frac{1}{2}$. Using the product rule, the probability of producing purple-flowered *PP* plant from a *Pp* × *Pp* cross is $\frac{1}{2} \times \frac{1}{2} = \frac{1}{4}$.

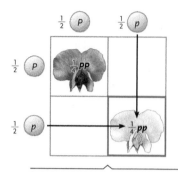

b. To produce an F₂ plant with the *pp* genotype, two *p* gametes must combine. The probability of selecting a *p* gamete from one F₁ parent is $\frac{1}{2}$, and the probability of selecting a *p* gamete from the other F₁ parent is also $\frac{1}{2}$. Using the product rule, the probability of producing a white-flowered *pp* plant from a *Pp* × *Pp* cross is $\frac{1}{2} \times \frac{1}{2} = \frac{1}{4}$.

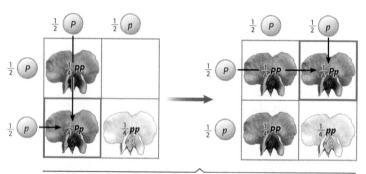

c. To produce an F₂ plant with the *Pp* genotype, a *P* gamete must combine with a *p* gamete. The cross *Pp* × *Pp* can produce *Pp* offspring in two different ways: (1) a *P* gamete from the first parent can combine with a *p* gamete from the second parent or (2) a *p* gamete from the first parent can combine with a *P* gamete from the second parent. We apply the sum rule to obtain the combined probability: each of the ways to get *Pp* has an individual probability of $\frac{1}{4}$, so the probability of *Pp*, purple-flowered offspring, is $\frac{1}{4} + \frac{1}{4} = \frac{1}{2}$.

Figure 10.7

Punnett square method for predicting offspring and their ratios in genetic crosses. The example is the F₁ × F₁ cross of purple-flowered plants from Figure 10.5, p. 222. Each cell shows the genotype and proportion of one type of F₂ plant.

this case, the rule of addition applies, because there are two ways to get purple flowers: genotypes *PP* and *Pp*. Adding the individual probabilities of these combinations, 1/4 *PP* + 1/2 *Pp*, gives a total of 3/4, indicating that three-fourths of the **F₂** offspring are expected to have purple flowers. Because the total probabilities must add up to 1, the remaining one-fourth of the offspring are expected to have white flowers (1/4 *pp*). These proportions give the ratio 3:1, which is close to the ratio Mendel obtained in his cross.

In Figure 10.7 we have just stepped through the **Punnett square** method for determining the genotypes

of offspring and their expected proportions. To use the Punnett square, write the probability that meiosis will produce gametes with each type of allele from one parent at the top of the diagram and write the chance of obtaining each type of allele from the other parent on the left side. Then fill in the cells by combining the alleles from the top and from the left and multiplying their individual probabilities.

10.1e Mendel Used a Testcross to Check the Validity of His Hypotheses

Mendel realized that he could assess the validity of his hypotheses by determining whether they could be used successfully to *predict* the outcome of a cross of a different type than he had tried so far. Accordingly, he crossed an F₁ plant with purple flowers, assumed to have the heterozygous genotype *Pp*, with a true-breeding white-flowered plant, with the homozygous genotype *pp* (**Figure 10.8**, Experiment 1). There are two expected classes of offspring, *Pp* and *pp*, both with a probability of 1/2. Thus, the phenotypes of the offspring are expected to be 1 purple-flowered : 1 white-flowered. Mendel's actual results closely approach the expected 1:1 ratio. Mendel also made the same type of cross with all the other traits used in his study, including those traits affecting seed shape, seed colour, and plant height, and found the same 1:1 ratio.

A cross between an individual with the dominant phenotype and a homozygous recessive individual, such as the one described, is called a **testcross**. Geneticists use a testcross as a standard test to determine whether an individual with a dominant trait is a heterozygote or a homozygote, because these cannot be distinguished phenotypically. If the offspring of the testcross are of two types, with half displaying the dominant trait and half the recessive trait, then the individual in question must be a heterozygote (see Figure 10.8, Experiment 1). If all the offspring display the dominant trait, the individual in question must be a homozygote. For example, the cross *PP* × *pp* gives all *Pp* progeny, which show the dominant purple phenotype (see Figure 10.8, Experiment 2).

Obviously, the testcross method cannot be used for humans. However, it can be used in reverse by noting the traits present in families over several generations and working backward to deduce whether a parent must have been a homozygote or a heterozygote (see also Chapter 11).

Experimental
Research Figure 10.8
Testing the predicted
outcome of two different
genetic crosses.

Experiment 1

1. F₁ purple plant × true-breeding white plant

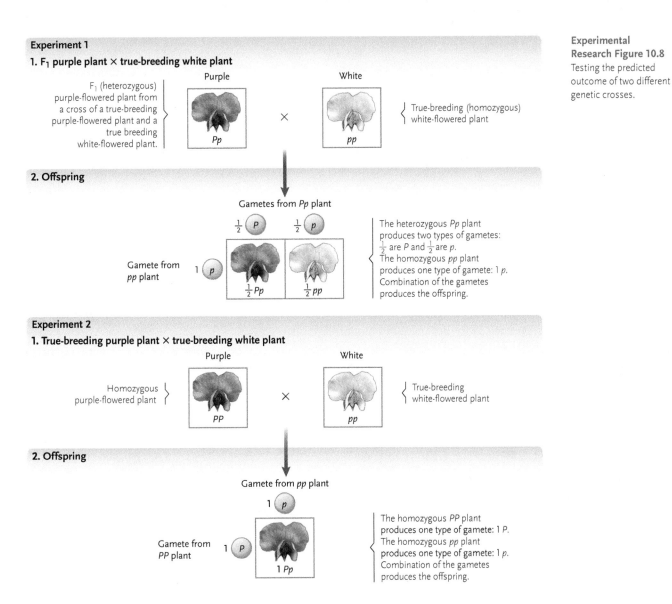

F₁ (heterozygous) purple-flowered plant from a cross of a true-breeding purple-flowered plant and a true breeding white-flowered plant.

Purple

Pp

×

White

pp

True-breeding (homozygous) white-flowered plant

2. Offspring

Gametes from *Pp* plant

$\frac{1}{2}$ *P* $\frac{1}{2}$ *p*

Gamete from *pp* plant   1 *p*

$\frac{1}{2}$ *Pp* $\frac{1}{2}$ *pp*

The heterozygous *Pp* plant produces two types of gametes: $\frac{1}{2}$ are *P* and $\frac{1}{2}$ are *p*. The homozygous *pp* plant produces one type of gamete: 1 *p*. Combination of the gametes produces the offspring.

Experiment 2

1. True-breeding purple plant × true-breeding white plant

Purple

PP

×

White

pp

Homozygous purple-flowered plant

True-breeding white-flowered plant

2. Offspring

Gamete from *pp* plant

1 *p*

Gamete from *PP* plant   1 *P*

1 *Pp*

The homozygous *PP* plant produces one type of gamete: 1 *P*. The homozygous *pp* plant produces one type of gamete: 1 *p*. Combination of the gametes produces the offspring.

10.1f Mendel Tested the Independence of Different Genes in Crosses

Mendel next asked what happens in crosses when more than one character is involved. Would the alleles of different characters be inherited independently, or would they interact to alter their expected proportions in offspring?

To answer these questions, Mendel crossed parental stocks that had differences in two of the hereditary characters he was studying: seed shape and seed colour. His single-character crosses had shown that each was controlled by a pair of alleles. For seed shape, the *RR* or *Rr* genotype produces round seeds and the *rr* genotype produces wrinkled seeds. For seed colour, yellow is dominant. The homozygous *YY* and heterozygous *Yy* genotypes produce yellow seeds; the homozygous *yy* genotype produces green seeds.

Mendel crossed plants that bred true for the production of round and yellow seeds (*RR YY*) with plants

that bred true for the production of wrinkled and green seeds (*rr yy*) **(Figure 10.9, p. 226)**. The cross, *RR YY* × *rr yy*, yielded an F₁ generation that consisted of all round yellow seeds, with the genotype *Rr Yy*. A zygote produced from a cross that involves two characters is called a **dihybrid** (*di* = two).

Mendel then planted the F₁ seeds, grew the plants to maturity, and selfed them; that is, he crossed the F₁ plants to themselves. A cross between two individuals that are heterozygous for two pairs of alleles—here *Rr Yy* × *Rr Yy*—is called a **dihybrid cross** (see Figure 10.9, p. 226). The seeds produced by these plants, representing the **F₂** generation, included 315 round yellow seeds, 101 wrinkled yellow seeds, 103 round green seeds, and 32 wrinkled green seeds. Mendel noted that these numbers were close to a 9:3:3:1 ratio (3:1 for round : wrinkled, and 3:1 for yellow : green).

This 9:3:3:1 ratio was consistent with Mendel's previous findings if he added one further hypothesis: *The alleles of the genes that govern the two characters*

Experimental
Research Figure 10.9
Mendel's experiment
illustrating the
principle of
independent
assortment for seed
shape and seed colour
in peas.

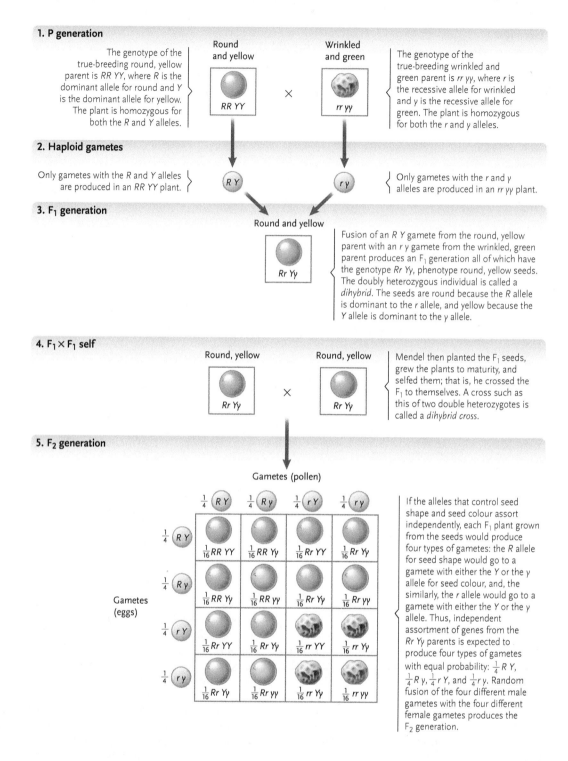

1. P generation

Round and yellow × Wrinkled and green

RR YY × *rr yy*

The genotype of the true-breeding round, yellow parent is *RR YY*, where *R* is the dominant allele for round and *Y* is the dominant allele for yellow. The plant is homozygous for both the *R* and *Y* alleles.

The genotype of the true-breeding wrinkled and green parent is *rr yy*, where *r* is the recessive allele for wrinkled and *y* is the recessive allele for green. The plant is homozygous for both the *r* and *y* alleles.

2. Haploid gametes

Only gametes with the *R* and *Y* alleles are produced in an *RR YY* plant.

R Y   *r y*

Only gametes with the *r* and *y* alleles are produced in an *rr yy* plant.

3. F$_1$ generation

Round and yellow

Rr Yy

Fusion of an *R Y* gamete from the round, yellow parent with an *r y* gamete from the wrinkled, green parent produces an F$_1$ generation all of which have the genotype *Rr Yy*, phenotype round, yellow seeds. The doubly heterozygous individual is called a *dihybrid*. The seeds are round because the *R* allele is dominant to the *r* allele, and yellow because the *Y* allele is dominant to the *y* allele.

4. F$_1$ × F$_1$ self

Round, yellow (*Rr Yy*) × Round, yellow (*Rr Yy*)

Mendel then planted the F$_1$ seeds, grew the plants to maturity, and selfed them; that is, he crossed the F$_1$ to themselves. A cross such as this of two double heterozygotes is called a *dihybrid cross*.

5. F$_2$ generation

Gametes (pollen)

$\frac{1}{4}$ *R Y* · $\frac{1}{4}$ *R y* · $\frac{1}{4}$ *r Y* · $\frac{1}{4}$ *r y*

Gametes (eggs)

$\frac{1}{4}$ *R Y* : $\frac{1}{16}$ *RR YY* · $\frac{1}{16}$ *RR Yy* · $\frac{1}{16}$ *Rr YY* · $\frac{1}{16}$ *Rr Yy*

$\frac{1}{4}$ *R y* : $\frac{1}{16}$ *RR Yy* · $\frac{1}{16}$ *RR yy* · $\frac{1}{16}$ *Rr Yy* · $\frac{1}{16}$ *Rr yy*

$\frac{1}{4}$ *r Y* : $\frac{1}{16}$ *Rr YY* · $\frac{1}{16}$ *Rr Yy* · $\frac{1}{16}$ *rr YY* · $\frac{1}{16}$ *rr Yy*

$\frac{1}{4}$ *r y* : $\frac{1}{16}$ *Rr Yy* · $\frac{1}{16}$ *Rr yy* · $\frac{1}{16}$ *rr Yy* · $\frac{1}{16}$ *rr yy*

If the alleles that control seed shape and seed colour assort independently, each F$_1$ plant grown from the seeds would produce four types of gametes: the *R* allele for seed shape would go to a gamete with either the *Y* or the *y* allele for seed colour, and, the similarly, the *r* allele would go to a gamete with either the *Y* or the *y* allele. Thus, independent assortment of genes from the *Rr Yy* parents is expected to produce four types of gametes with equal probability: $\frac{1}{4}$ *R Y*, $\frac{1}{4}$ *R y*, $\frac{1}{4}$ *r Y*, and $\frac{1}{4}$ *r y*. Random fusion of the four different male gametes with the four different female gametes produces the F$_2$ generation.

segregate independently during formation of gametes. That is, the allele for seed shape that the gamete receives (*R* or *r*) has no influence on which allele for seed colour it receives (*Y* or *y*) and vice versa. The two events are completely independent. Mendel termed this assumption **independent assortment**; it is now known as Mendel's **principle of independent assortment**.

To understand the effect of independent assortment in the cross, assume that the *RR YY* parent produces only *R Y* gametes and the *rr yy* parent produces only *r y* gametes. In the F$_1$ generation, all possible combinations of these gametes produce only one genotype, *Rr Yy*, in the offspring. As observed, all the F$_1$ will be round yellow seeds.

If the alleles that control seed shape and seed colour assort independently in gamete formation, each F$_1$ plant grown from the seeds will produce four types of gametes. As shown in **Figure 10.10**, the random

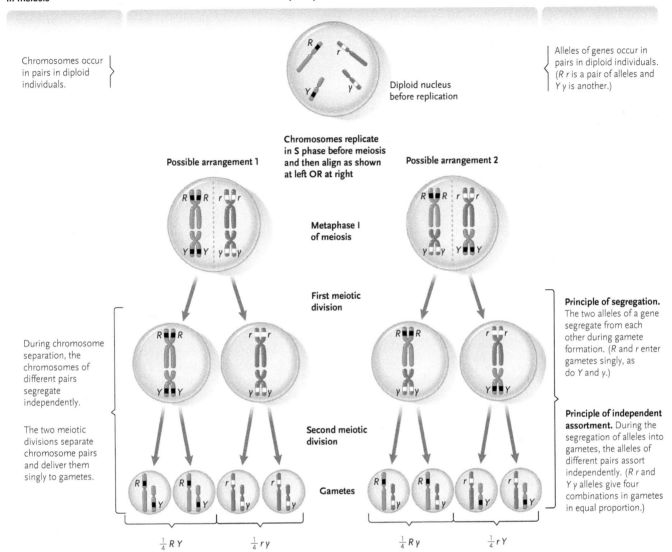

Chromosomes occur in pairs in diploid individuals.

Diploid nucleus before replication

Alleles of genes occur in pairs in diploid individuals. (*R r* is a pair of alleles and *Y y* is another.)

Chromosomes replicate in S phase before meiosis and then align as shown at left OR at right

Possible arrangement 1

Possible arrangement 2

Metaphase I of meiosis

First meiotic division

During chromosome separation, the chromosomes of different pairs segregate independently.

The two meiotic divisions separate chromosome pairs and deliver them singly to gametes.

Principle of segregation. The two alleles of a gene segregate from each other during gamete formation. (*R* and *r* enter gametes singly, as do *Y* and *y*.)

Second meiotic division

Gametes

Principle of independent assortment. During the segregation of alleles into gametes, the alleles of different pairs assort independently. (*R r* and *Y y* alleles give four combinations in gametes in equal proportion.)

$\frac{1}{4}$ *R Y* $\frac{1}{4}$ *r y* $\frac{1}{4}$ *R y* $\frac{1}{4}$ *r Y*

Figure 10.10

The parallels between the behaviour of chromosomes and genes and alleles in meiosis. The gametes show four different combinations of alleles produced by independent segregation of chromosome pairs.

alignment of homologous chromosome pairs in meiosis I ensures that the *R* allele for seed shape can be delivered independently to a gamete with either the *Y* or the *y* allele for seed colour, and, similarly, the *r* allele can be delivered to a gamete with either the *Y* or the *y* allele. Thus, the independent assortment of genes from the *Rr Yy* parents allows the organism to produce, overall, four types of gametes with equal probability: 1/4 *R Y*, 1/4 *R y*, 1/4 *r Y*, and 1/4 *r y*. These gametes and their probabilities are entered as the row and column headings of the Punnett square in Figure 10.9.

Filling in the cells of the diagram (see Figure 10.9) gives 16 combinations of alleles, all with an equal probability of 1 in every 16 offspring. Of these, the genotypes *RR YY*, *RR Yy*, *Rr YY*, and *Rr Yy* all have the same phenotype: round yellow seeds. These combinations occur in 9 of the 16 cells in the diagram, giving a total probability of 9/16. The genotypes *rr YY* and *rr Yy*, which produce wrinkled yellow seeds, are found in three cells, giving a probability of 3/16 for this phenotype. Similarly, the genotypes *RR yy* and *Rr yy*, which yield round green seeds, occur in three cells, giving a probability of 3/16. Finally, the genotype *rr yy*, which produces wrinkled green seeds, is found in only one cell and therefore has a probability of 1/16.

These probabilities of round yellow seeds, wrinkled yellow seeds, round green seeds, and wrinkled green seeds, in a 9:3:3:1 ratio, closely approximate the actual results of 315:101:108:32 obtained by Mendel. Thus, Mendel's first three hypotheses, with the added hypothesis of independent assortment, explain the observed results of his dihybrid cross. Mendel's testcrosses completely confirmed his hypotheses; for example, the testcross $Rr\ Yy \times rr\ yy$ produced 55 round yellow seeds, 51 round green seeds, 49 wrinkled yellow seeds, and 53 wrinkled green seeds. This distribution corresponds well to the expected 1:1:1:1 ratio in the offspring. (Try to set up a Punnett square for this cross and predict the expected classes of offspring and their frequencies.)

Mendel's first three hypotheses provided a coherent explanation of the pattern of inheritance for alternative traits of the same character, such as purple and white for flower colour. His fourth hypothesis, independent assortment, addressed the inheritance of traits for different characters, such as seed shape, seed colour, and flower colour, and showed that, instead of being inherited together, the traits of different characters were distributed independently to offspring.

10.1g Mendel's Research Founded the Field of Genetics

Mendel's techniques and conclusions were so advanced for his time that their significance was not immediately appreciated. Mendel's success was based partly on a good choice of experimental organism. He was also lucky. The characters he chose all segregate independently; that is, none of them are physically near each other on the chromosomes, a condition that would have given ratios other than 9:3:3:1, showing that they do not assort independently.

We now know that Mendel's findings demonstrated the patterns by which genes and chromosomes determine inheritance. Yet, when Mendel first reported his findings during the nineteenth century, the structure and function of chromosomes and the patterns by which they are separated and distributed to gametes were unknown; meiosis remained to be discovered. In addition, his use of mathematical analysis was a new and radical departure from the usual biological techniques of his day.

Mendel reported his results to a small group of fellow intellectuals in Brünn and presented his results in 1866 in a natural history journal published in the city. His article received little notice outside of Brünn, and those who read it were unable to appreciate the significance of his findings. His work was overlooked until the turn of the century, when three investigators—Hugo de Vries in Holland, Carl Correns in Germany, and Erich von Tschermak in Austria—independently performed a series of breeding experiments similar to Mendel's and reached the same conclusions. These investigators, in searching through previously published scientific articles, were surprised to discover Mendel's article about his experiments conducted three decades earlier. Each gave credit to Mendel's discoveries, and the quality and far-reaching implications of his work were at last realized. Mendel died in 1884, less than 20 years before the rediscovery of his experiments and conclusions; thus, he never received the recognition that he so richly deserved during his lifetime.

Mendel was unable to relate the behaviour of his "factors" (genes) to cell structures because the critical information he required was not obtained until later, through the discovery of meiosis during the 1890s. The next section describes how a genetics student familiar with meiosis was able to make the connection between Mendel's factors and chromosomes.

10.1h Sutton's Chromosome Theory of Inheritance Related Mendel's Genes to Chromosomes

By the time Mendel's results were rediscovered in the early 1900s, critical information from studies of meiosis was available. It was not long before a genetics student, Walter Sutton, recognized the similarities between the inheritance of the genes discovered by Mendel and the behaviour of chromosomes in meiosis and fertilization (Figure 10.10, p. 227).

In a historic article published in 1903, Sutton, then a graduate student at Columbia University in New York, drew all the necessary parallels between genes and chromosomes:

- Chromosomes occur in pairs in sexually reproducing, diploid organisms, as do the alleles of each gene.
- The chromosomes of each pair are separated and delivered singly to gametes, as are the alleles of a gene.
- The separation of any pair of chromosomes in meiosis and gamete formation is independent of the separation of other pairs (see Figure 10.10, p. 227), as in the independent assortment of the alleles of different genes in Mendel's dihybrid crosses.
- Finally, one member of each chromosome pair is derived in fertilization from the male parent, and the other member is derived from the female parent, in an exact parallel with the two alleles of a gene.

From this total coincidence in behaviour, Sutton correctly concluded that genes and their alleles are carried on the chromosomes, a conclusion known today as the **chromosome theory of inheritance.**

The exact parallel between the principles set forth by Mendel and the behaviour of chromosomes and genes during meiosis is shown in Figure 10.10 for an $Rr\ Yy$ diploid. For a cross of $Rr\ Yy \times Rr\ Yy$, when the gametes fuse randomly, the progeny will show a phenotypic ratio of 9:3:3:1. This mechanism explains the same ratio of gametes and progeny as the *Rr Yy* × *Rr Yy* cross in Figure 10.9, p. 226.

The particular site on a chromosome at which a gene is located is called the **locus** (plural, loci) of the gene. The locus is a particular DNA sequence that encodes a protein or RNA product responsible for the phenotype controlled by the gene. A locus for a gene with two alleles, *A* and *a*, on a homologous pair of chromosomes is shown in **Figure 10.11**. At the molecular level, different alleles consist of small differences in the DNA sequence of a gene, which may result in functional differences in the protein or RNA product encoded by the gene. These differences are detected as distinct phenotypes in the offspring of a cross.

All of the genetics research conducted since the early 1900s has confirmed Mendel's basic hypotheses about inheritance. This research has shown that Mendel's conclusions apply to all types of organisms, from yeast and fruit flies to humans, and has led to the rapidly growing field of human genetics. In humans, a number of easily seen traits show inheritance patterns that follow Mendelian principles **(Figure 10.12)**; for example, albinism, the lack of normal skin colour, is recessive to normal skin colour, and fingers with webs between them are recessive to normally separated fingers. Similarly, achondroplasia, the most frequent form of short-limb dwarfism, is a recessive trait that involves abnormal bone growth. Many human disorders that cannot be seen easily also show simple inheritance patterns. For instance, cystic fibrosis, in which a defect in the membrane transport of chloride ions leads to pulmonary and digestive dysfunctions and reduced life span, is a recessive trait.

The post-Mendel research has demonstrated additional patterns of inheritance (see the next section) that were not anticipated by Mendel and, in some

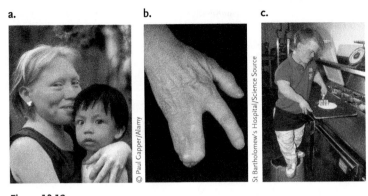

Figure 10.12

Human traits showing inheritance patterns that follow Mendelian principles. **(a)** Lack of normal skin colour (albinism). **(b)** Webbed fingers. **(c)** Achondroplasia or short-limb dwarfism.

circumstances, require modifications or additions to his hypotheses.

STUDY BREAK

1. What characteristics of the garden pea made this organism a good model system for Mendel?
2. How does independent assortment explain Mendel's dihybrid cross data?
3. How is an allele related to a locus?

10.2 Later Modifications and Additions to Mendel's Hypotheses

The rediscovery of Mendel's research in the early 1900s produced an immediate burst of interest in genetics. The research that followed greatly expanded our understanding of genes and their inheritance. That research fully supported Mendel's hypotheses, but also revealed many variations on the basic principles he had outlined. The following sections discuss each of these extensions of Mendel's fundamental principles.

10.2a In Incomplete Dominance, Dominant Alleles Do Not Completely Compensate for Recessive Alleles

Incomplete dominance occurs when the effects of recessive alleles can be detected to some extent in heterozygotes. Flower colour in snapdragons shows incomplete dominance **(Figure 10.13, p. 230)**. If true-breeding red-flowered and white-flowered snapdragon plants are crossed, all the F_1 offspring have pink flowers (see Figure 10.13, p. 230). The pink colour might make it appear that the pure red and white colours have blended—mixing red and white makes pink. However, when two F_1 plants are crossed, the red and white traits

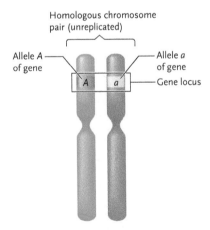

Homologous chromosome pair (unreplicated)

Allele *A* of gene

Allele *a* of gene

A   *a*

Gene locus

Figure 10.11

A locus, the site occupied by a gene on a pair of homologous chromosomes. Two alleles, *A* and *a*, of the gene are present at this locus in the homologous pair. These alleles have differences in the DNA sequence of the gene.

Experimental
Research Figure 10.13
Experiment showing
incomplete dominance
in the inheritance of
flower colour in
snapdragons.

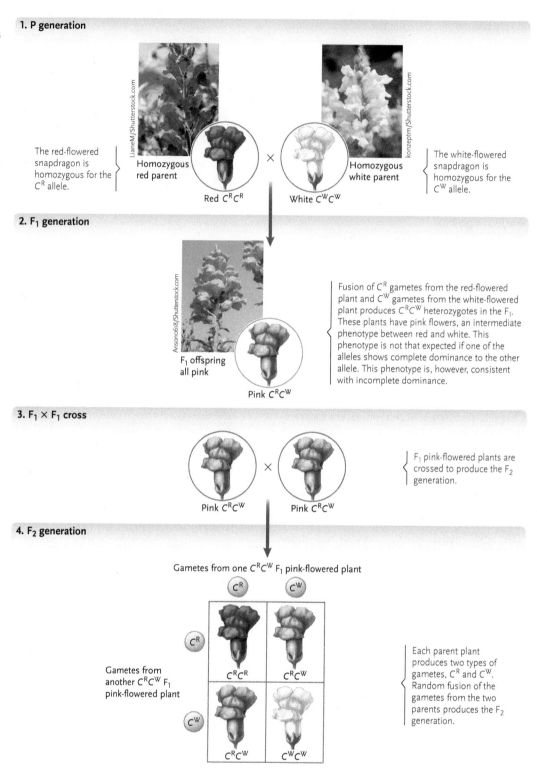

1. P generation

The red-flowered snapdragon is homozygous for the C^R allele.

Homozygous red parent

Red $C^R C^R$ × White $C^W C^W$

Homozygous white parent

The white-flowered snapdragon is homozygous for the C^W allele.

2. F_1 generation

F_1 offspring all pink

Pink $C^R C^W$

Fusion of C^R gametes from the red-flowered plant and C^W gametes from the white-flowered plant produces $C^R C^W$ heterozygotes in the F_1. These plants have pink flowers, an intermediate phenotype between red and white. This phenotype is not that expected if one of the alleles shows complete dominance to the other allele. This phenotype is, however, consistent with incomplete dominance.

3. $F_1 \times F_1$ cross

Pink $C^R C^W$ × Pink $C^R C^W$

F_1 pink-flowered plants are crossed to produce the F_2 generation.

4. F_2 generation

Gametes from one $C^R C^W$ F_1 pink-flowered plant

C^R C^W

Gametes from another $C^R C^W$ F_1 pink-flowered plant

C^R

C^W

$C^R C^R$ $C^R C^W$

$C^R C^W$ $C^W C^W$

Each parent plant produces two types of gametes, C^R and C^W. Random fusion of the gametes from the two parents produces the F_2 generation.

both reappear in the **F_2** generation, which has red, pink, and white flowers in numbers approximating a 1:2:1 ratio.

This outcome can be explained by incomplete dominance between a C^R allele for red colour and a C^W allele for white colour. When one allele is not completely

dominant to the other, we use a superscript to signify the character. In this case, C signifies the character for flower colour and the superscripts indicate the alleles (R for red and W for white). Therefore, the initial cross is $C^R C^R$ (red) × $C^W C^W$ (white), which produces $C^R C^W$ F_1 (pink) plants. The C^R allele encodes an enzyme that

Why Mendel's Dwarf Pea Plants Were So Short

Two independent research teams worked out the molecular basis for one of the seven characters Mendel studied—dwarfing, which is governed by stem length in garden peas. The investigators, including Diane Lester and her colleagues at the University of Tasmania in Australia and David Martin and his coworkers at Oregon State University, were interested in learning the molecular differences in the alleles of the gene that produced tall or dwarf plants. The dominant T allele (T = tall) of the gene produces plants of normal height; the recessive t allele produces dwarf plants with short stems. How can a single gene control the overall height of a plant?

Lester's team discovered that the gene encodes an enzyme that carries out a preliminary step in the synthesis of the plant hormone gibberellin, which, among other effects, causes the stems of plants to elongate. Martin's group cloned the gene and determined its complete DNA sequence. (Cloning techniques and DNA sequencing are described in Sections 15.1 and 16.2.) Comparisons of the DNA sequences from the T and t alleles revealed two versions of the enzyme that catalyzes gibberellin synthesis that differ by only a single amino acid. Lester's group found that the faulty enzyme encoded by the t allele carries out its step

(addition of a hydroxyl group to a precursor) much more slowly than the enzyme encoded by the normal T allele. As a result, plants with the t allele have only about 5% as much gibberellin in their stems as T plants. The reduced gibberellin levels limit stem elongation, producing the dwarf plants.

Thus, the methods of molecular biology allowed contemporary researchers to study a gene first discovered in the mid-nineteenth century. The findings leave little doubt that a change in a single amino acid leads to the dwarf phenotype Mendel observed in his monastery garden.

---

produces a red pigment, but two alleles ($C^R C^R$) are necessary to produce enough of the active form of the enzyme to produce fully red flowers. The enzyme is completely inactive in $C^W C^W$ plants, which produce colourless flowers that appear white because of the scattering of light by cell walls and other structures. With their single C^R allele, the $C^R C^W$ heterozygotes of the F_1 generation can produce only enough pigment to give the flowers a pink colour. When the pink $C^R C^W$ F_1 plants are crossed, the fully red and white colours reappear, together with the pink colour, in the F_2 generation, in a ratio of 1/4 $C^R C^R$ (red), 1/2 $C^R C^W$ (pink), and 1/4 $C^W C^W$ (white). This ratio is exactly the same as the ratio of genotypes produced from a cross of two heterozygotes in Mendel's experiments (e.g., see Figure 10.7, p. 224).

Some human disorders show incomplete dominance. For example, sickle cell disease (see the introduction to this chapter) is characterized by an alteration in the hemoglobin molecule that changes the shape of red blood cells when oxygen levels are low. An individual with sickle cell disease is homozygous for a recessive allele that encodes a defective form of one of the polypeptides of the hemoglobin molecule. Individuals heterozygous for that recessive allele and the normal allele have a condition known as *sickle cell trait*, which is a milder form of the disease because the individuals still produce normal polypeptides from the normal allele.

Familial hypercholesterolemia is another example of incomplete dominance. The gene involved encodes the low-density lipoprotein (LDL) receptor, a cell membrane protein responsible for removing excess cholesterol from the blood. Individuals with familial

hypercholesterolemia are homozygous for a defective LDL receptor gene, produce no LDL receptors, and have a severe form of the disease. These individuals have six times the normal level of cholesterol in the blood and therefore are very prone to atherosclerosis (hardening of the **arteries**). Many individuals with familial hypercholesterolemia have heart attacks as children. Heterozygous individuals have half the normal number of receptors, which results in a milder form of the disease. Their symptoms are twice the normal blood cholesterol level, an unusually high risk of atherosclerosis, and a high risk of heart attacks before age 35.

Many alleles that appear to be completely dominant are actually incomplete in their effects when analyzed at the biochemical or molecular level. For example, for pigments that produce fur or flower colours, biochemical studies often show that even though heterozygotes may produce enough pigment to make them look the same externally as homozygous dominants, a difference in the amount of pigment is measurable at the biochemical level. Thus, whether dominance between alleles is complete or incomplete often depends on the level at which the effects of the alleles are examined.

A similar situation occurs in humans who carry the recessive allele that causes Tay–Sachs disease. Children who are homozygous for the recessive allele do not have a functional version of an enzyme that breaks down gangliosides, a type of membrane lipid. As a result, gangliosides accumulate in the brain, leading to mental impairment and eventually to death. Heterozygotes are without symptoms of the disease, even though they have one copy of the recessive allele.

Phenylthiocarbamide (PTC)

Have you ever sat down to a plate of Brussels sprouts, only to find that they taste unpleasantly bitter? This sensation arises because receptors in the membranes of taste cells on your tongue are binding to compounds such as isothiocyanate (which is toxic to your thyroid in large doses). Much of our understanding of the molecular nature of bitter taste perception has grown out of an accidental observation that a synthetic chemical, phenylthiocarbamide (PTC), tastes intensely bitter to some people and yet is tasteless to others. PTC "nontasters" make up 20 to 30% of almost all populations of humans, chimps, and gorillas studied. Although several genes influence the limits of PTC detection, one particular member of the bitter receptor gene family on human chromosome 7 is mainly responsible for PTC tasting ability. The two most common alleles of this gene, "taster" and "nontaster," show a codominant inheritance pattern in families. Since PTC is not found in nature, it is likely that the two very common alleles detect naturally occurring toxic compounds containing the bitter-tasting thiourea chemical structure shown in the diagram ($N-C=S$).

Figure 1

The chemical structure of phenylthiocarbamide (PTC). Note the $N-C=S$ component.

However, at the biochemical level, reduced breakdown of gangliosides can be detected in heterozygotes, evidently due to a reduced quantity of the active enzyme.

CONCEPT FIX Since all of Mendel's traits show "simple" or "complete" dominance, you might get the idea that most traits in nature are governed by one dominant and one recessive allele. However, the above examples illustrate that only a minority of human genetic disorders show such simple dominance. ⬡

10.2b In Codominance, the Effects of Different Alleles Are Equally Detectable in Heterozygotes

Codominance occurs when alleles have approximately equal effects in individuals, making the two alleles equally detectable in heterozygotes. The inheritance of the human blood types M, MN, and N is an example of codominance. These are different blood types from the familiar blood types of the ABO blood group. The L^M and L^N alleles of the MN blood group gene that control this character encode different forms of a glycoprotein molecule located on the surface of red blood cells. If the genotype is $L^M L^M$, only the M form of the glycoprotein is present and the blood type is M; if it is $L^N L^N$, only the N form is present and the blood type is N. In heterozygotes with the $L^M L^N$ genotype, both glycoprotein types are present and can be detected, producing the blood type MN. Because each genotype has a different phenotype, the inheritance pattern for the MN blood group alleles is generally the same as for incompletely dominant alleles. That is, you would not be able to distinguish between codominance and incomplete dominance just by comparing the ratio of offspring from crosses.

The MN blood types do not affect blood transfusions and have relatively little medical importance. However, they have been invaluable in tracing human evolution and prehistoric migrations, and they are frequently used in initial tests to determine the paternity of a child. Among their primary advantages in research and paternity determination is that the genotype of all individuals, including heterozygotes, can be detected directly—and inexpensively—from their phenotype, with no requirement for further genetic tests or analysis.

10.2c In Multiple Alleles, More Than Two Alleles of a Gene Are Present in a Population

One of Mendel's major and most fundamental assumptions was that alleles occur in pairs in individuals; in the pairs, the alleles may be the same or different. After the rediscovery of Mendel's principles, it soon became apparent that although alleles do indeed occur in pairs in individuals, **multiple alleles** (more than two different alleles of a gene) may be present if all the individuals of a population are taken into account. For example, for a gene B, there could be the normal allele, B, and several alleles with alterations in the gene named, for example, b1, b2, b3, and so on. Some individuals in a population may have the B and b1 alleles of a gene; others, the b2 and b3 alleles; still others, the b3 and b5 alleles; and so on, for all possible combinations. Thus, although any one individual can have only two alleles of the gene, there are more than two alleles in the population as a whole. One of the genes that plays a part in the acceptance or rejection of organ transplants in humans has more than 200 different alleles!

The multiple alleles of a gene each contain nucleotide differences at one or more locations in their DNA sequences **(Figure 10.14)**, and these often cause detectable alterations in the structure and function of gene products encoded by the alleles. Despite the presence of multiple alleles at the population level, each diploid individual still has only two of the alleles, allowing gametes to be predicted and traced through crosses by the usual methods.

Human ABO Blood Group. The human ABO blood group provides a real example of multiple alleles, in a system that also exhibits both dominance and codominance. Karl Landsteiner, an Austrian biochemist, discovered the ABO blood group in 1901 while investigating the fact that attempts to transfer whole blood from one person to another were sometimes fatal. Landsteiner found that only certain combinations of four blood types, designated A, B, AB, and O, can be mixed safely in transfusions **(Table 10.1)**.

Landsteiner determined that, in certain combinations, red blood cells from one blood type are agglutinated or clumped by an agent in the serum of another type (the serum is the fluid in which the blood cells are suspended). The clumping was later found to depend on the action of an **antibody** in the blood serum. (Antibodies, protein molecules that interact with specific substances called antigens, are discussed in Chapter 51.)

The antigens responsible for the blood types of the ABO blood group are the carbohydrate parts of glycoproteins located on the surfaces of red blood cells (unrelated to the glycoprotein carbohydrates responsible for the blood types of the MN blood group). People with type A blood have *antigen A* on their red blood cells, and people with type B blood have *antigen B* on their red blood cells. At the same time, people with type A blood have antibodies against antigen B, and people with type B blood have antibodies against antigen A. People with type O blood have neither

Table 10.1	Blood Types of the Human ABO Blood Group		
Blood Type	Antigens	Antibodies	Blood Types Accepted in a Transfusion
A	A	Anti-B	A or O
B	B	Anti-A	B or O
AB	A and B	None	A, B, AB, or O
O	None	Anti-A, anti-B	O

antigen A nor antigen B on their red blood cells, but they have antibodies against both of these antigens. People with type AB blood have neither anti-A nor anti-B antibodies, but they have both the A and B antigens, and their red blood cells are clumped by antibodies in the blood of all the other groups.

The four blood types—A, B, AB, and O—are produced by different combinations of multiple (three) alleles of a single gene *I* **(Figure 10.15)**. The three alleles, designated I^A, I^B, and i, produce the following blood types:

$$I^A I^A = \text{type A blood}$$
$$I^A i = \text{type A blood}$$
$$I^A I^B = \text{type AB blood}$$
$$I^B I^B = \text{type B blood}$$
$$I^B i = \text{type B blood}$$
$$ii = \text{type O blood}$$

In addition, I^A and I^B are codominant alleles that are each dominant to the *i* allele.

10.2d In Epistasis, Genes Interact, with the Activity of One Gene Influencing the Activity of Another Gene

The genetic characters discussed so far in this chapter, such as flower colour, seed shape, and the blood types of the ABO group, are all produced by the alleles of single genes, with each gene functioning on its own.

B allele	5′...ATGCAGATACCGATTACAGACCATAGG...3′
	3′...TACGTCTATGGCTAATGTCTGGTATCC...5′
b_1 allele	5′...ATGCAGA**G**ACCGATTACAGACCATAGG...3′
	3′...TACGTCT**C**TGGCTAATGTCTGGTATCC...5′
b_2 allele	5′...ATGCAGATACCGA**C**TACAGACCATAGG...3′
	3′...TACGTCTATGGCT**G**ATGTCTGGTATCC...5′
b_3 allele	5′...ATGCAGATACCGATTACAG**T**CCATAGG...3′
	3′...TACGTCTATGGCTAATGTC**A**GGTATCC...5′

Figure 10.14

Multiple alleles. Multiple alleles consist of small differences in the DNA sequence of a gene at one or more points, which result in detectable differences in the structure of the protein encoded by the gene. The *B* allele is the normal allele, which encodes a protein with normal function. The three *b* alleles each have alterations of the normal protein-coding DNA sequence that may adversely affect the function of that protein.

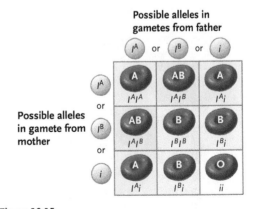

Possible alleles in gametes from father

Figure 10.15

Inheritance of the blood types of the human ABO blood group. Note that although there are three possible alleles in the population, each individual parent carries only two.

NEL

CHAPTER 10 MENDEL, GENES, AND INHERITANCE | 233

233

This is not the case for every trait. In **epistasis** (*epi* = on or over; *stasis* = standing or stopping), genes interact, with one or more alleles of a gene at one locus inhibiting or masking the effects of one or more alleles of a gene at a different locus. The result of epistasis is that some expected phenotypes do not appear among offspring.

Labrador retrievers may have black, chocolate brown, or yellow fur **(Figure 10.16)**. The different colours result from variations in the amount and distribution in hairs of a brownish-black pigment called melanin. One gene, coding for an enzyme involved in melanin production, determines how much melanin is produced. The dominant *B* allele of this gene produces black fur colour in *BB* or *Bb* Labs; less pigment is produced in *bb* dogs, which are chocolate brown. However, another gene at a different locus determines whether the black or chocolate colour appears at all, by controlling the deposition of pigment in hairs. The dominant *E* allele of this second gene permits pigment deposition, so that the black colour in *BB* or *Bb* individuals, or the chocolate colour in *bb* individuals, actually appears in the fur. Pigment deposition is almost completely blocked in homozygous recessive *ee* individuals, so the fur lacks melanin and has a yellow colour whether the genotype for the *B* gene is *BB*, *Bb*, or *bb*. Thus, the *E* gene is said to be epistatic to the *B* gene.

Epistasis by the *E* gene eliminates some of the expected classes from crosses among Labs. Rather than two separate classes, as would be expected from a dihybrid cross without epistasis, the *BB ee*, *Bb ee*, *bB ee*, and *bb ee* genotypes produce a single yellow phenotype, giving the distribution 9/16 black, 3/16 chocolate, and 4/16 yellow. That is, the ratio is 9:3:4 instead of the expected 9:3:3:1 ratio. Many other dihybrid crosses that involve epistatic interactions produce distributions that differ from the expected 9:3:3:1 ratio.

In human biology, researchers believe that gene interactions and epistasis are common. The current thinking is that epistasis is an important factor in determining an individual's susceptibility to common human diseases. That is, the different degrees of susceptibility are the result of different gene interactions in the individuals. A specific example is insulin resistance, a disorder in which muscle, fat, and liver cells do not use insulin correctly, with the result that glucose and insulin levels become high in the blood. This disorder is believed to be determined by several genes often interacting with one another.

10.2e In Polygenic Inheritance, a Character Is Controlled by the Common Effects of Several Genes

Some characters follow a pattern of inheritance in which there is a more or less even gradation of types, forming a continuous distribution, rather than "on" or "off"

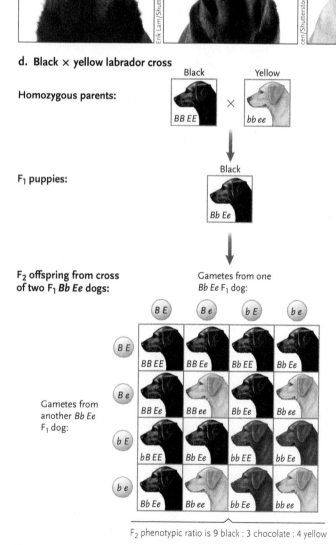

a. Black labrador

b. Chocolate brown labrador

c. Yellow labrador

Erik Lam/Shutterstock.com

cen/Shutterstock.com

cen/Shutterstock.com

d. Black × yellow labrador cross

Black   Yellow

Homozygous parents: *BB EE*   ×   *bb ee*

F₁ puppies: Black   *Bb Ee*

F₂ offspring from cross of two F₁ *Bb Ee* dogs:

Gametes from one *Bb Ee* F₁ dog:

B E   *B e*   *b E*   *b e*

Gametes from another *Bb Ee* F₁ dog:

B E   →   *BB EE*   *BB Ee*   *Bb EE*   *Bb Ee*

B e   →   *BB Ee*   *BB ee*   *Bb Ee*   *Bb ee*

b E   →   *bB EE*   *Bb Ee*   *bb EE*   *bb Ee*

b e   →   *Bb Ee*   *Bb ee*   *bb Ee*   *bb ee*

F₂ phenotypic ratio is 9 black : 3 chocolate : 4 yellow

Figure 10.16

An example of epistasis: the inheritance of coat colour in Labrador retrievers.

(discontinuous) effects such as the production of only purple or white flowers in pea plants. For example, human adults range from short to tall, in a continuous distribution of height between limits of about 1 and 2 m. Typically, a continuous distribution of this type is the result of **polygenic inheritance**, in which several to many different genes contribute to the same character. Other characters that undertake a similar continuous distribution include skin colour and body weight in humans, ear length in corn, seed colour in wheat, and colour spotting in mice. These characters are also known as **quantitative traits.**

Polygenic inheritance can be detected by defining classes of variation, such as human body height of 180 cm in one class, 181 cm in the next class, 182 cm in the next class, and so on. The number of individuals in each class is then plotted as a graph. If the plot produces a bell-shaped curve, with fewer individuals at the extremes and the greatest numbers clustered around the midpoint, it is a good indication that the trait is quantitative **(Figure 10.17).**

The expression of a genetic phenotype can be influenced by the environment; this is particularly common with quantitative traits like body size. For example, poor nutrition during infancy and childhood is one environmental factor that can limit growth and prevent individuals from reaching the height expected from purely genetic contributions; good nutrition can have the opposite effect. Thus, the average young adult in Japan today is several inches taller than the average adult in the 1930s, when nutrition was poorer.

CONCEPT FIX At first glance, the wide variation shown in a quantitative trait might appear to support the old idea that the characteristics of parents are blended in their offspring. Commonly, people believe that the children in a family with one tall and one short parent will be of intermediate height. Although the children of such parents are indeed most likely to be of intermediate height, careful genetic analysis of hundreds of such families shows that their offspring actually range over a continuum from short to tall, forming a typical bell-shaped curve. Some children are not intermediate relative to their parents; they are either taller or shorter than both parents. Careful analysis of the inheritance of skin colour produces the same result. Although the skin colour of children is most often intermediate between that of their parents, a typical bell-shaped distribution is obtained in which some children at the extremes are lighter or darker than either parent. Thus, genetic analysis does not support the idea of blending or even mixing of parental traits in quantitative characteristics such as body size or skin colour. ⬡

a. Students at Brigham Young University, arranged according to height

Dan Fairbanks/Brigham Young University

Figure 10.17
Continuous variation in height due to polygenic inheritance.

b. Actual distribution of individuals in the photo according to height

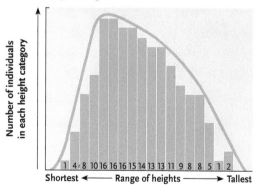

Number of individuals in each height category

1 4 8 10 16 16 15 14 13 13 11 9 8 8 5 1 2

Shortest ← Range of heights → Tallest

c. Idealized bell-shaped curve for a population that displays continuous variation in a trait

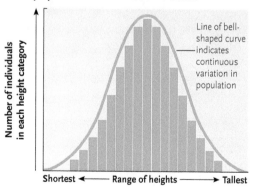

Number of individuals in each height category

Line of bell-shaped curve indicates continuous variation in population

Shortest ← Range of heights → Tallest

If the sample in the photo included more individuals, the distribution would more closely approach this ideal.

10.2f In Pleiotropy, Two or More Characters Are Affected by a Single Gene

In the previous section, we saw several genes affecting the same trait. In this section we see the reverse situation: single genes affecting more than one character of an organism in a process called **pleiotropy**. For example, sickle cell disease (see earlier discussion) is caused by a recessive allele of a single gene that affects hemoglobin structure and function. However, the altered hemoglobin protein, the primary phenotypic change of the sickle cell mutation, leads to blood vessel blockage, which can damage many tissues and organs in the body and thus affect many body functions, producing wide-ranging symptoms such as fatigue, abdominal pain, heart failure, paralysis, and pneumonia **(Figure 10.18)**. Physicians recognize these wide-ranging pleiotropic effects as symptoms of sickle cell disease.

CONCEPT FIX Although Mendel's simple, single gene experiments in peas provided a valuable scientific model for understanding inheritance, modern analyses in a wide variety of organisms are finding that many traits are quantitative and most genes have some pleiotropic effects. ⬡

The next chapter describes additional patterns of inheritance that were not anticipated by Mendel, including the effects of recombination during meiosis. These additional patterns also extend, rather than contradict, Mendel's fundamental principles.

STUDY BREAK

1. Distinguish between alleles that are incompletely dominant and those that are codominant.
2. How might you know that a trait is polygenic?

Figure 10.18

Pleiotropy, as demonstrated by the wide-ranging, multiple effects of the single mutant allele responsible for sickle cell disease. (Not all effects are shown.)

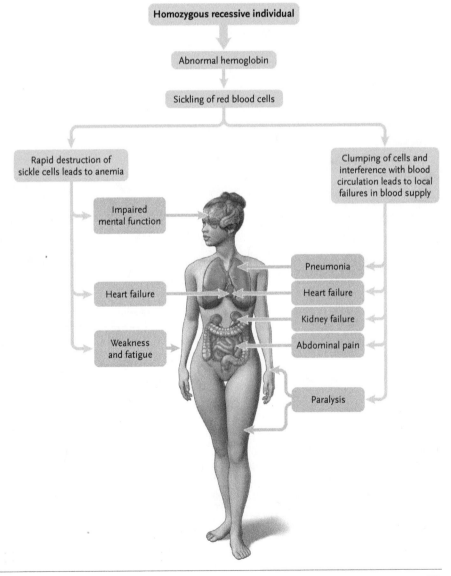

PEOPLE BEHIND BIOLOGY 10.3

Dr. Charles Scriver, Professor Emeritus, *McGill University, Montréal*

A *paradigm* is a particular way of thinking about a subject, and as Charles Scriver began his career, the way of thinking about genetic disease was beginning to shift. The old paradigm of "nothing can be done" was giving way to an understanding

that disease phenotypes have both a genetic *and* an environmental component. Through a combination of basic research, public education, newborn-screening programs, and online archiving of hundreds of mutations, Scriver brought this

paradigm shift to our understanding of the underlying biology, treatment, and prevention of diseases such as phenylketonuria, vitamin D–deficient rickets, Tay–Sachs disease, and thalassemia.

Review

To access course materials such as Aplia and other companion resources, please visit www.NELSONbrain.com.

10.1 The Beginnings of Genetics: Mendel's Garden Peas

- Mendel made a good choice of experimental organism in that garden peas offered simple cultivation; clearly defined, true-breeding characters (such as flower colour or seed shape); and an opportunity to make controlled pollinations.

- By analyzing his results quantitatively, Mendel showed that traits are passed from parents to offspring as hereditary factors (now called genes and alleles) in predictable ratios and combinations, disproving the notion of blended inheritance (see Figures 10.3, 10.4, and 10.5).

- Mendel realized that his results with crosses involving single characters (monohybrid crosses) could be explained if three hypotheses were true: (1) the genes that govern genetic characters occur in pairs in individuals; (2) if different alleles of a gene are present in a pair within an individual, one allele is dominant over the other; and (3) the two alleles of a gene segregate and enter gametes singly (see Figures 10.5 and 10.7).

- Mendel confirmed his hypotheses by a testcross between an F₁ heterozygote and a homozygous recessive parent. This type of testcross is still used to determine whether an individual is homozygous or heterozygous for a dominant allele (see Figure 10.8).

- To explain the results of his crosses with individuals showing differences in two characters—dihybrid crosses—Mendel added an additional hypothesis: the alleles of the genes that govern the two characters segregate independently during formation of gametes (see Figure 10.9). That is, the dihybrid cross *Aa Bb* × *Aa Bb* can be treated as two separate monohybrid crosses: *Aa* × *Aa* and *Bb* × *Bb*. The monohybrid crosses would give phenotypic ratios of 3/4 *A__*: 1/4 *aa* and 3/4 *B__*: 1/4 *bb*, respectively. The standard dihybrid ratios arise from combinations of these monohybrid ratios. That is, 9/16 *A__ B__* results from 3/4 *A__* × 3/4 *B__*, 3/16 *aa B__* results from 1/4 *aa* × 3/4 *B__*, and so on.

- Walter Sutton was the first person to note the similarities between the inheritance of genes and the behaviour of chromosomes in meiosis and fertilization. These parallels made it obvious that genes and alleles are carried on the chromosomes, and are called the chromosome theory of inheritance (see Figure 10.10).

- A locus is the particular site where a given gene is found on the chromosomes of an organism (see Figure 10.11). An allele is just a particular version of the DNA sequence of a gene. Therefore, if an individual were heterozygous for the stem length gene of Mendel's peas, it would have a *T* allele on one homologue and a *t* allele on the other. These two alleles would each be located at exactly the same locus on their respective chromosomes.

10.2 Later Modifications and Additions to Mendel's Hypotheses

- Incomplete dominance arises when, in a heterozygote, the activity of one allele is insufficient to compensate for the inactivity of another. Codominance arises when, in a heterozygote, both alleles are equally active. In both cases, the phenotype of heterozygotes is different from that of either homozygote (see Figure 10.13).

- Many genes may have multiple alleles if all the individuals in a population are taken into account. However, any diploid individual in a population has only two alleles of these genes, which are inherited and passed on according to Mendel's principles (see Figures 10.14 and 10.15).

- In epistasis, genes interact, with alleles of one locus inhibiting or masking the effects of alleles at a different locus. The result is that some expected phenotypes do not appear among offspring (see Figure 10.16).

- A character that is subject to polygenic inheritance shows a more or less continuous variation from one extreme to another. Plotting the distribution of such characters among individuals typically produces a bell-shaped curve (see Figure 10.17).

- In pleiotropy, one gene affects more than one character of an organism (see Figure 10.18).

Questions

Self-Test Questions

1. Imagine an organism with the genotype *Rr*. If the diagrams below represent the replicated chromosomes of this organism early in meiosis, which one shows the correct location of the *R* and *r* alleles?

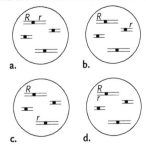

2. Kernel colour in corn is influenced by the *C* gene. The dominant *C* allele produces coloured kernels, and plants homozygous for the recessive *c* allele have colourless (white) kernels. What gamete genotypes, and in what proportions, would be produced by the plants in the following crosses? What kernel colour, and in what proportions, would be expected in the offspring of the crosses?
   a. *CC × Cc*
   b. *Cc × Cc*
   c. *Cc × cc*

3. In peas, the allele *T* produces tall plants and the allele *t* produces dwarf plants. The *T* allele is dominant to *t*. If a tall plant is crossed with a dwarf and the offspring are distributed about equally between tall and dwarf plants, what are the genotypes of the parents?

4. The ability of humans to taste the bitter chemical phenylthiocarbamide (PTC) is a genetic trait. People with at least one copy of the normal, dominant allele of the *PTC* gene can taste PTC; those who are homozygous for a mutant, recessive allele cannot taste it. Could two parents able to taste PTC have a nontaster child? Could nontaster parents have a child able to taste PTC? A pair of taster parents, both of whom had one parent able to taste PTC and one nontaster parent, is expecting their first child. What are the chances that the child will be either able or unable to taste PTC? Suppose the first child is a nontaster; what is the chance that their second child will also be unable to taste PTC?

5. One gene has the alleles *A* and *a*; another gene has the alleles *B* and *b*. Alleles of the *A* and *B* genes assort independently. For each of the following genotypes, what genotypes of gametes will be produced, and in what proportions?
   a. *AA BB*
   b. *Aa BB*
   c. *Aa bb*
   d. *Aa Bb*

6. Which genotypes, and in what frequencies, will be present in the offspring from the following matings?
   a. *AA BB × aa BB*
   b. *Aa Bb × Aa Bb*
   c. *Aa Bb × aa bb*
   d. *Aa BB × AA Bb*

7. In addition to the two genes in question 5, assume you now study a third independently assorting gene that has the alleles *C* and *c*. For each of the following genotypes, indicate what types of gametes will be produced.
   a. *AA BB CC*
   b. *Aa BB cc*
   c. *Aa BB Cc*
   d. *Aa Bb Cc*

8. Imagine that you are helping a friend with genetics problems. He has drawn the Punnett square below to answer questions about a dihybrid cross: *Mm Hh × Mm Hh*. Use the principles of meiosis to explain why this diagram is incorrect.

	M	H	h	m
M				
h				
H				
m				

9. A man is homozygous dominant for alleles at 10 different genes that assort independently. How many genotypically different types of sperm cells can he produce? A woman is homozygous recessive for the alleles of 8 of these 10 genes, but she is heterozygous for the other 2 genes. How many genotypically different types of eggs can she produce? What hypothesis can you suggest to describe the relationship between the number of different possible gametes and the number of heterozygous and homozygous genes that are present?

10. In guinea pigs, an allele for rough fur (*R*) is dominant over an allele for smooth fur (*r*); an allele for black coat (*B*) is dominant over that for white (*b*). You have an animal with rough, black fur. What cross would you use to determine whether the animal is homozygous for these traits? What phenotype would you expect in the offspring if the animal were homozygous?

11. You cross a lima bean plant from a variety that breeds true for green pods with another lima bean from a variety that breeds true for yellow pods. You note that all the F$_1$ plants have green pods. These green-pod F$_1$ plants, when crossed to each other, yield 675 plants with green pods and 217 with yellow pods. How many genes likely control pod colour in this experiment? Give the alleles letter designations. Which is dominant?

12. Some recessive alleles have such a detrimental effect that they are lethal when present in both chromosomes of a pair. Homozygous recessives cannot survive, and die at some point during embryonic development. Suppose that the allele *r* is lethal in the homozygous *rr* condition. What genotypic ratios would you expect among the living offspring of the following crosses?
   a. *RR × Rr*
   b. *Rr × Rr*

13. In garden peas, the genotypes *GG* and *Gg* produce green pods and *gg* produces yellow pods; *TT* and *Tt* plants are tall and *tt* plants are dwarfed; *RR* and *Rr* produce round seeds and *rr* produces wrinkled seeds. If a plant of a true-breeding tall variety with green pods and round seeds is crossed with a plant of a true-breeding dwarf variety with yellow pods and wrinkled seeds, what phenotypes are expected, and in what ratios, in the F_1 generation? What phenotypes, and in what ratios, are expected if F_1 individuals are crossed?

14. In chickens, a gene called *F* influences leg feathering. Feathered legs are produced by a dominant allele *F*, while featherless legs result in individuals who are homozygous for the *f* allele. A second gene, *P*, on another chromosome, influences comb shape. The dominant allele *P* produces pea combs; a recessive allele *p* of this gene causes single combs. A breeder makes the following crosses with birds 1, 2, 3, and 4; all parents have feathered legs and pea combs.

Cross	Offspring
1 × 2	all feathered, pea comb
1 × 3	3/4 feathered, 1/4 featherless, all pea comb
1 × 4	9/16 feathered, pea comb; 3/16 featherless, pea comb; 3/16 feathered, single comb; 1/16 featherless, single comb

What are the genotypes of the four birds?

15. A mixup in a hospital ward causes a mother with O and MN blood types to think that a baby given to her really belongs to someone else. Tests in the hospital show that the doubting mother is able to taste PTC (see question 4). The baby given to her has O and MN blood types and has no reaction when the bitter PTC chemical is placed on its tongue. The mother has four other children with the following blood types and tasting abilities for PTC.
   a. type A and MN blood, taster
   b. type B and N blood, nontaster
   c. type A and M blood, taster
   d. type A and N blood, taster

   Without knowing the father's blood types and tasting ability, can you determine whether the child is really hers? (Assume that all her other children have the same father.)

16. In cats, the genotype *AA* produces tabby fur colour; *Aa* is also a tabby, and *aa* is black. Another independently assorting gene at a different locus is epistatic to the gene for fur colour. When present in its dominant *W* form (*WW* or *Ww*), this gene blocks the formation of fur colour and all the offspring are white; *ww* individuals develop normal fur colour. What fur colours, and in what proportions, would you expect from the cross *Aa Ww* × *Aa Ww*?

17. Having malformed hands with shortened fingers is a dominant trait controlled by a single gene; people who are homozygous for the recessive allele have normal hands and fingers. Having woolly hair is a dominant trait controlled by a different, independently assorting gene; homozygous recessive individuals have normal, nonwoolly hair. Suppose a woman with normal hands and nonwoolly hair marries a man who has malformed hands and woolly hair. Their first child has normal hands and nonwoolly hair. What are the genotypes of the mother, the father, and the child? If this couple has a second child, what is the probability that it will have normal hands and woolly hair?

Questions for Discussion

1. The eyes of brown-eyed people are not alike but rather vary considerably in shade and pattern. What do you think causes these differences?

2. Explain how individuals of an organism that are phenotypically alike can produce different ratios of progeny phenotypes.

3. ABO blood type tests can be used to exclude paternity. Suppose a defendant who is the alleged father of a child takes a blood-type test and the results do not exclude him as the father. Do the results indicate that he is the father? What arguments could a lawyer make based on the test results to exclude the defendant from being the father? (Assume the tests were performed correctly.)

11

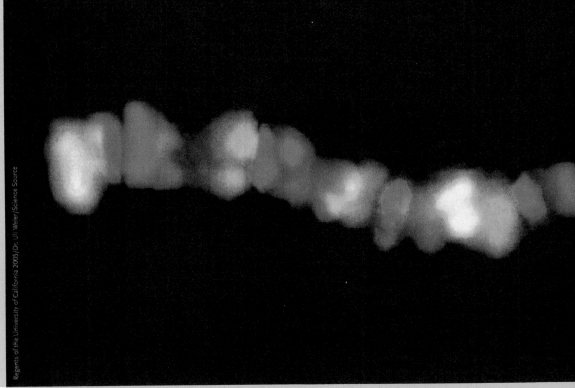

Regents of the University of California 2005/Dr. Uli Weier/Science Source

Genes, Chromosomes, and Human Genetics

WHY IT MATTERS

Imagine being 10 years old and trapped in a body that each day becomes more shrivelled, frail, and old. You are just tall enough to peer over the top of the kitchen counter, and you weigh less than 16 kg. Already you are bald, and you probably have only a few more years to live. But if you are like Mickey Hayes or Fransie Geringer (**Figure 11.1**), you still have not lost your courage or your childlike curiosity about life. Like them, you still play, laugh, and celebrate birthdays.

Progeria, the premature aging that afflicts Mickey and Fransie, is caused by a genetic error that occurs once in every 8 million human births. The error is perpetuated each time cells of the embryo—then of the child—duplicate their chromosomes and divide. The outcome of that rare mistake is an acceleration of aging and a greatly reduced life expectancy.

Progeria affects both boys and girls. Usually, symptoms begin to appear before the age of 2. The rate of body growth declines to abnormally low levels. Skin becomes thinner, muscles become flaccid, and limb bones start to degenerate. Children with progeria never reach puberty, and most die in their early teens from a stroke or heart attack brought on by hardening of the arteries, a condition typical of advanced age.

The plight of Mickey and Fransie provides a telling and tragic example of the dramatic effects that gene defects can have on living organisms. The characteristics of each individual, from humans to pine trees to protozoa, depend on the combination of genes, alleles, and chromosomes inherited from its parents, as well as on environmental effects. This chapter delves into genes and the role of chromosomes in inheritance.

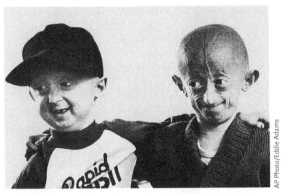

Figure 11.1

Two boys, both younger than 10, who have progeria, a genetic disorder characterized by accelerated aging and extremely reduced life expectancy.

11.1 Genetic Linkage and Recombination

In the historic experiments described in the previous chapter, Gregor Mendel carried out crosses with seven different characters in garden peas, controlled by seven different genes. He found that his observations from crosses were consistent with the hypothesis that each of the genes assorted independently of all of the others. If Mendel had extended his study to additional characters, he would soon have found exceptions to this principle. This should not be surprising because an organism has many more genes than chromosomes. Conceptually, then, chromosomes contain many genes, with each gene at a particular location, or locus. Genes located on different chromosomes assort independently during meiosis because the two chromosomes behave independently of one another during as they line up on the metaphase plate (see Chapter 9 for a review of chromosome behaviour during meiosis). Genes located on the same chromosome may be inherited together in genetic crosses—that is, they do not assort independently—because the chromosome is inherited as a single physical entity in meiosis. Genes on the same chromosome are known as **linked genes**, and the phenomenon is called **linkage**.

11.1a The Principles of Linkage and Recombination Were Determined with *Drosophila*

In the early part of the twentieth century, Thomas H. Morgan and coworkers at Columbia University used the fruit fly, *Drosophila melanogaster*, as a model organism to investigate Mendel's principles in animals. (For more information about *Drosophila* as a model research organism, see *The Purple Pages*.) Groups of genes that tended to assort together in crosses were believed to be carried on the same chromosome. It was an undergraduate student named Alfred Sturtevant, working in Morgan's lab, who developed the insight that resulted in the construction of the first genetic map showing the relative order of genes on a chromosome. This map also estimated the distance separating the genes. These brilliant and far-reaching hypotheses were typical of Morgan's group, which founded genetics research in the United States, developed *Drosophila* as a research organism, and made discoveries that were likely as significant to the development of genetics as those of Mendel.

Although it is tempting to assume that genetic maps could be made simply by looking down a microscope, finding the genes, and measuring the distance between them, the technology to do this was simply not available. Instead, Morgan's group used an indirect measure of distance. They reasoned that genes sitting relatively far apart on a chromosome would be more likely to be separated from one another during meiotic crossing-over than genes lying closer together. Figure 9.13, Chapter 9, illustrates this process of recombination occurring in the space separating two genes as they appear on chromosomes paired during meiosis. Obviously, if recombination is to be used as a measure of the distance separating genes, it must be detectable. That is why the organism used in Figure 9.13, Chapter 9, is heterozygous for all genes; the chromatids resulting from recombination are then different from the original, nonrecombinant, ones and can be identified. Following meiosis I and II, each of the four different chromatids will become a chromosome in a separate gamete (review the basic mechanisms of meiosis in Figure 9.10, Chapter 9). Which chromosome, recombinant or not, is carried by a given gamete is most clearly revealed only in offspring resulting from fertilization with a homozygous recessive gamete. That is why, in the cross originally done by Morgan in 1911, you will notice that one parent is heterozygous and the other is homozygous recessive **(Figure 11.2, p. 242).**

To understand the following crosses, you need to learn to work with the genetic symbolism developed by Morgan instead of the *A/a* system used in Chapter 10. Although *Drosophila* notation might appear counterintuitive at first, understanding a few basic principles will help you see the logic behind it. First, note that geneticists working with fruit flies have all agreed on a "normal," or "wild-type," genotype; any change from wild type is, by definition, a mutant. Mutant alleles are named based on the altered phenotype of the organism that expresses them. The names for dominant mutant alleles are written with the first letter in uppercase, whereas those for recessive mutant alleles are written with the first letter in lowercase. For example, a dominant mutant allele transforming an antenna into a leg is called Antennapedia (*Antp*), whereas a recessive mutant allele altering eye colour is called vermilion (*v*). The notation for a wild-type allele is always made by simply adding a superscripted plus (+) sign to the

Experimental Research
Figure 11.2 Evidence for gene linkage.

QUESTION: Do the purple-eye vestigial-wing genes of *Drosophila* assort independently?

EXPERIMENT: Morgan crossed true-breeding wild-type flies with red eyes and normal wings with purple-eyed, vestigial-winged flies. The F₁ dihybrids were all wild type in phenotype. Next he crossed the F₁ dihybrid flies with purple-eyed, vestigial-winged flies (this is a testcross) and analyzed the phenotypes of the progeny.

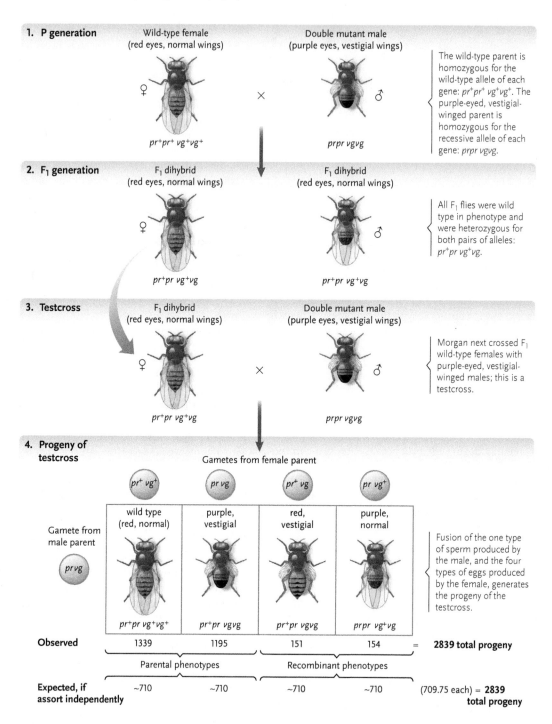

1. **P generation**

Wild-type female (red eyes, normal wings) ♀ $pr^+pr^+\ vg^+vg^+$ × Double mutant male (purple eyes, vestigial wings) ♂ $prpr\ vgvg$

The wild-type parent is homozygous for the wild-type allele of each gene: $pr^+pr^+\ vg^+vg^+$. The purple-eyed, vestigial-winged parent is homozygous for the recessive allele of each gene: $prpr\ vgvg$.

2. **F₁ generation**

F₁ dihybrid (red eyes, normal wings) ♀ $pr^+pr\ vg^+vg$ F₁ dihybrid (red eyes, normal wings) ♂ $pr^+pr\ vg^+vg$

All F₁ flies were wild type in phenotype and were heterozygous for both pairs of alleles: $pr^+pr\ vg^+vg$.

3. **Testcross**

F₁ dihybrid (red eyes, normal wings) ♀ $pr^+pr\ vg^+vg$ × Double mutant male (purple eyes, vestigial wings) ♂ $prpr\ vgvg$

Morgan next crossed F₁ wild-type females with purple-eyed, vestigial-winged males; this is a testcross.

4. **Progeny of testcross**

Gametes from female parent: $pr^+\ vg^+$ $pr\ vg$ $pr^+\ vg$ $pr\ vg^+$

Gamete from male parent: $prvg$

	wild type (red, normal)	purple, vestigial	red, vestigial	purple, normal
	$pr^+pr\ vg^+vg^+$	$pr^+pr\ vgvg$	$pr^+pr\ vgvg$	$prpr\ vg^+vg$
Observed	1339	1195	151	154

= 2839 total progeny

Parental phenotypes — Recombinant phenotypes

| **Expected, if assort independently** | ~710 | ~710 | ~710 | ~710 |

(709.75 each) = **2839 total progeny**

Fusion of the one type of sperm produced by the male, and the four types of eggs produced by the female, generates the progeny of the testcross.

RESULTS: 2534 of the testcross progeny flies were parental—wild-type or purple, vestigial—while 305 of the progeny were recombinant—red, vestigial or purple, normal. If the genes assorted independently, the expectation is for a 1:1:1:1 ratio for testcross progeny: approximately 1420 of both parental and recombinant progeny.

CONCLUSION: The purple-eye and vestigial-wing genes do not assort independently. The simplest alternative is that the two genes are linked on the same chromosome.

mutant allele notation. You know you understand this system if you agree that *Antp⁺* refers to a *recessive* allele giving a normal phenotype when homozygous.

Morgan began a specific breeding program using true-breeding fruit flies with normal red eyes and normal wing length (genotype *pr⁺pr⁺ vg⁺vg⁺*), along with a true-breeding fly with the recessive traits of purple eyes and vestigial (that is, short and crumpled) wings (genotype *prpr vgvg*) (Figure 11.2, step 1).

The F_1 (first-generation) offspring were all dihybrid *pr⁺pr vg⁺vg*, and because of the dominance of the wild-type alleles, they all had red eyes and normal wings (see Figure 11.2, step 2). Morgan then selected these wild-type F_1 females as the dihybrid parent and mated them to homozygous recessive males (with purple eyes and vestigial wings) as the testcross parent. If the purple and vestigial genes were carried on different chromosomes, Mendel's principle of independent assortment (see Section 10.1) would predict four classes of phenotypes in the offspring, in the approximate 1:1:1:1 ratio of red eyes, normal wings : purple, vestigial : red, vestigial : purple, normal. Given over 2800 offspring from several females, about 700 should have been in each class. However, Morgan observed two types of progeny in which the counts were much higher than 700 (red, normal and purple, vestigial) and two types with counts that were much lower (red, vestigial, and purple, normal) (see Figure 11.2, step 4).

Morgan's hypothesis to explain this non-Mendelian distribution is illustrated in **Figure 11.3, p. 244.** He suggested that the two genes are linked genetically—physically associated on the same chromosome. That is, *pr* and *vg* are linked genes. He further hypothesized that the behaviour of these linked genes is explained by *chromosome recombination* during meiosis. Furthermore, he proposed that the frequency of this recombination is a function of the distance between linked genes.

The *pr⁺pr vg⁺vg* F_1 dihybrid parents produce four types of gametes (see Figure 11.3). The two parental gametes, *pr⁺ vg⁺* and *pr vg*, are generated by simple segregation of the chromosomes during meiosis without any crossing-over (recombination) between the genes. The two recombinant gametes, *pr⁺ vg* and *pr vg⁺*, result from crossing-over between the homologous chromatids when they are paired in prophase I of meiosis (see Figures 9.10 and 9.13, Chapter 9). The offspring of the cross are produced by fusion of each of these four gametes with a *pr vg* gamete produced by the *prpr vgvg* male parent. The phenotypes of the offspring directly reflect the genotypes of the gametes produced by the dihybrid parent.

CONCEPT FIX Students of genetics sometimes assume that the wild-type and purple vestigial offspring in the above cross are called "parental" because they *look like* the parents. However, the term *parental* actually refers to genotype, not phenotype; parental offspring are the ones that *inherit chromosomes that were NOT involved in*

recombination in the dihybrid parent. Parental offspring, therefore, do not always resemble the parents of the cross. ⬢

Although Morgan could not look down a microscope and measure the distance between genes directly, he could look down a microscope and identify the phenotypes of recombinant offspring from dihybrid fruit fly testcrosses. Thus, the relative frequency of recombinant progeny became his "measure" of the distance separating genes. The example in Figure 11.3 reveals that purple eyes and vestigial wings are on the same chromosome and are separated by a recombinant offspring frequency distance of 10.7%.

11.1b Recombination Frequency Can Be Used to Map Chromosomes

The recombinant offspring frequency of 10.7% for the *pr* and *vg* genes of *Drosophila* means that 10.7% of the gametes originating from the *pr⁺pr vg⁺vg* parent contained recombined chromosomes (i.e., either *pr⁺ vg* or *pr vg⁺*). That recombinant offspring frequency is characteristic for those two genes. In other crosses that involve linked genes, Morgan found that the recombinant offspring frequency was characteristic of the two particular genes involved, and varied from less than 1% up to a maximum of 50% (see the next section).

From these observations, Alfred Sturtevant realized that the variation in recombinant offspring frequencies could be used as a means of mapping genes on chromosomes. Sturtevant himself later recalled his light bulb moment:

> I suddenly realized that the variations in the strength of linkage already attributed by Morgan to difference in the spatial separation of the gene offered the possibility of determining sequence in the linear dimensions of a chromosome. I went home and spent most of the night (to the neglect of my other homework) producing the first chromosome map.

Therefore, recombinant offspring frequencies can be used to make a **linkage map** of a chromosome showing the relative locations of genes. For example, assume that the three genes *a*, *b*, and *c* are carried together on the same chromosome. Crosses reveal a 9.6% frequency of recombinants for *a* and *b*, an 8% frequency for *a* and *c*, and a 2% frequency for *b* and *c*. These recombinant offspring frequencies allow the genes to be arranged in only one sequence on the chromosomes as follows:

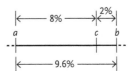

Figure 11.3

Recombinant offspring, the result of crossing-over between homologous chromosomes in the dihybrid parent. The testcross of Figure 11.2, p. 242, is redrawn here to show the two linked genes on chromosomes. The two parental homologues in the dihybrid parent (female, on the left) are coloured differently to allow us to follow them during the cross. The parental offspring inherit one or the other of the chromosomes unchanged from the dihybrid parent. The recombinant offspring inherit one or the other of the recombined chromosomes from the dihybrid parent.

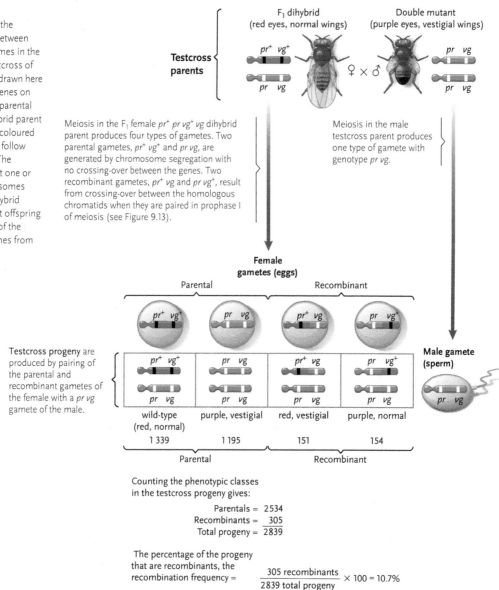

Testcross parents

F₁ dihybrid (red eyes, normal wings) pr^+ vg^+ / pr vg ♀ × ♂   Double mutant (purple eyes, vestigial wings) pr vg / pr vg

Meiosis in the F₁ female pr^+ pr vg^+ vg dihybrid parent produces four types of gametes. Two parental gametes, pr^+ vg^+ and pr vg, are generated by chromosome segregation with no crossing-over between the genes. Two recombinant gametes, pr^+ vg and pr vg^+, result from crossing-over between the homologous chromatids when they are paired in prophase I of meiosis (see Figure 9.13).

Meiosis in the male testcross parent produces one type of gamete with genotype pr vg.

Female gametes (eggs)

Parental | Recombinant

pr^+ vg^+ | pr vg | pr^+ vg | pr vg^+

Testcross progeny are produced by pairing of the parental and recombinant gametes of the female with a pr vg gamete of the male.

Male gamete (sperm) pr vg

| pr^+ vg^+ / pr vg | pr vg / pr vg | pr^+ vg / pr vg | pr vg^+ / pr vg |

wild-type (red, normal) | purple, vestigial | red, vestigial | purple, normal

1 339 | 1 195 | 151 | 154

Parental | Recombinant

Counting the phenotypic classes in the testcross progeny gives:

Parentals = 2534
Recombinants = 305
Total progeny = 2839

The percentage of the progeny that are recombinants, the recombination frequency = $\dfrac{305 \text{ recombinants}}{2839 \text{ total progeny}} \times 100 = 10.7\%$

You will note that the *a–b* recombinant offspring frequency does not exactly equal the sum of the *a–c* and *c–b* frequencies. This is because genes farther apart on a chromosome are more likely to have more than one cross-over occur between them. Whereas a single cross-over between two genes gives recombinant chromatids, a double cross-over (two single cross-overs occurring in the same meiosis) between two genes gives the parental arrangement of alleles (and is therefore undetectable and would not be counted). You can see this simply by drawing single and double cross-overs between two genes on a piece of paper. In our example, the undetectable double cross-overs that occur between *a* and *b* have slightly decreased the overall recombinant offspring frequency between these two genes.

Using this method, Sturtevant created the first linkage map showing the arrangement of six genes on

the *Drosophila* X chromosome. (A partial linkage map of a *Drosophila* chromosome is shown in **Figure 11.4.**)

Since the time of Morgan, many *Drosophila* genes and those of other eukaryotic organisms widely used for genetic research, including *Neurospora* (a fungus), yeast, maize (corn), and the mouse, have been mapped using the same approach. Recombinant offspring frequencies, together with the results of other techniques, have been used to create linkage maps of the locations of genes in the DNA of prokaryotic organisms such as *Escherichia coli*.

The unit of a linkage map, called a **map unit** (abbreviated mu), is equivalent to a recombinant offspring frequency of 1%. The map unit is also called the **centimorgan** (cM) in honour of Morgan's discoveries of linkage and recombination. Map units are not absolute physical distances such as micrometres or nanometres; rather, they are *relative*, showing the positions

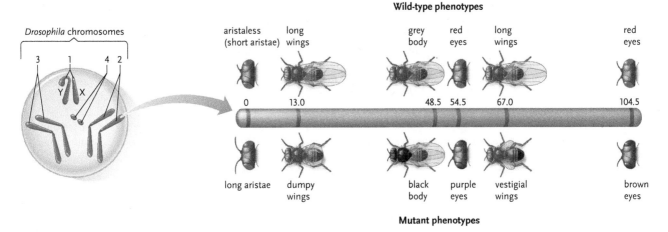

Wild-type phenotypes

aristaless (short aristae) / long wings — grey body / red eyes / long wings — red eyes

0   13.0   48.5   54.5   67.0   104.5

long aristae / dumpy wings — black body / purple eyes / vestigial wings — brown eyes

Mutant phenotypes

Figure 11.4

Relative map locations of several genes on chromosome 2 of *Drosophila*, as determined by frequencies of recombinant offspring from dihybrid testcrosses. For each gene, the diagram shows the normal or wild-type phenotype on the top and the mutant phenotype on the bottom. Mutant alleles at two different locations alter wing structure, one producing the dumpy-wing phenotype and the other the vestigial-wing phenotype; the normal allele at these locations results in normal long-wing structure. Mutant alleles at two different locations also alter eye colour.

of genes with respect to each other. One of the reasons that the units are relative and not absolute distances is that the frequency of crossing-over giving rise to recombinant offspring varies to some extent from one position to another along chromosomes.

In recent years, DNA sequencing of whole genomes has supplemented the linkage maps of a number of species. DNA sequencing shows the precise physical locations of genes right down to the number of base pairs separating them.

11.1c Widely Separated Linked Genes Assort Independently

Genes can be so widely separated on a chromosome that recombination is almost certain to occur at some point between them in every cell undergoing meiosis. When this is the case, the genes assort independently even though they are on the same chromosome. The map distance separating them will be 50 mu. (Fifty map units reflect 50% recombinant offspring. This is the same proportion of recombinant offspring observed when genes are on different chromosomes.)

To understand why this is, first recall Figure 9.13, Chapter 9, showing that a recombination event in a given cell creates 2 recombinant and 2 nonrecombinant chromatids. Next, imagine 100 meiocytes going through meiosis as usual to yield 400 gametes. If a recombination event occurred in the space separating 2 given genes in 10 of those cells, then 20 recombinant chromatids would be produced during prophase I. Twenty gametes would eventually receive recombinant chromosomes, and 20/400 = 5% of the total testcross progeny would be recombinant. We would conclude that these genes are 5 mu apart. Now assume that a recombination event occurs along the chromosome in

the space separating the two genes in *every one of the 100* cells going through meiosis. Two hundred recombinant offspring would result out of the total of 400; 50% would be recombinants; 50 mu would separate the genes.

Linkage between such widely separated genes can still be detected, however, by testing their linkage to one or more genes that lie between them. For example, the genes *a* and *c* in **Figure 11.5** are located so far apart that they assort independently and show no linkage. However, crosses that show *a* and *b* are 23 mu apart (recombinant offspring frequency of 23%), and other crosses show *b* and *c* are 34 mu apart. Therefore, *a* and *c* must

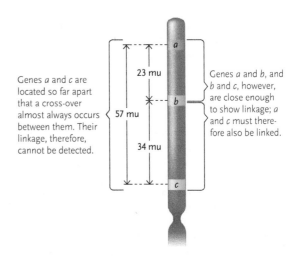

Genes *a* and *c* are located so far apart that a cross-over almost always occurs between them. Their linkage, therefore, cannot be detected.

23 mu

57 mu

34 mu

Genes *a* and *b*, and *b* and *c*, however, are close enough to show linkage; *a* and *c* must therefore also be linked.

Figure 11.5

Genes far apart on the same chromosome. Genes *a* and *c* are far apart and will not show linkage, suggesting that they are on different chromosomes. However, linkage between such genes can be established by noting their linkage to another gene or genes located between them—gene *b* here.

also be linked and carried on the same chromosome at 23 mu + 34 mu = 57 mu apart. Obviously, we could not see a recombinant offspring frequency of 57% in testcross progeny because the maximum frequency of recombinant chromatids is 50%, as described above.

We now know that some of the genes Mendel studied are actually on the same chromosome. For example, although the genes for flower colour and seed colour are actually located on the same chromosome, they are so far apart that frequent recombination between them made them assort independently in Mendel's analysis.

STUDY BREAK

1. What type of cross is typically used to discover whether two genes are linked or not?
2. How can two genes be on the same chromosome and yet assort independently (as if they were on separate chromosomes)?

11.2 Sex-Linked Genes

In many organisms, one or more pairs of chromosomes are different in males from those in females. Genes located on these chromosomes, the *sex chromosomes*, are called **sex-linked genes**; they are inherited differently in males and females.

CONCEPT FIX Note that the word "linked" in the phrase "sex-linked gene" means only that the gene is on a sex chromosome. The use of the word "linked" when considering two or more genes means that the genes are on the same chromosome. Linked genes might be on a sex chromosome or an autosome. ⬡

Chromosomes other than the sex chromosomes are called **autosomes**; genes on these chromosomes have the same patterns of inheritance in both sexes. In humans, chromosomes 1 to 22 are the autosomes.

11.2a Females Are XX and Males Are XY in Both Humans and Fruit Flies

In most species with sex chromosomes, females have two copies of a chromosome known as the **X chromosome**, forming a fully homologous XX pair, whereas males have only one X chromosome. Another chromosome, the Y chromosome, occurs in males but not in females. The Y chromosome has a short region of homology with the X chromosome that allows them to pair during meiosis. The XX human chromosome complement is shown in Figure 8.10, Chapter 8.

Each normal gamete produced by an XX female carries an X chromosome. Half the gametes produced by an XY male carry an X chromosome and half carry a Y. When a sperm cell carrying an X chromosome fertilizes an X-bearing egg cell, the new individual develops into an XX female. Conversely, when a sperm cell carrying a Y chromosome fertilizes an X-bearing egg cell, the combination produces an XY male. The Punnett square (see **Figure 11.6**) shows that fertilization is expected to produce females and males with an equal probability of 1/2. This expectation is closely matched in the human and *Drosophila* populations.

Other sex chromosome arrangements have been found, as in some insects with XX females and XO males (the O means there is no Y chromosome). In birds, butterflies, and some reptiles, the situation is reversed: males have a homologous pair of sex chromosomes (ZZ instead of XX), and females have the equivalent of an XY combination (ZW).

11.2b Human Sex Determination Depends on the *SRY* Gene

One gene carried on the Y chromosome, *SRY* (for sex-determining region of the Y), appears to be the master switch that directs development toward maleness at an early point in embryonic development.

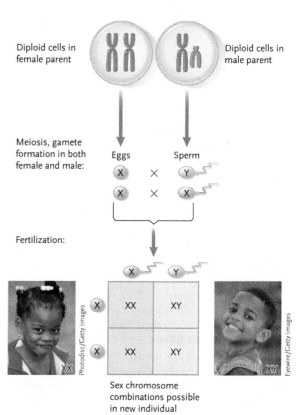

Sex chromosome combinations possible in new individual

Figure 11.6

Sex chromosomes and the chromosomal basis of sex determination in humans. Females have two X chromosomes and therefore all gametes (eggs) have the X sex chromosome. Males have one X and one Y chromosome and therefore produce equal numbers of gametes containing an X chromosome versus a Y chromosome. Males transmit their Y chromosome to their sons, but not to their daughters. Males receive their X chromosome only from their mother.

MOLECULE BEHIND BIOLOGY 11.1

Drosopterin

The brick-red eyes of wild-type fruit flies owe their colour to a mixture of two types of pigment: bright red drosopterin and brown ommochrome. Drosopterin is the final product of a multistep biochemical pathway beginning with guanine. Mutations can alter the function of enzymes that act at different steps in this pathway to result in novel eye colours such as purple, brown, and sepia.

For the first month or so of embryonic development in humans and other mammals, the rudimentary structures that give rise to reproductive organs and tissues are the same in XX and XY embryos. After six to eight weeks, the *SRY* gene becomes active in XY embryos, producing a protein that regulates the expression of other genes, thereby stimulating part of these structures to develop as testes. As a part of stimulation by hormones secreted in the developing testes and elsewhere, tissues degenerate that would otherwise develop into female structures such as the vagina and oviducts. The remaining structures develop into the penis and scrotum. In XX embryos, which do not have a copy of the *SRY* gene, development proceeds toward female reproductive structures. The rudimentary male structures degenerate in XX embryos because the hormones released by the developing testes in XY embryos are not present. Further details of the *SRY* gene and its role in human sex determination are presented in Chapter 42.

CONCEPT FIX Although the X and Y chromosomes are called *sex chromosomes*, only a few genes they carry have any influence on sex determination or sexual function. For instance, most of the roughly 2400 known genes on the human X chromosome code for phenotypes needed by both sexes, such as colour perception, blood clotting, and DNA replication. Conversely, genes governing structures needed by only one sex or the other, such as breast development, penis structure, and facial hair, are coded on autosomes. If you are male, you have inherited the genes needed for uterine development and you will pass them along to your offspring to be used by daughters. You do not express these genes in your body. If you are female, a comparable situation is the case for genes coding for penis structure, and so on. You inherited these genes but you don't express them. ⬡

11.2c Sex-Linked Genes Were First Discovered in *Drosophila*

Since males and females have different sets of sex chromosomes, the genes carried on these chromosomes can be inherited in a distinctly non-Mendelian pattern called sex linkage. Sex linkage arises from two differences between males and females: (1) males have one X chromosome and therefore one allele for each gene on this chromosome (males are hemizygous for X-linked genes, *hemi* = half); females have two copies of the X chromosome and therefore two alleles for all genes on the X chromosome; (2) males also have one copy of the Y chromosome and one allele for each gene on this chromosome; females have no Y chromosome and therefore no Y alleles at all. Y chromosomes are present in males but not females.

Morgan discovered sex-linked genes and their pattern of sex linkage in 1910. The story of discovery started when he found a male fly in his stocks with white eyes instead of the normal red eyes **(Figure 11.7)**. He crossed the white-eyed male with a true-breeding female with red eyes and observed that all the F_1 flies had red eyes **(Figure 11.8a, p. 248)**. He concluded that the white-eye trait was recessive. Next, he allowed the F_1 flies to interbreed. Based on Mendel's principles, he expected that both male and female F_2 flies would show a 3:1 ratio of red-eyed flies to white-eyed flies. Morgan was surprised to find that all the F_2 females had red eyes, *but half of the F_2 males had red eyes and half had white eyes* (Figure 11.8b).

a.

b.

Figure 11.7
Eye colour phenotypes in *Drosophila*. **(a)** Normal, red, wild-type eye colour. **(b)** Mutant white eye colour caused by a recessive allele of a sex-linked gene carried on the X chromosome.

QUESTION: How is the white-eye gene of *Drosophila* inherited?

EXPERIMENT: Morgan crossed a white-eyed male *Drosophila* with a true-breeding female with red eyes and then crossed the F_1 flies to produce the F_2 generation. He also performed the reciprocal cross in which the phenotypes were switched in the parental flies—true-breeding white-eyed female × red-eyed male.

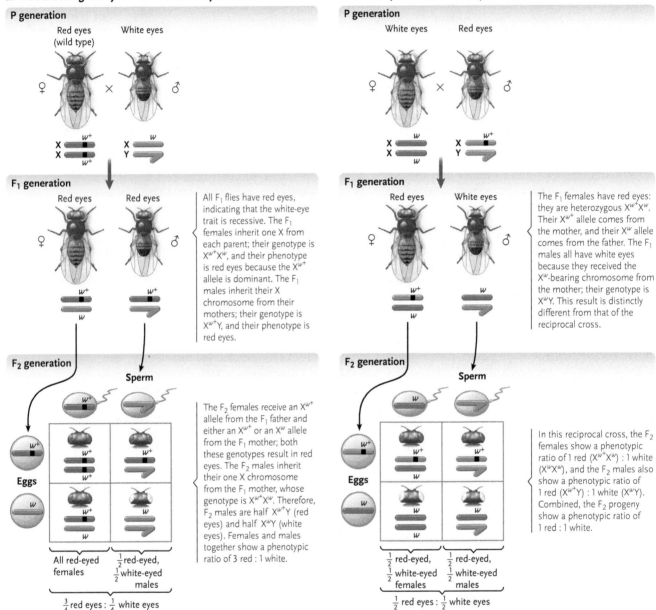

a. True-breeding red-eyed female × white-eyed male

P generation

Red eyes (wild type) × White eyes

All F_1 flies have red eyes, indicating that the white-eye trait is recessive. The F_1 females inherit one X from each parent; their genotype is $X^{w+}X^w$, and their phenotype is red eyes because the X^{w+} allele is dominant. The F_1 males inherit their X chromosome from their mothers; their genotype is $X^{w+}Y$, and their phenotype is red eyes.

F₁ generation

Red eyes   Red eyes

F₂ generation

Sperm

Eggs

The F_2 females receive an X^{w+} allele from the F_1 father and either an X^{w+} or an X^w allele from the F_1 mother; both these genotypes result in red eyes. The F_2 males inherit their one X chromosome from the F_1 mother, whose genotype is $X^{w+}X^w$. Therefore, F_2 males are half $X^{w+}Y$ (red eyes) and half X^wY (white eyes). Females and males together show a phenotypic ratio of 3 red : 1 white.

All red-eyed females $\frac{1}{2}$ red-eyed, $\frac{1}{2}$ white-eyed males

$\frac{3}{4}$ red eyes : $\frac{1}{4}$ white eyes

b. White-eyed female × red-eyed male

P generation

White eyes × Red eyes

The F_1 females have red eyes: they are heterozygous $X^{w+}X^w$. Their X^{w+} allele comes from the mother, and their X^w allele comes from the father. The F_1 males all have white eyes because they received the X^w-bearing chromosome from the mother; their genotype is X^wY. This result is distinctly different from that of the reciprocal cross.

F₁ generation

Red eyes   White eyes

F₂ generation

Sperm

Eggs

In this reciprocal cross, the F_2 females show a phenotypic ratio of 1 red ($X^{w+}X^w$) : 1 white (X^wX^w), and the F_2 males also show a phenotypic ratio of 1 red ($X^{w+}Y$) : 1 white (X^wY). Combined, the F_2 progeny show a phenotypic ratio of 1 red : 1 white.

$\frac{1}{2}$ red-eyed, $\frac{1}{2}$ white-eyed females $\frac{1}{2}$ red-eyed, $\frac{1}{2}$ white-eyed males

$\frac{1}{2}$ red eyes : $\frac{1}{2}$ white eyes

RESULTS: Differences were seen in both the F_1 and F_2 generations for the red ♀ × white ♂ and white ♀ × red ♂ crosses.

CONCLUSION: The segregation pattern for the white-eye trait showed that the white-eye gene is a sex-linked gene located on the X chromosome.

Morgan hypothesized that the alleles segregating in the cross were of a gene located on the X chromosome—now termed a sex-linked gene. The white-eyed male parent in the cross had the genotype X^wY—an X chromosome with a white (X^w) allele—and no other allele of that gene on the Y chromosome. The red-eyed female parent in the cross had the genotype $X^{w+}X^w$—each X chromosome carries the dominant normal allele for red eyes, X^{w+}.

We can follow the alleles in this cross (see Figure 11.8a). The F_1 flies of a cross $X^{w+}X^w × X^wY$ are produced as follows. The X chromosome of each male comes from his mother; therefore, his genotype is $X^{w+}Y$, and his phenotype is red eyes. Each female receives one X from each parent; therefore, her genotype is $X^{w+}X^{w}$, and her phenotype is red eyes due to the dominance of the X^{w+} allele.

In the F_2 generation, each female receives an X^{w+} allele from her father (F_1) and either an X^{w+} or X^{W} allele from her mother (F_1); these genotypes result in red eyes (see Figure 11.8a). Each male receives his one X chromosome from his mother (F_1), who has the genotype $X^{w+}X^{w}$. Therefore, F_2 males are half $X^{w+}Y$ (red eyes) and half $X^{W}Y$ (white eyes).

Morgan also made a *reciprocal cross* of the one just described; that is, the phenotypes were switched between the parents. The reciprocal cross here was a white-eyed female ($X^{W}X^{W}$) with a red-eyed male ($X^{w+}Y$) (see Figure 11.8b). All F_1 males had white eyes because they received the X^{W}-bearing chromosome from their mother; thus, their genotype is $X^{W}Y$. The F_1 females have red eyes; they are all heterozygous $X^{w+}X^{w}$. *This result is clearly different from the reciprocal cross shown in Figure 11.8a.*

In the F_2 generation of this second cross, both male and female flies showed a 1:1 ratio of red eyes to white eyes (see Figure 11.8b). Again, this result differs markedly from that of the cross in Figure 11.8a.

In summary, Morgan's work showed that there is a distinctive pattern in the phenotypic ratios for reciprocal crosses in which the gene involved is on the X chromosome. A key indicator of this sex linkage is when all male offspring of a cross between a true-breeding mutant female and a wild-type male have the mutant phenotype. As we have seen, this occurs because a male receives his X chromosome from his female parent.

11.2d Sex-Linked Genes in Humans Are Inherited as They Are in *Drosophila*

For obvious reasons, experimental genetic crosses cannot be conducted with humans. However, a similar analysis can be made by interviewing and testing living members of a family and reconstructing the genotypes and phenotypes of past generations from family records. The results are summarized in a chart called a **pedigree**, which shows all parents and offspring for as many generations as possible, the sex of individuals in the different generations, and the presence or absence of the trait of interest. Females are designated by a circle and males by a square; a solid circle or square indicates the presence of the trait.

In humans, as in fruit flies, sex-linked recessive traits appear more frequently among males than females because males need to receive only one copy of the allele on the X chromosome inherited from their mothers to develop the trait. Females must receive two copies of the recessive allele, one from each parent, to express the trait. Two examples of human sex-linked traits are red–green colour-blindness, a recessive trait

in which the affected individual is unable to distinguish between the colours red and green because of a defect in light-sensing cells in the retina, and hemophilia, a recessive trait in which affected individuals have a defect in blood clotting.

CONCEPT FIX Colour-blindness does not mean that people see only black and white. The inability to see any colour at all is very rare. As shown in Figure 11.16, p. 258, colour-blindness reduces the variety of colours that can be distinguished. ⬡

People with hemophilia are "bleeders"; that is, they bleed uncontrollably if they are injured because a protein required for forming blood clots is not produced in functional form. Males are bleeders if they receive an X chromosome that carries the recessive allele. The disease also develops in females with the recessive allele on both of their X chromosomes—a rare combination. With luck and good care, affected people can reach maturity, but their lives are tightly circumscribed by the necessity to avoid injury. Even internal bleeding from slight bruises can be fatal. The disease, which affects about 1 in 7000 males, can be treated by injection of the required clotting protein.

Hemophilia has had effects reaching far beyond individuals who inherit the disease. The most famous cases occurred in the royal families of Europe descended from Queen Victoria of England **(Figure 11.9, p. 250)**. The disease was not recorded in Queen Victoria's ancestors, so the recessive allele for the trait probably appeared as a spontaneous mutation in the queen or one of her parents. Queen Victoria was heterozygous for the recessive hemophilia allele; that is, she was a **carrier**, meaning that she carried the mutant allele and could pass it on to her offspring, but she did not have symptoms of the disease. A carrier is indicated in a pedigree by a male or female symbol with a central dot.

Note in Queen Victoria's pedigree in Figure 11.9 that Leopold, Duke of Albany, had hemophilia, as did his grandson, Rupert, Viscount Trematon. The trait appears in males in alternate generations (i.e., it skips a generation) because it passes with the X chromosome from mother to son. Mothers do not express the trait because they are heterozygous carriers. The sons, in turn, must pass the X chromosome with the affected allele to their daughters (and the Y chromosome to their sons), as did the Duke of Albany. The appearance of a trait in the males of alternate generations therefore suggests that the allele under study is recessive and carried on the X chromosome.

At one time, 18 of Queen Victoria's 69 descendants were affected males or female carriers. Because so many sons of European royalty were affected, the trait influenced the course of history. In Russia, Crown Prince Alexis was one of Victoria's descendants with hemophilia. His affliction drew together his parents, Czar Nicholas II and Czarina Alexandra (a granddaughter of Victoria and a carrier), and the hypnotic monk Rasputin, who manipulated the family to his advantage by

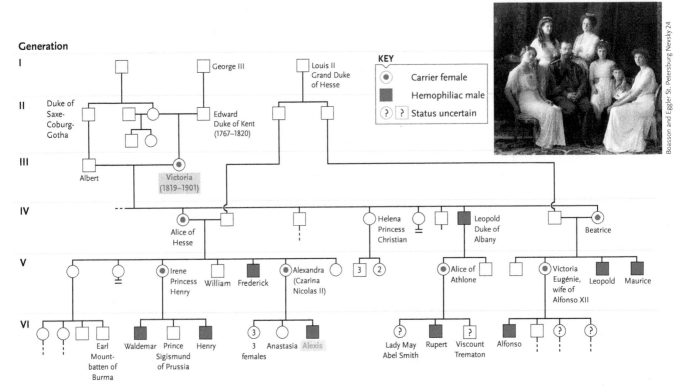

Generation

KEY

- Carrier female
- Hemophiliac male
- ? Status uncertain

Figure 11.9

Inheritance of hemophilia in descendants of Queen Victoria of England. The photograph shows the Russian royal family in which the son, Crown Prince Alexis, had hemophilia. His mother was a carrier of the mutated gene.

convincing them that only he could control the boy's bleeding. The situation helped trigger the Russian Revolution of 1917, which ended the Russian monarchy and led to the establishment of a Communist government in the former Soviet Union, a significant event in twentieth-century history.

Hemophilia affected only sons in the royal lines but could have affected daughters if a hemophiliac son had married a carrier female. Because the disease is rare in the human population as a whole, the chance of such a mating is so low that only a few hemophiliac females have been recorded.

11.2e Inactivation of One X Chromosome Evens out Gene Effects

Although mammalian females have twice as many copies of genes carried on the X chromosome as males, it is unlikely that they require twice as much of the products of those genes. Theoretically, products from genes on the X chromosome could be equalized in males and females if (1) expression of genes on the single male X chromosome were doubled, or (2) expression of genes on both female X chromosomes were halved, or (3) one X chromosome were "turned off" in females. All of these dosage compensation

mechanisms are known in nature, but mammals use the latter; females with two X chromosomes inactivate most of the genes on one X chromosome or the other in most body cells.

As a result of the equalizing mechanism, the activity of most genes carried on the X chromosome is essentially the same in the cells of males and females. The inactivation occurs by a condensation process that folds and packs the chromatin of one of the two X chromosomes into a tightly coiled state similar to the condensed state of chromosomes during cell division. The inactive, condensed X chromosome can be seen within the nucleus in cells of females as a dense mass of chromatin called the **Barr body.**

The inactivation occurs during embryonic development. Which of the two X chromosomes becomes inactive in a particular embryonic cell line is a random event. But once one of the X chromosomes is inactivated in a cell, that same X is inactivated in all descendants of the cell. Thus, within one female, one of the X chromosomes is active in particular cells and inactive in others, and vice versa.

If the two X chromosomes carry different alleles of a gene, one allele will be active in cell lines in which one X chromosome is active, and the other allele will be active in cell lines in which the other X chromosome is active. For many sex-linked alleles, such as the recessive allele that causes hemophilia, random inactivation of either X chromosome has little overall whole-body effect in heterozygous females because the dominant allele is active in enough of the critical cells to produce a normal phenotype. However, for some genes, the inactivation of either X chromosome in heterozygotes produces recognizably different effects in distinct regions of the body.

For example, the orange and black patches of fur in calico cats result from inactivation of one of the two X chromosomes in regions of the skin of heterozygous females (Figure 11.10). Males, which get only one of the two alleles, normally have either black or orange fur. Similarly, in humans, females who are heterozygous for an allele on the X chromosome that blocks development of sweat glands may have a patchy distribution of skin areas with and without the glands. Females with the patchy distribution are not seriously affected and may be unaware of the condition.

As we have seen, the discovery of genetic linkage, recombination, and sex-linked genes led to the elaboration and expansion of Mendel's principles of inheritance. Next, we examine what happens when patterns of inheritance are modified by changes in the chromosomes.

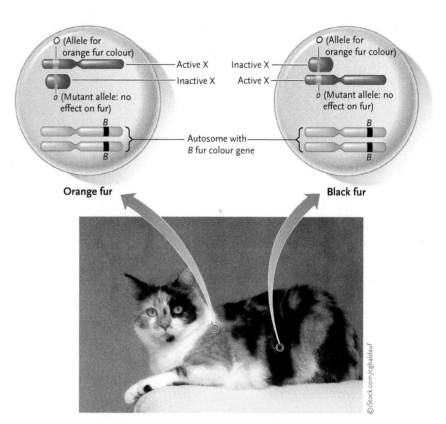

Figure 11.10

A female cat with the calico colour pattern in which patches of orange and black fur are produced by random inactivation of one of the two X chromosomes. Two genes control the black and orange colours: the *O* gene on the X chromosome is for orange fur colour, and the *B* gene on an autosome is for black fur colour. A calico cat has the genotype *Oo BB* (or *Oo Bb*). An orange patch results when the X chromosome carrying the mutant *o* allele is inactivated. In this case, the *O* gene masks the expression of the *B* gene and orange fur is produced. (This in an example of epistasis; see Section 10.2d.) A black patch results when the X chromosome carrying the *O* allele is inactivated. In this case, the mutant *o* allele cannot mask *B* gene expression and black fur results. The white patches result from interactions with a third, autosomal, gene that entirely blocks pigment deposition in the fur.

STUDY BREAK

1. What are the differences in sex chromosomes that underlie sex linkage inheritance patterns?
2. How could you determine if a given gene is sex-linked or not?

11.3 Chromosomal Alterations That Affect Inheritance

Although chromosomes are relatively stable structures, they are sometimes altered by breaks in the DNA, which can be generated by agents such as radiation or certain chemicals or by enzymes encoded in some infecting viruses. The broken chromosome fragments may be lost or they may reattach to the same or different chromosomes. The resulting changes in chromosome structure may have genetic consequences if alleles are eliminated, mixed in new combinations, duplicated, or placed in new locations by the alterations in cell lines that lead to the formation of gametes.

Genetic changes may also occur through changes in chromosome number, including addition or loss of one or more chromosomes or even entire sets of chromosomes. Both chromosomal alterations and changes in chromosome number can be a source of disease and disability, as well as a source of variability during evolution.

11.3a Deletions, Duplications, Translocations, and Inversions Are the Most Common Chromosomal Alterations

Chromosomal alterations after breakages occur in four major forms (Figure 11.11, p. 252):

- A **deletion** occurs if a broken segment is lost from a chromosome.
- A **duplication** occurs if a segment is broken from one chromosome and inserted into its homologue. In the receiving homologue, the alleles in the

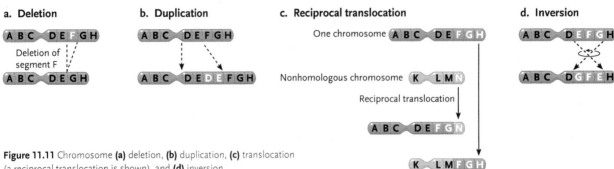

Figure 11.11 Chromosome **(a)** deletion, **(b)** duplication, **(c)** translocation (a reciprocal translocation is shown), and **(d)** inversion.

inserted fragment are added to the ones already there.

- A **translocation** occurs if a broken segment is attached to a different, nonhomologous chromosome.
- An **inversion** occurs if a broken segment reattaches to the same chromosome from which it was lost, but in reversed orientation, so that the order of genes is reversed.

To be inherited, chromosomal alterations must occur or be included in cells of the germ line leading to development of eggs or sperm.

Deletions and Duplications. A deletion (see Figure 11.11a) may cause severe problems if the missing segment contains genes that are essential for normal development or cellular functions. For example, one deletion from human chromosome 5 typically leads to severe cognitive impairment and a malformed larynx. The cries of an affected infant sound more like a meow than a human cry—hence the name of the disorder, *cri-du-chat* (meaning "cat's cry").

A duplication (see Figure 11.11b) may have effects that vary from harmful to beneficial, depending on the genes and alleles contained in the duplicated region. Although most duplications are likely to be detrimental, some have been important sources of evolutionary change. That is, because there are duplicate genes, one copy can mutate into new forms without seriously affecting the basic functions of the organism. For example, mammals have genes that encode several types of hemoglobin that are not present in vertebrates such as sharks that evolved earlier; the additional hemoglobin genes of mammals are believed to have appeared through duplications, followed by mutations in the duplicates that created new and beneficial forms of hemoglobin as further evolution took place. Duplications sometimes arise during recombination in meiosis, if crossing-over occurs unequally, so that a segment is deleted from one chromosome of a homologous pair and inserted into the other.

Translocations and Inversions. In a translocation, a segment breaks from one chromosome and attaches to another, nonhomologous, chromosome. In many cases, a translocation is reciprocal, meaning that two nonhomologous chromosomes exchange segments (see Figure 11.11c). Reciprocal translocations resemble genetic recombination, except that the two chromosomes involved in the exchange do not contain the same genes.

For example, a particular cancer of the human immune system, Burkitt lymphoma, is caused by a translocation that moves a segment of human chromosome 8 to the end of chromosome 14. The break does not interrupt any genes required for normal cell function, but the translocated segment contains a gene that influences cell division. Although this cell division gene is precisely regulated at its normal location, it is overexpressed in the new location. This can result in uncontrolled cell division and the development of a cancer in certain tissues.

In an inversion, a chromosome segment breaks and then reattaches to the same chromosome, but in reverse order (see Figure 11.11d). Inversions have essentially the same effects as translocations—genes may be broken internally by the inversion, with loss of function, or they may be transferred intact to a new location within the same chromosome, producing effects that range from beneficial to harmful.

Inversions and translocations have been important factors in the evolution of plants and some animals, including insects and primates. For example, five of the chromosome pairs of humans show evidence of translocations and inversions that are not present in one of our nearest primate relatives, gorillas. Therefore, the changes must have occurred after the gorilla and human evolutionary lineages split.

11.3b The Number of Entire Chromosomes May Also Change

At times, whole single chromosomes are lost or gained from cells entering or undergoing meiosis, resulting in a change of chromosome number. Most often, these changes occur through **nondisjunction**, the failure of homologous pairs to separate during the first meiotic division, or through misdivision, the failure of chromatids to separate during the second meiotic division (see Chapter 9 and **Figure 11.12**). As a result,

a.

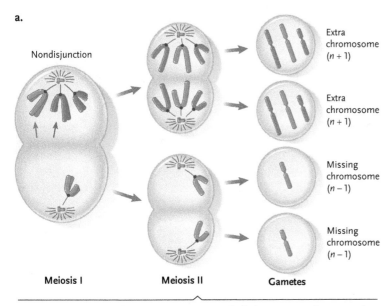

Nondisjunction

Extra chromosome (*n* + 1)

Extra chromosome (*n* + 1)

Missing chromosome (*n* − 1)

Missing chromosome (*n* − 1)

Meiosis I   **Meiosis II**   **Gametes**

Nondisjunction during the first meiotic division causes both chromosomes of one pair to be delivered to the same pole of the spindle. The nondisjunction produces two gametes with an extra chromosome and two with a missing chromosome.

b.

Misdivision

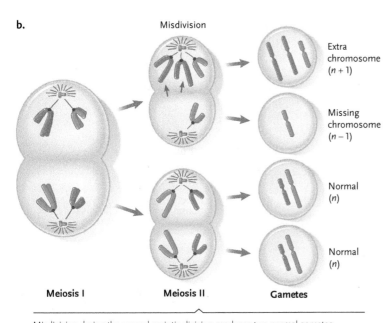

Extra chromosome (*n* + 1)

Missing chromosome (*n* − 1)

Normal (*n*)

Normal (*n*)

Meiosis I   **Meiosis II**   **Gametes**

Misdivision during the second meiotic division produces two normal gametes, one gamete with an extra chromosome, and one gamete with a missing chromosome.

Figure 11.12

(a) Nondisjunction during the first meiotic division and **(b)** misdivision during the second meiotic division.

products of meiosis are produced that lack one or more chromosomes or contain extra copies of the chromosomes. *Note that failure of homologues to disjoin in meiosis I does not affect meiosis II; chromatids will most likely separate normally in meiosis II.* Fertilization by such gametes produces an individual with extra or missing chromosomes. Such individuals are called **aneuploids**,

whereas individuals with a normal set of chromosomes are called **euploids**.

Changes in chromosome number can also occur through duplication of entire sets, meaning individuals may receive one or more extra copies of the entire haploid complement of chromosomes. Such individuals are called **polyploids**. *Triploids* have three copies of each chromosome instead of two; *tetraploids* have four copies of each chromosome. Multiples higher than tetraploids also occur.

Aneuploids. The effects of addition or loss of whole chromosomes vary depending on the chromosome and the species. In animals, aneuploidy of autosomes usually produces debilitating or lethal developmental abnormalities. These abnormalities also occur in humans; addition or loss of an autosomal chromosome causes embryos to develop so abnormally that they are aborted naturally. For reasons that are not understood, aneuploidy is as much as 10 times as frequent in humans as in other mammals. Of human embryos that have been miscarried and examined, about 70% are aneuploids.

In some cases, autosomal aneuploids survive. This is the case with humans who receive an extra copy of chromosome 21—one of the smallest chromosomes **(Figure 11.13a, p. 254)**. Many of these individuals survive well into adulthood. The condition produced by the extra chromosome, called *Down syndrome* or *trisomy 21,* is characterized by short stature and some degree of cognitive impairment. About 40% of individuals with Down syndrome have heart defects, and skeletal development is slower than normal. Most do not mature sexually and remain sterile. However, with attentive care and appropriate educational opportunities, individuals with Down syndrome can successfully participate in many activities.

Most Down syndrome arises from nondisjunction or misdivision of chromosome 21 during meiosis, primarily in women (about 5% of nondisjunctions that lead to Down syndrome occur in men). The

Figure 11.13

Down syndrome.
(a) The chromosomes of a human female with Down syndrome showing three copies of chromosome 21 (circled in red). **(b)** The incidence of Down syndrome increases with the age of the mother, as determined in a study conducted in Victoria, Australia, between 1942 and 1957.

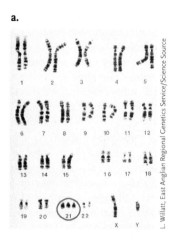

a.

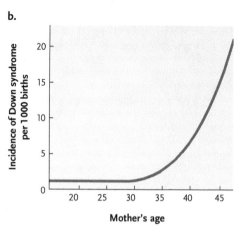

b.

nondisjunction occurs more frequently as women age, increasing the chance that a child may be born with the syndrome (Figure 11.13b). Around the world, about 1 in every 800 children is born with Down syndrome, making it one of the most common serious human genetic defects.

Aneuploidy of sex chromosomes can also arise by nondisjunction or misdivision during meiosis (**Figure 11.14** and **Table 11.1**). Unlike autosomal aneuploidy, which usually has drastic effects on survival, altered numbers of X and Y chromosomes are often tolerated, producing individuals who progress through embryonic development and grow to adulthood. In the case of multiple X chromosomes, the X-chromosome inactivation mechanism converts all but one of the X chromosomes to a Barr body, so the dosage of active X-chromosome genes is the same as in normal XX females and XY males. Triple X females may be taller than usual and may be at higher risk for learning disability, reduced muscle tone, and menstrual irregularities.

Because sexual development in humans is pushed toward male or female reproductive organs primarily by the presence or absence of the *SRY* gene on the Y chromosome, people with a Y chromosome are externally malelike, no matter how many X chromosomes are present. If no Y chromosome is present, X chromosomes in various numbers give rise to femalelike individuals. (Table 11.1 lists the effects of some alterations

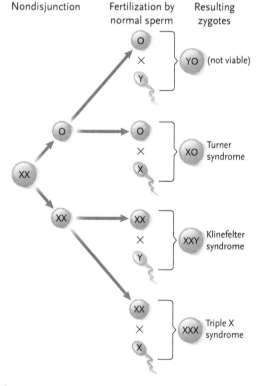

Figure 11.14

Some abnormal combinations of sex chromosomes resulting from nondisjunction of X chromosomes in females.

Table 11.1	Effects of Unusual Combinations of Sex Chromosomes in Humans		
Combination of Sex Chromosomes	Approximate Frequency	Effects	
XO	1 in 5000 births	Turner syndrome: females with underdeveloped ovaries; sterile; intelligence and external genitalia are normal; typically, individuals are short in stature with underdeveloped breasts	
XXY	1 in 2000 births	Klinefelter syndrome: male external genitalia with very small and underdeveloped testes; sterile; intelligence usually normal; sparse body hair and some development of the breasts; similar characteristics in XXXY and XXXXY individuals	
XYY	1 in 1000 births	XYY syndrome: apparently normal males but often taller than average	
XXX	1 in 1000 births	Triple-X syndrome: apparently normal female with normal or slightly delayed mental development	

PEOPLE BEHIND BIOLOGY 11.2

Dr. Irene Ayako Uchida, *McMaster University*

In the early 1940s, the world was at war and Irene Uchida was studying English literature at the University of British Columbia and writing for a student newspaper. On returning home from a visit to Japan, she was prevented from continuing her studies. Fearing a Japanese invasion, and suspecting the Japanese people living on the Pacific coast to be a threat to national security, the Canadian government forced Uchida's family and thousands of other Japanese-Canadians to relocate to internment camps in the interior of British Columbia. During this difficult time, Uchida was head of a school for the children of internees.

She was later able to resume her education, this time at the University of Toronto, where she was encouraged to take up the field of genetics rather than her intended career in social work. Graduating with a Ph.D. in 1951, Uchida became a pioneer in the emerging field of medical cytogenetics and an international authority on the relationship between radiation and trisomies such as 18 and 21 (Down syndrome).

Uchida was made an officer of the Order of Canada in 1993, and retired in 1995 after a long and rewarding career. She died in 2013.

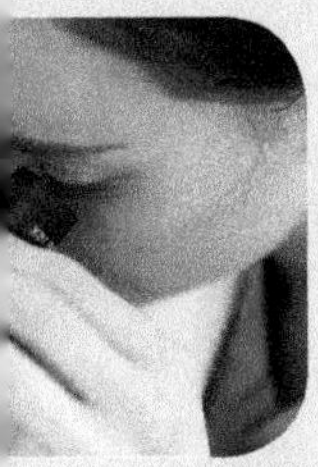

in sex chromosome number.) Similar abnormal combinations of sex chromosomes also occur in other animals, including *Drosophila,* with varying effects on viability.

Polyploids. Polyploidy often originates from failure of the spindle to function normally during mitosis in cell lines leading to germ-line cells. In these divisions, the spindle fails to separate the duplicated chromosomes, which are therefore incorporated into a single nucleus with twice the usual number of chromosomes. Eventually, meiosis takes place and produces products with two copies of each chromosome instead of one. Fusion of one such gamete with a normal haploid gamete produces a triploid zygote, and fusion of two such gametes produces a tetraploid zygote.

The effects of polyploidy vary widely between plants and animals. In plants, polyploids are often hardier and more successful in growth and reproduction than the diploid plants from which they were derived. As a result, polyploidy is common and has been an important source of variability in plant evolution. About half of all flowering plant species are polyploids, including important crop plants such as wheat and other cereals, cotton, and strawberries. One particularly widespread use of polyploids is in triploid bananas. Since triploid plants have difficulty disjoining homologues properly in meiosis, they are often sterile or, in this case, seedless.

By contrast, polyploidy is uncommon among animals because it usually has lethal effects during embryonic development. For example, in humans, all but about 1% of polyploids die before birth, and the few who are born die within a month. The lethality is probably due to disturbance of animal developmental pathways, which are typically much more complex than those of plants.

We now turn to a description of the effects of altered alleles on human health and development.

STUDY BREAK

What mechanisms are responsible for
(a) duplication of a chromosome segment,
(b) generation of a Down syndrome individual,
(c) a chromosome translocation, and
(d) polyploidy?

11.4 Human Genetics and Genetic Counselling

We have already noted a number of human genetic traits and conditions caused by mutant alleles or chromosomal alterations (see **Table 11.2, p. 256,** for a more detailed list). All of these traits are of interest as examples of patterns of inheritance that amplify and extend Mendel's basic principles. Those with harmful effects are also important because of their impact on human life and society.

11.4a In Autosomal Recessive Inheritance, Heterozygotes Are Carriers and Homozygous Recessives Are Affected by the Trait

Sickle cell disease and cystic fibrosis are examples of human traits caused by recessive alleles on autosomes. Alleles of these particular traits code for defective proteins that function poorly, if at all. Many other human genetic traits follow a similar pattern of inheritance (see Table 11.2, p. 256). These traits are passed on

Table 11.2	Examples of Human Genetic Traits
Trait	Adverse Health Effects
Autosomal Recessive Inheritance	
Albinism	Absence of pigmentation (melanin)
Attached earlobes	None
Cystic fibrosis	Excess mucus in lungs and digestive cavities
Sickle cell disease	Severe tissue and organ damage
Galactosemia	Brain, liver, and eye damage
Phenylketonuria	Severe cognitive impairment.
Tay–Sachs disease	Severe cognitive impairment, death
Autosomal Dominant Inheritance	
Free earlobes	None
Achondroplasia	Defective cartilage formation that causes dwarfism
Early balding in males	None
Campodactyly	Rigid, bent small fingers
Curly hair	None
Huntington disease	Progressive, irreversible degeneration of nervous system
Syndactyly	Webbing between fingers
Polydactyly	Extra digits
Brachydactyly	Short digits
Progeria	Premature aging
X-Linked Inheritance	
Hemophilia A	Deficient blood clotting
Red–green colour-blindness	Inability to distinguish red from green
Testicular feminizing syndrome	Absence of male organs, sterility
Changes in Chromosome Structure	
Cri-du-chat	Severe cognitive impairment, malformed larynx
Changes in Chromosome Number	
Down syndrome	Developmental delays, cognitive impairment, heart defects

according to the pattern known as **autosomal recessive inheritance**, in which individuals who are homozygous for the dominant allele are free of symptoms and are not carriers; heterozygotes are usually symptom free but are carriers. People who are homozygous for the recessive allele show the trait.

Between 10% and 15% of African Americans in the United States are carriers of sickle cell disease—that is, they have the sickle cell trait (see Section 10.2a). Although carriers make enough normal hemoglobin through the activity of the dominant allele to be essentially unaffected, the mutant, sickle cell form of the hemoglobin molecule is also present in their red blood cells. Carriers can be identified by a simple test for the mutant hemoglobin. In countries where malaria is common, including several countries in Africa, sickle cell carriers are less susceptible to contracting malaria, which helps explain the increased proportions of the recessive allele among races that originated in malarial areas.

Cystic fibrosis, one of the most common genetic disorders among people of Northern European descent, is another autosomal recessive trait **(Figure 11.15)**. About 1 in every 25 people from this line of descent is an unaffected carrier with one copy of the recessive allele, and about 1 in 2500 is homozygous for the recessive allele. The homozygous recessives have an altered membrane transport protein that results in excess Cl$^-$ (chloride ions) in the extracellular fluids. Through pathways that are not completely understood, the alteration in chloride transport causes thick, sticky mucus to collect in airways of the lungs, in the ducts of glands such as the pancreas, and in the digestive tract. The accumulated mucus impairs body functions and, in the lungs, promotes pneumonia and other infections. With current management procedures, the life expectancy for a person with cystic fibrosis is about 40 years. The prevalence of cystic fibrosis alleles may have a similar explanation to those for sickle cell disease; heterozygotes may enjoy some resistance to infectious diseases such as tuberculosis or cholera.

Another autosomal recessive disease, *phenylketonuria* (PKU), appears in about 1 of every 15 000 births. Affected individuals cannot produce an enzyme that converts the amino acid phenylalanine to another amino acid, tyrosine. As a result, phenylalanine builds up in the blood and is converted into other products, including phenylpyruvate. Elevations in both phenylalanine and phenylpyruvate damage brain tissue and

Figure 11.15
A child affected by cystic fibrosis. Daily chest thumps, back thumps, and repositioning dislodge thick mucus that collects in airways to the lungs.

FOCUS ON RESEARCH 11.3
Achondroplastic Dwarfing by a Single Amino Acid Change

Researchers recently found that the gene responsible for achondroplastic dwarfing is on chromosome 4. The gene codes for a receptor that binds the *fibroblast growth factor* (*FGF*), a growth hormone that stimulates a wide range of mammalian cells to grow and divide. This fibroblast growth factor receptor (FGFR) gene is active in chondrocytes—cells that form cartilage and bone.

Arnold Munnich and his colleagues isolated the gene that encodes the FGFR and obtained its DNA sequence. They found two versions of the gene's sequence with a single difference—one version had an adenine–thymine (A-T) base pair and the other had a guanine–cytosine (G-C) base pair at the same position in the DNA

sequence. The change substitutes arginine for glycine at one position in the amino acid sequence of the encoded protein. Arginine and glycine have very different chemical properties. The substitution occurs in a segment of the protein that extends across the membrane, connecting a hormone-binding site outside the cell with a site inside the cell that triggers the internal response.

The investigators then looked for the A-T–to–G-C substitution in the mutant form of the gene on chromosome 4 that causes achondroplastic dwarfing. The substitution was present in copies of the gene isolated from 6 families of achondroplastic dwarfs but absent in 120 people who lack the trait. This result supported the hypothesis that a

mutant allele of the FGFR on chromosome 4 is responsible for achondroplastic dwarfism.

How does the single amino acid substitution cause dwarfing? The cause is not known exactly. The change may inhibit the transmission of the signal triggered by a hormone binding to the receptor on the outer membrane. As a result, chondrocytes divide improperly and inhibit normal elongation of the limb bones. This helps explain why the achondroplasia mutation is dominant.

Identification of the gene responsible for achondroplastic dwarfing opens the future to finding a cure for the condition, possibly through gene therapy for infants or young children who carry the mutation.

---

can lead to cognitive impairment. However, if diagnosed early enough, an affected infant can be placed on a phenylalanine-restricted diet, which can prevent the PKU symptoms. Screening newborns for PKU is routine in the developed world and is becoming more established in the developing world as well. This is a wonderful example of how the expression of a genetic trait can be influenced by the environment.

You may have seen warnings on certain foods and drinks for phenylketonuriacs (individuals with PKU) not to use them. This is because they contain the artificial sweetener aspartame (trade name NutraSweet). Aspartame is a small molecule consisting of the amino acids aspartic acid and phenylalanine. Aspartame binds to taste receptors, signalling that the substance is sweet. Once ingested, aspartame is broken down and phenylalanine is released in amounts that might be harmful for people with PKU.

11.4b In Autosomal Dominant Inheritance, Only Homozygous Recessives Are Unaffected

Some human traits follow a pattern of **autosomal dominant inheritance** (see Table 11.2). In this case, the allele that causes the trait is dominant, and people who are either homozygous or heterozygous for the dominant allele are affected. Individuals homozygous for the recessive normal allele are unaffected.

Achondroplasia, a type of dwarfing that occurs in about 1 in 10 000 people, is caused by an autosomal dominant allele of a gene on chromosome 4. Of individuals with the dominant allele, only heterozygotes survive embryonic development; homozygous dominants are usually stillborn. When limb bones develop in heterozygous children, cartilage formation is defective, leading to disproportionately short arms and legs. The trunk and head, however, are of normal size. Affected adults are usually not much more than 122 cm tall. Achondroplastic dwarfs are of normal intelligence, are fertile, and can have children.

11.4c Males Are More Likely to Be Affected by X-Linked Recessive Traits

Red–green colour-blindness **(Figure 11.16, p. 258)** and hemophilia have already been presented as examples of human traits that demonstrate **X-linked recessive inheritance**, that is, traits due to inheritance of recessive alleles carried on the X chromosome. Another X-linked recessive human disease trait is Duchenne muscular dystrophy. In affected individuals, muscle tissue begins to degenerate late in childhood; by the onset of puberty, most individuals with this disease are unable to walk. Muscular weakness progresses, with later involvement of the heart muscle; the average life expectancy for individuals with Duchenne muscular dystrophy is 25 years.

Figure 11.16

Punnett square showing sex-linked recessive inheritance of colour-blindness in humans. Note that the mother carries the defective allele on one of her X chromosomes but is unaffected. Half of her daughters will be carriers and half of her sons will be colour-blind. Images indicate how the normal and colour-blind sons perceive a particular flower and leaves.

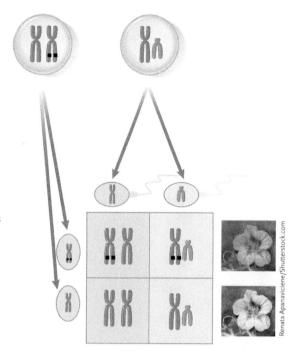

Renata Apanaviciene/Shutterstock.com

11.4d Human Genetic Disorders Can Be Predicted, and Many Can Be Treated

Each year, roughly 8 million children around the world are born with a severe disease or disability with a significant genetic component. The rate of such births in middle- and low-income countries is double that for high-income countries. Why might this be? One contributing factor has already been mentioned: in areas where malaria is endemic, the frequency of the sickle cell allele tends to be higher and the incidence of new-born sickle cell disease is higher. Nutritional deficiencies, consanguinous (blood relative) marriage practices, and higher numbers of children born to older mothers may also elevate birth defect rates in certain societies. In addition to improvements in basic financial, health, and nutritional standards, programs offering genetic counselling, prenatal diagnosis, and genetic screening can help reduce the suffering associated with genetic disorders.

Genetic counselling allows prospective parents to assess the possibility that they might have an affected child. For example, parents may seek counselling if they, a close relative, or one of their existing children has a genetic disorder. Genetic counselling begins with identification of parental genotypes through pedigrees or direct testing for an altered protein or DNA sequence. With this information in hand, counsellors can often predict the chances of having a child with the trait in question. Couples can then make an informed decision about whether to have a child.

Genetic counselling is often combined with techniques of **prenatal diagnosis**, in which cells derived from a developing embryo or its surrounding tissues or fluids are tested for the presence of mutant alleles or chromosomal alterations. In **amniocentesis**, cells are obtained from the amniotic fluid—the watery fluid surrounding the embryo in the mother's uterus **(Figure 11.17)**. In **chorionic villus sampling**, cells are obtained from portions of the placenta that develop from tissues of the embryo. More than 100 genetic disorders can now be detected by these tests. If prenatal diagnosis detects a serious genetic defect, the prospective parents

Figure 11.17

Amniocentesis, a procedure used for prenatal diagnosis of genetic defects. The procedure is complicated and costly, and, therefore, it is used primarily in high-risk cases.

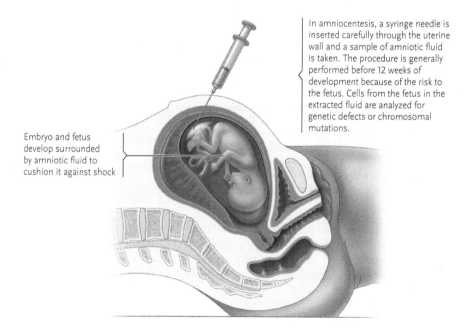

Embryo and fetus develop surrounded by amniotic fluid to cushion it against shock

In amniocentesis, a syringe needle is inserted carefully through the uterine wall and a sample of amniotic fluid is taken. The procedure is generally performed before 12 weeks of development because of the risk to the fetus. Cells from the fetus in the extracted fluid are analyzed for genetic defects or chromosomal mutations.

can reach an informed decision about whether to continue the pregnancy, including religious and moral considerations, as well as genetic and medical advice.

Once a child is born, inherited disorders are identified by **genetic screening**, in which biochemical or molecular tests for disorders are routinely applied to children and adults or to newborn infants in hospitals. The tests can detect inherited disorders early enough to start any available preventive measures before symptoms develop. As mentioned previously, worldwide newborn screening for PKU identifies affected children in time for them to avoid the debilitating symptoms of this disease. The first generation of people to survive childhood with PKU are now adults.

The characters and traits described so far in this chapter all depend on genes carried by chromosomes in the nucleus. But what of the genes located on DNA in mitochondria and chloroplasts? The following section addresses such interesting cases.

STUDY BREAK

1. What inheritance pattern would suggest that a trait is dominant and carried on an autosome?
2. How are inherited disorders detected before symptoms arise?

11.5 Nontraditional Patterns of Inheritance

We consider two examples of nontraditional patterns of inheritance in this section. In **cytoplasmic inheritance**, the pattern of inheritance follows that of genes in the cytoplasmic organelles: mitochondria or chloroplasts. In **genomic imprinting**, the expression of an allele of a particular nuclear gene is based on whether an individual organism inherits the allele from the male or female parent.

11.5a Cytoplasmic Inheritance Follows the Pattern of Inheritance of Mitochondria or Chloroplasts

Organelle DNA contains genes and alleles that, like nuclear genes, are also subject to being mutated. Mutant genes in some cases result in altered phenotypes, but the inheritance pattern of these mutant genes is fundamentally different from that of mutant genes carried on chromosomes in the nucleus. The two major differences are as follows: (1) ratios typical of Mendelian segregation are *not* found because genes are not segregating by meiosis, and (2) genes usually show uniparental inheritance from generation to generation. In *uniparental inheritance,* all progeny (both males and females) inherit the genotype of only one of the parents. For most multicellular eukaryotes, the mother's

genotype is passed on in a phenomenon called *maternal inheritance.* Maternal inheritance occurs because the amount of cytoplasm in the female gamete usually far exceeds that in the male gamete. Hence, a zygote receives most of its cytoplasm, including mitochondria and (in plants) chloroplasts, from the female ("egg" parent) and little from the male parent.

CONCEPT FIX Many people believe that they inherit half of their DNA from each of their parents. Although this idea is roughly true for nuclear DNA, recall that mitochondria also contain DNA and they are inherited exclusively from mothers. You have considerably more of your mother's DNA than your father's. ⬡

In humans, several inherited diseases have been traced to mutations in mitochondrial genes (Table 11.3). Recall that the mitochondrion plays a critical role in synthesizing adenosine triphosphate (ATP), the energy source for many cellular reactions. The mutations producing the diseases in Table 11.3 are in mitochondrial genes that encode components of the ATP-generating system of the organelle. The resulting mitochondrial defects are especially destructive to the organ systems most dependent on mitochondrial reactions for energy: the central nervous system, skeletal and cardiac muscle, the liver, and the kidneys. These inherited diseases show maternal inheritance.

11.5b In Gene Imprinting, the Allele Inherited from One of the Parents Is Expressed whereas the Other Allele Is Silent

Genomic imprinting is a phenomenon in which the expression of an allele of a gene is determined by the parent that contributed it. In some cases, the paternally derived allele is expressed; in others, the maternally derived allele is expressed. The silent allele—the one that is not expressed—is called the *imprinted allele.* The imprinted allele is not inactivated by mutation. Rather, it is silenced by chemical modification (methylation) of certain bases in its sequence.

Table 11.3	Some Human Diseases Caused by Mutations in Mitochondrial Genes	
Disease	**Symptoms**
Kearns–Sayre syndrome	May include muscle weakness, mental deficiencies, abnormal heartbeat, short stature
Leber hereditary optic neuropathy	Vision loss from degeneration of the optic nerve, abnormal heartbeat
Mitochondrial myopathy and encephalomyopathy	May include seizures, strokelike episodes, hearing loss, progressive dementia, abnormal heartbeat, short stature
Myoclonic epilepsy	Vision and hearing loss, uncoordinated movement, jerking of limbs, progressive dementia, heart defects

As an example of how imprinting is involved in human disease, Prader–Willi syndrome (PWS) and Angelman syndrome (AS) in humans are both caused by genomic imprinting of a particular gene on a chromosome inherited from one parent, coincident with deletion of the same gene on the homologous chromosome inherited from the other parent. The syndromes differ with respect to the gene imprinted. Both PWS and AS occur in about 1 in 15 000 births and are characterized by serious developmental, mental, and behavioural problems. PWS individuals are compulsive overeaters (leading to obesity), have short stature, have small hands and feet, and show mild to moderate cognitive impairment. AS individuals are hyperactive, are unable to speak, have seizures, show severe cognitive impairment, and display a happy disposition with bursts of laughter.

How is genomic imprinting responsible for these two syndromes? PWS is caused when an individual has a normal maternally derived chromosome 15 and a paternally derived chromosome 15 with a deletion of a small region of several genes that includes the PWS gene. The PWS gene is imprinted, and therefore silenced, on maternally derived chromosomes. As a result, when there is no PWS gene on the paternally derived chromosome, there is no PWS gene activity, and PWS results. Similarly, AS is caused when an individual has a normal paternally derived chromosome 15 and a maternally derived chromosome 15 with a deletion of the same region; that region also includes the AS gene, the normal function of which is also required for normal development. In this case, genomic imprinting silences the AS gene on the paternally derived chromosome, and because there is no AS gene on the maternally derived chromosome, there is no AS gene activity, and AS syndrome develops.

CONCEPT FIX Although imprinted traits can show a *parent of origin effect*, imprinting is not the same as sex-linkage. Imprinted traits are not necessarily carried on sex chromosomes, and any given sex-linked allele can be inherited from either a mother or a father. ⬡

The mechanism of imprinting involves the modification of the DNA in the region that controls the expression of a gene by the binding or regulatory proteins, resulting in the addition of methyl (–CH3) groups to cytosine nucleotides. The methylation of the control region of a gene usually prevents it from being expressed. The regulation of gene expression by methylation of DNA is discussed further in Section 14.2. Genomic imprinting occurs in the gametes where the allele destined to be inactive in the new embryo after fertilization—either the father's or the mother's, depending on the gene—is methylated. That methylated (silenced) state of the gene is passed on as the cells grow and divide to produce the somatic (body) cells of the organism.

A number of cancers are associated with the failure to imprint genes. For instance, the mammalian *Igf2* (insulin growth factor 2) gene encodes a growth factor, a molecule that stimulates cells to grow and divide. *Igf2* is an imprinted gene, with the paternally derived allele "on" and the maternally derived allele "off." In some cases, the imprinting mechanism for this gene does not work, resulting in both alleles of *Igf2* being active, a phenomenon known as **loss of imprinting**. The resulting double dose of the growth factor disrupts the cell division cycle, increasing the risk of uncontrolled growth and cancer.

In this chapter, we have discussed genes and the role of chromosomes in inheritance. In the next chapter, we will turn to the molecular structure and function of the genetic material and learn about the molecular mechanism by which DNA is replicated.

STUDY BREAK

Which inheritance pattern would suggest that a trait is coded by the mitochondrial genome?

Review

 aplia

To access course materials such as Aplia and other companion resources, please visit www.NELSONbrain.com.

11.1 Genetic Linkage and Recombination

- Genes consist of sequences of nucleotides in DNA and are arranged linearly in chromosomes.
- Genes carried on the same chromosome are linked in their transmission from parent to offspring. Linked genes are inherited in patterns similar to those of single genes, except for changes in the linkage due to recombination (see Figure 11.2).
- As a result of recombination, the order of a particular collection of alleles linked on any given chromosome is mixed up as a result of exchange with corresponding alleles on the other homologous chromosome. The exchanges occur while homologues pair during prophase I of meiosis.
- The likelihood of recombination between any two genes located on the same chromosome pair reflects the physical distance between them on the chromosome. The greater this distance, the greater the chance that chromatids will exchange segments at points between the genes and the greater the frequency of recombinant products of meiosis (gametes in animals, spores in plants).

- The relationship between separation and recombinant offspring frequencies is used to produce chromosome maps in which genes are assigned relative locations with respect to each other (see Figure 11.4).
- Testcrosses ($AaBb \times aabb$) can be used to detect linkage. If all progeny classes are equally frequent, then the genes are not linked.
- Genes carried on the same chromosome may not show genetic linkage (i.e., assort independently) if they are quite far apart.

11.2 Sex-Linked Genes

- Sex linkage is a pattern of inheritance produced by genes carried on sex chromosomes: chromosomes that differ between males and females. Sex-linked inheritance patterns arise because, in humans and fruit flies, females have two copies of the X chromosome and therefore two alleles for each gene. Males have only one copy of the X chromosome and therefore only one allele for each gene. Only males have an allele for genes carried on the Y chromosome.
- Sex linkage is suggested by a particular, non-Mendelian pattern of inheritance when the progeny of reciprocal crosses are different (see Figure 11.8).
- Since males have only one X chromosome, any recessive alleles that they inherit on that X chromosome will be expressed. Females must receive two copies of the recessive allele, one from each parent, to develop the trait (see Figures 11.6–11.8).
- In mammals, inactivation of one of the two X chromosomes in cells of the female makes the dosage of X-linked genes the same in males and females (see Figure 11.10).
- Parents can influence the expression of certain alleles in their offspring through DNA methylation called imprinting.

11.3 Chromosomal Alterations That Affect Inheritance

- Inheritance is influenced by processes that delete, duplicate, or invert segments within chromosomes or translocate segments between chromosomes (see Figure 11.11).
- Chromosomes also change in number by addition or removal of individual chromosomes or entire sets of chromosomes. Changes in single chromosomes usually occur through nondisjunction, in which homologous pairs fail to separate during meiosis I, or by misdivision, when sister chromatids fail to separate during meiosis II. As a result, one set of meiotic products receives an extra copy of a chromosome and the other set is deprived of the chromosome.

- Polyploids have one or more extra copies of the entire chromosome set. Polyploids usually arise when the spindle fails to function during meiosis in cell lines leading to gamete formation, producing zygotes that contain double the number of chromosomes typical for the species (see Figures 11.12–11.14).

11.4 Human Genetics and Genetic Counselling

- Three modes of inheritance are most significant in human heredity: autosomal recessive, autosomal dominant, and X-linked recessive inheritance.
- In autosomal recessive inheritance, males or females carry a recessive allele on an autosome. Heterozygotes are carriers that are usually unaffected, but homozygous individuals show symptoms of the trait. Affected children born to unaffected parents suggest autosomal recessive inheritance.
- In autosomal dominant inheritance, a dominant gene is carried on an autosome. Individuals that are homozygous or heterozygous for the trait show symptoms of the trait; homozygous recessives are normal.
- In X-linked recessive inheritance, a recessive allele for the trait is carried on the X chromosome. Male individuals with the recessive allele on their X chromosome or female individuals with the recessive allele on both X chromosomes show symptoms of the trait. Heterozygous females are carriers but usually show no symptoms of the trait.
- Genetic counselling, based on identification of parental genotypes by constructing family pedigrees and prenatal diagnosis, allows prospective parents to reach an informed decision about whether to have a child or continue a pregnancy.

11.5 Nontraditional Patterns of Inheritance

- Cytoplasmic inheritance depends on genes carried on DNA in mitochondria or chloroplasts. Cytoplasmic inheritance follows the maternal line: it parallels the inheritance of the cytoplasm in fertilization, in which most or all of the cytoplasm of the zygote originates from the egg cell. That is, all of the offspring of affected mothers would be affected; none of the offspring of affected fathers would be affected.
- Genomic imprinting is a phenomenon in which the expression of an allele of a gene is determined by the parent that contributed it. In some cases, the allele inherited from the father is expressed; in others, the allele from the mother is expressed. The silencing of the other allele is often the result of methylation of the region adjacent to the gene that is responsible for controlling the expression of that gene.

Questions

Self-Test Questions

1. In humans, red–green colour-blindness is an X-linked recessive trait. If a man with normal vision and a colour-blind woman have a son, what is the chance that the son will be colour-blind? What is the chance that a daughter will be colour-blind?

2. The following pedigree shows the pattern of inheritance of red–green colour-blindness in a family. Females are shown as circles and males as squares; the squares or circles of individuals affected by the trait are filled in black.

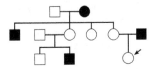

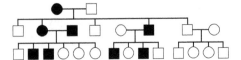

What is the chance that a son of the third-generation female indicated by the arrow will be colour-blind if the father is a normal man? If the father is colour-blind?

3. Individuals affected by a condition known as polydactyly have extra fingers or toes. The following pedigree shows the pattern of inheritance of this trait in one family:

From the pedigree, can you tell if polydactyly comes from a dominant or recessive allele? Is the trait sex linked? As far as you can determine, what is the genotype of each person in the pedigree with respect to the trait?

4. A number of genes carried on the same chromosome are tested and show the following cross-over frequencies. What is their sequence in the map of the chromosome?

Genes	Cross-over Frequencies between Them
C and A	7%
B and D	3%
B and A	4%
C and D	6%
C and B	3%

5. In *Drosophila*, two genes, one for body colour and one for eye colour, are carried on the same chromosome. The wild-type grey body colour is dominant to black body colour, and wild-type red eyes are dominant to purple eyes. You make a cross between a fly with a grey body and red eyes and a fly with a black body and purple eyes. Among the offspring, about half have grey bodies and red eyes and half have black bodies and purple eyes. A small percentage have (a) black bodies and red eyes or (b) grey bodies and purple eyes. Which alleles are carried together on the chromosomes in each of the flies used in the cross? Which alleles are carried together on the chromosomes of the F₁ flies with black bodies and red eyes, and those with grey bodies and purple eyes?

6. Another gene in *Drosophila* determines wing length. The dominant wild-type allele of this gene produces long wings; a recessive allele produces vestigial (short) wings. A female that is true-breeding for red eyes and long wings is mated with a male that has purple eyes and vestigial wings.

F₁ females are then crossed with purple-eyed, vestigial-winged males. From this second cross, a total of 600 offspring are obtained with the following combinations of traits:

252 with red eyes and long wings
276 with purple eyes and vestigial wings
42 with red eyes and vestigial wings
30 with purple eyes and long wings

Are the genes linked, unlinked, or sex linked? If they are linked, how many map units separate them on the chromosome?

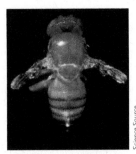

Drosophila with vestigial wings

7. One human gene, which is suspected to be carried on the Y chromosome, controls the length of hair on men's ears. One allele produces nonhairy ears, and another produces hairy ears. If a man with hairy ears has sons, what percentage will also have hairy ears? What percentage of his daughters will have hairy ears?

8. You conduct a cross in *Drosophila* that produces only half as many male as female offspring. What might you suspect as a cause?

Questions for Discussion

1. Can a linkage map be made for a haploid organism that reproduces sexually?

2. Crossing-over does not occur between any pair of homologous chromosomes during meiosis in male *Drosophila*. From what you have learned about meiosis and crossing-over, propose one hypothesis for why this might be the case.

3. Even though X inactivation occurs in XXY (Klinefelter syndrome) humans, they do not have the same phenotype as normal XY males. Similarly, even though X inactivation occurs in XX individuals, they do not have the same phenotype as XO (Turner syndrome) humans. Why might this be the case?

4. All mammals have evolved from a common ancestor. However, the chromosome number varies among mammals. By what mechanism might this have occurred?

5. Assume that genes *a, b, c, d, e,* and *f* are linked. Explain how you would construct a linkage map that shows the order of these six genes and the map units between them.

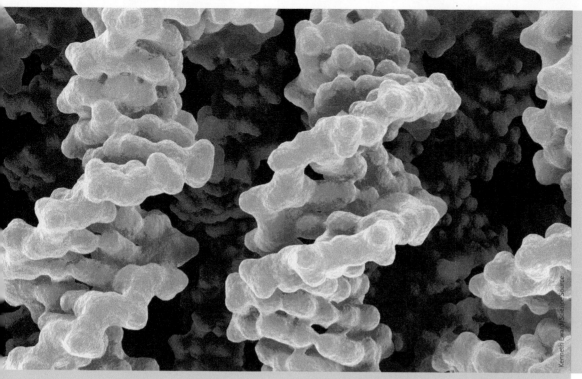

A digital model of DNA (based on data generated by X-ray crystallography).

Kenneth Eward/Science Source

DNA Structure, Replication, and Organization

WHY IT MATTERS

Imagine a scene 40 thousand years ago in what is now called the Drachenlock Cave in Switzerland. Flickering torchlight reflects from a collection of large bear skulls as a Neanderthal shaman arranges one, then the next, to face toward the entrance to the cave. Now fast-forward to the present to find cave bear bones and teeth once again carefully arranged by human hands, this time on the bench of a modern, ultraclean research laboratory. The scientist is completely covered by a protective gown, gloves, and a face mask. The surface of the specimens is bleached and irradiated with high-intensity ultraviolet light. A small drill bores into the interior of a molar tooth, where researchers hope to recover ancient DNA (aDNA) from *Ursus spelaeus*, a long-extinct relative of modern bears.

As much as characterization of aDNA sequences promises to enhance our understanding of the genetic history and composition of modern populations, this field is overshadowed by two significant problems: DNA damage and contamination. The double helix of DNA is subject to breakages in one or both strands in addition to inappropriate cross-linking and chemical modification of individual bases. Living cells very successfully prevent or repair most of this DNA damage, but post-mortem degradation can be extensive after thousands of years. Sustained cold temperatures preserve aDNA relatively well, facilitating successful recovery of sequences from frozen mammoths and bison in **permafrost**, penguins in ice, and the human "Ice Man" frozen in a glacier. Ancient bacterial DNA sequences have been recovered from 500 thousand-year-old sections of ice cores, and the complete genome has been sequenced from a 700 thousand-year-old horse bone recovered from permafrost.

The natural degradation of DNA over time usually means that aDNA sequences remaining in a given tissue sample are very rare and therefore prone to contamination by DNA from modern or ancient sources—hence the need for ultraclean laboratories, decontamination procedures, and authentication protocols. Suspicions of contamination have clouded some of the most dramatic reports of aDNA recovery from specimens 10 to 100 million years old.

As the future brings better techniques for the recovery and characterization of authentic aDNA sequences on Earth, we will undoubtedly turn these skills toward the search for evidence of past or present life on other planets. The Martian polar ice caps are very cold and very persistent, providing ideal conditions for preservation of DNA from any organisms that may have inhabited the Red Planet in the past.

Our current ability to find, characterize, and manipulate DNA arises ultimately from the work of a Swiss physician and physiological chemist, Johann Friedrich Miescher. In 1868, Miescher was engaged in a study of the composition of the cell nucleus. He collected pus cells from discarded bandages and extracted large quantities of an acidic substance with a high phosphorus content. He called the unusual substance *nuclein*. Nuclein is now known by its modern name, **deoxyribonucleic acid**, or **DNA**, the molecule that is the genetic material of all living organisms and, as indicated by ancient DNA studies, all extinct organisms as well.

At the time of Miescher's discovery, scientists knew nothing about the molecular basis of heredity and very little about genetics. Although Mendel had already published the results of his genetic experiments with garden peas, the significance of his findings was not widely known or appreciated. It was not known which chemical substance in cells actually carries the instructions for reproducing parental traits in offspring. Not until 1952, more than 80 years after Miescher's discovery, did scientists fully recognize that the hereditary molecule was DNA.

After DNA was established as the hereditary molecule, the focus of research changed to the three-dimensional structure of DNA. Among the scientists striving to work out the structure were James D. Watson, a young American postdoctoral student at Cambridge University in England, and the Englishman Francis H.C. Crick, then a graduate student at Cambridge University. Using chemical and physical information about DNA, in particular Rosalind Franklin's analysis of the arrangement of atoms in DNA, the two investigators assembled molecular models from pieces of cardboard and bits of wire. Eventually, they constructed a model for DNA that fit all the known data **(Figure 12.1)**. Their discovery was of momentous importance in biology. The model enabled scientists to understand key processes in cells for the first time in terms of the structure and interaction of molecules. For example, the model immediately made

Figure 12.1
James D. Watson and Francis H.C. Crick demonstrating their 1953 model for DNA structure, which revolutionized the biological sciences.

it possible to understand how genetic information is stored in the structure of DNA and how DNA replicates. Unquestionably, the discovery launched a molecular revolution within biology, making it possible for the first time to relate the genetic traits of living organisms to a universal molecular code present in the DNA of every cell. In addition, Watson and Crick's discovery opened the way for numerous advances in fields such as medicine, forensics, pharmacology, and agriculture and eventually gave rise to the current rapid growth of the biotechnology industry.

12.1 Establishing DNA as the Hereditary Molecule

In the first half of the twentieth century, many scientists believed that proteins were the most likely candidates for the hereditary molecules because they appeared to offer greater opportunities for information coding than did nucleic acids. That is, proteins contain 20 types of amino acids, whereas nucleic acids have only 4 different nitrogenous bases available for coding. Other scientists believed that nucleic acids were the hereditary molecules. In this section, we describe the experiments showing that DNA, not protein, is the genetic material.

12.1a Experiments Began When Griffith Found a Substance That Could Genetically Transform Pneumonia Bacteria

In 1928, Frederick Griffith, a British medical officer, observed an interesting phenomenon in his experiments with the bacterium *Streptococcus pneumoniae*, which causes a severe form of pneumonia in mammals. Griffith was trying to make a vaccine to prevent pneumonia infections in the epidemics that occurred after World War I. He used two strains of the bacterium in his attempts. The smooth strain, S, has a polysaccharide capsule surrounding each cell and forms colonies that appear smooth and glossy when grown on a culture plate. When he injected the S strain into mice, it was virulent (highly infective, or pathogenic), causing pneumonia and killing the mice in a day or two (**Figure 12.2**, step 1). The rough strain, R, does not have a polysaccharide capsule and forms colonies with a nonshiny, rough appearance. When Griffith injected the R strain into mice, it was avirulent (not infective, or nonpathogenic); the mice lived (step 2). Evidently, the capsule was responsible for the virulence of the S strain. We now know that the capsule hinders the ability of the host's immune system to detect the *Streptococcus* cells. The smooth strain could therefore live long enough to multiply and cause fatal pneumonia.

If Griffith killed the S bacteria by heating before injecting them into the mice, the mice remained healthy (step 3). However, quite unexpectedly, Griffith found that if he injected living R bacteria along with the heat-killed S bacteria, many of the mice died (step 4). Also, he was able to isolate living S bacteria with polysaccharide capsules from the infected mice. In some way, living R bacteria had acquired the ability to make the polysaccharide capsule from the dead S bacteria, and they had changed—transformed—into virulent S cells. The transformed bacteria were altered permanently; the smooth, infective trait was stably inherited by the descendants of the transformed bacteria. Griffith called the conversion of R bacteria to S bacteria *transformation* and the agent responsible the *transforming principle*. What was the nature of the molecule responsible for the transformation? Carbohydrates, lipids, proteins, and nucleic acids are the four main types of biological macromolecules. The structure of carbohydrates and lipids tends to be highly repetitive and therefore not very likely to carry information. However, proteins and nucleic acids are built of various combinations of different amino acids and nucleotides, respectively. This gives them a complexity of structure that makes them likely candidates for carrying the information needed for transformation.

12.1b Avery and His Coworkers Identified DNA as the Molecule That Transforms Avirulent Rough *Streptococcus* to the Virulent Smooth Form

In the 1940s, Oswald Avery, a physician and medical researcher at the hospital at the Rockefeller Institute for Medical Research in New York, and his coworkers, Colin MacLeod and Maclyn McCarty, performed an experiment designed to identify the chemical nature of the

QUESTION: What is the nature of the genetic material?

EXPERIMENT: Frederick Griffith studied the conversion of a nonvirulent (noninfective) R form of the bacterium *Streptococcus pneumoniae* to a virulent (infective) S form. The S form has a capsule surrounding the cell, giving colonies of it on a laboratory dish a smooth, shiny appearance. The R form has no capsule, so the colonies have a rough, nonshiny appearance. Griffith injected the bacteria into mice and determined how the mice were infected.

1 Mice injected with live S cells (control to show effect of S cells)

2 Mice injected with live R cells (control to show effect of R cells)

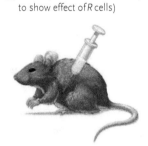

RESULT: Mice die. Live S cells in their blood; shows that S cells are virulent.

RESULT: Mice live. No live R cells in their blood; shows that R cells are nonvirulent. Evidently the capsule is responsible for virulence of the S strain.

3 Mice injected with heat-killed S cells (control to show effect of dead S cells)

4 Mice injected with heat-killed S cells plus live R cells

RESULT: Mice live. No live S cells in their blood; shows that live S cells are necessary to be virulent to mice.

RESULT: Mice die. Live S cells in their blood; shows that living R cells can be converted to virulent S cells with some factor from dead S cells.

CONCLUSION: Griffith concluded that some molecules released when S cells were killed could change living nonvirulent R cells genetically to the virulent S form. He called the molecule the *transforming principle* and the process of genetic change *transformation*.

Experimental Research Figure 12.2 Griffith's experiment with infective and noninfective strains of *Streptococcus pneumoniae*.

transforming principle that can change the avirulent *rough* form of *Streptococcus* bacteria into the infective *smooth* form. Rather than working with mice, they attempted to reproduce the transformation using bacteria growing in culture tubes. They used heat to kill virulent S bacteria and then treated the macromolecules extracted from the cells with enzymes that break down each of the three main candidate molecules for the hereditary material—protein; DNA; and the other nucleic acid, ribonucleic acid (RNA). When they destroyed proteins or RNA, the researchers saw no effect;

the extract of *S* bacteria still transformed *R* bacteria into virulent *S* bacteria—the cells had polysaccharide capsules and produced smooth colonies on culture plates. When they destroyed DNA, however, no transformation occurred—no smooth colonies were seen on culture plates.

In 1944, Avery and his colleagues published their discovery that the transforming principle was DNA. At the time, many scientists firmly believed that the genetic material was protein. So although their findings were clearly revolutionary, Avery and his colleagues presented their conclusions in the paper cautiously, offering several interpretations of their results. Although some scientists accepted these data almost immediately, others remained unconvinced. After all, it seemed unlikely that a molecule like DNA, with only four different components (adenine, thymine, cytosine, and guanine), could hold the complex information required of the genetic material in a cell. Protein, with its 20 different amino acid components, seemed a far superior medium for coding information. Those who believed that the genetic material was protein argued that it was possible that not all protein was destroyed by Avery's enzyme treatments, and, as contaminants in their DNA transformation reaction, these remaining proteins were, in fact, responsible for the transformation. Further experiments were needed to convince all scientists that DNA is the hereditary molecule.

12.1c Hershey and Chase Found the Final Evidence Establishing DNA as the Hereditary Molecule

A final series of elegant experiments conducted in 1952 by bacteriologist Alfred D. Hershey and his laboratory assistant Martha Chase at the Cold Spring Harbor Laboratory removed any remaining doubts that DNA is the hereditary molecule. Hershey and Chase studied the infection of the bacterium *Escherichia coli* by bacteriophage T2. *Escherichia coli* is a bacterium normally found in the intestines of mammals. **Bacteriophages** (or simply **phages;** see Chapters 9 and 23) are viruses that infect bacteria. A **virus** is an infectious agent that contains either DNA or RNA surrounded by a protein coat. Viruses cannot reproduce except in a host cell. When a virus infects a cell, it can use the cell's resources to produce more virus particles.

The phage replication cycle begins when a phage attaches to the surface of a bacterium. For phages such as T2, the infected cell quickly stops producing its own molecules and instead starts making progeny phages. After about 100 to 200 phages are assembled inside the bacterial cell, a viral enzyme breaks down the cell wall, killing the cell and releasing the new phages. The whole cycle takes approximately 90 minutes.

The T2 phage that Hershey and Chase studied consists of only a core of DNA surrounded by proteins.

Therefore, one of these molecules must be the genetic material that enters the bacterial cell and directs the infective cycle within. But which one? Hershey and Chase prepared two batches of phages, one with the protein tagged with a radioactive label and the other with the DNA tagged with a radioactive label. To obtain labelled phages, they added T2 to *E. coli* growing in the presence of either the radioactive isotope of sulfur (^{35}S) or the radioactive isotope of phosphorus (^{32}P) (**Figure 12.3,** step 1). The progeny phages produced in the ^{35}S medium had labelled proteins and unlabelled DNA because sulfur is a component of proteins but not of DNA. The phages produced in the ^{32}P medium had labelled DNA and unlabelled proteins because phosphorus is a component of DNA but not of proteins.

Hershey and Chase then infected separate cultures of *E. coli* with the two types of labelled phages (step 2). After a short period to allow the genetic material to enter the bacterial cell, they mixed the bacteria in a kitchen blender. They reasoned that only the genetic material was injected into the bacterial cell, leaving the rest of the phage outside. By mixing the cells in a blender, they could shear off the phage parts that did not enter the bacteria and collect them separately for analysis.

When they infected the bacteria with phages that contained labelled protein coats, they found no **radioactivity** in the bacterial cells but could easily measure it in the material removed by the blender (step 3, top). They also found no radioactivity in the progeny phages (step 4, top). However, if the infecting phages contained radioactive DNA, they found radioactivity inside the infected bacteria but none in the phage coats removed by the blender (step 3, bottom). In addition, radioactivity *was* seen in the progeny phages (step 4, bottom). The results were unequivocal: the genetic material of the phage was DNA, not protein.

When taken together, the experiments of Griffith, Avery and his coworkers, and Hershey and Chase established that DNA, not proteins, carries genetic information. Their research also established the term *transformation,* which is still used in molecular biology. **Transformation** is the conversion of a cell's hereditary type by the uptake of DNA released by the breakdown of another cell, as in the Griffith and Avery experiments. Having identified DNA as the hereditary molecule, scientists turned next to determining its structure.

STUDY BREAK

How did Hershey and Chase exploit the reproductive cycle of a phage to gain evidence for DNA as the hereditary material?

QUESTION: Is DNA or protein the genetic material?

EXPERIMENT: Hershey and Chase performed a definitive experiment to show whether DNA or protein is the genetic material. They used phage T2 for their experiment; it consists only of DNA and protein.

1. They infected *E. coli* growing in the presence of radioactive ^{32}P or ^{35}S with phage T2. The progeny phages were labelled either in their protein with ^{35}S (top), or in their DNA with ^{32}P (bottom).
2. Separate cultures of *E. coli* were infected with the radioactively labelled phages.
3. After a short period of time to allow the genetic material to enter the bacterial cell, the bacteria were mixed in a blender. The blending sheared from the cell surface the phage coats that did not enter the bacteria. The components were analyzed for radioactivity.
4. Progeny phages were analyzed for radioactivity.

RESULT: No radioactivity within cell; ^{35}S in phage coat.

RESULT: No radioactivity in progeny phages.

RESULT: ^{32}P within cell; not in phage coat.

RESULT: ^{32}P in progeny phages.

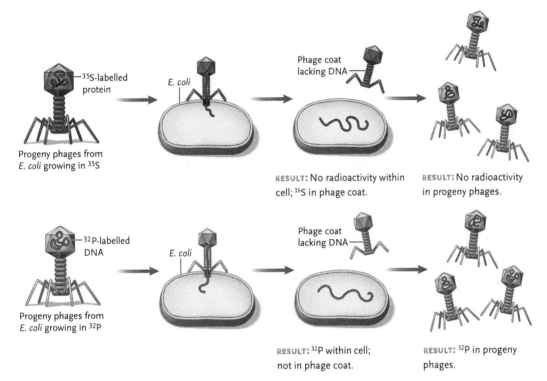

CONCLUSION: ^{32}P, the isotope used to label DNA, was found within phage-infected cells and in progeny phages, indicating that DNA is the genetic material. ^{35}S, the **radioisotope** used to label proteins, was found in phage coats after infection but was not found in the infected cell or in progeny phages, showing that protein is not the genetic material.

Experimental Research Figure 12.3 The Hershey and Chase experiment demonstrating that DNA is the hereditary molecule.

12.2 DNA Structure

The experiments that established DNA as the hereditary molecule were followed by a highly competitive scientific race to discover the structure of DNA. The race ended in 1953 when Watson and Crick elucidated the structure of DNA, ushering in a new era of molecular biology.

12.2a Watson and Crick Brought Together Information from Several Sources to Work Out DNA Structure

Before Watson and Crick began their research, other investigators had established that DNA contains four different nucleotides. Each nucleotide consists of the five-carbon sugar *deoxyribose* (carbon atoms on deoxyribose are numbered with primes from 1′ to 5′);

a phosphate group; and one of the four nitrogenous bases—adenine (A), guanine (G), thymine (T), and cytosine (C) **(Figure 12.4)**. Two of the bases, **adenine** and **guanine**, are *purines*, nitrogenous bases built from a pair of fused rings of carbon and nitrogen atoms. The other two bases, **thymine** and **cytosine**, are *pyrimidines*, built from a single carbon ring. An organic chemist, Erwin Chargaff, measured the amounts of nitrogenous bases in DNA and discovered that they occur in definite ratios. He observed that the number of purines equals the number of pyrimidines, but, more specifically, the amount of adenine equals the amount of thymine, and the amount of guanine equals the amount of cytosine; these relationships are known as *Chargaff's rules.*

Researchers had also determined that DNA contains nucleotides joined to form a *polynucleotide chain*. In a polynucleotide chain, the deoxyribose sugars are linked by phosphate groups in an alternating sugar–phosphate–sugar–phosphate pattern, forming a **sugar–phosphate backbone** (highlighted in grey in Figure 12.4). Each phosphate group is a "bridge" between the 3′ carbon of one sugar and the 5′ carbon of the next sugar; the entire linkage, including the bridging phosphate group, is called a **phosphodiester bond**.

The polynucleotide chain of DNA has polarity, or directionality. That is, the two ends of the chain are not the same: at one end, a phosphate group is bound to the 5′ carbon of a deoxyribose sugar, whereas at the other end, a **hydroxyl group** is bonded to the 3′ carbon of a deoxyribose sugar (see Figure 12.4). Consequently, the two ends are called the **5′ end** and the **3′ end**, respectively.

These were the known facts when Watson and Crick began their collaboration in the early 1950s. However, the number of polynucleotide chains in a DNA molecule and the manner in which they fold or twist in DNA were unknown. Watson and Crick themselves did not conduct experiments to study the structure of DNA; instead, they used the research data of others for their analysis, relying heavily on data gathered by physicist Maurice H.F. Wilkins and research associate Rosalind Franklin **(Figure 12.5a)** at King's College, London. These researchers were using **X-ray diffraction** to study the structure of DNA (Figure 12.5b). In X-ray diffraction, an X-ray beam is directed at a molecule in the form of a regular solid, ideally in the form of a crystal. Within the crystal, regularly arranged atoms bend and reflect the X-rays into smaller beams that exit the crystal at definite angles determined by the arrangement of atoms in the structure of the crystal. If a photographic film is placed behind the crystal, the exiting beams produce a pattern of exposed spots. From that pattern, researchers can deduce the positions of the atoms in the crystal.

Wilkins and Franklin did not have DNA crystals to work with, but they were able to obtain X-ray diffraction

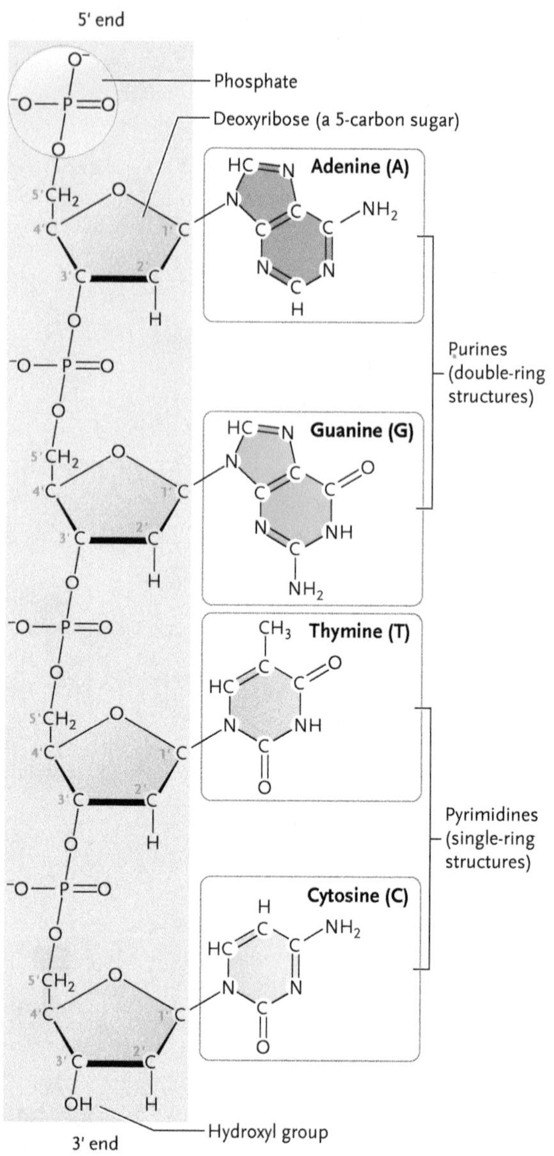

Figure 12.4
The four nucleotide subunits of DNA, linked into a polynucleotide chain. The sugar–phosphate backbone of the chain is highlighted in grey. The connection between adjacent deoxyribose sugars is a phosphodiester bond. The polynucleotide chain has polarity: at one end (5′), a phosphate group is bound to the 5′ carbon of a deoxyribose sugar, whereas at the other end (3′), a hydroxyl group is bound to the 3′ carbon of a deoxyribose sugar.

patterns from a sample of DNA molecules that had been pulled out into a fibre (see Figure 12.5). The patterns indicated that the DNA molecules within the fibre were cylindrical and about 2 nm in diameter. Separations between the spots showed that major patterns of atoms repeat at intervals of 0.34 nm and 3.4 nm within the DNA. Franklin correctly interpreted an X-shaped distribution of spots in the diffraction pattern (see dashed lines in Figure 12.5) to mean that DNA has a helical structure.

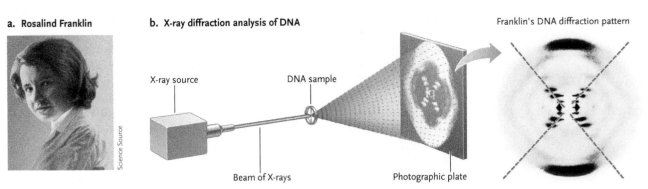

a. Rosalind Franklin

b. X-ray diffraction analysis of DNA

Franklin's DNA diffraction pattern

X-ray source

DNA sample

Beam of X-rays

Photographic plate

Science Source

Science Source

Figure 12.5

X-ray diffraction analysis of DNA. **(a)** Rosalind Franklin. **(b)** The X-ray diffraction method to study DNA and the diffraction pattern Rosalind Franklin obtained. The X-shaped pattern of spots (dashed lines) was correctly interpreted by Franklin to indicate that DNA has a helical structure similar to a spiral staircase.

12.2b The New Model Proposed That Two Polynucleotide Chains Wind into a DNA Double Helix

Watson and Crick constructed scale models of the four DNA nucleotides and fitted them together in different ways until they arrived at an arrangement that satisfied both Wilkins's and Franklin's X-ray data and Chargaff's chemical analysis. Watson and Crick's trials led them to a double-stranded model for DNA structure in which two polynucleotide chains twist around each other in a right-handed way, like a double-spiral staircase **(Figure 12.6, p. 270)**. They were the first to propose the famous double-helix model for DNA.

In the **double-helix model**, the two sugar–phosphate backbones are separated from each other by a regular distance. The bases extend into and fill this central space. A purine and a pyrimidine, if paired together, are exactly wide enough to fill the space between the backbone chains in the double helix. However, a purine–purine base pair is too wide to fit the space exactly, and a pyrimidine–pyrimidine pair is too narrow. From Chargaff's data, Watson and Crick proposed that the purine–pyrimidine base pairs in DNA are A-T and G-C pairs. That is, wherever an A occurs in one strand, a T must be opposite it in the other strand; wherever a G occurs in one strand, a C must be opposite it. This feature of DNA is called **complementary base-pairing**, and one strand is said to be *complementary* to the other. The base pairs, which fit together like pieces of a jigsaw puzzle, are stabilized by hydrogen bonds—two between A and T and three between G and C (see Figure 12.6; hydrogen bonds are discussed in *The Purple Pages*). The hydrogen bonds between the paired bases, repeated along the double helix, hold the two strands together in the helix.

CONCEPT Although this text follows the generally common convention of referring to the DNA double helix as a *DNA molecule,* you should be aware that this terminology is, strictly speaking, inaccurate. If a molecule is defined as a collection of atoms connected by covalent bonds, then *each* of the two sugar–phosphate backbones of the double helix qualifies as a molecule. The double helix is technically composed of *two* polynucleotide molecules held together by hydrogen bonds. ⬡

The base pairs lie in flat planes almost perpendicular to the long axis of the DNA helix. In this state, each base pair occupies a length of 0.34 nm along the long axis of the double helix (see Figure 12.6). This spacing accounts for the repeating 0.34 nm pattern noted in the X-ray diffraction patterns. The larger 3.4 nm repeat pattern was interpreted to mean that each full turn of the double helix takes up 3.4 nm along the length of the molecule; therefore, 10 base pairs are packed into a full turn.

Watson and Crick also realized that the two strands of a double helix fit together in a stable chemical way only if they are **antiparallel**, that is, only if they run in opposite directions (see Figure 12.6, arrows). In other words, the 3′ *end* of one strand is opposite the 5′ *end* of its complementary strand. This antiparallel arrangement is highly significant for the process of replication, which is discussed in the next section.

As hereditary material, DNA must faithfully store and transmit genetic information for the entire life cycle of an organism. Watson and Crick recognized that this information is coded into the DNA by the particular sequence of the four nucleotides. This sequence is preserved by robust covalent bonds between the molecules in a DNA double helix. Although only four different kinds of nucleotides exist, combining them in groups allows an essentially infinite number of different sequences to be "written," just as the 26 letters of the alphabet can be combined in groups to write a virtually unlimited number of words. Chapter 13 shows how taking the four nucleotides in groups of three forms enough words to spell out the structure of any conceivable protein.

Watson and Crick announced their model for DNA structure in a brief but monumental paper published in the journal *Nature* in 1953. Watson and Crick shared a Nobel Prize with Wilkins in 1962 for their discovery

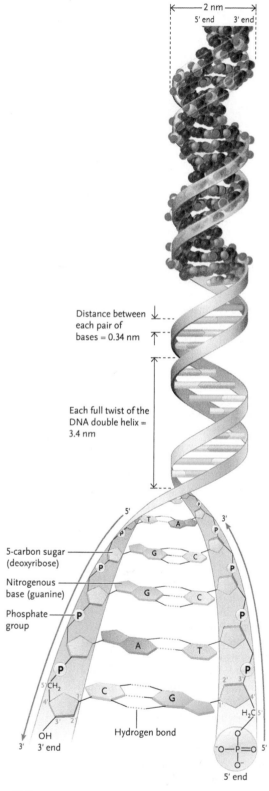

Figure 12.6

DNA double helix. Arrows and labelling of the ends show that the two polynucleotide chains of the double helix are antiparallel—that is, they have opposite polarity in that they run in opposite directions. In the space-filling model at the top, the spaces occupied by atoms are indicated by spheres. There are 10 base pairs per turn of the helix; only 8 base pairs are visible because the other 2 are obscured where the backbones pass over each other.

Labels in figure: 2 nm; 5' end; 3' end; Distance between each pair of bases = 0.34 nm; Each full twist of the DNA double helix = 3.4 nm; 5-carbon sugar (deoxyribose); Nitrogenous base (guanine); Phosphate group; Hydrogen bond; OH; 3' end; 5' end

of the molecular structure of DNA. Rosalind Franklin might have been a candidate for a Nobel Prize had she not died of cancer at age 38 in 1958. (The Nobel Prize is normally given only to living investigators.) Unquestionably, Watson and Crick's discovery of DNA structure opened the way to molecular studies of genetics and heredity, leading to our modern understanding of gene structure and action at the molecular level.

STUDY BREAK

1. Which bases in DNA are purines? Which are pyrimidines?
2. What bonds form between complementary base pairs? Between a base and the deoxyribose sugar?
3. Which features of the DNA molecule did Watson and Crick describe?

12.3 DNA Replication

Once they had discovered the structure of DNA, Watson and Crick realized immediately that complementary base-pairing could explain how DNA replicates (**Figure 12.7**). They imagined that, for replication, the hydrogen bonds between the two strands break, allowing them to unwind and separate. Each strand then acts as a template for the synthesis of its partner. When replication is complete, there are two double helices, each with one strand derived from the parental DNA molecule base-paired with a newly synthesized one. Most important, each of the two new double helices consists of the identical base-pair sequences as the parental DNA.

The model of replication Watson and Crick proposed is termed **semiconservative replication** (**Figure 12.8a, p. 272**). Other scientists proposed two other models for replication. In the *conservative replication model,* each of the two strands of original DNA serves as a template for a new DNA double helix (Figure 12.8b). After the two complementary copies separate from their templates, they wind together into an all "new" DNA double helix. In the *dispersive replication model,* neither parental molecule remains intact; both chains of each replicated double helix contain old and new segments (Figure 12.8c, p. 272).

12.3a Meselson and Stahl Showed That DNA Replication Is Semiconservative

A definitive experiment published in 1958 by Matthew Meselson and Franklin Stahl of the California Institute of Technology demonstrated that DNA replication is semiconservative (**Figure 12.9, p. 273**). In their experiment, Meselson and Stahl had to be able to distinguish parental DNA molecules from newly synthesized

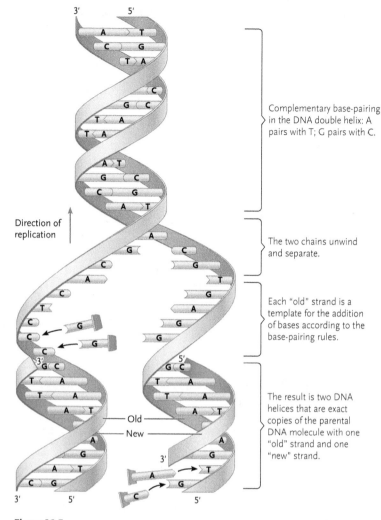

Figure 12.7

Watson and Crick's model for DNA replication. The original DNA is shown in grey. A new polynucleotide chain (red) is assembled on each original chain as they unwind. The template and complementary copy chains remain together when replication is complete, producing DNA double helices that are half old and half new. The model is known as the semiconservative model for DNA replication.

Complementary base-pairing in the DNA double helix: A pairs with T; G pairs with C.

The two chains unwind and separate.

Each "old" strand is a template for the addition of bases according to the base-pairing rules.

The result is two DNA helices that are exact copies of the parental DNA molecule with one "old" strand and one "new" strand.

Direction of replication

Old

New

of the cells and extracted the DNA (step 3).

Meselson and Stahl then mixed the DNA samples with cesium chloride (CsCl) and centrifuged the mixture at very high speed (step 4). During the centrifugation, the CsCl forms a density gradient and DNA double helices move to a position in the gradient where their density matches that of the CsCl. Therefore, DNA of different densities is separated into bands, with the densest DNA settling closer to the bottom of the tube. In Figure 12.9 "Result" shows the outcome of these experiments, and "Conclusions" shows why the results were compatible with only the semiconservative replication model.

12.3b DNA Polymerases Are the Primary Enzymes of DNA Replication

During replication, complementary polynucleotide chains are assembled from individual deoxyribonucleotides by enzymes known as **DNA polymerases**. More than one kind of DNA polymerase is required for DNA replication in all cells. *Deoxyribonucleoside triphosphates* are the substrates for the polymerization reaction catalyzed by DNA polymerases **(Figure 12.10, p. 274)**. A nucleoside triphosphate is a nitrogenous base linked to a sugar, which is linked, in turn, to a chain of three phosphate groups. You have encountered a nucleoside triphosphate before, namely the ATP produced in cellular respiration (see Chapter 6). In that case, the sugar is ribose, making ATP a ribonucleoside triphosphate. The deoxyribonucleoside triphosphates used in DNA replication have the sugar *deoxyribose* rather than the sugar *ribose*. Because four different bases are found in DNA—adenine (A), guanine (G), cytosine (C), and thymine (T)—four different deoxyribonucleoside triphosphates are used for DNA replication. In keeping with the ATP naming convention, the deoxyribonucleoside triphosphates for DNA replication are given the short names dATP, dGTP, dCTP, and dTTP, where the "d" stands for "deoxyribose."

Figure 12.10, p. 274, presents a section of a DNA polynucleotide chain being replicated, showing how DNA polymerase catalyzes the assembly of a new DNA strand that is complementary to the template strand. To understand Figure 12.10, remember that the carbons

DNA. To do this, they used a nonradioactive "heavy" nitrogen isotope to tag the parental DNA. The heavy isotope, ^{15}N, has one more neutron in its nucleus than the normal ^{14}N isotope. Molecules containing ^{15}N are measurably heavier (denser) than molecules of the same type containing ^{14}N.

As the first step in their experiment, Meselson and Stahl grew *E. coli* bacteria in a culture medium containing the heavy ^{15}N isotope (see Figure 12.9, step 1). The heavy isotope was incorporated into the nitrogenous bases of DNA, resulting in the entire DNA being labelled with ^{15}N. Then they transferred the bacteria to a culture medium containing the light ^{14}N isotope (step 2). All new DNA synthesized after the transfer contained the light isotope. Just before the transfer to the medium with the ^{14}N isotope, and after each round of replication following the transfer, they took a sample

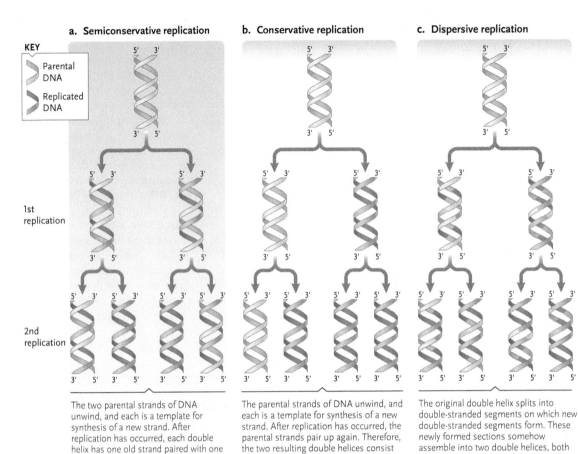

Figure 12.8
Three theoretical models for DNA replication. Experimental data support the semiconservative mechanism.

a. Semiconservative replication

KEY

Parental DNA

Replicated DNA

1st replication

2nd replication

The two parental strands of DNA unwind, and each is a template for synthesis of a new strand. After replication has occurred, each double helix has one old strand paired with one new strand. This model was the one proposed by Watson and Crick themselves.

b. Conservative replication

The parental strands of DNA unwind, and each is a template for synthesis of a new strand. After replication has occurred, the parental strands pair up again. Therefore, the two resulting double helices consist of one with two old strands, and the other with two new strands.

c. Dispersive replication

The original double helix splits into double-stranded segments on which new double-stranded segments form. These newly formed sections somehow assemble into two double helices, both of which are a mixture of the original double-stranded DNA interspersed with new double-stranded DNA.

in the deoxyriboses of nucleotides are numbered with primes. Each DNA strand has two distinct ends: the 5′ end has an exposed phosphate group attached to the 5′ carbon of the sugar, and the 3′ end has an exposed hydroxyl group attached to the 3′ carbon of the sugar. As you learned earlier, because of the antiparallel nature of the DNA strands within a double helix, the 5′ end of one strand is opposite the 3′ end of the other. DNA polymerase can add a nucleotide *only* to the 3′ end of an existing nucleotide chain. As a new DNA strand is assembled, a 3′ –OH group is always exposed at its "newest" end; the "oldest" end of the new chain has an exposed 5′ phosphate. DNA polymerases are therefore said to assemble nucleotide chains in the 5′ → 3′ direction.

Because of the antiparallel nature of DNA, the template strand is "read" in the 3′ → 5′ direction for this new synthesis. DNA polymerases of bacteria, archaeans, and eukaryotes all consist of several polypeptide subunits arranged to form different domains (see polypeptides in *The Purple Pages*). The polymerases share a shape that is said to resemble a partially closed human right hand in which the template DNA lies over the "palm" in a groove formed by the "fingers" and "thumb" **(Figure 12.11a, p. 275)**. The palm domain is evolutionarily related among the polymerases of

bacteria, archaea, and eukaryotes, while the finger and thumb domains are different sequences in each of these three types of organisms. The template strand does not pass through the tunnel formed by the thumb and finger domains, however. Instead, the template strand and the 3′ –OH of the new strand meet at the active site for the polymerization reaction of DNA synthesis, located in the palm domain. A nucleotide is added to the new strand when an incoming dNTP enters the active site carrying a base complementary to the template strand base positioned in the active site. By moving along the template strand, one nucleotide at a time, DNA polymerase extends the new DNA strand, as we saw in Figure 12.10.

Figure 12.11b, p. 275, shows the representation of DNA polymerase used in the following DNA replication figures, and it also shows a sliding DNA clamp. The **sliding DNA clamp** is a protein that encircles the DNA and binds to the rear of the DNA polymerase in terms of the enzyme's forward movement during replication. The function of the sliding DNA clamp is to tether the DNA polymerase to the template strand. Tethering the DNA polymerase makes replication more efficient because without it, the enzyme will detach from the template after only a few dozen polymerizations.

Experimental Research Figure 12.9 The Meselson and Stahl experiment demonstrating that the semiconservative model is correct.

QUESTION: Does DNA replicate semiconservatively?

EXPERIMENT: Matthew Meselson and Franklin Stahl proved that the semiconservative model of DNA replication is correct and that the conservative and dispersive models are incorrect.

1 Bacteria grown in ^{15}N (heavy) medium. The heavy isotope is incorporated into the bases of DNA, resulting in all the DNA being heavy, that is, labelled with ^{15}N.

2 Bacteria transferred to ^{14}N (light) medium and allowed to grow and divide for several generations. All new DNA is light.

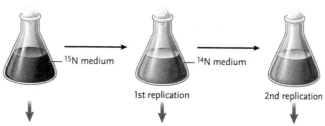

^{15}N medium → 1st replication → ^{14}N medium → 2nd replication

3 DNA extracted from bacteria cultured in ^{15}N medium and after each generation in ^{14}N medium.

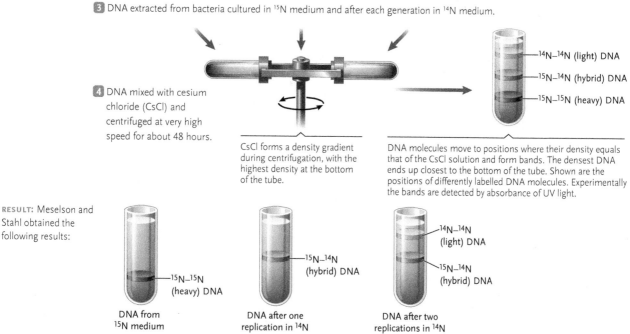

4 DNA mixed with cesium chloride (CsCl) and centrifuged at very high speed for about 48 hours.

^{14}N–^{14}N (light) DNA
^{15}N–^{14}N (hybrid) DNA
^{15}N–^{15}N (heavy) DNA

CsCl forms a density gradient during centrifugation, with the highest density at the bottom of the tube.

DNA molecules move to positions where their density equals that of the CsCl solution and form bands. The densest DNA ends up closest to the bottom of the tube. Shown are the positions of differently labelled DNA molecules. Experimentally the bands are detected by absorbance of UV light.

RESULT: Meselson and Stahl obtained the following results:

^{15}N–^{15}N (heavy) DNA

DNA from ^{15}N medium

^{15}N–^{14}N (hybrid) DNA

DNA after one replication in ^{14}N

^{14}N–^{14}N (light) DNA
^{15}N–^{14}N (hybrid) DNA

DNA after two replications in ^{14}N

CONCLUSION: The predicted DNA banding patterns for the three DNA replication models were as follows:

	^{15}N medium	One replication in ^{14}N	Two replications in ^{14}N	
Semiconservative				√ Matches results
Conservative				X Does not match results
Dispersive				X Does not match results

The results support the semiconservative model.

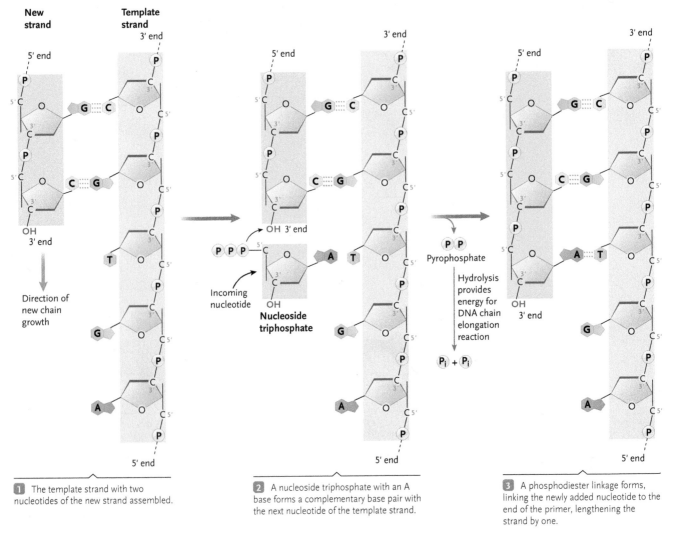

New strand   **Template strand**

1 The template strand with two nucleotides of the new strand assembled.

2 A nucleoside triphosphate with an A base forms a complementary base pair with the next nucleotide of the template strand.

3 A phosphodiester linkage forms, linking the newly added nucleotide to the end of the primer, lengthening the strand by one.

Figure 12.10

Reactions assembling a complementary chain in the 5′ → 3′ direction on a template DNA strand, showing the phosphodiester linkage created when the DNA polymerase enzyme adds each nucleotide to the chain.

But, with the clamp, many tens of thousands of polymerizations occur before the enzyme detaches. Overall, the rate of DNA synthesis is much faster because of the sliding DNA clamp.

In sum, the key molecular events of DNA replication are as follows:

1. The two strands of the DNA molecule unwind for replication to occur.
2. DNA polymerase can add nucleotides only to an existing chain.
3. The overall direction of new synthesis is in the 5′ → 3′ direction, which is a direction antiparallel to that of the template strand.
4. Nucleotides enter into a newly synthesized chain according to the A-T and G-C complementary base-pairing rules.

The following sections describe how enzymes and other proteins conduct these molecular events. Our focus is on the well-characterized replication system of *E. coli*. Replication in archaeans and eukaryotes is highly similar, although there are differences in the replication machinery. The replication machinery of archaeans is strikingly similar to that of eukaryotes and is clearly different from that of bacteria.

12.3c Helicases Unwind DNA for New DNA Synthesis, and Other Proteins Stabilize the DNA at the Replication Fork

In semiconservative replication, the two strands of the parental DNA molecule unwind and separate to expose the template strands for new DNA synthesis **(Figure 12.12, p. 276).** Unwinding of the DNA for replication occurs at a small, specific sequence in the bacterial chromosome known as the **origin of replication** (*ori*). Specific proteins bind to an *ori* sequence and, in turn, promote binding of **DNA helicase,** which

a. Bacterial DNA polymerase

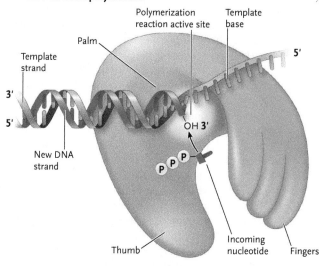

b. How a DNA polymerase and sliding clamp are shown in the book

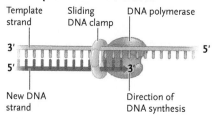

Figure 12.11

DNA polymerase structure. **(a)** Stylized drawing of a bacterial DNA polymerase. The enzyme viewed from the side resembles a human right hand. The polymerization reaction site lies on the palm. When the incoming nucleotide is added, the thumb and fingers close over the site to facilitate the reaction. **(b)** How DNA polymerase is shown in subsequent figures of DNA replication. The figure also shows a sliding DNA clamp tethering the DNA polymerase to the template strand.

unwinds the DNA strands. The unwinding produces a Y-shaped structure called a **replication fork**, which consists of the two unwound template strands transitioning to double-helical DNA.

Single-stranded binding proteins (SSBs) coat the exposed single-stranded DNA segments, stabilizing the DNA and keeping the two strands from pairing back together (see Figure 12.12). The SSBs are displaced as the replication enzymes make the new polynucleotide chain on the template strands. For circular chromosomes, such as the genomes of most bacteria, unwinding the DNA will eventually cause the still-wound DNA ahead of the unwinding to become highly twisted. You can visualize this phenomenon with some string. Take two equal lengths of string and twist them around each other. Now tie the two ends of each string together. You have created a model of a circular DNA double helix. Pick anywhere in the circle and pull apart

the two pieces of string. The more you pull, the more the region where the two strings are still together becomes highly twisted. In the cell, the twisting of DNA during replication is relieved by **topoisomerase**. This enzyme cuts the DNA ahead of the replication fork, turns the DNA on one side of the break in the opposite direction of the twisting force, and rejoins the two strands (see Figure 12.12).

12.3d RNA Primers Provide the Starting Point for DNA Polymerase to Begin Synthesizing a New DNA Chain

If DNA polymerases can only add nucleotides to the 3′ end of an existing strand, how can a new strand begin when there is no existing strand in place? The answer lies in a short chain a few nucleotides long called a **primer**, which is made of RNA instead of DNA **(Figure 12.13, p. 276)**. The primer is synthesized by the enzyme **primase**. Primase then leaves the template, and DNA polymerase takes over, extending the RNA primer with DNA nucleotides as it synthesizes the new DNA chain. RNA primers are removed and replaced with DNA later in replication.

12.3e One New DNA Strand Is Synthesized Continuously; the Other, Discontinuously

DNA polymerases synthesize a new DNA strand on a template strand in the 5′ → 3′ direction. Because the two strands of a DNA double helix are antiparallel, only one of them runs in a direction that allows DNA polymerase to make a 5′ → 3′ complementary copy in the direction of unwinding. That is, on this template strand—top strand in **Figure 12.14, p. 277**—new DNA is synthesized continuously in the direction of unwinding of the double helix. However, the other template strand—bottom strand in Figure 12.14—runs in the opposite direction; this means DNA polymerase has to copy it in the direction opposite to the unwinding direction. How is new DNA polymerized in the direction opposite to the unwinding? The polymerases make this strand in short lengths that are synthesized in the direction opposite to that of DNA unwinding (see Figure 12.14). The short lengths produced by this **discontinuous replication** are then covalently linked into a single continuous polynucleotide chain. The short lengths are called **Okazaki fragments**, after Reiji Okazaki, the scientist who first detected them. The new DNA strand synthesized in the direction of DNA unwinding is called the **leading strand** of DNA replication; the template for that strand is the

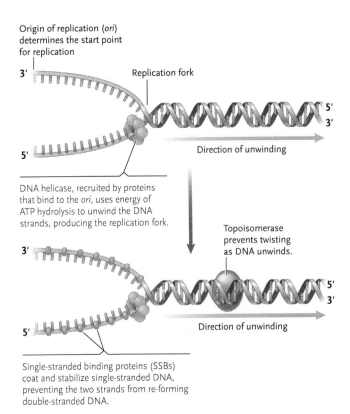

Origin of replication (*ori*) determines the start point for replication

3′

Replication fork

5′

DNA helicase, recruited by proteins that bind to the *ori*, uses energy of ATP hydrolysis to unwind the DNA strands, producing the replication fork.

5′

3′

Direction of unwinding

3′

Topoisomerase prevents twisting as DNA unwinds.

5′

3′

5′

Direction of unwinding

Single-stranded binding proteins (SSBs) coat and stabilize single-stranded DNA, preventing the two strands from re-forming double-stranded DNA.

Figure 12.12
The roles of DNA helicase, single-stranded binding proteins (SSBs), and topoisomerase in DNA replication.

Figure 12.13
Initiation of a new DNA strand by synthesis of a short RNA primer by primase, and the extension of the primer as DNA by DNA polymerase.

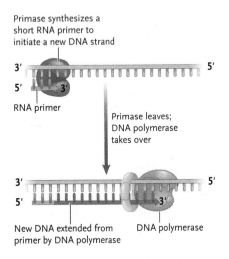

Primase synthesizes a short RNA primer to initiate a new DNA strand

3′   5′

5′

3′

RNA primer

Primase leaves; DNA polymerase takes over

3′   5′

5′

3′

New DNA extended from primer by DNA polymerase

DNA polymerase

leading strand template. The strand synthesized discontinuously in the opposite direction is called the **lagging strand;** the template strand for that strand is the **lagging strand template.**

12.3f Multiple Enzymes Coordinate Their Activities in DNA Replication

Figure 12.15, p. 278, shows how the enzymes and proteins we have introduced act in a coordinated way to replicate DNA. Primase initiates all new strands by synthesizing an RNA primer. **DNA polymerase III,** the main polymerase, extends the primer by adding DNA nucleotides. For the lagging strand, **DNA polymerase I** removes the RNA primer at the 5′ end of the previous newly synthesized Okazaki fragment, replacing the RNA nucleotides one by one with DNA nucleotides. RNA nucleotide removal uses the 5′ → 3′ exonuclease activity of the enzyme. (An exonuclease removes nucleotides from the end of a molecule; the primer is digested from its 5′ end toward its 3′ end.) DNA polymerase I stops replacing RNA and leaves the template when it encounters the first DNA nucleotide that was synthesized in the Okazaki fragment (Figure 12.15). Therefore, the DNA base replacing the last RNA base of the primer ends up right beside the first DNA base of the Okazaki fragment. The needed covalent bond in the backbone is made by **DNA ligase** (*ligare* = to tie).

The replication process continues in the same way until the entire DNA double helix is copied. **Table 12.1, p. 279,** summarizes the activities of the major enzymes replicating DNA. Replication advances at a rate of about 500 to 1000 nucleotides per second in *E. coli* and other bacteria, and at a rate of about 50 to 100 per second in eukaryotes. The entire process is so rapid that the RNA primers and nicks left by discontinuous synthesis persist for only seconds or fractions of a second. A short distance behind the fork, the new DNA chains are fully continuous and wound into complete DNA double helices. Each helix consists of one "old" and one "new" polynucleotide. Researchers identified the enzymes that replicate DNA through experiments with a variety of bacteria and eukaryotes and with viruses that infect both types of cells. Experiments with the bacterium *E. coli* have provided the most complete information about DNA replication, particularly in the laboratory of Arthur Kornberg at Stanford University. Kornberg received a Nobel Prize in 1959 for his discovery of the mechanism for DNA synthesis.

12.3g Multiple Replication Origins Enable Rapid Replication of Large Chromosomes

Unwinding at an *ori* within a DNA molecule actually produces two replication forks: two Ys joined together at their tops to form a **replication bubble.** Typically, each of the replication forks moves away from the ori as DNA replication proceeds, with the events at each fork mirroring those in the other **(Figure 12.16, p. 280).** For small circular genomes, such as those found in many bacteria and archaeans, there is a single *ori*. Eukaryotic genomes, by contrast, are distributed among several linear chromosomes, each of which can be very long. The average human chromosome, for instance, is about 25 times as long as the *E. coli* chromosome. Nonetheless, replication of long, eukaryotic chromosomes is relatively rapid—sometimes faster than the *E. coli*

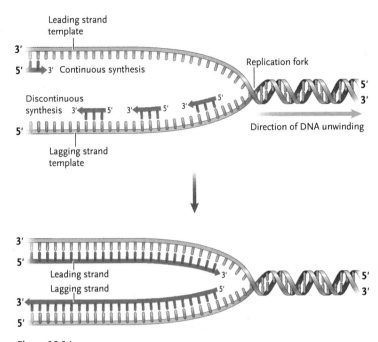

Figure 12.14
Replication of antiparallel template strands at a replication fork. Synthesis of the new DNA strand on the top template strand is continuous. Synthesis on the new DNA strand on the bottom template strand is discontinuous—short lengths of DNA are made, which are then joined into a continuous chain. The overall effect is synthesis of both strands in the direction of replication fork movement.

chromosome—because there are many, sometimes hundreds, of origins of replication along eukaryotic chromosomes. Replication initiates at each origin, forming a replication bubble at each (**Figure 12.17, p. 280**). Movement of the two forks in opposite directions from each origin extends the replication bubbles until the forks eventually meet along the chromosomes to produce fully replicated DNA molecules. Normally, a replication origin is activated only once during the S phase of a eukaryotic cell cycle, so no portion of the DNA is replicated more than once.

CONCEPT FIX Figures 12.12 and 12.14 show that one strand of DNA is replicated continuously (leading strand), while the other is replicated discontinuously (lagging strand). This might lead you to believe that any one particular strand of DNA on a chromosome is replicated either continuously or discontinuously along its entire length. However, if

---

MOLECULE BEHIND BIOLOGY 12.1

Acyclic Nucleoside Phosphonates as Antiviral Drugs

Viruses are obligate parasites that exploit the cellular machinery of infected host cells for replication and gene expression. Such intimate association with host biochemistry makes it difficult for scientists to find an exclusively viral "target" for antiviral drug binding.

However, herpes viruses provide such a target when, once inside the nucleus of an infected cell, they

transcribe a gene coding for their own distinctive DNA polymerase. This novel polymerase replicates viral DNA, drawing from the cellular pool of nucleotide triphosphates.

It has been possible to selectively "poison" viral DNA replication with acyclic nucleoside phosphonates such as cidofovir (shown below) because they (1) are converted to their triphosphate form by infected cells, (2) are

then selectively incorporated into viral DNA (instead of the normal nucleotides) by viral polymerase, and (3) block further DNA synthesis.

These drugs are part of a large class of compounds called base analogues that are incorporated into DNA by "mistake." Compare the structures below with those of the standard bases shown in Figure 12.4, p. 268, and notice why these drugs are called "acyclic."

Cidofovir   Adefovir dipivoxil   Tenofovir disoproxil fumarate

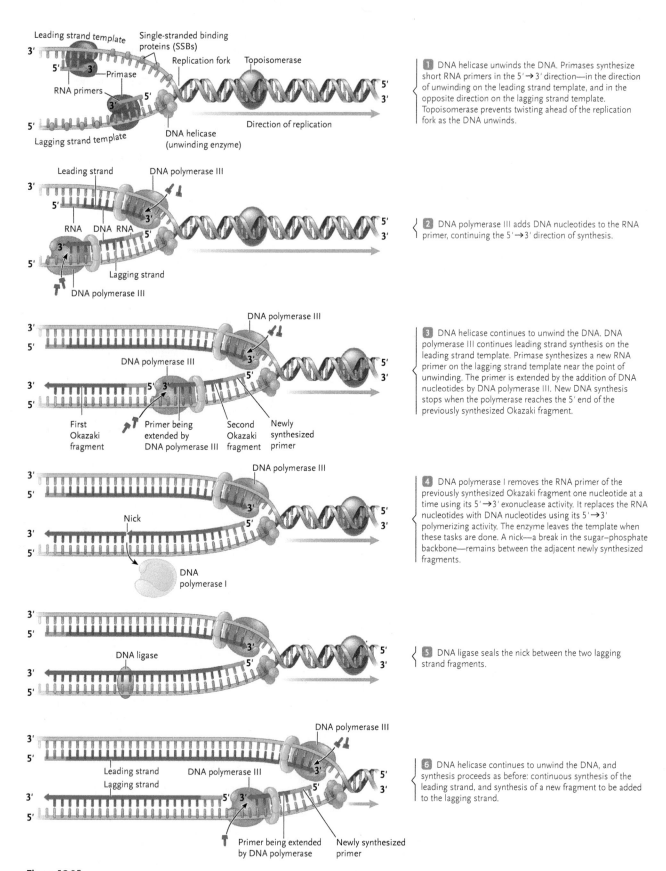

1 DNA helicase unwinds the DNA. Primases synthesize short RNA primers in the 5'→3' direction—in the direction of unwinding on the leading strand template, and in the opposite direction on the lagging strand template. Topoisomerase prevents twisting ahead of the replication fork as the DNA unwinds.

2 DNA polymerase III adds DNA nucleotides to the RNA primer, continuing the 5'→3' direction of synthesis.

3 DNA helicase continues to unwind the DNA. DNA polymerase III continues leading strand synthesis on the leading strand template. Primase synthesizes a new RNA primer on the lagging strand template near the point of unwinding. The primer is extended by the addition of DNA nucleotides by DNA polymerase III. New DNA synthesis stops when the polymerase reaches the 5' end of the previously synthesized Okazaki fragment.

4 DNA polymerase I removes the RNA primer of the previously synthesized Okazaki fragment one nucleotide at a time using its 5'→3' exonuclease activity. It replaces the RNA nucleotides with DNA nucleotides using its 5'→3' polymerizing activity. The enzyme leaves the template when these tasks are done. A nick—a break in the sugar–phosphate backbone—remains between the adjacent newly synthesized fragments.

5 DNA ligase seals the nick between the two lagging strand fragments.

6 DNA helicase continues to unwind the DNA, and synthesis proceeds as before: continuous synthesis of the leading strand, and synthesis of a new fragment to be added to the lagging strand.

Figure 12.15

Molecular model of DNA replication. The drawings simplify the process. In reality, the enzymes assemble at the fork, replicating both strands from that position as the template strands fold and pass through the assembly.

Table 12.1	Major Proteins of DNA Replication
Protein	**Activity**
Helicase	Unwinds DNA helix 
Single-stranded binding proteins	Stabilize single-stranded DNA and prevent the two strands at the replication fork from re-forming double-stranded DNA
Topoisomerase	Avoids twisting of the DNA ahead of the replication fork (in circular DNA) by cutting the DNA, turning the DNA on one side of the break in the direction opposite to that of the twisting force, and rejoining the two strands 
Primase	Assembles RNA primers in the 5' → 3' direction to initiate a new DNA strand 
DNA polymerase III	Main replication enzyme in *E. coli*; extends the RNA primer by adding DNA nucleotides to it 
DNA polymerase I	*Escherichia coli* enzyme that uses its 5' → 3' exonuclease activity to remove the RNA of the previously synthesized Okazaki fragment, and uses its 5' → 3' polymerization activity to replace the RNA nucleotides with DNA nucleotides 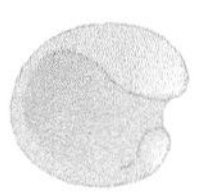
Sliding clamp	Tethers DNA polymerase III to the DNA template, making replication more efficient 
DNA ligase	Seals nick left between adjacent bases after RNA primers replaced with DNA 

you look carefully at the replication bubble in Figure 12.16, you will see that a bubble consists of two replication forks travelling in opposite directions. You will see that any one particular strand of DNA on a chromosome is replicated continuously at one fork but discontinuously at the other fork. ⬢

12.3h Telomerases Solve a Special Replication Problem at the Ends of Linear DNA Molecules in Eukaryotes

The requirement for an RNA primer to initiate DNA replication (see Figures 12.13, p. 276, and 12.15, p. 278) results in the linear chromosomes of eukaryotes getting shorter at each round of replication. Think about the end of a linear DNA molecule. New DNA synthesis on the 3' → 5' template strand must be started with an RNA primer. When that primer is subsequently removed, as usual, a gap will be left in its place at the 5' end of the new DNA strand (Figure 12.18, p. 281). Everywhere else on the chromosome, such gaps are filled in by DNA polymerase by elongating the 3' end of a neighbouring nucleotide. However, at the very ends of chromosomes, there is no existing nucleotide chain that can be elongated. Therefore, DNA polymerase cannot fill in the gap with the required DNA nucleotides and the resulting newly synthesized strand will be too short. (You should agree that this problem occurs on both ends of the chromosome, just on opposite strands of the double helix.) When these new, now shortened, DNA strands are used as a template for the next round of DNA replication, the resulting chromosomes will be shorter still. Indeed, when most somatic cells go through the cell cycle, their chromosomes shorten with each division. Such loss of DNA sequences can eventually have lethal consequences for the cell.

Most eukaryotic chromosomes can afford to lose some DNA sequence because a buffer of highly repetitive noncoding DNA protects genes near the ends of chromosomes. This region of noncoding DNA is called the **telomere** (*telo* = end, *mere* = segment). A telomere consists of a short DNA sequence that is repeated hundreds to thousands of times. In humans, the repeated sequence, the *telomere repeat*, is 5'-TTAGGG-3' on the template strand (the top strand in Figure 12.18, step 1, p. 281). With each replication, a fraction of the telomere repeats is lost by the mechanism described above but the genes are unaffected. The buffering fails only when the entire telomere is lost.

The length of telomeres can be maintained by the action of an unusual enzyme, called **telomerase**, which adds DNA to the ends of chromosomes. Since telomerase makes DNA, it is a type of DNA polymerase. Recall that DNA polymerases require a free 3' OH to extend, a supply of dNTPs, and a template strand. If you look closely at Figure 12.18, you might predict that telomerase elongates the 5' end of the bottom strand to fill in the gap. Although this solution appears easiest,

Figure 12.16
Synthesis of leading and lagging strands in the two replication forks of a replication bubble formed at an origin of replication.

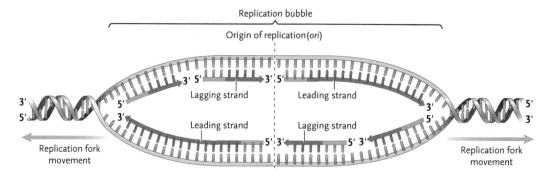

Figure 12.17
Replication from multiple origins in the linear chromosomes of eukaryotes.

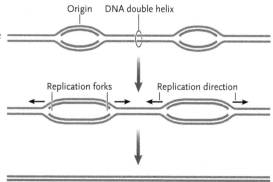

it is impossible since *there are no known polymerases capable of elongating a 5′ end.* So, instead, telomerase must elongate the available 3′ end of the top strand. But now there is a different problem—what to use for a template strand? The lack of a template on the chromosome is solved by *telomerase carrying its own template* in the form of single-stranded RNA molecule. Telomerase adds a telomere repeat to the 3′ end of the DNA using the RNA as a template (see Figure 12.18). Then it shifts toward the end of the chromosome and adds another, and another. Once several hundred repeats are added to the top strand, it is primed and used as a template as usual. When the RNA primer is removed, there will be a single-stranded region at the end of the chromosome as before.

CONCEPT FIX It is important to understand that telomerase does not directly prevent the mechanism that causes the shortening of chromosomes. Telomerase just acts against this mechanism by lengthening chromosomes. ⬢

In most multicellular organisms, telomerase is not active in somatic cells, meaning telomeres shorten when such cells divide. As a result, somatic cells are capable of only a certain number of mitotic divisions before they stop dividing and die. Telomerase is normally active only in the rapidly dividing cells of the early embryo, and in germ cells to ensure that chromosomes of gametes have telomeres restored before passing to the next generation.

Telomerase explains how cancer cells can divide indefinitely and not be limited to a certain number

of divisions as a result of telomere shortening. For many cancers, as normal cells develop into cancer cells, their telomerases are reactivated, preserving chromosome length during the rapid divisions characteristic of cancer. A positive side of this discovery is that it may lead to an effective cancer treatment if a means can be found to switch off the telomerases in tumour cells. The chromosomes in the rapidly dividing cancer cells would then eventually shorten to the length at which they break down, leading to cell death and elimination of the tumour. Elizabeth Blackburn, Carol Greider, and Jack Szostak were awarded a Nobel Prize in 2009 for their discovery of how chromosomes are protected by telomeres and the enzyme telomerase.

STUDY BREAK

1. What is the importance of complementary base-pairing to DNA replication?
2. Why is a primer needed for DNA replication on both strands?
3. Two DNA polymerases are used in DNA replication. What are their roles?
4. Why are telomeres important?

12.4 Mechanisms That Correct Replication Errors

DNA polymerases make very few errors as they assemble new molecules. Most of the mistakes that do occur, called **base-pair mismatches**, are corrected, either by a proofreading mechanism carried out during replication by the DNA polymerases themselves or by a DNA repair mechanism that corrects mismatched base pairs after replication is complete.

12.4a Proofreading Depends on the Ability of DNA Polymerases to Reverse and Remove Mismatched Bases

The **proofreading mechanism**, first proposed in 1972 by Arthur Kornberg and Douglas L. Brutlag of Stanford University in California, depends on the ability of DNA

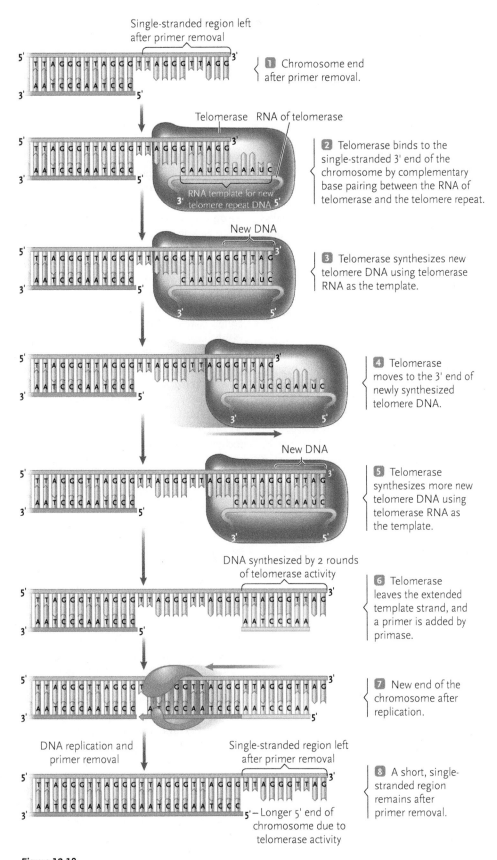

Figure 12.18
Addition of telomere repeats to the 3' end of a eukaryotic linear chromosome by telomerase.

CHAPTER 12   DNA STRUCTURE, REPLICATION, AND ORGANIZATION | 281

polymerases to back up and remove mispaired nucleotides from a DNA strand. Only when the most recently added base is correctly paired with its complementary base on the template strand can the DNA polymerases continue to add nucleotides to a growing chain. The correct pairs allow the fully stabilizing hydrogen bonds to form **(Figure 12.19**, step 1). If a newly added nucleotide is mismatched (step 2), the DNA polymerase reverses using a built-in deoxyribonuclease to remove the newly added incorrect nucleotide (step 3). The enzyme resumes working forward, now inserting the correct nucleotide (step 4).

Several experiments have confirmed that the major DNA polymerases of replication can actually proofread their work in this way. For example, when the primary DNA polymerase that replicates DNA in bacteria is intact, with its reverse activity working, its overall error rate is astonishingly low—only about 1 mispair persists in the DNA for every 1 million nucleo-

tides assembled in the test tube. If the proofreading activity of the enzyme is experimentally inhibited, the error rate increases to about 1 mistake for every 1000 to 10 000 nucleotides assembled. Experiments with eukaryotes have yielded similar results.

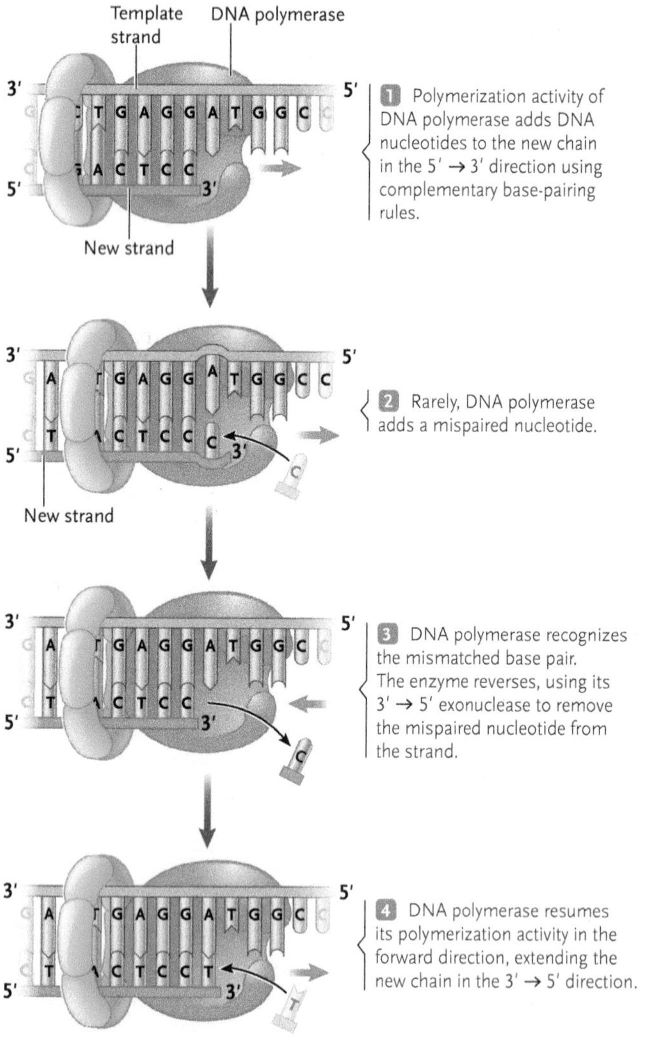

12.4b DNA Repair Corrects Errors That Escape Proofreading

Any base-pair mismatches that remain after proofreading face still another round of correction by **DNA repair mechanisms**. These **mismatch repair** mechanisms increase the accuracy of DNA replication well beyond the one-in-a-million errors that persist after proofreading. As noted earlier, the "correct" A-T and G-C base pairs fit together like pieces of a jigsaw puzzle, and their dimensions separate the sugar–phosphate backbone chains by a constant distance. Mispaired bases are too large or small to maintain the correct separation, and they cannot form the hydrogen bonds characteristic of the normal base pairs. As a result, base mismatches distort the structure of the DNA helix. These distortions provide recognition sites for the enzymes catalyzing mismatch repair.

The repair enzymes move along the double helix, "scanning" the DNA for distortions in the newly synthesized nucleotide chain. If the enzymes encounter a distortion, they remove a portion of the new chain, including the mismatched nucleotides **(Figure 12.20**, step 1). The gap left by the removal (step 2) is then filled by a DNA polymerase, using the template strand as a guide (step 3). The repair is completed by a DNA ligase, which seals the nucleotide chain into a continuous DNA molecule (step 4).

The same repair mechanisms also detect and correct alterations in DNA caused by the damaging effects of chemicals and radiation, including the ultraviolet light in sunlight. Some idea of the importance of the repair mechanisms comes from the unfortunate plight of individuals with *Xeroderma pigmentosum*, a hereditary disorder in which the repair mechanism is faulty. Because of the effects of unrepaired alterations in their DNA, skin cancer can develop quickly in these individuals if they are exposed to sunlight.

The rare replication errors that remain in DNA after proofreading and DNA repair are a primary source of **mutations**, differences in DNA sequence that appear and remain in the replicated copies. When a mutation occurs in a gene, it can alter the property of the protein encoded by the gene, which, in turn, may alter how the organism functions. Hence, mutations are highly important to the evolutionary process because they are the ultimate source of the variability in offspring acted on by natural selection.

We now turn from DNA replication and error correction to the arrangements of DNA in eukaryotic and prokaryotic cells. These arrangements organize

1 Polymerization activity of DNA polymerase adds DNA nucleotides to the new chain in the 5' → 3' direction using complementary base-pairing rules.

2 Rarely, DNA polymerase adds a mispaired nucleotide.

3 DNA polymerase recognizes the mismatched base pair. The enzyme reverses, using its 3' → 5' exonuclease to remove the mispaired nucleotide from the strand.

4 DNA polymerase resumes its polymerization activity in the forward direction, extending the new chain in the 3' → 5' direction.

Figure 12.19
Proofreading by a DNA polymerase.

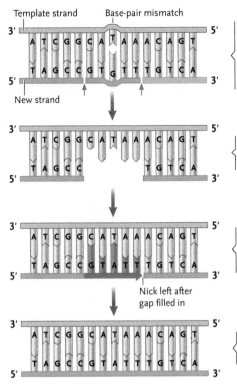

Template strand   Base-pair mismatch

1 Repair enzymes move along the DNA, scanning for distortions in the double helix due to a mispaired base. The enzymes break the backbone of the new strand on each side of the mismatch.

New strand

2 The enzymes remove several bases, including the mismatched base, leaving a gap in the DNA.

3 DNA polymerase fills in the gap with its 5′ → 3′ polymerizing activity, using the template strand as a guide.

Nick left after gap filled in

4 DNA ligase seals the nick left after gap-filling to complete the repair.

Figure 12.20
Repair of mismatched bases in replicated DNA.

superstructures that fit the long DNA molecules into the microscopic dimensions of cells and also contribute to the regulation of DNA activity.

STUDY BREAK

Why is a proofreading mechanism important for DNA replication?

12.5 DNA Organization in Eukaryotic versus Prokaryotic Cells

Enzymatic proteins are the essential catalysts of every step in DNA replication. In addition, numerous proteins of other types organize the DNA in both eukaryotic and prokaryotic cells in addition to controlling its expression.

In eukaryotes, two major types of proteins, the histone and nonhistone proteins, are associated with DNA structure and regulation in the nucleus. These proteins are known collectively as the **chromosomal proteins** of eukaryotes. The complex of DNA and its associated proteins, termed **chromatin**, is the structural building block of a chromosome.

By comparison, the single DNA molecule of a prokaryotic cell is more simply organized and has fewer associated proteins. However, prokaryotic DNA is still

associated with two classes of proteins with functions similar to those of the eukaryotic histones and nonhistones: one class that organizes the DNA structurally and one that regulates gene activity. We begin this section with the major DNA-associated proteins of eukaryotes as they relate to packaging. The role of chromatin structure in gene regulation is addressed in Chapter 14.

12.5a Histones Pack Eukaryotic DNA at Successive Levels of Organization

The **histones** are a class of small, positively charged (basic) proteins that are complexed with DNA in the chromosomes of eukaryotes. (Most other cellular proteins are larger and are neutral or negatively charged.) The histones link to DNA by an attraction between their positive charges and the negatively charged phosphate groups of the DNA.

Five types of histones exist in most eukaryotic cells: H1, H2A, H2B, H3, and H4. The amino acid sequences of these proteins are highly similar among eukaryotes, suggesting that they perform the same functions in all eukaryotic organisms.

One function of histones is to pack DNA molecules into the narrow confines of the cell nucleus. For example, each human cell nucleus contains 2 m of DNA. Combination with the histones compacts this length so much that it fits into nuclei that are only about 10 μm in diameter.

Histones and DNA Packing. The histones pack DNA at several levels of chromatin structure. In the most fundamental structure, called a **nucleosome**, two molecules each of H2A, H2B, H3, and H4 combine to form a beadlike, eight-protein **nucleosome core particle** around which DNA winds for almost two turns **(Figure 12.21, p. 284)**. A short segment of DNA, the **linker**, extends between one nucleosome and the next. Under the electron microscope, this structure looks like beads on a string. The diameter of the beads (the nucleosomes) gives this structure its name—the **10 nm chromatin fibre** (see Figure 12.21).

Each nucleosome and linker includes about 200 base pairs of DNA. Nucleosomes compact DNA by a factor of about 7; that is, a length of DNA becomes about one-seventh the length when it is wrapped into nucleosomes.

Histones and Chromatin Fibres. The fifth histone, H1, brings about the next level of chromatin packing. One H1 molecule binds both to the nucleosomes and to the linker DNA. This binding causes the nucleosomes to package into a coiled structure 30 nm in diameter, called the **30 nm chromatin fibre** or **solenoid**, with about six nucleosomes per turn (see Figure 12.21).

The arrangement of DNA in nucleosomes and solenoids compacts the DNA and probably also protects it from chemical and mechanical damage. In the test tube, DNA wound into nucleosomes and chromatin fibres is much more resistant to degradation by deoxyribonuclease (a DNA-digesting enzyme) than when it is not bound to histone proteins.

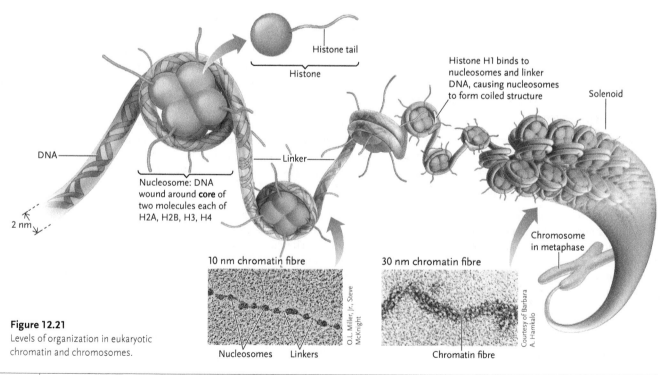

Figure 12.21
Levels of organization in eukaryotic chromatin and chromosomes.

Packing at Still Higher Levels: Euchromatin and Heterochromatin. In interphase nuclei, chromatin fibres are loosely packed in some regions and densely packed in others. The loosely packed regions are known as **euchromatin** (*eu* = true, regular, or typical), and the densely packed regions are called **heterochromatin** (*hetero* = different). Chromatin fibres also fold and pack into the thick, rodlike chromosomes that become visible during mitosis and meiosis.

Several experiments indicate that heterochromatin represents large blocks of genes that have been turned off and placed in a compact storage form. For example, recall the process of X-chromosome inactivation in mammalian females (see Section 11.2). As one of the two X chromosomes becomes inactive in cells early in development, it packs down into a block of heterochromatin called the *Barr body,* which is large enough to see under the light microscope. These findings support the idea that, in addition to organizing nuclear DNA, histones play a role in regulating gene activity.

12.5b Many Nonhistone Proteins Have Key Roles in the Regulation of Gene Expression

Nonhistone proteins are loosely defined as all the proteins associated with DNA that are not histones. Nonhistones vary widely in structure; most are negatively charged or neutral, but some are positively charged. They range in size from polypeptides smaller than histones to some of the largest cellular proteins.

Many nonhistone proteins help control the expression of individual genes. (The regulation of gene expression is the subject of Chapter 14.) For example, expression of a gene requires that the enzymes and proteins for that process be able to access the gene in the chromatin. If a gene is packed into heterochromatin, it is unavailable for activation. If the gene is in the more extended euchromatin, it is more accessible. Many nonhistone proteins affect gene accessibility by modifying histones to change how they associate with DNA in chromatin, either loosening or tightening the association. Other nonhistone proteins are regulatory proteins that activate or repress the expression of a gene. Yet others are components of the enzyme–protein complexes that are needed for the expression of any gene.

12.5c DNA Is Organized More Simply in Prokaryotes than in Eukaryotes

Several features of DNA organization in prokaryotic cells differ fundamentally from eukaryotic DNA. In contrast to the linear DNA in eukaryotes, the primary DNA molecule of most prokaryotic cells is circular, with only one copy per cell. In parallel with eukaryotic terminology, the DNA molecule is called a **bacterial chromosome.** The chromosome of the best-known bacterium, *E. coli,* includes about 1360 μm of DNA, which is equivalent to 4.6 million base pairs. There are exceptions: some bacteria have two or more different chromosomes in the cell, and some bacterial chromosomes are linear.

Replication begins from a single origin in the DNA circle, forming two forks that travel around the circle in opposite directions. Eventually, the forks meet at the opposite side from the origin to complete replication **(Figure 12.22).**

Inside prokaryotic cells, the DNA circle is packed and folded into an irregularly shaped mass called the **nucleoid** (shown in Figure 2.7, Chapter 2). The DNA of the nucleoid is suspended directly in the cytoplasm with no surrounding membrane.

Figure 12.22
Replication from a single origin of replication in a circular bacterial chromosome.

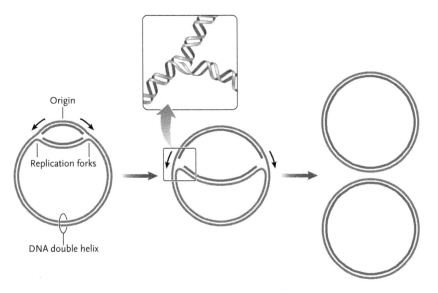

Origin

Replication forks

DNA double helix

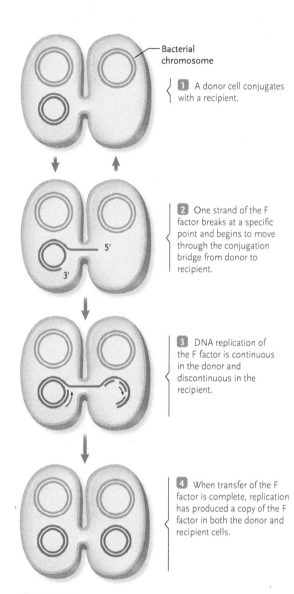

- Bacterial chromosome

1 A donor cell conjugates with a recipient.

2 One strand of the F factor breaks at a specific point and begins to move through the conjugation bridge from donor to recipient.

5′

3′

3 DNA replication of the F factor is continuous in the donor and discontinuous in the recipient.

4 When transfer of the F factor is complete, replication has produced a copy of the F factor in both the donor and recipient cells.

Figure 12.23

Transfer of F factor by rolling circle replication during conjugation. One of the two strands of the plasmid is nicked and the 5′ end moves from the donor into a recipient cell. The remaining circular strand "rolls" like a tape dispenser. DNA synthesis is continuous in the donor cell and discontinuous in the recipient (arrows), resulting in two complete plasmids.

Many prokaryotic cells also contain other DNA molecules, called **plasmids**, in addition to the main chromosome of the nucleoid. Most plasmids are circular, although some are linear. Plasmids have replication origins and are duplicated and distributed to daughter cells together with the bacterial chromosome during cell division. Chapter 9 describes the process of conjugation, in which plasmids are replicated while being transferred from a donor cell to a recipient cell. The DNA is replicated by a mechanism called rolling circle replication, in which one strand of the plasmid is cut and travels into a recipient cell as a linear molecule; the other strand remains circular in the donor cell **(Figure 12.23)**. DNA replication restores both strands to double-strandedness, and the linear molecule recircularizes. Although rolling circle replication follows the usual rules of DNA replication, notice that the leading and lagging strand synthesis occur in separate cells rather than at one replication fork.

Although bacterial DNA is not organized into nucleosomes, there are positively charged proteins that combine with bacterial DNA. Some of these proteins help organize the DNA into loops, thereby providing some compaction of the molecule. Bacterial DNA also combines with many types of genetic regulatory proteins that have functions similar to those of the nonhistone proteins of eukaryotes (see Chapter 14).

With this description of prokaryotic DNA organization, our survey of DNA structure and its replication and organization is complete. The next chapter revisits the same structures and discusses how they function in the expression of information encoded in DNA.

STUDY BREAK

1. What is the structure of the nucleosome?
2. What is the role of histone H1 in eukaryotic chromosome structure?

Review

To access course materials such as Aplia and other companion resources, please visit www.NELSONbrain.com.

12.1 Establishing DNA as the Hereditary Molecule

- Griffith found that a substance derived from killed virulent *Streptococcus pneumoniae* bacteria could transform nonvirulent living *S. pneumoniae* bacteria to the virulent type (Figure 12.2).

- Avery and his coworkers showed that DNA, and not protein or RNA, was the molecule responsible for transforming *S. pneumoniae* bacteria into the virulent form.

- Hershey and Chase showed that the DNA of a phage, not the protein, enters bacterial cells to direct the life cycle of the virus. Taken together, the experiments of Griffith, Avery and his coworkers, and Hershey and Chase established that DNA is the hereditary molecule (Figure 12.3).

12.2 DNA Structure

- Watson and Crick discovered that a DNA molecule consists of two polynucleotide chains twisted around each other into a right-handed double helix. Each nucleotide of the chains consists of deoxyribose; a phosphate group; and one of adenine, thymine, guanine, and cytosine. The deoxyribose sugars are linked by phosphate groups to form an alternating sugar–phosphate backbone. The two strands are held together by hydrogen bonded adenine–thymine (A-T) and guanine–cytosine (G-C) base pairs. Each full turn of the double helix involves 10 base pairs (Figures 12.4 and 12.6).
- The two strands of the DNA double helix are antiparallel.

12.3 DNA Replication

- DNA is duplicated by semiconservative replication, in which the two strands of a parental DNA molecule unwind and each serves as a template for the synthesis of a complementary copy (Figures 12.7–12.9).
- Several enzymes catalyze DNA replication. Helicase unwinds the DNA; primase synthesizes an RNA primer used as a starting point for nucleotide assembly by DNA polymerases. DNA polymerases assemble nucleotides into a polymer, one at a time, in a sequence complementary to the sequence of bases in the template. After a DNA polymerase removes the primers and fills in the resulting gaps, DNA ligase closes the remaining single-strand nicks (Figures 12.10–12.12 and 12.15).
- As the DNA helix unwinds, only one template runs in a direction that allows the new DNA strand to be made continuously in the direction of unwinding. The other template strand is copied in short lengths that run in the direction opposite to unwinding. The short lengths produced by this discontinuous replication are then linked into a continuous strand (Figures 12.14 and 12.15).
- DNA synthesis begins at sites that act as replication origins and proceeds from the origins as two replication forks moving in opposite directions (Figures 12.16 and 12.17).
- The ends of eukaryotic chromosomes consist of telomeres: short sequences repeated hundreds to thousands of times. These repeats provide a buffer against chromosome shortening during replication. Although most somatic cells show this chromosome shortening, some cell types do not because they have a telomerase enzyme that adds telomere repeats to the chromosome ends (Figure 12.18).

12.4 Mechanisms That Correct Replication Errors

- In proofreading, the DNA polymerase reverses and removes the most recently added base if it is mispaired as a result of a replication error. The enzyme then resumes DNA synthesis in the forward direction (Figure 12.19).
- In DNA mismatch repair, enzymes recognize distorted regions caused by mispaired base pairs and remove a section of DNA that includes the mispaired base from the newly synthesized nucleotide chain. A DNA polymerase then resynthesizes the section correctly, using the original template chain as a guide (Figure 12.20).

12.5 DNA Organization in Eukaryotic versus Prokaryotic Cells

- Eukaryotic chromosomes consist of DNA complexed with histone and nonhistone proteins.
- In eukaryotic chromosomes, DNA is wrapped around a core consisting of two molecules each of histones H2A, H2B, H3, and H4 to produce a nucleosome. Linker DNA connects adjacent nucleosomes. The chromosome structure in this form is the 10 nm chromatin fibre. The binding of histone H1 causes the nucleosomes to package into a coiled structure called the 30 nm chromatin fibre (Figure 12.21).
- Chromatin is distributed between euchromatin, a loosely packed region in which genes are active in RNA transcription, and heterochromatin, densely packed masses in which genes, if present, are inactive. Chromatin also folds and packs to form thick, rodlike chromosomes during nuclear division.
- Nonhistone proteins help control the expression of individual genes.
- The bacterial chromosome is a closed, circular double helix of DNA; it is packed into the nucleoid region of the cell. Replication begins from a single origin and proceeds in both directions. Many bacteria also contain plasmids, which replicate independently of the host chromosome (Figure 12.22).
- Bacterial DNA is organized into loops through interaction with proteins. Other proteins similar to eukaryotic nonhistones regulate gene activity in prokaryotic organisms.

Questions

Self-Test Questions

1. Working on the Amazon River, a biologist isolated DNA from two unknown organisms, P and Q. He discovered that the adenine content of P was 15% and the cytosine content of Q was 42%. Which of the following conclusions can be drawn?
   a. The amount of adenine in Q is 42%.
   b. The amount of guanine in P is 15%.
   c. The amount of guanine and cytosine combined in P is 70%.
   d. The amount of thymine in Q is 21%.

2. The Hershey and Chase experiment involved infecting bacterial cells with radioactively labelled viruses. What did this experiment show?
   a. ^{35}S-labelled DNA ended up inside the virus progeny.
   b. ^{32}P-labelled DNA entered bacterial cells.
   c. ^{35}S-labelled protein was incorporated into bacterial cells.
   d. ^{32}P-labelled protein was incorporated into virus coats.

3. Which of the following would appear on a list of pyrimidines?
   a. cytosine and thymine
   b. cytosine and guanine
   c. adenine and thymine
   d. adenine and guanine

4. Which of the following statements about DNA replication is true?
   a. DNA polymerase III extends an RNA primer.
   b. Some DNA polymerases can add new bases to the 5′ end of a growing strand.
   c. Each eukaryotic chromosome has a single origin of replication.
   d. Okazaki fragments are made only of RNA.

5. Which of the following statements about DNA structure is true?
   a. Each DNA strand has a 3′ OH on one end and a 5′ OH on the other end.
   b. Each strand of the double helix runs parallel to the other.
   c. The binding of adenine to thymine is through three hydrogen bonds.
   d. Bonds between components of the backbone (i.e., sugar–phosphate) are stronger than those between one strand and the other.

6. In the Meselson and Stahl experiment, the DNA in the parental generation was all $^{15}N^{15}N$, and after one round of replication, the DNA was all $^{15}N^{14}N$. What ratio of DNA would be seen after three rounds of replication?
   a. one $^{15}N^{14}N$: one $^{14}N^{14}N$
   b. one $^{15}N^{14}N$: two $^{14}N^{14}N$
   c. one $^{15}N^{14}N$: three $^{14}N^{14}N$
   d. one $^{15}N^{14}N$: four $^{14}N^{14}N$

7. Since DNA is synthesized in the 5′ → 3′ direction, which of the following must be true?
   a. The template must be read in the 5′ → 3′ direction.
   b. Polymerase must add successive nucleotides to the 3′ –OH end of the newly forming chain.
   c. Ligase must unwind the two DNA strands in opposite directions.
   d. Primase must add RNA nucleotides to the growing 5′ end.

8. Which of the following is a characteristic of telomerase?
   a. It is active in cancer cells.
   b. It is more active in adult than in embryonic cells.
   c. It has telomeres made of RNA.
   d. It shortens the ends of chromosomes.

9. What does the process of mismatch repair accomplish?
   a. It seals Okazaki fragments with ligase into a continual DNA strand.
   b. It removes RNA primers and replaces them with the correct DNA.
   c. It restores DNA sequence that is lost during the replication of the ends of chromosomes.
   d. It replaces incorrect bases that escape proofreading by DNA polymerase.

10. The DNA of prokaryotic organisms differs from that of eukaryotes. In what way?
    a. Prokaryotic DNA is surrounded by densely packed histones; eukaryotic DNA is not.
    b. Prokaryotic DNA has many sites for the initiation of DNA replication; eukaryotic DNA does not.
    c. Prokaryotic DNA is typically single stranded; eukaryotic DNA is typically double stranded.
    d. Prokaryotic DNA is rarely packaged in linear chromosomes; eukaryotic DNA is commonly packaged in linear chromosomes.

Questions for Discussion

1. Chargaff's data suggested that adenine pairs with thymine and guanine pairs with cytosine. What other data available to Watson and Crick suggested that adenine–guanine and cytosine–thymine pairs normally do not form?

2. Exposing cells to radioactive thymidine can label eukaryotic chromosomes during the S phase of interphase. If cells are exposed to radioactive thymidine during the S phase, would you expect both or only one of the sister chromatids of a duplicated chromosome to be labelled at metaphase of the following mitosis (see Section 8.3)?

3. If the cells in question 2 finish division and then enter another round of DNA replication in a medium that has been washed free of radioactive label, would you expect both or only one of the sister chromatids of a duplicated chromosome to be labelled at metaphase of the following mitosis?

4. During replication, an error uncorrected by proofreading or mismatch repair produces a DNA molecule with a base mismatch at the indicated position:

   AATTCCGACTCCTATGG

   TTAAGGTTGAGGATACC
   ↑

   This DNA molecule is received by one of the two daughter cells produced by mitosis. In the next round of replication and division, the mutation appears in only one of the two daughter cells. Develop a hypothesis to explain this observation.

5. Strains of bacteria that are resistant to an antibiotic sometimes appear spontaneously among other bacteria of the same type that are killed by the antibiotic. In view of the information in this chapter about DNA replication, what might account for the appearance of this resistance?

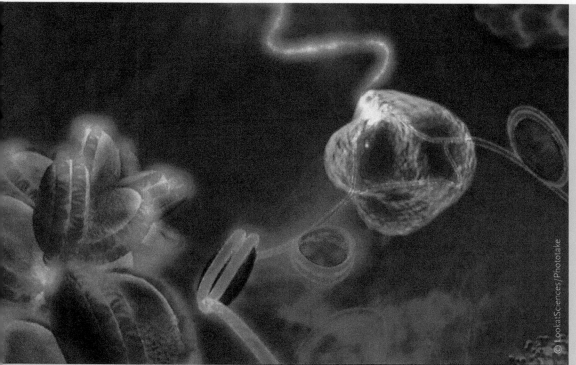

Transcription of a eukaryotic gene to produce messenger RNA (mRNA), a type of RNA that acts as a template for protein synthesis. The DNA of the gene unwinds from the nucleosome (left side) and is copied by an RNA polymerase (centre) into mRNA (exiting the top).

Gene Structure and Expression

WHY IT MATTERS

The marine mussel *Mytilus* **(Figure 13.1, p. 290)** lives in one of the most demanding environments on Earth—it clings permanently to rocks pounded by surf day in and day out, constantly in danger of being dashed to pieces or torn loose by foraging predators. The mussel is remarkably resistant to disturbance. If you try to pry one loose, you will find how difficult it is to tear the tough, elastic fibres that hold it fast. They are even hard to cut with a knife.

The fibres holding mussels to rocks are proteins secreted by the muscular foot of the animal. The proteins include keratin (an intermediate filament protein) and another resinous protein. Along with other proteins, they form a tough, adhesive material called byssus.

Byssus is one of the world's premier underwater adhesives. It fascinates biochemists, adhesive manufacturers, dentists, and surgeons looking for better ways to hold repaired body parts together. Genetic engineers are inserting segments of mussel DNA into yeast cells, which reproduce in large numbers and serve as "factories," translating the mussel genes into proteins. Among the proteins produced are those of byssus, allowing investigators to figure out how to use or imitate the mussel glue for human needs. This exciting work, like the mussel's own byssus building, starts with one of life's universal truths: *Every protein is assembled on ribosomes according to instructions dictated by genes coded in DNA.*

In this chapter, we trace the basic process that produces proteins in all organisms, beginning with the instructions encoded in DNA and leading through RNA to the sequence of amino acids in a protein. Many enzymes and other proteins are players as well as products in this story, as are several kinds of RNA and the cell's protein-making machines, the ribosomes. As your understanding of the fundamental elements of all protein production grows, be sure to notice the differences in the kinds of information coded in DNA, differences in the mechanisms in prokaryotic

Dennis Hallinan

Figure 13.1

The marine mussel *Mytilus* and its natural habitat.

electerra/Shutterstock.com

cells versus eukaryotes, and differences in the structure of genes that code for protein versus those that code for RNA.

13.1 The Connection between DNA, RNA, and Protein

Although the relationship between proteins and nucleic acids was once uncertain, it is now common knowledge that proteins are encoded by genes made of DNA. In this section, you will learn how that connection was discovered. We also present an overview of the molecular steps needed to go from gene to protein: transcription and translation.

13.1a Genes Specify Either Protein or RNA Products

How do we know that genes encode—that is, specify the amino acid sequence of—proteins? Two key pieces of research involving defects in metabolism illustrated this connection unequivocally. The first began in 1896 with Archibald Garrod, an English physician. He studied *alkaptonuria*, a human disease that does little harm but is detected easily by the fact that a patient's urine turns black when exposed to oxygen. Garrod and William Bateson, a geneticist, studied families of patients with the disease and concluded that it is an inherited trait. Garrod also found that people with alkaptonuria excrete a particular compound, homogentisic acid, in their urine. Garrod concluded that normal people are able to metabolize the homogentisic acid, whereas people with alkaptonuria cannot. By 1908, Garrod had concluded that the disease was an inborn error of metabolism. Garrod's work was the first to show a specific relationship between genes and metabolism.

In the second piece of research, George Beadle and Edward Tatum, working in the 1940s with the orange bread mould *Neurospora crassa*, collected data showing a direct relationship between genes and enzymes. Beadle and Tatum chose *Neurospora* for their work because it is a haploid fungus with simple nutritional needs. That is, wild-type *Neurospora*—the form of the mould found in nature—grows readily on a minimal medium (MM) consisting of a number of inorganic salts, sucrose, and a vitamin. The researchers reasoned that the fungus uses only simple chemicals in the medium to synthesize all of the more complex molecules needed for growth and reproduction, including amino acids for proteins and nucleotides for DNA and RNA.

Beadle and Tatum exposed spores of wild-type *Neurospora* to X-rays that caused mutations. They found that some of the treated spores would not germinate and grow unless MM was supplemented with additional nutrients, such as amino acids or vitamins. Mutant strains that are unable to grow on MM are called auxotrophs (*auxo* = increased; *troph* = eater), or nutritional mutants. Beadle and Tatum hypothesized that each auxotrophic strain had a defect in a gene coding for an enzyme needed to synthesize a nutrient that now had to be added to the MM. The wild-type strain could make the nutrient for itself from raw materials in the MM, but the mutant strain could grow only if the researchers supplied the nutrient. By testing to see if each mutant strain would grow on MM supplemented with a given nutrient, Beadle and Tatum discovered which specific nutrient each mutant needed to grow and, therefore, which gene defect it had. For example, a mutant that required the addition of the amino acid arginine to grow had a defect in a gene for an enzyme involved in the synthesis of arginine. Such arginine auxotrophs are known as *arg* mutants. The assembly of arginine from raw materials is a multi-step "assembly-line" process with a different enzyme catalyzing each step. Therefore, different *arg* mutants might have defects in different enzymes and therefore have blocks at different steps in the assembly line. (This is conceptually similar to Lederberg's work with auxotrophic bacteria, described in Chapter 9.)

Beadle and Tatum determined where in the arginine synthesis pathway each of four mutants (*argE*, *argF*, *argG*, and *argH*) was blocked. They tested whether each mutant could grow on MM or on MM supplemented with one of ornithine, citrulline, argininosuccinate (three compounds known to be involved in the synthesis of arginine), and arginine itself **(Figure 13.2).** While none of the four mutants could grow on MM because it was lacking arginine, they all grew well on MM + arginine. Each of the *arg* mutants showed a different pattern of growth on the supplemented MM (see Figure 13.2). Beadle and

Tatum deduced that the biosynthesis of arginine occurred in a number of steps, with each step controlled by a gene that encoded the enzyme for the step (see Figure 13.2). For example, the *argH* mutant grows on MM + arginine but not on MM + any of the other three compounds; this means that the mutant is blocked at the last step in the pathway, which produces arginine. Similarly, the *argG* mutant grows

QUESTION: Do genes specify enzymes?

EXPERIMENT: Test *arg* mutants of the orange bread mould *Neurospora crassa* for growth on MM (minimal medium), MM + ornithine, MM + citrulline, MM + argininosuccinate, and MM + arginine. *Arg* mutants are unable to synthesize the amino acid arginine, which is essential for growth.

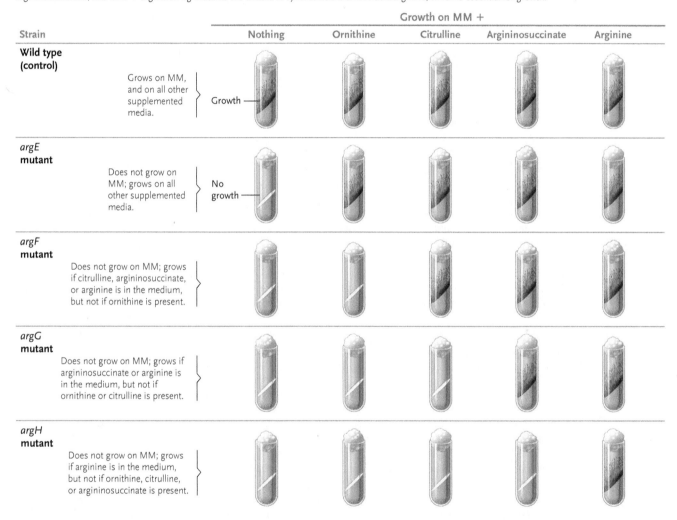

CONCLUSION: Arginine is synthesized in a biochemical pathway. Each step of the pathway is catalyzed by an enzyme, and each enzyme is encoded by a gene.

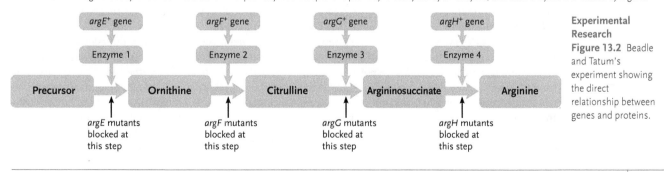

Experimental Research
Figure 13.2 Beadle and Tatum's experiment showing the direct relationship between genes and proteins.

on MM + arginine or argininosuccinate but not on MM + any of the other supplements; this means that *argG* is blocked in the pathway before argininosuccinate is made (see Figure 13.2). With similar analysis, the researchers deduced the whole pathway from precursor to arginine and showed which gene encoded the enzyme that carried out each step. In sum, Beadle and Tatum had shown the direct relationship between genes and enzymes, which they put forward as the **one gene–one enzyme hypothesis**. Their experiment was a keystone in the development of molecular biology. As a result of their work, they were awarded a Nobel Prize in 1958.

It is important to understand that protein structure and function are now known to be more complex than suggested by the work of Beadle and Tatum. Many proteins consist of more than one subunit. Each of these subunits is a separate molecule, called a polypeptide, that is coded by a separate gene. Polypeptides can assemble to create a functional cluster of molecules called a protein. For instance, the protein hemoglobin is made up of four polypeptides, two each of an α-subunit and a β-subunit; this composition gives the protein its functional property of transporting oxygen rather than catalyzing a chemical reaction. Two different genes are needed to encode the hemoglobin protein: one for the α-polypeptide and one for the β-polypeptide. Beadle and Tatum's hypothesis was therefore later restated as the **one gene–one polypeptide hypothesis**. It is important to keep the distinction between protein, the functional collection of polypeptides, and polypeptide, the molecule encoded by a gene, clear in your mind as we discuss transcription and translation in the rest of this chapter.

13.1b The Pathway from Gene to Polypeptide Involves Transcription and Translation

The pathway from gene to polypeptide has two major steps, transcription and translation. **Transcription** is the mechanism by which the information encoded in DNA is made into a complementary RNA copy. It is called transcription because the information in one nucleic acid type is transferred to another nucleic acid type. **Translation** is the use of the information encoded in the RNA to assemble amino acids into a polypeptide. It is called translation because the information in a nucleic acid, in the form of nucleotides, is converted into a different kind of molecule—amino acids. In 1956, Francis Crick gave the name Central Dogma to the flow of information from DNA to RNA to protein.

In transcription, the enzyme **RNA polymerase** creates an RNA sequence that is complementary to the DNA sequence of a given gene. The process follows the same basic rules of complementary base-pairing and nucleic acid chemistry that we first encountered in DNA replication (see Chapter 12). For each of the

several thousand genes that will be appropriate to express in a given cell, one DNA strand or the other is the **template strand** and is read by the RNA polymerase. The RNA transcribed from a gene encoding a polypeptide is called **messenger RNA (mRNA)**.

In translation, an mRNA associates with a **ribosome**, a particle on which amino acids are linked into polypeptide chains. As the ribosome moves along the mRNA, the amino acids specified by the mRNA are joined one by one to form the polypeptide encoded by the gene.

The processes of transcription and translation are similar in prokaryotic and eukaryotic cells **(Figure 13.3)**. One key difference is that whereas prokaryotic cells can transcribe and translate a given gene simultaneously, eukaryotic cells transcribe and process mRNA in the nucleus before exporting it to the cytoplasm for translation on ribosomes.

13.1c The Genetic Code Is Written in Three-Letter Words Using a Four-Letter Alphabet

Conceptually, the transcription of DNA into RNA is straightforward. The DNA "alphabet" consists of the four letters A, T, G, and C, representing the four DNA nucleotide bases, adenine, thymine, guanine, and cytosine, and the RNA alphabet consists of the four letters A, U, G, and C, representing the four RNA bases, adenine, uracil, guanine, and cytosine. In other words, both nucleic acids share three of the four bases but differ in the other one: T in DNA is equivalent to U in RNA. But whereas there are 4 RNA bases, there are 20 amino acids. How is nucleotide information in an mRNA translated into the amino acid sequence of a polypeptide?

Breaking the Genetic Code. The nucleotide information that specifies the amino acid sequence of a polypeptide is called the **genetic code**. Scientists hypothesized that the 4 bases in an mRNA (A, U, G, C) would have to be used in combinations of at least 3 to provide the capacity to code for 20 amino acids. One- and 2-letter words were eliminated because if the code used 1-letter words, only 4 different amino acids could be specified (that is, 4^1); if 2-letter words were used, only 16 different amino acids could be specified (that is, 4^2). But if the code used 3-letter words, 64 different amino acids could be specified (that is, 4^3), more than enough to specify 20 amino acids. We know now that the genetic code is indeed a three-letter code; each three-letter word (triplet) is called a **codon**. **Figure 13.4** illustrates the relationship among a gene, codons in an mRNA, and the amino acid sequence of a polypeptide. Genetic information in DNA is first transcribed into complementary three-letter RNA codons (the RNA complement to adenine [A] in the template strand is uracil [U] instead of thymine [T]).

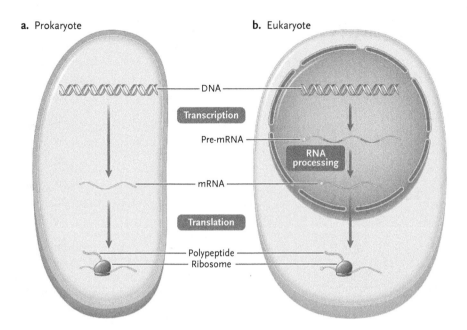

a. Prokaryote

b. Eukaryote

DNA

Transcription

Pre-mRNA

RNA processing

mRNA

Translation

Polypeptide
Ribosome

Figure 13.3
Transcription and translation in **(a)** prokaryotic and **(b)** eukaryotic cells. In prokaryotic cells, RNA polymerase synthesizes an mRNA molecule that is immediately available for translation on ribosomes. In eukaryotes, RNA polymerase synthesizes a precursor–mRNA (pre-mRNA molecule) containing extra segments that are removed by RNA processing to produce a translatable mRNA. That mRNA exits the nucleus through a nuclear pore and is translated on ribosomes in the cytoplasm. Note that only a small segment of DNA is shown. In prokaryotic cells the chromosome is circular.

CONCEPT FIX The template strand for a given gene is always read 3′ to 5′. For gene *a* in Figure 13.4, the bottom strand is the template and is therefore read left to right. However, the template for gene *b* might be the top strand; RNA polymerase would then have to be read right to left. ⬡

How do the codons correspond to the amino acids? Marshall Nirenberg and Philip Leder of the National Institutes of Health (NIH) in the United States established the identity of most of the codons in 1964. These researchers found that short, artificial mRNAs of codon length—three nucleotides—could bind to ribosomes in a test tube and cause a single transfer RNA (tRNA), with its linked amino acid, to bind to the ribosome. (As we will discuss in Section 13.4, tRNAs are a special class of RNA molecules that bring amino acids to the ribosome for assembly into the polypeptide chain.) Nirenberg and Leder then made 64 of the short mRNAs, each consisting of a different, single codon. They added the mRNAs, one at a time, to a mixture in a test tube containing ribosomes and all the different tRNAs, each linked to its own amino acid. The idea was that, from the mixture of tRNAs, each single-codon mRNA would link to the tRNA carrying the amino acid corresponding to the codon. The experiment worked for 50 of the 64 codons, allowing those codons to be assigned to amino acids definitively.

Another approach, carried out in 1966 by H. Ghobind Khorana and his coworkers, used long, artificial mRNA molecules containing only one nucleotide repeated continuously or different nucleotides in repeating patterns. Each artificial mRNA was added to ribosomes in a test tube, and the

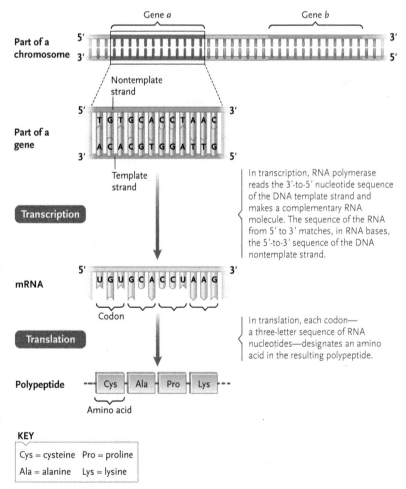

In transcription, RNA polymerase reads the 3′-to-5′ nucleotide sequence of the DNA template strand and makes a complementary RNA molecule. The sequence of the RNA from 5′ to 3′ matches, in RNA bases, the 5′-to-3′ sequence of the DNA nontemplate strand.

In translation, each codon—a three-letter sequence of RNA nucleotides—designates an amino acid in the resulting polypeptide.

KEY

Cys = cysteine	Pro = proline
Ala = alanine	Lys = lysine

Figure 13.4
Relationship among a gene, codons in an mRNA, and the amino acid sequence of a polypeptide.

Second base of codon

First base of codon	U	C	A	G	Third base of codon
U	UUU Phe	UCU Ser	UAU Tyr	UGU Cys	U
U	UUC Phe	UCC Ser	UAC Tyr	UGC Cys	C
U	UUA Leu	UCA Ser	UAA	UGA	A
U	UUG Leu	UCG Ser	UAG	UGG Trp	G
C	CUU Leu	CCU Pro	CAU His	CGU Arg	U
C	CUC Leu	CCC Pro	CAC His	CGC Arg	C
C	CUA Leu	CCA Pro	CAA Gln	CGA Arg	A
C	CUG Leu	CCG Pro	CAG Gln	CGG Arg	G
A	AUU Ile	ACU Thr	AAU Asn	AGU Ser	U
A	AUC Ile	ACC Thr	AAC Asn	AGC Ser	C
A	AUA Ile	ACA Thr	AAA Lys	AGA Arg	A
A	AUG Met	ACG Thr	AAG Lys	AGG Arg	G
G	GUU Val	GCU Ala	GAU Asp	GGU Gly	U
G	GUC Val	GCC Ala	GAC Asp	GGC Gly	C
G	GUA Val	GCA Ala	GAA Glu	GGA Gly	A
G	GUG Val	GCG Ala	GAG Glu	GGG Gly	G

KEY

Ala = alanine
Arg = arginine
Asn = asparagine
Asp = aspartic acid
Cys = cysteine
Gln = glutamine
Glu = glutamic acid
Gly = glycine
His = histidine
Ile = isoleucine
Leu = leucine
Lys = lysine
Met = methionine
Phe = phenylalanine
Pro = proline
Ser = serine
Thr = threonine
Trp = tryptophan
Tyr = tyrosine
Val = valine

Figure 13.5
The genetic code, written as the codons appear in mRNA being read 5′ to 3′. The AUG initiator codon, which codes for methionine, is shown in green; the three terminator codons are boxed in red.

sequence of amino acids in the polypeptide chain made by the ribosomes was analyzed. For example, an artificial mRNA containing only uracil nucleotides in the sequence UUUUUU... resulted in a polypeptide containing only the amino acid phenylalanine; they deduced that UUU must be the codon for phenylalanine. Khorana's approach, combined with the results of Nirenberg and Leder's experiments, identified the coding assignments of all the codons. Nirenberg and Khorana received a Nobel Prize in 1968 for solving the nucleic acid code.

Features of the Genetic Code. By convention, scientists write the codons in the 5′ → 3′ direction as they appear in mRNAs, substituting U for the T of DNA **(Figure 13.5)**. Of the 64 codons, 61 specify amino acids. One of these codons, AUG, specifies the amino acid methionine. It is the first codon translated in any mRNA in both prokaryotic cells and eukaryotes. In that position, AUG is called a **start** or **initiator codon**. The three codons that do not specify amino acids—UAA, UAG, and UGA—are **stop codons** (also called **nonsense** or **termination codons**) that act as "periods" indicating the end of a polypeptide-encoding sentence. When a ribosome reaches one of the stop codons, polypeptide synthesis stops and the new polypeptide chain is released from the ribosome.

Only two amino acids, methionine and tryptophan, are specified by a single codon. All the rest are represented by at least two; some by as many as six. In other words, there are many synonyms in the nucleic acid code, a feature known as **degeneracy** (or redundancy). For example, UGU and UGC both specify cysteine, and CCU, CCC, CCA, and CCG all specify proline.

Another feature of the genetic code is that it is **commaless**; that is, the words of the nucleic acid code are sequential, with no indicators such as commas or spaces to mark the end of one codon and the beginning of the next. Therefore, the code can be read correctly only by starting at the right place—at the first base of the first three-letter codon at the beginning of a coded message (the start codon)—and reading three nucleotides at a time. In other words, there is only one correct **reading frame** for each mRNA. For example, if you read the message SADMOMHASMOPCUTOFFBOYTOT three letters at a time, starting with the first letter of the first "codon," you would find that a mother reluctantly had her small child's hair cut. However, if you start incorrectly at the second letter of the first codon, you read the gibberish message ADM OMH ASM OPC UTO FFB OYT OT.

The code is also **universal**. With a few exceptions, the same codons specify the same amino acids in all living organisms, and even in viruses. The universality of the nucleic acid code indicates that it was established in its present form very early in the evolution of life and has remained virtually unchanged through billions of years of evolutionary history. Consistency in the genetic code makes genetic engineering possible. In Chapter 15, you will see how genes from one organism can be transferred to, and interpreted, by another.

STUDY BREAK

1. On the basis of their work with auxotrophic mutants of the fungus *Neurospora crassa*, Beadle and Tatum proposed the one gene–one enzyme hypothesis. Why was this hypothesis updated subsequently to the one gene–one polypeptide hypothesis?
2. Why is the sequence of bases in the mRNA different from that in the DNA of a given gene?

13.2 Transcription: DNA-Directed RNA Synthesis

Transcription is the process by which information coded in sequential DNA bases is transferred to a complementary RNA strand. Although certain aspects of this mechanism **(Figure 13.6)** are similar to those of

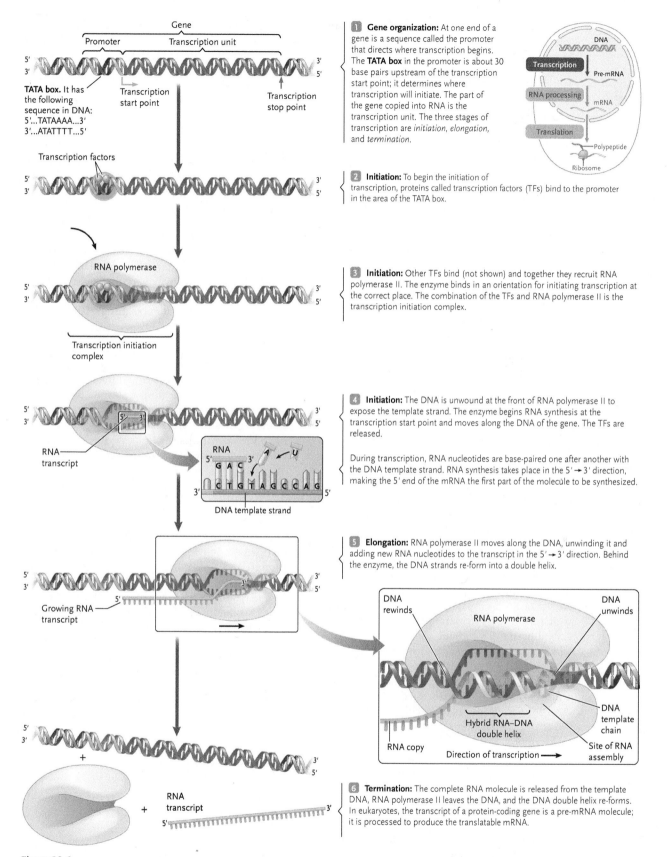

1 **Gene organization:** At one end of a gene is a sequence called the promoter that directs where transcription begins. The **TATA box** in the promoter is about 30 base pairs upstream of the transcription start point; it determines where transcription will initiate. The part of the gene copied into RNA is the transcription unit. The three stages of transcription are *initiation*, *elongation*, and *termination*.

2 **Initiation:** To begin the initiation of transcription, proteins called transcription factors (TFs) bind to the promoter in the area of the TATA box.

3 **Initiation:** Other TFs bind (not shown) and together they recruit RNA polymerase II. The enzyme binds in an orientation for initiating transcription at the correct place. The combination of the TFs and RNA polymerase II is the transcription initiation complex.

4 **Initiation:** The DNA is unwound at the front of RNA polymerase II to expose the template strand. The enzyme begins RNA synthesis at the transcription start point and moves along the DNA of the gene. The TFs are released.

During transcription, RNA nucleotides are base-paired one after another with the DNA template strand. RNA synthesis takes place in the 5′ → 3′ direction, making the 5′ end of the mRNA the first part of the molecule to be synthesized.

5 **Elongation:** RNA polymerase II moves along the DNA, unwinding it and adding new RNA nucleotides to the transcript in the 5′ → 3′ direction. Behind the enzyme, the DNA strands re-form into a double helix.

6 **Termination:** The complete RNA molecule is released from the template DNA, RNA polymerase II leaves the DNA, and the DNA double helix re-forms. In eukaryotes, the transcript of a protein-coding gene is a pre-mRNA molecule; it is processed to produce the translatable mRNA.

Figure 13.6

Transcription of a eukaryotic protein-coding gene. Transcription has three stages: initiation, elongation, and termination. RNA polymerase moves along the gene, separating the two DNA strands to allow RNA synthesis in the 5′ → 3′ direction using the 3′ → 5′ DNA strand as template.

DNA replication (see Figure 12.15), it is important for you to understand how these processes are different. In transcription,

- for a given gene, *only one of the two DNA nucleotide strands acts as a template* for synthesis of a complementary copy, instead of both, as in replication.
- only a relatively small part of a DNA molecule—the sequence encoding a single gene—serves as a template, rather than all of both strands, as in DNA replication.
- RNA polymerases catalyze the assembly of nucleotides into an RNA strand, rather than the DNA polymerases that catalyze replication.
- the RNA molecules resulting from transcription are single polynucleotide chains, not double ones, as in DNA replication.
- wherever adenine appears in the DNA template chain, a uracil is matched to it in the RNA transcript instead of thymine, as in DNA replication.

Although the mechanism of transcription is similar in prokaryotic cells and eukaryotes, watch for the important differences pointed out in this section.

13.2a Transcription Proceeds in Three Steps

Figure 13.6 illustrates the general structure of a eukaryotic protein-coding gene and shows how it is transcribed. The gene consists of two main parts, a **promoter**, which is a control sequence for transcription, and a **transcription unit**, the section of the gene that is copied into an RNA molecule. Transcription takes place in three steps: (1) initiation, in which the molecular machinery that carries out transcription assembles at the promoter and begins synthesizing an RNA copy of the gene; (2) elongation, in which the RNA polymerase moves along the gene extending the RNA chain; and (3) termination, in which transcription ends and the RNA molecule—the transcript—and the RNA polymerase are released from the DNA template. Roger Kornberg of Stanford University in California received a Nobel Prize in 2006 for describing the molecular structure of the eukaryotic transcription apparatus and how it acts in transcription.

Similarities and differences in transcription of eukaryotic and bacterial protein-coding genes are as follows:

- Gene organization is the same, although the specific sequences in the promoter where the transcription apparatus assembles differ.
- In eukaryotes, RNA polymerase II, the enzyme that transcribes protein-coding genes, cannot bind directly to DNA; it is recruited to the promoter

once proteins called **transcription factors** have bound. In bacteria, RNA polymerase binds directly to DNA; it is directed to the promoter by a protein factor that is then released once transcription begins.
- Elongation is essentially identical in the two types of organisms.
- In prokaryotic cells, there are two types of specific DNA sequences, called **terminators**, that signal the end of transcription of the gene. Both types of terminator sequences act *after they are transcribed*. In the first case, the terminator sequence on the mRNA uses complementary base-pairing with itself to form a "hairpin." In the second case, a protein binds to a particular terminator sequence on the mRNA. Both of these mechanisms trigger the termination of transcription and the release of the RNA and RNA polymerase from the template. In eukaryotes, there are no equivalent "transcription terminator" sequences. Instead, the 3′ end of the mRNA is specified by a different process, which is discussed in a later section.

Once an RNA polymerase molecule has started transcription and progressed past the beginning of a gene, another molecule of RNA polymerase may start transcribing as soon as there is room at the promoter. In most genes this process continues until there are many RNA polymerase molecules spaced closely along a gene, each making an RNA transcript.

13.2b Transcription of Non–Protein Coding Genes Occurs in a Similar Way

Non–protein coding genes include, for example, those for tRNAs and rRNAs. In eukaryotes, RNA polymerase II transcribes protein-coding genes, RNA polymerase III transcribes tRNA genes and the gene for one of the four rRNAs, and RNA polymerase I transcribes the genes for the three other rRNAs. The promoters for these non–protein coding genes are different from those of protein-coding genes, being specialized for the assembly of the transcription machinery that involves the correct RNA polymerase type. In bacteria a single type of RNA polymerase transcribes all types of genes. The promoters for bacterial non–protein coding genes are essentially the same as those of protein-coding genes.

STUDY BREAK

1. If the DNA template strand has the sequence 3′-CAAATTGGCTTATTACCGGATG-5′, what is the sequence of an RNA transcribed from it?
2. What is the role of the promoter in transcription?

13.3 Processing of mRNAs in Eukaryotes

Although mRNAs obviously contain regions that code for protein, they also contain noncoding regions that, although not specifying an amino acid, nevertheless play key roles in the process of protein synthesis. For instance, in prokaryotic mRNAs the coding region is flanked by untranslated ends, the 5′ untranslated region (5′ UTR) and a 3′ untranslated region (3′ UTR). These same elements are present in eukaryotic mRNAs along with additional types of noncoding elements. The following section looks at the structure and function of genes, with particular focus on the synthesis of mRNA in eukaryotes.

13.3a Eukaryotic Protein-Coding Genes Are Transcribed into Precursor mRNAs That Are Modified in the Nucleus

A eukaryotic protein-coding gene is typically transcribed into a **precursor mRNA (pre-mRNA)** that must be processed in the nucleus to produce translatable mRNA (see Figure 13.3, p. 293, **Figure 13.7**, and **Figure 13.8, p. 298**). The mature mRNA exits the nucleus and is translated by ribosomes in the cytoplasm.

Modifications of Pre-mRNA and mRNA Ends. At the 5′ end of the pre-mRNA is the 5′ guanine cap, consisting of a guanine-containing nucleotide that is reversed so that its 3′ –OH group faces the beginning rather than the end of the molecule. A capping enzyme adds this **5′ cap** to the pre-mRNA (without the need for complementary base-pairing) soon after RNA polymerase II begins transcription. The cap, which is connected to the rest of the chain by three phosphate groups, remains when pre-mRNA is processed to mRNA. The cap protects the mRNA from degradation and is the site where ribosomes attach at the start of translation.

Transcription of a eukaryotic protein-coding gene is terminated differently from that of a prokaryotic gene (Figure 13.7). The eukaryotic gene has no terminator sequence in the DNA that, after transcription into RNA, signals RNA polymerase to stop transcribing. Instead, near the 3′ end of the gene is a DNA sequence that is transcribed into the pre-mRNA. Proteins bind to this *polyadenylation signal* in the RNA and cleave it just downstream. This signals the RNA polymerase to stop transcription. Then the enzyme poly(A) polymerase adds a chain of 50 to 250 adenine nucleotides, one nucleotide at a time, to the newly created 3′ end of the pre-mRNA.

CONCEPT FIX No complementary base-pairing with a template is needed for this particular type of RNA synthesis. There is no "poly(T)" sequence in the DNA corresponding to the poly(A) sequence in the pre-mRNA.

Figure 13.7

Relationship between a eukaryotic protein-coding gene, the pre-mRNA transcribed from it, and the mRNA processed from the pre-mRNA.

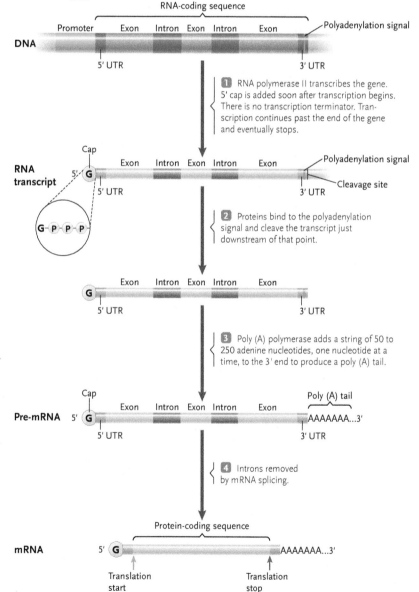

The string of adenine nucleotides, called the **poly (A) tail**, enables the mRNA produced from the pre-mRNA to be translated efficiently and protects it from attack by RNA-digesting enzymes in the cytoplasm.

Sequences Interrupting the Protein-Coding Sequence. The transcription unit of a protein-coding gene—the RNA-coding sequence—also contains non–protein coding sequences called **introns** that interrupt the protein-coding sequence (shown in Figure 13.8). The introns are transcribed into pre-mRNAs but are removed from pre-mRNAs during processing in the nucleus. The amino acid–coding sequences that are retained in finished mRNAs are called **exons**. The mechanisms by which introns originated in genes remain a mystery.

Introns were discovered by several methods, including direct comparisons between the nucleotide sequences of mature mRNAs and either pre-mRNAs or the genes encoding them. Although many eukaryotic genes do not contain introns, most have at least one; some contain more than 60. In humans, introns are, on average, 6 times the length of exons. The original discoverers of introns, Richard Roberts and Phillip Sharp, received a Nobel Prize in 1993 for their findings.

13.3b Introns Are Removed during Pre-mRNA Processing to Produce Translatable mRNA

A process called **mRNA splicing**, which occurs in the nucleus, removes introns from pre-mRNAs and joins exons together. As an illustration of one type of mRNA splicing, Figure 13.8 shows the processing of a pre-mRNA with a single intron to produce a mature mRNA. mRNA splicing takes place in a **spliceosome**, a complex formed between the pre-mRNA and a handful of **small ribonucleoprotein particles**. A ribonucleoprotein particle is a complex of RNA and proteins. The small ribonucleoprotein particles involved in mRNA splicing are located in the nucleus; each consists of a relatively short *small nuclear RNA* (snRNA) bound to a number of proteins. The particles are therefore known as snRNPs, pronounced "snurps." The snRNPs bind in a particular order to an intron in the pre-mRNA and form the active spliceosome. The spliceosome cleaves the pre-mRNA to release the intron, and joins the flanking exons.

Complementary base-pairing between regions of snRNA and mRNA ensures that the cutting and splicing are so exact that not a single base of an intron is retained in the finished mRNA, nor is a single base removed from the exons. Without this precision, removing introns would change the reading frame of the coding portion of the mRNA, producing the wrong codons from the point of a mistake onward.

13.3c Introns Contribute to Protein Variability

Introns seem wasteful in terms of the energy and raw materials required to replicate and transcribe them and the elaborate cellular machinery

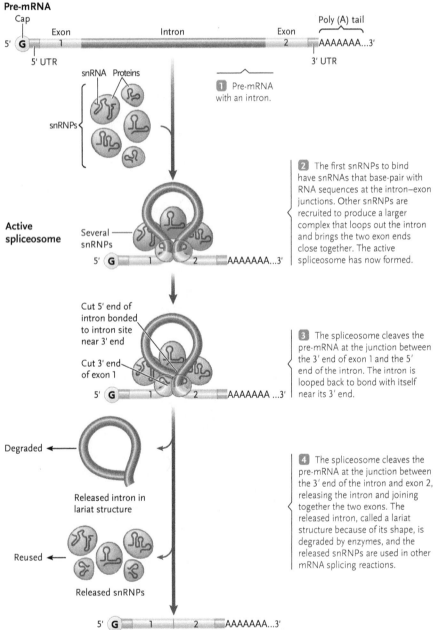

Pre-mRNA

1 Pre-mRNA with an intron.

2 The first snRNPs to bind have snRNAs that base-pair with RNA sequences at the intron–exon junctions. Other snRNPs are recruited to produce a larger complex that loops out the intron and brings the two exon ends close together. The active spliceosome has now formed.

3 The spliceosome cleaves the pre-mRNA at the junction between the 3' end of exon 1 and the 5' end of the intron. The intron is looped back to bond with itself near its 3' end.

4 The spliceosome cleaves the pre-mRNA at the junction between the 3' end of the intron and exon 2, releasing the intron and joining together the two exons. The released intron, called a lariat structure because of its shape, is degraded by enzymes, and the released snRNPs are used in other mRNA splicing reactions.

Figure 13.8
mRNA splicing—the removal from pre-mRNA of introns and joining of exons in the spliceosome.

required to remove them during pre-mRNA processing. Why are they present in mRNA-encoding genes? Among a number of possibilities, introns may provide a selective advantage to organisms by increasing the coding capacity of existing genes through a process called alternative splicing and in a process that generates new proteins called exon shuffling.

Alternative Splicing. The removal of introns from a given pre-mRNA is not absolute. That is, in particular tissues or sexes, or under certain environmental conditions, different regions of a given pre-mRNA may be identified as introns and removed in different combinations to produce different mature mRNAs. *Regions that are exon in one situation may well be removed as intron in another situation* **(Figure 13.9).** As an example, the pre-mRNA transcript of the mammalian α-tropomyosin gene is spliced in various ways in different tissues—smooth muscle (for example, muscles of the intestine and bladder), skeletal muscle (for example, biceps, glutes), fibroblast (connective tissue cell that makes collagen), liver, and brain—to produce different forms of the α-tropomyosin protein. Figure 13.9 shows the splicing of the α-tropomyosin pre-mRNA to the mRNAs found in smooth muscle and skeletal muscle. Exons 2 and 12 are found only in the smooth muscle mRNA, whereas exons 3, 10, and 11 are found only in the skeletal muscle mRNA.

The mechanism, called **alternative splicing**, greatly increases the number and variety of proteins encoded in the cell nucleus without increasing the size of the genome. For example, current data suggest that three-quarters of all human pre-mRNAs are subjected to alternative splicing. In each case, the different mRNAs produced from the parent pre-mRNA are translated to produce a family of related proteins with various combinations of amino acid sequences derived from the exons. Each protein in the family, then, varies in its function. Alternative splicing helps us understand why humans have only about 20 000 genes but can make over 100 000 proteins. As a result of alternative splicing, the number of diverse protein products far exceeds the number of genes. Ultimately, it is the diversity of proteins available, not the amount or diversity of DNA sequence, that determines the relative complexity of an organism's functions.

The polypeptides made from the two related tropomyosin mRNAs in Figure 13.9 have some identical stretches of amino acids, along with others that differ. As described in *The Purple Pages*, the primary structure of a protein—its amino acid

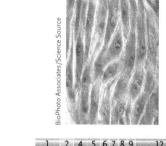

Smooth muscle: Found in walls of tubes and cavities of the body, including blood vessels, the stomach and intestine, the bladder, and the uterus. Contraction of smooth muscles typically produces a squeezing motion.

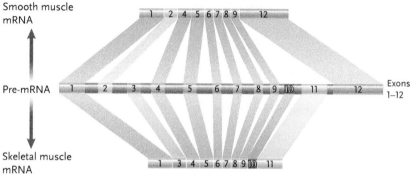

Figure 13.9
Alternative splicing of the α-tropomyosin pre-mRNA to distinct mRNA forms found in smooth muscle and skeletal muscle. All of the introns are removed in both mRNA splicing pathways, but exons 3, 10, and 11 are also removed to produce the smooth muscle mRNA, and exons 2 and 12 are also removed to produce the skeletal muscle mRNA.

Skeletal muscle: Most muscles of this type are attached by tendons to the skeleton. Their function is locomotion and movement of body parts. The human body has more than 600 skeletal muscles, ranging in size from the small muscles that move the eyeballs to the large muscles that move the legs.

structure—directs the folding of the chain into its three-dimensional shape. Therefore, the two forms of tropomyosin fold into related, but different, shapes. In its role in muscle contraction in smooth muscles and skeletal muscles, tropomyosin interacts with other proteins. The interactions depend upon the specific structural form of the tropomyosin, and, as you might expect, the two forms participate in different types of muscle action; typically smooth muscles perform squeezing actions in blood vessels and internal organs, whereas skeletal muscles pull on the bones of the skeleton to move body parts.

Alternative splicing causes us to further reconsider the one gene–one polypeptide hypothesis introduced earlier in the chapter. We must now accept the fact that for some genes at least, one gene may specify a number of polypeptides, each of which has a related function.

Exon Shuffling. Another advantage provided by introns may come from the fact that intron–exon junctions often fall at points dividing major functional regions in encoded proteins. The functional divisions may have allowed new proteins to evolve by exon shuffling, a process by which existing protein regions or domains, already selected for due to their useful functions, are mixed into novel combinations to create new proteins. Evolution by this mechanism would produce new proteins with novel functions much more quickly than by changes in individual nucleotides at random points (see Section 16.4b).

STUDY BREAK

1. What are the similarities and differences between pre-mRNAs and mRNAs?
2. What is the role of base-pairing in mRNA splicing?
3. How is it possible for an organism to produce more proteins than it has genes for?

13.4 Translation: mRNA-Directed Polypeptide Synthesis

Translation is the assembly of amino acids into polypeptides on ribosomes. In prokaryotic organisms, translation takes place throughout the cell, whereas in eukaryotes it occurs in the cytoplasm. (However, a few specialized genes are transcribed and translated in mitochondria and chloroplasts.)

Figure 13.10 summarizes the translation process. In prokaryotic cells, the mRNA produced by transcription is not confined within a nucleus and is therefore available immediately for translation. However, for eukaryotes the mRNA produced by splicing of the pre-mRNA first exits the nucleus and is then translated in the cytoplasm. In translation, the mRNA associates with a ribosome and another type of RNA, transfer RNA (tRNA), which brings amino acids to the complex to be joined, one by one, into the polypeptide chain. The sequence of amino acids in the polypeptide chain is determined by the sequence of codons in the mRNA. The mRNA is read from the 5' end to the 3' end; the polypeptide is assembled from the **N-terminal end** to the **C-terminal end**.

In this section, we will start by discussing the key players in the process, the tRNAs and ribosomes, and then walk through the translation process from a start codon to a stop codon.

13.4a tRNAs Are Small RNAs of a Highly Distinctive Structure That Bring Amino Acids to the Ribosome

Transfer RNAs (tRNAs) bring amino acids to the ribosome for addition to the polypeptide chain.

tRNA Structure. tRNAs are small RNAs, about 75 to 90 nucleotides long (mRNAs are typically hundreds of nucleotides long), with a highly distinctive structure that accomplishes their role in translation **(Figure 13.11)**. All tRNAs can base-pair with themselves to wind into four double-helical segments, forming a cloverleaf pattern in two dimensions. At the tip of one of the double-helical segments is the **anticodon**, the three-nucleotide segment that base-pairs with a codon in mRNAs. At the other end of the cloverleaf, opposite the anticodon, is a free 3' end of the molecule that links to the amino acid corresponding to the anticodon. For example, a tRNA that

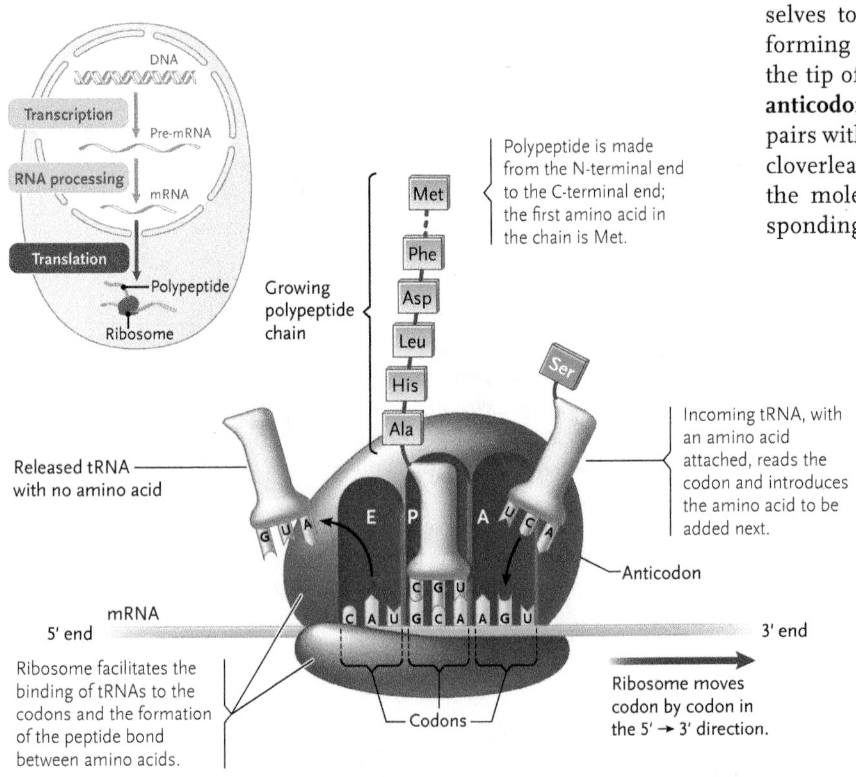

Polypeptide is made from the N-terminal end to the C-terminal end; the first amino acid in the chain is Met.

Incoming tRNA, with an amino acid attached, reads the codon and introduces the amino acid to be added next.

Released tRNA with no amino acid

Ribosome facilitates the binding of tRNAs to the codons and the formation of the peptide bond between amino acids.

Ribosome moves codon by codon in the 5' → 3' direction.

Figure 13.10

An overview of translation, in which ribosomes assemble amino acids into a polypeptide chain. The figure shows a ribosome in the process of translation. A tRNA molecule with an amino acid bound to it is entering the ribosome on the right. The anticodon on the tRNA will pair with the codon in the mRNA. Its amino acid will then be added to the growing polypeptide that is currently attached to the tRNA in the middle of the ribosome. As it assembles a polypeptide chain, the ribosome moves from one codon to the next along the mRNA in the 5' → 3' direction.

Dr. Steve Zimmerly, *University of Calgary*

Steve Zimmerly and his colleagues think they know where introns came from.

Biology students (and researchers) often wonder about the origins of introns, and to investigate this question, Zimmerly collected and analyzed a large number of examples of a type of intron called "Group II" from plant organelles and bacteria. Group II introns have two fascinating abilities. First, they can splice themselves out of RNA without the need for snRNPs. Second, they are mobile; these elements can copy themselves and insert at a new location **(Figure 1)**.

The Zimmerly lab proposed a model for intron evolution that suggests the introns in nuclear genes of higher eukaryotes evolved from mobile Group II introns originating in prokaryotic cells. These Group II introns may have spread to eukaryotes at the time when their bacterial hosts

were engulfed by eukaryotic cells to become endosymbiotic mitochondria and chloroplasts. Over evolutionary time, the nuclear introns lost their mobility and became dependent on spliceosomes for accurate splicing.

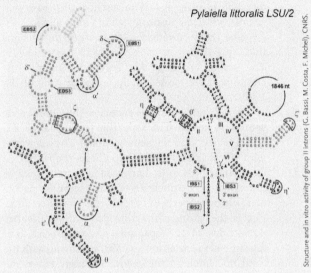

Pylaiella littoralis LSU/2

Structure and in vitro activity of group II introns (C. Bassi, M. Costa, F. Michel), CNRS.

Figure 1
Sequence of a Group II intron showing extensive complementary base-pairing with itself.

a. A tRNA molecule in two dimensions (yeast alanine tRNA)

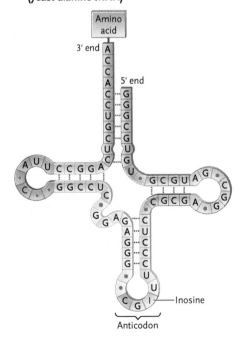

b. A tRNA molecule in three dimensions

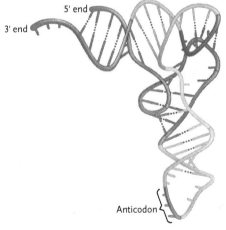

c. How an aminoacyl–tRNA complex is shown in this book

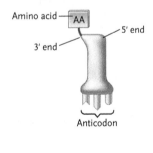

Figure 13.11
tRNA structure. The red dots show sites where bases are chemically modified into other forms; chemical modification of certain bases is typical of tRNAs. This tRNA has the purine inosine (I) in the anticodon, which has relatively loose base-pairing ability, allowing this single tRNA to pair with each of three alanine codons: 5'-GCU-3', 5'-GCC-3', and 5'-GCA-3'. This tRNA also has the unusual base pair G–U. Unusual base pairs, allowed by the greater flexibility of short RNA chains, are common in tRNAs.

is linked to serine (Ser) pairs with the codon 5'-AGU-3' in mRNA (see Figure 13.11). The anticodon of the tRNA that pairs with this codon is 3'-UCA-5'.

CONCEPT FIX The anticodon and codon pair in an antiparallel manner, as do the two strands in the DNA helix. We will therefore write anticodons in the $3' \rightarrow 5'$ direction to make it easy to see how they pair with codons, which are normally written $5' \rightarrow 3'$. ●

The tRNA cloverleaf folds in three dimensions into the L-shaped structure shown in Figure 13.11b. The anticodon and the segment binding the amino acid are located at the opposite ends of the L structure.

Recall that 61 of the 64 codons of the genetic code specify an amino acid. Does this mean that 61 different tRNAs read the **sense codons?** The answer is no. Francis Crick's **wobble hypothesis** proposed that the complete set of 61 sense codons can be read by fewer than 61 distinct tRNAs because of the particular pairing properties of the bases in the anticodons. That is, the pairing of the anticodon with the first two nucleotides of the codon is always precise, but the anticodon has more flexibility in pairing with the third nucleotide of the codon. In many cases, the same tRNA's anticodon can read codons that have either U or C in the third position; for example, a tRNA carrying phenylalanine can read both codons 5'-UUU-3' and 5'-UUC-3'. Similarly, the same tRNA's anticodon can read two codons that have A or G in the third position; for example, a tRNA carrying glutamine can pair with both 5'-CAA-3' and 5'-CAG-3' codons. The special purine called inosine in the alanine tRNA shown in Figure 13.11a allows even more extensive wobble by allowing the tRNA to pair with codons that have one of U, C, and A in the third position.

Addition of Amino Acids to Their Corresponding tRNAs. The correct amino acid must be present on a tRNA if translation is to be accurate. The process of adding an amino acid to a tRNA is called **aminoacylation** (literally, the addition of an amino acid) or **charging** (because the process adds free energy as the amino acid–tRNA combinations are formed).

The finished product of charging, a tRNA linked to its "correct" amino acid, is called an **aminoacyl–tRNA**. A collection of different enzymes called **aminoacyl–tRNA synthetases** catalyzes aminoacylation, as shown in **Figure 13.12**. This energy in the aminoacyl–tRNA eventually drives the formation of the **peptide bond** linking amino acids during translation.

With the tRNAs attached to their corresponding amino acids, our attention moves to the ribosome, where the amino acids are removed from tRNAs and linked into polypeptide chains.

13.4b Ribosomes Are rRNA–Protein Complexes That Work as Automated Protein Assembly Machines

Ribosomes are ribonucleoprotein particles that carry out protein synthesis by translating mRNA into chains of amino acids. Like some automated machines, such as those forming complicated metal parts by a series of machining steps, ribosomes use an information tape—an mRNA molecule—as the directions required to accomplish a task. For ribosomes, the task is to join amino acids into ordered sequences to make a polypeptide chain.

In prokaryotic cells, ribosomes carry out their assembly functions throughout the cell. In eukaryotes, ribosomes function only in the cytoplasm, either suspended freely in the cytoplasmic solution or attached to the membranes of the endoplasmic reticulum (ER), the system of membrane-bound tubular or flattened sacs in the cytoplasm. A finished ribosome is made up of two parts of dissimilar size, called the *large* and *small ribosomal subunits* **(Figure 13.13)**. Each subunit is made up of a combination of ribosomal RNA (rRNA) and ribosomal proteins.

CONCEPT FIX The endosymbiotic origin of chloroplasts and mitochondria in eukaryotic cells is reflected by the fact that these organelles still code for their own "prokaryotic" ribosomes that are distinct from those in the cytoplasm. ●

Prokaryotic and eukaryotic ribosomes are similar in structure and function. However, the differences in their molecular structure, particularly in the ribosomal proteins, give them distinct properties. For example, the antibiotics streptomycin and erythromycin are effective antibacterial agents because they inhibit bacterial, but not eukaryotic, ribosomes.

To fulfill its role in translation, the ribosome has special binding sites active in bringing together mRNA with aminoacyl–tRNAs (see Figure 13.13 and refer also to Figure 13.10, p. 300). One such site is where the mRNA threads a bent path through the ribosome. The **A site** (aminoacyl site) is where the incoming aminoacyl–tRNA (carrying the next amino acid to be added to the polypeptide chain) binds to the mRNA. The **P site** (peptidyl site) is where the tRNA carrying the growing polypeptide chain is bound. The **E site** (exit site) is where an exiting tRNA binds as it leaves the ribosome.

13.4c Translation Initiation Brings the Ribosomal Subunits, an mRNA, and the First Aminoacyl–tRNA Together

There are three major stages of translation: *initiation, elongation,* and *termination.* During initiation, the translation components assemble on the start codon of the mRNA. In elongation, the assembled complex reads the string of codons in the mRNA one at a time

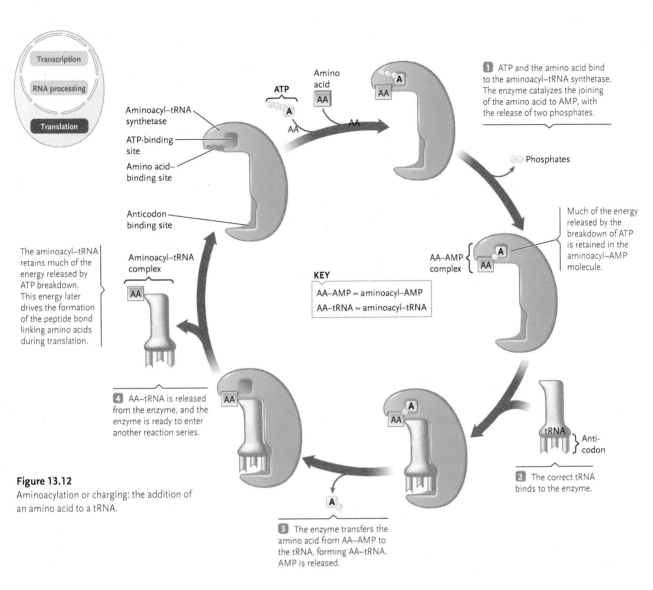

Aminoacyl–tRNA synthetase

ATP-binding site

Amino acid–binding site

Anticodon binding site

The aminoacyl–tRNA retains much of the energy released by ATP breakdown. This energy later drives the formation of the peptide bond linking amino acids during translation.

Aminoacyl–tRNA complex

1 ATP and the amino acid bind to the aminoacyl–tRNA synthetase. The enzyme catalyzes the joining of the amino acid to AMP, with the release of two phosphates.

Phosphates

Much of the energy released by the breakdown of ATP is retained in the aminoacyl–AMP molecule.

AA–AMP complex

KEY

AA–AMP = aminoacyl–AMP
AA–tRNA = aminoacyl–tRNA

tRNA

Anticodon

2 The correct tRNA binds to the enzyme.

4 AA–tRNA is released from the enzyme, and the enzyme is ready to enter another reaction series.

Figure 13.12
Aminoacylation or charging: the addition of an amino acid to a tRNA.

3 The enzyme transfers the amino acid from AA–AMP to the tRNA, forming AA–tRNA. AMP is released.

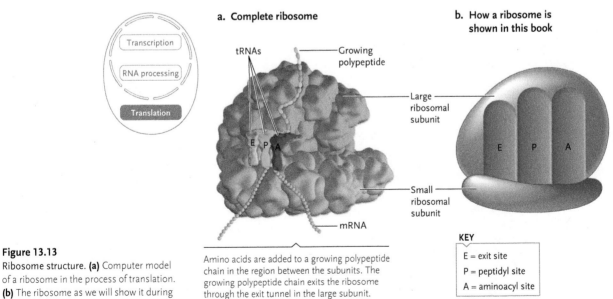

a. Complete ribosome

tRNAs

Growing polypeptide

Large ribosomal subunit

E P A

Small ribosomal subunit

mRNA

b. How a ribosome is shown in this book

Large ribosomal subunit

E P A

Small ribosomal subunit

KEY

E = exit site
P = peptidyl site
A = aminoacyl site

Figure 13.13
Ribosome structure. **(a)** Computer model of a ribosome in the process of translation. **(b)** The ribosome as we will show it during translation in this book.

Amino acids are added to a growing polypeptide chain in the region between the subunits. The growing polypeptide chain exits the ribosome through the exit tunnel in the large subunit.

while joining the specified amino acids into the polypeptide. Termination completes the translation process when the complex disassembles after the last amino acid of the polypeptide specified by the mRNA has been added to the polypeptide.

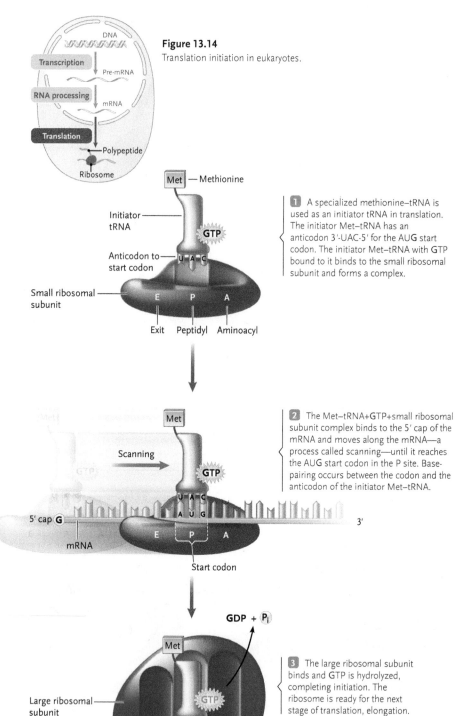

Figure 13.14
Translation initiation in eukaryotes.

1 A specialized methionine–tRNA is used as an initiator tRNA in translation. The initiator Met–tRNA has an anticodon 3'-UAC-5' for the AUG start codon. The initiator Met–tRNA with GTP bound to it binds to the small ribosomal subunit and forms a complex.

2 The Met–tRNA+GTP+small ribosomal subunit complex binds to the 5' cap of the mRNA and moves along the mRNA—a process called scanning—until it reaches the AUG start codon in the P site. Base-pairing occurs between the codon and the anticodon of the initiator Met–tRNA.

3 The large ribosomal subunit binds and GTP is hydrolyzed, completing initiation. The ribosome is ready for the next stage of translation, elongation.

Figure 13.14 illustrates the steps of translation initiation in eukaryotes. In bacteria, translation initiation is similar in using a special initiator Met–tRNA and GTP, but the way in which the ribosome assembles at the start codon is different than in eukaryotes. Rather than scanning from the 5' end of the mRNA, the small ribosomal subunit, the initiator Met–tRNA and GTP bind directly to the region of the mRNA with the AUG start codon. This initiation complex is then guided by the **ribosome binding site**—a short, specific RNA sequence—just upstream of the start codon on the mRNA that base-pairs with a complementary sequence of rRNA in the small ribosomal subunit. The large ribosomal subunit then binds to the small subunit to complete the ribosome. GTP hydrolysis then begins translation.

After the initiator tRNA pairs with the AUG initiator codon, the subsequent stages of translation simply read the codons one at a time on the mRNA. The initiator tRNA–AUG pairing thus establishes the correct **reading frame**—the series of codons for the polypeptide encoded by the mRNA. This is often referred to as the open reading frame.

13.4d Polypeptide Chains Grow during the Elongation Stage of Translation

The central reactions of translation take place in the elongation stage, which adds amino acids one at a time to a growing polypeptide chain. The individual steps of elongation depend on the binding properties of the P, A, and E sites of the ribosome. The P site, with one exception, can bind only to a **peptidyl–tRNA**, that is, a tRNA linked to a growing polypeptide chain containing two or more amino acids. The exception is the initiator tRNA, which is recognized by the P site as a peptidyl–tRNA even though it carries only a single amino acid, methionine. The A site can bind only to an aminoacyl–tRNA. The tRNA that was previously in the P site is shifted to the E site and then leaves the ribosome.

Figure 13.15 shows the elongation cycle of translation. The cycle begins at the point when an initiator tRNA with its attached methionine is bound to the P site, and the A site is empty (top of figure). The first step in each round of the cycle is the binding of the appropriate aminoacyl–tRNA to the codon in the A site of the ribosome (step 1). This binding is facilitated by a protein **elongation factor (EF)** that is bound to the aminoacyl–tRNA and that is released once the tRNA binds to the codon. Another EF is used when the ribosome translocates along the mRNA to the next codon (step 3). Each EF is released after its job is completed. GTP hydrolysis is used to power the ribosome along the mRNA. In elongation, a peptide bond is formed between the C-terminal end of the growing polypeptide on the P site tRNA and the amino acid on the A site tRNA (step 2). **Peptidyl transferase** catalyzes this reaction. As we noted in an earlier example of the splicing reaction, researchers have demonstrated that the enzyme activity in the large ribosomal subunit is not a protein but a ribozyme (catalytic RNA) within the large subunit.

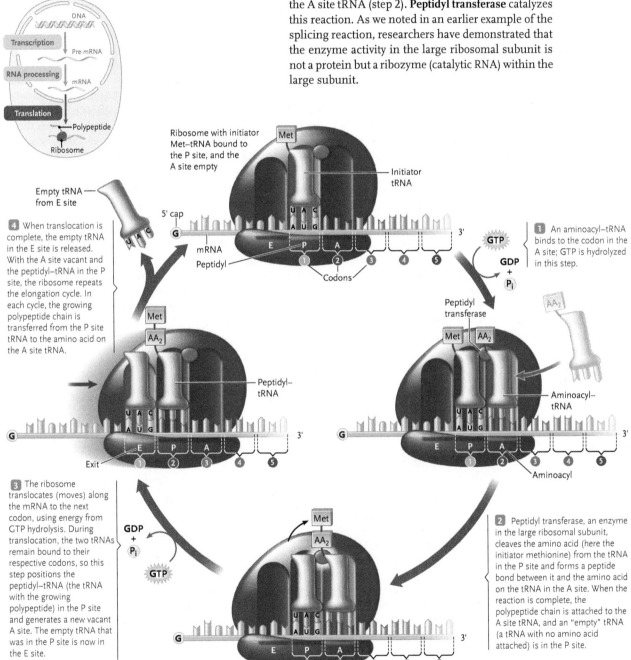

Figure 13.15

Translation elongation. A protein elongation factor (EF) complexes with the aminoacyl–tRNA to bring it to the ribosome, and another EF is needed for ribosome translocation. For simplicity, the EFs are not shown in the figure.

The elongation cycle is quite similar in prokaryotic cells and eukaryotes, turning at the rate of about 1 to 3 times per second in eukaryotes versus 15 to 20 times per second in bacteria.

13.4e Termination Releases a Completed Polypeptide from the Ribosome

Translation termination is similar in prokaryotic and eukaryotic cells; it takes place when one of the stop codons on the mRNA, UAG, UAA, or UGA arrives in the A site of a ribosome **(Figure 13.16)**. A protein **release factor (RF;** also called a **termination factor)** binds in the A site and causes the ribosome to disassemble into its subunits.

CONCEPT FIX Since the termination factor is a protein, and not a tRNA, it cannot base-pair with the stop codon. It has a similar shape as tRNA and simply wins the competition to occupy the A site of the ribosome since there are no competing tRNAs that recognize termination codons. ⬡

13.4f Multiple Ribosomes Simultaneously Translate a Single mRNA

Once the first ribosome has begun translation, another one can assemble with an initiator tRNA as soon as there is room at the 5′ UTR of the mRNA. Ribosomes continue to attach as translation continues and become spaced along the mRNA like beads on a string. The entire structure of an mRNA molecule and the multiple ribosomes attached to it is known as a **polysome** (a contraction of *polyribosome;* **Figure 13.17, p. 308**). The multiple ribosomes greatly increase the overall rate of polypeptide synthesis from a single mRNA. The total number of ribosomes in a polysome depends on the length of the coding region of its mRNA molecule, ranging from a minimum of one or two ribosomes on the smallest mRNAs to as many as 100 on the longest mRNAs.

In prokaryotic cells, because of the absence of a nuclear envelope, transcription and translation are typically coupled. As soon as the 5′ end of a new mRNA emerges from the RNA polymerase, ribosomal subunits attach and initiate translation. By the time the mRNA is completely transcribed, it is covered with ribosomes from end to end, each assembling a copy of the encoded polypeptide. Meanwhile, several other RNA polymerases have likely begun transcribing the same gene, each one trailing a collection of translating ribosomes **(Figure 13.18, p. 308)**. Such a system allows prokaryotic cells to regulate the production very quickly in response to changing environmental conditions.

13.4g Newly Synthesized Polypeptides Are Processed and Folded into Finished Form

Most eukaryotic proteins are in an inactive, unfinished form when ribosomes release them. Processing reactions that convert the new proteins into the finished form include the removal of amino acids from the ends or interior of the polypeptide chain and the addition of larger organic groups, including carbohydrate or lipid structures.

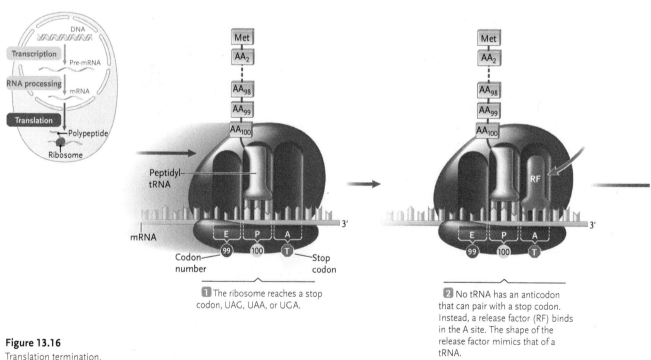

1 The ribosome reaches a stop codon, UAG, UAA, or UGA.

2 No tRNA has an anticodon that can pair with a stop codon. Instead, a release factor (RF) binds in the A site. The shape of the release factor mimics that of a tRNA.

Figure 13.16
Translation termination.

MOLECULE BEHIND BIOLOGY 13.2

Amanitin

Alpha-amanitin is one of several potent toxins found in various species of the mushroom *Amanita* (Figure 1). Although composed of many amino-acid backbones linked in a ring, this interesting molecule is not a protein. It is the product of a metabolic pathway; it is not produced by translation. In the laboratory, amanitin is a useful inhibitor of eukaryotic RNA polymerase. However, on the dinner table, amanitin is a powerful poison. People suffering from amanitin poisoning show extensive, and usually fatal, liver and kidney damage.

a.

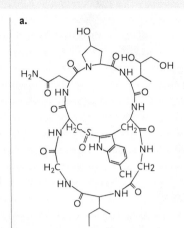

b.

Figure 1
(a) The very striking double circular structure of amanitin. (b) Amanita phalloides.

Proteins fold into their final three-dimensional shapes as the processing reactions take place. For many proteins, helper proteins called chaperones or chaperonins assist the folding process by combining with the folding protein, promoting correct three-dimensional structures and inhibiting incorrect ones.

In some cases, the same initial polypeptide may be processed by alternative pathways that produce different mature polypeptides, usually by removing different, long stretches of amino acids from the interior of the polypeptide chain. Alternative processing is another mechanism, distinct from alternative splicing of mRNA, that increases the number of proteins encoded by a single gene.

Other proteins are processed into an initial, inactive form that is later activated at a particular time or location

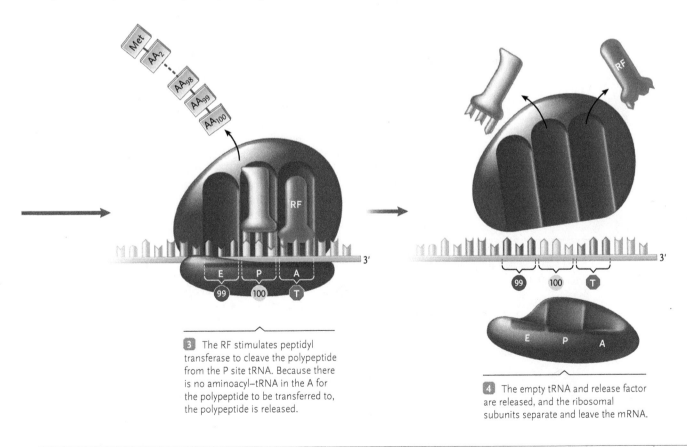

3 The RF stimulates peptidyl transferase to cleave the polypeptide from the P site tRNA. Because there is no aminoacyl–tRNA in the A for the polypeptide to be transferred to, the polypeptide is released.

4 The empty tRNA and release factor are released, and the ribosomal subunits separate and leave the mRNA.

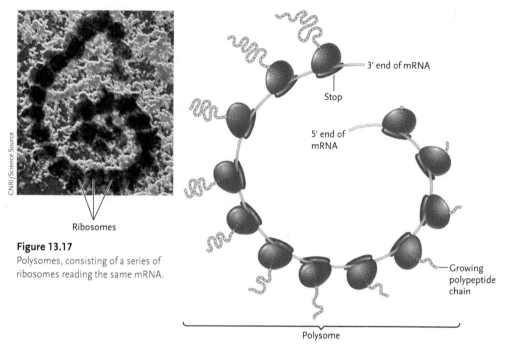

Figure 13.17
Polysomes, consisting of a series of ribosomes reading the same mRNA.

3' end of mRNA

Stop

5' end of mRNA

Growing polypeptide chain

Polysome

sorting and delivery system, cells would wind up as a jumble of proteins floating about in the cytoplasm, with none of the spatial organization that makes cellular life possible.

Although translation of all proteins begins on free ribosomes in the cytosol, there are three types of final destination compartments where the final products may be needed: (1) the cytosol; (2) the endomembrane system, which includes the Golgi complex, lysosomes, secretory vesicles, the nuclear envelope, and the plasma membrane; and (3) other membrane-bound organelles distinct from the endomembrane system, including the nucleus, mitochondria, chloroplasts, and microbodies (for example, **peroxisomes**).

by removal of a covering segment of the amino acid chain. The digestive enzyme pepsin, for example, is made by cells lining the stomach in an inactive form called **pepsinogen**. When the cells secrete pepsinogen into the stomach, the high acidity of that organ triggers removal of a segment of amino acids, thus converting the enzyme into an active form that rapidly degrades food proteins in food particles. The initial production of the protein as inactive pepsinogen protects the cells that make it from having their own proteins degraded by the enzyme.

13.4h Finished Proteins Are Sorted to the Cellular Locations Where They Function

Eukaryotic cells are structurally compartmentalized, with various organelles performing specialized functions. Therefore, every protein that is made must be delivered to its appropriate compartment. Without a

Protein Sorting to the Cytoplasm. Proteins that function in the cytosol are simply released from ribosomes once translation is completed. Examples of proteins that function in the cytoplasm are cytoskeleton proteins (for example, tubulin and keratin) and the enzymes that carry out glycolysis (see Section 6.3).

Protein Sorting to the Endomembrane System. The endomembrane system is a major traffic network for proteins. Polypeptides that sort to the endomembrane system begin their synthesis on free ribosomes in the cytosol and produce a short segment of amino acids called a **signal sequence** (also called a **signal peptide**) near their N-terminal ends. As **Figure 13.19** shows, the signal sequence is recognized by a signal recognition particle that initiates a series of steps that ultimately result in the polypeptide entering the lumen (interior) of the rough ER. This mechanism is called **cotranslational import** because import of the polypeptide into the ER occurs simultaneously with translation of the mRNA encoding the polypeptide.

▶ CONCEPT FIX Ribosomes engaged in cotranslational import stud the surface of the ER and give rise to the term *rough*. Note that ribosomes do not sit on the rough ER waiting for mRNA to translate. Rather, they only associate with the ER *after* they have begun translation as free ribosomes in the cytosol. ⬡

The signal sequence was discovered in 1975 by Günter Blobel, B. Dobberstein, and colleagues at Rockefeller University in New York when they observed that proteins sorted through the endomembrane system initially contain extra amino acids at their N-terminal ends. Blobel received a Nobel Prize

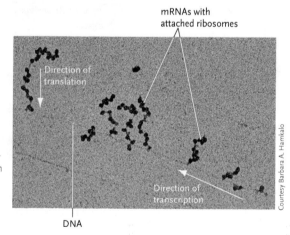

mRNAs with attached ribosomes

Direction of translation

Direction of transcription

DNA

Courtesy Barbara A. Hamkalo

Figure 13.18
Simultaneous transcription and translation in progress in an electron microscope preparation extracted from *E. coli*, × 5 700 000.

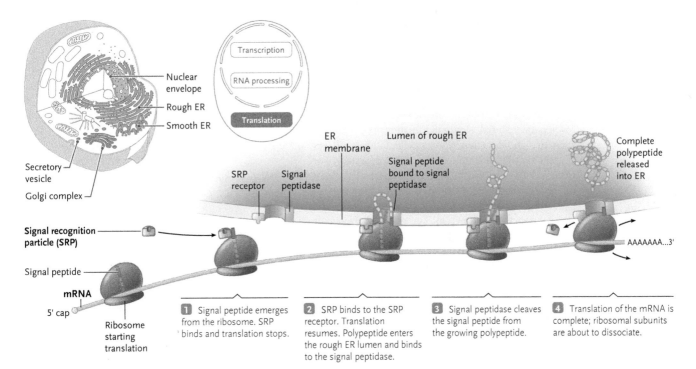

Figure 13.19
The signal mechanism directing proteins to the ER. The figure shows several ribosomes at different stages of translation of the mRNA.

Labels in figure:
- Nuclear envelope
- Rough ER
- Smooth ER
- Transcription
- RNA processing
- Translation
- Secretory vesicle
- Golgi complex
- ER membrane
- Lumen of rough ER
- Signal peptide bound to signal peptidase
- Complete polypeptide released into ER
- SRP receptor
- Signal peptidase
- Signal recognition particle (SRP)
- Signal peptide
- mRNA
- 5' cap
- Ribosome starting translation
- AAAAAAA...3'

1. Signal peptide emerges from the ribosome. SRP binds and translation stops.

2. SRP binds to the SRP receptor. Translation resumes. Polypeptide enters the rough ER lumen and binds to the signal peptidase.

3. Signal peptidase cleaves the signal peptide from the growing polypeptide.

4. Translation of the mRNA is complete; ribosomal subunits are about to dissociate.

in 1999 for his work with the mechanism of sorting proteins in cells.

Once inside the lumen of the rough ER, proteins fold into their final form. They also have, or obtain, a type of tag—a postal code if you will—that targets each protein for sorting to its final destination. Depending on the protein and its destination, the tag may be an amino acid sequence already coded in the protein, or a functional group or short sugar chain added to the protein in the lumen. Some proteins remain in the ER, whereas others are transported to the Golgi complex, where they may be modified further. From the Golgi complex, proteins are packaged into vesicles, which may deliver them to lysosomes, secrete them from the cell (digestive enzymes, for example), or deposit them in the plasma membrane (cell surface receptors, for instance).

Protein Sorting to the Nucleus, Mitochondria, Chloroplasts, and Microbodies. Proteins are sorted to the nucleus, mitochondria, chloroplasts, and microbodies after they have been made on free ribosomes in the cytosol. This mechanism of sorting is called **posttranslational import**. Proteins destined for the mitochondria, chloroplasts, and microbodies have short amino acid sequences called **transit sequences** at their N-terminal ends that target them to the appropriate organelle. The protein is taken up into the correct organelle by interactions between its transit sequences and organelle-specific transport complexes in the membrane of the appropriate organelle. A transit peptidase enzyme within the organelle then removes the transit sequence.

Proteins sorted to the nucleus, such as the enzymes for DNA replication and RNA transcription, have short amino acid sequences called **nuclear localization signals**. A cytosolic transport protein binds to the signal and moves the nuclear protein to the nuclear pore complex, where it is then transported into the nucleus. The localization signal is never removed from nuclear proteins because they need to reenter the nucleus each time the nuclear envelope breaks down and reforms during the cell division cycle.

Although prokaryotic cells are structurally simpler than eukaryotes, the same basic system of molecular sorting signals distributes proteins throughout prokaryotic cells. In prokaryotic organisms, signals similar to the ER-directing signals of eukaryotes direct newly synthesized bacterial proteins to the plasma membrane (bacteria do not have ER membranes); further information built into the proteins keeps them in the plasma membrane or allows them to enter the cell wall or to be secreted outside the cell. Proteins without sorting signals remain in the cytoplasm. The similarity of mechanisms across all cells suggests that protein sorting is a very ancient evolutionary innovation.

13.4i Mutations Can Affect Protein Structure and Function

To this point in the chapter, we have been building an understanding of how the sequence of DNA bases in genes is directly related to the structure and function of the polypeptides that they encode. We will close the chapter with consideration of how various types of small changes in the DNA sequence might affect protein structure. (Contrast these small changes with the rather large-scale changes associated with the movement of mobile genetic elements in Chapter 9 and the chromosomal rearrangements in Chapter 11.)

Mutations are changes in the sequence of bases in the genetic material. How will mutations affect protein structure and function? Your understanding of this chapter should lead you to respond, "It depends." For instance, let's consider several different mutations in the protein-coding region of a gene, as shown in **Figure 13.20**. The normal (unmutated) DNA and amino acid sequences are shown in Figure 13.20a. **Base-pair substitution mutations** involve a change of one particular base to another in the genetic material. This will cause a change in a base in a codon in mRNA.

If a mutation alters the codon to specify a different amino acid, then the resulting protein will have a different amino acid sequence. We call this a **missense mutation** because although an amino acid is placed in the polypeptide, it is the wrong one (see Figure 13.20b). Whether the polypeptide's function is altered significantly or not depends on which amino acid is changed and what it is changed to. A missense mutation in the gene for one of the two hemoglobin polypeptides **(Figure 13.21)** results in the genetic disorder sickle cell disease, described in Chapter 10.

A second type of base-pair substitution mutation is a **nonsense mutation** (see Figure 13.20c). In this case, the mutation changes a sense (amino acid–coding) codon to a nonsense (termination) codon in the mRNA. Translation of an mRNA containing a nonsense mutation results in a premature "stop" and a shorter-than-normal polypeptide. This polypeptide will likely be partially functional at best.

Because of the degeneracy of the genetic code, some base-pair substitution mutations do not alter the amino acid specified by the gene because the changed codon specifies the same amino acid as in the normal polypeptide. Such mutations are known as **silent mutations** (see Figure 13.20d).

If a single base pair is deleted or inserted in the coding region of a gene, the reading frame of the resulting mRNA is altered. That is, after that point, the ribosome reads codons that are not the same as for the normal mRNA, typically producing a completely different amino acid sequence in the polypeptide from then on. This type of mutation is called a **frameshift mutation** (see Figure 13.20e; insertion mutation shown); the resulting polypeptide is usually nonfunctional because of the significantly altered amino acid sequence. The protein may be longer or shorter than usual, depending on where the stop codons occur in the shifted reading frame.

Figure 13.20

Effects of base-pair mutations in protein-coding genes on the amino acid sequence of the encoded polypeptide.

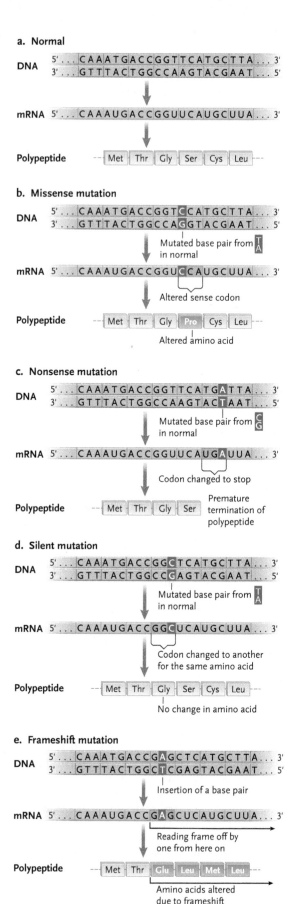

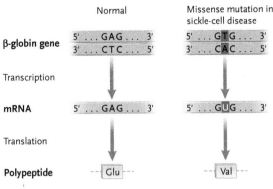

	Normal	Missense mutation in sickle-cell disease
β-globin gene	5′ ...GAG... 3′ 3′ ...CTC... 5′	5′ ...GTG... 3′ 3′ ...CAC... 5′
Transcription	↓	↓
mRNA	5′ ...GAG... 3′	5′ ...GUG... 3′
Translation	↓	↓
Polypeptide	--⌐Glu¬--	--⌐Val¬--

Figure 13.21

Missense mutation in a gene for one of the two polypeptides of hemoglobin that is the cause of sickle cell disease.

Both transcription and translation are steps in the process of gene expression, the realization of the gene's coded information in the makeup and activities of a cell. However, we will see in the next chapter that the flow of information is not one way; organisms and cells also exert control over how their genes are expressed.

STUDY BREAK

1. How does translation initiation occur in eukaryotes versus prokaryotic cells?
2. Distinguish among the E, P, and A sites of the ribosome.
3. How are proteins directed to different parts of a eukaryotic cell?

Review

To access course materials such as Aplia and other companion resources, please visit www.NELSONbrain.com.

13.1 The Connection between DNA, RNA, and Protein

- In their genetic experiments with *Neurospora crassa*, Beadle and Tatum found a direct correspondence between gene mutations and alterations of enzymes. Their one gene–one enzyme hypothesis is now restated as the one gene–one polypeptide hypothesis (Figure 13.2).
- The pathway from genes to proteins involves transcription and then translation. In transcription, a sequence of nucleotides in DNA is copied into a complementary sequence in an RNA molecule. In translation, the sequence of nucleotides in an mRNA molecule specifies an amino acid sequence in a polypeptide (Figure 13.4).
- The genetic code is a triplet code. AUG at the beginning of a coded message establishes a reading frame for reading the codons three nucleotides at a time. The code is redundant: most of the amino acids are specified by more than one codon (Figure 13.5).
- The genetic code is essentially universal.
- Aside from genes that code for protein through translation of mRNA, other genes code directly for RNA products (such as tRNA, rRNA, and snRNA) that are not translated.

13.2 Transcription: DNA-Directed RNA Synthesis

- Transcription is the process by which information coded in DNA is transferred to a complementary RNA copy (Figure 13.6).
- Transcription begins when an RNA polymerase binds to a promoter sequence in the DNA and starts synthesizing an RNA molecule. The enzyme then adds RNA nucleotides in sequence according to the DNA template. At the end of the transcribed sequence, the enzyme and the completed RNA transcript release from the DNA template. The mechanism of termination is different in eukaryotes and prokaryotic cells.

- In addition to sequences coding for amino acids, the DNA of protein-coding genes also contains several types of sequences that regulate transcription and translation.

13.3 Processing of mRNAs in Eukaryotes

- A gene encoding an mRNA molecule includes the promoter, which is recognized by the regulatory proteins and transcription factors that promote DNA unwinding and the initiation of transcription by an RNA polymerase. Transcription in eukaryotes produces a pre-mRNA molecule that consists of a 5′ cap, the 5′ untranslated region, interspersed exons (amino acid–coding segments) and introns, the 3′ untranslated regions, and the 3′ poly (A) tail. All are copied from DNA except the 5′ cap and poly (A) tail, which are added during transcription (Figure 13.7).
- Introns in pre-mRNAs are removed to produce functional mRNAs by splicing. snRNPs bind to the introns, loop them out of the pre-mRNA, clip the intron at each exon boundary, and join the adjacent exons together (Figure 13.8).
- Many pre-mRNAs are subjected to alternative splicing, a process that joins exons in different combinations to produce different mRNAs encoded by the same gene. Translation of each mRNA produced in this way generates a protein with a different function (Figure 13.9).

13.4 Translation: mRNA-Directed Polypeptide Synthesis

- Translation is the assembly of amino acids into polypeptides. Translation occurs on ribosomes. The P, A, and E sites of the ribosome are used for the stepwise addition of amino acids to the polypeptide as directed by the mRNA (Figures 13.10 and 13.13).
- Amino acids are brought to the ribosome attached to specific tRNAs. Amino acids are linked to their

corresponding tRNAs by aminoacyl-tRNA synthetases. By matching amino acids with tRNAs, the reactions also provide the ultimate basis for the accuracy of translation (Figures 13.14 and 13.15).

- Translation proceeds through the stages of initiation, elongation, and termination. In initiation, a ribosome assembles with an mRNA molecule and an initiator methionine-tRNA. In elongation, amino acids linked to tRNAs are added one at a time to the growing polypeptide chain. In termination, the new polypeptide is released from the ribosome and the ribosomal subunits separate from the mRNA (Figure 13.16).

- After they are synthesized on ribosomes, polypeptides are converted into finished form by processing reactions, which include removal of one or more amino acids from the protein chains, addition of

organic groups, and folding guided by chaperones.

- Proteins are distributed in cells by means of signals spelled out by amino acid sequences at the N-terminal end of the newly translated polypeptide (Figure 13.19).

- Mutations in the DNA template alter the mRNA and can lead to changes in the amino acid sequence of the encoded polypeptide. A missense mutation changes one codon to one that specifies a different amino acid, a nonsense mutation changes a codon to a stop codon, and a silent mutation changes one codon to another codon that specifies the same amino acid. A base-pair insertion or deletion is a frameshift mutation that alters the reading frame beyond the point of the mutation, leading to a different amino acid sequence from then on in the polypeptide (Figures 13.20 and 13.21).

Questions

Self-Test Questions

1. Which statement about the following pathway is true?

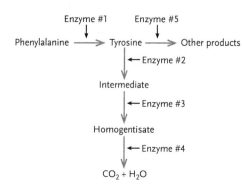

a. A mutation for enzyme #1 causes tyrosine to build up.
b. A mutation for enzyme #2 prevents tyrosine from being synthesized.
c. A mutation at enzyme #3 prevents homogentisate from being synthesized.
d. A mutation for enzyme #4 could hide a mutation in enzyme #1.

2. Which of the following statements describes *eukaryotic* mRNA?
a. It uses snRNPs to cut out introns and seal together translatable exons.
b. It is translated by ribosomes as it is being transcribed by RNA polymerase.
c. It has a guanine cap on its 3′ end and a poly (A) tail on its 5′ end.
d. It is a polymer of adenine, thymine, guanine, and cytosine bases.

3. A segment strand of DNA has a base sequence of 5′-GCATTAGAC-3′. What would be the sequence of an RNA molecule complementary to that sequence?
a. 5′-GUCTAATGC-3′
b. 5′-GCAUUAGAC-3′
c. 5′-CGTAATCTG-3′
d. 5′-GUCUAAUGC-3′

4. Which of the following statements about the initiation phase of translation in prokaryotic cells is true?
a. GTP is synthesized.
b. A region of the 5′ UTR of mRNA binds to rRNA.
c. 5′-UAC-3′ on the Met tRNA binds 3′-AUG-5′ on mRNA.
d. tRNA attaches first to the small ribosomal subunit.

5. Which of the following types of bonding involves complementary base-pairing?
a. tRNA to amino acid
b. signal peptide to signal recognition particle
c. release factor to stop codon
d. DNA to RNA during transcription of rRNA gene

6. Translation is in progress, with methionine bound to a tRNA in the P site, and a phenylalanine bound to a tRNA in the A site. What is the order of the next steps in the elongation cycle?
a. the ribosome translocates → a new aminoacyl-tRNA enters the A site → peptidyl transferase catalyzes a peptide bond between the two amino acids → empty tRNA is released from the ribosome
b. peptidyl transferase catalyzes a peptide bond between the two amino acids → a new aminoacyl-tRNA enters the A site → empty tRNA is released from the ribosome → the ribosome translocates

c. peptidyl transferase catalyzes a peptide bond between the two amino acids → the ribosome translocates → empty tRNA is released from the ribosome → a new aminoacyl-tRNA enters the A site

d. the ribosome translocates → peptidyl transferase catalyzes a peptide bond between the two amino acids → empty tRNA is released from the ribosome → a new aminoacyl-tRNA enters the A site

7. Which of the following statements about translation is true?
   a. ATP is the preferred energy source during various stages of translation.
   b. Peptide bond formation between amino acids is catalyzed by a ribozyme.
   c. When the mRNA codon UGG reaches the ribosome, there is no tRNA to bind to it.
   d. Forty-two amino acids of a protein are encoded by 84 nucleotides of the mRNA.

8. Which of the following items binds to the SRP receptor and to the signal sequence to guide a newly synthesized protein to be secreted to its proper channel?
   a. a ribosome
   b. a signal peptidase
   c. a signal recognition particle
   d. a rough ER

9. A part of an mRNA molecule with the sequence 5'-UGC GCA-3' is being translated by a ribosome. The following activated tRNA molecules are available. Which two of them can correctly bind the mRNA, resulting in a dipeptide?

tRNA Anticodon	Amino Acid
3'-GGC-5'	Proline
3'-CGU-5'	Alanine
3'-UGC-5'	Threonine
3'-CCG-5'	Glycine
3'-ACG-5'	Cysteine
3'-CGG-5'	Alanine

   a. cysteine–alanine
   b. proline–cysteine
   c. glycine–proline
   d. threonine–glycine

10. If a single base insertion mutation occurred within the first exon of a eukaryotic gene, what would be the likely result?
    a. improper splicing by spliceosome
    b. a longer mature mRNA
    c. a failure of the initiation of translation
    d. a silent mutation

Questions for Discussion

1. Would you expect rRNA genes to have start codons? Why or why not?

2. A mutation appears that alters an anticodon in a tRNA from AAU to AUU. What effect will this change have on protein synthesis in cells carrying this mutation?

3. The normal form of a gene is shown below, starting with the start codon (3' and 5' UTR are not visible):

   5'-ATGCCCGCCTTTGCTACTTGGTAG-3'

   3'-TACGGGCGGAAACGATGAACCATC-5'

   When this gene is transcribed, the result is the following mRNA molecule:

   5'-AUGCCCGCCUUUGCUACUUGGUAG-3'

   In a mutated form of the gene, two extra base pairs (underlined) are inserted:

   5'-ATGCCCGCCTAATTGCTACTTGGTAG-3'

   3'-TACGGGCGGATTAACGATGAACCATC-5'

   What effect will this mutation have on the structure of the protein encoded in the gene?

4. A geneticist is attempting to isolate mutations in the genes for four enzymes acting in a metabolic pathway in the bacterium *Escherichia coli*. The end product E of the pathway is absolutely essential for life:

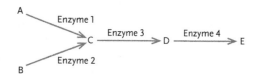

   The geneticist has been able to isolate mutations in the genes for enzymes 1 and 2, but not for enzymes 3 and 4. Develop a hypothesis to explain why.

5. How could you show experimentally that the genetic code is universal, namely, that it is the same in bacteria as it is in eukaryotes such as fungi, plants, and animals?

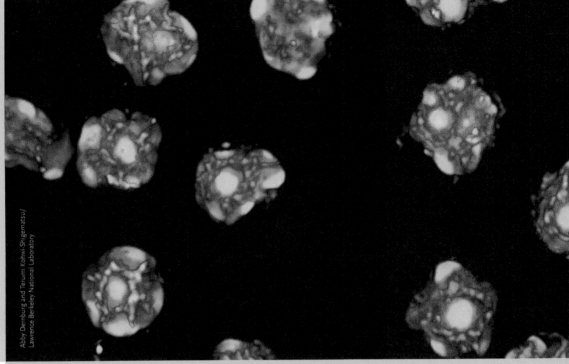

Chromatin remodelling proteins (gold) binding to chromatin (blue). Chromatin remodelling, a change in chromosome structure in the region of a gene, is a key step in the activation of genes in eukaryotes.

14

Control of Gene Expression

WHY IT MATTERS

A human egg cell is almost completely inactive metabolically when it is released from the ovary. It remains quiescent as it travels down a fallopian tube leading from the ovary to the uterus, carried along by movements of cilia lining the walls of the tube **(Figure 14.1)**. It is here, in the fallopian tube, that the egg meets sperm cells and embryonic development begins. Within seconds after the cells unite, the fertilized egg breaks its quiescent state and begins a series of divisions that continues as the egg moves through the fallopian tube and enters the uterus. Subsequent divisions produce specialized cells that *differentiate* into the distinct types tailored for the myriad specific functions in the body, from muscle cells to cells of the lens of the eye.

At first glance, you might think it most efficient for the cells in each differenti- ated tissue to retain only those genes needed to carry out its specific function; that is, liver cells might be expected to have a different collection of genes than bone cells. However, biochemical and cytogenetic analyses do not support this model and have, in fact, demonstrated that all nucleated cells of a developing embryo retain essentially the same set of genes that was created in the original single-celled zygote at fertilization. Structural and functional differences in cell types result from the presence or absence of the *products resulting from expression of genes* rather than the presence or absence of the genes themselves. As you saw in the previous chapter, all gene expression initially results in RNA products made by transcrip- tion. One type of RNA product, mRNA, further directs the synthesis of protein products by translation. But what determines when the product is produced, where, and how much? For example, the products of some genes, known as

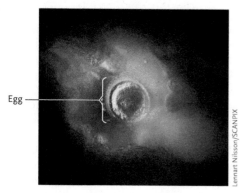

Figure 14.1
A human egg at the time of its release from the ovary. The outer layer, appearing light blue in colour, is a coat of polysaccharides and glycoproteins that surrounds the egg. Within the egg, genes and regulatory proteins are poised to enter the pathways, initiating embryonic development.

Egg

housekeeping genes, are expressed in nearly all cells, whereas the products of other genes may be found only in certain cell types at specific times under particular environmental conditions. To illustrate this point, consider that all cells contain genes coding for the rRNA molecules needed for ribosome function, as well as genes coding for various hemoglobin polypeptides. While rRNA gene products are abundant in all cells, particular hemoglobins are found only in those cells that give rise to red blood cells in the fetus, newborn, or adult.

The material in the previous chapter on transcription and translation hinted at possible regulatory mechanisms of gene expression. Usually, when we say that a gene is "turned on," we mean that it is more likely to be transcribed actively. Beyond transcription, the expression of gene products is subject to further controls affecting the processing of ribonucleic acid (RNA), possible translation into protein, and the activity and "life span" of the product itself.

You saw in the previous chapter that transcription and translation are coincident in prokaryotic cells. This enables a rapid response to environmental conditions through regulation of transcription initiation. Eukaryotes, particularly multicellular organisms, exhibit a variety of mechanisms not used by prokaryotic organisms. In this chapter, we examine the mechanisms of transcriptional regulation and its fine-tuning by additional controls at the posttranscriptional, translational, and posttranslational levels. Our discussion begins with bacterial systems, where researchers first discovered a mechanism for transcriptional regulation, and then moves to eukaryotic systems, where the regulation of gene activity is more complex. The chapter closes with a look at the loss of regulatory controls in cancer cells. The ways in which genes regulate development are discussed in Chapters 36 and 42.

14.1 Regulation of Gene Expression in Prokaryotic Cells

Transcription and translation are closely regulated in prokaryotic cells in ways that reflect prokaryotic life histories. Prokaryotic organisms tend to be single celled and relatively simple, with generation times measured in minutes. Rather than the complex patterns of long-term cell differentiation and development typical of multicellular eukaryotes, prokaryotic cells typically undergo rapid and reversible alterations in biochemical pathways that allow them to adapt quickly to changes in their environment.

The bacterium *Escherichia coli*, for example, can find itself in the intestinal tract of a cow one minute and then in a treated municipal water supply soon after. Sugars such as lactose might be more available in the aquatic environment, and genes coding for enzymes needed to metabolize this energy source must be turned on. Other nutrients, such as the amino acid tryptophan, may be abundant in the intestinal tract. Therefore, genes coding for enzymes needed to manufacture the amino acid from scratch must be turned off. A versatile and responsive control system allows the bacterium to make the most efficient use of the particular array of nutrients and energy sources available at any given time.

14.1a The Operon Is a Unit of Transcription

For a typical metabolic process, several genes are involved, and they must be regulated in a coordinated fashion. For example, three genes encode proteins for the metabolism of lactose by *E. coli*. In the absence of lactose, the three genes are transcribed very little, whereas in the presence of lactose, the genes are transcribed quite actively. That is, the on/off control of these genes is at the level of transcription.

In 1961, François Jacob and Jacques Monod of the Pasteur Institute in Paris proposed the *operon model* for the control of the expression of genes for lactose metabolism in *E. coli*. Subsequently, data have shown the operon model to be widely applicable to the regulation of gene expression in bacteria and their viruses. Jacob and Monod received the Nobel Prize in 1965 for their explanation of bacterial operons and their regulation by repressors.

An **operon** is a cluster of prokaryotic genes and the DNA sequences involved in their regulation. The promoter, as we saw in the previous chapter, is a region where the RNA polymerase begins transcription. Another regulatory DNA sequence in the operon is the **operator**, a short segment that is a binding sequence for a **regulatory protein**. A gene that is separate from the operon encodes the regulatory protein. Some operons are controlled by a regulatory protein termed a **repressor**, which, when bound to the DNA, reduces the likelihood that genes will be transcribed. Other operons are controlled by a regulatory protein termed an **activator**, which, when bound to the DNA, increases the likelihood that genes will be transcribed. Many operons are controlled by more than one regulatory mechanism, and a number of the repressors or activators control more than one operon. The result is a complex network of superimposed controls that provides regulation of transcription, allowing almost instantaneous global responses to changing environmental conditions.

Each operon, which can contain several to many genes, is transcribed as a unit from the promoter into a single messenger RNA (mRNA), and, as a result, the mRNA contains codes for several proteins. The cluster of genes transcribed into a single mRNA is called a **transcription unit**. A ribosome translates the entire mRNA from one end to the other, sequentially making each protein encoded in the mRNA. Typically, the proteins encoded by genes in the same operon catalyze steps in the same process, such as enzymes acting in sequence in a biochemical pathway.

14.1b The *lac* Operon for Lactose Metabolism Is Transcribed When an Inducer Inactivates a Repressor

Jacob and Monod researched the genetic control of lactose metabolism in *E. coli* through a series of brilliantly creative genetic and biochemical approaches. Their studies showed that metabolism of lactose as an energy source involves three genes: *lacZ*, *lacY*, and *lacA* **(Figure 14.2)**. These three genes are adjacent to one another on the chromosome in the order Z-Y-A. The genes are transcribed as a unit into a single mRNA starting with the *lacZ* gene; the promoter for the transcription unit is upstream of *lacZ*.

The *lacZ* gene encodes the enzyme β-galactosidase, which catalyzes the conversion of the disaccharide sugar, lactose, into the monosaccharide sugars, glucose and galactose. These sugars are then further metabolized by other enzymes, producing energy for the cell by glycolysis and Kreb's cycle. The *lacY* gene encodes a permease enzyme that transports lactose actively into the cell, and the *lacA* gene encodes a transacetylase enzyme, the function of which is more relevant to metabolism of compounds other than lactose.

Jacob and Monod called the cluster of genes and adjacent sequences that control their expression the *lac* operon (see Figure 14.2). They coined the name *operon* from the key DNA sequence they discovered for regulating transcription of the operon—the operator. The operator was named because it controls the operation of the genes adjacent to it. For the *lac* operon, the operator is a short DNA sequence between the promoter and the *lacZ* gene.

These two investigators showed that the *lac* operon was controlled by a regulatory protein that they termed the *Lac repressor*. The Lac repressor is encoded by the regulatory gene *lacI*, which is nearby but separate from the *lac* operon (see Figure 14.2), and is synthesized in active form. When lactose is absent from the medium, the Lac repressor binds to the operator, thereby blocking the RNA polymerase from binding to the promoter **(Figure 14.3a)**. Repressor binding is a kind of equilibrium; while it is bound to the operator most of the time, it occasionally comes off. In moments when the repressor is not bound, polymerase can successfully transcribe. As a result, *there is always a low concentration of lac operon gene products in the cell.*

When lactose is added to the medium, the *lac* operon is turned on and all three enzymes are synthesized rapidly (Figure 14.3b). How does this occur?

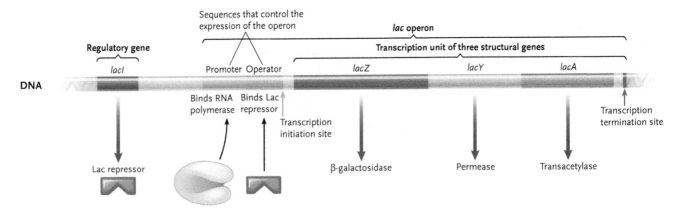

Figure 14.2

The *E. coli lac* operon. The *lacZ*, *lacY*, and *lacA* genes encode the enzymes taking part in lactose metabolism. The separate regulatory gene, *lacI*, encodes the Lac repressor, which plays a pivotal role in the control of the operon. The promoter binds RNA polymerase, and the operator binds the activated Lac repressor. The transcription unit, which extends from the transcription initiation site to the transcription termination site, contains the genes.

a. Lactose absent from medium: structural genes expressed at very low levels

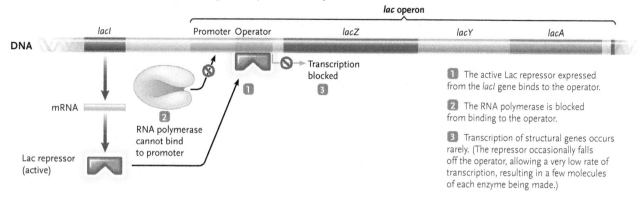

1. The active Lac repressor expressed from the *lacI* gene binds to the operator.

2. The RNA polymerase is blocked from binding to the operator.

3. Transcription of structural genes occurs rarely. (The repressor occasionally falls off the operator, allowing a very low rate of transcription, resulting in a few molecules of each enzyme being made.)

b. Lactose present in medium: structural genes expressed at high levels

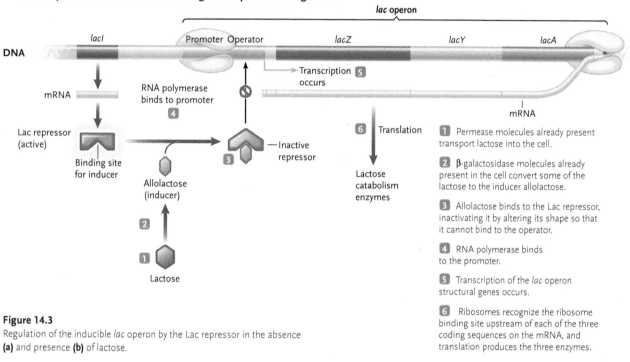

1. Permease molecules already present transport lactose into the cell.

2. β-galactosidase molecules already present in the cell convert some of the lactose to the inducer allolactose.

3. Allolactose binds to the Lac repressor, inactivating it by altering its shape so that it cannot bind to the operator.

4. RNA polymerase binds to the promoter.

5. Transcription of the *lac* operon structural genes occurs.

6. Ribosomes recognize the ribosome binding site upstream of each of the three coding sequences on the mRNA, and translation produces the three enzymes.

Figure 14.3

Regulation of the inducible *lac* operon by the Lac repressor in the absence **(a)** and presence **(b)** of lactose.

Lactose enters the cell and the low levels of β-galactosidase molecules already present convert some of it to *allolactose,* an isomer of lactose. Allolactose is an **inducer** for the *lac* operon. It binds to the Lac repressor, altering its shape so that the repressor can no longer bind to the operator DNA. With the repressor out of the way, RNA polymerase is then able to bind freely to the promoter and transcribe the three genes at a dramatically elevated rate. Because an inducer molecule increases its expression, the *lac* operon is called an **inducible operon.**

As the lactose is used up, the regulatory system switches the *lac* operon off. That is, the absence of lactose means that there are no allolactose inducer molecules to inactivate the repressor; the repressor binds to the operator, reducing transcription of the operon. These controls are aided by the fact that bacterial mRNAs are very short lived, about three minutes on average. This quick turnover permits the cytoplasm to be cleared quickly of the mRNAs transcribed from an operon. The enzymes themselves also have short lifetimes and are quickly degraded.

14.1c Transcription of the *lac* Operon Is Also Controlled by a Positive Regulatory System

Several years after Jacob and Monod proposed their negatively regulated operon model for the lactose metabolism genes, researchers found a *positive gene regulation* system that makes expression of the *lac* operon responsive to the availability of glucose. Glucose can be used directly in the glycolysis pathway to produce energy for the cell (see Chapter 6). However, lactose must first be converted into glucose by biochemical reactions that require energy. The net yield of energy from other sugars is therefore less than that for glucose, and cells will grow best if they ensure the preferential metabolism of glucose whenever it is available.

Figure 14.4 shows that the *lac* operon is sensitive to the availability of glucose through the binding of an activator protein called CAP (catabolite activator protein). The CAP binding site is on the DNA, just upstream of the *lac* promoter. When bound at this site, CAP bends the DNA in ways that make the promoter more accessible to RNA polymerase and transcription increases. To understand how CAP binding is related to the availability of glucose, you need to know that (1) CAP is synthesized in an inactive form that can only bind to DNA *after* it is activated by binding with **cyclic AMP (cAMP;** a nucleotide that plays a role in regulating cellular processes in both

a. Lactose present and glucose low or absent: structural genes expressed at very high levels

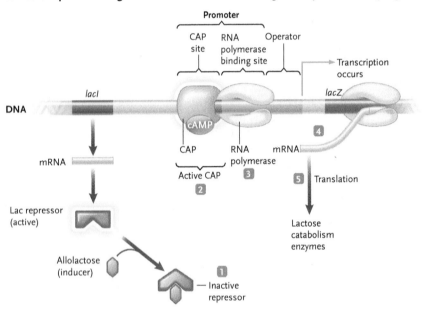

1. Lactose is converted to the inducer, allolactose, which inactivates the Lac repressor.

2. Active adenylyl cyclase synthesizes cAMP to high levels. cAMP binds to the activator CAP, activating it. Activated CAP binds to the CAP site in the promoter.

3. RNA polymerase binds efficiently to the promoter.

4. Genes of the operon are transcribed to high levels.

5. Translation produces high amounts of enzymes.

b. Lactose present and glucose present: structural genes expressed at low levels

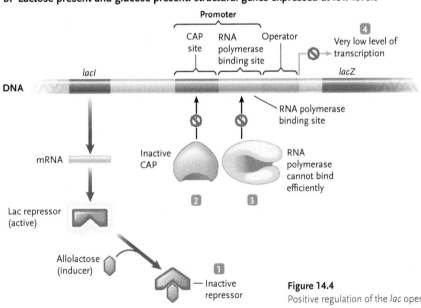

1. Lactose is converted to the inducer, allolactose, which inactivates the Lac repressor.

2. Catabolism of incoming glucose leads to inactivation of adenylyl cyclase, which causes the amount of cAMP in the cell to drop to a level too low to activate CAP. Inactive CAP cannot bind to the CAP site.

3. RNA polymerase is unable to bind to the promoter efficiently.

4. Transcription occurs at a low level: because the Lac repressor is not present to block RNA polymerase from binding to the promoter, the level of transcription is higher than when lactose is absent, but far lower than when lactose is present and glucose is absent.

Figure 14.4

Positive regulation of the *lac* operon through binding of the CAP activator protein.

prokaryotic and eukaryotic cells), and (2) cAMP levels are inversely related to the uptake of glucose from the growth medium; when glucose is abundant, cAMP levels tend to be low (meaning CAP is mostly inactive). When glucose is absent from the environment, cAMP concentration tends to be high inside the cell, leading to an increased level of activated CAP.

Taken together, the negative control by the Lac repressor and the positive control by CAP/cAMP ensure that cells express the *lac* operon most strongly only when lactose is present and glucose is not. Let's walk through one illustrative example to emphasize the interrelationships among the various players. Imagine cells growing on glucose only. In the presence of glucose, very little cAMP is available to bind to CAP. Therefore, CAP/cAMP binding will be rare and there will be very little stimulation of expression. In the absence of lactose, the Lac repressor will be bound to the operator site most of the time and very little synthesis of the *lac* genes will occur. For these two reasons, expression of the *lac* operon will be at its lowest level. If we then add lactose to the environment, it will be metabolized to the inducer, allolactose, which will bind to and inactivate the Lac repressor. RNA polymerase will then bind to the promoter and transcribe the *lac* operon genes at a low level. Expression will increase further as glucose is metabolized from the surrounding medium, allowing cAMP levels to rise, activated CAP to bind, and the *lac* promoter to become even more available to RNA polymerase.

CONCEPT FIX Inducing *lac* operon expression through negative control and repressing expression through positive control may sound confusing. How can negative control make expression increase? The answer to this apparent paradox lies in focusing your attention on the DNA-binding proteins: the Lac repressor and CAP. In general, if the binding of a protein to DNA results in decreased gene expression, that is negative control. If the binding of a protein results in increased gene expression, that is positive control. Therefore, the binding of the Lac repressor is a clear example of negative control. When this repression is *released*, the *lac* operon is induced and expression increases. *Whether gene expression is under negative or positive control depends on the impact of the respective DNA-binding proteins, not on the impact of the available substrates such as glucose or lactose.* ⬡

The same positive gene regulation system using CAP and cAMP regulates a large number of other operons that control the metabolism of many sugars. In each case, the system functions so that glucose, if it is present in the growth medium, is metabolized first. This type of regulatory system, in which several operons are under the control of a common regulator, is called a regulon.

14.1d Transcription of the *trp* Operon Genes for Tryptophan Biosynthesis Is Repressed When Tryptophan Activates a Repressor

Tryptophan is an essential amino acid used in the synthesis of proteins. If tryptophan is absent from the medium, *E. coli* must manufacture it. If tryptophan is present in the medium, then the cell will use that source rather than make its own.

The genes involved in tryptophan biosynthesis are coordinately controlled in an operon called the *trp* operon **(Figure 14.5, p. 320)**. The five genes in this operon, *trpA* to *trpE*, encode the enzymes for the steps in the tryptophan biosynthesis pathway. Upstream of the *trpE* gene are the operon's promoter and operator sequences. Expression of the *trp* operon is controlled by the Trp repressor, a regulatory protein encoded by the *trpR* gene, which is located elsewhere in the genome (not nearby, as was the case for the repressor gene for the *lac* operon). In contrast to the Lac repressor, the Trp repressor is synthesized in an inactive form in which it cannot bind to the operator.

When tryptophan is absent from the medium and must be made by the cell, the *trp* operon genes are expressed (see Figure 14.5a). This is the default state; since the Trp repressor is inactive and cannot bind to the operator, RNA polymerase can bind to the promoter and transcribe the operon. The resulting mRNA is translated to produce the five tryptophan biosynthetic enzymes that catalyze the reactions for tryptophan synthesis.

If tryptophan is present, there is no need for the cell to make it, so the *trp* operon is shut off (see Figure 14.5b). This occurs because the tryptophan entering the cell binds to the Trp repressor and activates it. The active Trp repressor then binds to the operator of the *trp* operon and blocks RNA polymerase from binding to the promoter—the operon cannot be transcribed.

For the *trp* operon, then, the presence of tryptophan represses the expression of the tryptophan biosynthesis genes; hence, this operon is an example of a **repressible operon**. Here, tryptophan acts as a **corepressor**, a regulatory molecule that combines with a repressor to activate it and thus shut off the operon.

Let's compare and contrast the two operons we have discussed: (1) In the *lac* operon, the repressor is synthesized in an active form. When the inducer (allolactose) is present, it binds to the repressor and inactivates it. The operon is then transcribed. (2) In the *trp* operon, the repressor is synthesized in an inactive form. When the corepressor (tryptophan) is present, it binds to the repressor and activates it. The active repressor blocks transcription of the operon.

CONCEPT FIX Inducible and repressible operons both illustrate *negative gene regulation* because both are

a. Tryptophan absent from medium: tryptophan must be made by the cell—structural genes transcribed

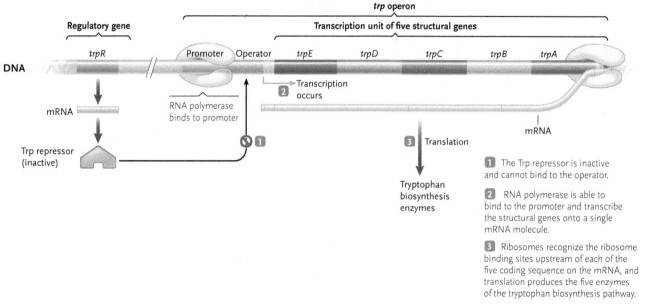

b. Tryptophan present in medium: cell uses tryptophan in medium rather than synthesizing it—structural genes not transcribed

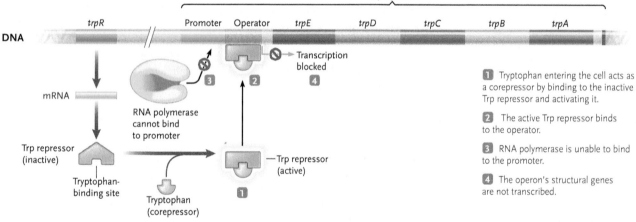

Figure 14.5

Regulation of the repressible *trp* operon by the Trp repressor protein in the absence **(a)** and presence **(b)** of the amino acid tryptophan.

regulated by a repressor that turns off gene expression when it binds DNA. ⬡

In summary, regulation of gene expression in prokaryotic cells occurs primarily at the transcription level. There are also, however, some examples of regulation at the translation level. For example, some proteins can bind to the mRNAs that produce them and modulate their translation. This serves as a feedback mechanism to fine-tune the amounts of the proteins in the cell. In the remainder of the chapter, we discuss the regulation of gene expression in eukaryotes. You will see that regulation occurs at several points in the gene expression pathway and that regulatory mechanisms are more complex than those in prokaryotic cells.

STUDY BREAK

1. Suppose the *lacI* gene is mutated so that the Lac repressor is not made. How does this mutation affect the regulation of the *lac* operon?
2. Answer the equivalent question for the *trp* operon: How would a mutation that prevents the Trp repressor from being made affect the regulation of the *trp* operon?

AI-2

Bacterial cells can communicate with one another through the production and detection of molecules called auto-inducers. When an autoinducer accumulates to high concentration in the local environment, it binds to membrane receptors that initiate a signal cascade, resulting in transcriptional activation of genes. This process, called quorum sensing, provides a mechanism for populations of cells to determine their density and thus coordinate gene expression as a community. For instance, although it is rather futile for an isolated single cell of *Vibrio harveyi* to express genes from its *lux* operon in order to bioluminesce,

hundreds of millions of cells, all expressing *lux* genes, collectively produce biologically significant amounts of light. Such large populations of bioluminescent bacteria are found in the light organs of squid. In a way, these populations of bacterial cells behave like multicellular organisms. Although various autoinducers are known to mediate communication among members of the same species, a novel compound, called AI-2 **(Figure 1),** has been found to facilitate communication between members of *different* species. AI-2 is unlike any other known autoinducer and is particularly interesting in that it

contains an atom of boron, an element whose function in biological systems has been quite mysterious.

Figure 1
AI-2, a universal autoinducer containing boron.

14.2 Regulation of Transcription in Eukaryotes

The molecular mechanisms in prokaryotic operon function are a simple means of coordinating synthesis of proteins with related functions. In eukaryotes, the coordinated synthesis of proteins with related functions also occurs, but without the need to organize genes under the control of a single promoter in an operon.

There are two general categories of eukaryotic gene regulation. Short-term regulation involves regulatory events in which gene sets are quickly turned on or off in response to changes in environmental or physiological conditions in the cell's or organism's environment. This type of regulation is most similar to prokaryotic gene regulation. Long-term gene regulation involves regulatory events required for an organism to develop and differentiate. Long-term gene regulation occurs in multicellular eukaryotes and not in simpler, unicellular eukaryotes. The mechanisms we discuss in this and the next section are applicable to both short-term and long-term regulation.

14.2a In Eukaryotes, Regulation of Gene Expression Occurs at Several Levels

The regulation of gene expression is more complicated in eukaryotes than in prokaryotic cells because eukaryotic cells are more complex, because the nuclear DNA is organized with histones into chromatin, and because multicellular eukaryotes produce large numbers and different types of cells. Further, the eukaryotic nuclear envelope separates the processes of transcription and translation, whereas in prokaryotic cells, translation

can start on an mRNA that is still being made. Consequently, gene expression in eukaryotes is regulated at more levels. That is, there is transcriptional regulation, posttranscriptional regulation, translational regulation, and posttranslational regulation **(Figure 14.6, p. 322).** The most important of these is transcriptional regulation.

14.2b Regulation of Transcription Initiation Involves the Effects of Proteins Binding to a Gene's Promoter and Regulatory Sites

Transcription initiation is the most common level at which the regulation of gene expression takes place.

Organization of a Eukaryotic Protein-Coding Gene. **Figure 14.7, p. 322,** shows a eukaryotic gene, emphasizing the regulatory sites involved in its expression. Immediately upstream of the transcription unit is the promoter. The promoter in the figure contains a **TATA box**, a sequence about 25 base pairs (bp) upstream of the start point for transcription that, as we will shortly see, plays an important role in transcription initiation in many promoters. The TATA box has the 7-bp consensus sequence

$$5'\text{-TATAAAA-}3'$$

$$3'\text{-ATATTTT-}5'$$

Promoters without TATA boxes have other sequence elements that play a similar role. In the following discussions, we describe transcription initiation involving a TATA box–containing promoter.

RNA polymerase II itself cannot recognize the promoter sequence. Instead, proteins called **transcription**

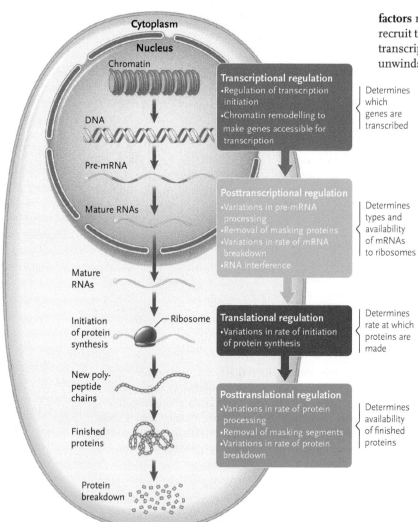

Transcriptional regulation
•Regulation of transcription initiation
•Chromatin remodelling to make genes accessible for transcription

Determines which genes are transcribed

Posttranscriptional regulation
•Variations in pre-mRNA processing
•Removal of masking proteins
•Variations in rate of mRNA breakdown
•RNA interference

Determines types and availability of mRNAs to ribosomes

Translational regulation
•Variations in rate of initiation of protein synthesis

Determines rate at which proteins are made

Posttranslational regulation
•Variations in rate of protein processing
•Removal of masking segments
•Variations in rate of protein breakdown

Determines availability of finished proteins

Figure 14.6

Steps in transcriptional, posttranscriptional, translational, and posttranslational regulation of gene expression in eukaryotes.

factors recognize and bind to the TATA box and then recruit the polymerase. Once the RNA polymerase II–transcription factor complex forms, the polymerase unwinds the DNA and transcription begins. Adjacent to the promoter, farther upstream, is the **promoter proximal region**, which contains regulatory sequences called **promoter proximal elements.** Regulatory proteins that bind to promoter proximal elements may stimulate or inhibit the rate of transcription initiation. More distant from the beginning of the gene is the **enhancer.** Regulatory proteins binding to regulatory sequences within an enhancer also stimulate or inhibit the rate of transcription initiation. Next we see more specifically how these regulatory sequences are involved in transcription initiation.

Activation of Transcription. To initiate transcription, proteins called **general transcription factors** (also called *basal transcription factors*) bind to the promoter in the area of the TATA box **(Figure 14.8).** These factors recruit the enzyme RNA polymerase II, which alone cannot bind to the promoter, and orient the enzyme to start transcription at the correct place. The combination of general transcription factors with RNA polymerase II is the **transcription initiation complex.** On its own, this complex brings about only a low rate of transcription initiation, which leads to just a few mRNA transcripts.

Figure 14.7

Organization of a eukaryotic gene. The transcription unit is the segment that is transcribed into the pre-mRNA; it contains the 5′UTR (untranslated region), exons, introns, and 3′UTR. Immediately upstream of the transcription unit is the promoter, which often contains the TATA box. Adjacent to the promoter and farther upstream of the transcription unit is the promoter proximal region, which contains regulatory sequences called promoter proximal elements. More distant from the gene is the enhancer, which contains regulatory sequences that control the rate of transcription of the gene. Transcription of the gene produces a pre-mRNA molecule with a 5′cap and 3′poly(A) tail; processing of the pre-mRNA to remove introns generates the functional mRNA (see Chapter 13).

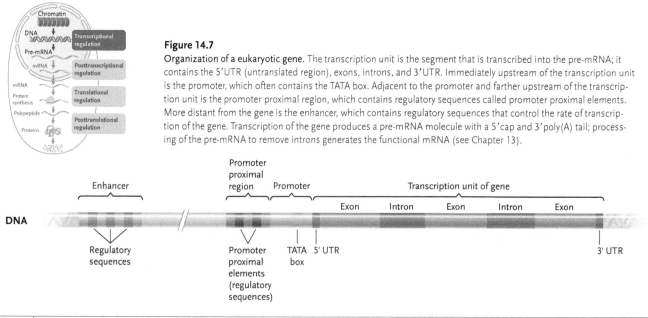

Activators are regulatory proteins that play a role in a positive regulatory system that controls the expression of one or more genes. Activators that bind to the promoter proximal elements interact directly with the general transcription factors at the promoter to stimulate transcription initiation so many more transcripts are synthesized in a given time. Housekeeping genes—genes that are expressed in all cell types for basic cellular functions such as glucose metabolism—have promoter proximal elements that are recognized by activators present in all cell types. By contrast, genes expressed only in particular cell types or at particular times have promoter proximal elements that are recognized by activators found only in those cell types, or at those times when transcription of these genes needs to be activated. To turn this around, the particular set of activators present within a cell at a given time is responsible for determining which genes in that cell are expressed to a significant level.

The DNA-binding and activation functions of activators are properties of two distinct domains in the proteins. (Protein domains are introduced in *The Purple Pages*.) The three-dimensional arrangement of amino acid chains within and between domains also produces highly specialized regions called **motifs**. Several types of motifs, each with a specialized function, are found in proteins, including motifs that insert into the DNA double helix. Motifs found in the DNA-binding domains of regulatory proteins, such as activators, include the helix-turn-helix, zinc finger, and leucine zipper **(Figure 14.9)**.

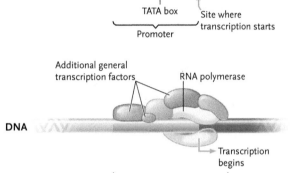

Figure 14.8
Formation of the transcription complex on the promoter of a protein-coding gene by the combination of general transcription factors with RNA polymerase. The general transcription factors are needed for RNA polymerase to bind and initiate transcription at the correct place.

1 The first general transcription factor recognizes and binds to the TATA box of a protein-coding gene's promoter.

2 Additional general transcription factors and then RNA polymerase add to the complex. A general transcription factor unwinds the promoter DNA, and then transcription begins.

a. Helix-turn-helix

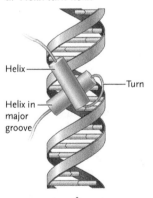

A helix-turn-helix motif is part of a protein bound to DNA. One of the α-helices binds to base pairs in the major groove of the DNA. A looped region of the protein—the turn—connects to a second α-helix, which helps hold the first helix in place.

b. Zinc finger

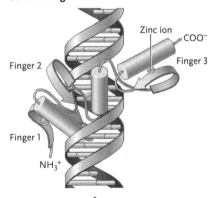

Zinc finger motifs are parts of proteins named for their resemblance to fingers projecting from a protein, and the presence of a bound zinc atom. Zinc fingers bind to specific base pairs in the grooves of DNA.

c. Leucine zipper

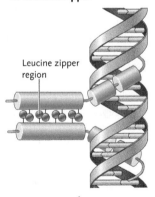

Leucine zipper proteins are dimers, with each monomer consisting of α-helical segments. Hydrophobic interactions between leucine residues within the leucine zipper motif hold the two monomers together. Other α-helices bind to DNA base pairs in the major groove.

Figure 14.9
Three DNA-binding motifs found in activators and other regulatory proteins.

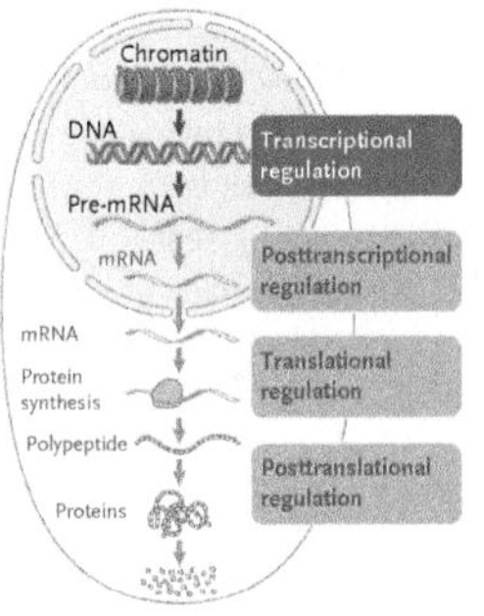

Figure 14.10

Interactions between activators at the enhancer, a coactivator, and general transcription factors at the promoter lead to maximal transcription of the gene.

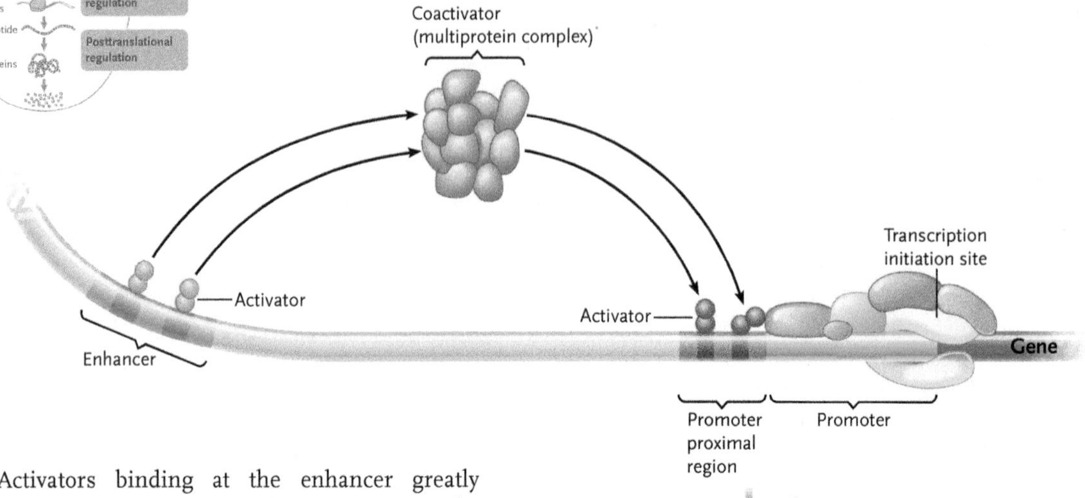

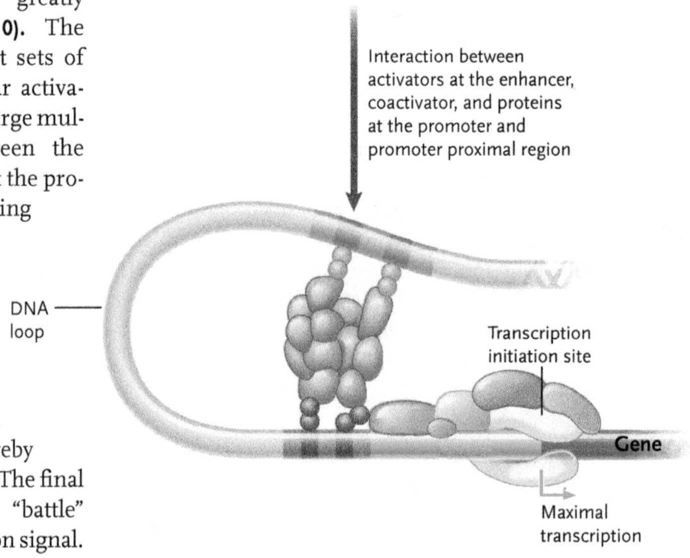

Activators binding at the enhancer greatly increase transcription rates **(Figure 14.10).** The enhancers of different genes have different sets of regulatory sequences, which bind particular activators. A **coactivator** (also called a *mediator*), a large multiprotein complex, forms a bridge between the activators at the enhancer and the proteins at the promoter and promoter proximal region, causing the DNA to form a loop. The interactions between the activators at the enhancer, the coactivator, the proteins at the promoter, and the RNA polymerase greatly stimulate transcription up to its maximal rate.

Repression of Transcription. In some genes, repressors oppose the effect of activators, thereby blocking or reducing the rate of transcription. The final rate of transcription then depends on the "battle" between the activation signal and the repression signal.

Repressors in eukaryotes work in various ways. Some repressors bind to the same regulatory sequence to which activators bind (often in the enhancer), thereby preventing activators from binding to that site. Other repressors bind to their own specific site in the DNA near where the activator binds and interact with the activator so that it cannot interact with the coactivator. Yet other repressors bind to specific sites in the DNA and recruit corepressors, multiprotein complexes analogous to coactivators except that they are negative regulators, inhibiting transcription initiation.

Combinatorial Gene Regulation. Let's review the key elements of transcription regulation for a protein-coding gene. General transcription factors bind to certain promoter sequences, such as the TATA box, and recruit RNA polymerase II; this results in a basal level of transcription. Specific activators bind to promoter proximal elements and stimulate the rate of transcription initiation. Activators also bind to the enhancer to greatly stimulate transcription of the gene.

How are these events coordinated in regulating gene expression? Any given gene has a specific number and types of promoter proximal elements. In some genes, there may be only one regulatory element, but genes under complex regulatory control have many regulatory elements. Similarly, the number and types of regulatory sequences in the enhancer are specific for each gene.

Both promoter proximal regions and enhancers are important in regulating the transcription of a gene. Each regulatory sequence in these two regions binds a specific regulatory protein. Since some regulatory proteins are activators and others are repressors, the overall effect of regulatory sequences on transcription depends on the particular proteins that bind to them. If activators bind both to the regulatory sequences in the promoter proximal region and to the enhancer, transcription is activated maximally, meaning a high rate of transcription and therefore the production of a high level of the mRNA encoded by the gene. But, if a repressor binds to the enhancer and an activator binds to the promoter proximal element, the amount of gene expression depends upon the relative effects of these two regulatory proteins. For example, if the repressor is strong, gene expression, in terms of the rate of transcription and the consequent level of the mRNA encoded by the gene, will be reduced.

A relatively small number of regulatory proteins (activators and repressors) control transcription of all protein-coding genes. By combining a few regulatory proteins in particular ways, the transcription of a wide array of genes can be controlled. The process is called **combinatorial gene regulation**. Consider a theoretical example of two genes, each with activators already bound to the respective promoter proximal elements **(Figure 14.11)**. Maximal transcription of gene *A* requires

activators 2, 5, 7, and 8 binding to their regulatory sequences in the enhancer, whereas maximal transcription of gene *B* requires activators 1, 5, 8, and 11 binding to its enhancer. Looked at another way, both genes require activators 5 and 8 combined with other different activators for full activation.

This operating principle solves a basic dilemma in gene regulation—if each gene were regulated by a single, distinct protein, the number of genes encoding regulatory proteins would have to equal the number of genes to be regulated. Regulating the regulators would require another set of genes of equal number, and so on until the coding capacity of any chromosome set, no matter how large, would be exhausted. But because different genes require different combinations of regulatory proteins, the number of genes encoding regulatory proteins can be much lower than the number of genes the regulatory proteins control.

Coordinated Regulation of Transcription of Genes with Related Functions. In the discussion of prokaryotic operons, you learned that genes with related function are often clustered *and* they are transcribed from one promoter onto a single mRNA. That mRNA is translated to produce the several proteins encoded by the genes. There are no operons in eukaryotes, yet the transcription of genes with related function is coordinately controlled. The preceding discussion of regulatory sequences and binding proteins gives an indication of how coordinated control is accomplished in eukaryotes.

All genes that are coordinately regulated have the same regulatory sequences associated with them. Therefore, with one signal, the transcription of all of the genes can be controlled simultaneously. Consider

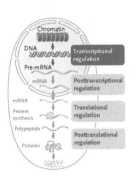

a. A unique combination of activators controls gene A.

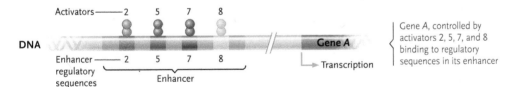

Gene *A*, controlled by activators 2, 5, 7, and 8 binding to regulatory sequences in its enhancer

b. A different combination of activators controls gene B.

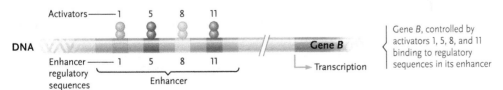

Gene *B*, controlled by activators 1, 5, 8, and 11 binding to regulatory sequences in its enhancer

Figure 14.11

Combinatorial gene regulation. A relatively small number of regulatory proteins control transcription of all protein-coding genes. Different combinations of activators bind to enhancer regulatory sequences to control the rate of transcription of each gene.

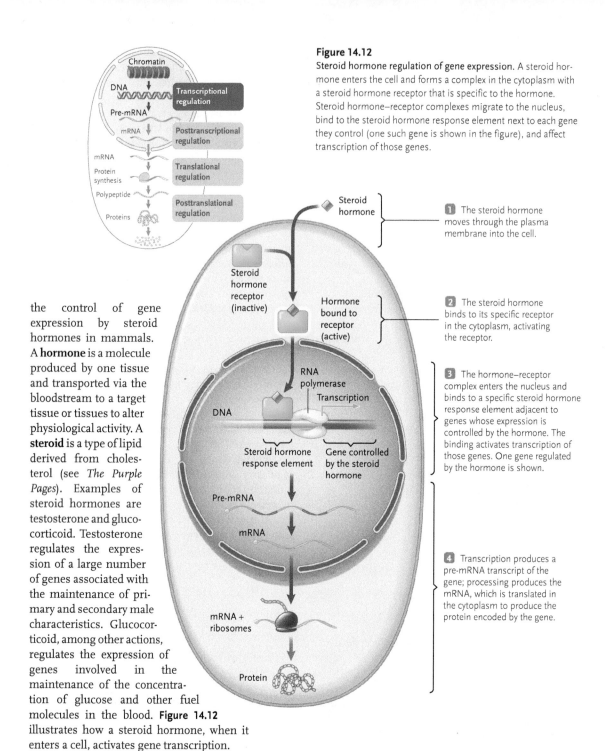

Figure 14.12

Steroid hormone regulation of gene expression. A steroid hormone enters the cell and forms a complex in the cytoplasm with a steroid hormone receptor that is specific to the hormone. Steroid hormone–receptor complexes migrate to the nucleus, bind to the steroid hormone response element next to each gene they control (one such gene is shown in the figure), and affect transcription of those genes.

1 The steroid hormone moves through the plasma membrane into the cell.

2 The steroid hormone binds to its specific receptor in the cytoplasm, activating the receptor.

3 The hormone–receptor complex enters the nucleus and binds to a specific steroid hormone response element adjacent to genes whose expression is controlled by the hormone. The binding activates transcription of those genes. One gene regulated by the hormone is shown.

4 Transcription produces a pre-mRNA transcript of the gene; processing produces the mRNA, which is translated in the cytoplasm to produce the protein encoded by the gene.

the control of gene expression by steroid hormones in mammals. A **hormone** is a molecule produced by one tissue and transported via the bloodstream to a target tissue or tissues to alter physiological activity. A **steroid** is a type of lipid derived from cholesterol (see *The Purple Pages*). Examples of steroid hormones are testosterone and glucocorticoid. Testosterone regulates the expression of a large number of genes associated with the maintenance of primary and secondary male characteristics. Glucocorticoid, among other actions, regulates the expression of genes involved in the maintenance of the concentration of glucose and other fuel molecules in the blood. **Figure 14.12** illustrates how a steroid hormone, when it enters a cell, activates gene transcription.

A steroid hormone acts on specific target tissues in the body because only cells in those tissues have **steroid hormone receptors** in their cytoplasm that recognize and bind the hormone (see Chapter 5). The steroid hormone moves through the plasma membrane into the cytoplasm and the receptor binds to it (Figure 14.12). The hormone–receptor complex then enters the nucleus and binds to specific regulatory sequences that are adjacent to the genes whose expression is controlled by the hormone. This binding activates transcription of those genes, and

proteins encoded by the genes are synthesized rapidly.

A single steroid hormone can regulate many different genes because all of the genes have an identical DNA sequence—a **steroid hormone response element**—to which the hormone–receptor complex binds. For example, all genes controlled by glucocorticoid have a glucocorticoid response element associated with them. Therefore, the release of glucocorticoid into the bloodstream coordinately activates the transcription of genes with that response element.

14.2c Methylation of DNA Can Control Gene Transcription

Although binding proteins to DNA is a common mechanism for regulating transcription, similar effects can also be achieved by modifying the DNA directly. In vertebrates, plants, fungi, and bacteria, **DNA methylation** enzymes add a methyl group ($-CH_3$) directly onto bases in the DNA. Methylated bases in promoter regions can prevent the binding of transcription factors, turning the gene off.

Silencing by methylation is common among vertebrates, but it is not universal among eukaryotes; very little methylation is found in the model organisms *Drosophila* and *Caenorhabditis elegans.*

14.2d Chromatin Structure Plays an Important Role in Whether a Gene Is Active or Inactive

Eukaryotic DNA is organized into chromatin by combination with histone proteins (discussed in Section 12.5). Recall that DNA is wrapped around a core of two molecules each of histones H2A, H2B, H3, and H4, forming the nucleosome (see Figure 12.21). Higher levels of chromatin organization occur when histone H1 links adjacent nucleosomes.

A eukaryotic promoter can exist in two states. In the inactive state, which is the normal state in eukaryotic cells, the nucleosomes in normal chromatin prevent general transcription factors and RNA polymerase II from binding so transcription does not occur. However, regulatory transcription factors can bind to the DNA and lead to a change in chromatin to make it active so transcription can occur. In the active state, general transcription factors and RNA polymerase II bind to the promoter and, controlled by the molecular events already discussed, transcription regulation can occur. A key regulatory event for regulating transcription initiation, then, is controlling the transition between the inactive and active states of chromatin in the region of a promoter.

Acetylation of histone tails (see Figure 12.21) is one mechanism that plays an important role in determining whether chromatin is inactive or active. In inactive chromatin, the histone tails are not acetylated and, in this form, the tails form a tight association with the DNA wrapped around the histone octamer of a nucleosome **(Figure 14.13).** When a regulatory transcription factor binds to a regulatory sequence associated with a gene, it can recruit protein complexes that include *histone acetyltransferase,* an enzyme that acetylates (adds acetyl groups; CH_3COO) to specific amino acids of the histone tails. Acetylation changes the charge of the histone tails and results in a loosening of the association of the histones with the DNA (see Figure 14.13). Usually acetylation of histones is not enough to make the chromatin completely active. Typically large multiprotein complexes bind to displace the acetylated nucleosomes in the promoter region from the DNA, or move them along the DNA away from the promoter. This type of change in chromatin structure is called **chromatin remodelling.** Then, general transcription factors and RNA polymerase II are free to bind and initiate transcription.

Inactivation of an active gene involves essentially the opposite of this process. With respect to the histones, the enzyme *histone deacetylase* catalyzes the removal of acetyl groups from the histone tails, restoring the inactive state of the chromatin in that region (see Figure 14.13).

The tails of histones can also be modified at specific positions by the enzyme-catalyzed covalent addition of methyl groups or phosphate groups. These chemical modifications can also affect chromatin structure and gene expression. Histone methylation, for instance, is associated with gene inactivation. Like acetylation, methylation and phosphorylation of histone tails are reversible. Overall, the conclusion is that the patterns of modification of histone tails are important in determining chromatin structure and gene activity. This has led to the concept of the **histone code,** which is a regulatory mechanism for altering chromatin structure and, therefore, gene activity, based on signals in histone tails represented by chemical modification patterns.

Once mRNAs are transcribed from active genes, further regulation occurs at each of the major steps in

Figure 14.13

Conversion of inactive chromatin to active chromatin by acetylation of histone tails, and the reverse by deacetylation of histone tails.

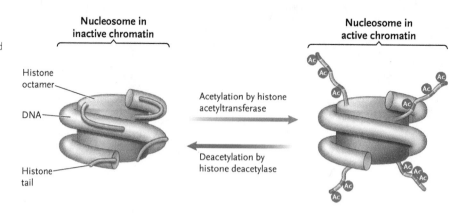

the pathway from genes to proteins: during pre-mRNA processing and the movement of finished mRNAs to the cytoplasm (posttranscriptional regulation), during protein synthesis (translational regulation), and after translation is complete (posttranslational regulation). The next section takes up the regulatory mechanisms operating at each of these steps.

STUDY BREAK

1. What is the role of histones in gene expression? How does acetylation of the histones affect gene expression?
2. What are the roles of general transcription factors, activators, and coactivators in transcription of a protein-coding gene?

14.3 Posttranscriptional, Translational, and Posttranslational Regulation

The previous sections describe several mechanisms that determine which mRNAs are produced under various conditions. The following sections illustrate that once a given mRNA is made, there are several opportunities to fine-tune expression through posttranscriptional, translational, and posttranslational controls (refer again to Figure 14.6, p. 322).

14.3a Posttranscriptional Regulation Controls mRNA Availability

Posttranscriptional regulation directs translation by controlling the availability of mRNAs to ribosomes. The controls work by several mechanisms, including changes in pre-mRNA processing and the rate at which mRNAs are degraded.

Variations in Pre-mRNA Processing. In Chapter 13, we noted that mRNAs are transcribed initially as pre-mRNA molecules. These pre-mRNAs are

variously processed to produce the finished mRNAs, which then enter protein synthesis. Variations in pre-mRNA processing can regulate *which* proteins are made in cells. As described in Section 13.3, pre-mRNAs can be processed by *alternative splicing*. Alternative splicing produces different mRNAs from the same pre-mRNA by removing different combinations of exons (the amino acid–coding segments) along with the introns (the noncoding spacers). The resulting mRNAs are translated to produce a family of related proteins with various combinations of amino acid sequences derived from the exons. Alternative splicing itself is under regulatory control. Regulatory proteins specific to the type of cell control which exons are removed from pre-mRNA molecules by binding to regulatory sequences within those molecules. The outcome of alternative splicing is that appropriate proteins within a family are synthesized in cell types or tissues in which they function optimally. Perhaps three-quarters of human genes are alternatively spliced at the pre-mRNA level.

Posttranscriptional Control by Masking Proteins. Some posttranscriptional controls operate by means of *masking* proteins that bind to mRNAs and make them unavailable for protein synthesis. These controls are important in many animal eggs, keeping mRNAs in an inactive form until the egg has been fertilized and embryonic development is under way. When an mRNA is to become active, other factors—other proteins, made as part of the developmental pathway—remove the masking proteins and allow the mRNA to enter protein synthesis.

Variations in the Rate of mRNA Breakdown. The rate at which eukaryotic mRNAs break down can also be controlled posttranscriptionally. The mechanism involves a regulatory molecule, such as a steroid hormone, directly or indirectly affecting the mRNA breakdown steps, either slowing or increasing the rate of those steps. For example, in the mammary gland of the rat, the mRNA for casein (a milk protein) has a half-life of about 5 hours (meaning that it takes 5 hours for half of the mRNA present at a given time to break down). The half-life of casein mRNA changes to about 92 hours if the peptide hormone prolactin is present. Prolactin is synthesized in the brain and in other tissues, including the breast. The most important effect of prolactin is to stimulate the **mammary glands** to produce milk (that is, it stimulates lactation). During milk production, a large amount of casein must be synthesized, and this is accomplished in part by radically decreasing the rate of breakdown of the casein mRNA.

Nucleotide sequences in the 5′ UTR (untranslated region; see Section 13.3) also appear to be important in determining mRNA half-life. If the 5′ UTR is transferred experimentally from one mRNA to another, the half-life of the receiving mRNA becomes the same as that of the donor mRNA. The controlling sequences in the 5′ UTR of an mRNA might be recognized by proteins that regulate its stability.

Regulation of Gene Expression by Small RNAs. Until relatively recently, the commonly accepted view was that regulation of gene expression in prokaryotic and eukaryotic cells involved only protein-based mechanisms. However, in 1998, Andrew Fire of the Stanford University School of Medicine and Craig Mello of the University of Massachusetts Medical School showed that RNA silenced the expression of a particular gene in the nematode worm, *C. elegans*. They called the phenomenon **RNA interference (RNAi)**. Their discovery revolutionized the way scientists thought about and studied gene regulation in eukaryotes. They now understand that posttranscriptional regulation may be carried out, not only by regulatory proteins, but also by noncoding single-stranded RNAs that can bind to mRNAs and affect their translation. We now know that RNAi is widespread among eukaryotes. Fire and Mello received a Nobel Prize in 2006 for their discovery of RNA interference.

Two major groups of small regulatory RNAs are involved in RNAi: **microRNAs (miRNAs)** and **short interfering RNAs (siRNAs)**. The transcription of an miRNA gene and the processing of the transcript to produce the functional miRNA molecule are shown in **Figure 14.14**. The miRNA, in a protein complex called the **miRNA-induced silencing complex (miRISC)**, binds to sequences in the 3′ UTRs of target mRNAs. If the miRNA and mRNA pair imperfectly, the double-stranded segment formed between the miRNA and the mRNA blocks ribosomes from translating the mRNA (shown in Figure 14.14). In this case, the target mRNA is not destroyed, but its expression is silenced. If the miRNA and mRNA pair perfectly, an enzyme in the protein complex cleaves the target mRNA where the miRNA is bound to it, destroying the mRNA and silencing its expression. RNAi by imperfect pairing and translation inhibition is the most common

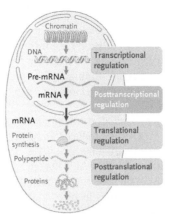

Figure 14.14
RNA interference—regulation of gene expression by microRNAs (miRNAs).

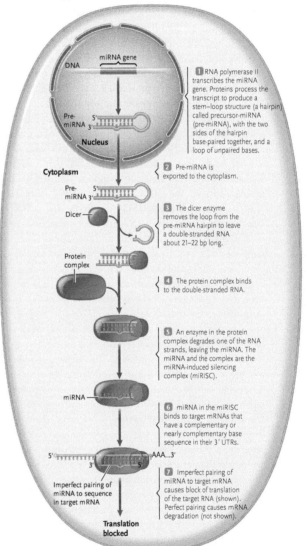

1 RNA polymerase II transcribes the miRNA gene. Proteins process the transcript to produce a stem–loop structure (a hairpin) called precursor-miRNA (pre-miRNA), with the two sides of the hairpin base-paired together, and a loop of unpaired bases.

2 Pre-miRNA is exported to the cytoplasm.

3 The dicer enzyme removes the loop from the pre-miRNA hairpin to leave a double-stranded RNA about 21–22 bp long.

4 The protein complex binds to the double-stranded RNA.

5 An enzyme in the protein complex degrades one of the RNA strands, leaving the miRNA. The miRNA and the complex are the miRNA-induced silencing complex (miRISC).

6 miRNA in the miRISC binds to target mRNAs that have a complementary or nearly complementary base sequence in their 3′ UTRs.

7 Imperfect pairing of miRNA to target mRNA causes block of translation of the target RNA (shown). Perfect pairing causes mRNA degradation (not shown).

mechanism in animals. RNAi by perfect pairing and RNA degradation is the most common mechanism in plants.

miRNA genes have been found in all multicellular eukaryotes that have been examined, and also in some unicellular ones. miRNAs play central roles in controlling gene expression in a variety of cellular, physiological, and developmental processes in animals and plants. In animals, for example, miRNAs help regulate specific developmental timing events, gene expression in neurons, brain development, cancer progression, and stem cell division.

The other major type of small regulatory RNAs is the siRNA. Whereas miRNA is produced from RNA that is encoded in the cell's genome, siRNA is produced from double-stranded RNA that is *not* encoded by nuclear genes. For example, the replication cycle of many viruses with RNA genomes involves a double-stranded RNA stage. Cells attacked by such a virus can defend themselves using siRNA that they produce from the virus's own RNA. The viral double-stranded RNA enters the cell's RNAi process in a way very similar to that described for miRNAs; double-stranded RNA is cut by Dicer (see Figure 14.14, p. 329) into short double-stranded RNA molecules, and then a protein complex binds to the molecules and degrades one of the RNA strands to produce single-stranded siRNA. The protein complex is similar to one that acts on the double-stranded RNA precursors of miRNAs. The siRNA with the protein complex in this case is the **siRNA-induced silencing complex (siRISC)**. In the RNAi process, the siRNA in the siRISC acts like the miRNA in the miRISC—single-stranded RNAs complementary to the siRNA are targeted and, in this case, the target RNA is cleaved and the pieces are then degraded. In our viral example, the targeted RNAs would be viral mRNAs for proteins the virus uses to replicate itself, or a single-stranded RNA that is the viral genome itself, or that is produced from the viral genome during replication.

The expression of any gene can be knocked down to low levels or knocked out completely in experiments involving RNAi with siRNA. To silence a gene, researchers introduce into the cell a double-stranded RNA that can be processed by Dicer and the protein complex into an siRNA complementary to the mRNA transcribed from that gene. Knocking down or knocking out the function of a gene is equivalent to creating a mutated version of that gene, but without changing the gene's DNA sequence. Researchers use this experimental approach to identify the functions of genes whose presence has been detected by sequencing complete genomes, but whose function is completely unknown. After an siRNA specific to a gene of interest is introduced into the cell, researchers look for a change in phenotype, such as properties relating to growth or metabolism. If such a change is seen, the researchers now have some insight into the gene's function, and they can investigate the gene with more focus. RNAi using siRNAs may also have some applications in medicine, perhaps to regulate the expression of genes associated with particular human diseases.

14.3b Translational Regulation Controls the Rate of Protein Synthesis

At the next regulatory level, translational regulation controls the rate at which mRNAs are used in protein synthesis. Translational regulation occurs in essentially all cell types and species. For example, translational regulation is involved in cell cycle control in all eukaryotes and in many processes during development in multicellular eukaryotes, such as red blood cell differentiation in animals. Significantly, many viruses exploit translational regulation to control their infection of cells and to shut off the host cell's own genes.

Let's consider the general role of translational regulation in animal development. During early development of most animals, little transcription occurs. The changes in protein synthesis patterns seen in developing cell types and tissues instead derive from the activation, repression, or degradation of maternal mRNAs, the mRNAs that were present in the mother's egg before fertilization. One important mechanism for translational regulation involves adjusting the length of the poly(A) tail of the mRNA. (Recall from Section 13.3 that the poly(A) tail—a string of adenine-containing nucleotides—is added to the 3' end of the pre-mRNA and is retained on the mRNA produced from the pre-mRNA after introns are removed.) That is, enzymes can change the length of the poly(A) tail on an mRNA in the cytoplasm in either direction: by shortening it or lengthening it. Increases in poly(A) tail length result in increased translation; decreases in length result in decreased translation. For example, during embryogenesis (the formation of the embryo) of the fruit fly, *Drosophila*, key proteins are synthesized when the poly(A) tails on the mRNAs for those proteins are lengthened in a regulated way. Evidence for this came from experiments in which poly(A) tail lengthening was blocked; the result was that embryogenesis was inhibited. But although researchers know that the length of poly(A) tails is regulated in the cytoplasm, how this process occurs is not completely understood.

14.3c Posttranslational Regulation Controls the Availability of Functional Proteins

Posttranslational regulation controls the availability of functional proteins in three primary ways: chemical modification, processing, and degradation. Chemical modification involves the addition or removal of chemical groups, which reversibly alters the activity of the protein. For example, you saw in Section 5.7 how the addition of phosphate groups to proteins involved in signal transduction pathways either stimulates or inhibits the activity of those proteins. Further, in Section 8.5, you learned how the addition of phosphate groups to target proteins plays a crucial role in regulating how a cell progresses through the cell division cycle. And in Section 14.2, you saw how acetylation of histones altered the properties of the nucleosome, loosening its association with DNA in chromatin.

In processing, proteins are synthesized as inactive precursors, which are converted to an active form under regulatory control. For example, you saw in Section 13.4 that the digestive enzyme pepsin is synthesized as pepsinogen, an inactive precursor that activates by removal of a segment of amino acids. Similarly, the glucose-regulating hormone insulin is synthesized as a precursor called proinsulin; processing of the precursor removes a central segment but leaves the insulin molecule, which consists of two polypeptide chains linked by disulfide bridges.

The rate of degradation of proteins is also under regulatory control. Some proteins in eukaryotic cells last for the lifetime of the individual, whereas others persist only for minutes. Proteins with relatively short cellular lives include many of the proteins regulating transcription. Typically, these short-lived proteins are marked for breakdown by enzymes that attach a "doom tag" consisting of a small protein called *ubiquitin* (**Figure 14.15,** step 1). The protein is given this name because it is indeed ubiquitous—present in almost the same form in essentially all eukaryotes. The ubiquitin tag labels the doomed proteins so that they are recognized and attacked by a *proteasome,* a large cytoplasmic complex of a number of different proteins (step 2). The proteasome unfolds the protein, and protein-digesting enzymes within the core digest the protein into small peptides. The peptides are released from the proteasome, and cytosolic enzymes further digest the peptides into individual amino acids, which are recycled for use in protein synthesis or oxidized as an energy source (step 3). The ubiquitin protein and proteasome are also recycled. Aaron Ciechanover and Avram Hershko, both of the Israel Institute of Technology in Haifa, Israel, and Irwin Rose of the University of California, Irvine, received a Nobel Prize in 2004 for the discovery of ubiquitin-mediated protein degradation.

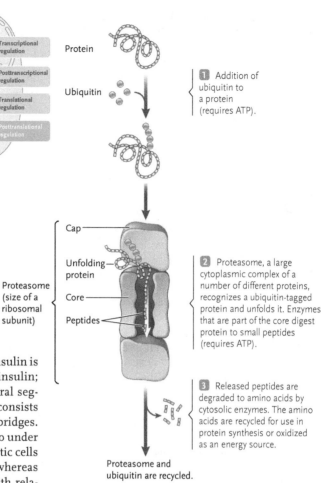

1 Addition of ubiquitin to a protein (requires ATP).

2 Proteasome, a large cytoplasmic complex of a number of different proteins, recognizes a ubiquitin-tagged protein and unfolds it. Enzymes that are part of the core digest protein to small peptides (requires ATP).

3 Released peptides are degraded to amino acids by cytosolic enzymes. The amino acids are recycled for use in protein synthesis or oxidized as an energy source.

Proteasome and ubiquitin are recycled.

Figure 14.15
Protein degradation by ubiquitin addition and enzymatic digestion within a proteasome.

We now describe cancer, a collection of diseases in which the control of gene expression goes awry.

14.3d Epigenetic Regulation Persists through Cell Division

The previous sections of this chapter outline several mechanisms for regulating changes in gene expression that are readily reversible and usually transient. *Lac* operon expression increases when lactose is present but decreases when lactose is absent. Certain genes are turned on when testosterone is present but then shut off again when hormone levels fall. However, there are many situations in which an established pattern of gene expression persists into the next cell or even organismal generation. For example, genes encoding the blood protein hemoglobin are present but inactive in most lines of vertebrate body cells. In the cell lines giving rise to red blood cells, hemoglobin genes are activated. In certain pathogenic strains of *E. coli*, genes for cell surface structures associated with virulence are turned off in most cells. Cells that happen to be involved in an active infection maintain expression of virulence genes in subsequent generations. In the case of genomic imprinting in mice (Section 11.5), an allele of a given gene is silenced during gametogenesis. This allele remains turned off in the fertilized zygote and resulting offspring. In all of these diverse examples, the appropriate pattern of gene expression is inherited from parent cells rather than having to be independently determined anew by each daughter cell.

This type of gene regulation is called **epigenetic** in that it persists through cell or organismal generations but does not result from changes in the DNA sequence. Although the notion of epigenetic regulation is not new, a wide variety of potential underlying mechanisms are still being actively investigated and debated. Two of the most well-documented epigenetic mechanisms are feedback loops and chromatin packaging.

Feedback Loops. One way that control of gene expression can be maintained over cell generations is by a self-sustaining regulatory loop. Such a loop arises when the product of a particular gene associates with its own promoter and stimulates its own transcription. A classic example of this comes from studies of phage lambda (λ), which can remain dormant in the chromosome of infected *E. coli* cells for several generations (Figure 23.5). Early in the infection cycle of this phage, the lambda repressor protein (cI) shuts down expression of other phage genes but stimulates expression of its own gene. As a result, high levels of repressor protein are maintained, even as the host cell divides, replicating the phage DNA along with the rest of its chromosome.

Comparable feedback loops are important in the differentiation of multicellular tissue types and figure prominently in the dramatic dedifferentiation of mouse adult fibroblast cells into stem cells. The creation of these induced stem cells, resulting from the introduction of only four transcription factors, won a share of the 2012 Nobel Prize in Medicine and Physiology for Shinya Yamanaka from Tokyo University, Japan.

Chromatin Packaging. Another strategy to achieve longer-term control of gene expression is to regulate the packaging of DNA and its associated proteins, known as chromatin. Section 12.5 describes the role of nucleosomes in chromatin structure. Figure 14.13 shows that this packaging is affected by chemical modifications of the histone proteins that make up nucleosomes. Densely compacted regions are called heterochromatin, and (most) genes in these regions are silenced. The specific genomic regions to be compacted into heterochromatin in a given cell are identified by DNA-binding proteins or small RNAs that, in turn, recruit additional protein complexes responsible for modifying histones and/or DNA. Histones may be modified by acetylation, methylation, or phosphorylation. DNA modification is typically methylation of cytosine in vertebrates or adenine in bacteria (Section 14.2c).

One dramatic example of regulation that is maintained through many cell divisions is the inactivation of specific X chromosomes in mammalian females described in Section 11.2e. Although the detailed mechanism is still being discovered, it is now certain that silencing of this entire chromosome involves tightly compacting chromatin in concert with DNA methylation, histone modification, and the association of a noncoding RNA called *Xist*. Mechanisms to explain how epigenetic modifications are maintained through mitosis, binary fission, and meiosis are the subject of active research.

STUDY BREAK

1. How does miRNA silence gene expression?
2. If the poly(A) tail on an mRNA were removed, what would likely be the effect on the translation of that mRNA?

14.4 The Loss of Regulatory Controls in Cancer

Chapter 8 showed that the cell division cycle in all eukaryotes is carefully regulated by genes (see Section 8.5 and Figure 8.18). For normal cells, it is the balance between internal or external factors that stimulate cell division and corresponding factors that inhibit cell division that governs whether the cell remains in a nondividing state or whether it grows and divides.

Occasionally, differentiated cells of complex multicellular organisms deviate from their normal genetic program and begin to grow and divide inappropriately, giving rise to tissue masses called *tumours* (see Figure 8.19). Such cells have lost their normal regulatory controls and have reverted toward an embryonic developmental state in a process called *dedifferentiation* (**Figure 14.16**). If the altered cells stay together in a single mass, the tumour is *benign*. Benign tumours are usually not life-threatening, and their surgical removal generally results in a complete cure.

However, if the cells of a tumour invade and disrupt surrounding tissues, the tumour is *malignant* and is called a cancer. Sometimes, cells from malignant tumours break off and move through the blood system or lymphatic system, forming new tumours at other

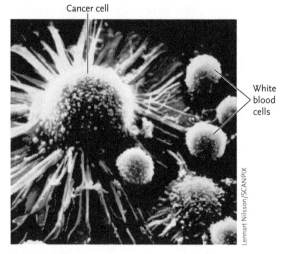

Cancer cell

White blood cells

Lennart Nilsson/SCANPIX

Figure 14.16
A scanning electron micrograph of a cancer cell surrounded by several white blood cells.

locations in the body. The spreading of a malignant tumour is called *metastasis* (meaning "change of state"). Malignant tumours can result in debilitation and death in various ways, including damage to critical organs, metabolic imbalances, hemorrhage, and secondary malignancies. In some cases, malignant tumours can be eliminated from the body by surgery or be destroyed by chemicals (*chemotherapy*) or radiation.

14.4a Cancers Are Genetic Diseases

Experimental evidence of various kinds shows that cancers are genetic diseases:

1. Particular cancers can have a high incidence in some human families. Cancers that run in families are known as **familial (hereditary) cancers.** Cancers that do not appear to be inherited are known as **sporadic (nonhereditary) cancers.** Familial cancers are less frequent than sporadic cancers.
2. Descendants of cancer cells are all cancer cells. In fact, it is the cloned descendants of certain cancer cells that form a tumour.
3. The incidence of cancers increases upon exposure to mutagens, agents that cause mutations in DNA. Particular chemicals and certain kinds of radiation are effective mutagens.
4. Particular chromosomal mutations are associated with specific forms of cancer (see Section 11.3 and Figure 11.12). In these cases, chromosomal breakage affects the expression of genes associated with the regulation of cell division.
5. Some viruses can induce cancer. Some viruses carry "cancer genes" with them, while others contain viral genes that disrupt normal cell cycle control of host cells.

All of the characteristics of cancer cells that have been mentioned—dedifferentiation, uncontrolled division, and metastasis—reflect changes in gene expression.

14.4b Three Main Classes of Genes Are Implicated in Cancer

Three major classes of genes are altered frequently in cancers: *proto-oncogenes, tumour suppressor genes,* and miRNA genes.

Proto-oncogenes. **Proto-oncogenes** (*onkos* = bulk or mass) are genes in normal cells that encode various kinds of proteins that stimulate cell division. Examples are growth factors, receptors on target cells that are activated by growth factors (see Chapter 5), components of cellular signal transduction pathways triggered by cell division stimulatory signals (see Chapter 5), and transcription factors that regulate the expression of the structural genes for progression through the cell cycle. In cancer cells, the proto-oncogenes are deregulated and become **oncogenes,** genes that stimulate the cell to progress to the cancerous state of the unregulated cell cycle. Only one of the two proto-oncogene alleles in a cell needs to be altered for the cellular changes to occur. Alterations that can convert a proto-oncogene into an oncogene include the following:

- A mutation in a gene's promoter or other control sequences results in the gene becoming abnormally active.
- A mutation in the coding segment of the gene may produce an altered form of the encoded protein that is abnormally active.
- Translocation, a process in which a segment of a chromosome breaks off and attaches to a different chromosome (discussed in Section 11.3), may move the gene to a new location under the control of an inappropriately powerful promoter or enhancer sequence.
- Infecting viruses may introduce genes whose expression disrupts cell cycle control or alters regulatory proteins to turn genes on in the host.

Tumour Suppressor Genes. **Tumour suppressor genes** are genes in normal cells encoding proteins that inhibit cell division. The best known tumour suppressor gene is *TP53*, so called because its encoded protein, p53, has a molecular weight of 53 000 **daltons.** Among other activities, normal p53 stops cell division by combining with and inhibiting cyclin-dependent protein kinases that trigger the cell's transition from the G_1 phase to the S phase of the cell cycle (discussed in Section 8.5). This activity is particularly important if the cell has sustained DNA damage. If such a cell undergoes DNA replication and divides, the damage may result in mutation in progeny cells. Mutations can deregulate gene expression and cause a cell to progress toward cancer. However, such cancers may be avoided if p53's action to block the cell from entering S phase gives the cell time to repair the damage or, if the damage cannot be repaired, to trigger the cell to undergo programmed cell death (apoptosis: see Chapter 8). If the *TP53* gene is mutated so that the p53 protein is not produced or is produced in an inactive form, the cyclin-dependent protein kinases are continually active in triggering cell division. As a result, many mutations can result in progeny cells. Inactive *TP53* genes are found in at least 50 percent of all cancers. In general, mutations of tumour suppressor genes contribute to the onset of cancer because the mutations result in a decrease in the inhibitory action of the cell cycle controlling proteins they encode.

Both alleles of a tumour suppressor gene must be inactivated for inhibitory activity to be lost in cancer cells. **Figure 14.17** illustrates inactivation of the tumour-suppressor gene *BRCA1* (*breast cancer 1*) in sporadic and familial forms of breast cancer. *BRCA1* is involved in repair of DNA damage. Inactivating both alleles of *BRCA1* is not by itself sufficient for the development of breast cancer but is one of the gene changes typically involved. Since sporadic breast cancer requires the mutational inactivation of two normal alleles of *BRCA1*, this form of the disease typically occurs later in life than the familial form. For familial breast cancer and other familial cancers, we use the term *predisposition*

for the cancer. This term relates to the inactivation mechanism just described. That is, an individual is predisposed to develop a particular cancer if they inherit one mutant allele of an associated tumour suppressor disease, because then a mutation inactivating the other allele is all that is needed to lose the growth inhibitory properties of the tumour suppressor gene's product.

miRNA Genes. Earlier in this chapter, we discussed the role of miRNAs in regulating expression of target mRNAs. In human cancers, many miRNA genes show altered, cancer-specific expression patterns. Studying these miRNA genes has given scientists insight into the normal activities of their encoded miRNAs in cell cycle control. Some miRNAs regulate the expression of mRNAs that are the transcripts of tumour suppressor genes. If these miRNAs are overexpressed because of alterations of the genes encoding them, expression of the target mRNAs can be completely blocked, thereby removing or decreasing inhibitory signals for cell proliferation. Other miRNAs regulate the translation of mRNAs that are transcripts of particular proto-oncogenes. If these miRNA genes are inactivated, or expression of these genes is markedly reduced, expression of the proto-oncogenes is higher than normal and cell proliferation is stimulated.

CONCEPT FIX This section shows that *cancer genes* are just deregulated versions of the genes that are essential for the normally controlled growth of all cells. ⬡

Figure 14.17
Mutational inactivation of tumour suppressor gene alleles in sporadic **(a)** and familial **(b)** cancers as exemplified by the *BRCA1* gene associated with breast cancer.

a. Sporadic breast cancer. Two independent mutations of the *BRCA1* tumour suppressor.

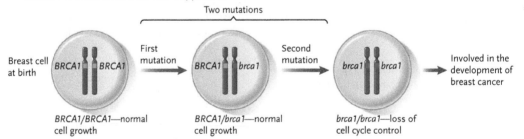

b. Familial breast cancer. An individual has a predisposition for breast cancer because of inheriting one mutated *brca1* allele; mutation of the other normal *BRCA1* allele then occurs.

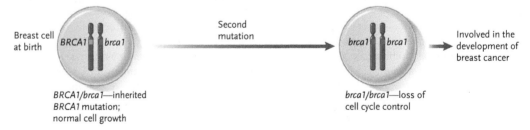

14.4c Cancer Develops Gradually by Multiple Steps

Cancer rarely develops by alteration of a single proto-oncogene to an oncogene, or inactivation of a single tumour suppressor gene. Rather, in almost all cancers, successive alterations in several to many genes gradually accumulate to transform normal cells to cancer cells. This gradual mechanism is called the *multistep progression of cancer*. One example of the steps that can occur, in this case for a form of colorectal cancer, is shown in **Figure 14.18.**

The ravages of cancer, probably more than any other example, bring home the critical extent to which humans and all other multicellular organisms depend on the mechanisms controlling gene expression to develop and live normally. In a sense, the most amazing thing about these control mechanisms is that in spite of their complexity, they operate without failures throughout most of the lives of all eukaryotes.

STUDY BREAK

1. What is the normal function of a tumour suppressor gene? How do mutations in tumour suppressor genes contribute to the onset of cancer?
2. What is the normal function of a proto-oncogene? How can mutations in proto-oncogenes contribute to the onset of cancer?
3. How can changes in expression of miRNA genes contribute to the onset of cancer?

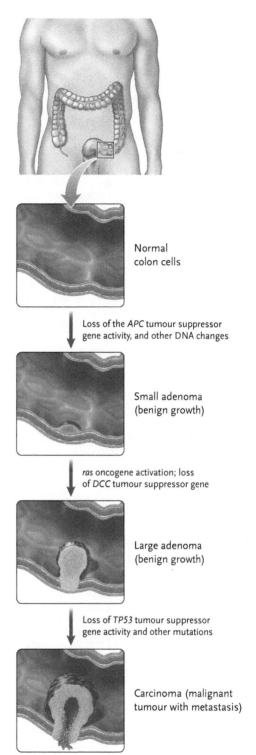

Normal colon cells

Loss of the *APC* tumour suppressor gene activity, and other DNA changes

Small adenoma (benign growth)

ras oncogene activation; loss of *DCC* tumour suppressor gene

Large adenoma (benign growth)

Loss of *TP53* tumour suppressor gene activity and other mutations

Carcinoma (malignant tumour with metastasis)

Figure 14.18
A multistep model for the development of a type of colorectal cancer.

Review

14.1 Regulation of Gene Expression in Prokaryotic Cells

- Transcriptional control in prokaryotic cells involves short-term changes that turn specific genes on or off in response to changes in environmental conditions. The changes in gene activity are controlled by regulatory proteins that recognize operators of operons (Figure 14.2).

- Regulatory proteins may be repressors, which slow the rate of transcription of operons, or activators, which increase the rate of transcription.

- Some repressors are made in an active form, in which they bind to the operator of an operon and inhibit its transcription. Combination with an inducer blocks the activity of the repressor and allows the operon to be transcribed (Figure 14.3).

- Activators are typically made in inactive form, in which they cannot bind to their binding site next to an operon. Combining with another molecule, often a nucleotide, converts the activator into the form in which it binds with its binding site and recruits RNA polymerase, thereby stimulating transcription of the operon (Figure 14.4).

- Other repressors are made in an inactive form, in which they are unable to inhibit transcription of an operon unless they combine with a corepressor (Figure 14.5).

14.2 Regulation of Transcription in Eukaryotes

- Operons are not found in eukaryotes. Instead, genes that encode proteins with related functions are typically scattered through the genome, while being regulated in a coordinated manner.

- Two general types of gene regulation occur in eukaryotes. Short-term regulation involves relatively rapid changes in gene expression in response to changes in environmental or physiological conditions. Long-term regulation involves changes in gene expression that are associated with the development and differentiation of an organism.

- Gene expression in eukaryotes is regulated at the transcriptional level (where most regulation occurs) and at posttranscriptional, translational, and posttranslational levels (Figures 14.6–14.8).

- Regulation of transcription initiation involves proteins binding to a gene's promoter and regulatory sites. At the promoter, general transcription factors bind and recruit RNA polymerase II, giving a very low level of transcription. Activator proteins bind to promoter proximal elements and increase the rate of transcription. Other activators bind to the enhancer and, through interaction with a coactivator, which also binds to the proteins at the promoter, greatly stimulate the rate of transcription (Figures 14.9–14.11).

- The overall control of transcription of a gene depends on the particular regulatory proteins that bind to promoter proximal elements and enhancers. The regulatory proteins are cell-type specific and may be activators or repressors. This gene regulation is achieved by a relatively low number of regulatory proteins, acting in various combinations (Figure 14.11).

- The coordinate expression of genes with related functions is achieved by each of the related genes having the same regulatory sequences associated with them.

- Transcriptionally active genes have a looser chromatin structure than transcriptionally inactive genes. The change in chromatin structure that accompanies the activation of transcription of a gene involves chromatin remodelling—specific histone modifications—particularly in the region of a gene's promoter (Figure 14.13).

- Sections of chromosomes or whole chromosomes can be inactivated by DNA methylation, a phenomenon called silencing. DNA methylation is also involved in genomic imprinting, in which transcription of either the inherited maternal or the inherited paternal allele of a gene is inhibited permanently.

14.3 Posttranscriptional, Translational, and Posttranslational Regulation

- Posttranscriptional, translational, and posttranslational controls operate primarily to regulate the quantities of proteins synthesized in cells (Figure 14.6).

- Posttranscriptional controls regulate pre-mRNA processing, mRNA availability for translation, and the rate at which mRNAs are degraded. In alternative splicing, different mRNAs are derived from the same pre-mRNA. In another process, small single-stranded RNAs complexed with proteins bind to mRNAs that have complementary sequences, and either the mRNA is cleaved or translation is blocked (Figure 14.14).

- Translational regulation controls the rate at which mRNAs are used by ribosomes in protein synthesis.

- Posttranslational controls regulate the availability of functional proteins. Mechanisms of regulation include the alteration of protein activity by chemical modification, protein activation by processing of inactive precursors, and affecting the rate of degradation of a protein.

- Epigenetic regulation of gene expression may persist through cell and organismal generations. Such regulation does not depend on changes to the DNA sequence but, rather, on transcription factors that regulate their own production in a feedback loop or on persistent changes to DNA packaging.

14.4 The Loss of Regulatory Controls in Cancer

- In cancer, cells partially or completely dedifferentiate, divide rapidly and uncontrollably, and may break loose to form additional tumours in other parts of the body.

- Proto-oncogenes, tumour suppressor genes, and miRNA genes are typically altered in cancer cells. Proto-oncogenes encode proteins that stimulate cell division. Their altered forms, oncogenes, are abnormally active. Tumour suppressor genes in their normal form encode proteins that inhibit cell division. Mutated forms of these genes lose this inhibitory activity (Figure 14.17). miRNA genes control the activity of mRNA transcripts of particular tumour suppressor genes and proto-oncogenes. Alteration of activity of such an miRNA gene can lead to a lower than normal activity of tumour suppressor gene products or a higher than normal activity of proto-oncogene products depending on the target of the miRNA. In either case, cell proliferation can be stimulated.

- Most cancers develop by multistep progression involving the successive alteration of several to many genes (Figure 14.18).

Questions

Self-Test Questions

1. Some genes are under negative regulation. Which of the following is an example of negative regulation in the *lac* operon?
   a. Binding of allolactose makes the Lac repressor unable to bind DNA.
   b. When lactose levels decrease, *lacZ* expression goes down.
   c. When Lac repressor binds the operator, *lacZ* expression goes down.
   d. When glucose levels are high, *lacZ* expression goes down.

2. For the *E. coli lac* operon, which of the following events occurs when glucose is absent and lactose is added?
   a. β-galactosidase decreases in the cell.
   b. The *lacI* gene cannot make Lac repressor protein.
   c. Allolactose binds the Lac repressor protein to remove it from the operator.
   d. The genes *lacZ, lacY,* and *lacA* are turned off.

3. Imagine a mutation in the *E. coli lac* operon that results in constitutive expression (always on). Further analysis confirms that normal amounts of functional Lac repressor protein are present. Where must the mutation be?
   a. in the *lac* promoter
   b. in the operator
   c. in the *lacZ* gene
   d. in the CAP binding site

4. Which of the following statements about the *trp* operon is correct?
   a. Tryptophan is an inducer.
   b. When end-product tryptophan binds to the Trp repressor, it stops transcription of the tryptophan biosynthesis genes.
   c. Trp repressor is synthesized in active form.
   d. Low levels of tryptophan bind to the *trp* operator and block transcription of the tryptophan biosynthesis genes.

5. How does chromatin remodelling activate gene expression?
   a. It allows repressors to disengage from the promoter.
   b. It winds genes tightly around histones.
   c. It inserts nucleosomes into chromatin.
   d. It recruits a protein complex that displaces nucleosomes from the promoter.

6. Which statement about activation of transcription is correct?
   a. RNA polymerase II binds the TATA box.
   b. A coactivator called a mediator forms a bridge between the promoter and the gene to be transcribed.
   c. Transcription factors bind the promoter and RNA polymerase.
   d. Enhancer regions bind to promoter regions.

7. The delivery of mature mRNA to the cytoplasm in eukaryotes is highly controlled. At which level of regulation is this control achieved?
   a. translational regulation
   b. posttranslational regulation
   c. transcriptional regulation
   d. posttranscriptional regulation

8. Perky ears in a certain mammal are coded by a dominant allele; the recessive allele codes for droopy ears. In males of these mammals, the gene encoding ear shape is transcribed only from the chromosome received from the female parent. This is because the gene from the male parent is silenced by methylation. What will be the result of a cross of a droopy female and a homozygous perky male?
   a. Daughters' ears will be perky and sons' ears will be droopy.
   b. All offspring will have perky ears.
   c. Sons will have one perky ear and one droopy ear.
   d. There will be equal numbers of perky-eared and droopy-eared sons and daughters.

9. Which of the following statements describes miRNA accurately?
   a. miRNA is encoded by non–protein coding genes.
   b. miRNA has a precursor that is folded and then elongated by a Dicer enzyme.
   c. miRNA forms complementary base pairs with tRNA.
   d. miRNA is translated in the cytoplasm.

10. Which of the following characteristics is exhibited by typical cancer cells?
    a. They convert oncogenes into proto-oncogenes.
    b. Oncogenes are near repressor genes.
    c. They have a balance of oncogenes and tumour suppressor genes.
    d. *TP53* mutations are one of several likely changes in DNA.

Questions for Discussion

1. In a mutant strain of *E. coli,* the CAP protein is unable to combine with its target region of the *lac* operon. How would you expect the mutation to affect transcription when cells of this strain are subjected to the following conditions?
   a. Lactose and glucose are both available.
   b. Lactose is available, but glucose is not.
   c. Both lactose and glucose are unavailable.

2. Duchenne muscular dystrophy, an inherited genetic disorder, affects boys almost exclusively. Early in childhood, muscle tissue begins to break down in affected individuals, who typically die in their teens or early twenties as a result of respiratory failure. Muscle samples from women who carry the mutation reveal some regions of degenerating muscle tissue adjacent to other regions that are normal. Develop a hypothesis explaining these observations.

3. Eukaryotic transcription is generally controlled by binding of regulatory proteins to DNA sequences rather than by modification of RNA polymerases. Develop a hypothesis explaining why this is so.

Protein microarray, a key tool of proteomics, the study of the complete set of proteins that can be expressed by an organism's genome. Each coloured dot is a protein, with a specific colour for each protein being studied.

DNA Technologies

WHY IT MATTERS

Have you ever wished you could create a new organism that would solve a real-world problem? Maybe you would create a fungus that converts toxic waste into fuel. Artificial blood requires some sort of cell to carry the oxygen; could you design such a cell? What if you could program the bacteria that normally make yogurt to produce different flavours on demand? Or maybe you could invent a multicellular organism that could measure and report the concentration of specific compounds in air.

The age of do-it-yourself (DIY) biology has arrived, and the basic tools of genetic engineering developed since the 1970s are now in the hands of undergraduates like you. Teams of students are collaborating with scientists and engineers in classrooms, labs, and informal makerspaces all over the world to develop innovative entries in the annual International Genetically Engineered Machine Competition (iGEM). In an open-source spirit of creating and sharing, teams of passionate students start with over a thousand standardized interchangeable BioBrick DNA sequences, plasmid backbones, and living cells. Adding their own custom-created parts, teams assemble parts into devices that, in turn, are combined to create innovative pathways and systems—all housed in living cells. Each year, teams present their novel living machines to address issues in categories such as art, energy, environment, food, health, measurement, and manufacturing.

The competition also highlights and promotes consideration of the broad range of risks and controversies surrounding genetic engineering, as well as the scientific, social, and ethical questions related to its rapidly expanding role in society.

In this chapter we look at the topic of **genetic engineering** as the latest addition to the broad area known as **biotechnology**, which is any technique applied to biological systems or living organisms to make or modify products or processes for a specific purpose. Thus, biotechnology includes manipulations that do not involve **DNA technologies**, such as the use of naturally occurring yeast to brew beer and bake bread and the use of bacteria to make cheese. With respect to biotechnologies that do involve the direct manipulation of genes for basic and applied research, we begin our discussion with a description of methods used to obtain genes in large quantities, an essential step for their analysis or further application.

15.1 DNA Cloning

Technologies designed to manipulate DNA must, of course, have DNA to work with. Three main sources of DNA sequences are commonly used in research:

i)   DNA sequences can be extracted from the genome of cells (and viruses) using specialized enzymes, as shown in Figures 15.1 and 15.3 (pages 341 and 343).

ii) DNA can be synthesized from an mRNA template by the reverse transcriptase enzyme, as shown in Figure 15.4 (page 344).

iii) DNA sequences of choice can be created by automated chemical synthesis in the laboratory using a DNA synthesizer responding to computer input. Although existing "gene machines" can create specified sequences up to a few thousand base pairs, this capacity is expanding rapidly.

Once a DNA sequence of choice has been obtained from nature or created artificially, the number of copies of the sequence can be increased dramatically, as described in the following sections.

Remember from Chapter 8 that a *clone* is a line of genetically identical cells or individuals derived from a single ancestor. By similar reasoning, DNA cloning is a method for producing many copies of a piece of DNA; the piece of DNA is referred to as a *gene of interest*, which is a gene that a researcher wants to study or manipulate. Scientists clone DNA for many reasons. For example, a researcher might be interested in how a particular human gene functions. Each human cell contains only two copies of most genes, amounting to a very small fraction of the total amount of DNA in a diploid cell. In its natural state in the genome, the gene is extremely difficult to study. However, through DNA cloning, a researcher can produce a sample large enough for scientific experimentation.

Cloned genes are used in basic research to find out about their biological functions. For example, researchers can determine the DNA sequence of a cloned gene, giving them the ultimate information about its structure. Also, by manipulating the gene and inducing mutations in it, they can gain information about its function and about how its expression is regulated. Cloned genes can be expressed in bacteria, and the proteins encoded by the cloned genes can be produced in quantity and purified. Those proteins can be used in basic research, or, in the case of genes that

encode proteins of pharmaceutical or clinical importance, they can be used in applied research.

An overview of one common method for cloning a gene of interest from a genome is shown in **Figure 15.1**; the method uses bacteria (commonly *Escherichia coli*) and plasmids, the small circular DNA molecules that replicate separately from the bacterial chromosome. The researcher first extracts DNA from cells containing the gene of interest and then cuts this DNA into fragments. One of these fragments will likely carry the desired gene. Each of the fragments is inserted into a plasmid, thus producing a collection of *recombinant DNA molecules*—**recombinant DNA** is DNA from two or more different sources that are joined together. These recombinant plasmids are then introduced into bacteria; each bacterium receives a different plasmid. The bacterium continues growing and dividing, and as it does, the recombinant plasmid DNA is also replicated. The final step is to identify which bacterium contains the plasmid carrying the gene of interest and isolate it for further study.

Cloned genes and other cloned DNA sequences from genomes are used in both basic research and applied research. In **basic research**, a researcher might want to study a cloned gene to learn about its structure, including its DNA sequence and sequences that regulate its expression. A researcher might also want to study the gene's function, including how its expression is regulated, and the nature of the gene's product. For protein-coding genes, for instance, the cloned gene could be used to produce the protein product in large quantities in a microorganism host to facilitate study of that protein's structure and function. As part of this research, the cloned gene could be manipulated in the laboratory to help dissect a gene's function.

In **applied research**, the interest in cloned genes or other cloned DNA sequences is not in the structure and function of a gene or sequence; that typically is understood, at least to a significant degree, at the beginning of research projects. Rather, cloned genes or cloned DNA sequences are used, for instance, for medical, forensic, agricultural, or commercial applications. Some examples are

- Gene therapy to correct or treat genetic diseases.
- Diagnosis of genetic diseases, such as sickle cell disease.
- DNA fingerprinting in forensics.
- Production of pharmaceuticals, such as humulin, human insulin to treat diabetes, and tissue plasminogen activator to break down blood clots.
- Generation of genetically modified animals and plants, including animals that synthesize pharmaceuticals, and plants that are nutritionally enriched, insect resistant, or herbicide resistant.
- Modification of bacteria to use in cleanup of oil spills or toxic waste.

15.1a Bacterial Enzymes Called Restriction Endonucleases Form the Basis of DNA Cloning

The key to DNA cloning is the specific joining of two DNA molecules from different sources, such as a genomic DNA fragment and a bacterial plasmid (see Figure 15.1). This specific joining of DNA is made possible, in part, by bacterial enzymes called **restriction endonucleases** (also called **restriction enzymes**), which were discovered in the late 1960s. Restriction enzymes recognize short, specific DNA sequences called *restriction sites,* typically four to eight base pairs long, and cut the DNA at specific locations within those sequences. The DNA fragments produced by cutting a long DNA molecule with a restriction enzyme are known as **restriction fragments.**

The *restriction* in the name of the enzymes refers to their normal role inside bacteria, in which the enzymes defend against viral attack by breaking down (restricting) the DNA molecules of infecting viruses. Why don't such enzymes break down the cell's own DNA? The bacterium "hides" the restriction sites in its own DNA by attaching methyl groups to bases in those sites, thereby blocking the binding of its restriction enzyme.

Hundreds of different restriction enzymes have been identified, each one cutting DNA at a specific restriction site. As illustrated by the restriction site of *Eco*RI **(Figure 15.2, p. 342),** most restriction sites are symmetrical in that the sequence of nucleotides read in the $3' \rightarrow 5'$ direction on one strand is the same as the sequence read in the $3' \rightarrow 5'$ direction on the complementary strand. A given enzyme always recognizes the same short DNA sequence as its cut site and always cuts at the same place within the sequence. The restriction enzymes most used in cloning—such as *Eco*RI—cleave the sugar–phosphate backbones of DNA to produce DNA fragments with single-stranded ends (Figure 15.2, step 1). The ends are called **sticky ends** because the short, single-stranded regions can form hydrogen bonds with complementary sticky ends

1 Isolate genomic DNA containing the gene of interest from the cells and cut the DNA into fragments.

2 Cut a circular bacterial plasmid to make it linear.

3 Insert the genomic DNA fragments into plasmids to make recombinant DNA molecules. Here, the recombinant DNA molecules are the recombinant plasmids.

Inserted genomic DNA fragment

Recombinant DNA molecules

4 Introduce recombinant molecules into the bacterial cells; each bacterium receives a different plasmid. As the bacteria grow and divide, the recombinant plasmids replicate, amplifying the piece of DNA inserted into the plasmid.

Bacterium

Bacterial chromosome

Progeny bacteria

5 Identify the bacterium containing the plasmid with the gene of interest inserted into it. Grow that bacterium in culture to produce large amounts of the plasmid for experiments with the gene of interest.

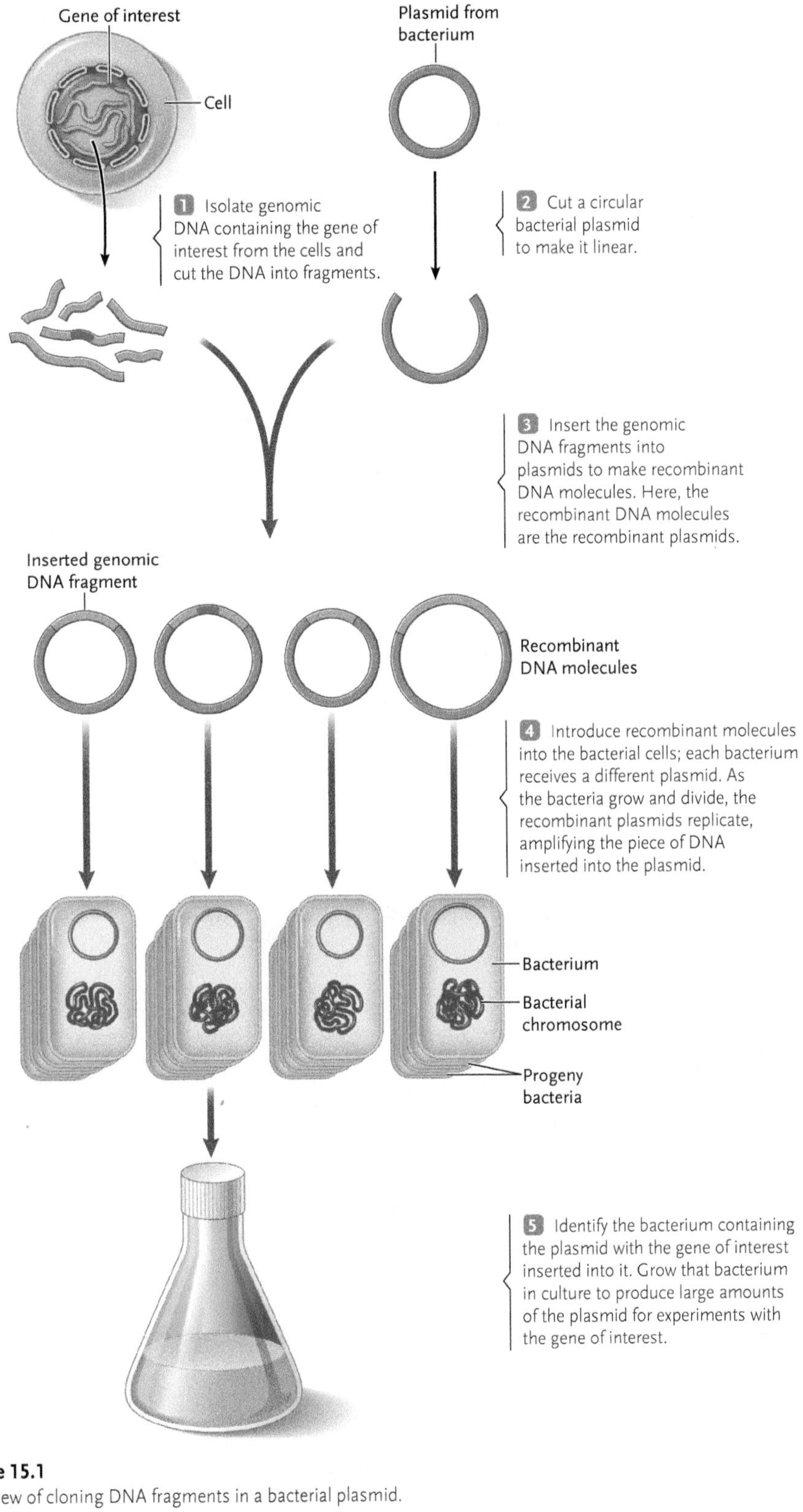

Figure 15.1
Overview of cloning DNA fragments in a bacterial plasmid.

on any other DNA molecules cut with the same enzyme. For example, step 2 shows the insertion of a DNA molecule with sticky ends produced by *Eco*RI between two other DNA molecules with the same sticky ends. The pairings leave nicks in the sugar–phosphate backbones of the DNA strands that are sealed by *DNA ligase,* an enzyme that has the same function in DNA replication (step 3). The result is DNA from two different sources joined together—a recombinant DNA molecule.

15.1b Bacterial Plasmids Illustrate the Use of Restriction Enzymes in Cloning

The bacterial plasmids used for cloning are examples of cloning vectors—DNA molecules into which a DNA fragment can be inserted to form a recombinant DNA molecule for cloning. Plasmid cloning vectors are usually natural plasmids that have been modified to have special features. Commonly, plasmid cloning vectors are engineered to contain two genes that are useful in the final steps of a cloning experiment for distinguishing bacteria that have recombinant plasmids from those that do not. The *amp*^R gene encodes an enzyme that breaks down the antibiotic ampicillin; when the plasmid is introduced into *E. coli* and the

amp^R gene is expressed, the bacteria become resistant to ampicillin. The *lacZ*^+ gene encodes β-galactosidase (part of the *lac* operon from Section 14.1), which hydrolyzes the sugar lactose, as well as a number of synthetic substrates. Restriction sites are located within the *lacZ*^+ gene but do not alter the gene's function. For a given cloning experiment, one of these restriction sites is chosen.

Cloning a Gene of Interest. **Figure 15.3** expands on the overview of Figure 15.1 to show the steps used to clone a gene of interest using a plasmid cloning vector and restriction enzymes. In outline, the steps are as follows:

- Isolate genomic DNA and digest that DNA with a restriction enzyme (step 1).
- Digest the plasmid cloning vector with the same restriction enzyme (step 2).
- Ligate cut genomic DNA fragments and cut plasmid DNA together using DNA ligase (step 3). This produces a mixture of recombinant plasmids (plasmids with DNA fragments inserted into the cloning vector), nonrecombinant plasmids (resealed cloning vectors with no DNA fragment inserted), and joined-together pieces of genomic DNA with no cloning vector involved.
- Transform the DNA into *E. coli* (step 4). Some bacteria will take up a plasmid, whereas others will not.
- *Selection:* Spread the bacterial cells on growth medium containing ampicillin and X-gal and incubate to allow colonies to grow (step 5). Bacteria containing plasmids are selected for because of the ampicillin in the growth medium. Within each cell of a colony, the plasmids replicate until approximately 100 copies are present.
- *Screening:* The X-gal in the medium distinguishes between bacteria that have been transformed with recombinant plasmids and nonrecombinant plasmids by *blue–white screening* (see Figure 15.3, Interpreting the Results). White colonies contain recombinant plasmids, whereas blue colonies contain nonrecombinant plasmids. Among the white colonies is the one with a recombinant plasmid that contains the gene of interest. We will see a little later how we can identify that particular plasmid.

Three researchers, Paul Berg, Stanley N. Cohen, and Herbert Boyer, in 1973 pioneered the development of DNA cloning techniques using restriction enzymes and bacterial plasmids. Berg received a Nobel Prize in 1980 for his research.

15.1c DNA Libraries Contain Collections of Cloned DNA Fragments

As you have seen, the starting point for cloning a gene of interest is a large set of plasmid clones carrying fragments representing the entire DNA of an

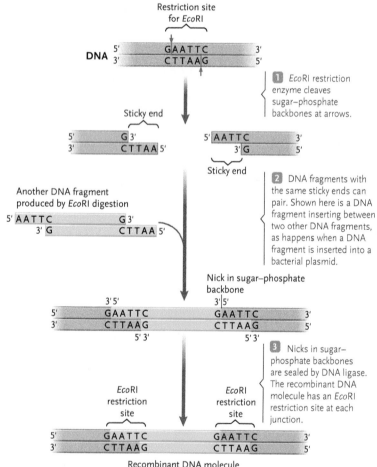

Figure 15.2

The restriction site for the restriction enzyme *Eco*RI, and the generation of a recombinant DNA molecule by complementary base-pairing of DNA fragments produced by digestion with the same restriction enzyme.

Research Method Figure 15.3 Cloning a gene of interest in a plasmid cloning vector.

PURPOSE: Cloning a gene produces many copies of a gene of interest that can be used, for example, to determine the DNA sequence of the gene, to manipulate the gene in basic research experiments, to understand its function, and to produce the protein encoded by the gene.

PROTOCOL:

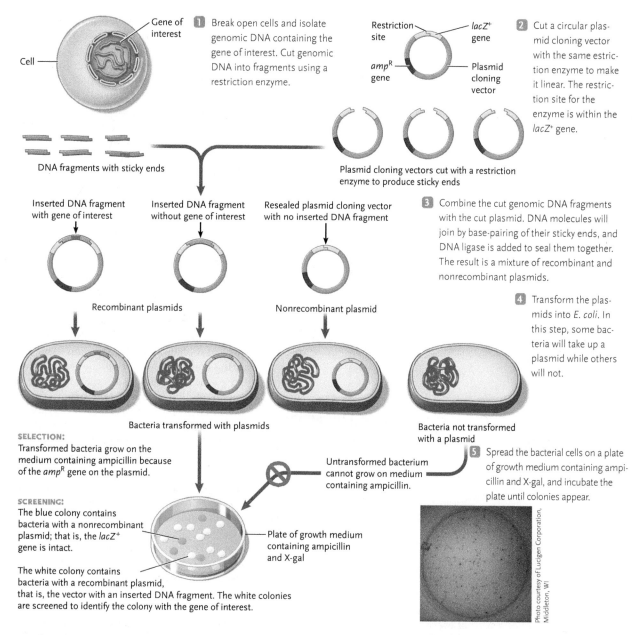

1 Break open cells and isolate genomic DNA containing the gene of interest. Cut genomic DNA into fragments using a restriction enzyme.

2 Cut a circular plasmid cloning vector with the same restriction enzyme to make it linear. The restriction site for the enzyme is within the *lacZ⁺* gene.

DNA fragments with sticky ends

Plasmid cloning vectors cut with a restriction enzyme to produce sticky ends

Inserted DNA fragment with gene of interest

Inserted DNA fragment without gene of interest

Resealed plasmid cloning vector with no inserted DNA fragment

3 Combine the cut genomic DNA fragments with the cut plasmid. DNA molecules will join by base-pairing of their sticky ends, and DNA ligase is added to seal them together. The result is a mixture of recombinant and nonrecombinant plasmids.

Recombinant plasmids

Nonrecombinant plasmid

4 Transform the plasmids into *E. coli*. In this step, some bacteria will take up a plasmid while others will not.

Bacteria transformed with plasmids

Bacteria not transformed with a plasmid

SELECTION:
Transformed bacteria grow on the medium containing ampicillin because of the *amp^R* gene on the plasmid.

Untransformed bacterium cannot grow on medium containing ampicillin.

5 Spread the bacterial cells on a plate of growth medium containing ampicillin and X-gal, and incubate the plate until colonies appear.

SCREENING:
The blue colony contains bacteria with a nonrecombinant plasmid; that is, the *lacZ⁺* gene is intact.

Plate of growth medium containing ampicillin and X-gal

The white colony contains bacteria with a recombinant plasmid, that is, the vector with an inserted DNA fragment. The white colonies are screened to identify the colony with the gene of interest.

Photo courtesy of Lucigen Corporation, Middleton, WI

INTERPRETING THE RESULTS: All of the colonies on the plate contain plasmids because the bacteria that form the colonies are resistant to the ampicillin present in the growth medium. Blue-white screening distinguishes bacterial colonies with nonrecombinant plasmids from those with recombinant plasmids. Blue colonies have nonrecombinant plasmids. These plasmids have intact *lacZ⁺* genes and produce β-galactosidase, which changes X-gal to a blue product. White colonies have recombinant plasmids. These plasmids have DNA fragments inserted into the *lacZ⁺* gene, so they do not produce β-galactosidase. As a result, they cannot convert X-gal to the blue product and the colonies are white. Among the white colonies is a colony containing the plasmid with the gene of interest. Further screening is done to identify that particular white colony (see Figure 15.4, p. 344). Once identified, the colony is cultured to produce large quantities of the recombinant plasmid for analysis or manipulation of the gene.

Figure 15.4

Synthesis of DNA from mRNA using reverse transcriptase.

PURPOSE: To produce double-stranded, complementary DNA (cDNA) copies of mRNA molecules isolated from cells.

PROTOCOL:

1 Isolate mRNAs from cells. One mRNA is shown.

2 Add primer of T DNA nucleotides (dT). The primer base-pairs to the poly (A) tail of the mRNa.

3 Reverse transcriptase uses DNA precursors to synthesize a DNA copy of the mRNA in the 5'-to-3' direction. The result is a hybrid nucleic acid molecule consisting of the mRNA base paired with a DNA strand.

4 An RNAase enzyme degrades the mRNA stand, leaving a single strand of DNA.

5 DNA polymerase uses DNA precursors to synthesize the second strand of DNA. Experimentally different methods are available for the use of primers in this reaction. The result is a double-stranded complementary DNA (cDNA) copy of the starting mRNA.

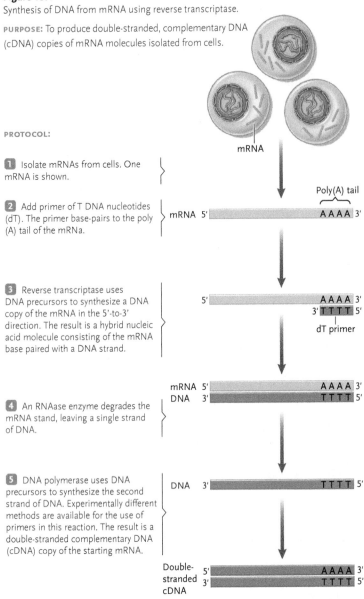

OUTCOME: The outcome is a population of double-stranded cDNA molecules that have base-pair sequences corresponding to the base sequences of the mRNA molecules isolated from the cell.

organism's genome. A collection of clones that contains a copy of every DNA sequence in a genome is called a **genomic library**. A genomic library can be made using plasmid cloning vectors or any other kind of cloning vector. The number of clones in a genomic library increases with the size of the genome. For example, a yeast genomic library of plasmid clones consists of hundreds of plasmids, whereas a human genomic library of plasmid clones consists of thousands of plasmids.

A genomic library is a resource containing the entire DNA of an organism cut into pieces. Just as for a book library, where you can search through the same

set of books on various occasions to find different passages of interest, you can search through the same genomic library on various occasions to find and isolate different genes or other DNA sequences.

Researchers also commonly use another kind of DNA library that is made starting with mRNA molecules isolated from a cell **(Figure 15.4)**. To convert single-stranded mRNA to double-stranded DNA for cloning (RNA cannot be cloned), first the researchers use the enzyme *reverse transcriptase* (made by retroviruses) to make a single-stranded DNA that is complementary to the mRNA. Then they degrade the mRNA strand with an enzyme and use DNA polymerase to make a second DNA strand that is complementary to the first. The result is **complementary DNA (cDNA)**. After adding restriction sites to each end, the researchers insert the cDNA into a cloning vector as described for the genomic library. The entire collection of cloned cDNAs made from the mRNAs isolated from a cell is a **cDNA library**.

Not all genes are active in every cell. Therefore, a cDNA library is limited in that it includes copies of only the genes that were active in the cells used as the starting point for creation of the library. This limitation can be an advantage, however, in identifying genes active in one cell type and not another. cDNA libraries are useful, therefore, for providing clues to the changes in gene activity that are responsible for cell differentiation and specialization. An ingenious method for comparing the cDNA libraries produced by different cell types—the DNA chip—is described in the next chapter.

cDNA libraries provide a critical advantage to genetic engineers who wish to insert eukaryotic genes into bacteria, particularly when the bacteria are to be used as "factories" for making the protein encoded in the gene. The genes in eukaryotic nuclear DNA typically contain many *introns*, spacer sequences that interrupt the amino acid–coding sequence of a gene (see Section 13.3). Because bacterial DNA does not contain introns, bacteria are not equipped to process eukaryotic genes correctly. However, the cDNA copy of a eukaryotic mRNA already has the introns removed, so bacteria can transcribe and translate it accurately to make eukaryotic proteins.

Screening a DNA Library for a Gene of Interest. One method used to screen a DNA library to identify a clone containing a gene of interest is based on the fact that a gene has a unique DNA sequence. In this technique, called **DNA hybridization**, a gene of interest is identified in the set of clones when it base-pairs with a short, single-stranded complementary DNA or RNA molecule called a *nucleic acid probe* **(Figure 15.5)**. The figure illustrates screening for a gene of interest in a genomic library. Similarly, the approach can be used to screen a cDNA library for the cDNA corresponding to a gene of interest. The probe is labelled with a radioactive or a nonradioactive tag, so investigators can detect it. In our

Research Method Figure 15.5 DNA hybridization to identify a DNA sequence of interest.

PURPOSE: Hybridization with a specific DNA probe allows researchers to detect a specific DNA sequence, such as a gene, within a population of DNA molecules. Here, DNA hybridization is used to screen a genomic library of plasmid clones to identify those containing a recombinant plasmid with a gene of interest.

PROTOCOL:

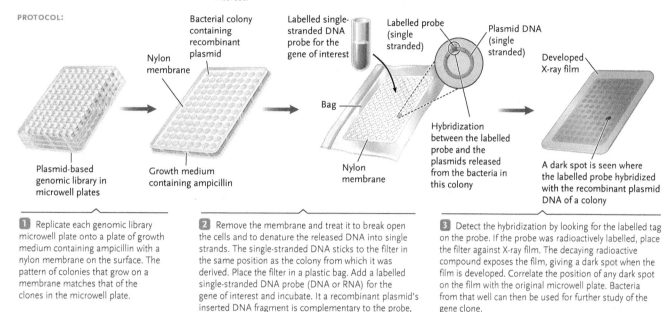

Plasmid-based genomic library in microwell plates

Growth medium containing ampicillin

Nylon membrane

Bacterial colony containing recombinant plasmid

Labelled single-stranded DNA probe for the gene of interest

Labelled probe (single stranded)

Plasmid DNA (single stranded)

Bag

Nylon membrane

Hybridization between the labelled probe and the plasmids released from the bacteria in this colony

Developed X-ray film

A dark spot is seen where the labelled probe hybridized with the recombinant plasmid DNA of a colony

1 Replicate each genomic library microwell plate onto a plate of growth medium containing ampicillin with a nylon membrane on the surface. The pattern of colonies that grow on a membrane matches that of the clones in the microwell plate.

2 Remove the membrane and treat it to break open the cells and to denature the released DNA into single strands. The single-stranded DNA sticks to the filter in the same position as the colony from which it was derived. Place the filter in a plastic bag. Add a labelled single-stranded DNA probe (DNA or RNA) for the gene of interest and incubate. It a recombinant plasmid's inserted DNA fragment is complementary to the probe, the two will hybridize, that is form base pairs. Wash off excess labelled probe.

3 Detect the hybridization by looking for the labelled tag on the probe. If the probe was radioactively labelled, place the filter against X-ray film. The decaying radioactive compound exposes the film, giving a dark spot when the film is developed. Correlate the position of any dark spot on the film with the original microwell plate. Bacteria from that well can then be used for further study of the gene clone.

INTERPRETING THE RESULTS: DNA hybridization with a labelled probe enables a researcher to identify a sequence of interest. If the probe is for a particular gene, it allows the specific identification of a colony containing bacteria with recombinant plasmids carrying that gene. The specificity of the method depends directly on the probe used. The same collection of bacterial clones can be used again and again to search for recombinant plasmids carrying different genes or different plasmids of interest simply by changing the probe used in the experiment.

example, if we know the sequence of part of a gene of interest, we can use that information to design and synthesize a nucleic acid probe. Or, we can take advantage of DNA sequence similarities of evolutionarily related organisms. For instance, we could make a probe for the human actin gene based on the sequence of the cloned mouse actin gene and expect that the two nucleic acids would hybridize because of the evolutionary conservation of that gene. Once a colony containing plasmids with a gene of interest has been identified, that colony can be used to produce large quantities of the cloned gene.

15.1d The Polymerase Chain Reaction Amplifies DNA *In Vitro*

Producing multiple DNA copies by cloning requires a series of techniques and considerable time. A much more rapid process, **polymerase chain reaction (PCR)**, produces an extremely large number of copies of a specific DNA sequence from a DNA mixture without having to clone the sequence in a host organism. The process is called *amplification* because it increases the amount of DNA to the point where it can be analyzed or manipulated easily. Developed in 1983 by Kary B. Mullis and F. Faloona at Cetus Corporation

(Emeryville, California), PCR has become one of the most important tools in modern molecular biology, finding wide application in all areas of biology. Mullis received a Nobel Prize in 1993 for his role in the development of PCR.

How PCR is performed is shown in **Figure 15.6, p. 346.** PCR is essentially a special case of DNA replication in which a DNA polymerase replicates just a portion of a DNA molecule rather than the whole molecule. PCR takes advantage of a characteristic common to all DNA polymerases: these enzymes add nucleotides only to the 3′ end of an existing chain called the *primer* (see Section 12.3). For replication to begin, a primer must be available, base-paired to the template chain. By cycling 20 to 30 times through a series of priming and replication steps, PCR amplifies the target sequence, producing millions of copies.

Since the primers used in PCR are designed to bracket only the sequence of interest, the cycles replicate only this sequence from a mixture of essentially any DNA molecules. Thus, PCR not only finds the "needle in the haystack" among all the sequences in a mixture but also makes millions of copies of the "needle"—the DNA sequence of interest. Usually, no further purification of the amplified sequence is necessary.

Research Method Figure 15.6

The polymerase chain reaction (PCR).

PURPOSE: To amplify—produce large numbers of copies of—a target DNA sequence in the test tube without cloning.

PROTOCOL: A PCR mixture has four key elements: (1) the DNA with the target sequence to be amplified; (2) a pair of DNA primers, one complementary to one end of the target sequence and the other complementary to the other end of the target sequence; (3) the four nucleoside triphosphate precursors for DNA synthesis (dATP, dTTP, dGTP, and dCTP); and (4) DNA polymerase. Since PCR uses high temperatures that would break down normal DNA polymerases, a heat-stable DNA polymerase is used. Heat-stable polymerases are isolated from microorganisms that grow in a high-temperature area such as a thermal pool or near a deep-sea vent.

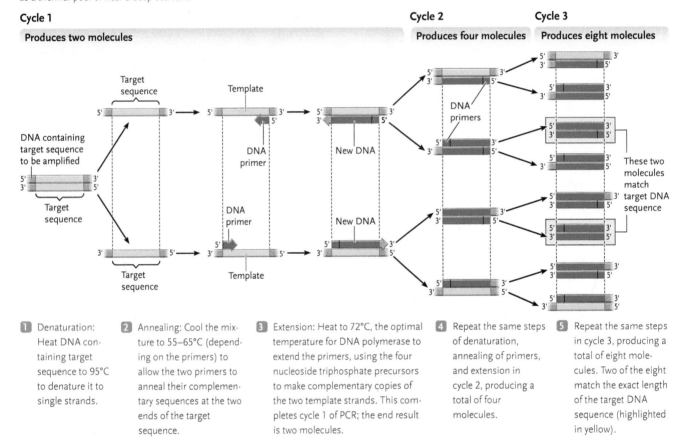

Cycle 1

Produces two molecules

Cycle 2

Produces four molecules

Cycle 3

Produces eight molecules

1. Denaturation: Heat DNA containing target sequence to 95°C to denature it to single strands.

2. Annealing: Cool the mixture to 55–65°C (depending on the primers) to allow the two primers to anneal their complementary sequences at the two ends of the target sequence.

3. Extension: Heat to 72°C, the optimal temperature for DNA polymerase to extend the primers, using the four nucleoside triphosphate precursors to make complementary copies of the two template strands. This completes cycle 1 of PCR; the end result is two molecules.

4. Repeat the same steps of denaturation, annealing of primers, and extension in cycle 2, producing a total of four molecules.

5. Repeat the same steps in cycle 3, producing a total of eight molecules. Two of the eight match the exact length of the target DNA sequence (highlighted in yellow).

INTERPRETING THE RESULTS: After three cycles, PCR produces a pair of molecules matching the target sequence. Subsequent cycles amplify these molecules to the point where they outnumber all other molecules in the reaction by many orders of magnitude.

CONCEPT FIX Careful attention to Figure 15.6 can help you avoid the common pitfalls in understanding PCR. Notice that

1. the primers are made of DNA, not RNA as in natural DNA replication;
2. the left primer binds to one strand while the right primer binds to the opposite strand of the original DNA;
3. of all the DNA sequences put into the PCR reaction tube, only the *target sequence,* the sequence between the primers, is amplified; and
4. although the diagram shows DNA being synthesized left to right on the bottom strand, and right to left on the top strand, the DNA polymerase is reading the template 3′ to 5′ in both cases.

The characteristics of PCR allow extremely small DNA samples to be amplified to concentrations high enough for analysis. PCR is used, for example, to produce enough DNA for analysis from the root of a single human hair, or from a small amount of blood, semen, or saliva, such as the traces left at the scene of a crime. It is also used to extract and multiply DNA sequences from skeletal remains; ancient sources such as mammoths, Neanderthals, and Egyptian mummies; and, in rare cases, amber-entombed fossils, fossil bones, and fossil plant remains.

A successful outcome of PCR is shown by analyzing a sample of the amplified DNA using **agarose gel electrophoresis** to see if the copies are the same length as the target **(Figure 15.7).** Gel electrophoresis is a technique by which DNA, RNA, or protein molecules are separated in a gel subjected to an electric field. The type of gel and the conditions used vary with the experiment, but in each case, the gel functions as a molecular sieve to separate the macromolecules based on size, electrical charge, or other properties. To separate large DNA molecules, such as those typically produced by PCR, a gel made of agarose, a natural molecule isolated from seaweed, is used because of its large pore size.

For PCR experiments, the size of the amplified DNA is determined by comparing the position of the

Research Method Figure 15.7 Separation of DNA fragments by agarose gel electrophoresis.

PURPOSE: Gel electrophoresis separates DNA molecules, RNA molecules, or proteins according to their sizes, electrical charges, or other properties through a gel in an electric field. Different gel types and conditions are used for different molecules and types of applications. A common gel for separating large DNA fragments is made of agarose.

PROTOCOL:

1 Prepare a gel consisting of a thin slab of agarose and place it in a gel box between two electrodes. The gel has wells for placing the DNA samples to be analyzed. Add **buffer** to cover the gels.

2 Load DNA sample solutions, such as PCR products, into wells of the gel, alongside a well loaded with marker DNA fragments of known sizes. (The DNA samples, as well as the marker DNA sample, have a dye added to help see the liquid when loading the wells. The dye migrates during electrophoresis, enabling the progress of electrophoresis to be followed.)

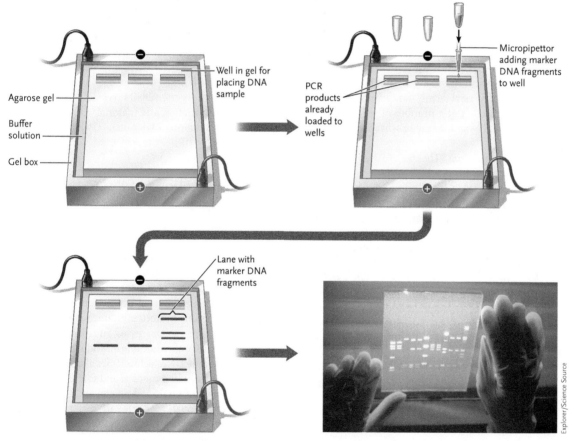

Well in gel for placing DNA sample

Agarose gel

Buffer solution

Gel box

Micropipettor adding marker DNA fragments to well

PCR products already loaded to wells

Lane with marker DNA fragments

Explorer/Science Source

3 Apply an electric current to the gel; DNA fragments are negatively charged, so they migrate to the positive pole. Shorter DNA fragments migrate faster than longer DNA fragments. At the completion of separation, DNA fragments of the same length have formed bands in the gel. At this point, the bands are invisible.

4 Stain the gel with a dye that binds to DNA. The dye fluoresces under UV light, enabling the DNA bands to be seen and photographed. An actual gel showing separated DNA bands stained and visualized this way is shown.

INTERPRETING THE RESULTS: Agarose gel electrophoresis separates DNA fragments according to their length. The lengths of the DNA fragments being analyzed are determined by measuring their migration distances and comparing these distances to a calibration curve of the migration distances of the marker bands, which have known lengths. For PCR, agarose gel electrophoresis shows whether DNA of the correct length was amplified. For restriction enzyme digests, this technique shows whether fragments are produced as expected.

DNA band with the positions of DNA fragments of known size separated on the gel at the same time. If that size matches the predicted size for the target DNA, PCR is deemed successful. In some cases, such as DNA from ancient sources, a size prediction may not be possible; in this case, agarose gel electrophoresis analysis simply indicates whether there was DNA in the sample that could be amplified.

The advantages of PCR have made it the technique of choice for researchers, law enforcement agencies, and forensic specialists whose primary interest is in the amplification of specific DNA fragments up to a practical maximum of a few thousand base pairs. Cloning remains the technique of choice for amplification of longer fragments. The major limitation of PCR relates to the primers. To design a primer for PCR, the researcher must first have sequence information about the target DNA. By contrast, cloning can be used to amplify DNA of unknown sequence.

Review of Some of the Materials, Concepts, and Techniques Introduced in This Section. In this chapter so far we have discussed many research methods—so there are a lot of new terms and techniques to learn! Here is a collection of a number of these terms and techniques and what they are or what they do:

- *Genetic engineering*. The use of DNA technologies to alter genes for practical purposes.
- *DNA cloning*. A method for producing many copies of a piece of DNA.
- *Gene cloning*. DNA cloning that involves a gene.
- *Recombinant DNA*. DNA fragments from two or more sources that have joined together.
- *Restriction enzyme (restriction endonuclease)*. An enzyme that recognizes a specific DNA sequence and cuts the DNA within that sequence. Fragments produced by cutting DNA with a restriction enzyme are *restriction fragments.*
- *Ligation*. The process of joining two or more DNA fragments together to make one DNA molecule.
- *DNA ligase*. The enzyme that seals together DNA fragments generated by restriction enzyme digestion to produce a recombinant DNA molecule.
- *Cloning vector*. DNA molecules into which a DNA fragment can be inserted to form a recombinant DNA molecule that can be replicated in a host organism for the purpose of cloning the DNA fragment.
- *Genomic DNA library*. A set of clones that collectively contains a copy of every DNA sequence in a genome.
- *cDNA (complementary DNA)*. A double-stranded DNA copy of a single-stranded mRNA molecule.
- *cDNA library*. A collection of cloned cDNAs made from the mRNAs isolated from a cell.

- *DNA hybridization*. A technique to identify a gene of interest in a set of clones using a nucleic acid probe that can base-pair with the DNA sequence of the gene.
- *Polymerase chain reaction (PCR)*. A DNA replication-based technique for amplifying DNA sequences, including genes, without cloning.
- *Agarose gel electrophoresis*. A technique in which an electric field passing through an agarose gel is used to separate DNA or RNA molecules on the basis of size.

STUDY BREAK

1. What features do restriction enzymes have in common? How do they differ?
2. Plasmid cloning vectors are one type of cloning vector that can be used with *E. coli* as a host organism. What features of a plasmid cloning vector make it useful for constructing and cloning recombinant DNA molecules?
3. What is a cDNA library, and from what cellular material is it derived? How does a cDNA library differ from a genomic library?
4. What information and materials are needed to amplify a region of DNA using PCR?

15.2 Applications of DNA Technologies

The ability to clone pieces of DNA—genes, especially—and to amplify specific segments of DNA by PCR revolutionized biology. These and other DNA technologies are now used for research in all areas of biology, including cloning genes to determine their structure, function, and regulation of expression; manipulating genes to determine how their products function in cellular or developmental processes; and identifying differences in DNA sequences among individuals in ecological studies. The same DNA technologies also have practical applications, including medical and forensic detection, modification of animals and plants, and the manufacture of commercial products. In this section, case studies provide examples of how the techniques are used to answer questions and solve problems.

15.2a DNA Technologies Are Used in Molecular Testing for Many Human Genetic Diseases

Many human genetic diseases are caused by defects in enzymes or other proteins that result from mutations at the DNA level. Once scientists have identified the specific mutations responsible for human genetic diseases, they can often use DNA technologies to develop molecular tests for those diseases. One example is sickle cell disease (see "Why It Matters" in Chapter 10; Section 10.2f; and Section 11.4a). People with this disease are homozygous for a DNA mutation that affects hemoglobin, the oxygen-carrying molecule of the blood. Hemoglobin consists of two copies each of the α-globin and β-globin polypeptides. The mutation, which is in the β-globin gene, alters one amino acid in the polypeptide. As a consequence, the function of hemoglobin is significantly impaired in individuals homozygous for the mutation (who have sickle cell disease) and mildly impaired in individuals heterozygous for the mutation (who have sickle cell trait).

The sickle cell mutation changes a restriction site in the DNA **(Figure 15.8)**. Three restriction sites for *Mst*II are associated with the normal β-globin gene, two within the coding sequence of the gene and one upstream of the gene. The sickle cell mutation eliminates the middle site of the three. Cutting the β-globin gene with *Mst*II produces two DNA fragments from the normal gene and one fragment from the mutated gene (see Figure 15.8). Restriction enzyme–generated DNA fragments of different lengths from the same region of the genome such as in this example are known as **restriction fragment length polymorphisms** (RFLPs, pronounced "riff-lips").

RFLPs are typically analyzed using **Southern blot analysis** (named after its inventor, researcher Edward Southern) **(Figure 15.9, p. 351)**. In this technique, genomic DNA is digested with a restriction enzyme, and the DNA fragments are separated using agarose gel electrophoresis. The fragments are then transferred—blotted—to a filter paper, and a labelled probe is used to identify a DNA sequence of interest from among the many thousands of fragments on the filter paper.

Analyzing DNA for the sickle cell mutation by *Mst*II digestion and Southern blot analysis is straightforward (see Figure 15.9). An individual with sickle cell disease will have one DNA band of 376 bp detected by the probe (lane A), a healthy individual will have two DNA bands of 175 and 201 bp (lane B), and an individual with sickle cell trait (heterozygous for normal and mutant alleles) will have three DNA bands of 376 bp (mutant allele) and 201 and 175 bp (normal allele) (lane C). The same probe detects all three RFLP fragments by binding to all or part of the sequence.

Restriction enzyme digestion and Southern blot analysis may be used to test for a number of other human genetic diseases, including phenylketonuria and Duchenne muscular dystrophy. In some cases, restriction enzyme digestion is combined with PCR for a quicker, easier analysis. The gene or region of the gene with the restriction enzyme variation is first amplified using PCR, and the amplified DNA is then cut with the diagnostic restriction enzyme. Amplification produces enough DNA so that separation by

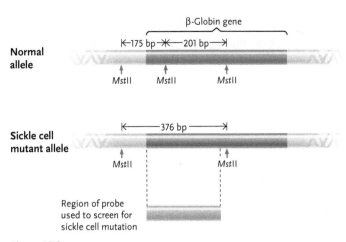

Figure 15.8
Restriction site differences between the normal and sickle cell mutant alleles of the β-globin gene. The figure shows a DNA segment that can be used as a probe to identify these alleles in subsequent analysis (see Figure 15.9, p. 351).

size on an agarose gel produces clearly visible bands, positioned according to fragment length. Researchers can then determine whether the fragment lengths match a normal or abnormal RFLP pattern. This method eliminates the need for a probe or for Southern blotting.

15.2b DNA Fingerprinting Is Used to Identify Human Individuals and Individuals of Other Species

Just as each human has a unique set of fingerprints, each also has unique combinations and variations of DNA sequences (with the exception of identical twins) known as *DNA fingerprints*. **DNA fingerprinting** is a technique used to distinguish between individuals of the same species using DNA samples. Invented by Sir Alec Jeffreys in 1985, DNA fingerprinting has become a mainstream technique for distinguishing human individuals, notably in forensics and paternity testing. Although the technique can be applied to all kinds of animals and plants, in this chapter we focus on humans.

DNA Fingerprinting Principles. In DNA fingerprinting, scientists use molecular techniques, most typically PCR, to analyze DNA variations at various loci in the genome. Several loci in noncoding regions of the genome are used for analysis. Each locus is an example of a *short tandem repeat* (STR) sequence, meaning that it has a short sequence of DNA repeated in series, with each repeat about 3 to 5 bp. Each locus has a different repeated sequence, and the number of repeats varies among individuals in a population. For example, one STR locus has the sequence AGAT repeated between 8 and 20 times. As a further source of variation, a given individual is either homozygous or heterozygous for

Ethidium Bromide

Figure 15.7, p. 347, shows an agarose gel containing DNA fragments separated by electrophoresis. The fragments appear orange because a stain has bound to the DNA and is fluorescing under ultraviolet light. The stain is ethidium bromide **(Figure 1)**. This relatively flat molecule slides

Figure 1
Ethidium bromide.

neatly between the bases of DNA by a process called intercalation—hence, its usefulness as a stain. However, intercalation into DNA around replication forks can increase the frequency of addition/deletion mutations in cultured cells.

---

an STR allele; perhaps you are homozygous for the 11-repeat allele or heterozygous for a 9-repeat allele and a 15-repeat allele. Likely your DNA fingerprint for this locus is different from most of the others in your class. Because each individual has an essentially unique combination of alleles (identical twins are the exception), analysis of multiple STR loci can discriminate between DNA of different individuals.

Figure 15.10, p. 352, illustrates how PCR is used to obtain a DNA fingerprint for a theoretical STR locus with three alleles of 9, 11, and 15 tandem repeats (see Figure 15.10a). Using primers that flank the STR locus, the locus is amplified from genomic DNA using PCR, and the PCR products are analyzed by gel electrophoresis (see Figure 15.10b).

CONCEPT FIX Notice in Figure 15.10b that the first lane has only one band, even though the cell that was the source of DNA was diploid and had two copies of all alleles. In this case, both alleles produce the same size fragment by PCR analysis. Therefore, fragments from both alleles migrate the same distance in the gel. Notice how this band is thicker than the others, indicating more DNA. ⬡

DNA Fingerprinting in Forensics. DNA fingerprints are routinely used to identify criminals or eliminate innocent people as suspects in legal proceedings. For example, a DNA fingerprint prepared from a hair found at the scene of a crime or from a semen sample might be compared with the DNA fingerprint of a suspect to link the suspect with the crime. Or a DNA fingerprint of blood found on a suspect's clothing or possessions might be compared with the DNA fingerprint of a victim. Typically, the evidence is presented in terms of the probability that the particular DNA sample could have come from a random individual. Hence, the media report probability values, such as one in several million, or in several billion, that a person other than the accused could have left his or her DNA at the crime scene.

Although courts initially met with legal challenges to the admissibility of DNA fingerprints, experience has shown that they are highly dependable as a line of evidence if DNA samples are collected and prepared with care and if a sufficient number of polymorphic loci are examined. There is always concern, however, about the possibility of contamination of the sample with DNA from another source during the path from crime scene to forensic lab analysis. Moreover, in some cases, criminals themselves have planted fake DNA samples at crime scenes to confuse the investigation.

There are many examples of the use of DNA fingerprinting to identify a criminal. For example, in a case in England, the DNA fingerprints of more than 4000 men were made during an investigation of the rape and murder of two teenage girls. The results led to the release of a man wrongly imprisoned for the crimes and to the confession and conviction of the actual killer. And the application of DNA fingerprinting techniques to stored forensic samples has led to the release of a number of people wrongly convicted for rape or murder.

DNA Fingerprinting in Testing Paternity and Establishing Ancestry. DNA fingerprints are also widely used as evidence of paternity because parents and their children share common alleles in their DNA fingerprints. That is, each child receives one allele of each locus from one parent and the other allele from the other parent. A comparison of DNA fingerprints for a number of loci can prove almost infallibly whether a child has been fathered or mothered by a given person. DNA fingerprints have also been used for other investigations, such as confirming that remains discovered in a remote region of Russia were actually those of Czar Nicholas II and members of his family, murdered in 1918 during the Russian revolution.

DNA fingerprinting is also widely used in studies of other organisms, including other animals, plants, and bacteria. Examples include testing for pathogenic *E. coli* in food sources such as hamburger meat, investigating cases of wildlife poaching, detecting genetically modified organisms among living organisms or in food, and comparing the DNA of ancient organisms with that of present-day descendants.

Research Method Figure 15.9 Southern blot analysis.

PURPOSE: The Southern blot technique allows researchers to identify DNA fragments of interest after separating DNA fragments on a gel. One application is to compare different samples of genomic DNA cut with a restriction enzyme to detect specific RFLPs. Here the technique is used to distinguish between individuals with sickle cell disease, individuals with sickle cell trait, and normal individuals.

PROTOCOL:

1 Isolate genomic DNA and digest with a restriction enzyme. Here, genomic DNA is isolated from three individuals: A, sickle cell disease (homozygous for the sickle cell mutant allele); B, normal (homozygous for the normal allele); and C, sickle cell trait (heterozygous for sickle cell mutant allele). Digest the DNA with *Mst*II.

2 Separate the DNA fragments by agarose gel electrophoresis. The thousands of differently sized DNA fragments produce a smear of DNA down the length of each lane in the gel, which can be seen after staining the DNA. (Gel electrophoresis and gel staining are shown in Figure 15.7, p. 347.)

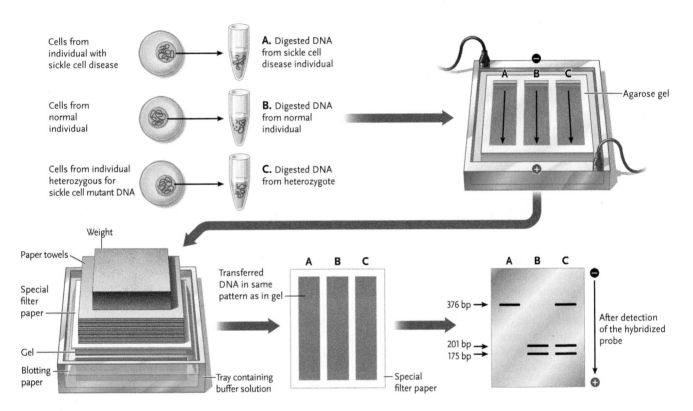

3 Hybridization with a labelled DNA probe to identify DNA fragments of interest cannot be done directly with an agarose gel. Edward Southern devised a method to transfer the DNA fragments from a gel to a special filter paper. First, treat the gel with a solution to denature the DNA into single strands. Next, place the gel on a piece of blotting paper with the ends of the paper in the buffer solution and place the special filter paper on top of the gel. Capillary action wicks the buffer solution in the tray up the blotting paper, through the gel and special filter paper, and into the weighted stack of paper towels on top of the gel. The movement of the solution transfers— blots—the single-stranded DNA fragments to the filter paper, where they stick. The pattern of DNA fragments is the same as it was in the gel.

4 To focus on a particular region of the genome, use DNA hybridization with a labelled probe. That is, incubate a labelled, single-stranded probe with the filter and, after washing off excess probe, detect hybridization of the probe with DNA fragments on the filter. For a radioactive probe, place the filter against photographic film, which, after development, will show a band or bands where the probe hybridized. In this experiment, the probe is a cloned piece of DNA from the area shown in Figure 15.8, p. 349 (the β-globin gene) that can bind to all three of the *Mst*II fragments of interest.

INTERPRETING THE RESULTS: The hybridization result indicates that the probe has identified a very specific DNA fragment or fragments in the digested genomic DNA. The RFLPs for the β-globin gene can be seen in Figure 15.8, p. 349. DNA from the sickle cell disease individual cut with *Mst*II results in a single band of 376 bp detected by the probe, while DNA from the normal individual results in two bands, of 201 bp and 175 bp. DNA from a sickle cell trait heterozygote results in three bands, of 376 bp (from the sickle cell mutant allele), and 201 bp and 175 bp (both from the normal allele). This type of analysis in general is useful for distinguishing normal and mutant alleles of genes where the mutation involved alters a restriction site.

a. Alleles at an STR locus

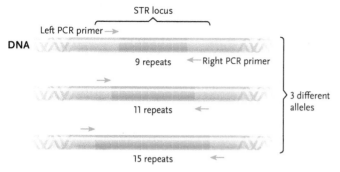

Figure 15.10

Using PCR to obtain a DNA fingerprint for an STR locus.

b. DNA fingerprint analysis of the STR locus by PCR

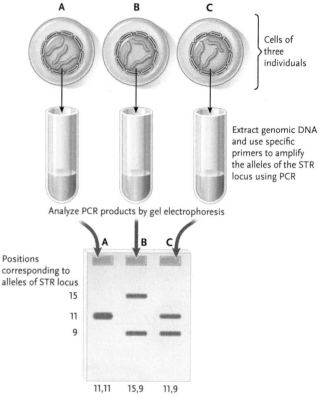

15.2c Genetic Engineering Uses DNA Technologies to Alter the Genes of a Cell or Organism

We have seen the many ways scientists use DNA technologies to ask and answer questions that were once completely inaccessible. Genetic engineering goes beyond gathering information; it is the use of DNA technologies to modify genes of a cell or organism. The goals of genetic engineering include using prokaryotic cells, fungi, animals, and plants as factories for the production of proteins needed in medicine and scientific research; correcting hereditary disorders; and improving animals and crop plants of agricultural importance. In many of these areas, genetic engineering has already been spectacularly successful. The successes and potential benefits of genetic engineering, however, are tempered by ethical and social concerns about its use, along with the fear that the methods may produce toxic or damaging foods or release dangerous and uncontrollable organisms to the environment.

Genetic engineering uses DNA technologies of the kind already discussed in this chapter. DNA—perhaps a modified gene—is introduced into target cells of an organism. Organisms that have undergone a gene transfer are called **transgenic**, meaning that they have been modified to contain genetic information—the *transgene*—from an external source.

The following sections discuss examples of applications of genetic engineering to bacteria, animals, and plants and assess major controversies arising from these projects.

Genetic Engineering of Bacteria to Produce Proteins. Transgenic bacteria have been made, for example, to synthesize proteins for medical applications, break down toxic wastes such as oil spills, produce industrial chemicals such as alcohols, and process minerals. *E. coli* is the organism of choice for many of these applications of DNA technologies.

Using *E. coli* to make a protein from a foreign source is conceptually straightforward (**Figure 15.11**). First, the gene for the protein is cloned from the appropriate organism. Then the gene is inserted into an **expression vector** that, in addition to the usual features of a cloning vector, contains the regulatory sequences that allow transcription and translation of the gene. For a bacterial expression vector, this means having a promoter and a transcription terminator that are recognized by the *E. coli* transcriptional machinery and having the ribosome binding site needed for the bacterial ribosome to recognize the start codon of the transgene (see Section 13.1). The regulatory sequences flank the cluster of restriction sites of the expression vector that are used for cloning so that the inserted gene is correctly placed for transcription and translation when the recombinant plasmid is transformed into *E. coli*.

As we mentioned earlier while discussing DNA libraries, a cDNA copy of a eukaryotic gene is used when we want to use bacteria to express the protein encoded by the gene (see Figure 15.11). This is because the gene itself typically contains introns, which bacteria cannot remove when they transcribe a eukaryotic gene. However, the eukaryotic mRNA that is copied by reverse transcriptase to synthesize cDNA has had its introns removed; thus, when that cDNA is expressed in bacteria it can be transcribed and translated to make the encoded eukaryotic protein. The protein is either extracted from the bacterial cells and purified or, if the protein is secreted, purified from the culture medium.

Expression vectors are available for a number of organisms. They vary in the regulatory sequences they contain and the selectable marker they carry so that the host organism transformed with the vector carrying a gene of interest can be detected and the host can express that gene.

For example, *E. coli* bacteria have been genetically engineered to make the human hormone insulin; the commercial product is called Humulin. Insulin is required by people with some forms of diabetes. Humulin is a perfect copy of the human insulin hormone. Many other proteins, including human growth hormone to treat human growth disorders, tissue plasminogen activator to dissolve blood clots that cause heart attacks, and a vaccine against foot-and-mouth disease of cattle and other cloven-hoofed animals (a highly contagious and sometimes fatal viral disease), have been developed for commercial production in bacteria using similar methods.

A concern is that genetically engineered bacteria may be released accidentally into the environment, where possible adverse effects of the organisms are currently unknown. Scientists minimize the danger of accidental release by growing the bacteria in laboratories that follow appropriate biosafety protocols. In addition, the bacterial strains typically used are genetic mutants that cannot survive outside the growth media used in the laboratory.

Genetic Engineering of Animals. Many animals, including fruit flies, fish, mice, pigs, sheep, goats, and cows, have been altered successfully by genetic engineering. There are many purposes for these alterations, including basic research, correcting genetic disorders in humans and other mammals, and producing pharmaceutically important proteins.

Genetic Engineering Methods for Animals. Several methods are used to introduce a gene of interest into animal cells. The gene may be introduced into *germ-line cells,* which develop into sperm or eggs and thus enable the introduced gene to be passed from generation to generation. Or, the gene may be introduced into *somatic* (body) *cells,* differentiated cells that are not part of lines producing sperm or eggs, in which case the gene is not transmitted from generation to generation.

Germ-line cells of embryos are often used as targets for introducing genes, particularly in mammals **(Figure 15.12, p. 354).** The treated cells are then cultured in quantity and reintroduced into early embryos. If the technique is successful, some of the introduced cells become founders of cell lines that develop into eggs or sperm with the desired genetic information integrated into their DNA. Individuals produced by crosses using the engineered eggs and sperm then contain the

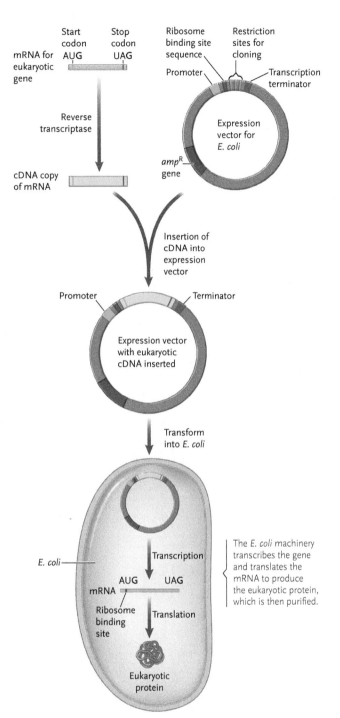

Figure 15.11
Using an expression vector to synthesize a eukaryotic protein.

introduced sequences in all of their cells. Several genes have been introduced into the germ lines of mice by this approach, resulting in permanent, heritable changes in the engineered individuals.

A related technique involves introducing desired genes into **stem cells,** which are cells capable of undergoing many divisions in an unspecialized, undifferentiated state, but which can also differentiate into

Research Method Figure 15.12 Introduction of genes into mouse embryos using embryonic germ-line cells.

PURPOSE: To make a transgenic animal that can transmit the transgene to offspring. The embryonic germ-line cells that receive the transgene develop into the reproductive cells of the animal.

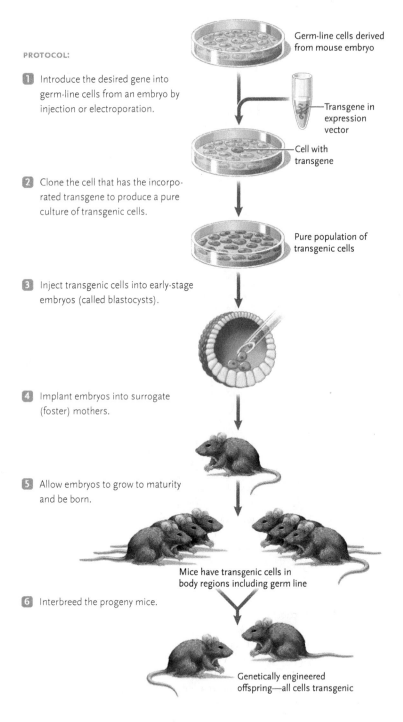

PROTOCOL:

1 Introduce the desired gene into germ-line cells from an embryo by injection or electroporation.

Germ-line cells derived from mouse embryo

Transgene in expression vector

Cell with transgene

2 Clone the cell that has the incorporated transgene to produce a pure culture of transgenic cells.

Pure population of transgenic cells

3 Inject transgenic cells into early-stage embryos (called blastocysts).

4 Implant embryos into surrogate (foster) mothers.

5 Allow embryos to grow to maturity and be born.

Mice have transgenic cells in body regions including germ line

6 Interbreed the progeny mice.

Genetically engineered offspring—all cells transgenic

INTERPRETING THE RESULTS: The result of the breeding is some offspring in which all cells are transgenic—a genetically engineered animal has been produced.

specialized cell types. In mammals, **embryonic stem cells** are found in a mass of cells inside an early-stage embryo (the blastocyst) (see Figure 15.12, step 3) and can differentiate into all of the tissue types of the embryo, whereas **adult stem cells** function to replace specialized cells in various tissues and organs. In mice and other nonhuman mammals, transgenes are introduced into embryonic stem cells, which are then injected into early-stage embryos as in Figure 15.12 (step 3). The stem cells then differentiate into a variety of tissues along with cells of the embryo itself, including sperm and egg cells. Males and females are then bred, leading to offspring that are either homozygotes, containing two copies of the introduced gene, or heterozygotes, containing one introduced gene and one gene that was native to the embryo receiving the engineered stem cells.

Introduction of genes into stem cells has been performed mostly in mice. One of the highly useful results is the production of a *knockout mouse*, a homozygous recessive that receives two copies of a gene altered to a nonfunctional state and thus has no functional copies. The effect of the missing gene on the knockout mouse is a clue to the normal function of the gene. In some cases, knockout mice are used to model human genetic diseases.

For introducing genes into somatic cells, somatic cells are typically removed from the body, cultured, and then transformed with DNA containing the transgene. The modified cells are then reintroduced into the body, where the transgene functions. Because germ cells and their products are not involved, the transgene remains in the individual and is not passed to offspring.

Gene Therapy: Correcting Genetic Disorders. The path to **gene therapy**—correcting genetic disorders—in humans began with experiments using mice. In 1982, Richard Palmiter at the University of Washington, Ralph Brinster of the University of Pennsylvania, and their colleagues injected a growth hormone gene from rats into fertilized mouse eggs and implanted the eggs into a surrogate mother. She gave birth to some normal-sized mouse pups that grew more quickly than normal and became about twice the size of their normal litter mates. These *giant mice* (**Figure 15.13**) attracted extensive media attention from around the world.

Palmiter and Brinster next attempted to cure a genetic disorder by gene therapy. In this experiment, they were able to correct a genetic growth hormone deficiency that produces dwarf mice. They introduced a normal copy of the growth hormone gene into fertilized eggs taken from mutant dwarf mice and implanted the eggs into a surrogate mother. The transgenic mouse pups grew to slightly larger than normal, demonstrating that the genetic defect in these mice had been corrected.

This sort of experiment, in which a gene is introduced into germ-line cells of an animal to correct a genetic disorder, is called **germ-line gene therapy.** For ethical reasons, germ-line gene therapy is not permitted with humans. Instead, humans are treated with **somatic gene therapy**, in which genes are introduced into somatic cells (as described in the previous section).

The first successful use of somatic gene therapy with a human subject who had a genetic disorder was carried out in the 1990s by W. French Anderson and his colleagues at the National Institutes of Health (NIH) in the United States. The subject was a young girl with *adenosine deaminase deficiency (ADA)*. Without the adenosine deaminase enzyme, white blood cells cannot mature (see Chapter 51); without normally functioning white blood cells, the body's immune response is so deficient that most children with ADA die of infections before reaching puberty. The researchers successfully introduced a functional ADA gene into mature white blood cells isolated from the patient. Those cells were reintroduced into the girl, and expression of the ADA gene provided a temporary cure for her ADA deficiency. The cure was not permanent because mature white blood cells, produced by differentiation of stem cells in the bone marrow, are nondividing cells with a finite lifetime. Therefore, the somatic gene therapy procedure has to be repeated every few months. Indeed, the subject of this example still receives periodic gene therapy to maintain the necessary levels of the ADA enzyme in her blood. In addition, she receives direct doses of the normal enzyme. More recent improved protocols have resulted in successful treatment of over 30 ADA patients worldwide without adverse affects or the need for ongoing therapy.

Successful somatic gene therapy has also been achieved for sickle cell disease. In December 1998, a 13-year-old boy's bone marrow cells were replaced with stem cells from the **umbilical cord** of an unrelated infant. The hope was that the stem cells would produce healthy bone marrow cells, the source of blood cells. The procedure worked, and the patient has been declared cured of the disease.

However, despite enormous efforts, human somatic gene therapy has not been the panacea people expected. Relatively little progress has been made since the first gene therapy clinical trial for ADA deficiency was described, and, in fact, there have been major setbacks. In 1999, for example, a teenage patient in a somatic gene therapy trial died as a result of a severe immune response to the viral vector being used to introduce a normal gene to correct his genetic deficiency. Furthermore, some children in gene therapy trials involving the use of retrovirus vectors to introduce genes into blood stem cells have developed a leukemia-like condition. In short, somatic gene therapy is not yet an effective treatment for human genetic disease, even though the approach has been successful in a number of cases to correct models of human genetic disorders in experimental mammals. Although no commercial human gene therapy product has been

approved for use, roughly 100 new clinical trials are approved worldwide each year, focusing on improved therapies for a long list of conditions, including cancer, congenital blindness, Parkinson's disease, malaria, multiple sclerosis, arthritis, Type I diabetes, cystic fibrosis, and muscular dystrophy, as well as various blood and immunological disorders.

Turning Domestic Animals into Protein Factories. Another successful application of genetic engineering turns animals into pharmaceutical factories for the production of proteins required to treat human diseases or other medical conditions. Most of these *pharming* projects, as they are called, engineer the animals to produce the desired proteins in milk, making the production, extraction, and purification of the proteins harmless to the animals.

One of the first successful applications of this approach was carried out with sheep engineered to produce a protein required for normal blood clotting in humans. The protein, called a *clotting factor*, is deficient in people with one form of hemophilia, who require frequent injections of the factor to avoid bleeding to death from even minor injuries. Using DNA-cloning techniques, researchers joined the gene encoding the normal form of the clotting factor to the promoter sequences of the β-lactoglobin gene, which encodes a protein secreted in milk, and introduced it into fertilized eggs. These cells were implanted into a surrogate mother, and the transgenic sheep born were allowed to mature. The β-lactoglobin promoter controlling the clotting factor gene became activated in mammary gland cells of females, resulting in the production of clotting factor. The clotting factor was then secreted into the milk. Production in the milk is harmless to the sheep and yields the protein in a form that can easily be obtained and purified.

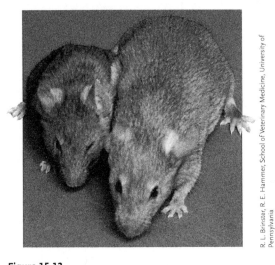

R. L. Brinster, R. E. Hammer, School of Veterinary Medicine, University of Pennsylvania

Figure 15.13
A genetically engineered giant mouse (right) produced by the introduction of a rat growth hormone gene into the animal.
A mouse of normal size is on the left.

Experimental Research Figure 15.14 The first cloning of a mammal.

QUESTION: Does the nucleus of an adult mammal contain all the genetic information to specify a new organism? In other words, can mammals be cloned starting with adult cells?

EXPERIMENT: Ian Wilmut, Keith Campbell, and their colleagues fused a mammary gland cell from an adult sheep with an unfertilized egg cell from which the nucleus had been removed, and tested whether that fused cell could produce a lamb.

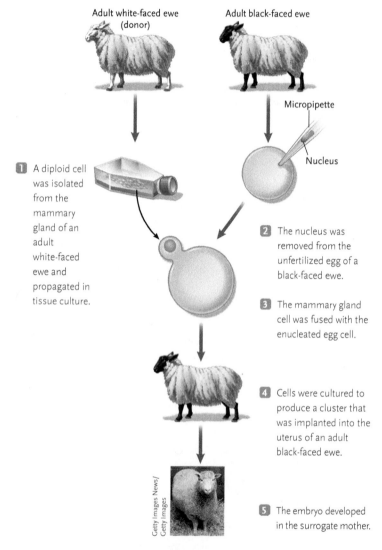

Adult white-faced ewe (donor)

Adult black-faced ewe

Micropipette

Nucleus

1 A diploid cell was isolated from the mammary gland of an adult white-faced ewe and propagated in tissue culture.

2 The nucleus was removed from the unfertilized egg of a black-faced ewe.

3 The mammary gland cell was fused with the enucleated egg cell.

4 Cells were cultured to produce a cluster that was implanted into the uterus of an adult black-faced ewe.

5 The embryo developed in the surrogate mother.

Getty Images News/ Getty Images

RESULT: Dolly was born and grew normally. She was white faced—a clone of the donor ewe. DNA fingerprinting using STR loci showed her DNA matched that of the donor ewe and neither the ewe who donated the egg nor the ewe who was the surrogate mother.

CONCLUSION: An adult nucleus of a mammal contains all the genetic material necessary to direct the development of a normal new organism, a clone of the original. Dolly was the first cloned mammal. The success rate for Wilmut and Campbell's experiment was very low—Dolly represented less than 0.4% of the fused cells they made—but its significance was huge.

Based on I. Wilmut et al. "Viable offspring derived from fetal and mammalian cells." *Nature.* 1997 Feb 27; 385(6619): 810–3.

Other similar projects are under development to produce particular proteins in transgenic mammals. These include a protein to treat cystic fibrosis, collagen to correct scars and wrinkles, human milk proteins to be added to infant formulas, and normal hemoglobin for use as an additive to blood transfusions.

Producing Animal Clones. Making transgenic mammals is expensive and inefficient. And because only one copy of the transgene typically becomes incorporated into the treated cell, not all progeny of a transgenic animal inherit that gene. Scientists reasoned that an alternative to breeding a valuable transgenic mammal to produce progeny with the transgene would be to clone the mammal. Each clone would be identical to the original, including the expression of the transgene. That this is possible was shown in 1997 when two scientists, Ian Wilmut and Keith H. S. Campbell of the Roslin Institute, Edinburgh, Scotland, announced that they had successfully cloned a sheep from a single somatic cell derived from an adult sheep **(Figure 15.14)**—the first cloned mammal.

Since the successful cloning experiment producing Dolly, many additional mammals have been cloned, including mice, goats, pigs, monkeys, rabbits, dogs, a male calf appropriately named Gene, and a domestic cat called CC (for *Copy Cat*).

Cloning farm animals has been so successful that several commercial enterprises now provide cloned copies of champion animals. One example is a clone of an American Holstein cow, Zita, who was the U.S. national champion milk producer for many years. Animal breeders estimate that there are now more than 100 cloned animals on U.S. farms, and breeders plan to produce entire herds if government approval is granted.

The cloning of domestic animals has its drawbacks. Many cloning attempts fail, leading to the death of the transplanted embryos. Cloned animals often suffer from conditions such as birth defects and poor lung development. Genes may be lost during the cloning process or may be expressed abnormally in the cloned animal. For example, molecular studies have shown that the expression of perhaps hundreds of genes in the genomes of clones is regulated abnormally.

CONCEPT FIX In studying Figures 15.12, p. 354, and 15.14, both related to manipulating animal embryos, it may be tempting to see Dolly as an advance in stem cell research. However, Dolly resulted from the transfer of a somatic cell nucleus to an egg cell that was lacking a nucleus. This cloning technique, called somatic cell nuclear transfer (SCNT), doesn't involve stem cells.

Genetic Engineering of Plants. Genetic engineering of plants has led to increased resistance to pests and disease; greater tolerance to heat, drought, and salinity; greater crop yields; faster growth; and resistance to herbicides. Another aim is to produce seeds with higher levels of amino acids. The essential amino acid lysine, for example, is present only in limited quantities in cereal grains such as wheat, rice, oats, barley, and corn; the seeds of legumes such as beans, peas, lentils, soybeans, and peanuts are deficient in the essential amino acid methionine or cysteine. Increasing the amounts of the deficient amino acids in plant seeds by genetic engineering would greatly improve the diet of domestic animals and human populations that rely on seeds as a primary food source. Efforts are also under way to increase the content of vitamins and minerals in crop plants.

Another possibility for plant genetic engineering is plant pharming to produce pharmaceutical products. Plants are ideal for this purpose because they are primary producers at the bottom rung of the **food chain** and can be grown in huge numbers with maximum conservation of the Sun's energy captured in photosynthesis.

Some plants, such as *Arabidopsis*, tobacco, potato, cabbage, and carrot, have special advantages for genetic engineering because individual cells can be removed from an adult, altered by the introduction of a desired gene, and then grown in cultures into a multicellular mass of cloned cells called a *callus*. Subsequently, roots, stems, and leaves develop in the callus, forming a young plant that can then be grown in containers or fields by the usual methods. In the plant, each cell contains the introduced gene. The gametes produced by the transgenic plants can then be used in crosses to produce offspring, some of which will have the transgene, as in the similar experiments with animals.

Methods Used to Insert Genes into Plants. Genes are inserted into plant cells by several techniques. One commonly used method takes advantage of a natural process that causes crown gall disease, which is characterized by bulbous, irregular growths—tumours, essentially—that can develop at wound sites on the trunks and limbs of deciduous trees **(Figure 15.15)**. Crown gall disease is caused by the bacterium *Rhizobium radiobacter* (formerly *Agrobacterium tumefaciens*, recently reclassified on the basis of genome analysis). This bacterium contains a large, circular plasmid called the **Ti (tumour-inducing) plasmid.** The interaction between the bacterium and the plant cell it infects stimulates the excision of a segment of the Ti plasmid called *T DNA* (for transforming DNA), which then integrates into the plant cell's genome. Genes on the T DNA are then expressed; the products stimulate the transformed cell to grow and divide and therefore to produce a tumour. The tumours provide essential nutrients for the bacterium. The Ti plasmid is used as a vector for making transgenic plants in much the same way as bacterial plasmids are used as vectors to introduce genes into bacteria **(Figure 15.16, p. 358).**

Gall

Figure 15.15

A crown gall tumour on the trunk of a California pepper tree. The tumour, stimulated by genes introduced from the bacterium *Rhizobium radiobacter*, is the bulbous, irregular growth extending from the trunk.

Successful Plant Genetic Engineering Projects. An early visual demonstration of the successful use of genetic engineering techniques to produce a transgenic plant is the glowing tobacco plant **(Figure 15.17, p. 358).** The transgenic plant contained luciferase, the gene for the firefly enzyme. When the plant was soaked in the substrate for the enzyme, it became luminescent.

The most widespread application of genetic engineering of plants involves the production of transgenic crops. Thousands of such crops have been developed and field tested, and many have been approved for commercial use. If you analyze the processed plant-based foods at a national supermarket chain, you will likely find that at least two-thirds contain products made from transgenic plants.

In many cases, plants are modified to make them resistant to insect pests, viruses, or herbicides. Crops modified for insect resistance include corn, cotton, and potatoes. The most common approach to making plants resistant to insects is to introduce the gene from the bacterium *Bacillus thuringiensis* that encodes the *Bt* toxin, an organic pesticide. This toxin has been used in powder form to kill insects in agriculture for many years, and now transgenic plants making their own *Bt* toxin are resistant to specific groups of insects that feed on them. Millions of acres of crop plants planted in the United States and Canada are *Bt*-engineered varieties.

Virus infections cause enormous crop losses worldwide. Transgenic crops that are virus resistant would be highly valuable to the agricultural community. There is some promise in this area. By some unknown process, transgenic plants expressing certain viral proteins become resistant to infections by whole viruses that contain these same proteins. Two

Research Method Figure 15.16 Using the Ti plasmid of *Rhizobium radiobacter* to produce transgenic plants.

PURPOSE: To make transgenic plants. This technique is one way to introduce a transgene into a plant for genetic engineering purposes.

PROTOCOL:

1 Isolate the Ti plasmid from *Rhizobium radiobacter*. The plasmid contains a segment called T DNA (T = transforming), which induces tumours in plants.

Rhizobium radiobacter
T DNA
Bacterial chromosome
Restriction site
T DNA
Ti plasmid

2 Digest the Ti plasmid with a restriction enzyme that cuts within the T DNA. Mix with a gene of interest on a DNA fragment that was produced by digesting with the same enzyme. Use DNA ligase to join the two DNA molecules together to produce a recombinant plasmid.

DNA fragment with gene of interest

Recombinant plasmid

3 Transform the recombinant Ti plasmid into a disarmed *A. Rhizobium radiobacter* that cannot induce tumours, and use the transformed bacterium to infect cells in plant fragments in a test tube. In infected cells, the T DNA with the inserted gene of interest excises from the Ti plasmid and integrates into the plant cell genome.

Rhizobium radiobacter disarmed so it cannot induce tumours

Plant cell (not to scale)

Nucleus

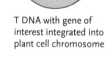

T DNA with gene of interest integrated into plant cell chromosome

Regenerated transgenic plant

4 Culture the transgenic plant fragments to regenerate whole plants.

INTERPRETING THE RESULTS: The plant has been genetically engineered to contain a new gene. The transgenic plant will express a new trait based on that gene, perhaps resistance to a herbicide or production of an insect toxin, according to the goal of the experiment.

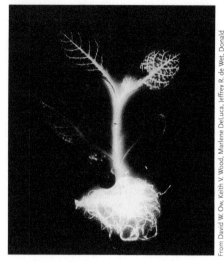

From David W. Ow, Keith V. Wood, Marlene DeLuca, Jeffrey R. de Wet, Donald R. Helinski and Stephen H. Howell, "Transient and stable expression of the firefly luciferase gene in plant cells and transgenic plants." *Science* 14 November 1986, Vol. 234 no. 4778 pp. 856–859. Reprinted with permission from AAAS.

Figure 15.17
A genetically engineered tobacco plant, made capable of luminescence by the introduction of a firefly gene coding for the enzyme luciferase.

virus-resistant genetically modified crops made so far are papaya and squash.

Several crops have also been engineered to become resistant to herbicides. For example, *glyphosate* (commonly known by its brand name, Roundup) is a highly potent herbicide that is widely used in weed control. The herbicide works by inhibiting a particular enzyme in the chloroplast. Unfortunately, it also kills crops. But transgenic crops have been made in which a bacterial form of the chloroplast enzyme has been added to the plants. The bacteria-derived enzyme is not affected by Roundup, and farmers who use these herbicide-resistant crops can spray fields of crops to kill weeds without killing the crops. Now most of the corn, soybean, canola, and cotton plants grown in North America are the genetically engineered, glyphosate-resistant ("Roundup-ready") varieties.

Crop plants are also being engineered to alter their nutritional qualities. For example, a strain of rice plants has been produced with seeds rich in β-carotene, a precursor of vitamin A, as well as iron **(Figure 15.18)**. The new rice, which is given a yellow or golden colour

Regular rice   Genetically engineered golden rice containing β-carotene

Golden Rice Humanitarian Board www.goldenrice.org

Figure 15.18
Rice genetically engineered to contain β-carotene.

by the carotene, may provide improved nutrition for the billions of people who depend on rice as a diet staple. In particular, the rice may help improve the nutrition of children younger than age 5 in southeast Asia, 70% of whom suffer from impaired vision because of vitamin A deficiency.

Plant pharming is also an active area both in university research labs and at biotechnology companies. Plant pharming involves the engineering of transgenic plants to produce medically valuable products. The approach is one described earlier: the gene for the product is cloned into a cloning vector adjacent to a promoter, in this case one active in plants, and the recombinant DNA molecule is introduced into plants. Products under development include vaccines for various bacterial and viral diseases, protease inhibitors to treat or prevent virus infections, collagen to treat scars and wrinkles, and aprotinin to reduce bleeding and clotting during heart surgery.

In contrast to animal genetic engineering, genetically altered plants have been widely developed and appear to be here to stay as mainstays of agriculture. But, as the next section discusses, both animal and plant genetic engineering have not proceeded without concerns.

15.2d DNA Technologies and Genetic Engineering Are a Subject of Public Concern

When recombinant DNA technology was developed in the early 1970s, researchers quickly recognized that in addition to the many anticipated benefits, there might be deleterious outcomes. One key concern at the time was that a bacterium carrying a recombinant DNA molecule might escape into the environment. Perhaps it could transfer that molecule to other bacteria and produce new, potentially harmful, strains. To address these concerns, the U.S. scientists who developed the technology drew up safety guidelines for recombinant DNA research in the United States. Adopted by the NIH, the guidelines listed the precautions to be used in the laboratory when constructing recombinant DNA molecules and included the design and use of host organisms that could survive only in growth media in the laboratory. Since that time, countless experiments involving recombinant DNA molecules have been done in laboratories around the world. These experiments have shown that recombinant DNA manipulations can be done safely. Over time, therefore, the recombinant DNA guidelines have become more relaxed. Nonetheless, stringent regulations still exist for certain areas of recombinant DNA research that pose significant risk, such as cloning genes from highly pathogenic bacteria or viruses, or gene therapy experiments. In essence, as the risk increases, the research facility must increase its security and must obtain more levels of approval by peer scientist groups.

Guidelines for genetic engineering also extend to research in several areas that have been the subject of public concern and debate. Although the public does not seem to be very concerned about genetically engineered microorganisms, for example, those cleaning up oil spills and hazardous chemicals, it is concerned about possible problems with **genetically modified organisms (GMOs)** used as food. A GMO is a transgenic organism; the majority of GMOs are crop plants. Issues are the safety of GMO-containing food and the possible adverse effects of the GMOs to the environment, such as by interbreeding with natural species or by harming beneficial insect species. For example, could introduced genes providing herbicide or insect resistance move from crop plants into related weed species through cross-pollination, producing "superweeds" that might be difficult or impossible to control? *Bt*-expressing corn was originally thought to have adverse effects on monarch butterflies who fed on the pollen. The most recent of a series of independent studies investigating this possibility has indicated that the risk to the butterflies is extremely low.

More broadly, different countries have reacted to GMOs in different ways. In Canada, transgenic crops are quite widely planted and harvested. Before commercialization, such GMOs are evaluated for potential risk by appropriate government regulatory agencies, including Health Canada, the Canadian Food Inspection Agency, and Environment Canada.

Political opposition to GMOs has been greater in Europe, dampening the use of transgenic crop plants in the fields and GMOs in food. In 1999, the European Union (EU) imposed a six-year moratorium on all GMOs, leading to a bitter dispute with the United States, Canada, and Argentina, the leading growers of transgenic crops. More recently, the EU has revised the GMO regulations in all member states. Basically, the EU has decided that using genetic engineering in agriculture and food production is permissible provided that the GMO or food containing it is safe for humans, animals, and the environment. All use of GMOs in the field or in food requires authorization following a careful review process.

On a global level, an international agreement, the **Cartagena Protocol on Biosafety**, "promotes biosafety by establishing practical rules and procedures for the safe transfer [between countries], handling and use of GMOs." Separate procedures have been set up for GMOs that are to be introduced into the environment and those that are to be used as food or feed or for processing. Although 167 countries have signed and implemented the Protocol, several others, mainly GMO exporters such as Canada, the United States, and Argentina, have not.

In sum, the use of DNA technologies in biotechnology has the potential for tremendous benefits to humankind. Such experimentation is not without risk, so for each experiment, researchers must assess that risk and make a judgment about whether to proceed

Dr. Michael Smith, *University of British Columbia*

The discipline of genetics was originally built on the study of rare, naturally occurring mutations. Researchers routinely screened thousands (or sometimes millions) of individuals to collect a handful of useful mutations. Agents that increased the frequency of mutations were often used, but they tended to be nonspecific, and the isolation of particular mutations in specific genes remained a lottery with unfavourable odds.

Michael Smith changed all of that in the late 1970s by demonstrating that *in vitro* DNA synthesis techniques could be used to create mutated sequences. This method of site-directed mutagenesis allowed specific mutations to be introduced into any given DNA sequence. For the first time, geneticists could create the exact changes they were interested in. Smith's work was recognized with the 1993 Nobel Prize in Chemistry.

In addition to his legacy as a scientist, Smith was a generous philanthropist and a strong supporter of public education in science. He died in 2000, three years after retiring from UBC.

---

and, if so, how to do so safely. Furthermore, agreed-upon guidelines and protocols should ensure a level of biosafety for researchers, consumers, politicians, and governments.

15.2e Synthetic Biologists Engineer New Systems in Living Cells

Although the technologies for manipulation and transfer of genes into new hosts, as described at the beginning of this chapter, have long been known as genetic engineering, the influence of fundamental ideas and approaches of formal engineering is relatively recent. In the late 1990s, engineers, physicists, and software designers began working with molecular biologists to apply engineering design principles to biological systems. This collaboration gave rise to the new interdisciplinary field of synthetic biology. Synthetic biologists combine standardized parts (DNA sequences) to design and build modified regulatory networks to study the organization of natural systems in living cells and to create novel networks with potential benefits in a wide range of biotechnologies. (The iGEM competition described in "Why it Matters" is a good example of the approaches and potential of the field of synthetic biology.)

Using genes "mined" from organisms in the environment, or sequences created from scratch by DNA synthesizers, scientists in this field can insert new enzymes into biosynthetic pathways, resulting in cells that produce novel products such as biodiesel, gasoline, and bioplastics. This work has culminated in the creation of a yeast strain containing an engineered biochemical pathway producing artemisinin (an antimalarial drug normally produced by the wormwood plant) on an industrial scale.

The logical end point of synthetic biology is the creation of artificial life, that is, the assembly of living systems entirely from nonliving parts. Such studies would provide a powerful model for understanding the possible origin of life, as well as the dynamics of basic cellular functioning. Synthetic cells, designed entirely from off-the-shelf parts in a laboratory, could be customized to serve a staggering array of applications in biotechnology.

Since synthetic cells would require a genome, one avenue of research toward the goal of artificial life is the top-down approach, which asks, "What is the minimum collection of genes required by a living cell?" Insights into the answer to this question come from characterizing organisms that have very small genomes, as well as studies that note the effect of inactivating every gene of an organism's genome, one at a time. Although the true minimal genome has yet to be established, it is likely in the range of about 300 genes for a free-living prokaryotic cell. In 2010, Craig Venter's group published an account of a replicating strain of a bacterium, *Mycoplasma mycoides*, they had engineered to contain a 1-million-base-pair synthetic genome. The genome was synthesized in 1000-base-pair segments from digitized sequence information, and then the segments were assembled in yeast before being transferred to the *Mycoplasma*. This was the first known life form that did not obtain its genome from a parent cell, proving the concept that a cell could be "booted up" by synthesized DNA.

A complementary approach to creating synthetic life is the bottom-up interest in building a functional cell, and its various components, from nonliving parts. Early research is well under way toward the creation of various types of primitive protocells that contain simple metabolism and nucleic acid biochemistry. The rapid advance of synthetic biology has led many researchers to predict that the first truly artificial living cells will be created in the near future.

In this chapter you have learned about how individual genes can be isolated and manipulated using various DNA technologies. But a gene is just a part of a genome. Researchers also want to know about the set of genes in a complete genome, and how genes and their gene products work together in networks to control life. They also want to know more generally about the organization of the genome with respect to both genes and nongene sequences. Genomes and proteomes (the complete sets of proteins expressed by a genome) are the subjects of the next chapter.

STUDY BREAK

1. What are the principles of DNA fingerprinting?
2. What is a transgenic organism?
3. What is the difference between using germ-line cells and somatic cells for gene therapy?

Review

15.1 DNA Cloning

- Producing multiple copies of genes by cloning is a common first step for studying the structure and function of genes or for manipulating genes. Cloning involves cutting genomic DNA and a cloning vector with the same restriction enzyme, joining the fragments to produce recombinant plasmids, and introducing those plasmids into a living cell such as a bacterium, where replication of the plasmid takes place (see Figures 15.1–15.3).

- A clone containing a gene of interest may be identified among a population of clones by using DNA hybridization with a labelled nucleic acid probe (see Figure 15.5).

- A genomic library is a collection of clones that contains a copy of every DNA sequence in the genome. A cDNA (complementary DNA) library is the entire collection of cloned cDNAs made by reverse transcriptase from the mRNAs isolated from a cell. A cDNA library contains only sequences from the genes that are active in the cell when the mRNAs are isolated.

- PCR amplifies a specific target sequence in DNA, such as a gene, defined by a pair of primers. PCR increases DNA quantities by successive cycles of denaturing the template DNA, annealing the primers, and extending the primers in a DNA synthesis reaction catalyzed by DNA polymerase; with each cycle, the amount of DNA doubles (see Figure 15.6).

15.2 Applications of DNA Technologies

- Recombinant DNA and PCR techniques are used in DNA molecular testing for human genetic disease mutations. One approach exploits restriction site differences between normal and mutant alleles of a gene

that create restriction fragment length polymorphisms (RFLPs) detectable by DNA hybridization with a labelled nucleic acid probe (see Figures 15.8 and 15.9).

- Human DNA fingerprints are produced from a number of loci in the genome characterized by tandemly repeated sequences that vary in number in all individuals (except identical twins). To produce a fingerprint, the PCR is used to amplify the region of genomic DNA for each locus, and the lengths of the PCR products indicate the alleles an individual has for the repeated sequences at each locus. DNA fingerprints are widely used to establish paternity, ancestry, or criminal guilt (see Figure 15.10).

- Genetic engineering is the introduction of new genes or genetic information to alter the genetic makeup of humans, other animals, plants, and microorganisms such as bacteria and yeast. Genetic engineering primarily aims to correct hereditary defects; improve domestic animals and crop plants; and provide proteins for medicine, research, and other applications (see Figures 15.11, 15.12, and 15.15).

- Genetic engineering has enormous potential for research and applications in medicine, agriculture, and industry. Potential risks include unintended damage to living organisms or the environment.

- Collaborations among molecular biologists, software designers, physicists and engineers have given rise to a new discipline of synthetic biology based on formal engineering principles. Synthetic biologists can choose from a wide variety of standardized components to construct cells for use in biotechnological applications. The ultimate aim of synthetic biology is to create living systems from nonliving components. Progress is being made toward this goal through production of primitive protocells as well as determination of the minimum set of genes necessary to sustain a living cell.

Questions

Self-Test Questions

1. Restriction enzymes are used in genetic engineering to degrade DNA. How?
   a. They digest DNA, one base at a time, from the 3′ end of the DNA of interest.
   b. They remove mismatched base pairs resulting from errors in ligation.
   c. They break sugar–phosphate bonds in the DNA backbone between particular bases.
   d. They cut PCR primers away from the template DNA.

2. How are genomic libraries and cDNA libraries similar?
   a. They can both be used to express eukaryotic proteins in bacteria.
   b. They both contain the same genes: one in DNA form, one in cDNA form.
   c. They both contain all of the genes in the genome of an organism.
   d. They both depend on bacteria to reproduce the cloned DNA of interest.

3. All of the following enzymes can make nucleic acid polymers. Which one is used in PCR?
   a. DNA polymerase
   b. RNA polymerase
   c. primase
   d. reverse transcriptase

4. Which of the following statements about the separation of DNA fragments by gel electrophoresis is true?
   a. Smaller fragments travel more quickly than larger fragments.
   b. Smaller fragments travel in the opposite direction of larger fragments.
   c. Smaller fragments float to the top of the gel, while larger fragments sink to the bottom.
   d. Smaller fragments are visible under UV illumination, while larger fragments are not.

5. Recall that in gene-cloning experiments of the kind illustrated in Figure 15.3, plasmid vectors are cut open and then the DNA of interest is ligated to the resulting sticky ends. However, ligation is a random process and sometimes vectors simply recircularize without incorporating any fragments of the DNA of interest. All of these vectors in the ligation mix, those carrying the DNA of interest as well as those that are "empty," are then transformed into bacterial hosts for replication. How can colonies of bacteria transformed with empty vectors be identified relative to those colonies of bacteria transformed with "full" vectors carrying passenger DNA?
   a. Full vectors carry DNA that interrupts and inactivates the *lacZ* gene. Colonies are white.
   b. Full vectors make their hosts more antibiotic resistant. Colonies are larger.
   c. Full vectors make their hosts replicate more slowly. Colonies are smaller.
   d. Full vectors have more restriction enzymes to degrade X-Gal. Colonies are blue.

6. Which of the following statements about DNA fingerprinting is correct?
   a. It compares one particular stretch of the same DNA between two or more people.
   b. It measures different lengths of DNA produced from digestion of many repeating noncoding regions.
   c. It requires the several DNA fragments to separate on a gel with the longest lengths running the greatest distance.
   d. It can easily differentiate DNA between identical twins.

7. Dolly, a sheep, was an example of reproductive (germ-line) cloning. Which of the following examples of cell fusion was required to perform this process?
   a. the fusion of a somatic cell from one strain with an enucleated egg of another strain
   b. the fusion of an egg from one strain with the egg of a different strain
   c. the fusion of an embryonic diploid cell of one strain with an adult haploid cell (gamete) from another strain
   d. the fusion of two nucleated mammary cells from two different strains

8. Which of the following statements about somatic cell gene therapy is correct?
   a. Red blood cells can be used as a target tissue.
   b. The technique is potentially useful for all types of genetic diseases.
   c. The inserted genes are passed on to the offspring.
   d. The desired DNA can be introduced to somatic cells cultured outside the body.

9. Which of the following characteristics of the Ti plasmid makes this vector particularly useful in genetic engineering?
   a. It is circular.
   b. It carries antibiotic resistance.
   c. It can be taken up by plant cells.
   d. It has sites that are cut by restriction endonucleases.

10. What is the minimum number of genes that a free-living prokaryotic cell likely requires?
    a. about 50
    b. about 300
    c. about 10 000
    d. about 1 000 000

Questions for Discussion

1. Do you think that genetic engineering is worth the risk? Who do you think should decide whether genetic engineering experiments and projects should be carried out: scientists, judges, politicians?

2. Do you think that human germ-line cells should be modified by genetic engineering to cure birth defects? To increase intelligence or beauty?

3. Write a paragraph supporting genetic engineering and one arguing against it. Which argument carries more weight, in your opinion?

4. A forensic scientist obtained a small DNA sample from a crime scene. To examine the sample, he increased its quantity by PCR. He estimated that there were 50 000 copies of the DNA in his original sample. Derive a simple formula and calculate the number of copies he will have after 15 cycles of PCR.

5. A market puts out a bin of tomatoes that have outstanding colour, flavour, and texture. A sign posted above them identifies them as genetically engineered produce. Most shoppers pick unmodified tomatoes in an adjacent bin, even though they are pale, mealy, and nearly tasteless. Which tomatoes would you pick? Why?

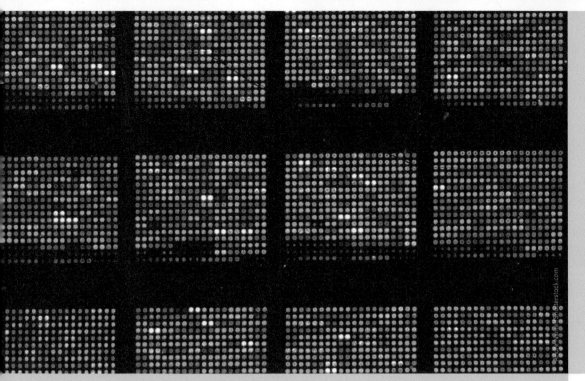

Results of DNA microarray analysis. DNA microarrays can be used, at a genomic level, to study which protein-coding genes are being expressed and the relative levels of expression of those genes.

Genomes and Proteomes

WHY IT MATTERS

You are sitting at the kitchen table with the spit kit in your hand. All you have to do is provide a small sample of saliva for the Personal Genome Project and mail it away. You want to do your part to increase knowledge of the human genome but the questions in your mind dry up your mouth. You just aren't sure this is the right thing to do.

The goal of the project sounds so important. In the years since the Human Genome Project (HGP) published the first glimpse of our 3 billion base pairs, hopes have been high that this new perspective would quickly lead to greater understanding of how genes influence our behaviour, diseases, and aging. What we got instead was greater understanding that we need to know the genome sequence of many more people. So, hundreds of volunteers have already contributed their genome sequence, along with medical and lifestyle information, to the Personal Genome Project database. Bioinformatics researchers use these large datasets to catalogue the range of human genetic variation and tease out relationships among genetics, environment, and well-being.

However, you wonder if you really want to read what is written in *your personal copies* of the human genome. What if your sequence suggests that you have an elevated risk of cancer or diabetes? Who will help you turn this knowledge into appropriate lifestyle choices? What if there is nothing you can do? You are healthy but what if you discover that you carry alleles for cystic fibrosis or Tay–Sachs disease or phenylketonuria or Mediterranean fever or G6PD deficiency? Will your fiancé(e) still be interested in you?

The project consent form explains that your genetic and personal information will be anonymous but will be publicly available online. Could someone put the pieces together to discover who you are? Could an identity thief steal your very genetic code? You know that Canada has been slow to outlaw genetic discrimination; might you be at risk of being denied health insurance or employment if your DNA sequence is public? And what about your brother and sister? They share much of your genome; should they not also share in your decision to publish family gene sequences? What if your sequence reveals a valuable variation, one that dramatically advances development of effective drugs? Will you benefit?

The Personal Genome Project is just one, definitely personal, example of research in the field of genomics, the characterization of whole genomes, including their structures (sequences), functions, and evolution. In this chapter, you will learn about the technologies underlying genomics and some of the insights that have come from genome analysis. You will also learn about proteomics, the study of the proteome, which is the complete set of proteins that can be produced by a genome. Proteomics involves characterizing the structures and functions of all expressed proteins of an organism, and the interactions among proteins in the cell. Research at the intersection of genomics and proteomics reveals highly networked interactions among genes and proteins and contributes to yet another emerging discipline, **systems biology**.

16.1 Genomics: An Overview

Genomics is the characterization of whole genomes, including their structures (sequences), functions, and evolution. Having the complete sequence of a genome makes it possible to study the complete set of genes in an organism or a virus, as well as other important sequences of their genomes. Having the complete sequence of a genome enables researchers to study the organization of genes in the genome as a whole and to determine how genes function together in networks.

Modern DNA sequencing techniques are advances on methods originally used to analyze the sequences of cloned DNA sequences and DNA sequences amplified by polymerase chain reaction (PCR; see Section 15.1).

The complete sequencing of the approximately 3-billion-base-pair human genome—the HGP—began in 1990. The task was completed in 2003 by an international consortium of researchers and by a private company, Celera Genomics (headed by J. Craig Venter). As part of the official HGP, the genomes of several important model organisms commonly used in genetic studies were sequenced for comparison: E. coli (representing prokaryotic cells), the yeast Saccharomyces cerevisiae (representing single-celled eukaryotes), Drosophila melanogaster and Caenorhabditis elegans (the fruit fly and a nematode worm, representing multicellular invertebrate animals), and Mus musculus (the mouse, representing nonhuman mammals). The sequences of the genomes of many organisms and viruses not part of the official HGP, including plants, have since been completed or are in progress.

Advances in many areas of scientific study have resulted from genomic approaches. For example, Genome Canada oversees diverse projects addressing topics such as Atlantic cod aquaculture, forestry breeding, agricultural crops, microorganisms active in mining and oilsands extraction, industrial production of fungal enzymes, and human health issues including autism and infectious disease.

A vast amount of DNA sequence data has been generated by genome sequencing projects. For those sequences to be useful, they need to be available centrally for access by all researchers. DNA sequences from genome sequencing projects are deposited into databases that are publicly available via the Internet. For example, GenBank® is an "annotated collection of all publicly available DNA sequences" at the National Institutes of Health (NIH). The Internet link is http://www.ncbi.nlm.nih.gov/genbank/. Currently there are over 150 billion bases in the DNA sequence records at GenBank®. Computational tools at GenBank® enable researchers and others, such as students like yourself, to perform various analyses with the sequence data.

Many other genomics databases are accessible using the Internet, with sequence data organized in different ways (perform an Internet search for "DNA sequence database"). For example, there are organism-specific sequence databases as well as databases that include summaries of particular genomics studies. The databases are available for individual researchers to use and also for collaborative efforts involving researchers all over the world. One of the main benefits of collaborative research of this kind is that researchers with different specialties can tackle a particular question or questions at a genomic or multigenomic level.

Genomics consists of three main areas of study:

1. Genome sequence determination and annotation, which means obtaining the sequences of complete genomes and analyzing them to locate putative protein-coding and noncoding RNA genes and other functionally important sequences in the genome.

2. Determining the functions of genes (a somewhat outdated term for this is **functional genomics**), which means using genome sequence data as a basis to study and understand the functions of genes and other parts of the genome. With respect to genes, this includes developing an understanding of how their expression is regulated. For protein-coding genes it also includes determining what proteins they encode, and how these proteins function in the organism's metabolic processes.

3. Studying how genomes have evolved, which means comparing genome sequence data to develop an understanding of how genes, particularly protein-coding genes, originated and genes and genomes changed over evolutionary time. Studies of genome sequences for a number of organisms represent an area of genomics known as **comparative genomics**.

Advances in each of these areas of study are accelerating as techniques are developed and improved for automating experimental procedures, and more sophisticated computer algorithms for data analysis are generated. Methods that facilitate the handling of many samples simultaneously, whether those samples are DNA molecules for sequencing or genes for analysis, are called high-throughput techniques. The next three sections of the chapter discuss each of the three areas of genomics in turn.

STUDY BREAK

What additional biological questions can be answered if we have the complete sequence of an organism's genome as compared with the sequences of individual genes?

DNA Sequencing Methods. All DNA sequencing methods have in common the following steps:

1. DNA purification;
2. DNA fragmentation;
3. amplification of fragments;
4. sequencing each fragment; and
5. assembly of fragment sequences into genome sequences.

The methods differ in how the amplification is done, the lengths of the fragments, how many fragments are sequenced simultaneously, and how the sequencing reactions themselves are done.

For decades the method devised by Frederick Sanger was by far the most common DNA sequencing

16.2 Genome Sequence Determination and Annotation

Genome sequence determination and annotation means obtaining the sequence of bases in a genome using DNA sequencing techniques and then analyzing the sequence data using computer-based approaches to identify genes and other sequences of interest, which include gene regulatory sequences, origins of replication, repetitive sequences, and transposable elements.

16.2a Genome Analysis Begins with DNA Sequencing

DNA sequencing was developed in the late 1970s by Allan M. Maxam, a graduate student, and his mentor, Walter Gilbert, of Harvard University. A few years later, Frederick Sanger, of Cambridge University, designed a method that became the one commonly used in research. Gilbert and Sanger were awarded a Nobel Prize in 1980. DNA sequencing technology has evolved since its development, and particularly rapidly in the past few years.

Whole-Genome Shotgun Sequencing. Before we discuss methods of DNA sequencing, let us consider the strategy generally used to determine the sequence of a genome, whole-genome shotgun sequencing **(Figure 16.1)**. In this method, genomic DNA is isolated and purified, and that DNA is broken into thousands to millions of random, overlapping fragments. Each fragment is amplified to produce many copies, and then the sequence of the fragment is determined. The entire genome sequence is then assembled using computer algorithms that search for the sequence overlaps between fragments and stitch together the sequence reads to produce longer contiguous sequences.

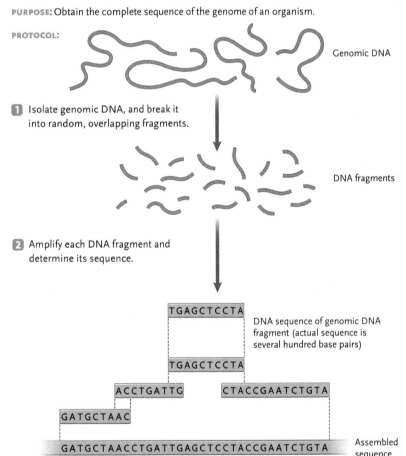

PURPOSE: Obtain the complete sequence of the genome of an organism.

PROTOCOL:

Genomic DNA

1 Isolate genomic DNA, and break it into random, overlapping fragments.

DNA fragments

2 Amplify each DNA fragment and determine its sequence.

TGAGCTCCTA

DNA sequence of genomic DNA fragment (actual sequence is several hundred base pairs)

TGAGCTCCTA

ACCTGATTG   CTACCGAATCTGTA

GATGCTAAC

GATGCTAACCTGATTGAGCTCCTACCGAATCTGTA

Assembled sequence

3 Enter the DNA sequences of the fragments into a computer, and use the computer to assemble overlapping sequences into the continuous sequence of each chromosome of the organism. This technique is analogous to taking 10 copies of a book that has been torn randomly into smaller sets of a few pages each and, by matching overlapping pages of the leaflets, assembling a complete copy of the book with the pages in the correct order.

INTERPRETING THE RESULTS: The method generates the complete sequence of the genome of an organism.

Research Method Figure 16.1 Whole-genome shotgun sequencing.

technique used. The Sanger method is a DNA synthesis–based method for DNA sequencing. It is based on the properties of nucleotides known as dideoxyribonucleotides, which have a —H on the 3′ carbon of the deoxyribose sugar instead of the —OH found in normal deoxyribonucleotides; therefore, the method, explained in **Figure 16.2,** is also called dideoxy sequencing.

PURPOSE: Obtain the sequence of a piece of DNA, such as in gene sequencing or genome sequencing. The method is shown here with a typical automated sequencing system.

PROTOCOL:

1 A dideoxy sequencing reaction contains (1) the fragment of DNA to be sequenced (denatured to single strands); (2) a DNA primer that will bind to the 3′ end of the sequence to be determined; (3) a mixture of the four deoxyribonucleotide precursors for DNA synthesis; (4) a mixture of the four dideoxyribonucleotide (dd) precursors, at about 1/100 the concentration of the deoxyribonucleotides, each labelled with a different fluorescent molecule; and (5) DNA polymerase to catalyze the DNA synthesis reaction.

2 DNA polymerase synthesizes the new DNA strand in the 5′ → 3′ direction starting at the 3′ end of the primer. New synthesis continues until a dideoxyribonucleotide is incorporated randomly into the DNA. The dideoxyribonucleotide acts as a terminator for DNA synthesis because it has no 3′-OH group for the addition of the next base (see Section 12.3). For a large population of template DNA strands, the dideoxy sequencing reaction produces a series of new strands, with lengths from one up. At the 3′ end of each new strand is the fluorescently labelled dideoxyribonucleotide that terminated the synthesis.

3 The labelled strands are separated by electrophoresis using a polyacrylamide gel prepared in a capillary tube. The principle of separation is the same as for agarose gel electrophoresis (see Figure 15.7), but this gel can discriminate between DNA strands that differ in length by one nucleotide. As the bands of DNA fragments move near the bottom of the tube, a laser beam shining through the gel excites the fluorescent labels on each DNA fragment. The fluorescence is registered by a detector, with the wavelength of the fluorescence indicating whether ddA, ddT, ddG, or ddC is at the end of the fragment in each case.

INTERPRETING THE RESULTS: The data from the laser system are sent to a computer that interprets which of the four possible fluorescent labels is at the end of each DNA strand. The results show, on a computer screen or in printouts, colours for the labels as the DNA bands passed the detector. The sequence of the newly synthesized DNA, which is complementary to the template strand, is read from left (5′) to right (3′). (The sequence shown here begins after the primer.)

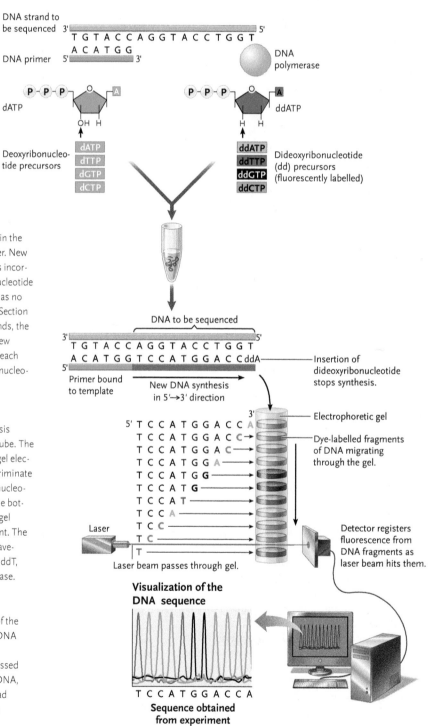

Research Method Figure 16.2 Dideoxy (Sanger) method for DNA sequencing.

In recent years the dideoxy sequencing method has been replaced largely, but not completely, by faster, cheaper, and more automated techniques. In general, these newer high-throughput techniques have decreased sequencing costs by reducing the pre-paratory steps, automating more of the process, and sequencing up to a billion different DNA fragments in parallel.

Figure 16.3 outlines a next-generation DNA sequencing technique that is widely used in genome

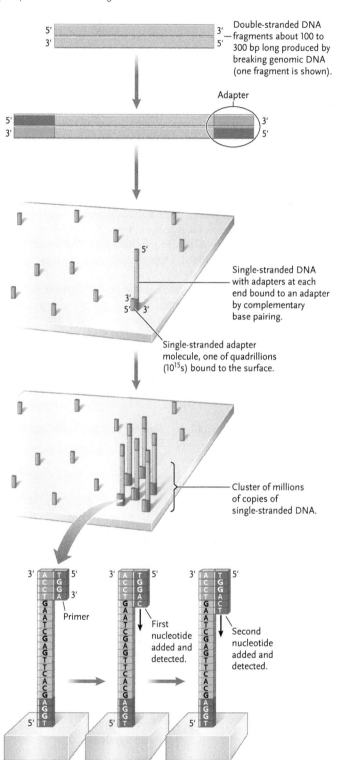

PURPOSE: Automated, massively parallel sequencing of up to a billion DNA fragments.

PROTOCOL:

1️⃣ DNA ligase attaches short double-stranded DNA adapter molecules to each end of 100- to 300-bp genomic DNA fragments.

2️⃣ The DNA fragments are denatured to single strands, which are added to a cell in an automated machine through which liquid can flow. Over the glass surface of the cell are bound about one quadrillion (1 × 1015) single-stranded adapter molecules that have complementary sequences to those of the adapters added to the DNA in step 1. Each DNA fragment to be sequenced binds to one of the glass-bound adapter molecules by complementary base-pairing. The massive number of glass-bound adapters allows many DNA strands to be sequenced simultaneously.

3️⃣ An amplification process generates millions of copies of each of the DNA fragments that bound initially to one of the glass-bound adapters, clustered around the place on the cell where that DNA bound. Up to one billion different clusters can be produced in the sequencing cell simultaneously.

4️⃣ The DNA fragments are now ready for synthesis-based DNA sequencing. One fragment is shown for the sequencing steps.

5️⃣ DNA primers are added to the cell. A primer anneals to each DNA strand (it is the complementary strand to the adapter sequence at its end), and DNA synthesis is done in a cyclic manner one nucleotide at a time using four different fluorescently labelled DNA nucleotide precursors. Each time a labelled nucleotide is added, synthesis stops and the machine uses laser technology to measure the fluorescence so as to identify the base added. That base is the same for all strands in a cluster. By repeated cycles of addition of a nucleotide and laser detection, the sequence of the strand is obtained. Up to about 100 bases of each fragment can be sequenced.

INTERPRETING THE RESULTS: The DNA sequence obtained is complementary to the initial single-stranded DNA strand that paired with the glass-bound adapter. The DNA sequence data from all of the clusters of DNA fragments are analyzed by computer to determine overlaps between fragments, and, by the principles described in Figure 16.2 the complete sequence of a genome is assembled.

Research Method Figure 16.3 Illumina/Solexa method for DNA sequencing.

Double-stranded DNA fragments about 100 to 300 bp long produced by breaking genomic DNA (one fragment is shown).

Single-stranded DNA with adapters at each end bound to an adapter by complementary base pairing.

Single-stranded adapter molecule, one of quadrillions (10^15s) bound to the surface.

Cluster of millions of copies of single-stranded DNA.

sequencing projects, the DNA synthesis–based Illumina/Solexa method. This is an example of massively parallel DNA sequencing, because up to one billion different DNA fragments can be sequenced simultaneously.

As a result of the lower cost of sequencing, and the automated, massively parallel DNA sequencing methods that are used, the genomes of many species beyond those targeted in the HGP have been determined. Although the question, "How many different genomes have been sequenced to date?" seems reasonable, it is rather hard to answer for three main reasons. One reason is that the answer depends on how you define one genome as different from another. Does "different" mean a single genome from two different species? Or can "different" mean a genome from two alternative strains, breeds, or cultivars of the same species? A second reason that this number is hard to pin down has to do with completion. Genome sequences don't need to be entirely complete in order to be informative and useful. Some genome projects stop at the "good enough" stage when the work of completing the entire sequence would be of little additional benefit. The third factor that makes the number of sequenced genomes elusive is that it keeps changing. In 2000, about 100 genome sequences were added to repositories per year, one every three days. Now, only 15 years later, the rate of new genome sequence additions is approaching 10 000 per year, more than 1 per hour! By 2020 the rate will certainly exceed 100 000 sequences per year. By that time, we will likely stop asking if our favourite genome has been sequenced and just assume that it has.

Table 16.1 presents a snapshot of completed genome sequences in one database. The values

represent total numbers of completed genomes. Sometimes several genomes are included for a given species. Notice the very large number of bacterial species sequenced. This reflects both the relative ease of sequencing smaller genomes and the popularity of these organisms in research.

16.2a Genome Sequences Are Annotated to Identify Genes and Other Sequences of Importance

A raw genome sequence is simply a string of A, T, G, and C letters; it tells us practically nothing about the organism from which it derives, other than the total length of its genome. Therefore, once the complete sequence of a genome has been determined, the next step is annotation, the identification of functionally important features in the genome. These include the following:

- Protein-coding genes.
- Noncoding RNA genes. As mentioned earlier, "noncoding" means that the RNA transcript of the gene is not translated. Rather, the transcript is the final functional product of the gene. Noncoding RNA genes include genes for tRNAs, rRNAs, and snRNAs (see Chapter 13), and genes for microRNAs (miRNAs; see Chapter 14).
- Regulatory sequences associated with genes (see Chapter 15).
- Origins of replication (see Chapter 12).
- Transposable elements, viruses, and sequences related to them (see Chapter 9).
- Pseudogenes. A **pseudogene** is very similar to a functional gene at the DNA sequence level, but one or more inactivating mutations have changed the gene so that it can no longer produce a functional gene product (e.g., deletion of the promoter). Most pseudogenes are derived from protein-coding genes and are recognized by their sequence similarities to functional genes.
- Short repetitive sequences. These are sequences that are repeated a few too many times in the genome. The short tandem repeat (STR) sequences discussed in Section 15.2 are examples of short repetitive sequences.

Annotation is performed by researchers in the field of **bioinformatics**, which is the application of mathematics and computer science to extract information from biological data, including those related to genome structure, function, and evolution.

Some examples of genome annotation for protein-coding genes are illustrated in the following subsections.

Identifying Open Reading Frames by Computer Search of Genome Sequences. As outlined in Chapter 13, proteins are specified in mRNA molecules by a series of codons starting with the initiation codon AUG and

Table 16.1	Number of Organismal Genomes Sequenced*	
Organism		Number of Genomes
Prokaryotic Cells		
Archaea		330
Bacteria		17 360
	Total prokaryotic cells:	17 690
Eukaryotes		
Animals		
Mammals		20
Fishes		25
Insects		77
Other animals		64
	Total animals	186
Plants		69
Fungi		384
Protists		159
	Total eukaryotes	798
	Total all organisms	18 488

*As of May 2014, http://www.genomesonline.org.

ending with one of the three termination codons: UAG, UAA, or UGA. The span of codons from start to stop codon is called an **open reading frame (ORF)**, and ORFs that are longer than 100 codons almost always indicate the presence of a protein-coding gene. Computer algorithms are used to identify possible protein-coding genes in a genome sequence by searching for ORFs. In a DNA sequence, this means searching for ATG, separated from a stop codon (TAG, TAA, or TGA) by a multiple of three nucleotides. The search is complicated because either of the two DNA strands could be the template for a given gene. Theoretically, then, each DNA sequence has six reading frames for the three-letter genetic code, three on one strand and three on the other strand. An ORF can be in any one of these frames. This is illustrated in **Figure 16.4** for a theoretical 30-nucleotide segment of DNA. Note that each single-stranded DNA sequence generated by DNA sequencing can be used to infer the sequence of the complementary DNA strand. If an ORF is present in a particular DNA sequence, it will be in one of these frames.

We can start looking for an ORF going in the $5' \rightarrow 3'$ direction in the top strand of Figure 16.4, starting at the leftmost A nucleotide. In this case, reading in groups of three nucleotides will lead you to the TAG at the right end, which is the stop codon. We have found an ORF in the sequence, and it is coded by the entire length of the top strand. However, if instead we start looking for an ORF in the top strand starting at either the second nucleotide (the T) or the third nucleotide (the G), we do not find a start codon, so we have not found an ORF. For the bottom strand, none of the three frames has a start codon. Computer algorithms can search easily for ORFs in all six reading frames of a DNA sequence.

CONCEPT FIX Figure 16.4 shows an ORF on the top strand, reading $5' \rightarrow 3'$ from ATG. Although it is tempting to assume that the top strand containing the ORF is used as the template for transcription, this is not possible; RNA polymerases only read template DNA in the $3' \rightarrow 5'$ direction. Therefore, template DNA for this ORF is the bottom strand, not the top. ⬡

Searching for protein-coding ORFs is straightforward in prokaryotic genomes because few genes have introns. Eukaryotic protein-coding genes typically have introns, so more sophisticated algorithms must be used to identify such genes. For example, the algorithms may search for particular

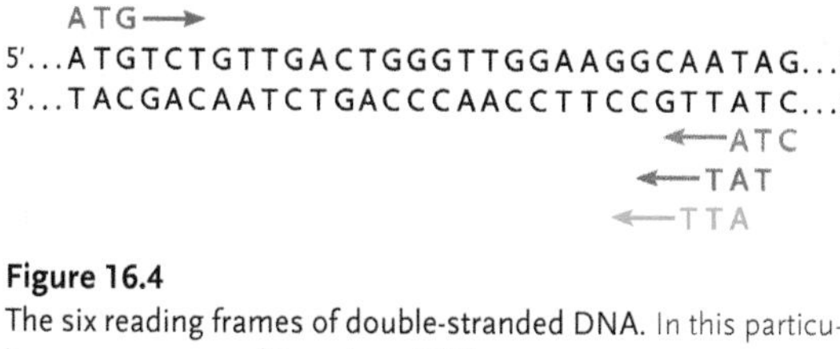

characteristics of protein-coding genes, such as junctions between exons and introns, sequences that are characteristic of eukaryotic promoters, and overrepresentation of certain three-base codons relative to others.

Computer identification is typically the first step in identifying protein-coding genes. However, other evidence is needed before biologists can be confident that the sequence they have annotated is a functioning protein-coding gene. Two approaches to obtaining such evidence are described in the next two subsections.

Identifying Protein-Coding Genes by Sequence Similarity Searches. One way of testing whether candidate protein-coding genes found by searching for ORFs are functioning protein-coding genes is by comparing their sequences with known, identified, and verified genes in databases. This is a sequence similarity search. Such searches can be done using an Internet browser to access the computer programs and the databases. For example, to use the BLAST (Basic Local Alignment Search Tool) program at the National Center for Biotechnology Information (http://blast .ncbi.nlm.nih.gov), a researcher pastes the putative ORF DNA sequence, or the amino acid sequence of the protein it would encode, into a browser window and sets the program to begin searching. The BLAST program searches the databases of known sequences and returns the best matches, if any. The matches are listed in order, from the closest match to the least likely match. Finding a known gene's sequence that matches the putative ORF sequence closely is good evidence that the ORF is in fact a protein-coding gene and that it encodes a protein functionally related to that of the matching gene sequence. The principle here is that genes of living organisms tend to be similar to each other because they have evolved from ancestral genes in ancestral organisms. Genes that have highly conserved sequences because they have evolved from a gene in a common ancestor are called **homologous genes**. For example, if a gene in the mouse has been characterized experimentally and its sequence is known, and that gene is evolutionarily conserved in mammals, there should be a match for that gene in the human genome sequence.

With sequence similarity searches, ORFs can be sorted into ones with known and unknown functions. For the latter, experiments are required to show whether they are real protein-coding genes and, if so, what their functions are. For example, analysis of the human genome sequence initially identified more than a thousand putative ORFs with no sequence similarities to known genes. Most of these function-unknown genes have now been shown to be pseudogenes. Such uncertainty makes it difficult to determine the exact number of protein-coding genes in a genome just from its sequence.

```
                GTC ⟶
              TGT ⟶
            ATG ⟶
5'...ATGTCTGTTGACTGGGTTGGAAGGCAATAG...3'
3'...TACGACAATCTGACCCAACCTTCCGTTATC...5'
                          ⟵ATC
                        ⟵TAT
                      ⟵TTA
```

Figure 16.4
The six reading frames of double-stranded DNA. In this particular sequence, one of them is an ORF.

Identifying Protein-Coding Genes from Sequences of Gene Transcripts. The gold standard for identifying protein-coding genes in a genome sequence is the demonstration that the sequences are transcribed in

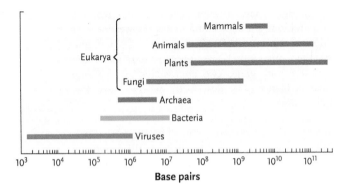

Figure 16.5
Ranges of genome sizes for viruses, bacteria, archaea, and eukaryotes. Note that the Domain Archaea has not been studied as extensively as the Domain Bacteria, so there may be representatives with substantially larger or smaller genomes than the range given.

Table 16.2	Genome Sizes and Estimated Number of Protein-Coding Genes for Selected Members of Domains Bacteria, Archaea, and Eukarya		
Domain and Organism		Genome Size (millions of base pairs, Mb)	Protein-Coding Genes
Bacteria			
Mycoplasma genitalium		0.58	475
Escherichia coli		4.6	4 146
Archaea			
Thermoplasma acidophilum		1.56	1 484
Methanosarcina acetivorans		5.75	4 540
Eukarya			
Protists			
Tetrahymena thermophila (a ciliated protist)		146	>20 000
Fungi			
Saccharomyces cerevisiae (a budding yeast)		12.1	~ 6 000
Neurospora crassa (orange bread mould)		40	~ 10 100
Plants			
Arabidopsis thaliana (thale cress)		120	~ 26 000
Oryza sativa (rice)		411	~ 56 000
Capsicum annum (hot pepper)		~ 3480	~ 34 500
Invertebrates			
Caenorhabditis elegans (a nematode worm)		100	~ 20 000
Drosophila melanogaster (fruit fly)		165	~ 13 700
Locusta migratoria (swarming locust)		6500	~ 17 300
Vertebrates			
Takifugu rubripes (pufferfish)		393	~ 27 000
Mus musculus (mouse)		2600	~ 22 000
Homo sapiens (human)		3200	~ 20 500

cells to make mRNAs. One approach to doing this makes use of the sequences of transcripts represented in cDNA libraries. Recall from Section 15.1 that a cDNA library is made starting with mRNA molecules isolated from a cell. If the mRNA molecules are isolated under different conditions and from different cell types in a multicellular organism, they will represent the activity of many of the organism's protein-coding genes. However, protein-coding genes that are rarely transcribed or that produce very few mRNA molecules are likely to be missed by this approach.

The single-stranded mRNA molecules are converted to double-stranded DNA molecules using reverse transcriptase, and these DNA molecules are cloned to produce the cDNA library. Some part of each cloned mRNA (as cDNA) is sequenced using a sequencing primer that pairs with the DNA just adjacent to the inserted cDNA fragment in the clone. Using computer algorithms, each cDNA sequence is compared with the genome sequence of the organism to map the location of the sequence and, therefore, the protein-coding gene from which the original transcript was derived.

This approach is also useful for cataloguing transcripts in humans and other eukaryotes to identify which genes are alternatively spliced. Recall from Section 14.3 that alternative splicing of pre-mRNA transcripts of protein-coding genes produces different mRNAs by using different splice sites that may remove different combinations of exons, or modify their lengths. The resulting mRNAs are translated to produce a family of related proteins having various combinations of amino acid sequences derived from the remaining exons.

16.2b Genome Landscapes Vary Markedly in Size, Gene Number, and Gene Density

With many genomes now sequenced, researchers can compare them to learn about genome sizes, the number of protein-coding genes, and the density of these genes (how widely spaced they are). A vast amount of new information is available about genome landscapes. Here we will present some generalizations and then provide a more detailed description of the *E. coli* genome and the human genome, as examples of bacterial and eukaryote genomes, respectively.

Figure 16.5 shows the ranges of genome sizes for viruses, bacteria, archaea, and different groups of eukaryotes, and **Table 16.2** gives examples of genome sizes and the number of protein-coding genes for some bacteria, archaea, and eukaryotes. We can arrive at some general conclusions about the data. Members of both the Domain Bacteria and the Domain Archaea have genomes that vary widely in size. In addition, their genes are densely packed in their genomes, with little noncoding space between them. Thus, the larger genomes of organisms in these two domains tend to reflect increased gene number.

Members of the domain Eukarya vary markedly in form and complexity, and their genomes also show great differences in size and gene density (Table 16.2). For example, the genome of yeast, *Saccharomyces cerevisiae*, is only about 0.4% the size of the human genome. However, yeast have just a little less than 30% of the number of protein-coding genes found in humans. Genes in yeast are therefore, on average, coded more closely together than in humans. Although this yeast versus human comparison might lead you to assume that there is a close relationship between organism complexity and genome size, this is not the case.

For instance, the fruit fly, *Drosophila melanogaster*, and the locust, *Schistocerca gregaria*, are both insects with similar overall physiological complexity. However, the genome of the locust, at 9300 Mb, is 52 times the size of the fruit fly genome. Even within a given genus, different species often have widely differing genome sizes. For example, there is a 50-fold variation in the genome size of the *Allium* species, which includes onions, leeks, shallots, and garlic. Among the vertebrates we again find great variation in genome size. For example, the genome of the mouse and human are about seven times as large as the pufferfish genome, *Takifugu rubripes*. And yet the pufferfish has more protein-coding genes than either the mouse or the human (Table 16.2). As we saw with yeast, the genes are coded more closely in the pufferfish genome than they are in either the mouse or the human genome.

It is important to think critically about the data presented for gene numbers in a genome. As you have learned, the determination of the protein-coding gene number involves both computer and experimental analysis. The outcomes of these analyses are therefore estimates of the number of genes present. Only when an entire genome has been studied experimentally to characterize every gene it contains can we be certain of an organism's exact gene number. For example, you have just read that the estimated number of protein-coding genes is greater than 22 thousand in the mouse genome and greater than 20 500 in the human genome. These numbers are not precise. Rather, at this point they likely reflect different extents of progress in annotating the two genomes, rather than suggesting that 2000 more protein-coding genes are necessary to create and run a mouse rather than a human.

Profile of the *E. coli* genome. *E. coli* is one of the most intensively studied model organisms, and the genome of laboratory

strain K12 is one of the best annotated. In many ways, *E. coli* has a typical bacterial genome, with the vast majority of its genes on a single circular chromosome with one origin of replication **(Figure 16.6a)**, and the remainder of its genes on one or more plasmids, each of which is much smaller than the circular chromosome. With about 4.6 Mb and about 4146 protein-coding genes, the *E. coli* K12 genome is in the middle range, sizewise, of bacterial genomes (see Figure 16.5). The noncoding genes are those for rRNAs and tRNAs. There are a small number of transposable elements and repetitive sequences.

Figure 16.6b shows a close-up of a 10-kb segment of the *E. coli* genome containing a number of protein-coding genes to illustrate the following characteristics:

- The genes are close together, with little space in between. Promoters for the genes are located immediately upstream of each transcription unit (not shown in the figure).
- Some of the genes are transcribed in the left-to-right direction (using the bottom strand as the template), whereas the others are transcribed in the right-to-left direction (using the top strand as

a. Map of the circular *E. coli* K12 genome showing the genes transcribed clockwise (blue) and the genes transcribed counterclockwise (orange) and the location of the origin of replication.

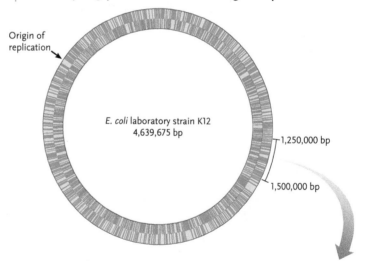

b. Detail of a 10-kb region of the *E. coli* K12 genome, from about 3:30 on the genome "clock."

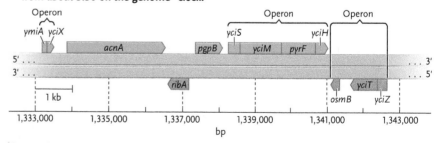

Figure 16.6

The genome of *E. coli*, laboratory strain K12.

Table 16.3	Comparison of the *E. coli* K12 and Human Genomes	
Property	*E. coli* K12 genome	*H. sapiens* genome
Chromosomes	1 circular (plus plasmids)	23 linear (pairs in diploid cells)*
Nucleotides	4.64 Mb	3 100 Mb
Protein-coding genes	4 146	~ 20 500
Noncoding RNA genes	176	~ 12 000
% coding DNA	88%	1.2%
Protein-coding genes per Mb	894	7
Introns per average gene	0	8
Average polypeptide size	330 amino acids	430 amino acids

*There are 24 different human chromosomes: 22 autosomes and the X and Y chromosomes. Each individual has 23 pairs of chromosomes.

the template). (The two template strands are transcribed in different directions because the two DNA molecules in a double helix are antiparallel; see Chapter 12.)

- Some genes are single transcription units, whereas others are organized into operons (see Chapter 14). In the genome as a whole, about one-half of protein-coding genes are organized into operons.
- The genes vary in length, reflecting the lengths of their encoded proteins.

CONCEPT FIX Look carefully at Figure 16.6, noticing that some genes are shown in blue and some in orange. Although you may have assumed that one particular strand of the double helix is used as the template

(i.e., read by RNA polymerase) for all genes on a chromosome, the figure shows this assumption to be false. One strand of the helix is used as a template for some genes (such as the blue genes in Figure 16.6), while the other strand is used as a template for other genes (the orange genes in Figure 16.6). Recall that templates have to be read $3' \rightarrow 5'$, so, in Figure 16.6, the blue genes are using the bottom strand as their template. ⬢

Table 16.3 summarizes some of what has been learned about the *E. coli* K12 genome to date with respect to its physical aspects, genes, and gene products.

Other bacterial genomes may be larger or smaller than the *E. coli* K12 genome, but their genome landscapes are similar to that of *E. coli* in several ways. For example, typically there is one origin of replication, 85 to 92% of the DNA codes for proteins, there is a mixture of operons and single-gene transcription units, some genes are transcribed using one DNA strand as the template whereas others are transcribed using the other strand, and there are relatively few transposable elements or repetitive sequences.

Profile of the Human Genome. At about 3.2 billion base pairs, the human genome is about 700 times as long as the *E. coli* genome. Each human individual has 23 pairs of chromosomes. Men have 24 different chromosomes, the 22 autosomes and the X and Y chromosomes, whereas women have 23 different chromosomes, the 22 autosomes and the X chromosome. **Figure 16.7a** displays the

Figure 16.7
The human genome.

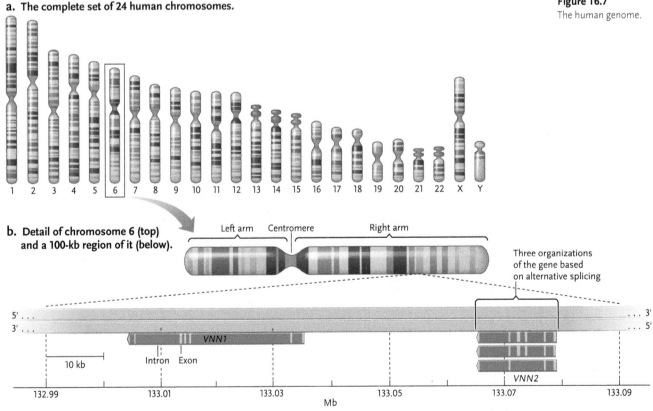

a. The complete set of 24 human chromosomes.

1 2 3 4 5 6 7 8 9 10 11 12 13 14 15 16 17 18 19 20 21 22 X Y

b. Detail of chromosome 6 (top) and a 100-kb region of it (below).

Left arm   Centromere   Right arm

Three organizations of the gene based on alternative splicing

5' ...   ... 3'
3' ...   ... 5'

VNN1

10 kb

Intron Exon

VNN2

132.99   133.01   133.03   133.05   133.07   133.09

Mb

complete set of human chromosomes, depicting the banding patterns that help researchers identify regions of chromosomes. (Figure 8.10 shows the banding patterns of stained human chromosomes.) Figure 16.7b shows chromosome 6 in more detail and then a close-up of a 100-kb segment of the long arm of that chromosome to show the protein-coding genes it contains. Compare this figure with Figure 16.6b, which shows a 10-kb segment of the *E. coli* chromosome, and note the following:

- Genes are relatively far apart, with a large amount of space in between. That is, even though the human genome segment shown is 10 times as long as the *E. coli* segment shown in Figure 16.6b, it contains only 2 protein-coding genes. Each of these genes consists of transcription units that are far longer than the genes in *E. coli*, largely because they consist of about 95% introns and 5% exons. The right-hand gene in Figure 16.7b illustrates at the DNA level the alternative splicing variants for that gene; note the different exons (light pink regions) for the three gene drawings. (Alternative splicing is described in Section 14.3.)
- As in the genomes of other organisms, some genes are transcribed from one of the strands of the double helix, while other genes are transcribed from the other strand. For the particular segment shown in Figure 16.7b, both genes happen to be transcribed from the same strand.
- All of the genes are single transcription units. Eukaryotic genes are rarely organized in operons.

Table 16.3 summarizes some of what researchers have learned about the human genome to date with respect to its physical aspects, genes, and gene products. Some of the key features of the human genome are as follows:

- There are about 20 500 protein-coding genes. On average, there are 8 exons per gene, with some human genes consisting of a single exon and others having over 100 exons. Introns make up about 95% of the average transcription unit. Since about 2% of the genome consists of protein-coding sequences, introns represent about 20 to 25% of the human genome.
- On average, more than 20 regulatory sequences are associated with each protein-coding gene. These sequences are distributed over thousands to tens of thousands of base pairs upstream and downstream of each gene, as well as being scattered within introns. The regulatory sequences are widely scattered within regions that encompass 15 to 25% of the human genome.
- There are about 12 000 noncoding RNA genes, which include genes for rRNA, tRNA, small nuclear RNA, and microRNAs (see Chapter 13 and Section 14.3).
- There are thousands of pseudogenes.

- There are many inserted DNA viruses and reverse-transcribed RNA viruses, totalling nearly 10% of the entire genome.
- About 45% of the genome consists of transposable element sequences (see Section 9.4). Only a tiny fraction of these transposable elements are functionally active. The others are inactive, being the transposable element version of pseudogenes.
- The genome contains a variety of short, repeated sequences, including those at the centromeres and telomeres, as well as others scattered throughout the rest of the chromosome.
- Replication begins at hundreds to thousands of origins of replication per chromosome. However, there are no consistent, sequence-specific replication origins, as in bacteria and yeast.

CONCEPT FIX Stop for a moment to total up the previous information about the composition of your genome. Notice that over half of your DNA sequence is transposable elements and viruses that are, or once were, mobile. Although these sequences may well contain genes, they are not coding for human proteins and are often referred to as "junk DNA." Add in the thousands of pseudogenes, introns, and nonessential repetitive sequences and you may be surprised to realize that junk DNA approaches 75% of your entire genome. ⬢

Genome-Wide Association Studies Catalogue Genetic Variation. Just as we have established the basic architecture of the genome that is common to all humans (Figure 16.7), we are well into the task of discovering the various types of diversity in the genomes of different people and how this variation interacts with environmental influences to produce the overall phenotype. One type of variation in the DNA sequence of different human genomes is a change in a single nucleotide. This difference is a called a single nucleotide polymorphism (SNP, pronounced "snip"). The International HapMap Project collected, mapped, and publicly released data on well over 10 million SNPs common among people of African, Asian, and European ancestry. Thomas Hudson, at McGill University, was a Canadian member of the HapMap Consortium, contributing data for chromosomes 2 and 4. Once common DNA variants are identified, many thousands of them can be used to create DNA microarray "chips" (Section 16.3c) that enable automated screening. This is how DNA in your saliva sample in "Why It Matters" would reveal your personal profile of genetic variation.

Studies that screen a large number of people for a large number of variants are called Genome-Wide Association Studies (GWAS). Analysis of GWAS datasets can find statistical correlations between particular genetic variations and specific diseases or other traits in a population. In recent years, this type of genomic analysis has been directed toward understanding the genetic basis of complex diseases such as schizophrenia.

Although family and twins studies show a significant genetic component to schizophrenia risk, no single gene can be identified as responsible. A recent GWAS study identified 22 sites associated with elevated risk, half of them previously unknown. Variation at these sites included over 8000 SNPs as well as insertion/deletion of larger chromosomal regions, called copy number variations (CNVs).

In the hands of healthcare professionals, genomic data from patients has led to better, more personalized treatment. An example of this is that a patient's variation at two genes, VKORC1 and CYP2C9, is now recognized on product labelling as an important factor in predicting the optimal dose of the common anticoagulant drug warfarin. This field of pharmacogenomics is expanding rapidly, exploring the potential of matching medical treatments to genotypes. Another application of genomics, personal genomics, is also developing rapidly. Several entrepreneurial companies now offer affordable personal genomic screening to the public, often including additional information concerning family relationships and ancestry as well as statistical estimates for expression of hundreds of traits and medical conditions. Such personal genetic profiles should be approached with caution for the scientific and psychosocial reasons highlighted in "Why It Matters."

Up to this point, we have focused on the features of the enormous portion of the human genome encoded within the linear chromosomes of the cell's nucleus. It is also important to remember that in a eukaryote, each mitochondrion also contains a circular mitochondrial genome, or mtDNA. The human mtDNA is 16.6 kb, much smaller than even a prokaryotic genome. Its 37 genes (13 of them are protein coding) perform essential functions related to cellular respiration. In addition, photosynthetic eukaryotes, including plants and algae, have a separate circular genome up to several hundred thousand bases in each of their chloroplasts: the cpDNA. Not surprisingly, this genome contains genes involved in photosynthesis.

Other mammalian genomes are very much like the human genome. But for other eukaryotes generally, particular features can vary considerably. For example, eukaryote genomes range from having a very low percentage of protein-coding DNA, as in mammals, to almost as high a percentage as is seen for bacteria.

STUDY BREAK

1. What is the principle behind whole-genome shotgun sequencing of genomes?
2. What are the key sequences identified by genome annotation?
3. How are possible protein-coding genes identified in a genome sequence of a bacterium? Of a mammal?
4. What general differences are there in the genome landscapes of bacteria and eukaryotes?

16.3 Determining the Functions of the Genes in a Genome

Once a genome is annotated, the next step is to use the genome sequence data to understand the functions of genes and other parts of the genome. "Gene function" is considered broadly here to include regulation of gene expression, the products genes encode, and the role of these products in the function of the organism. For protein-coding genes, the gene products are proteins. We study proteins to understand their structure and function, to discover how they participate in networks of interactions with other proteins and other nonprotein molecules in the cell, and to discover how these complexes are important functionally for the organism.

We also need to determine what genes there are for noncoding RNAs in the genome, and what the functions of the RNAs are. Several of the noncoding RNA genes can be assigned functions based on evolutionary conservation principles, that is, by looking for sequence similarity with known gene sequences. An example is the rRNA genes. However, identifying and determining the functions of miRNA genes is more challenging in part because of their diversity of sequences. In this section, we focus on protein-coding genes, again because of the importance of their products in controlling the functions of cells and, therefore, of organisms. Determining the functions of protein-coding genes typically relies on computer analysis and on laboratory experiments. The following subsections present examples of these approaches.

16.3a Gene Function May Be Predicted by a Sequence Similarity Search of Sequence Databases

You learned earlier that a DNA sequence can be identified as a likely protein-coding gene by using a sequence similarity search of sequences in databases. This approach can also be used to assign the function of a gene. A high degree of similarity between the sequence of a candidate gene of unknown function and the sequence of a gene of known function likely indicates that both sequences evolved from a gene in a common ancestor and that their sequences in the present day have been conserved significantly because they code for proteins that have similar functions. As explained earlier, genes with highly conserved sequences as a result of divergence from a common ancestral gene are homologous genes.

Using sequence similarity searches to determine if a candidate gene and a known gene are homologous is by far the most common method for assigning the functions of genes. Experimental investigation of the functions of genes is considerably more expensive

Dr. Stephen Scherer, *Centre for Applied Genomics, Hospital for Sick Children, Toronto, Fellow of the Royal Society of Canada*

The idea that offspring inherit one copy of each gene from each of their parents has been a universal principle of genetics since the days when Mendel himself was explaining inheritance of traits in pea plants. Thanks to the careful genomic work of Dr. Stephen Scherer and his collaborators, we now know that this universal principle is not so universal. A breakthrough paper from Scherer's group in 2007 outlined the discovery that some genes are present in only one copy, while others show up three times in a given diploid genome. This new type of variation was called copy number variation (CNV) and has since been shown to be a surprisingly common type of genetic difference between one human and another.

The CNV discovery arose out of Scherer's determined work to understand the role of genetic variation in Autism Spectrum Disorder (ASD). Ongoing extensive international collaborative work has since identified disease-susceptibility variants on several different chromosomes, leading to the development of early diagnostic tests. Recent whole-genome sequencing studies have identified previously unknown, very rare variants in both coding and noncoding regions of the genome.

and time-consuming than DNA sequence comparisons; therefore, it is not feasible to repeat experiments in every species whose genome is sequenced. As a result, experimental data are available only for a small fraction of organisms. And because the functions of homologous protein-coding genes are so well conserved during the evolution of organisms, information about the function of a gene in one well-studied species very often applies to the homologous genes in another.

In some cases, the outcome of a sequence similarity search will indicate that the entire candidate gene's sequence is homologous to a known gene's sequence. In other cases, only part of the candidate gene sequence may match closely a sequence in a known gene. Typically this result indicates that the candidate gene encodes a protein with a domain that is related evolutionarily to a domain-encoding region of the known gene. (Protein domains are discussed in the Genome Evolution section later in this chapter.)

16.3b Gene Function May Be Determined Using Experiments That Alter the Expression of a Gene

If a researcher can determine how the phenotype of a cell or organism is affected when the expression of a gene is turned off, or reduced significantly, functional properties of the encoded protein may be inferred. In a simple example, if cells grow larger, the gene may be involved in regulating cell size.

Two main kinds of manipulations are used to turn off or reduce significantly the expression of a gene in genome-scale experiments—gene knockout and gene knockdown.

1. Gene knockout. In this approach, researchers replace a normal gene on its chromosome with a defective gene that cannot express a functional protein. Usually, the replacement lacks the ORF that encodes the gene's protein product. In effect, this is a deletion mutation that has been engineered genetically. A deletion mutation is a null mutation because there is zero expression of the gene's protein product. For a haploid organism, there is only one copy of each gene to knock out, whereas in diploid organisms both copies of each gene must be knocked out. On a genomic scale, experimental manipulations can be done to knock out each gene systematically one by one. The phenotypic consequences of zero expression of each gene can then be ascertained. Major projects have been done, or are being done, to knock out systematically the function of each gene in the genomes of several organisms, including yeast, the fruit fly, the nematode worm, and the mouse (knockout mice were introduced in Section 15.2).

2. Gene knockdown. Knocking down a gene's expression is typically done using RNA interference (RNAi). As discussed in Section 14.3, RNAi reduces the expression of a gene at the translation level. In RNAi, a small regulatory RNA (like a natural miRNA) is transcribed from an expression plasmid introduced into the cell. The sequence of that regulatory RNA forms complementary base pairs with the mRNA of a gene of interest. The base-pairing triggers the RNAi molecular mechanisms (see Figure 14.14), which knock down the expression of the gene by causing degradation of that gene's mRNA or by blocking its translation. For example, RNAi has been used to knock down gene expression of each of the approximately 20 000 genes of the nematode worm one by one. The advantage of RNAi over gene knockouts is that the decrease in function of a gene can be temporary.

Characterizing genes by studying the effects on the phenotype of knockouts or knockdowns can be very expensive and time-consuming. In a genome-wide study, thousands of knockout or knockdown strains have to be engineered genetically, and then each one has to be screened for a battery of possible phenotypic changes. The most ambitious studies of this kind have examined hundreds of phenotypes for each gene, which is only a fraction of the phenotypes that could be characterized. To make this approach really productive in the future will require further development of high-throughput methods that automate the measurement of phenotypic changes.

16.3c Transcriptomics Determines at the Genome Level When and Where Genes Are Transcribed

Some genes are transcribed in all cell types, whereas others are transcribed only when and where they are needed (see Chapter 14). Determining when and where genes are transcribed can shed light on their function. For instance, a researcher might be interested in determining at a genomic scale the gene expression patterns in different cell types, at different stages of embryonic development, at different points of the cell division cycle, or in response to mutation or changes in the environment. A medical example is identifying gene expression differences between normal cells and cells that have become cancerous. The experimental analysis itself may be qualitative—analyzing whether or not genes are expressed—or quantitative—analyzing how the level of expression of genes varies.

The complete set of transcripts in a cell is called the **transcriptome**, and the study of the transcriptome is called **transcriptomics**. Transcriptomics includes cataloguing transcripts and quantifying the changes in expression levels of each transcript during development, in different cell types, under different physiological conditions, and with other variations.

Analysis of transcriptomes is done using high-throughput hybridization or, increasingly, by sequence-based approaches. A hybridization-based approach uses **DNA microarrays**, also called **DNA chips**. The surface of a DNA microarray is divided into a microscopic grid of about 60 000 spaces. On each space of the grid, a computerized system deposits a microscopic spot containing about 10 000 000 copies of a DNA probe that is about 20 nucleotides long.

Studies of gene activity using DNA microarrays involve comparing gene expression under a defined experimental condition with expression under a reference (control) condition. As a theoretical example, **Figure 16.8** shows how a DNA microarray can be used to compare gene expression patterns in normal cells

and cancer cells in humans. mRNAs are isolated from each cell type and cDNAs are made from them, incorporating different fluorescent labels: green for one cDNA, red for the other. The two cDNAs are mixed and added to the DNA microarray, where they hybridize with whichever spots on the microarray contain complementary DNA probes. A laser excites the fluorescent labels, and the resulting green and red fluorescence is detected and quantified, enabling a researcher to see which genes are expressed in the cells. This technique is semiquantitative because it is also able to approximately quantify differences in gene expression between the two cell types (see "Interpreting the Results" in the figure).

Examples of DNA microarray analysis are screening individuals for mutations associated with genetic diseases (such as breast cancer), as well as studying changing gene expression profiles during Drosophila development, the growth of a gingivitis-causing bacterium under different conditions, flower development in plants, and the lives sea urchin larvae under different pH conditions.

A newer, sequence-based approach to analyzing transcriptomes is **RNA-seq** (whole-transcriptome sequencing). This technique uses high-throughput sequencing of cDNAs to identify and quantify RNA transcripts in a sample. For transcriptomic analysis of protein-coding genes using RNA-seq, mRNAs are isolated and converted to cDNAs (see Figure 15.4). About 30 to 400 nucleotides of each cDNA are sequenced using high-throughput techniques, and the results are aligned with the genome sequence of the organism under study. A single RNA-seq study can identify over 100 000 sequence reads, each one of which indicates the presence of a specific mRNA in the cells being studied. While a relatively new technique, RNA-seq is rapidly becoming the replacement for DNA microarrays in transcriptomics because of its decreasing cost and its greater precision for quantifying transcripts.

16.3d Proteomics Is the Characterization of All Expressed Proteins

Genome research also includes analysis of the proteins encoded by a genome, because proteins are largely responsible for cell function and, therefore, for most of the functions of an organism. The term **proteome** has been coined to refer to the complete set of proteins that can be expressed by an organism's genome. A cellular proteome is a subset of those proteins—the collection of proteins found in a particular cell type under a particular set of environmental conditions.

The study of the proteome is the field of **proteomics**. The number of possible proteins encoded by the genome is larger than the number of protein-coding genes in the

PURPOSE: DNA microarrays can be used in various experiments, including comparing the levels of gene expression in two different tissues, as illustrated here. The power of the technique is that the entire set of genes in a genome can be analyzed simultaneously.

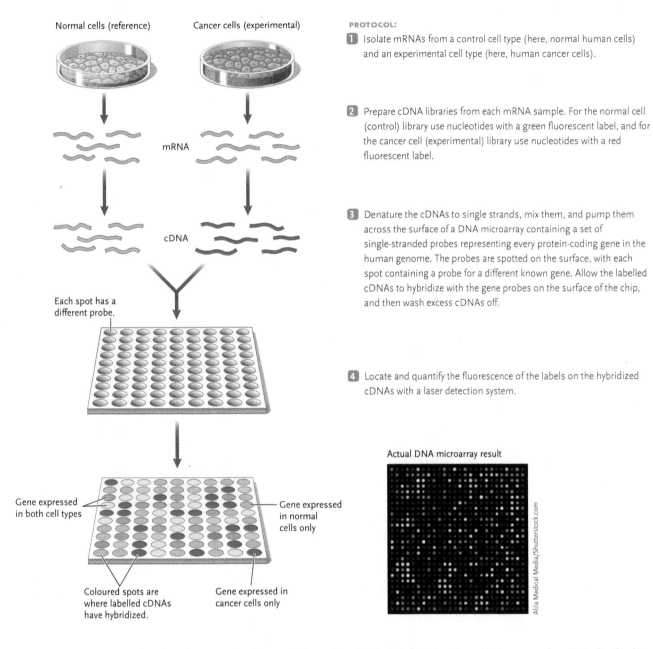

Normal cells (reference)   Cancer cells (experimental)

mRNA

cDNA

Each spot has a different probe.

Gene expressed in both cell types

Coloured spots are where labelled cDNAs have hybridized.

Gene expressed in normal cells only

Gene expressed in cancer cells only

Actual DNA microarray result

Alila Medical Media/Shutterstock.com

PROTOCOL:

1. Isolate mRNAs from a control cell type (here, normal human cells) and an experimental cell type (here, human cancer cells).

2. Prepare cDNA libraries from each mRNA sample. For the normal cell (control) library use nucleotides with a green fluorescent label, and for the cancer cell (experimental) library use nucleotides with a red fluorescent label.

3. Denature the cDNAs to single strands, mix them, and pump them across the surface of a DNA microarray containing a set of single-stranded probes representing every protein-coding gene in the human genome. The probes are spotted on the surface, with each spot containing a probe for a different known gene. Allow the labelled cDNAs to hybridize with the gene probes on the surface of the chip, and then wash excess cDNAs off.

4. Locate and quantify the fluorescence of the labels on the hybridized cDNAs with a laser detection system.

INTERPRETING THE RESULTS: The coloured spots on the microarray indicate where the labelled cDNAs have bound to the gene probes attached to the chip and, therefore, which genes were active in normal and/or cancer cells. Moreover, we can quantify the gene expression in the two cell types by the colour detected. A purely green spot indicates that the gene was active in the normal cell, but not in the cancer cell. A purely red spot indicates that the gene was active in the cancer cell, but not in the normal cell. A yellow spot indicates that the gene was equally active in the two cell types, and other colours tell us the relative levels of gene expression in the two cell types. For this particular experiment, we would be able to see how many genes have altered expression in the cancer cells, and exactly how their expression was changed.

Research Method Figure 16.8 DNA microarray analysis of gene expression levels.

genome, at least in eukaryotes. In eukaryotes, alternative splicing of gene transcripts and variation in protein processing means that expression of a gene may yield more than one protein product. The number of different proteins an organism can produce typically far exceeds the number of protein-coding genes.

Proteomics has three major goals: (1) to determine the structures and functions of all proteins, (2) to determine the location of each protein within or outside the cell, and (3) to identify physical interactions among proteins.

Determining Protein Structure. Protein structure may be determined as follows:

Clone the coding sequence of the gene into an expression vector (see Section 15.2).
↓
Transform the cloned gene into a host to express the protein.
↓
Purify the protein.
↓
Determine the structure of the protein using X-ray crystallography or nuclear magnetic resonance (NMR).

Protein structure may also be predicted nonexperimentally using computer algorithms based on the known chemistry of amino acids and how they interact.

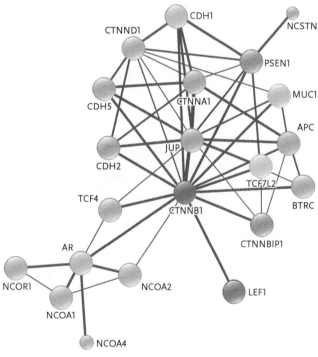

Figure 16.9
The protein-interaction network for human β-catenin (CTNNB1). Thicker lines show stronger associations between proteins.

Determining the Locations of Proteins in Cells. The location of a protein in a cell is important because it is key to its function. The cellular location of a protein can be studied by tagging the protein in some way and then visualizing the location of the tag microscopically. Different tags are used for visualization using light microscopy or electron microscopy.

Identifying Interactions among Proteins. Many proteins function by interacting with other proteins. In some cases, proteins (actually polypeptides) interact to form the quaternary structure—and therefore the functional form—of a protein (see *The Purple Pages*). Many multipolypeptide proteins exist, and you have encountered several in this book, for example, (1) hemoglobin is a four-polypeptide protein consisting of two α-globin polypeptides and two β-globin polypeptides and four associated heme groups (see "Molecule behind Biology," Box 40.1, Chapter 40); (2) RuBP carboxylase/oxygenase (rubisco), the first enzyme of the light-independent reactions of photosynthesis (see Section 9.3), consists of eight copies of a large polypeptide and eight copies of a small polypeptide; and (3) the Lac repressor protein that controls the expression of the lac operon in *E. coli* (see Section 14.1) consists of four copies of the same polypeptide.

In other interactions among proteins, the interaction is not permanent but serves to affect the function of one or other of the partners in the interaction. For example, in Chapter 5 you were introduced to protein kinases—enzymes that transfer a phosphate group from ATP to one or more sites on particular target proteins as part of a signal transduction pathway. The phosphorylation of the target proteins occurs as a result of the interaction between the enzymatic protein and each target protein. Once the target protein is phosphorylated, the two proteins no longer interact. Understanding the interactions among proteins is important, then, to help us understand how proteins work individually and together to determine the phenotype of a cell.

Thousands of interactions have been identified experimentally for a variety of organisms. The interaction data are assembled to produce protein-interaction networks, the analysis of which is informing us about the details and complexities of the functions of proteins in cells. **Figure 16.9** shows part of a protein-interaction network centred on the human protein β-catenin (cadherin-associated protein; the central CTNNB1 sphere in the figure). α-catenin is involved in the formation of adherens junctions (a type of cell junction; see Section 2.5) in epithelial cells where it links a-catenin (CTNNA1 in the figure) with E-cadherin (CDH1 in the figure; cadherins are discussed in Chapter 42). It also plays a key role in a signalling pathway that is important, for example, in regulating how cell fate is decided during development. Interactions with, for example, APC, LEF1, TCF4, and TCF7L2 occur as part of that signalling pathway's operation.

Just as for genomic DNA sequences, information about various properties of each protein are placed in databases, for example, Entrez (http://www.ncbi.nlm.nih.gov/Class/MLACourse/Original8Hour/Entrez/) and UniProt (http://www.uniprot.org), to create a dossier of that protein that is available to researchers worldwide.

Characterizing Protein Function. Through various approaches, researchers learn about the functions of proteins. **Figure 16.10a** shows an example of what we have learned about the functions of human protein-coding genes with respect to protein classes, and Figure 16.10b shows the functions of human protein-coding genes with respect to the biological processes involving these proteins.

STUDY BREAK

1. What are the ways by which the function of a gene identified in a genome sequence may be assigned?
2. How would you determine how a steroid hormone affects gene expression in human tissue culture cells?
3. What is the proteome, and what are the major goals of proteomics?

16.3f Systems Biology Highlights Interactions at Various Levels of Organization

The various "omics" projects have accumulated massive databases of information about the structures and functions of many thousands of individual genes, proteins, and RNAs. Fortunately, data visualization tools have enabled researchers to generate maps of interactions that reveal the structure of networks underlying the various levels of biological organization. We see that complexity is based not so much on how many genes an organism has, or how many proteins a cell can make, but rather on the networks of various interactions among these components at a given level and the interconnections among different levels.

The sum of all interactions of gene products with one another in a cell gives rise to an *interactome,* which, in turn, creates a particular array of active enzymes interacting with cofactors and substrates to create the *metabolome.* Metabolomes in all tissues and organs give rise to the overall *phenome* of an organism, which, if unhealthy, exhibits a *diseasome.* Overall, such research is leading to a more integrated and holistic understanding of living systems.

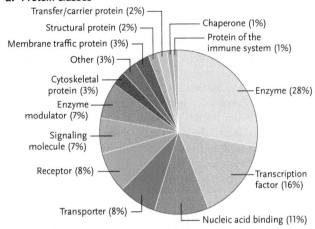

a. Protein classes

Transfer/carrier protein (2%)
Structural protein (2%)
Membrane traffic protein (3%)
Other (3%)
Cytoskeletal protein (3%)
Enzyme modulator (7%)
Signaling molecule (7%)
Receptor (8%)
Transporter (8%)
Chaperone (1%)
Protein of the immune system (1%)
Enzyme (28%)
Transcription factor (16%)
Nucleic acid binding (11%)

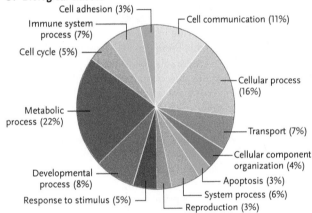

b. Biological classes

Cell adhesion (3%)
Immune system process (7%)
Cell cycle (5%)
Metabolic process (22%)
Developmental process (8%)
Response to stimulus (5%)
Cell communication (11%)
Cellular process (16%)
Transport (7%)
Cellular component organization (4%)
Apoptosis (3%)
System process (6%)
Reproduction (3%)

Figure 16.10
Functions of human protein-coding genes organized with respect to protein classes **(a)** and biological processes **(b).**

16.4 Genome Evolution

DNA genomes with protein-coding genes are thought to have evolved over 3.5 billion years ago (bya), by the time of the earliest fossil microorganisms that have been discovered. These early cells probably had at most a few hundred protein-coding genes. New genes evolved as life evolved and became more complex, so that most present-day organisms have thousands or tens of thousands of protein-coding genes. In this section you will learn how genes and genomes have evolved, and how genome sequences inform us about the evolutionary history of life.

16.4a Comparative Genomics Reveals the Evolutionary History of Genes and Genomes

Understanding how genes evolved and how genomes evolved are major goals of the field of comparative genomics. Because the genes in present-day genomes evolved from ancestral genes that were in the genomes of organisms living millions to billions of years ago, we can trace the evolutionary history of genes by comparing the genomes of different groups of present-day organisms. From such comparisons, we can estimate when new genes first appeared in ancient organisms, describe how they changed over time, and gain insights into what molecular processes cause new genes to evolve in the first place.

Comparative genomics has shown that some genes are found in the genomes of almost all present-day organisms. Examples are genes involved in core biological processes like transcription and protein synthesis, including genes for some subunits of RNA polymerase, genes for many of the proteins that make up part of the structure of a ribosome, and most of the aminoacyl–tRNA synthetase enzymes that attach amino acids to tRNA molecules. The proteins coded for by these genes not only perform the same function in every organism but are also related evolutionarily. This conclusion strongly suggests that the single-celled common ancestor of all living organisms had these genes in its genome, and that these genes have been passed down through the generations for billions of years.

Most genes do not appear in the genomes of all organisms but have a more restricted distribution. There are eukaryote-specific genes, bacteria-specific genes, archaea-specific genes, animal-specific genes, plant-specific genes, primate-specific genes, human-specific genes, and so on. For example, mitosis and meiosis genes are eukaryote-specific genes, genes for flowers are plant specific, and some genes related to brain function are primate specific.

Analyzing the evolutionary history of genes provides valuable information about how life evolved on the molecular level. For example, by comparing the functions of almost 4000 evolutionarily related groups of genes in 100 genomes of bacteria, archaea, and eukaryotes, researchers have identified a period about 3 bya when many new genes evolved. By analyzing the functions of these new genes, the researchers concluded that many of the new genes evolved as adaptations to changes in the amount of oxygen in Earth's atmosphere, following the development of the oxygen-producing photosynthetic reactions (see Chapter 3).

As mentioned in Section 3.5f, the ability of otherwise solitary single cells to grow collaboratively and communally has evolved multiple times in the tree of life—giving rise to an astonishing range of multicellular life forms. Some of the genetic renovations associated with the development of multicellular lifestyles have been discovered through genomic analysis of related species of algae, comparing *Chlamydomonas* with *Volvox*, specifically. These two species last shared a unicellular common ancestor about 200 million years ago (mya). However, since that time, *Chlamydomonas* has remained unicellular, while *Volvox* has developed a relatively sophisticated multicellular colonial structure (Figure 3.24).

Aside from duplication of some cyclin genes (associated with cell cycle control) as well as some extracellular matrix (ECM) genes (associated with cell wall proteins that hold the colony together) in *Volvox*, we find relatively little difference in the number, or types, of genes in these two modern species. Therefore, it seems that the emergence of multicellularity in this case relied more heavily on repurposing and reregulating existing genes than on the acquisition of new genes.

One such repurposed gene in *Volvox* is GlsA. While unicellular *Chlamydomonas* cells always divide symmetrically, creating daughter cells with identical structure and fate, *Volvox* development depends on several rounds of asymmetric cell division resulting in few cells that are relatively large. These large cells become reproductive cells, while the thousands of smaller cells function solely as nondividing somatic cells. Mutations in GlsA result in loss of asymmetric division. A genomic DNA database search discovered a very similar gene sequence in *Chlamydomonas* called GAR1 (Figure 16.12). GlsA in *Volvox* and GAR1 in *Chlamydomonas* are orthologues, since they are derived from the same gene in their common ancestor. However, since *Chlamydomonas* only divides symmetrically, it appears that the protein product of these two genes interacts in a different network, with different effects on the plane of cell division, in the two modern species.

A family of related genes, including RegA and RlsA, code for transcription factors that provide the control of cell division necessary for cooperative growth of multicellular algae. These genes are paralogues since they arose by gene duplication in the unicellular ancestor of *Volvox*, where they likely functioned to regulate growth depending on the availability of light and nutrients. However, in modern *Volvox*, at least some of these genes are now under developmental control, regulating growth depending on reproductive versus somatic cell type.

While comparative genomics provides new insights into the evolution of known genes and genomes, it has also led to the discovery of otherwise unknown organisms and novel genes. In the mid-2000s, maverick biologist J. Craig Venter renovated a private yacht to serve as an oceanic survey laboratory, collecting seawater samples from Halifax to the Galapagos Islands. Sequencing of the total DNA extracted from such samples revealed a staggering degree of genetic diversity among the unicellular microorganisms and viruses collected from the marine environment. Hundreds of new species were discovered, along with an equally impressive number of genes otherwise unknown to science.

Venter's survey of genetic diversity in the ocean is one of the earliest examples of the now burgeoning field of **metagenomics**, in which DNA or RNA from an entire community of organisms in a particular niche is harvested collectively, sequenced, and analyzed using some of the DNA technologies described in this chapter. This approach is significant because until very recently, our understanding of the genetics of the microbial world was based almost exclusively on the very small proportion of species that can be cultivated in the laboratory. With the tools of modern metagenomics, we gain access to the genomes of a whole new world of previously inaccessible organisms and viruses.

Multicellular eukaryotes have complex relationships with rich communities of organisms inhabiting their skin, digestive, and excretory tracts. Large-scale metagenomic and metatranscriptomic analyses are significantly improving our understanding of the role of such microbial communities in human health and disease. Mining the metagenomic data harvested from microbial communities in such diverse environments as the termite gut, deep-sea hydrothermal vents, glaciers, geysers, the bovine rumen, and desert soil will certainly identify tens of thousands of novel genes that code for enzymes that may have applications in industrial biofuel production, food processing, pollution control, and drug development.

Comparative genomics has also been applied to understanding human evolution. (Human evolution is discussed in Chapter 21.) The human genome was the first mammalian genome sequenced, and researchers now have the sequences of hundreds of human genomes to study and compare to discover what makes us human and what is responsible for human variation. We also have over 40 other mammalian genomes to compare with the human genome. These include genomes of primate species that are closely related to humans, such as the common chimpanzee and the mountain gorilla, as well as less closely related mammals, such as the cow and the duck-billed platypus. Comparing the human genome with the genomes of other primates reveals which features are common to all of these primates and which are unique to humans. The human and chimpanzee genomes are strikingly similar, with 96% DNA sequence identity across the entire genome. The annotation of the chimpanzee genome is not yet complete, but it is likely that these two species share virtually all of their genes, so the genomic changes that occurred in human evolution probably involved only subtle mutations in the protein-coding sequences of genes, and mutations to regulatory sequences that determine how and when each gene is expressed (see Chapter 14). By contrast, comparisons of primate genomes with those of other mammals have identified new genes that evolved only in primates. Further studies of the functions of these genes may shed light on how primates evolved the characteristics that distinguish them from other mammals. And, interestingly, the primate-specific genes in the human genome contain the highest fraction of disease-related genes—19.4%—of any group of genes.

DNA microarrays and RNA-seq (see Section 16.3) have been used to compare which genes are transcribed in which parts of the brain in humans, chimpanzees, and rhesus monkeys. Certain groups of genes are expressed in the brain only during embryonic and early postnatal development. In both chimpanzees and rhesus monkeys, many genes involved in the formation of new synapses (communicating junctions between neurons; see Chapter 45) are transcribed only in the first year after birth, while in humans expression of these genes continues up to age five. These differences are most prominent in the prefrontal **cortex**, which is an area of the brain involved in complex decision-making (see Chapter 44). These comparative findings provide clues to how our species evolved enhanced learning abilities.

Comparative genomics also provides information about how the arrangement of genes on chromosomes has evolved. In Section 11.3 you learned about chromosomal mutations that occur when part of a chromosome is translocated to another chromosome, or inverted in place. Nondisjunction in meiosis can also cause entire chromosomes to be duplicated (see Figure 11.12). Such chromosomal mutations are uncommon, and usually they are harmful. But when a nonharmful chromosomal mutation occurs and spreads to all members of a species, the order of genes on the chromosomes of that species may then be different from the order in closely related species. Comparing the genomes of a range of related species reveals that over the course of hundreds of millions of years of biological evolution, pieces of chromosomes have changed places repeatedly by translocation and inversion, rearranging the genes on chromosomes like shuffling a deck of cards. Even so, the chromosomal arrangement of some genes is preserved after all this reshuffling, even in distantly related organisms. For example, comparisons of the human genome with the genomes of distantly related animals such as insects and sea anemones reveal blocks of homologous genes that are on the same chromosome and arranged in the same order in all of these species. This means that the order of these genes on the chromosome has been preserved from the time that all of these species evolved from a common ancestor, even though that common ancestor lived over 500 mya.

16.4b New Genes Evolve by Duplication and Exon Shuffling

The evolution of a new gene is a rare event—much less common than a mutation in an existing gene. But, nonetheless, over millions of years of biological evolution many new genes have been produced. For example, a comparison of genome sequences among four species in the Drosophila genus of fruit flies identified over 200 genes that had evolved in just the past 13 million years (a comparatively short time in evolutionary history).

Throughout the history of life on Earth, the evolution of new biological functions has almost always involved the evolution of new genes. For example, photosynthesis became possible only with the evolution of genes coding for proteins that could harness the energy in photons to synthesize ATP and electron carrier molecules. And comparative analysis of mammalian genomes has revealed genes involved in milk production and other biological functions found only in mammals. Evolutionary biologists have described a number of molecular mechanisms to explain where these new genes come from. The most common molecular mechanism to explain the origin of new genes is gene duplication, which produces multigene families after a series of duplications of genes that all derive from the same ancestral gene. New types of genes are produced by a process called **exon shuffling**, which combines parts of two or more genes.

Gene Duplication. Gene duplication is any process that produces two identical copies of a gene in an organism's genome. There are three main mechanisms by which organisms might acquire duplicate copies of a gene: (1) whole-genome duplication (WGD), (2) unequal crossing-over of homologous chromosomes during meiosis, or (3) replication of transposable elements (see Section 9.4).

a. Normal crossing-over

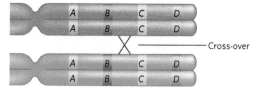

Cross-over

Crossing-over occurs between homologous chromatids during prophase I of meiosis (see Figure 11.5). Normally crossing-over occurs at the exact same point on each homolog and results in recombinant chromosomes after meiosis that have the same number of genes in each homolog.

Recombinant chromosomes (parental chromosomes not shown)

b. Unequal crossing-over

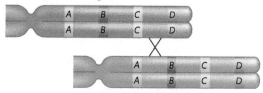

Unequal crossing-over results in recombinant chromosomes after meiosis that have a different number of genes. One (top) has duplicate genes, here *B* and *C*, whereas the other (bottom) has lost genes, here *B* and *C*.

Figure 16.11
Duplication of genes by unequal crossing-over.

Widespread failure of chromosome partitioning in meiosis or mitosis can result in zygotes and daughter cells having double the normal number of chromosomes. Such cells could give rise to polyploid organisms with **whole-genome duplication (WGD)**. Although polyploidy is relatively rare, there are many thousands of modern plant species (most domestic crops) and many hundreds of animal species (many insects, amphibians, and fish) that have more than two sets of chromosomes. An ancient WGD in the yeast *Saccharomyces cerevisiae* was the first to be revealed by comparative genomics. Subsequent analyses suggest that WGDs have occurred at least twice in the evolutionary history of the vertebrates, three times in the bony fish, and up to four times in the flowering plants.

Unequal crossing-over is the rare phenomenon in meiosis in which, instead of crossing-over occurring at the exact same point on each homologue of a homologous pair of chromosomes (**Figure 16.11a**), crossing-over occurs at different points (Figure 16.11b). The result of unequal crossing-over is that one of the recombinant chromosomes is missing one or more genes, while the other has duplicate copies of these genes. Unequal crossing-over produces tandem duplication of genes, with the duplicate copies clustered in the same region of the same chromosome.

Gene duplication may occur as a mistake when a transposable element copies itself and splices the DNA copies elsewhere in a genome. (Transposable element movement is discussed in Section 9.4.) Rarely, transposable elements copy adjacent DNA in addition to their own, producing duplicate copies of any genes in that DNA. This produces **dispersed duplication** of genes, meaning that the copies of the gene are found in different places in the genome—often on two different chromosomes.

At first, the duplicate copies of a gene have the same protein-coding sequences and encode identical proteins. The two genes are functionally redundant, meaning that one could be eliminated from the genome with no loss of biological functionality. Often, one of the redundant copies is mutated into a pseudogene, or lost by deletion. But if both genes remain functional, they will evolve slowly in different ways, as different mutations occur in each gene. Mutations in regulatory sequences may change how each duplicate gene is regulated, or mutations in protein-coding sequences may change the functional properties of the proteins produced by each gene. Over many generations, this evolutionary process can produce two homologous genes with similar but distinct functions.

For example, nitric oxide synthase enzymes catalyze a reaction that produces nitric oxide (NO), a molecule that cells use to communicate with each other. In the human genome, there are three genes for different nitric oxide synthase enzymes. One gene is expressed only in neurons, another only in the endothelial cells lining blood vessels, and the third in the liver and in a type of white blood cell called a macrophage (see

Chapter 51). Homologues of all three of these genes are found in other mammalian genomes as well as in the genomes of birds and reptiles, so the gene duplications by which these genes evolved must have happened over 200 mya. Evolution of tissue-specific expression patterns for each gene must have involved mutations to regulatory sequences that control transcription. The evolution of these genes also involved mutations to the protein-coding sequences, causing the proteins to have subtly different structures and functions. For example, the neuronal and endothelial nitric oxide synthase enzymes are regulated by Ca^{2+} ions, while the third enzyme is not. The three genes are found on three different chromosomes in the human genome, which suggests that they evolved by dispersed duplication.

Production of Multigene Families. Gene duplication is often followed by further duplication of one or both of the original duplicates. When this happens repeatedly over millions of years, a family of homologous genes called a **multigene family** evolves. The nitric oxide synthase enzymes described above are a small gene family, with three members in the human genome. Other multigene families contain tens to hundreds of genes. The members of a multigene family all evolve from one ancestral gene and therefore have similar DNA sequences and produce proteins with similar structures and functions. But because different mutations occur in each member of a multigene family, the genes gradually evolve subtly different characteristics.

Let us consider the OPT/YSL multigene family of the plant *Arabidopsis thaliana* as an example. The proteins coded for by these genes are oligopeptide transporters that shuttle short peptide molecules into the cytoplasm from organelles or the external environment. They are also important players in maintaining appropriate levels of heavy metals. This multigene family is found in other plant genomes as well as in the genomes of fungi and other eukaryotes. By comparing DNA sequences of OPT/YSL genes in the genomes of plants and other organisms, researchers have concluded that hundreds of millions of years ago and before the evolution of the plant kingdom, a gene duplication produced the ancestral OPT gene and the ancestral YSL gene. Mutations in each gene caused them to encode proteins specialized for transporting different oligopeptides. A series of more recent gene duplications occurred since the

a. Family tree showing evolutionary relationships among *OPT* and *YSL* genes

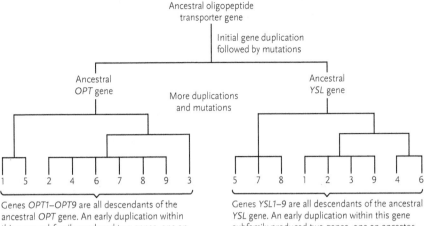

Genes *OPT1–OPT9* are all descendants of the ancestral *OPT* gene. An early duplication within this gene subfamily produced two genes, one an ancestor of *OPT1* and *OPT5* and the other an ancestor of the other seven *OPT* genes. A subsequent gene duplication in the latter group produced the ancestor of *OPT2, 4,* and *6–9,* and the ancestor of *OPT3.*

Genes *YSL1–9* are all descendants of the ancestral *YSL* gene. An early duplication within this gene subfamily produced two genes, one an ancestor of *YSL5, 7,* and *8* and the other an ancestor of the other six *YSL* genes. A subsequent gene duplication in the latter group produced the ancestor of *YSL1–3* and *9,* and the ancestor of *YSL4* and *6.*

b. Distribution of *OPT* genes on chromosomes in the *Arabidopsis thaliana* genome

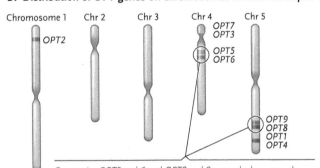

Gene pairs *OPT5* and *6* and *OPT8* and *9* are each close enough that they could have evolved by a recent tandem duplication. But only *OPT8* and *9* are near relatives in the *OPT* gene family tree (part **(a)** of figure). Therefore, we can hypothesize that *OPT8* and *9* likely resulted from a fairly recent tandem duplication, whereas *OPT6* is a dispersed duplicate of another *OPT* gene.

Figure 16.12

Evolution of the plant OPT/YSL multigene family. **(a)** Family tree showing evolutionary relationships among OPT and YSL genes. **(b)** Distribution of OPT genes on chromosomes in the Arabidopsis thaliana genome.

evolution of plants, but well before the evolution of Arabidopsis thaliana. Each duplicate gene in this family accumulated different mutations, producing the functionally diverse set of OPT genes and YSL genes now found in *Arabidopsis thaliana* and other plants.

Figure 16.12a illustrates the family relationships among the OPT/YSL genes using a phylogenetic tree, much as a family tree illustrates relationships in a human family (see Chapter 20 for more information on how phylogenetic trees are constructed). Figure 16.12b shows the distribution of the OPT genes on Arabidopsis thaliana chromosomes and outlines the possible evolutionary history of some of these genes.

The oligopeptide transporter gene family in *Arabidopsis thaliana* is larger than the nitric oxide synthase gene family in the human genome, but other multigene families are even larger. For example, some families of transcription factor proteins and membrane-bound receptor proteins include hundreds of genes. Some of the larger multigene families have members in all kingdoms of eukaryotes, or even in all three domains of living organisms. Such families each evolved from an ancestral gene that first appeared billions of years ago.

Exon Shuffling. The new genes produced by gene duplication evolve distinct functions, but they retain the same general function as other members of the multigene family into which they have been "born," so to speak. Our examples have illustrated that. By contrast, exon shuffling—the duplication and rearrangement of exons—is a molecular evolutionary process that combines exons of two or more existing genes to produce a gene that encodes a protein with an unprecedented function.

Remember from Section 13.3 that many protein-coding genes in eukaryotes contain introns, sequences that do not encode amino acids. The introns are present in the pre-mRNA transcripts of such genes but, by RNA processing, the introns are removed while the exons—the sequences encoding amino acids in the pre-mRNAs—are spliced together to make the mature mRNAs. In many genes, the junctions between exons fall at points within the protein-coding sequence between major functional regions in the protein. These functional regions correspond to the domains into which many proteins are divided.

Exon shuffling can occur in the following way. When a piece of DNA is cut out of a chromosome and reinserted elsewhere in the genome (through the activity of a transposable element, for example), the ends of the piece of DNA that moves may occur within the introns of a gene, causing one or more whole exons to be inserted somewhere else in a chromosome. If these exons are inserted into an intron in another gene, the amino acid sequence encoded by the exons may be added to the amino acid sequence of the encoded protein. Such a transfer of DNA can produce a new gene, coding for a protein that has one or more domains added to the other domains that it already had.

An exon shuffling event occurred very early in the evolution of animals (at least 700 mya) that produced a new gene coding for a protein that plays a key role in signalling between cells in animal tissues. Evidence for this exon shuffling event comes from comparing the genome sequence of the choanoflagellate *Monosiga brevicollis* with the sequences of a number of animal genomes, including Homo sapiens. Choanoflagellates (see Chapter 24) are single-celled or colonial protists that are thought to be related evolutionarily to animals. The evolution of multicellularity in the first animals is thought to have involved molecular mechanisms that enabled choanoflagellate-like cells to attach to and communicate with one another, so they could then specialize in performing different functions.

Figure 16.13 shows the exon shuffling event. It involves the Notch family of proteins, which are

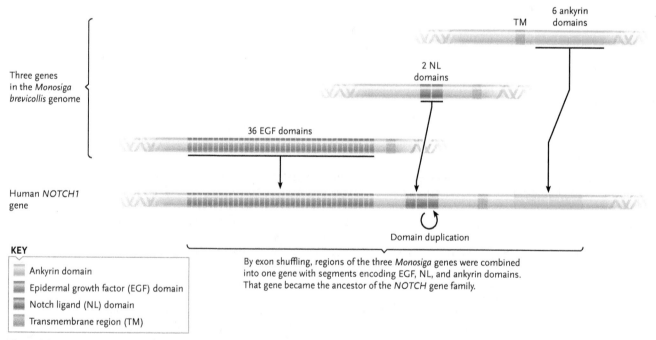

KEY

	Ankyrin domain
	Epidermal growth factor (EGF) domain
	Notch ligand (NL) domain
	Transmembrane region (TM)

By exon shuffling, regions of the three *Monosiga* genes were combined into one gene with segments encoding EGF, NL, and ankyrin domains. That gene became the ancestor of the *NOTCH* gene family.

Figure 16.13

Evolution of Notch domains in animals by exon shuffling. At the top are three genes in the *Monosiga brevicollis* genome that encode three transmembrane (TM) region–containing proteins, one with epithelial growth factor (EGF) domains, a second with Notch ligand (NL) domains, and a third with ankyrin domains. At the bottom is the human NOTCH1 gene, which encodes a protein with EFG, NL, and ankyrin domains.

MOLECULE BEHIND BIOLOGY 16.2

Myoglobin

Mammalian myoglobin is a relatively small, extensively studied protein composed of eight alpha helices that fold to enclose an internal oxygen-binding heme group **(Figure 1).** Having a higher affinity for oxygen than hemoglobin, myoglobin acts to store oxygen for use in muscle cells. High concentrations of myoglobin in muscle tissue is an adaptation that allows marine mammals such as elephant seals and sperm whales to extend their dive time for over an hour without taking a breath. Recent studies of myoglobin chemistry and genomics have

provided a glimpse into the lifestyle of the ancestors of modern whales as they ventured into the ocean depths.

Across a wide range of modern aquatic mammals, there is a strong correlation between high myoglobin concentrations and increased surface charge on the protein. Since surface charge is determined by amino acid composition, which, in turn, is determined by DNA sequence, it is therefore possible to estimate maximum myoglobin concentrations in muscle cells based on myoglobin gene sequence. Combining sequence data

with body mass data allows scientists to predict maximum dive times of aquatic animals. Since comparative genomics of ancient DNA (from extinct mammoths, for example) versus modern sequences allows us to deduce the gene sequences of evolutionary ancestors, and since we have fossil records of the size of ancestral whales, we can now estimate that the maximum dive time of an ancestor of modern whales, such as the *Basilosaurus* **(Figure 2),** was the same as that of a modern dolphin (about 15 minutes).

Figure 1
Myoglobin folded around heme group.

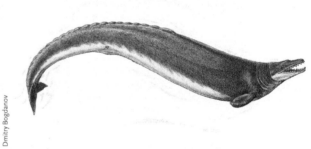

Figure 2
Basilosaurus, *an ancestor of modern whales from the Late Eocene, 40 mya.*

multidomain, membrane-spanning proteins. The human Notch1 protein, encoded by the NOTCH1 gene, contains a transmembrane (TM) region, 36 copies of an EGF domain, three copies of an NL domain, and six copies of an ankyrin domain. The TM region anchors the Notch1 protein in the plasma membrane. The three domains are key to the protein's function. The part of the protein that is outside the cell membrane includes the EGF and NL domains, which enables a Notch protein in one cell to bind to other proteins in adjacent cells in a tissue. The ankyrin domains within the cell enable it to attach to the microfilaments that make up part of the cytoskeleton (see Section 2.3).

Figure 16.13 also shows three different genes in the Monosiga brevicollis genome, one with a sequence encoding EGF domains, a second with a sequence encoding NL domains, and a third with a sequence encoding ankyrin domains. However, this organism lacks a gene homologous to the gene for the Notch protein. Researchers have hypothesized that through exon shuffling early in animal evolution, the sequences coding for the EGF, NL, and ankyrin domains in the three genes were combined in one gene, producing the ancestor of the NOTCH gene family. At some point, a duplication of the sequence coding for one NL domain occurred, since the *Monosiga brevicollis* gene has sequences coding for only two copies of that domain, while animal genes for Notch proteins have sequences coding for three copies.

The genes produced by gene duplication typically encode functional proteins because they are duplicates of an existing functional gene. Most instances of exon shuffling should theoretically produce nonfunctional proteins, because an existing functional protein is interrupted by one or more domains from an unrelated protein. But in a small number of cases, proteins produced by exon shuffling combine the functions of two or more proteins in a new and useful way, like the assembly of the gene for the Notch signalling protein (see Figure 16.13). Interestingly, exon shuffling is thought to account for perhaps one-third of newly evolved genes. The genes that are produced by exon shuffling have more novel functions than those produced by gene duplication. In cases like the Notch protein, they become the ancestors of

multigene families that evolve through subsequent gene duplications.

The domain structures of proteins in humans and other organisms provide evidence of how common exon shuffling has been in the evolution of proteins. The most widely used domains are found in thousands of different proteins, in dozens of different combinations with other domains.

STUDY BREAK

1. What molecular mechanisms cause tandem duplication of genes and dispersed duplication of genes?
2. Why do new genes produced by exon shuffling have more novel functions than new genes produced by gene duplication?

Review

To access course materials such as Aplia and other companion resources, please visit www.NELSONbrain.com.

16.1 Genomics: An Overview

- Genomics is the characterization of whole genomes, including their structures (sequences), functions, and evolution.
- Genome sequence data are in databases that may be accessed by researchers worldwide.
- Genomics consists of three main areas of study: genome sequence determination and annotation, the determination of complete genome sequences and identification of putative genes and other important sequences; functional genomics, the study of the functions of genes and other parts of the genome; and comparative genomics, the comparison of entire genomes or parts of them to understand evolutionary relationships and basic biological similarities and differences among species.

16.2 Genome Sequence Determination and Annotation

- The whole-genome shotgun method of sequencing a genome involves breaking up the entire genome into random, overlapping fragments, cloning each fragment, determining the sequence of the fragment in each clone, and using computer algorithms to assemble overlapping sequences into the sequence of the complete genome (Figure 16.1).
- DNA sequencing methods involve DNA purification; DNA fragmentation; amplification of fragments; sequencing each fragment; and assembly of fragment sequences into longer sequences, such as those of a genome (Figures 16.2 and 16.3).
- Once the complete sequence of a genome has been determined, it is annotated to identify key sequences, including protein-coding genes, noncoding RNA

genes, regulatory sequences associated with genes, origins of replication, transposable elements, pseudogenes, and short repetitive sequences. Annotation of a genome is the task of researchers in bioinformatics.
- Identifying protein-coding genes in a genome sequence can be done by using a computer search for open reading frames (ORFs), by searching databases for sequence similarity to genes of known function, and (the gold standard) by studying gene transcripts.
- Complete genome sequences have been obtained for many viruses, a large number of prokaryotic cells, and many eukaryotes, including humans. For organismal genomes, those of bacteria and archaea are generally smaller than those of eukaryotes, and their genes are densely packed in their genomes with little noncoding space between them. Prokaryotic genes are organized either into single transcription units or into operons. Genomes of eukaryotes vary greatly in size, but there is no correlation between genome size and type of organism. Gene density also varies, but in general it is significantly less than is seen for prokaryotic genes. Eukaryotic genes are organized into single transcription units (Figures 16.5–16.7; Tables 16.2 and 16.3).

16.3 Determining the Functions of the Genes in a Genome

- The function of a protein-coding gene may be assigned by a sequence similarity search of sequence databases, by using evidence from protein structure, or by using knockout or knockdown experiments that alter the expression of a gene.
- Transcriptomics is the study at the genome level of when and where genes are transcribed. One experimental method for studying the transcription of all or many of the genes in a genome simultaneously is the DNA microarray (DNA chip); this technique can generate qualitative information about gene transcription, such as the similarities and differences in gene expression in two cell types or in two developmental

stages, as well as quantitative information about the relative levels of gene transcription (Figure 16.8).

- Proteomics is the characterization of the complete set of proteins in an organism or in a particular cell type. Protein numbers, protein structures, protein functions, protein locations, and protein interactions are all topics of proteomics (Figures 16.9 and 16.10).

16.4 Genome Evolution

- Comparative genomics traces the evolution of genomes by analyzing similarities and differences in DNA sequences in the genomes of present-day organisms.
- Comparative analysis reveals how homologous protein-coding genes have evolved in groups of organisms, how regulation of gene expression has evolved through mutations in the regulatory sequences of genes, and how chromosome structure has evolved as parts of one chromosome have broken off and been attached to other chromosomes.
- New genes evolve by whole-genome duplication (WGD) or by tandem duplication when chromosomes cross over unequally in meiosis, producing a chromosome containing two copies of the DNA coding for

one or more genes (Figure 16.11). New genes evolve by dispersed duplication when transposable elements copy DNA coding for one or more genes and insert it at another location in the genome.

- Duplicate copies of genes evolve distinct functions as different mutations occur in the two copies. Mutations in protein-coding sequences produce proteins with slightly different structures, while mutations in regulatory sequences cause the genes to be expressed in different cell types and in response to different stimuli.
- Repeated cycles of duplication followed by mutation produce multigene families, which are collections of homologous genes that code for similar but functionally distinct proteins. The largest multigene families comprise hundreds of different genes (Figure 16.12).
- Exon shuffling produces functionally novel proteins by combining parts of two or more different genes. When exons that code for one or more domains of a protein are copied from one gene and inserted into the protein-coding sequence of another gene, those domains are added to the structure of the protein coded for by that gene. Adding new domains to a protein gives the protein new molecular functionalities (Figure 16.13).

Questions

Self-Test Questions

1. Why is the Solexa/Illumina DNA sequencing method faster and less expensive than the Sanger method?
   a. It sequences longer fragments of DNA.
   b. It sequences more DNA fragments at the same time.
   c. It does not require amplification of DNA fragments before sequencing.
   d. It does not require the use of computer algorithms to find places where sequence fragments overlap.

2. How do pseudogenes differ from genes?
   a. They are not transcribed.
   b. They contain longer ORFs.
   c. They do not have introns.
   d. They use a different genetic code.

3. What is the main reason that searching for ORFs is more useful for annotating bacterial protein-coding genes than it is for annotating eukaryote protein-coding genes?
   a. Eukaryote protein-coding genes contain introns.
   b. The density of protein-coding genes is much higher in eukaryote genomes.
   c. In most bacteria, all of the protein-coding genes are located on a single circular chromosome.
   d. Bacterial protein-coding genes are much longer than eukaryotic protein-coding genes.

4. Which of the following statements about genome size is true?
   a. Bacteria have genomes that vary widely in size.
   b. The human genome is the largest among eukaryotes.

   c. Organisms with large genomes tend to be more complex than organisms with small genomes.
   d. As genome size increases in a lineage, the number of genes also always increases.

5. Which of the following statements about the *E. coli* genome is true?
   a. It has a much lower gene density than the human genome.
   b. It contains longer genes than the human genome.
   c. All of the genes are transcribed from the same template strand of the DNA double helix.
   d. About half of the genes in the *E. coli* genome are grouped with other genes in operons.

6. Which of the following statements about the human genome is true?
   a. The protein-coding sequences occupy about 75% of the genome.
   b. About 45% of the genome consists of transposable element sequences.
   c. The genome sequence comprises approximately 30 million base pairs.
   d. Human cells have about 10 500 different protein-coding genes.

7. What makes up about 95% of the average human transcription unit?
   a. short repeat sequences
   b. protein-coding sequences
   c. regulatory sequences
   d. introns

8. Imagine that the DNA sequences of two protein-coding genes are similar, but only for part of the protein-coding sequence. What does this suggest?
   a. The two proteins have one or more domains in common.
   b. The two proteins were produced by duplication of an ancestral gene.
   c. The two proteins perform the same function.
   d. One of the two genes is actually a pseudogene.

9. Imagine two protein-coding genes have very similar nucleotide sequences and are located right next to each other on a chromosome. What does this suggest?
   a. One of them is a duplicate of the other, copied by a retrotransposon.
   b. One of them is a pseudogene.
   c. They were produced by unequal crossing-over.
   d. They are transcribed in the same cell types.

10. When do the proteins coded for by genes in a multigene family begin to evolve distinct functions?
   a. When gene duplication occurs.
   b. When exon shuffling occurs.
   c. When the genes are expressed by transcription and translation.
   d. When different mutations occur in each protein-coding sequence.

Questions for Discussion

1. Why are high-throughput techniques used so much in genomics research? Give examples from this chapter of different uses of high-throughput techniques.

2. Why does the Sanger DNA sequencing method work best when the concentration of dideoxyribonucleotides is much less than the concentration of deoxyribonucleotides? If you wanted to adjust the reaction mixture to produce a greater number of very long complementary sequence fragments, how would you change the relative concentration of dideoxyribonucleotides, and why?

3. Which of the methods for annotating protein-coding genes would you expect to do the best job of distinguishing functioning genes from pseudogenes, and why?

4. The genome of the yeast Saccharomyces cerevisiae is only about 0.4% the size of the human genome, yet it contains about 30% as many genes as are in the human genome. Given that, which of the features of the human genome would you expect to find many fewer of in the yeast genome?

5. How does sequencing the genomes of a greater number of animal species help in annotating and determining the functions of human protein-coding genes?

The Chemical, Physical, and Environmental Foundations of Biology

The Scientific Basis of Biology

The information contained in this textbook represents the culmination of hundreds of years of research involving a huge number of experiments carried out by countless scientists. The entire content of this book—every observation, experimental result, and generality—is the product of **biological research,** the collective effort of individuals who have worked to understand every aspect of the living world. This section describes how biologists working today pose and find answers to questions.

The Scientific Method

Beginning about 500 years ago in Europe, inquisitive people began to understand that direct observation is the most reliable and productive way to study natural phenomena. By the nineteenth century, researchers were using the **scientific method**—an investigative approach to acquiring knowledge in which scientists make observations about the natural world, develop working explanations about what they observe, and then test those explanations by collecting more information.

Application of the scientific method requires both curiosity and skepticism: successful scientists question the current state of our knowledge and challenge old concepts with new ideas and new observations. Explanations of natural phenomena must be backed up by objective evidence rooted in observation and measurement. Most important, scientists share their ideas and results by publishing their work.

Testing a Hypothesis Is Central to the Scientific Method

A **hypothesis** can be defined as a tentative explanation for an observation, phenomenon, or scientific problem that can be tested by further investigation. Scientific hypotheses have two fundamental elements. First, a hypothesis must be *testable*. That is, there must be some set of observations or experiments that can be undertaken to support the hypothesis. For example, you may be studying a gene in yeast that you find is activated when cells are placed under conditions of heat stress. You may hypothesize that the protein encoded by this gene is essential for the yeast to survive short-term exposure to high temperature. Using modern molecular techniques, you can test this hypothesis by inactivating the gene in a population of yeast cells and observing if there is a change in heat tolerance. Today, this hypothesis is easily testable. A scientist may have had a similar idea 30 years ago, but given the lack of molecular techniques, the hypothesis would not have been testable at that time.

The second key to a scientific hypothesis is that it must be *falsifiable*. That is, through observation or experimentation you must be able to show that the original hypothesis may not be correct. Getting back to the yeast analogy, it is very possible that through analysis you would find that inactivation of the gene does not change the ability of yeast cells to survive high temperatures.

Scientists test the predictions that come from hypotheses with experimental or observational tests that generate relevant data. And if data from just one study refute a scientific hypothesis (i.e., demonstrate that its predictions are incorrect), the scientist must modify the hypothesis and test it again or abandon it altogether.

No amount of data can prove beyond a doubt that a hypothesis is correct; there is always the chance that a contradictory example exists, and it is impossible to test every imaginable example. That is why scientists say that positive results are consistent with, support, or confirm a hypothesis.

Elements of the Scientific Method

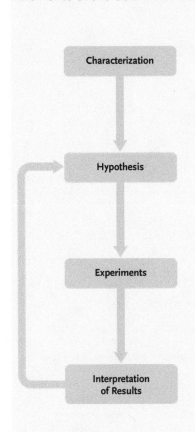

1 Before a new hypothesis is formulated, researchers today usually know a fair amount about the subject under study. This characterization comes from years of their own experiments as well as the published research of other scientists working in the same discipline.

2 Based on earlier findings, create a testable and falsifiable explanation (a hypothesis) of the information gathered. Hypotheses may be expressed in words or in mathematical equations.

3 Design and conduct a controlled experiment to test the predictions of the hypothesis, that is, what you would expect to observe if the hypothesis were correct. The experiment must be clearly defined so that it can be repeated by others.

4 Compare the results of the experiment with those predicted by the hypothesis. If the results do not match the predictions, the hypothesis is refuted, and it must be rejected or revised. If the prediction was correct, the hypothesis is confirmed. The data from one set of experiments are subsequently used to develop additional hypotheses to be tested.

Research Method Figure

An Example of Hypothesis Development and Testing

Consider this simple example of hypothesis development and testing. A friend gives you a plant that she grew on her windowsill. Under her care, the plant always flowered. You place the plant on your windowsill and water it regularly, but the plant never blooms. You know that your friend always gave fertilizer to the plant, and you wonder whether fertilizing the plant will make it flower. In other words, you create a hypothesis with a specific **prediction:** "This type of plant will flower if it receives fertilizer." This is a good hypothesis because it is not only testable but also falsifiable. To test the hypothesis, you would simply give the plant fertilizer. If it flowers, your hypothesis is confirmed. If it does not bloom, the data force you to reject or revise your hypothesis.

With all experiments it is important to include a **control**—a set of individuals that will not be subject to the treatment. To test this specific hypothesis, you need to compare plants that receive fertilizer (the experimental treatment) with plants grown without fertilizer (the control treatment). The presence or absence of fertilizer is the **experimental variable,** and in a controlled experiment, everything except the experimental variable—the flower pots, the soil, the amount of water, and exposure to sunlight—is kept the same between the treated and control individuals. This type of control ensures that any differences in flowering pattern observed between plants that receive the experimental treatment (fertilizer) and those that receive the control treatment (no fertilizer) can be attributed to the experimental variable.

Nearly all experiments in biology include **replicates,** multiple subjects that receive either the same experimental treatment or the same control treatment. Scientists use replicates in experiments because individuals typically vary in genetic makeup, size, health, or other characteristics—and because accidents may disrupt a few replicates. By exposing multiple subjects to both treatments, we can use a statistical test to compare the average result of the experimental treatment with the average result of the control treatment, giving us more confidence in the overall findings.

continued on next page

Question: Your friend fertilizes a plant that she grows on her windowsill, and it flowers. After she gives you the plant, you put it on your windowsill, but you do not give it any fertilizer and it does not flower. Will giving the plant fertilizer induce it to flower?

Friend added fertilizer.   You did not add fertilizer.

Experiment: Establish six replicates of an experimental treatment (identical plants grown with fertilizer) and six replicates of a control treatment (identical plants grown without fertilizer).

Experimental Treatment   **Control Treatment**

Possible Result 1: Neither experimental nor control plants flower.

Experimentals   **Controls**

Conclusion: Fertilizer alone does not cause the plants to flower. Consider alternative hypotheses and conduct additional experiments, each testing a different experimental treatment, such as the amount of water or sunlight the plant receives or the temperature to which it is exposed.

Possible Result 2: Plants in the experimental group flower, but plants in the control group do not.

Experimentals   **Controls**

Conclusion: The application of fertilizer induces flowering in this type of plant, confirming your original hypothesis. Pat yourself on the back and apply to graduate school in plant biology.

The Scientific Theory

When a hypothesis stands up to repeated experimental tests, it is gradually accepted as an accurate explanation of natural events. This acceptance may take many years, and it usually involves repeated experimental confirmations. When many different tests have consistently confirmed a hypothesis that addresses many broad questions, it may become regarded as a scientific **theory**—a scientifically acceptable, well-substantiated explanation of some aspect of the natural world. Most scientific theories are supported by exhaustive experimentation; thus, scientists usually regard them as established truths that are unlikely to be contradicted by future research.

In common usage, the word *theory* most often labels an idea as either speculative or downright suspect, as in the expression "It's only a theory." But when scientists talk about theories, they refer to concepts that have withstood the test of many experiments. Because of the difference between the scientific and common usage of the word *theory*, many people fail to appreciate the extensive evidence that supports scientific theories. For example, virtually every scientist accepts the theory of evolution as a fully supported scientific truth: all species change with time, new species are formed, and older species eventually die off. Although evolutionary biologists debate the details of how evolutionary processes bring about these changes, very few scientists doubt that the theory of evolution is essentially correct. Moreover, *no scientist who has tried to cast doubt on the theory of evolution has ever devised or conducted a study that disproves any part of it.* Unfortunately, the confusion between the scientific and common usage of the word *theory* has led, in part, to endless public debate about supposed faults and inadequacies in the theory of evolution.

Experimental versus Observational Science

In some scientific disciplines, the system under study may be too large or too complex to establish controlled experiments. In astronomy, for example, one cannot manipulate stars and galaxies as if they were potted plants. Astronomy is considered an observational science, as are research themes in ecology and evolutionary biology. Observational science relies on sophisticated statistical techniques to analyze detailed observational data in order to test hypotheses. The statistical tools provide a method for researchers to infer pattern and underlying cause from the collected data.

Many scientific disciplines rely on a combination of observational and experimental science. For example, ecology researchers studying global climate change often set up experiments that take place in the environment. These enable a certain level of control of variables under far more realistic conditions than would be possible in a laboratory. These so-called field experiments complement the analysis of observational data that may reflect changes to our climate that occurred hundreds of years ago.

Measurement and Scale

The SI system of Measurement

The International System of Units is the most widely used system of measurement in the world. Its abbreviation, *SI*, is from the French Système International d'Unités. It was adopted by the eleventh General Conference of Weights and Measures in 1960 and represents the latest modification of the metric system, which was first implemented by the French National Assembly in 1790.

The SI system uses seven base units, each of which measures or describes a different kind of physical quantity. Each unit is strictly defined, although the definitions have been modified (and made more accurate) over time. As an example, the metre was originally defined by the French Academy of Sciences as the length between two marks on a platinum–iridium bar that was designed to represent 1/10 000 000 of the distance from the equator to the North Pole through Paris. This definition was changed in 1983 by the International Bureau of Weights and Measures to become the distance travelled by light in absolute vacuum in 1/299 792 458 of a second.

The SI system also uses a series of prefix names and prefix symbols to form the names and symbols of the decimal multiples of the base SI units. Note that the base unit for mass is the kilogram, not the gram. One kilogram equals 1000 g ($1 \text{ kg} = 10^3 \text{ g}$). This list has been extended several times: prefixes now range from yotta, at 10^{24} (one septillion), to yocto, at 10^{-24} (one septillionth).

Factor	Prefix	Symbol	Factor	Prefix	Symbol
10^{24}	yotta	Y	10^{-1}	deci	d
10^{21}	zetta	Z	10^{-2}	centi	c
10^{18}	exa	E	10^{-3}	milli	m
10^{15}	peta	P	10^{-6}	micro	μ
10^{12}	tera	T	10^{-9}	nano	n
10^{9}	giga	G	10^{-12}	pico	p
10^{6}	mega	M	10^{-15}	femto	f
10^{3}	kilo	k	10^{-18}	atto	a
10^{2}	hecto	h	10^{-21}	zepto	z
10^{1}	deca	da	10^{-24}	yocto	y

The Seven Base Units of the SI System

Name	Symbol	Quantity
metre	m	length
kilogram	kg	mass
second	s	time
ampere	A	electric current
kelvin	K	temperature
mole	mol	amount of substance
candela	cd	luminous intensity

Derived SI Units

Several other units have been derived from combinations of the seven base units of measure. Three of the more common concern units of force (newton), pressure (pascal), and energy or heat (joule). The measurement of temperature in degrees Celsius is also considered a derived unit, even though one Celsius degree is the same size as one kelvin. However, 0°C = 273.16 K (note that no degree symbol is used when expressing temperature in kelvins).

Name	Symbol	Quantity	Expression
newton	N	force	$m \cdot kg \cdot s^{-2}$
pascal	Pa	pressure	$N \cdot m^{-2}$
joule	J	energy and work	$N \cdot m$

Non-SI Units in Common Usage

A number of units not derived from the base SI units are accepted for use with SI units.

Name	Symbol	Value in SI Units
minute	min	60 s
hour	h	3600 s
day	d	86 400 s
litre	L	$1 \text{ dm}^3 = 10^{-3} \text{ m}^3$
angstrom	Å	10^{-10} m
calorie, a measure of food energy*	cal	4.184 J
unified atomic mass unit or Dalton**	u or Da	$\sim 1.66054 \times 10^{-24}$ kg

*One food calorie = 1 Cal = 1000 cal
**Value determined experimentally to be 1/12 the mass of an unbound atom of carbon-12.

Why Everyone Should Use SI Units

In December 1998, NASA launched the Mars Climate Orbiter on a mission to study the Martian weather and climate. As it approached Mars, the spacecraft received instructions from flight control on Earth to fire thruster engines to enter into a proper orbit about 140 to 150 km above the Martian surface. However, as it approached the planet, a navigation error caused the spacecraft to descend into an orbit of only 57 km above the surface. The spacecraft was soon destroyed by the heat caused by atmospheric friction.

The review of the incident found that the root cause was a mix-up between the use of SI units and an older system of measure, imperial units (e.g., inches, feet, and pounds). More specifically, the software that was used to control the thruster engines of the spacecraft from the ground was written using the imperial unit of force, the pound-force, whereas onboard the spacecraft, information was interpreted in terms of newtons, the metric unit of force. Since 1 pound-force equals about 4.45 N, instructions from the ground were thus multiplied by 4.45.

The total cost of the mission was approximately $327 million.

Scale in Biology

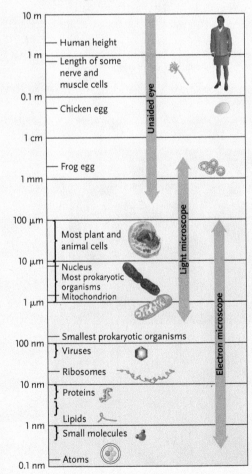

The Organization of Matter

Any substance in the universe that has mass and occupies space is defined as **matter.** The fundamental scientific concepts that explain how matter is organized in biological systems are no different from those for nonliving forms of matter. Living organisms are built from the same chemical building blocks as nonliving systems and abide by the same fundamental laws of chemistry and physics. Because of this, a basic understanding of how all matter is organized is important for a complete picture of the structure and function of organisms.

Elements and Compounds

All matter is composed of elements. An **element** is a pure substance composed of only one type of atom. Ninety-two different elements occur naturally on Earth. Living organisms are composed of about 25 elements, with only 4 elements—carbon, hydrogen, oxygen, and nitrogen—accounting for more than 96% of the mass of an organism. Seven other elements—calcium, phosphorus, potassium, sulfur, sodium, chlorine, and magnesium—contribute most of the remaining 4%. The proportions by mass of different elements differ markedly in sea water, the human body, a fruit, and Earth's crust, as shown below.

A **compound** is a substance that contains two or more elements. For example, hydrogen and oxygen are the elements that make up the compound water (H_2O). The chemical and physical properties of compounds are typically distinct from those of their atoms or elements.

Sea water		Human		Pumpkin		Earth's crust	
Oxygen	88.3	Oxygen	65.0	Oxygen	85.0	Oxygen	46.6
Hydrogen	11.0	Carbon	18.5	Hydrogen	10.7	Silicon	27.7
Chlorine	1.9	Hydrogen	9.5	Carbon	3.3	Aluminium	8.1
Sodium	1.1	Nitrogen	3.3	Potassium	0.34	Iron	5.0
Magnesium	0.1	Calcium	2.0	Nitrogen	0.16	Calcium	3.6
Sulfur	0.09	Phosphorus	1.1	Phosphorus	0.05	Sodium	2.8
Potassium	0.04	Potassium	0.35	Calcium	0.02	Potassium	2.6
Calcium	0.04	Sulfur	0.25	Magnesium	0.01	Magnesium	2.1
Carbon	0.003	Sodium	0.15	Iron	0.008	Other elements	1.5
Silicon	0.0029	Chlorine	0.15	Sodium	0.001		
Nitrogen	0.0015	Magnesium	0.05	Zinc	0.0002		
Strontium	0.0008	Iron	0.004	Copper	0.0001		
		Iodine	0.0004				

Andriano/Shutterstock.com

©iStock.com/Hon Lau

The Atom

Elements are composed of **atoms**—the smallest units that retain the chemical and physical properties of an element. Any given element has only one type of atom identified by a standard one- or two-letter symbol. The element carbon is identified by the single letter C, which stands for both the carbon atom and the element.

Atomic Number and Mass Number of the Most Common Elements in Living Organisms			
Element	Symbol	Atomic Number	Mass Number of the Most Common Form
Hydrogen	H	1	1
Carbon	C	6	12
Nitrogen	N	7	14
Oxygen	O	8	16
Sodium	Na	11	23
Magnesium	Mg	12	24
Phosphorus	P	15	31
Sulfur	S	16	32
Chlorine	Cl	17	35
Potassium	K	19	39
Calcium	Ca	20	40
Iron	Fe	26	56
Iodine	I	53	127

Each atom consists of an atomic nucleus surrounded by one or more smaller, fast-moving particles called electrons. All atomic nuclei contain one or more positively charged particles called **protons.** The number of protons in the nucleus of each kind of atom is referred to as the **atomic number.** This number does not vary and thus specifically identifies the atom. The smallest atom, hydrogen, has a single proton in its nucleus, so its atomic number is 1. Carbon with six protons, nitrogen with seven protons, and oxygen with eight protons have atomic numbers of 6, 7, and 8, respectively.

With one exception, the nuclei of all atoms also contain uncharged particles called **neutrons,** which occur in variable numbers approximately equal to the number of protons. The single exception is the most common form of hydrogen, which has a nucleus that contains only a single proton. Atoms are assigned a **mass number** based on the total number of protons and neutrons in the atomic nucleus. Electrons are ignored in determinations of atomic mass because the mass of an electron is very small.

Hydrogen   **Carbon**

Nucleus
(1 proton)

1 electron

6 protons
6 neutrons

2 electrons

4 electrons

Isotopes

All atoms of a specific element have the same number of protons, but they may differ in the number of neutrons. These distinct forms of an element, where atoms have the same atomic number but different atomic masses, are called **isotopes.** The nuclei of some isotopes are unstable and break down, or *decay*, giving off particles of matter and energy that can be detected as radioactivity. The decay transforms the unstable, radioactive isotope—called a radioisotope—into an atom of another element. For example, the carbon isotope ¹⁴C is unstable and undergoes radioactive decay in which one of its neutrons splits into a proton and an electron. The electron is ejected from the nucleus, but the proton is retained, giving a new total of seven protons and seven neutrons, which is characteristic of the most common form of nitrogen. Thus, the decay transforms the carbon atom into an atom of nitrogen.

Isotopes of hydrogen

^{1}H	^{2}H (deuterium)	^{3}H (tritium)
1 proton	1 proton	1 proton
	1 neutron	2 neutrons
atomic number = 1	atomic number = 1	atomic number = 1
mass number = 1	mass number = 2	mass number = 3

Isotopes of carbon

^{12}C	^{13}C	^{14}C
6 protons	6 protons	6 protons
6 neutrons	7 neutrons	8 neutrons
atomic number = 6	atomic number = 6	atomic number = 6
mass number = 12	mass number = 13	mass number = 14

THE CHEMICAL, PHYSICAL, AND ENVIRONMENTAL FOUNDATIONS OF BIOLOGY |

Use of Radioisotopes

Radioactive decay occurs at a steady, clocklike rate. The length of time it takes for one-half of a sample of a radioisotope to decay is termed its **half-life.** Each type of radioisotope has a characteristic half-life. For example, carbon-14 decays with a fixed half-life of 5730 years, while uranium-238 has a half-life of 4.5 billion years. Because unstable isotopes decay at a fixed rate that is not affected by chemical reactions or environmental conditions such as temperature or pressure, they are used to estimate the age of organic material, rocks, and fossils. These radiometric techniques have been vital in dating animal remains and tracing evolutionary lineages.

A number of radioisotopes that have short half-lives are used in medical imaging and in the treatment of diseases. These isotopes include iodine-123 and thalium-201, which have half-lives of only 13.3 and 3.1 days, respectively.

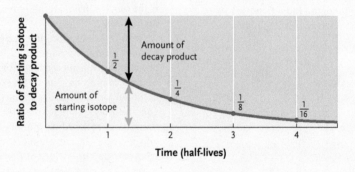

Electrons and Electron Shells

In an atom, the number of electrons is equal to the number of protons in the nucleus. Because electrons carry a negative charge and protons are positively charged, the total structure of an atom is electrically neutral.

Electrons move around the atomic nucleus in **orbitals,** which are grouped into **electron shells.** As shown below, the first shell (I) may be occupied by a maximum of two electrons. The second (II) and third (III) shells can hold a maximum of eight electrons each. The fourth shell can hold 18 electrons (not all shown). Atoms with more than four electron shells are very rare in biological molecules.

The chemical behaviour of an atom depends primarily on the number of electrons in its outermost shell. This is referred to as the valence shell, which holds **valence electrons.** Atoms in which the valence shell is not completely filled with electrons tend to be chemically reactive; those with a completely filled valence shell are nonreactive, or inert.

For example, as shown on the left, hydrogen has a single, unpaired electron in its outermost and only electron shell and is highly reactive; helium has two valence electrons filling its single orbital and is unreactive or inert. Along with helium, neon and argon are also referred to as inert gases because their outer electron shell is full.

Because an unfilled electron shell is less stable than a filled one, atoms with an incomplete outer shell have a strong tendency to interact with other atoms in a way that causes them to either gain or lose enough electrons to achieve a completed outermost shell. All elements commonly found in living organisms have valence shells that are not completely filled with electrons (purple balls in figure at left). Because of this, these atoms readily participate in chemical reactions with other atoms.

Atomic number

Element	I	II	III	IV
1 Hydrogen	○			
2 Helium	○○			
6 Carbon	○○	○○○○		
7 Nitrogen	○○	○○○○○		
8 Oxygen	○○	○○○○○○		
10 Neon	○○	○○○○○○○○		
11 Sodium	○○	○○○○○○○○	○	
12 Magnesium	○○	○○○○○○○○	○○	
15 Phosphorus	○○	○○○○○○○○	○○○○○	
16 Sulfur	○○	○○○○○○○○	○○○○○○	
17 Chlorine	○○	○○○○○○○○	○○○○○○○	
18 Argon	○○	○○○○○○○○	○○○○○○○○	
19 Potassium	○○	○○○○○○○○	○○○○○○○○	○
20 Calcium	○○	○○○○○○○○	○○○○○○○○	○○

Electron shell

Chemical Bonds

An atom with an incomplete valence shell has a strong tendency to interact with other atoms so that they have a completely filled valence shell. These interactions, called **chemical bonds,** are caused by closely associated atoms sharing or transferring electrons to complete the valence shell. Four types of chemical bonds are important in biological molecules: ionic bonds, covalent bonds, hydrogen bonds, and van der Waals forces. Because of their importance in hydrogen bonding, polar molecules are also discussed in this section.

Ionic Bonds

Ionic bonds form between atoms that gain or lose valence electrons completely. A sodium atom (Na) readily loses a single electron to achieve a full valence shell (see last section), and chlorine (Cl) readily gains an electron to do the same. After the transfer, the sodium atom, now with 11 protons and 10 electrons, carries a single positive charge. The chlorine atom, now with 17 protons and 18 electrons, carries a single negative charge. In this charged condition, the atoms are called **ions:** sodium, with a positive charge, is a **cation,** while chloride, with a negative charge, is an **anion.**

Ionic bonds are common among the forces that hold ions, atoms, and molecules together in living organisms because these bonds have three key features:

- They exert an attractive force over greater distances than any other chemical bond.
- Their attractive force extends in all directions.
- They vary in strength depending on the presence of other charged substances.

Ionic bond formation between sodium and chlorine

Crystals of sodium chloride (NaCl)

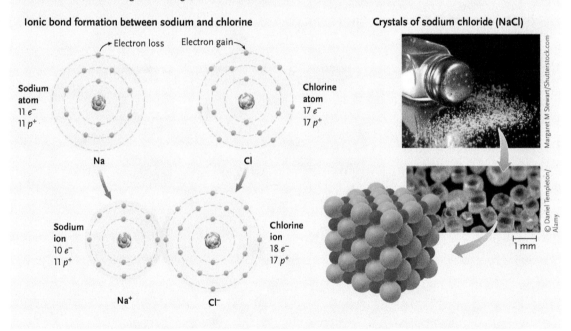

Electron loss   Electron gain

Sodium atom
11 e^-
11 p^+

Na

Chlorine atom
17 e^-
17 p^+

Cl

Sodium ion
10 e^-
11 p^+

Na^+

Chlorine ion
18 e^-
17 p^+

Cl^-

Margaret M Stewart/Shutterstock.com

© Daniel Templeton/ Alamy

1 mm

Covalent Bonds

Covalent bonds form between two atoms when they share valence electrons. This is distinct from ionic bonds, where electrons are gained or lost from atoms. The term **molecule** refers to two or more atoms held together by covalent bonds. The formation of molecular hydrogen, H_2, by two hydrogen atoms is the simplest example of a covalent bond. If two hydrogen atoms collide, the single electron of each atom may join in a new, combined two-electron orbital that surrounds both nuclei. The two electrons fill the orbital; thus, the hydrogen atoms tend to remain linked stably together. The linkage formed by the shared orbital is a covalent bond.

A structural formula represents a covalent bond of a pair of shared electrons as a single line. For example, in H_2, the covalent bond that holds the molecule together is represented as H:H or H—H. Generally speaking, the covalent bonding capacity of an atom is equal to the number of valence shell electrons necessary to fill the shell: hydrogen, 1; oxygen, 2; nitrogen, 3; and carbon, 4.

As shown below, a single oxygen atom has six valence shell electrons, and two oxygen atoms form a single molecule.

Carbon, with four unpaired outer electrons, typically forms four covalent bonds to complete its outermost energy level. An example is methane, CH_4, the main component of natural gas.

Unlike ionic bonds, which extend their attractive force in all directions, the shared orbitals that form covalent bonds extend between atoms at discrete angles and directions, giving covalently bound molecules distinct, three-dimensional forms. For biological molecules such as proteins, which are held together primarily by covalent bonds, the three-dimensional form imparted by these bonds is critical to their functions.

The four covalent bonds formed by the carbon atom are fixed at an angle of 109.5° from each other, forming a tetrahedron. The tetrahedral arrangement of the bonds allows carbon atoms to link extensively to each other in chains and rings in both branched and unbranched form. Such structures form the backbones of an almost unlimited variety of molecules. Carbon can also form double bonds, in which atoms share two pairs of electrons, and triple bonds, in which atoms share three pairs of electrons.

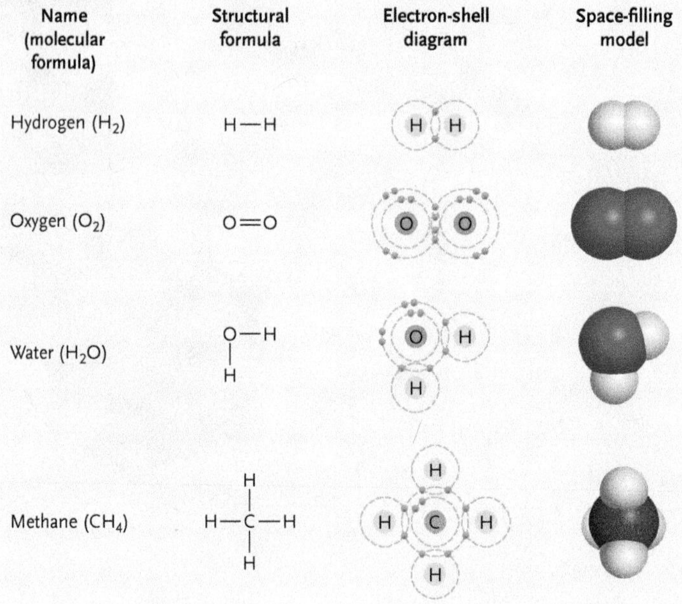

Name (molecular formula)	Structural formula	Electron-shell diagram	Space-filling model
Hydrogen (H_2)	H—H		
Oxygen (O_2)	O=O		
Water (H_2O)	O—H H (below O)		
Methane (CH_4)	H—C—H (with H above and H below C)		

Polarity and Hydrogen Bonding

All covalent bonds involve the sharing of valence electrons between two atoms. Yet the degree of electron sharing between the two atoms can differ widely. **Electronegativity** is the measure of an atom's attraction for the electrons it shares in a chemical bond with another atom. The more electronegative an atom is, the more strongly it attracts shared electrons. Oxygen is the most electronegative atom found in biological molecules, followed by nitrogen and sulfur. By comparison neither carbon nor hydrogen is considered electronegative.

The unequal sharing of electrons between two atoms that differ in their electronegativity results in a **polar covalent bond.** The atom that attracts the electrons more strongly carries a partial negative charge (denoted by the symbol d^-), and the atom deprived of electrons carries a partial positive charge (denoted by the symbol d^+). As shown below for a molecule of water, atoms carrying partial charges give the molecule partially positive and negative ends; this is referred to as polarity, and the molecule is termed **polar.**

Polar molecules attract and align themselves with other polar molecules and with charged ions and molecules. Polar molecules that associate readily with water because it is strongly polar are identified as **hydrophilic** (*hydro* = water; *philic* = preferring). Nonpolar substances that are excluded by water and other polar molecules are identified as **hydrophobic** (*phobic* = avoiding). Most common non-polar molecules consist primarily of C—H bonds (neither atom being electronegative).

Hydrogen atoms are made partially positive by sharing electrons unequally with oxygen, nitrogen, or sulfur. Because of this, the hydrogen atom may be attracted to other electronegative atoms that it is not directly bonded to (see figure below). his attractive force is the **hydrogen bond,** illustrated by a dotted line in structural diagrams of molecules. Hydrogen bonds may form between atoms in the same or different molecules.

Individual hydrogen bonds are about 1/20 the strength of a covalent bond. However, large biological molecules may offer many opportunities for hydrogen bonding, both within and between molecules. When numerous, hydrogen bonds are collectively strong and lend stability to the three-dimensional structure of molecules such as proteins.

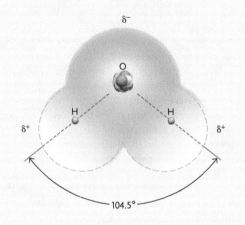

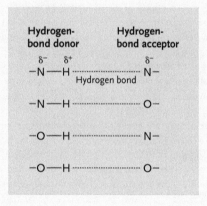

Van der Waals Forces

Van der Waals forces are even weaker than hydrogen bonds. These forces develop between nonpolar molecules or regions of molecules when, through their constant motion, electrons accumulate by chance in one part of a molecule or another. This process leads to zones of positive and negative charge, making the molecule polar. If they are oriented in the right way, the polar parts of the molecules are attracted electrically to one another and cause the molecules to stick together briefly. Although an individual bond formed with van der Waals forces is weak and transient, the formation of many bonds of this type can stabilize the shape of a large molecule, such as a protein.

A striking example of the collective power of van der Waals forces concerns the ability of geckos to cling to and walk up vertical smooth surfaces. The toes of the lizard are covered in millions of pads, each one forming a weak interaction—using van der Waals forces—with the molecules on the smooth surface.

Nathalie Speliers Ufermann/Shutterstock.com

Chemical Reactions

Chemical reactions occur when atoms or molecules interact to form new chemical bonds or break old ones. As a result of bond formation or breakage, atoms are added to or removed from molecules, or the linkages of atoms in molecules are rearranged. When any of these alterations occur, molecules change from one type to another, usually with different chemical and physical properties. In biological systems, chemical reactions are accelerated by *enzymes,* which are discussed in Chapter 4.

The atoms or molecules entering a chemical reaction are called the **reactants,** and those leaving a reaction are the **products.** A chemical reaction is written with an arrow showing the direction of the reaction; reactants are placed to the left of the arrow, and products are placed to the right. Both reactants and products are usually written in chemical shorthand as formulas.

For example, the overall reaction of photosynthesis, in which carbon dioxide and water are combined to produce sugars and oxygen (see Chapter 7), is written as follows:

$$6CO_2 + 6H_2O \rightarrow C_6H_{12}O_6 + 6O_2$$

Carbon dioxide · Water · A sugar · Molecular oxygen

The number in front of each formula indicates the number of molecules of that type among the reactants and products (the number 1 is not written). Notice that there are as many atoms of each element to the left of the arrow as there are to the right, even though the products are different from the reactants. This balance reflects the fact that in such reactions, atoms may be rearranged but not created or destroyed. Chemical reactions written in balanced form are known as **chemical equations.**

While some chemical reactions result in all the reactant molecules being converted into products, many reactions are reversible; that is, the products of the forward reaction can become the reactants of the reverse reaction. That a reaction is reversible is illustrated by using opposite-headed arrows. As an example, hydrogen and molecular nitrogen can react to produce ammonia, but ammonia can also break down to produce hydrogen and nitrogen:

$$3H_2 + N_2 \rightleftarrows 2NH_3$$

Water

All living organisms contain water, and many kinds of organisms live directly in water. Even those that live in dry environments contain water in all their structures—different organisms range from 50% to more than 95% water by mass. The water inside organisms is crucial for life: it is required for many important biochemical reactions and plays major roles in maintaining the shape and organization of cells and tissues.

Hydrogen Bonds and the Properties of Water

The properties of water molecules that make them so important to life depend to a great extent on their polar structure and their ability to link to each other by hydrogen bonds (See "Chemical Bonds").

Hydrogen bonds form readily between water molecules in both liquid water and ice. In liquid water, each water molecule establishes an average of 3.4 hydrogen bonds with its neighbours, forming an arrangement known as the **water lattice.** In liquid water, the hydrogen bonds that hold the lattice together constantly break and reform, allowing the water molecules to break loose from the lattice, slip past one another, and reform the lattice in new positions.

In ice, the water lattice is a rigid, crystalline structure in which each water molecule forms four hydrogen bonds with neighbouring molecules. The rigid ice lattice spaces the water molecules farther apart than the water lattice. Because of this greater spacing, water has the unusual property of being about 10% less dense when solid than when liquid. Imagine what Earth would be like if ice sank to the bottom, as most solids do.

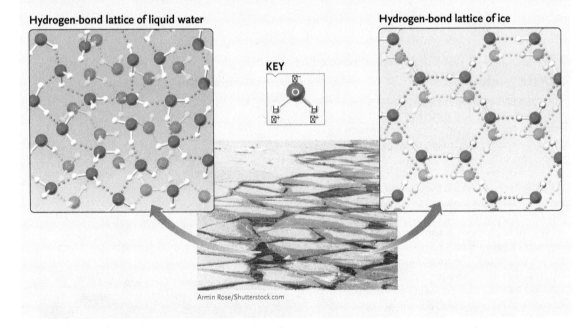

Hydrogen-bond lattice of liquid water

KEY

Hydrogen-bond lattice of ice

Armin Rose/Shutterstock.com

Specific Heat and Heat of Vaporization

The hydrogen-bond lattice of liquid water retards the escape of individual water molecules as the water is heated. As heat flows into water, much of it is absorbed in the breakage of hydrogen bonds. As a result, the temperature of water, reflected in the average motion of its molecules, increases relatively slowly as heat is added. This results in water having a high **specific heat,** defined as the amount of heat required to increase the temperature of a given quantity of water. For example, relatively high temperatures and the addition of considerable heat are required to break enough hydrogen bonds to make water boil. The high boiling point maintains water as a liquid over the wide temperature range of 0 to 100°C.

The unusual properties of water are more obvious if you compare it to H_2S, a molecule that has a similar molecular mass and structure. Compared to H_2O, H_2S boils at an astonishingly low temperature of $-60°C$.

The vast difference in boiling points between these two molecules is explained by oxygen being more electronegative than sulfur. This results in water being a more polar molecule and in turn being able to form a much stronger hydrogen bond lattice.

A large amount of heat, 586 cal/g, must be added to give water molecules enough energy of motion to break loose from liquid water and form a gas. This required heat, known as the **heat of vaporization,** allows humans and many other organisms to cool off when hot. In humans, water is released onto the surface of the skin by more than 2.5 million sweat glands; the heat energy absorbed by the water in sweat as the sweat evaporates cools the skin and the underlying blood vessels. The heat loss helps keep body temperature from increasing when environmental temperatures are high. Plants use a similar cooling mechanism as water evaporates from their leaves.

Surface Tension

The hydrogen-bond lattice of water results in water molecules staying together, a phenomenon called **cohesion.** For example, in land plants, cohesion holds water molecules in unbroken columns in the microscopic conducting tubes that extend from the roots to the highest leaves. As water evaporates from the leaves, water molecules in the columns, held together by cohesion, move upward through the tubes to replace the lost water.

Related to cohesion is **surface tension,** which is a measure of how difficult it is to stretch or break the surface of a liquid. The water molecules at surfaces facing air can form hydrogen bonds with water molecules beside and below them but not on the sides that face the air. This unbalanced bonding produces a force that places the surface water molecules under tension, making them more resistant to separation than the underlying water molecules. This force is strong enough to allow small insects such as water striders to walk on water.

Creation of surface tension by unbalanced hydrogen bonding

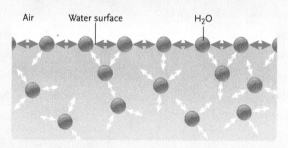

Air　　Water surface　　H_2O

Spider supported by water's surface tension

©iStock.com/Alasdair Thomson

Aqueous Solutions

Because water molecules are small and strongly polar, they readily surround other polar and charged molecules and ions. The surface coat, called a **hydration shell,** reduces the attraction between the molecules or ions and promotes their separation and entry into a **solution,** where they are suspended individually, surrounded by water molecules. Once in solution, the hydration shell prevents the polar molecules or ions from reassociating. In such an aqueous solution, water is called the **solvent,** and the molecules of a substance dissolved in water are called the *solute*.

Sodium chloride (salt) dissolves in water because water molecules quickly form hydration layers around the Na^+ and Cl^- ions in the salt crystals, reducing the attraction between the ions so much that they separate from the crystal and enter the surrounding water lattice as individual ions. In much the same way, hydration shells surround macromolecules such as nucleic acids and proteins, reducing their electrostatic interaction with other molecules.

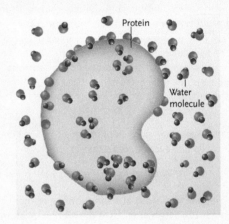

Calculating Solute Concentrations

In the cell, chemical reactions depend on solutes dissolved in aqueous solutions. To understand these reactions, you need to know the number of atoms and molecules involved. **Concentration** is the number of molecules or ions of a substance in a unit volume of space, such as 1 mL or 1 L. The number of molecules or ions in a unit volume cannot be counted directly, but it can be calculated indirectly by using the mass number of atoms as the starting point.

The mass number of an atom is equivalent to the number of protons and neutrons in its nucleus. From the mass number, and the fact that neutrons and protons have approximately the same mass (i.e., 1.66×10^{-24} g), you can calculate the mass of an atom of any substance. For an atom of the most common form of carbon, with six protons and six neutrons in its nucleus, the total mass is

$$12 \times (1.66 \times 10^{-24} \text{ g}) = 1.992 \times 10^{-23} \text{ g}$$

For an oxygen atom, with eight protons and eight neutrons in its nucleus, the total mass is

$$16 \times (1.66 \times 10^{-24} \text{ g}) = 2.656 \times 10^{-23} \text{ g}$$

Dividing the total mass of a sample of an element by the mass of a single atom gives the number of atoms in the sample. Suppose you have a carbon sample with a mass of 12 g—a mass in grams equal to the atom's mass number. (A mass in grams equal to the mass number is known as the atomic weight of an element.) Dividing 12 g by the mass of one carbon atom gives

$$\frac{12}{(10.992 \times 10^{-23} \text{ g})} = 6.02 \times 10^{23} \text{ atoms}$$

If you divide the atomic weight of oxygen (16 g) by the mass of one oxygen atom, you get the same result:

$$\frac{16}{(2.656 \times 10^{-23} \text{ g})} = 6.02 \times 10^{23} \text{ atoms}$$

In fact, dividing the atomic weight of any element by the mass of an atom of that element always produces the same number: 6.02×10^{23}. This number is called **Avogadro's number** after Amedeo Avogadro, the nineteenth-century Italian chemist who first discovered the relationship.

The same relationship holds for molecules. The **molecular weight** of any molecule is the mass in grams equal to the total mass number of its atoms. For NaCl, the total mass number is $23 + 35 = 58$ (a sodium atom has 11 protons and 12 neutrons, and a chlorine atom has 17 protons and 18 neutrons). The mass of an NaCl molecule is therefore

$$58 \times (1.66 \times 10^{-24} \text{ g}) = 9.628 \times 10^{-23} \text{ g}$$

Dividing the molecular weight of NaCl (58 g) by the mass of a single NaCl molecule gives

$$\frac{58}{(9.628 \times 10^{-23} \text{ g})} = 6.02 \times 10^{23} \text{ atoms}$$

When concentrations are described, the atomic weight of an element or the molecular weight of a compound—the amount that contains 6.02×10^{23} atoms or molecules—is known as a **mole** (abbreviated *mol*). The number of moles of a substance dissolved in 1 L of solution is known as the **molarity** (abbreviated *M*) of the solution. This relationship is highly useful in chemistry and biology because we know that two solutions with the same volume and molarity but composed of different substances will contain the same number of molecules of the substances.

Dissociation of Water and pH

The most critical property of water that is unrelated to its hydrogen-bond lattice is its ability to separate or dissociate. This occurs when a hydrogen atom that is involved in a hydrogen bond between two water molecules moves from one molecule to the other. The proton (H^+) is what actually leaves; the electron is left behind. This proton switch results in the formation of a hydroxide ion (OH^-) and a hydronium ion (H_3O^+).

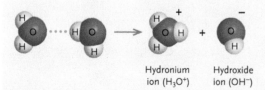

Hydronium
ion (H_3O^+)

Hydroxide
ion (OH^-)

It is convention to simply use H^+ (the hydrogen ion) to denote the hydronium ion. The proportion of water molecules that dissociate to release hydrogen and hydroxide ions is small. However, because of the dissociation, water always contains some H^+ and OH^- ions.

In pure water, the concentrations of H^+ and OH^- ions are equal. However, adding other substances may alter the relative concentrations of H^+ and OH^-, making them unequal. Some substances, called **acids,** are proton donors, which release hydrogen ions (and anions) when they are dissolved in water, effectively increasing the H^+ concentration. For example, hydrochloric acid (HCl) dissociates into H^+ and Cl^- when dissolved in water:

$$HCl \rightarrow H^+ + Cl^-$$

Other substances, called **bases,** are proton acceptors, which reduce the H^+ concentration of a solution. Most bases dissociate in water into hydroxide ions (OH^-) and cations. The hydroxide ion can act as a base by accepting a proton to produce water. For example, sodium hydroxide (NaOH) separates into Na^+ and OH^- ions when dissolved in water:

$$NaOH \rightarrow Na^+ + OH^-$$

The excess OH^- combines with H^+ to produce water,

$$OH^- + H^+ \rightarrow H_2O$$

thereby reducing the H^+ concentration. Basic solutions are also called *alkaline* solutions.

Other bases do not dissociate to produce hydroxide ions directly. For example, ammonia (NH_3), a poisonous gas, acts as a base when dissolved in water, directly accepting a proton from water, producing an ammonium ion, and releasing a hydroxide ion:

$$NH_3 + H_2O \rightarrow NH_4^+ + OH^-$$

The concentration of H^+ is measured on a numerical scale from 0 to 14, called the pH scale. Because the number of H^+ ions in solution increases exponentially as the acidity increases, the scale is based on logarithms of this number to make the values manageable:

$$pH = -\log_{10}[H^+]$$

In this formula, the brackets indicate concentration in moles per litre. The negative of the logarithm is used to give a positive number for the pH value. For example, in a water solution that is *neutral*—neither acidic nor basic—the concentration of *both* H^+ and OH^- ions is 1×10^{-7} M (0.000 000 1 M). The base 10 logarithm of 1×10^{-7} is -7. The negative of the logarithm -7 is 7. Acidic solutions have pH values less than 7, while basic solutions have pH values greater than 7. Each whole number on the pH scale represents a value 10 times or one-tenth the next number.

Hydrochloric acid (HCl)	Lemon juice, cola drinks, some acid rain		Black coffee		Urine (5.0–7.0)	$[H^+] = [OH^-]$	Pure water	Egg white (8.0)	Phosphate detergents, bleach, antacids		Household ammonia (10.5–11.9)		Oven cleaner	
			Tomatoes	Bread										
0	**1**	**2**	**3**	**4**	**5**	**6**	**7**	**8**	**9**	**10**	**11**	**12**	**13**	**14**
	Gastric fluid (1.0–3.0)	Vinegar, wine, beer, oranges	Bananas		Typical rainwater	Milk (6.6)	Blood (7.3–7.5)	Seawater (7.8–8.3)		Soapy solutions		Hair remover		Sodium hydroxide (NaOH)

pH

Buffers Keep pH within Limits

Acidity is important to cells because even small changes, on the order of 0.1 or even 0.01 pH unit, can drastically affect biological reactions. In large part, a small change in pH can cause structural changes in proteins that can damage or destroy the proteins' function. Consequently, all living organisms have elaborate systems that control their internal acidity by regulating H^+ concentration near the neutral value of pH 7.

Living organisms control the internal pH of their cells with *buffers*—substances that compensate for pH changes by absorbing or releasing hydrogen ions. When hydrogen ions are released in excess by biological reactions, buffers combine with them and remove them from the solution; if the concentration of hydrogen ions decreases, buffers release H^+ to restore the balance. Most buffers are weak acids, weak bases, or combinations of these substances that dissociate reversibly in water solutions to release or absorb H^+ or OH^-. (Weak acids, such as acetic acid, or weak

bases, such as ammonia, release relatively few H^+ or OH^- ions in an aqueous solution, whereas strong acids or bases dissociate extensively. HCl is a strong acid; NaOH is a strong base.)

The buffering mechanism that maintains blood pH near neutral values is a good example. In humans and many other animals, blood pH is buffered by a chemical system based on carbonic acid (H_2CO_3), a weak acid. In water solutions, carbonic acid dissociates readily into bicarbonate ions (HCO_3^-) and H^+:

$$H_2CO_3 \rightarrow HCO_3^- + H^+$$

The reaction is reversible. If hydrogen ions are present in excess, the reaction is pushed to the left—the excess H^+ ions combine with bicarbonate ions to form H_2CO_3. If the H^+ concentration declines below normal levels, the reaction is pushed to the right—H_2CO_3 dissociates into HCO_3^- and H^+, restoring the H^+ concentration. The back-and-forth adjustments of the buffer system help keep human blood close to its normal pH of 7.4.

Carbon Compounds

Carbon Bonding

Compounds that contain carbon form the structures of living organisms and take part in all biological reactions as well as serving as energy sources. Collectively, molecules based on carbon are known as organic molecules. All other substances, that is, those without carbon atoms in their structures, are **inorganic molecules.** A few of the smallest carbon-containing molecules that occur in the environment as minerals or atmospheric gases, such as $CaCO_3$ and CO_2, are also considered inorganic molecules.

Carbon's central role in life's molecules arises from its bonding properties: it can assemble into an astounding variety of chain and ring structures that form the backbones of all biological molecules. This is because carbon has four unpaired outer electrons that it readily shares to complete its outer most energy level, forming four covalent bonds. With different combinations of single, double, and even triple bonds, an almost limitless array of molecules is possible. Carbon atoms bond covalently to each other and to other atoms, chiefly hydrogen, oxygen, nitrogen, and sulfur, in molecular structures that range in size from a few to thousands or even millions of atoms. Molecules consisting of carbon linked only to hydrogen atoms are called hydrocarbons (*hydro-* refers to hydrogen, not water). The simplest hydrocarbon, CH_4 (methane), consists of a single carbon atom bonded to four hydrogen atoms. Removing one hydrogen atom from methane leaves a methyl group, which occurs in many biological molecules:

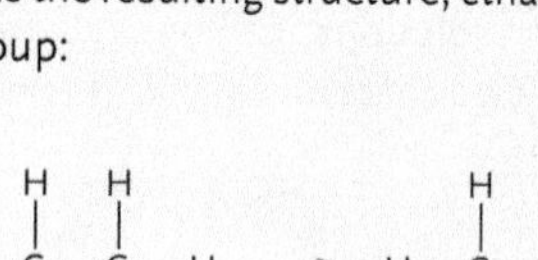

Methane   Methyl group

Now imagine bonding two methyl groups together. Removing a hydrogen atom from the maximum of four bonds, the number of hydrogen atoms in a molecule decreases as the resulting structure, ethane, produces an ethyl group:

Ethane   Ethyl group

Repeating this process builds a linear hydrocarbon chain:

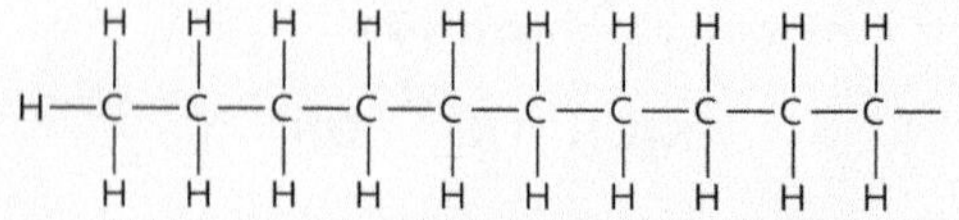

Branches can be added to produce a branched hydrocarbon chain:

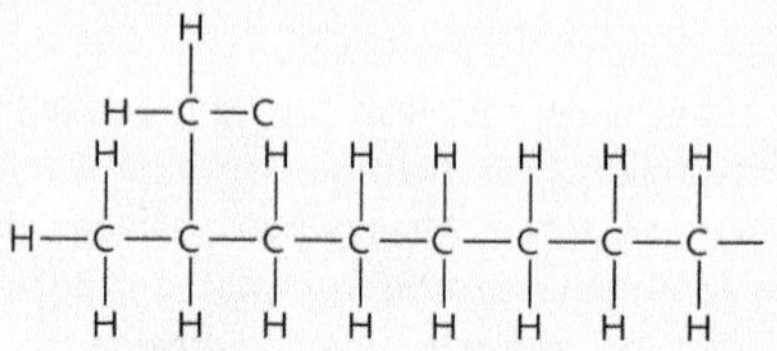

A chain can loop back on itself to form a ring. For example, cyclohexane, C_6H_{12}, has single covalent bonds between each pair of carbon atoms and two hydrogen atoms attached to each carbon atom:

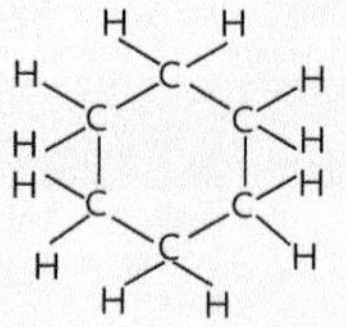

C_6H_{12}, cyclohexane

Hydrocarbons gain added complexity when neighbouring carbon atoms form double or triple bonds. Because each carbon atom can form a maximum of four bonds, the number of hydrogen atoms in a molecule decreases as the number of bonds between any two carbon atoms increases:

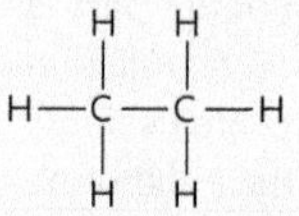

Single bonding: Double bonding: Triple bonding:
C_2H_6, ethane C_2H_4, ethene C_2H_2, ethyne
                  (ethylene)   (acetylene)

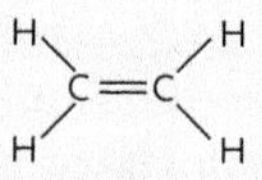

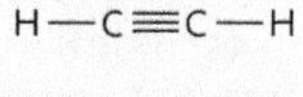

Double bonds between carbon atoms are also found in carbon rings:

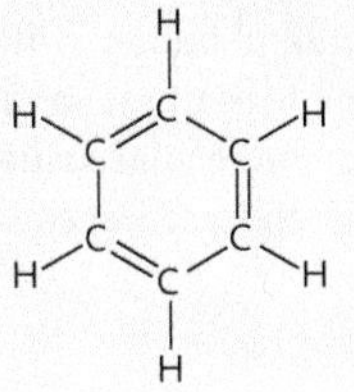

Notice how each carbon in the ring above still maintains four covalent bonds.

To simplify things, the ring structure above is often simply depicted like this:

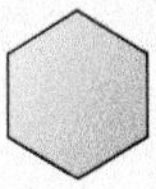

Many carbon rings can join together to produce larger molecules, as in the string of sugar molecules that makes up a polysaccharide chain:

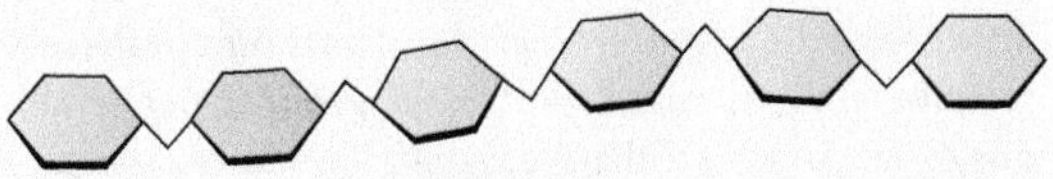

There is almost no limit to the number of different hydrocarbon structures that carbon and hydrogen can form. However, the molecules of living systems typically contain other elements in addition to carbon and hydrogen. These other elements confer functional properties on organic molecules, producing the four major classes of organic molecules: *carbohydrates, lipids, proteins,* and *nucleic acids.*

Dehydration and Hydrolysis Reactions

In many of the reactions that involve functional groups, the components of a water molecule, —H and —OH, are removed from or added to the groups as they interact. When the components of a water molecule are *removed* during a reaction, usually as part of the assembly of a larger molecule from smaller subunits, the reaction is called a **dehydration synthesis reaction** or a condensation reaction. For example, this type of reaction occurs when individual sugar molecules combine to form a starch molecule. In **hydrolysis**, the reverse reaction, the components of a water molecule are *added* to functional groups as molecules are broken into smaller subunits. For example, the breakdown of a protein molecule into individual amino acids occurs by hydrolysis.

Dehydration synthesis reactions

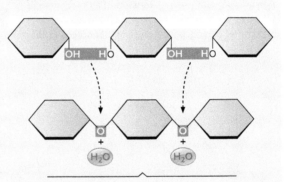

The components of a water molecule are removed as subunits join into a larger molecule.

Hydrolysis

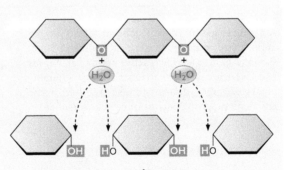

The components of a water molecule are added as molecules are split into smaller subunits.

Functional Groups

Carbohydrates, lipids, proteins, and nucleic acids are synthesized and degraded in living organisms through interactions between small, reactive groups of atoms attached to the organic molecules. The atoms in these reactive groups, called **functional groups,** occur in positions in which their covalent bonds are more readily broken or rearranged than the bonds in other parts of the molecules.

The functional groups that enter most frequently into biological reactions are the *hydroxyl, carbonyl, carboxyl, amino, phosphate,* and *sulfhydryl* groups. The unconnected covalent bonds written to the left of each structure link these functional groups to other atoms in biological molecules, usually carbon atoms. The symbol R is used to represent a chain of carbon atoms.

Common Functional Groups of Organic Molecules

Functional Group	Major Classes of Molecules	Example
Hydroxyl R—OH	Alcohols	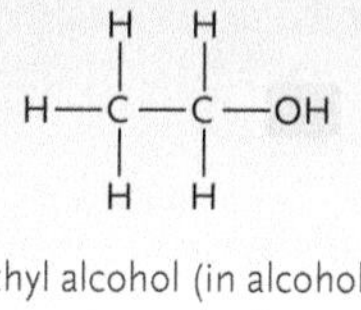 Ethyl alcohol (in alcoholic beverages)

A hydroxyl group (—OH) consists of an oxygen atom linked to a hydrogen atom. Hydroxyl groups are polar and confer polarity on the parts of the molecules that

contain them. The presence of the hydroxyl group enables an alcohol to form linkages to other organic molecules through dehydration synthesis reactions.

Carbonyl 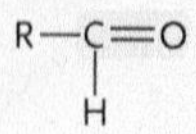
 	
R—C=O
    |
    H
	Aldehydes	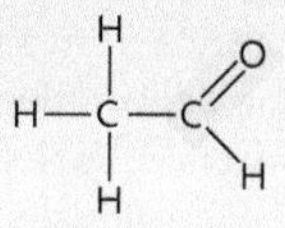
		Acetaldehyde

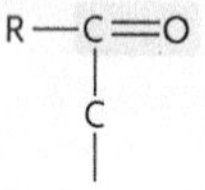 R—C=O
    |
    C
	Ketones	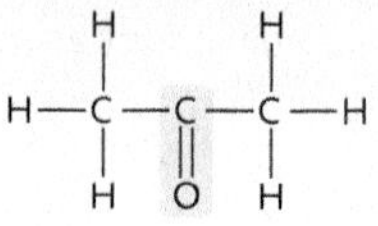
		Acetone (a solvent)

A carbonyl group (C=O) consists of an oxygen atom linked to a carbon atom by a double bond. Carbonyl groups are the reactive parts of aldehydes and ketones, molecules that act as major building blocks of carbohydrates and also take part in the reactions supplying energy for cellular activities. In

an aldehyde, the carbonyl group is linked—along with a hydrogen atom—to a carbon atom at the end of a carbon chain, along with a hydrogen atom, as in acetaldehyde. In a ketone, the carbonyl group is linked to a carbon atom in the interior of a carbon chain, as in acetone.

Carboxyl R—COOH or 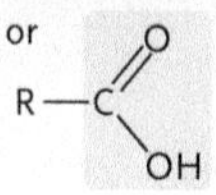 R—C=O (with OH)	Organic acids	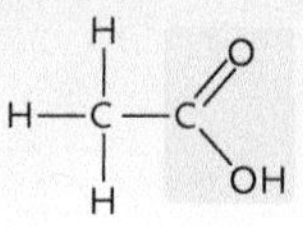 Acetic acid (in vinegar)

A carboxyl group (—COOH) is formed by the combination of a carbonyl group and a hydroxyl group. The carboxyl group is the characteristic functional group of organic acids (also called carboxylic acids). The carboxyl group gives organic molecules acidic properties because its —OH group readily releases the hydrogen as a proton (H^+) in solution.

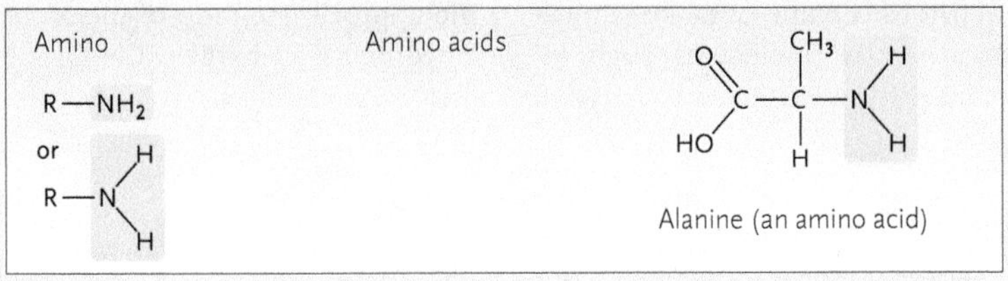

Amino — Amino acids

$R—NH_2$

or

Alanine (an amino acid)

The amino group (—NH_2) consists of a nitrogen atom bonded on one side to two hydrogen atoms; in a molecule it is linked to an R group on the other side, as in the amino acid alanine and all other amino acids.

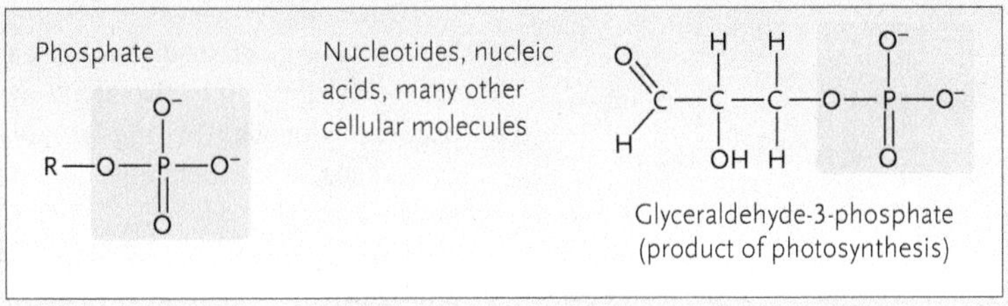

Phosphate — Nucleotides, nucleic acids, many other cellular molecules

Glyceraldehyde-3-phosphate (product of photosynthesis)

The phosphate group (—OPO_3^{2-}) consists of a central phosphorus atom bonded to four oxygen atoms, as shown at left. Among the large biological molecules linked by phosphate groups is the nucleic acid DNA. Phosphate groups are added to or removed from biological molecules as part of reactions that conserve or release energy. In addition, they control biological activity—the activity of many proteins is turned on or off by the addition or removal of phosphate groups.

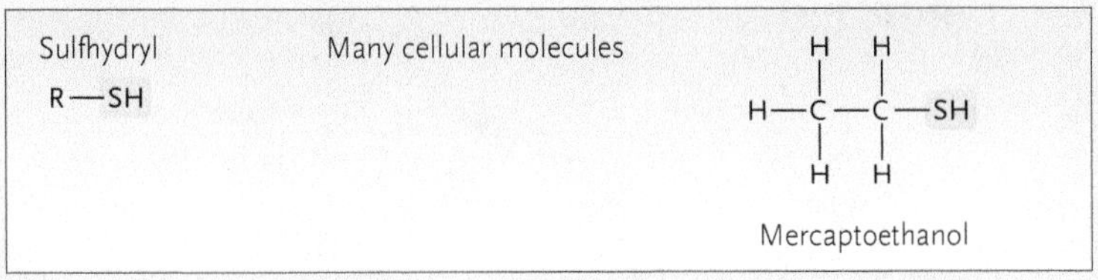

Sulfhydryl — Many cellular molecules

$R—SH$

Mercaptoethanol

In the sulfhydryl group (—SH), a sulfur atom is linked on one side to a hydrogen atom; in a molecule, the other side is linked to an R group. The sulfhydryl group is easily converted into a covalent linkage in which it loses its hydrogen atom as it binds. In many of these linking reactions, two sulfhydryl groups interact to form a disulfide linkage (—S—S—). In proteins, the disulfide bond contributes to tertiary structure.

Carbohydrates

Carbohydrates, the most abundant biological molecules, serve many functions. Together with fats, they act as the major fuel substances providing chemical energy for cellular activities. Chains of carbohydrate subunits also form structural molecules such as cellulose, one of the primary constituents of plant cell walls. Carbohydrates get their name because they contain carbon, hydrogen, and oxygen atoms, with the approximate ratio of the atoms being 1 carbon : 2 hydrogens : 1 oxygen (CH_2O).

Monosaccharides

Carbohydrates occur either as monosaccharides or as chains of monosaccharide units linked together. Monosaccharides are soluble in water, and most have a distinctly sweet taste. Of the monosaccharides, those that contain three carbons (*trioses*), five carbons (*pentoses*), and six carbons (*hexoses*) are most common in living organisms. All monosaccharides can occur in the linear form, where each carbon atom in the chain except one has both an —H and an —OH group attached to it.

Monosaccharides with five or more carbons can fold back on themselves to assume a ring form. Folding into a ring occurs through a reaction between two functional groups in the same monosaccharide, as occurs in glucose. The ring form of most five- and six-carbon sugars is much more common in cells than the linear form.

When glucose forms into a ring, two alternative arrangements are possible (α-glucose and β-glucose) that differ in the arrangements of the —OH group bound to the carbon at position 1. These two different forms of glucose are called isomers, which are discussed below.

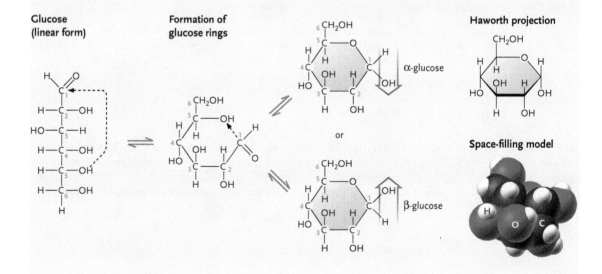

Glyceraldehyde (3 carbons; a triose)   Ribose (5 carbons; a pentose)   Mannose (6 carbons; a hexose)

Glucose (linear form)   Formation of glucose rings   α-glucose   or   β-glucose   Haworth projection   Space-filling model

Isomers of the Monosaccharides

Typically, one or more of the carbon atoms in a monosaccharide links to four different atoms or chemical groups. Carbons linked in this way are called *asymmetrical* carbons; they have important effects on the structure of a monosaccharide because they can take either of two fixed positions with respect to other carbons in a carbon chain. For example, the middle carbon of the three-carbon sugar glyceraldehyde is asymmetrical because it shares electrons in covalent bonds with four different atoms or groups: —H, —OH, —CHO, and —CH₂OH. The —H and —OH groups can take either of two positions, with the —OH extending to either the left or the right of the carbon chain relative to the —CHO and —CH₂OH groups:

CHO — H—C—OH — CH₂OH — **D-Glyceraldehyde** — CHO — HO—C—H — CH₂OH — **L-Glyceraldehyde**

Note that the two forms of glyceraldehyde have the same chemical formula, $C_3H_6O_3$. The difference between the two forms is similar to the difference between your two hands. Although both hands have four fingers and a thumb, they are not identical; rather, they are mirror images of each other. That is, when you hold your right hand in front of a mirror, the reflection looks like your left hand, and vice versa.

Two or more molecules with the same chemical formula but different molecular structures are called isomers. Isomers that are mirror images of each other, like the two forms of glyceraldehyde, are called enantiomers, or optical isomers. One of the enantiomers—the one in which the hydroxyl group extends to the left in the view just shown—is called the l-form (*laevus* = left). The other enantiomer, in which the —OH extends to the right, is called the d-form (*dexter* = right). The difference between l- and d-enantiomers is critical to biological function. Typically, one of the two forms enters much more readily into cellular reactions; just as your left hand does not fit readily into a right-hand glove, enzymes (proteins that accelerate chemical reactions in living organisms) fit best to one of the two forms of an enantiomer. For example, most of the enzymes that catalyze the biochemical reactions of monosaccharides react more rapidly with the d-form, making this form much more common among cellular carbohydrates than the l-form. Many other kinds of biological molecules besides carbohydrates form enantiomers; an example is the amino acids.

In the ring form of many five- or six-carbon monosaccharides, including glucose, the carbon at the 1 position of the ring is asymmetrical because its four bonds link to different groups of atoms. This asymmetry allows monosaccharides such as glucose to exist as two different enantiomers. The glucose enantiomer with an —OH group pointing below the plane of the ring is known as *alpha-glucose*, or *a-glucose*; the enantiomer with an —OH group pointing above the plane of the ring is known as *beta-glucose*, or *b-glucose*. Other five- and six-carbon monosaccharide rings have similar α- and β-configurations.

The α- and β-rings of monosaccharides can give the polysaccharides assembled from them vastly different chemical properties. For example, starches, which are assembled from α-glucose units, are biologically reactive polysaccharides easily digested by animals; cellulose, which is assembled from β-glucose units, is relatively unreactive and, for most animals, completely indigestible.

Another form of isomerism is found in monosaccharides, as well as in other molecules. Two molecules with the same chemical formula but atoms that are arranged in different ways are called structural isomers. The sugars glucose and fructose are examples of structural isomers.

Glucose
(an aldehyde)

Fructose
(a ketone)

Disaccharides

Disaccharides are typically assembled from two monosaccharides linked by a dehydration synthesis reaction. For example, the disaccharide maltose is formed by the linkage of two α-glucose molecules with oxygen as a bridge between the number 1 carbon of the first glucose unit and the number 4 carbon of the second glucose unit. Bonds of this type, which commonly link monosaccharides into chains, are known as glycosidic bonds. A glycosidic bond between a 1 carbon and a 4 carbon is written in chemical shorthand as a 1 → 4 linkage. Linkages such as 1 → 2, 1 → 3, and 1 → 6 are also common in carbohydrate chains. The linkages are designated as α or β depending on the orientation of the —OH group at the 1 carbon that forms the bond. In maltose, the —OH group is in the α position. Therefore, the link between the two glucose subunits of maltose is written as an α (1 → 4) linkage. Maltose, sucrose, and lactose are common disaccharides.

Formation of maltose

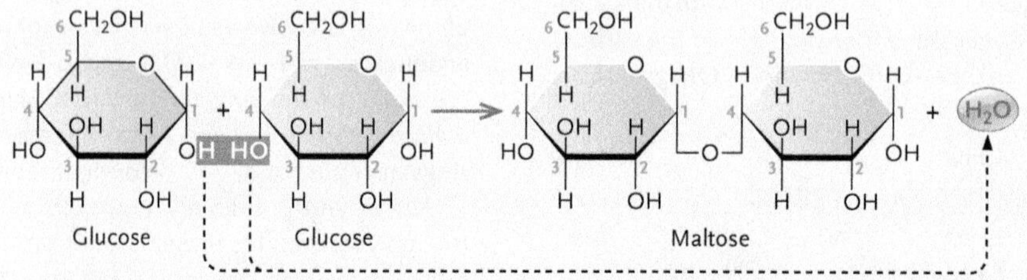

Sucrose

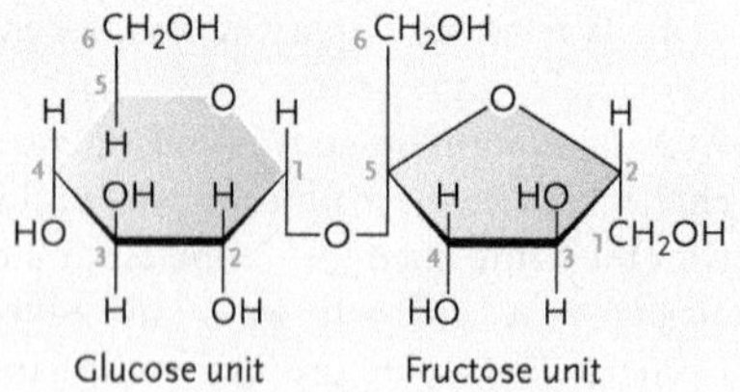

Glucose unit Fructose unit

Lactose

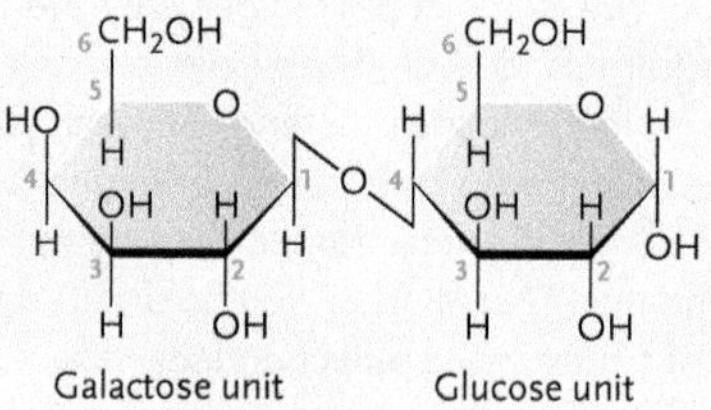

Galactose unit Glucose unit

Polysaccharides

Polysaccharides are longer chains formed by the end-to-end linking of monosaccharides through dehydration synthesis reactions. A polysaccharide is a type of macromolecule, which is a very large molecule assembled by the covalent linkage of smaller subunit molecules. The subunit for a polysaccharide is the monosaccharide.

The dehydration synthesis reactions that assemble polysaccharides from monosaccharides are examples of polymerization, in which identical or nearly identical subunits, called the monomers of the reaction, join like links in a chain to form a larger molecule called a polymer. Linkage of a relatively small number of nonidentical subunits can create highly diverse and varied biological molecules. Many kinds of polymers are found in cells, not just polysaccharides. DNA is a primary example of a highly diverse polymer assembled from various sequences of only four different types of monomers.

The most common polysaccharides—the plant starches glycogen and cellulose—are all assembled from hundreds or thousands of glucose units. Other polysaccharides are built up from a variety of different sugar units. Polysaccharides may be linear, unbranched molecules, or they may contain one or more branches in which side chains of sugar units are attached to a main chain.

Amylose, formed from α-glucose units joined end to end in α (1 → 4) linkages. The coiled structures are induced by the bond angles in the α-linkages.

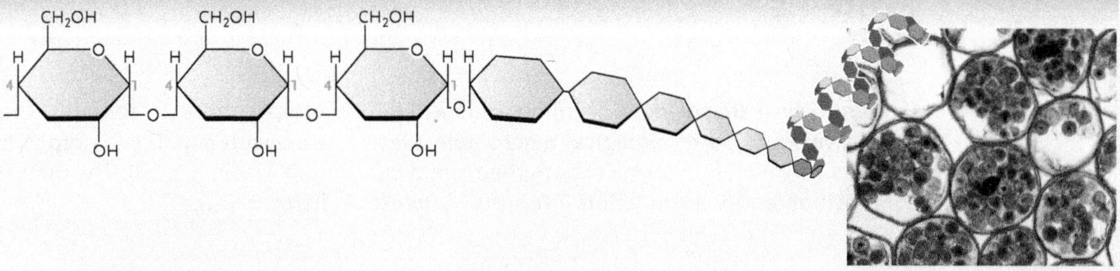

Amylose grains (purple) in plant root tissue

Ed Reschke

Glycogen, formed from glucose units joined in chains by α (1 → 4) linkages; side branches are linked to the chains by α (1 → 6) linkages (boxed in blue).

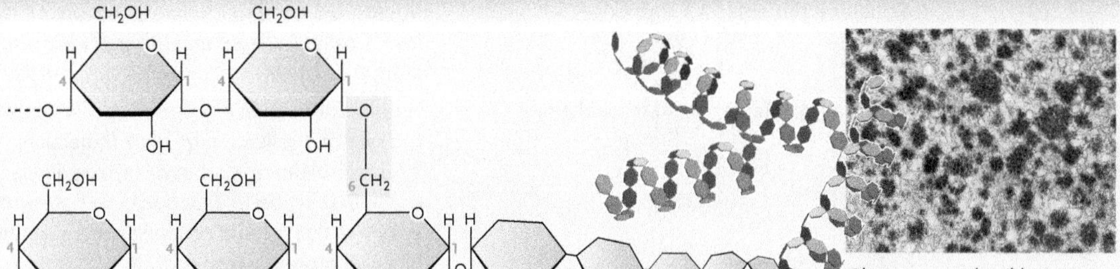

Glycogen particles (blue) in liver cell

Don W. Fawcett/Science Source. Colorization by: Mary Martin

Cellulose, formed from glucose units joined end to end by β (1 → 4) linkages. Hundreds to thousands of cellulose chains line up side by side, in an arrangement reinforced by hydrogen bonds between the chains, to form cellulose microfibrils in plant cells.

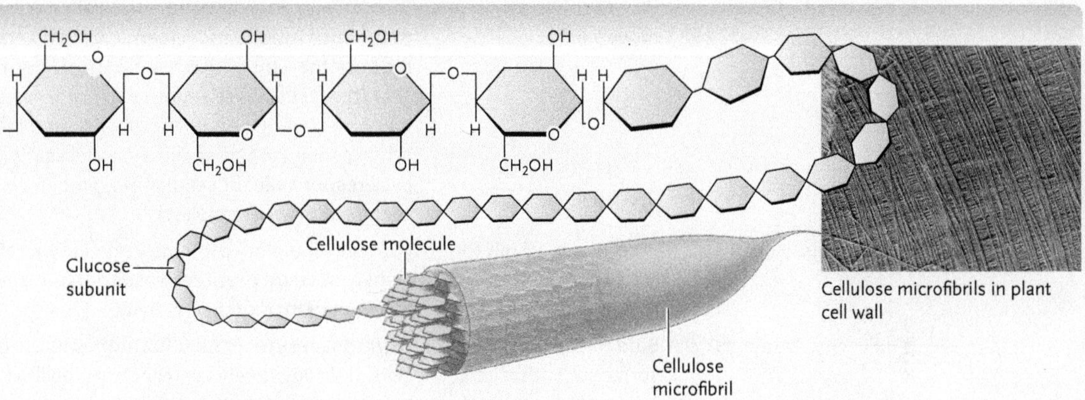

Glucose subunit

Cellulose molecule

Cellulose microfibril

Cellulose microfibrils in plant cell wall

Biophoto Associates/Science Source

Chitin, formed from β-linkages joining glucose units modified by the addition of nitrogen-containing groups. The external body armour of the tick is reinforced by chitin fibres.

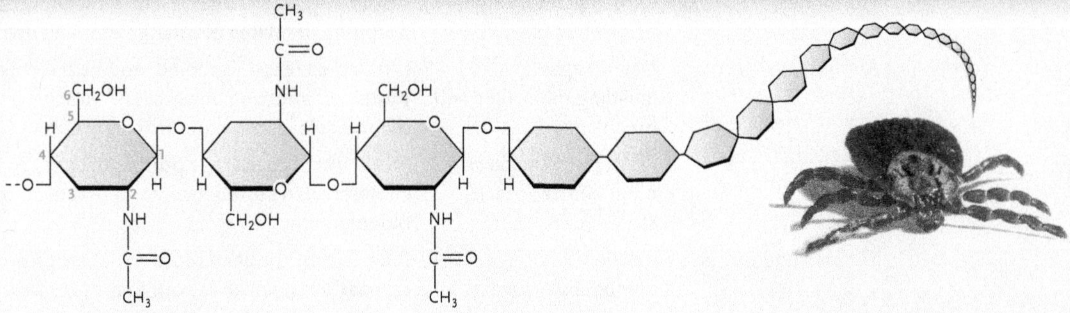

Sergey Toronto/Shutterstock.com

Proteins

Proteins, which are polymers of amino acids, are the most diverse group of biological macromolecules. Proteins vary hugely in terms of both their chemical composition and their function. Even the simplest prokaryotic cell contains thousands of proteins, each with a defined composition and specific function within the cell. The major protein functions are listed below.

Protein Type	Function	Examples
Structural proteins	Support	Microtubule and microfilament proteins form supporting fibres inside cells; collagen and other proteins surround and support animal cells; cell wall proteins support plant cells.
Enzymatic proteins	Increase the rate of biological reactions	Among thousands of examples, DNA polymerase increases the rate of duplication of DNA molecules; RuBP (ribulose 1,5-bisphosphate) carboxylase/oxygenase increases the rates of the first synthetic reactions of photosynthesis; the digestive enzymes lipases and proteases increase the rate breakdown of fats and proteins, respectively.
Membrane transport proteins	Speed up movement of substances across biological membranes	Ion transporters move ions such as Na^+, K^+, and Ca^{2+} across membranes; glucose transporters move glucose into cells; aquaporins allow water molecules to move across membranes.
Motile proteins	Produce cellular movements	Myosin acts on microfilaments (called thin filaments in muscle) to produce muscle movements; dynein acts on microtubules to produce the whipping movements of sperm tails, flagella, and cilia (the last two are whiplike appendages on the surfaces of many eukaryotic cells); kinesin acts on microtubules of the cytoskeleton (the three-dimensional scaffolding of eukaryotic cells responsible for cellular movement, cell division, and the organization of organelles).
Regulatory proteins	Promote or inhibit the activity of other cellular molecules	Nuclear regulatory proteins turn genes on or off to control the activity of DNA; protein kinases add phosphate groups to other proteins to modify their activity.
Receptor proteins	Bind molecules at cell surface or within cell; some trigger internal cellular responses	Hormone receptors bind hormones at the cell surface or within cells and trigger cellular responses; cellular adhesion molecules help hold cells together by binding molecules on other cells; LDL receptors bind cholesterol-containing particles to cell surfaces.
Hormones	Carry regulatory signals between cells	Insulin regulates sugar levels in the bloodstream; growth hormone regulates cellular growth and division.
Antibodies	Defend against invading molecules and organisms	Antibodies recognize, bind, and help eliminate essentially any protein of infecting bacteria and viruses, and many other types of molecules, both natural and artificial.
Storage proteins	Hold amino acids and other substances in stored form	Ovalbumin is a storage protein of eggs; apolipoproteins hold cholesterol in stored form for transport through the bloodstream.
Venoms and toxins	Interfere with competing organisms	Ricin is a castor bean protein that stops protein synthesis; bungarotoxin is a snake venom that causes muscle paralysis.

Amino Acids

All proteins are polymers of amino acids. The generalized structure of an amino acid has a central carbon atom attached to an amino group (—NH$_2$), a carboxyl group (—COOH), and a hydrogen atom:

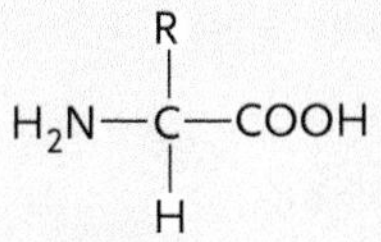

$$H_2N—\overset{\overset{\displaystyle R}{|}}{\underset{\underset{\displaystyle H}{|}}{C}}—COOH$$

The remaining bond of the central carbon is to 1 of 20 different side groups represented by the R. The R group, also called the side chain, ranges from a single hydrogen atom in the amino acid glycine to complex carbon chains or rings in some others. Differences in the side groups give the amino acids their individual properties. When discussing protein structure, amino acids are commonly referred to as amino acid residues or simply residues.

Proteins are synthesized from 20 different amino acids. These 20 are most commonly grouped according to the properties of their side chains. Here, the amino acids are shown in the ionic form common at the pH typical of a cell, 7.2.

Nonpolar amino acids

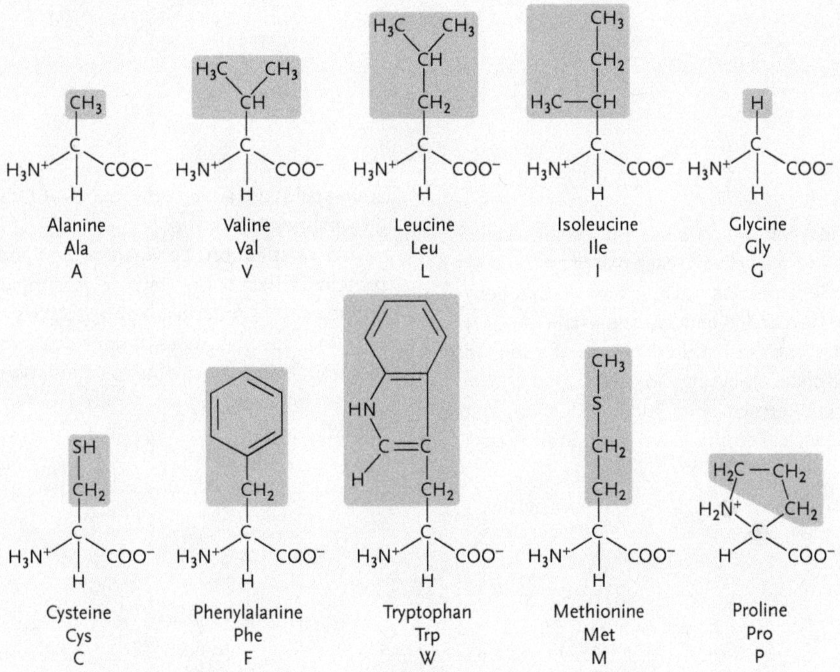

Alanine
Ala
A

Valine
Val
V

Leucine
Leu
L

Isoleucine
Ile
I

Glycine
Gly
G

Cysteine
Cys
C

Phenylalanine
Phe
F

Tryptophan
Trp
W

Methionine
Met
M

Proline
Pro
P

Uncharged polar amino acids

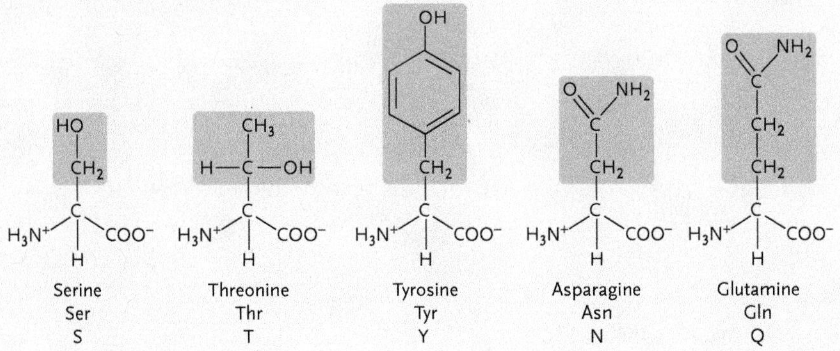

Serine
Ser
S

Threonine
Thr
T

Tyrosine
Tyr
Y

Asparagine
Asn
N

Glutamine
Gln
Q

continued on next page

THE CHEMICAL, PHYSICAL, AND ENVIRONMENTAL FOUNDATIONS OF BIOLOGY |

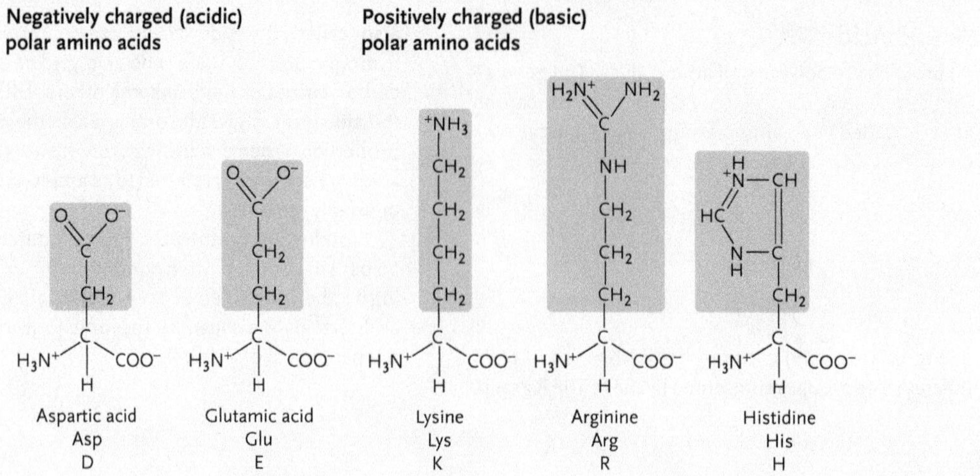

Negatively charged (acidic) polar amino acids

Positively charged (basic) polar amino acids

Aspartic acid	Glutamic acid	Lysine	Arginine	Histidine
Asp	Glu	Lys	Arg	His
D	E	K	R	H

Polypeptides

Covalent bonds link amino acids into chains called **polypeptides.** The link between each pair of amino acids in a polypeptide, a peptide bond, is formed by a dehydration synthesis reaction between the —NH_2 group of one amino acid and the —COOH group of a second. An amino acid chain always has an —NH_2 group at one end, called the N-terminal end, and a —COOH group at the other end, called the C-terminal end. In cells, amino acids are added only to the —COOH end of the growing peptide strand.

The distinction between a polypeptide and a protein is that a polypeptide is simply a string of amino acids. A protein is a polypeptide that has folded into the specific three-dimensional shape that is required for most proteins to be functional.

The following figure shows the formation of a peptide bond.

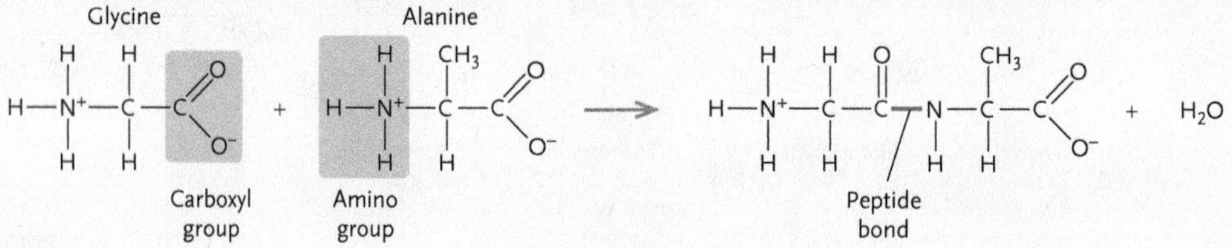

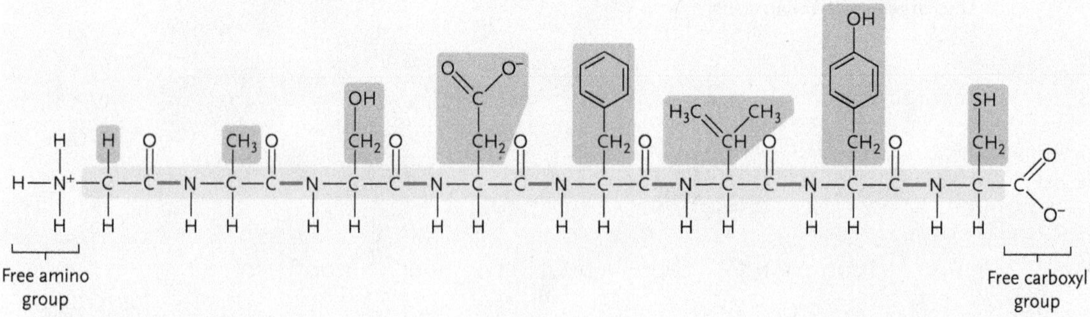

Glycine Alanine Carboxyl group Amino group Peptide bond H_2O

Free amino group Free carboxyl group

A polypeptide—a linear chain of amino acids.
The backbone of the polypeptide is highlighted in the bottom figure above. The amino end of the polypeptide is called the N-terminus, while the carboxyl end is called the C-terminus.

The Four Levels of Protein Structure

Proteins have four potential levels of structure, with each level imparting different characteristics and degrees of structural complexity to the molecule. **Primary structure** is the particular and unique sequence of amino acids forming a polypeptide; **secondary structure** is produced by the twists and turns of the amino acid chain. Tertiary structure is the folding of the amino acid chain, with its secondary structures, into the overall three-dimensional shape of a protein. All proteins have primary, secondary, and tertiary structures. Quaternary structure, when present, refers to the arrangement of polypeptide chains in a protein that is formed from more than one chain. Each structural level depends upon the level before it.

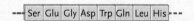
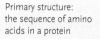

--- Ser | Glu | Gly | Asp | Trp | Gln | Leu | His ---

Primary structure: the sequence of amino acids in a protein

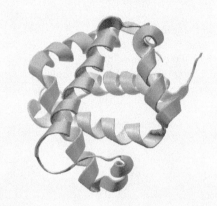

Secondary structure: regions of alpha helix, beta strand, or random coil in a polypeptide chain

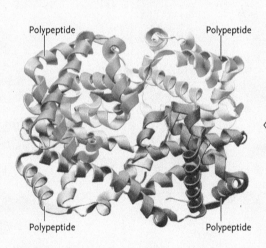

Tertiary structure: overall three-dimensional folding of a polypeptide chain

Quaternary structure: the arrangement of polypeptide chains in a protein that contains more than one chain

Polypeptide   Polypeptide

Polypeptide   Polypeptide

Primary Structure

The primary structure of a protein is simply its complete amino acid sequence. The primary sequence is determined by the nucleotide sequence of the coding region of the protein's corresponding gene.

H_3N^+ — | Phe | Val | Asn | Gln | His | Leu | Cys | Gly | Ser | His | Leu | Val | Glu | Ala | Leu | Tyr | Leu | Val | Cys | Gly | Glu | Arg | Gly | Phe | Phe | Tyr | Thr | Pro | Lys | Ala | — COO^-

Secondary Structure

The amino acid chain of a protein, rather than being stretched out in linear form, is folded into arrangements that form the protein's secondary structure. Secondary structure is based on hydrogen bonds between atoms of the backbone. More precisely, the hydrogen bonds form between the hydrogen atom attached to the nitrogen of the backbone and the oxygen attached to one of the carbon atoms of the backbone. Two highly regular secondary structures are the alpha helix and the beta sheet. A third, less regular arrangement, the random coil or loop, imparts flexibility to certain regions of the protein. Most proteins have segments of all three arrangements.

Experimental Research Figure

The α helix

A model of the α helix (left), a coil shape formed when hydrogen bonds form between every N—H group of the backbone and the C≡O group of the amino acid four residues earlier. In protein diagrams (right), the α helix is depicted as a cylinder or barrel.

The β sheet

A β sheet is formed by side-by-side alignment of β strands (picture shows two strands). The sheet is formed by hydrogen bonds between atoms of each strand. In protein diagrams, the β strands are depicted by ribbons with arrowheads pointing toward the C-terminal.

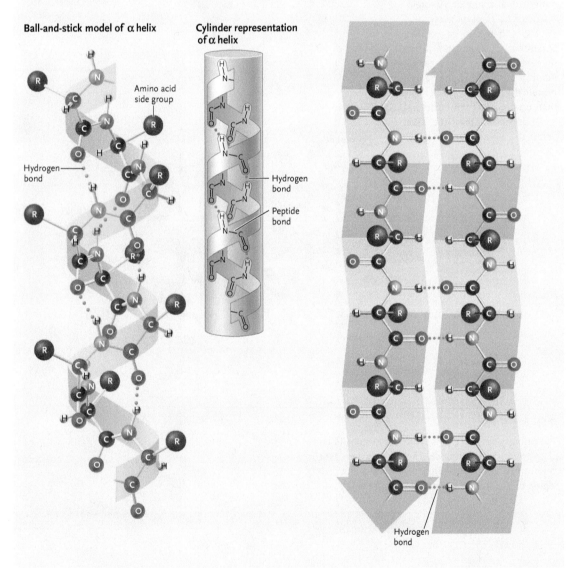

Ball-and-stick model of α helix

Cylinder representation of α helix

Amino acid side group

Hydrogen bond

Hydrogen bond

Peptide bond

Hydrogen bond

Tertiary Structure

The four major interactions between R groups that contribute to tertiary structure are shown below: (1) ionic bonds, (2) hydrogen bonds, (3) hydrophobic interactions, and (4) disulfide bridges. The tertiary structure of most proteins is flexible, allowing them to undergo limited alterations in three-dimensional shape known as conformational changes. These changes contribute to the function of many proteins, particularly enzymes, as well as other proteins involved in cellular movements or in the transport of substances across cell membranes.

Below are two representations of the three-dimensional structure of the enzyme lysozyme. In a ribbon diagram, α helices are shown as a cylinder, β strands are depicted as flat arrows, and random coils are shown as thin ropes. In a space-filling model, spheres represent different atoms. The sizes of the spheres and the intersphere distances are proportional to the actual dimensions. Atoms of different elements are represented by different colours. Disulfide bonds are shown in yellow.

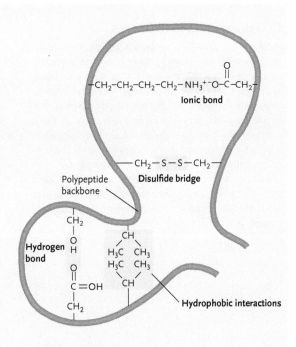

Lysozyme

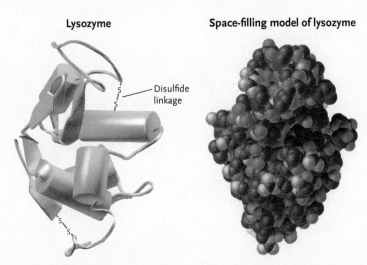

Disulfide linkage

Space-filling model of lysozyme

Quaternary Structure

Some proteins consist of two or more polypeptides that come together to form a functional protein. An example of a protein that exhibits quaternary structure is collagen. The collagen molecule consists of three helical polypeptides that aggregate to form a triple-helix structure. Collagen is a major component of the connective tissue, is found exclusively in animals, and is the most abundant protein in mammals.

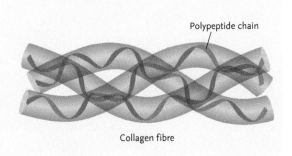

Polypeptide chain

Collagen fibre

Cofactors/Prosthetic Groups

A cofactor (also called a prosthetic group) is a nonprotein chemical compound that is bound to a protein and is required for the protein to function. Many enzymes require cofactors, which can be either organic or inorganic molecules. Many vitamins are essential to life because they act as key cofactors. A good example of a prosthetic group is the molecule heme, which is a key component of the oxygen-carrying protein hemoglobin. Each molecule of hemoglobin contains four heme molecules—one attached to each globin protein. Each heme contains a central iron atom that is responsible for binding molecules of oxygen.

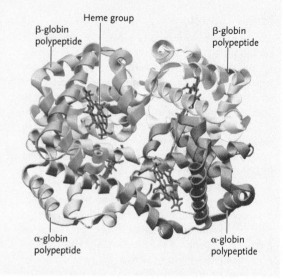

β-globin polypeptide

Heme group

β-globin polypeptide

α-globin polypeptide

α-globin polypeptide

Protein Domains

In many proteins, folding of the polypeptide(s) produces distinct, large structural subdivisions called domains. Often, one domain of a protein is connected to another by a segment of random coil. The hinge formed by the flexible random coil allows domains to move with respect to one another. That different domains of a protein are structurally distinct often reflects that they are functionally distinct as well.

Two domains in an enzyme that assembles DNA molecules

Domain a   Domain b

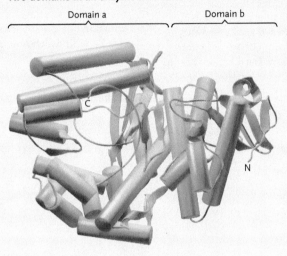

The same protein, showing the domain surfaces

Domain a   Domain b

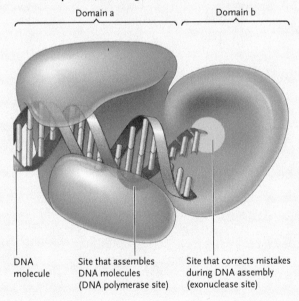

DNA molecule

Site that assembles DNA molecules (DNA polymerase site)

Site that corrects mistakes during DNA assembly (exonuclease site)

Protein Folding and Denaturation

A fundamental biochemical question is, "What determines how a protein will fold into the correct functional conformation?" The first insight came from a classic experiment published by Christian Anfinsen and Edgar Haber in 1962. The researchers studied ribonuclease, an enzyme that hydrolyzes RNA.

When they treated the enzyme chemically to break the disulfide linkages holding the protein in its functional state, the protein unfolded and had no enzyme activity. Unfolding a protein from its active conformation so that it loses its structure and function is called denaturation. This most often involves the use of specific chemicals or heat.

When they removed the denaturing chemicals, the ribonuclease slowly regained full activity because the disulfide linkages reformed, enabling the protein to reassume its functional conformation. The reversal of denaturation is called **renaturation.**

The key conclusion from this experiment was that the amino acid sequence itself specifies the tertiary structure of a protein. Nothing else is required. For this work, Christian Anfinsen received a Nobel Prize in 1972.

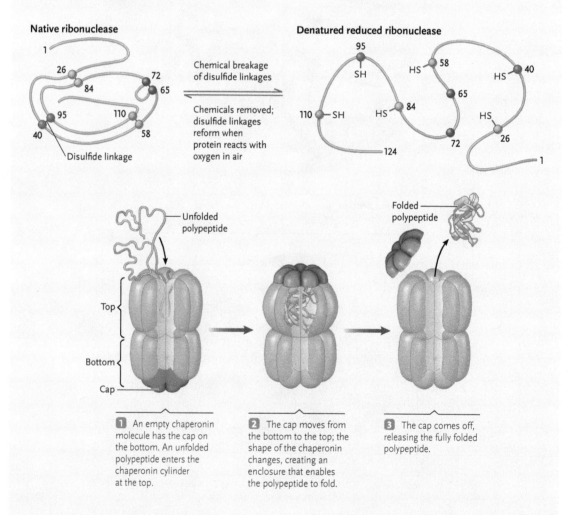

Native ribonuclease

1
26
84
72
65
95
110
40
58

Disulfide linkage

Chemical breakage of disulfide linkages

Chemicals removed; disulfide linkages reform when protein reacts with oxygen in air

Denatured reduced ribonuclease

95
SH
HS 58
HS 40
65
110 — SH
HS
84
HS
124
72
26
1

Unfolded polypeptide

Folded polypeptide

Top

Bottom

Cap

1 An empty chaperonin molecule has the cap on the bottom. An unfolded polypeptide enters the chaperonin cylinder at the top.

2 The cap moves from the bottom to the top; the shape of the chaperonin changes, creating an enclosure that enables the polypeptide to fold.

3 The cap comes off, releasing the fully folded polypeptide.

Within the cell, the high density of newly synthesized proteins may impede the proper folding of individual proteins. For many proteins, correct folding is helped by a group of proteins called **chaperone proteins** or **chaperonins** (see figure above).

They function by temporarily binding with newly synthesized proteins, directing their conformation toward the correct tertiary structure, and inhibiting incorrect arrangements as the new proteins fold.

Nucleic Acids

Two types of nucleic acids exist: DNA and RNA. Deoxyribonucleic acid (DNA) stores the hereditary information in all eukaryotes, bacteria, and archaea. In all organisms, ribonucleic acid (RNA) carries out a diversity of functions.

RNA carries the instructions for assembling proteins from DNA to the site of protein synthesis, the ribosome, which is itself composed partially of RNA. Another type of RNA serves to bring amino acids to the ribosome for their assembly into proteins.

Nucleotides

All nucleic acids are polymers of nucleotides. A **nucleotide** consists of three parts linked by covalent bonds: (1) a nitrogenous base formed from rings of carbon and nitrogen atoms; (2) a five-carbon, ring-shaped sugar; and (3) one to three phosphate groups.

In nucleotides, the nitrogenous bases link covalently to a five-carbon sugar, either **deoxyribose** or **ribose.** The carbons of the two sugars are numbered with a prime symbol—1′, 2′, 3′, 4′, and 5′. The prime symbols are added to distinguish the carbons in the sugars from those in the nitrogenous bases, which are written without primes. The two sugars differ only in the chemical group bound to the 2′ carbon: deoxyribose has an —H at this position, and ribose has an —OH group.

The two types of nitrogenous bases are pyrimidines, with one carbon–nitrogen ring, and purines, with two rings. Three pyrimidine bases—uracil (U), thymine (T), and cytosine (C)—and two purine bases—adenine (A) and guanine (G)—form parts of nucleic acids in cells.

Overall structural plan of a nucleotide

Chemical structures of nucleotides

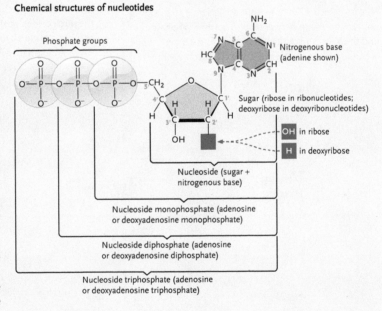

Pyrimidine and Purine Bases of Nucleic Acids

The figure shows the three single-ring pyrimidines and two double-ring purines that are the nitrogenous bases of nucleotides. The red arrows indicate where the bases link to ribose or deoxyribose sugars to form nucleotides.

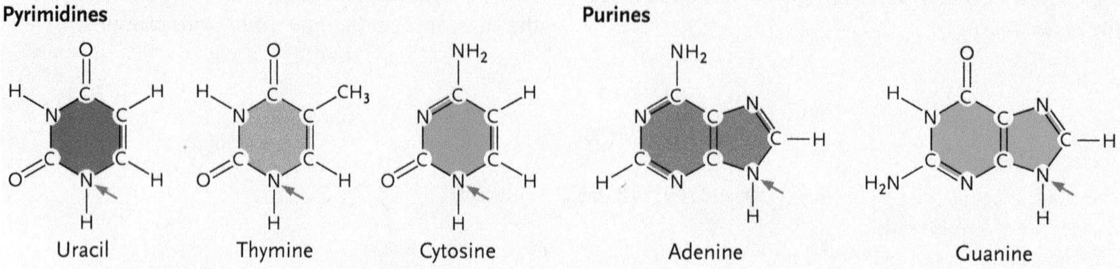

Pyrimidines

Uracil   Thymine   Cytosine

Purines

Adenine   Guanine

DNA and RNA Structure

Nucleotides in DNA and RNA are linked by a bridging phosphate group between the 5′ carbon of one sugar and the 3′ carbon of the next sugar in line. This linkage is called a phosphodiester bond. This arrangement of alternating sugar and phosphate groups forms the backbone of a nucleic acid. The nitrogenous bases of the nucleotides project from this backbone. Note that the nucleotide thymine (T) in DNA is not found in RNA; it is replaced by uracil (U).

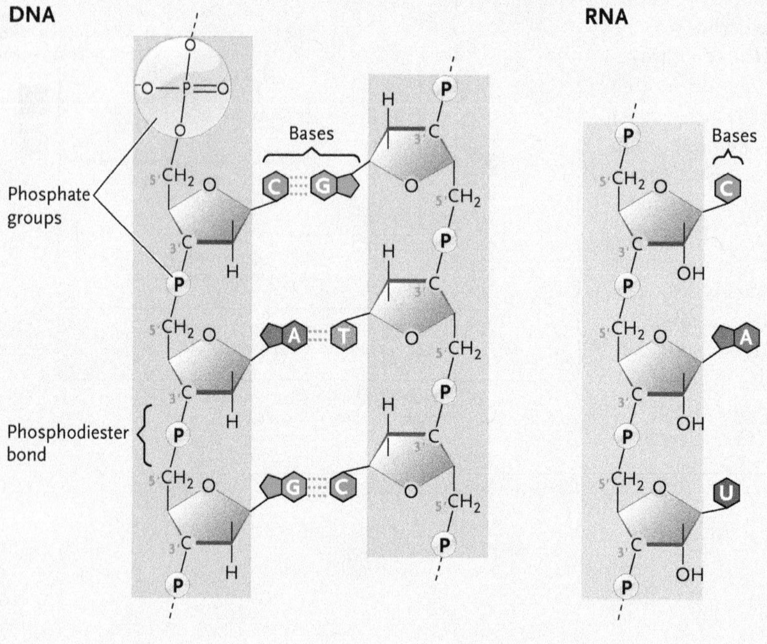

DNA

Phosphate groups

Bases

Phosphodiester bond

RNA

Bases

DNA Double Helix

In cells, DNA takes the form of a double helix: two nucleotide chains wrapped around each other in a spiral that resembles a twisted ladder. As shown below, the sides of the ladder are the sugar–phosphate backbones of the two chains, which twist around each other to form the double helix. The rungs of the ladder are the nitrogenous bases, which extend inward from the sugars toward the centre of the helix.

Each rung consists of a pair of nitrogenous bases held in a flat plane roughly perpendicular to the long axis of the helix. The two nucleotide chains of a DNA double helix are held together by hydrogen bonds between the base pairs. A DNA double-helix molecule is also referred to as double-stranded DNA. The space separating the sugar–phosphate backbones of a DNA double helix is just wide enough to accommodate a base pair that consists of one purine and one pyrimidine. Purine–purine base pairs are too wide and pyrimidine–pyrimidine pairs are too narrow to fit this space exactly. More specifically, of the possible purine–pyrimidine pairs, only two combinations, adenine with thymine and guanine with cytosine, can form stable hydrogen bonds so that the base pair fits precisely within the double helix. An adenine–thymine (A—T) pair forms two stabilizing hydrogen bonds; a guanine–cytosine (G—C) pair forms three.

DNA double helix, showing arrangement of sugars, phosphate groups, and bases

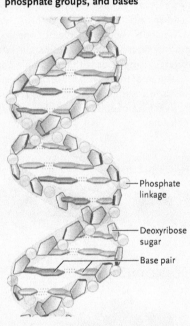

Phosphate linkage
Deoxyribose sugar
Base pair

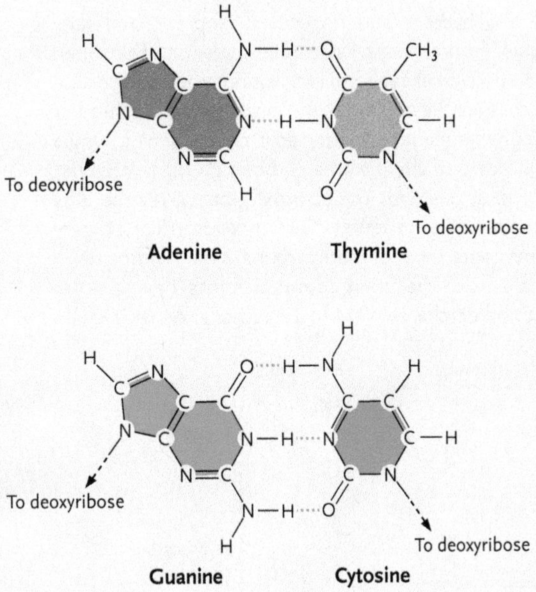

To deoxyribose
To deoxyribose
Adenine
Thymine
To deoxyribose
To deoxyribose
Guanine
Cytosine

Lipids

Lipids are a diverse group of water-insoluble, primarily nonpolar biological molecules composed mostly of hydrogen and carbon (hydrocarbons). The term *lipid* is a catch-all word for a range of nonpolar molecules. They are not large enough to be considered true macromolecules and, unlike nucleic acids and proteins, are not considered polymers of defined monomeric subunits. As a result of their nonpolar character, lipids typically dissolve much more readily in nonpolar solvents, such as acetone and chloroform, than in water. Their insolubility in water underlies their ability to form cell membranes. In addition, some lipids are stored and used in cells as an energy source. Other lipids serve as hormones that regulate cellular activities. Lipids in living organisms can be grouped into one of three categories—fats, phospholipids, and steroids.

Isoprenes and Fatty Acids

The structural backbone of all lipids is derived from one of two hydrocarbon molecules: isoprene and fatty acids. Isoprenes are five-carbon molecules that when linked together can form long hydrocarbon chains. Isoprenes are the structural unit in steroids and a number of phospholipids. A fatty acid consists of a single hydrocarbon chain with a carboxyl group (—COOH) linked at one end. The carboxyl group gives the fatty acid its acidic properties. The fatty acids in living organisms contain four or more carbons in their hydrocarbon chain, with the most common forms having even-numbered chains of 14 to 22 carbons. As their chain length increases, fatty acids become progressively less water soluble and more solid.

If the hydrocarbon chain of a fatty acid binds the maximum possible number of hydrogen atoms, so that only single bonds link the carbon atoms, the fatty acid is said to be saturated with hydrogen atoms. If one or more double bonds link the carbons, reducing the number of bound hydrogen atoms, the fatty acid is unsaturated. Fatty acids with one double bond are monounsaturated; those with more than one double bond are polyunsaturated. Unlike saturated fatty acids, the presence of double bonds imparts a "kink" in the molecule.

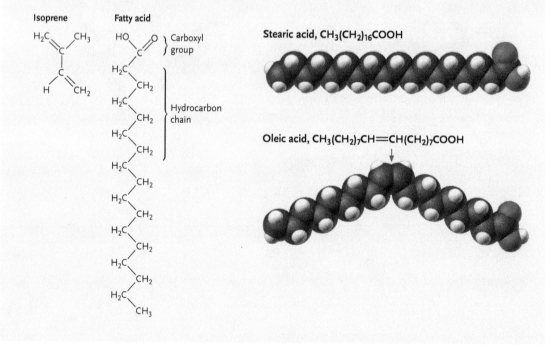

Stearic acid, $CH_3(CH_2)_{16}COOH$

Oleic acid, $CH_3(CH_2)_7CH{=}CH(CH_2)_7COOH$

Phospholipids

Phosphate-containing lipids, or phospholipids, are the primary lipids of cell membranes. In the most common phospholipids, glycerol forms the backbone for the molecule as in triglycerides, but only two of its binding sites are linked to fatty acids. The third site is linked to a polar phosphate group, which also binds to another polar unit. Thus, a phospholipid contains two hydrophobic fatty acids at one end, attached to a hydrophilic polar group, often called the head group. Molecules that contain both hydrophobic and hydrophilic regions are called amphipathic molecules.

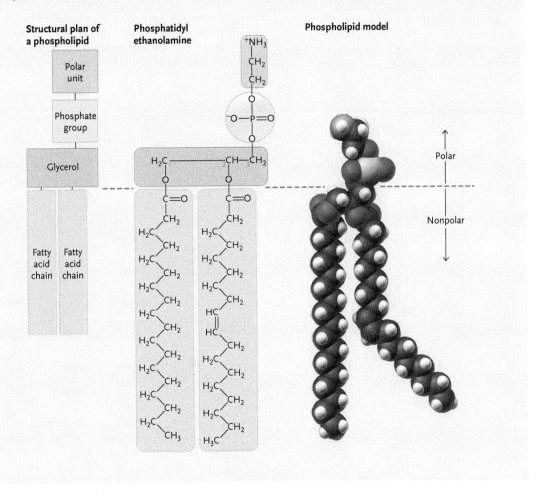

Fats

A fat consists of three fatty acid chains linked to a single molecule of glycerol. Because of this, fats are also often referred to as triacylglycerols or triglycerides. The three fatty acids linked to the glycerol may be different or the same. Different organisms usually have distinctive combinations of fatty acids in their triglycerides. As with individual fatty acids, triglycerides generally become less fluid as the length of their fatty acid chains increases; those with shorter chains remain liquid as oils at biological temperatures, and those with longer chains solidify.

Triglycerides are used widely as stored energy in animals. Gram for gram, they yield more than twice as much energy as carbohydrates. Therefore, fats are an excellent source of energy in the diet. Storing the equivalent amount of energy as carbohydrates rather than fats would add more than 45 kg to the mass of an average man or woman. A layer of fatty tissue just under the skin also serves as an insulating blanket in humans, other mammals, and birds. Triglycerides secreted from special glands in waterfowl and other birds help make feathers water repellent.

Formation of a triglyceride

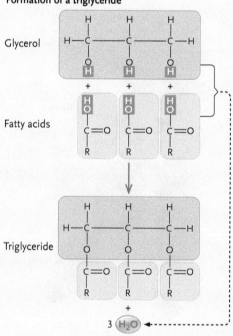

Glyceryl palmitate

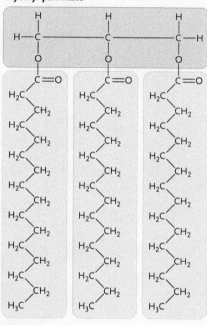

Triglyceride model

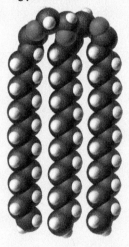

Steroids

Steroids are a group of lipids with structures based on a framework of four carbon rings that are derived from isoprene units. Small differences in the side groups attached to the rings distinguish one steroid from another. The most abundant steroids, the sterols, have a single polar —OH group linked to one end of the ring framework and a complex, nonpolar hydrocarbon chain at the other end. Although sterols are almost completely hydrophobic, the single hydroxyl group gives one end of the molecules a slightly polar, hydrophilic character. As a result, sterols also have dual solubility properties and, like phospholipids, tend to assume positions that satisfy these properties.

Cholesterol is an important component of the plasma membrane surrounding animal cells; similar sterols, called phytosterols, occur in plant cell membranes.

Arrangement of carbon rings in a steroid

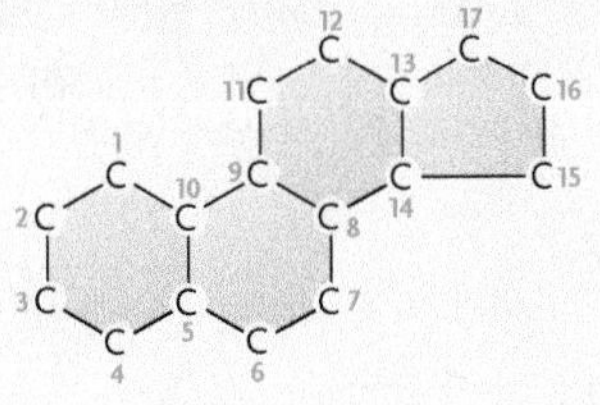

Cholesterol, a sterol

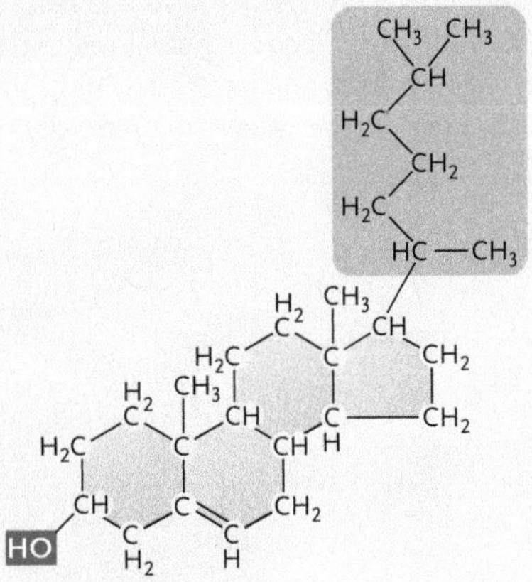

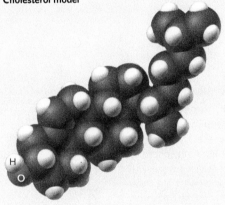

Cholesterol model

The Biosphere

The biosphere is the area occupied by life on Earth, from the depths of the ocean to the sky above. The various physical environments of Earth and their different abiotic factors, such as sunlight, temperature, humidity, wind speed, cloud cover, and rainfall, influence the evolution and diversity of organisms. These abiotic factors contribute to a region's climate, the weather conditions prevailing over an extended period of time. Climates vary on global, regional, and local scales and undergo seasonal changes almost everywhere.

Solar Radiation: Energy from the Sun

The global pattern of environmental diversity results from latitudinal variation in incoming solar radiation, Earth's rotation on its axis, and its orbit around the Sun. Earth's spherical shape causes the intensity of incoming solar radiation to vary from the equator to the poles. Solar radiation is more concentrated near the equator than it is at the poles, causing latitudinal variation in Earth's temperature.

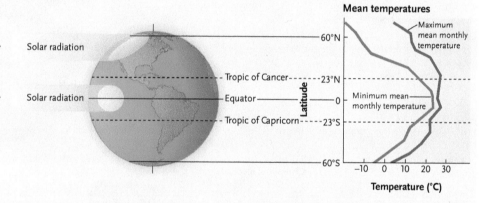

Solar radiation

Near the poles, solar radiation travels a long distance through the atmosphere and strikes a large surface area.

Near the equator, solar radiation travels a short distance through the atmosphere and strikes a small surface area.

Mean temperatures

Seasonality: Weather throughout the Year

Earth is tilted on its axis by 23.5°. This tilt produces seasonal variation in the intensity of incoming solar radiation. The northern hemisphere receives its maximum illumination, and the southern hemisphere its minimum, on the June solstice (around June 21), when the Sun shines directly over the Tropic of Cancer (23.5° N latitude). The reverse is true on the December solstice (around December 21), when the Sun shines directly over the Tropic of Capricorn (23.5° S latitude). Twice each year, on the vernal and autumnal equinoxes (around March 21 and September 21, respectively), the Sun shines directly over the equator. Only the Tropics, the latitudes between the tropics of Cancer and Capricorn, ever receive intense solar radiation from directly overhead. Moreover, the tropics experience only small seasonal changes in temperature and day length, with high temperatures and day length of approximately 12 hours throughout the year.

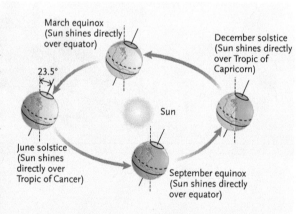

Seasonal variation in temperature and day length increases steadily toward the poles. Polar winters are long and cold, with periods of continuous darkness, and polar summers are short, with periods of continuous light.

Air Circulation: Wind Patterns

Sunlight warms air masses, causing them to expand, lose pressure, and rise in the atmosphere. The unequal heating of air at different latitudes initiates global air movements, producing three circulation cells in each hemisphere. Warm equatorial air masses rise to high altitude before spreading north and south. They eventually sink back to Earth at about 30° N and S latitude. At low altitude, some air masses flow back toward the equator, completing low-latitude circulation cells. Others flow toward the poles, rise at 60° latitude, and divide at high altitude. Some of this air flows toward the equator, completing the pair of middle-latitude circulation cells. The rest moves toward the poles, where it descends and flows toward the equator, forming the polar circulation cells.

The flow of air masses at low altitude creates winds near the planet's surface. But the planet's surface rotates beneath the atmosphere, moving rapidly near the equator, where Earth's diameter is greatest, and more slowly near the poles. Latitudinal variation in the speed of Earth's rotation deflects the movement of the rising and sinking air masses from a strictly north–south path into belts of easterly and westerly winds; this deflection is called the Coriolis effect. Winds near the equator are called the trade winds; those farther from the equator are the temperate westerlies and easterlies, named for their direction of flow.

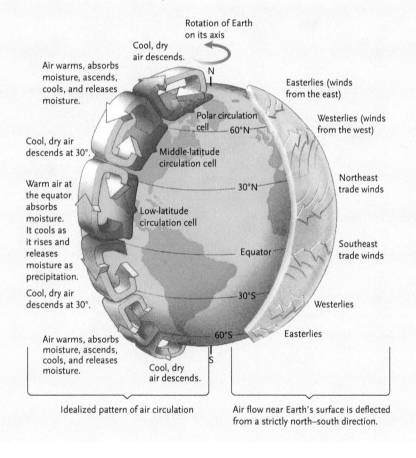

Rotation of Earth on its axis

Cool, dry air descends.

Air warms, absorbs moisture, ascends, cools, and releases moisture.

Cool, dry air descends at 30°.

Warm air at the equator absorbs moisture. It cools as it rises and releases moisture as precipitation.

Cool, dry air descends at 30°.

Air warms, absorbs moisture, ascends, cools, and releases moisture.

Cool, dry air descends.

Polar circulation cell
Middle-latitude circulation cell
Low-latitude circulation cell

60°N
30°N
Equator
30°S
60°S

Easterlies (winds from the east)
Westerlies (winds from the west)
Northeast trade winds
Southeast trade winds
Westerlies
Easterlies

Idealized pattern of air circulation

Air flow near Earth's surface is deflected from a strictly north–south direction.

Precipitation

Differences in solar radiation and global air circulation create latitudinal variations in rainfall. Warm air holds more water vapour than cool air does. As air near the equator heats up, it absorbs water, primarily from the oceans. However, the warm air masses expand as they rise, and their heat energy is distributed over a larger volume, causing their temperature to drop. A decrease in temperature without the actual loss of heat energy is called adiabatic cooling. After cooling adiabatically, the rising air masses release moisture as rain. Torrential rainfall is characteristic of warm equatorial regions, where rising, moisture-laden air masses cool as they reach high altitude.

As cool, dry air masses descend at 30° latitude, increased air pressure at low altitude compresses them, concentrating their heat energy, raising their temperature, and increasing their capacity to hold moisture. Descending air masses absorb water at these latitudes, which are typically dry. Some air masses continue moving poleward in the lower atmosphere. When they rise at 60° latitude, they cool adiabatically and release precipitation, creating moist habitats in the northern and southern temperate zones.

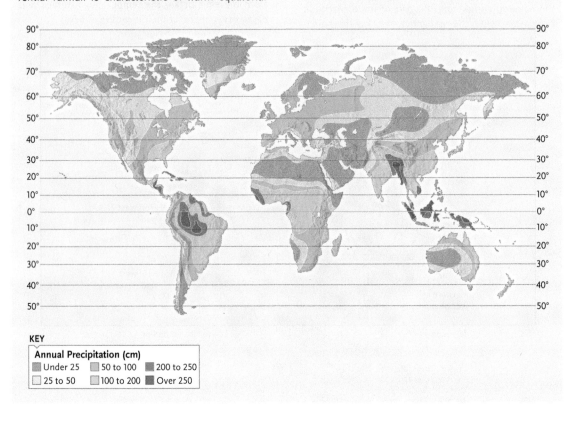

KEY

Annual Precipitation (cm)

- Under 25
- 25 to 50
- 50 to 100
- 100 to 200
- 200 to 250
- Over 250

Ocean Currents

Latitudinal variations in solar radiation also warm the oceans' surface water unevenly. Because the volume of water increases as it warms (5 decrease in density), sea level is about 8 cm higher at the equator than at the poles. The volume of water associated with this "slope" is enough to cause surface water to move in response to gravity. The trade winds and temperate westerlies also contribute to the mass flow of water at the ocean surface. Thus, surface water flows in the direction of prevailing winds, forming major currents. Earth's rotation, the positions of landmasses, and the shapes of ocean basins also influence the movements of these currents.

Oceanic circulation is generally clockwise in the northern hemisphere and counterclockwise in the southern hemisphere (see figure below). The trade winds push surface water toward the equator and westward until it contacts the eastern edge of a continent. Swift, narrow, and deep currents of warm, nutrient-poor water run toward the poles, parallel to the east coasts of continents. For example, the Gulf Stream flows northward along the east coast of North America, carrying warm water toward northwestern Europe. Cold water returns from the poles toward the equator in slow, broad, and shallow currents, such as the California Current, that parallel the west coasts of continents.

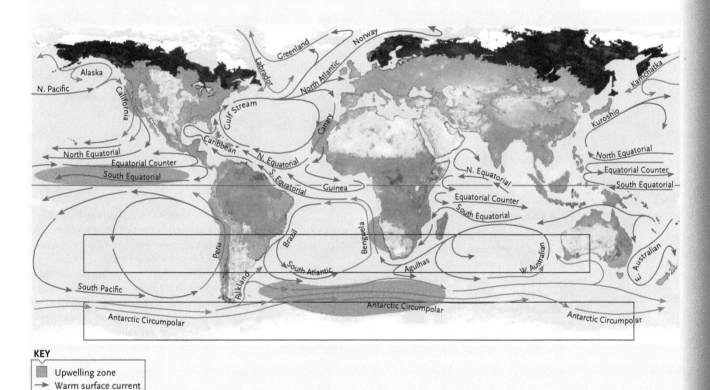

KEY
- Upwelling zone
- Warm surface current
- Cold surface current

Regional and Local Effects

Although global and seasonal patterns determine an area's climate, regional and local effects also influence abiotic conditions. Currents running along sea coasts exchange heat with air masses flowing above them, moderating the temperature over the nearby land. Breezes often blow from the sea toward the land during the day and in the opposite direction at night (see figure at right). These local effects sometimes override latitudinal variations in temperature. For example, the climate in London, England, is much milder than that in Winnipeg, even though Winnipeg is slightly farther south. London has a maritime climate, tempered by winds that cross the nearby North Atlantic Current, but Winnipeg's climate is continental, not moderated by the distant ocean.

Ocean currents also affect moisture conditions in coastal habitats. For example, the region off the southeast coast of Newfoundland known as the Grand Banks is one of the foggiest places on Earth. Here, as the warm Gulf Stream current meets the cold Labrador current, the air above the water cools and its water vapour condenses into heavy fog and rain.

Daytime: land warmer than sea

2 Cool air descends and replaces air over land through onshore flow.

1 Warm air ascends.

Nighttime: sea warmer than land

1 Warm air ascends.

2 Cool air descends and replaces air over sea through offshore flow.

The Effects of Topography

Mountains, valleys, and other topographic features are a major influence on regional climates. In the northern hemisphere, south-facing slopes are warmer and drier than north-facing slopes because they receive more solar radiation. In addition, adiabatic cooling causes air temperature to decline 3 to 6°C for every 1000 m increase in elevation. Mountains also establish regional and local rainfall patterns. For example, warm air masses pick up moisture from the Pacific Ocean and then move inland toward the Rocky Mountains. As air rises to cross the mountains, it cools adiabatically and loses moisture, releasing heavy rainfall on the windward side (see below). After the now-dry air crosses the peaks, it descends and warms, absorbing moisture and forming a rain shadow. Habitats on the leeward side of mountains, such as the eastern slopes of the Rocky Mountains in Alberta, are typically drier than those on the windward side.

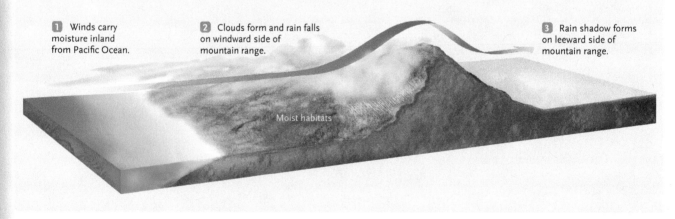

1 Winds carry moisture inland from Pacific Ocean.

2 Clouds form and rain falls on windward side of mountain range.

3 Rain shadow forms on leeward side of mountain range.

Moist habitats

Microclimate

Although climate influences the overall distributions of organisms, the abiotic conditions that immediately surround them, the microclimate, have the greatest effect on survival and reproduction. For example, a fallen log on the forest floor creates a microclimate in the underlying soil that is shadier, cooler, and moister than the surrounding soil, which is exposed to sun and wind. Many animals, including some insects, worms, salamanders, and snakes, occupy these sheltered sites and avoid the effects of prolonged exposure to the elements.

Aleksander Bolbot/Shutterstock.com

Biomes

Various climatic factors interact to create and regulate **biomes**—groups of ecosystems that share distinctive combinations of soils, vegetation, and animals. Fourteen different biomes have been defined (see below). Why is climate so important in defining biomes? Climatic factors, particularly temperature regimes and water availability, control the rate of photosynthesis by plants, which produce the organic molecules that provide the energy and carbon required by all other organisms in a biome.

In addition, climate influences the type of plants that make up the dominant vegetation of a biome through the selection pressures it creates: certain climatic regions favour certain adaptations and strategies. For example, in arid regions, the dominant plants have adaptations that store water or reduce water loss by evaporation, or that are metabolically active only in the wettest season, have an advantage over other plants. Biomes are often classified climatically (e.g., desert) or on the basis of the dominant vegetation (e.g., grassland, tropical rainforest).

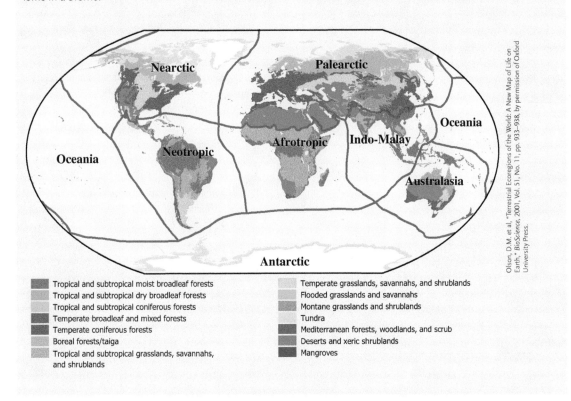

Olson, D.M. et al, "Terrestrial Ecoregions of the World: A New Map of Life on Earth," *BioScience*, 2001, Vol. 51, No. 11, pp. 933–938, by permission of Oxford University Press.

- Tropical and subtropical moist broadleaf forests
- Tropical and subtropical dry broadleaf forests
- Tropical and subtropical coniferous forests
- Temperate broadleaf and mixed forests
- Temperate coniferous forests
- Boreal forests/taiga
- Tropical and subtropical grasslands, savannahs, and shrublands
- Temperate grasslands, savannahs, and shrublands
- Flooded grasslands and savannahs
- Montane grasslands and shrublands
- Tundra
- Mediterranean forests, woodlands, and scrub
- Deserts and xeric shrublands
- Mangroves

History of Earth

Geological Time Scale and Major Evolutionary Events

The Geological Time Scale and Major Evolutionary Events

Eons (duration drawn to scale)	Eon	Era	Period	Epoch	Millions of Years Ago	Major Evolutionary Events
Phanerozoic — Cenozoic, Mesozoic, Paleozoic	Phanerozoic	Cenozoic	Quaternary	Holocene		
					0.01	
				Pleistocene		Origin of humans; major glaciations
					1.7	
				Pliocene		Origin of apelike human ancestors
					5.2	
			Tertiary	Miocene		Angiosperms and mammals further diversify and dominate terrestrial habitats
					23	
				Oligocene		Divergence of primates; origin of apes
					33.4	
				Eocene		Angiosperms and insects diversify; modern orders of mammals differentiate
					55	
				Paleocene		Grasslands and deciduous woodlands spread; modern birds and mammals diversify; continents approach current positions
Proterozoic		Mesozoic			65	
			Cretaceous			Many lineages diversify: angiosperms, insects, marine invertebrates, fishes, dinosaurs; asteroid impact causes mass extinction at end of period, eliminating dinosaurs and many other groups
					144	
			Jurassic			Gymnosperms abundant in terrestrial habitats; first angiosperms; modern fishes diversify; dinosaurs diversify and dominate terrestrial habitats; frogs, salamanders, lizards, and birds appear; continents continue to separate
					206	
			Triassic			Predatory fishes and reptiles dominate oceans; gymnosperms dominate terrestrial habitats; radiation of dinosaurs; origin of mammals; Pangaea starts to break up; mass extinction at end of period
					251	

Eons (duration drawn to scale)	Eon	Era	Period	Epoch	Millions of Years Ago	Major Evolutionary Events
Archaean	Phanerozoic (continued)	Paleozoic	Permian			Insects, amphibians, and reptiles abundant and diverse in swamp forests; some reptiles colonize oceans; fishes colonize freshwater habitats; continents coalesce into Pangaea, causing glaciation and decline in sea level; mass extinction at end of period eliminates 85% of species
					290	
			Carboniferous			Vascular plants form large swamp forests; first seed plants and flying insects; amphibians diversify; first reptiles appear
					354	
			Devonian			Terrestrial vascular plants diversify; fungi and invertebrates colonize land; first insects appear; first amphibians colonize land; major glaciation at end of period causes mass extinction, mostly of marine life
					417	
			Silurian			Jawless fishes diversify; first jawed fishes; first vascular plants on land
					443	
			Ordovician			Major radiations of marine invertebrates and fishes; major glaciation at end of period causes mass extinction of marine life
					490	
			Cambrian			Diverse radiation of modern animal phyla (Cambrian explosion); simple marine communities
					543	
	Proterozoic					High concentration of oxygen in atmosphere; origin of aerobic metabolism; origin of eukaryotic cells; evolution and diversification of protists, fungi, soft-bodied animals
					2500	
	Archaean					Evolution of prokaryotes, including anaerobic bacteria and photosynthetic bacteria; oxygen starts to accumulate in atmosphere
					3800	
						Formation of Earth at start of era; Earth's crust, atmosphere, and oceans form; origin of life at end of era
					4600	

Model Research Organisms

Certain species or groups of organisms have become favourite subjects for laboratory and field studies because their characteristics make them relatively easy research subjects. In most cases, such **model organisms** became popular because they have rapid development, short life cycles, and small adult size. Thus, researchers can rear and house large numbers of them in the laboratory. Also, as fuller portraits of their genetics and other aspects of their biology emerge, their appeal as research subjects tends to grow because biologists have a better understanding of the biological context within which specific processes occur. Because the fundamental elements of biochemistry, development, and evolution are common to all organisms, research on these small and often simple model organisms provides insight into biological processes that operate in and among larger and more complex organisms.

As a cautionary note, you should also be aware that the very characteristics that make model organisms valuable for research may make them poor representatives of other organisms in that group. Thus, specific findings from *Drosophila* or *Caenorhabditis elegans* may not be generally applicable to other insects or nematodes, respectively. The use of model organisms only, to the exclusion of others, may obscure the richness of biological diversity.

Escherichia coli

We probably know more about *Escherichia coli* than any other organism. For example, microbiologists have deciphered the complete DNA sequence of the genome of a standard laboratory strain of *E. coli*, including the sequence of the approximately 4400 genes in its genome. The functions of about one-third of these genes are still unidentified; however, *E. coli* got its start in laboratory research because of the ease with which it can be grown in cultures. Because *E. coli* cells divide about every 20 minutes under optimal conditions, a clone of 1 billion cells can be grown in a matter of hours in only 10 mL of culture medium. The same amount of medium can accommodate as many as 10 billion cells before the growth rate begins to slow. *E. coli* strains can be grown in the laboratory with minimal equipment, requiring little more than culture vessels in an incubator held at 37°C.

The study of naturally occurring plasmids in *E. coli* and of enzymes that cut DNA at specific sequences eventually resulted in the development of recombinant DNA techniques—procedures to combine DNA from different sources. Today, *E. coli* is used extensively for creating such molecules and for amplifying (cloning) them once they are made. In essence, the biotechnology industry has its foundation in molecular genetics studies of *E. coli*.

Large-scale *E. coli* cultures are widely used as "factories" for the production of desired proteins. For example, the human insulin hormone, required for treatment of certain forms of diabetes, can be produced by *E. coli* factories.

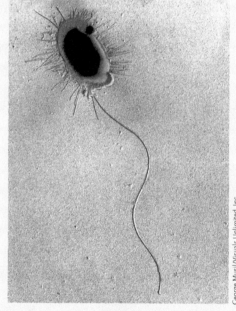

George Musil/Visuals Unlimited, Inc.

Saccharomyces cerevisiae

Commonly known as baker's yeast or brewer's yeast, *Saccharomyces cerevisiae* was probably the first microorganism to have been domesticated by humans—a beer-brewing vessel is basically a *Saccharomyces* culture. Favourite strains of baker's and brewer's yeasts have been kept in continuous cultures for centuries. The yeast has also been widely used in scientific research; its microscopic size and relatively short generation time make it easy and inexpensive to culture in large numbers in the laboratory.

The complete DNA sequence of *S. cerevisiae*, which includes more than 12 million base pairs that encode about 6000 genes, was the first eukaryotic genome to be determined. Plasmids, extrachromosomal segments of DNA, have been produced that are used to introduce genes into yeast cells. Using plasmids, researchers can experimentally alter any of the yeast genes to test their functions and can introduce genes or DNA samples from other organisms for testing or cloning. These genetic engineering studies have demonstrated that many mammalian genes can replace yeast genes when introduced into the fungi, confirming their close relationships, even though mammals and fungi are separated by millions of years of evolution. *S. cerevisiae* has been so important to genetic studies in eukaryotes that it is often called the eukaryotic *E. coli*. Research with another yeast, *Schizosaccharomyces pombe*, has been similarly productive, particularly in studies of genes that control the cell cycle.

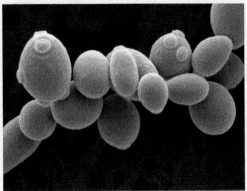

© Medical-on-Line/Alamy

Drosophila melanogaster

The pesky little fruit fly that appears seemingly from nowhere when rotting fruit or a fermented beverage is around is one of the mainstays of genetic research. It was first described in 1830 by C. F. Fallén, who named it *Drosophila*, meaning "dew lover." The species identifier became *melanogaster*, which means "black belly." The great geneticist Thomas Hunt Morgan began to culture *D. melanogaster* in 1909 in the famous "Fly Room" at Columbia University. Many important discoveries in genetics were made in the Fly Room, including sex-linked genes and sex linkage and the first chromosome map. The subsequent development of methods to induce mutations in *Drosophila* led, through studies of the mutants produced, to many other discoveries that collectively established or confirmed essentially all of the major principles and conclusions of eukaryotic genetics.

One reason for the success of *D. melanogaster* as a subject for genetics research is the ease of culturing it. It is usually grown at 25°C in small bottles stopped with a cotton or plastic foam wad and about one-third filled with a fermenting medium that contains water, cornmeal, agar, molasses, and yeast. The several hundred eggs laid by each adult female hatch rapidly and progress through larval and pupal stages to produce adult flies in about 10 days. These are ready to breed within 10 to 12 hours. Males and females can be identified easily with the unaided eye.

Many types of mutations produce morphological differences, such as changes in eye colour, wing shape, or the numbers and shapes of bristles, which can be seen with the unaided eye or under a low-power binocular microscope. The salivary gland cells of the fly larvae have giant chromosomes that are so large that differences can be observed directly with a light microscope. The availability of a wide range of mutants and comprehensive linkage maps of each of its chromosomes, and the ability to manipulate genes readily by molecular techniques, made the fruit fly genome one of the first to be sequenced. The sequencing of *Drosophila*'s genome was completed in 2001; it has approximately 14 000 genes in its 165-million-base-pair genome. (A database of the *Drosophila* genome is available at http://flybase.org.) Importantly, the relationship between fruit fly and human genes is close, to the point that many human disease genes have counterparts in the fruit fly genome. This similarity enables the fly genes to be studied as models of human disease genes to better understand the functions of those genes and how alterations in them can lead to disease.

The analysis of fruit fly embryonic development has also contributed significantly to the understanding of development in humans. For example, experiments on mutants that affect fly development have provided insight into the genetic basis of many human birth defects. Before making a career as an environmentalist, David Suzuki studied temperature-sensitive neurological mutants at the University of British Columbia.

Roblan/Shutterstock.com

Caenorhabditis elegans

Researchers studying the tiny, free-living nematode *C. elegans* have made many advances in molecular genetics, animal development, and neurobiology. It is so popular as a model research organism that most workers simply refer to it as "the worm." Several attributes make *C. elegans* a model research organism. The adult is about 1 mm long and thrives on cultures of *E. coli* or other bacteria; thus, thousands can be raised in a culture dish. It completes its life cycle from egg to reproductive adult within three days at room temperature. Furthermore, stock cultures can be kept alive indefinitely by freezing them in liquid nitrogen or in an ultracold freezer (−80°C). Researchers can therefore store new mutants for later research without having to clean, feed, and maintain active cultures. Best of all, the worm is anatomically simple; an adult contains just 959 cells (excluding the gonads). Having a fixed cell number is relatively uncommon among animals, and developmental biologists have made good use of this trait. The eggs, juveniles, and adults of the worm are completely transparent, and researchers can observe cell divisions and cell movements in living animals with straightforward microscopy techniques. There is no need to kill, fix, and stain specimens for study. And virtually every cell in the worm's body is accessible for manipulation by laser microsurgery, microinjection, and similar approaches.

The genome of *C. elegans*, which was sequenced in 1998, is also simple, consisting of 100 million base pairs organized into roughly 17 000 genes on 6 pairs of chromosomes. The genome, which is about the same size as 1 human chromosome, specifies the amino acid sequences of about 10 000 protein molecules—far fewer than are found in more complex animals.

The knowledge gained from research on *C. elegans* is highly relevant to studies of larger and more complex organisms, including vertebrates. Recent research demonstrates some striking similarities among nematodes, fruit flies, and mice in the genetic control of development; in some of the proteins that govern important events such as cell death; and in the molecular signals used for cell-to-cell communication. Using a relatively simple model such as *C. elegans*, researchers can answer research questions more quickly and more efficiently than they could if they studied larger and more complex animals.

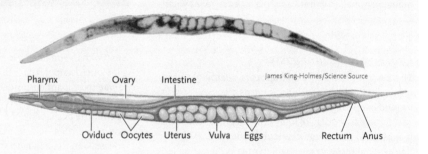

Pharynx   Ovary   Intestine   James King-Holmes/Science Source

Oviduct Oocytes Uterus Vulva Eggs   Rectum Anus

Arabidopsis thaliana

For plant geneticists, the little white-flowered thale cress, *Arabidopsis thaliana*, has attributes that make it a prime subject for genetic research. A tiny member of the mustard family, *Arabidopsis* is revealing answers to some of the biggest questions in plant development and physiology. Each plant grows only a few centimetres tall, so little laboratory space is required to house a large population. As long as *Arabidopsis* is provided with damp soil containing basic nutrients, it grows easily and rapidly in artificial light. Seeds grow to mature plants in just over a month and then flower and reproduce themselves in another three to four weeks. This permits investigators to perform desired genetic crosses and obtain large numbers of offspring with known, desired genotypes with relative ease.

The *Arabidopsis* genome was the first complete plant genome to be sequenced. Researchers have identified approximately 28 000 genes arranged on 5 pairs of chromosomes. The genome contains relatively little repetitive DNA, so it is fairly easy to isolate *Arabidopsis* genes, which can then be cloned using genetic engineering techniques. Cloned genes are inserted into bacterial plasmids, and the recombinant plasmids are transferred to the bacterial species *Agrobacterium tumefaciens*, which readily infects *Arabidopsis* cells. Amplified by the bacteria, the genes and their protein products can be sequenced or studied in other ways. Typically, researchers use chemical mutagens or recombinant bacteria to introduce changes in the *Arabidopsis* genome.

© Custom Life Science Images/Alamy

Danio rerio

The zebrafish (*Danio rerio*) is a small (3 cm) freshwater fish that gets its name from the black and white stripes running along its body. Native to India, it has spread around the world as a favourite aquarium fish. Beginning about 30 years ago, it began to be used in scientific laboratories as a model vertebrate organism for studying the roles of genes in development. Its use is now so widespread that it has been dubbed the "vertebrate fruit fly."

The zebrafish brings many advantages as a model research organism. It can be maintained easily in an ordinary aquarium on a simple diet. Although its generation time is relatively long (3 months for the zebrafish compared with 6 weeks for the mouse), a female zebrafish produces about 200 offspring at a time, compared with an average of 10 for the mouse. Embryonic development of the zebrafish takes place in eggs released to the outside by the female. The embryos develop rapidly, taking only three days from egg laying to hatching. Best of all, the eggs and embryos are transparent, providing an open window that allows researchers to observe developmental stages directly, with little or no disturbance to the embryo. Observational conditions are so favourable that the origin and fate of each cell can be traced from the fertilized egg to the hatchling. Individual nerve cells can be traced, for example, as they grow and make connections in the brain, spinal cord, and peripheral body regions. Removing or transplanting cells and tissues is also relatively easy. Biochemical and molecular studies can be carried out by techniques ranging from the simple addition of reactants to the water surrounding the embryos to injection of chemicals into individual cells.

The advantages of working with the zebrafish have spurred efforts to investigate its genetics, with particular interest in genes that regulate embryonic development. This work has already identified mutants of more than 2000 genes, including more than 400 genes that influence development. Most of the mechanisms controlled by the developmental genes resemble their counterparts in humans and other mammals. Developmental and physiological studies have revealed functions of some zebrafish genes that were previously unknown for their mammalian equivalents.

David Dohnal/Shutterstock.com

Mus musculus

The "wee, sleekit, cow'rin', tim'rous beastie," as the poet Robert Burns called the mouse (*Mus musculus*), has a much larger stature among scientists. The mouse and its cells have been used to great advantage as models for research on mammalian developmental genetics, immunology, and cancer. The availability of the mouse as a research tool enables scientists to carry out mammalian experiments that would not be practical or ethical with humans. Its small size makes the mouse relatively inexpensive and easy to maintain in the laboratory, and its short generation time, compared with most other mammals, allows genetic crosses to be carried out within a reasonable time span. Mice can be mated when they are 10 weeks old; in 18 to 22 days, the female gives birth to a litter of 5 to 10 offspring. A female may be rebred a little more than a day after giving birth.

Mice have a long and highly productive history as experimental animals. Gregor Mendel, the founder of genetics, is known to have kept mice as part of his studies. Toward the end of the nineteenth century, August Weissmann helped disprove an early evolutionary hypothesis, the inheritance of acquired characters, by cutting off the tails of mice for 22 successive generations and finding that it had no effect on tail length. The first example of a lethal allele was also found in mice, and pioneering experiments on the transplantation of tissues between individuals were conducted with mice. During the 1920s, Fred Griffith laid the groundwork for the research showing that DNA is the hereditary molecule in his work with pneumonia-causing bacteria in mice.

More recently, genetic experiments with mice have revealed more than 500 mutants that cause hereditary diseases, immunological defects, and cancer in mammals, including humans. The mouse has also been the mammal of choice for experiments that introduce and modify genes through genetic engineering. One of the most spectacular results of this research was the production of giant mice by introducing a human growth hormone gene into a line of dwarfed mice that were deficient for this hormone. Genetic engineering has also produced knockout mice (see "Knockouts: Genes and Behaviour," Chapter 47) in which a gene of interest is completely nonfunctional. The effects of this lack of function often help investigators determine the role of the normal form of the gene. Some knockout mice are defective in genes homologous to human genes that cause serious diseases, such as cystic

continued on next page

fibrosis, so researchers can study the disease in mice with the goal of developing cures or therapies.

The revelations in developmental genetics from studies with the mouse have been of great interest and importance in their own right. In 2002, the sequence of the mouse genome was reported. This sequence is enabling researchers to refine and expand their use of the mouse as a model organism for studies of mammalian biology and mammalian diseases. More and more, as we find that much of what applies to the mouse also applies to humans, the findings in mice have shed new light on human development and

opened pathways to the possible cures of human genetic diseases.

lostbear/Shutterstock.com

Anolis Lizards of the Caribbean

The lizard genus *Anolis* has been a model system for studies in ecology and evolutionary biology since the 1960s, when Ernest E. Williams of Harvard University's Museum of Comparative Zoology first began studying it. With more than 400 known species—and new ones being described all the time—*Anolis* is one of the most diverse vertebrate genera known. Most anoles are less than 10 cm long, not including the tail, and many occur at high densities, making it easy to collect a lot of data in a relatively short time. Male anoles defend territories, and their displays make them conspicuous even in dense forests.

Anolis species are widely distributed in South America and Central America, but nearly 40% occupy Caribbean islands. The number of species on an island is generally proportional to the island's size. Cuba, the largest island, has more than 50 species, whereas small islands have just one or two. Studies by Williams and others suggest that the anoles on some large islands are the products of independent adaptive radiations. Eight of the 10 *Anolis* species now found in Puerto Rico

probably evolved on that island from a common ancestor. Similarly, the seven *Anolis* species in Jamaica had a common ancestor, which was different from the ancestor of the Puerto Rican species. The anole faunas in Cuba and Hispaniola are the products of several independent radiations on each island. Williams discovered that these independent radiations had produced similar-looking species on different islands. He developed the concept of the *ecomorph,* a group of species that have similar morphological, behavioural, and ecological characteristics even though they are not closely related within the genus. Williams named the ecomorphs after the vegetation that they commonly used. For example, grass anoles are small, slender species that usually perch on low, thin vegetation. Trunk-ground anoles have chunky bodies and large heads, and they perch low on tree trunks, frequently jumping to the ground to feed. Although the grass anoles or the trunk-ground anoles on different islands are similar in many ways, they are not closely related to each other. Their resemblances are the products of convergent evolution.

A. krugi

Jason Patrick Ross/Shutterstock.com

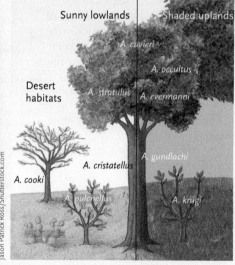

John Ford, *Department of Fisheries and Oceans and the University of British Columbia*

In 1973, Mike Biggs, working at the Pacific Biological Station in Nanaimo, British Columbia, revolutionized field studies of killer whales when he realized that the natural markings on the bodies of the whales could be used to identify individuals. By photographing the dorsal fin and grey "saddle" patch at the base of the fin, along with the unique pattern of nicks and scars, he developed a technique of photo-identification that allowed his group to begin to examine the natural history and population ecology of this charismatic species in detail **(Figure 1)**.

In 1977, John Ford began to study the underwater vocalizations of the whales with respect to their behaviour and social structure. Killer whales, like other toothed whales, produce a wide variety of sounds that serve different purposes. Rapid series of clicks are used for echolocation and navigation (like the bats mentioned at the start of this chapter), while other sounds resembling whistles, squeals,

squawks, and screams are used for social communication. A large percentage of these sounds are distinctly different in different groups of whales. These vocal variations, known as dialects, have allowed researchers to distinguish family groups. A group's dialect appears to be learned by each calf by mimicking its mother, and thus each pod of killer whales can be readily identified using sound analyzers. Dialects appear to be used by the whales as acoustic indicators of group identity and membership. As a result, they have been used to gain insight into the

social history of populations. Pods with similar dialects belong to a clan, a continuous lineage descended from a common ancestral pod. As pods grew in size over time, they gradually split into new pods and their common dialect drifted apart. Pods with similar dialects probably split in the recent past, while others with fewer similarities are likely more distantly related. Different clans have no dialect features in common and probably have very ancient links. Thus, vocal dialects of resident killer whale pods provide information on how communities have evolved in the past **(Figure 2)**.

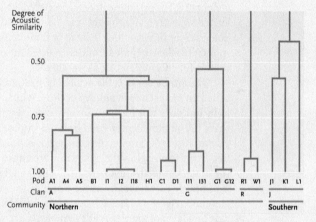

Figure 2

This diagram shows all 19 resident pods of killer whales organized according to the degree of similarity in their call repertoire. Pods with almost identical dialects are linked with a high index of acoustic similarity. Pods that have related dialects belong to the same clan. The four resident clans have no acoustic similarity and are not linked. The family tree shown for each clan reflects its historical genealogy.

Figure 1

A pod of killer whales foraging off the coast of British Columbia.

STUDY BREAK

1. How do most invertebrates detect sound? Give an example.
2. Explain in detail how a human detects sound. Is this fundamentally different from the way an invertebrate hears?
3. Why are the echolocation calls of many bats inaudible to humans despite their high intensity? If humans can't hear bats, how did they discover that bats could emit calls and hear in this frequency range?

45.4 Photoreceptors and Vision

The great majority of animals have receptors that can detect and respond to light. As animals evolved and became more complex, the complexity of their visual sensory receptors increased, leading to the highly developed eyes of cephalopods and vertebrates.

45.4a Vision Involves Detection and Perception of Radiant Energy

Photoreceptors detect light at particular wavelengths, and centres in a brain or central ganglion integrate signals arriving from the receptors into a perception of light. All animals use forms of a single lipidlike pigment, *retinal* (synthesized from vitamin A), in photoreceptors to absorb light energy. The simplest eyes are capable only of distinguishing light from dark; the most complex eyes distinguish shapes and colours and focus an accurate image of objects being viewed onto a layer of photoreceptors.

45.4b Invertebrate Eyes Take Many Forms

Some invertebrates, such as earthworms, do not have visual organs; instead, photoreceptors in their skin allow them to sense and respond to light. Earthworms respond negatively to light, as you can easily discover by shining a flashlight on an earthworm outside its burrow at night.

The eyes of other invertebrates are diverse, ranging from collections of photoreceptors with no lens and no image-forming capability to eyes remarkably like those of vertebrates. The photoreceptors of invertebrates are depolarized when they absorb light, and they generate action potentials or increase their release of neurotransmitter molecules when they are stimulated. Vertebrate photoreceptors function differently, as we will see.

The simplest eye is the **ocellus** (plural, *ocelli;* also called an *eyespot* or *eyecup*). An ocellus, which detects light but does not form an image, consists of fewer than 100 photoreceptor cells lining a cup or pit. In planarians, for example, photoreceptor cells in a cup-like depression below the epidermis are connected to the dendrites of afferent neurons, which are bundled into nerves that travel from the ocelli to the cerebral ganglion **(Figure 45.12)**. Each ocellus is covered on one side by a layer of pigment cells that blocks most of the light rays arriving from the opposite side of the animal. As a result, most of the light received by the pigment cells enters the ocellus from the side that it faces. Through integration of information transmitted to the cerebral ganglion from the eyecups, planarians orient themselves so that the amount of light falling on the two ocelli is equal and diminishes as they swim. This reaction carries them directly away from the source of the light. Similar ocelli are found in a variety of animals, including insects, arthropods, and molluscs.

Two main types of image-forming eyes have evolved in invertebrates: compound eyes and single-lens eyes. The **compound eye** of insects, crustaceans, and a few annelids and molluscs contains hundreds to thousands of faceted visual units called **ommatidia** (*omma* = eye) fitted closely together **(Figure 45.13)**. Each ommatidium samples a small part of the visual field. In insects, light entering an ommatidium is focused by a transparent **cornea** and a *crystalline cone* (just below the cornea) onto a bundle of photoreceptor cells. Microvilli of these cells interdigitate like the fingers of clasped hands, forming a central axis rich in rhodopsin, a retinal-containing **photopigment** (light-absorbing pigment). Absorption of light by rhodopsin causes action potentials to be generated in afferent neurons connected to the base of the ommatidium. From these signals, the brain receives a mosaic image of the world. Because even the slightest motion is detected simultaneously by many ommatidia, compound eyes are extraordinarily adept at detecting movement—a lesson soon learned by fly-swatting humans.

The **single-lens eye** of cephalopods **(Figure 45.14)** resembles a vertebrate eye in that both types operate like a camera. In the cephalopod eye, light enters through the transparent cornea; a **lens** concentrates the light; and a layer of photoreceptors at the back of the eye, the **retina**, records the image. Behind the cornea is the **iris**, which surrounds the **pupil**, the opening through which light enters the eye. Muscles in the iris adjust the size of the pupil to vary the amount of light entering the eye. When the light is bright, circular muscles in the iris contract, shrinking the size of the pupil and reducing the amount of light that enters. In dim light, radial muscles contract and enlarge the pupil, increasing the amount of light that enters the eye. Muscles move the lens forward and back with respect to the retina to focus the image. This is an example of **accommodation**, a process by which the lens changes to enable the eye to focus on objects at different distances. A neural network lies under the retina, meaning that light rays do not have to pass through the neurons to reach the photoreceptors. The vertebrate eye has the opposite arrangement. This and other differences in structure and function indicate that cephalopod and vertebrate eyes evolved independently but are remarkably similar.

Figure 45.12

The ocellus of a planarian flatworm, and the arrangement of pigment cells on which its orientation response is based.

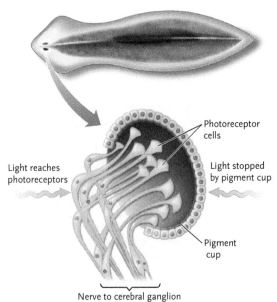

Photoreceptor cells

Light reaches photoreceptors

Light stopped by pigment cup

Pigment cup

Nerve to cerebral ganglion

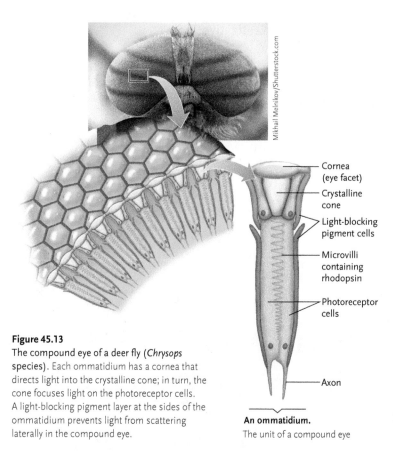

Figure 45.13
The compound eye of a deer fly (*Chrysops* species). Each ommatidium has a cornea that directs light into the crystalline cone; in turn, the cone focuses light on the photoreceptor cells. A light-blocking pigment layer at the sides of the ommatidium prevents light from scattering laterally in the compound eye.

Cornea (eye facet)
Crystalline cone
Light-blocking pigment cells
Microvilli containing rhodopsin
Photoreceptor cells
Axon

An ommatidium.
The unit of a compound eye

45.4c Vertebrate Eyes Have a Complex Structure

The human eye **(Figure 45.15, p. 1110)** has similar structures—cornea, iris, pupil, lens, and retina—to those of the cephalopod eye just described. Light entering the eye through the cornea passes through the iris and then the lens. The lens focuses an image on the retina, and the axons of afferent neurons originating in the retina converge to form the optic nerve leading from the eye to the brain. A clear fluid called the **aqueous humour** fills the space between the cornea and the lens. This fluid carries nutrients to the lens and cornea, which do not contain any blood vessels. The main chamber of the eye, located between the lens and the retina, is filled with the jellylike **vitreous humour** (*vitrum* = glass). The outer wall of the eye contains a tough layer of connective tissue (the *sclera*). Inside it is a darkly pigmented layer (the *choroid*) that prevents light from entering except through the pupil. It also contains the blood vessels nourishing the retina.

Two types of photoreceptors, rods and cones, occur in the retina along with layers of neurons that carry out an initial integration of visual information before it is sent to the brain. The **rods** are specialized for detection of light at low intensities; the **cones** are specialized for detection of different wavelengths

(colours). Accommodation does not occur by forward and backward movement of the lens, as described for cephalopods. Rather, the lens of most terrestrial vertebrates is focused by changing its shape. The lens is held in place by fine ligaments that anchor it to a surrounding layer of connective tissue and muscle, the **ciliary body**. These ligaments keep the lens under tension when the ciliary muscle is relaxed. The tension flattens the lens, which is soft and flexible, and focuses light from distant objects on the retina **(Figure 45.16a, p. 1111)**. When the ciliary muscles contract, they relieve the tension of the ligaments, allowing the lens to assume a more spherical shape and focusing light from nearby objects on the retina (Figure 45.16b).

45.4d The Retina of Mammals and Birds Contains Rods and Cones and a Complex Network of Neurons

The retina of a human eye contains about 120 million rods and 6 million cones organized into a densely packed single layer. Neural networks of the retina are layered on top of the photoreceptor cells, so that light rays focused by the lens on the retina must pass through the neurons before reaching the photoreceptors. The light must also pass through a layer of fine blood vessels covering the surface of the retina.

In mammals and birds with eyes specialized for daytime vision, cones are concentrated in and around a small region of the retina, the **fovea** (see Figure 45.15). The image focused by the lens is centred on the fovea, which is circular and less than a millimetre in diameter in humans. The rods are spread over the remainder of

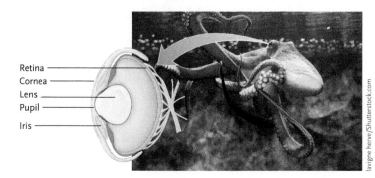

Retina
Cornea
Lens
Pupil
Iris

Figure 45.14
The eye of an octopus, a cephalopod mollusc.

Seeing with your Feet: Using the Genome as an Investigative Tool

It is one thing to demonstrate that an animal responds behaviourally to external stimuli, but it can be very challenging to determine how the stimuli were detected. For example, there is evidence of animals such as garden toads (*Bufo bufo*) changing their behaviour in advance of an earthquake, but we do not know what cues trigger the response.

For some time, it has been clear that echinoderms such as sea urchins respond to changing light conditions, but nobody had found photoreceptors in these animals (see Chapter 1 for a discussion of the significance of light and light sensing). The publication of the genome of purple urchins (*Strongylocentrotus purpuratus*) **(Figure 1)** provided biologists with a means of investigating photoreception in these animals.

Specifically, data in the genome showed that sea urchins possess several genes that code for a widely occurring eye protein, opsin. Discovering this, the researchers designed antibodies against different opsin proteins and performed *in situ* hybridization (see Chapters 15 and 16 for discussions of DNA technologies and genomics). They found that the urchins possess *Sp-opsin4* and *Sp-pax6*, two proteins that regulate phototaxis. This approach also allowed them to visualize where the photoreceptor cells were located—in the urchin's tube feet. The sea urchin photoreceptive cells are microvillar r-opsin, previously known only from protostomes. Since tube feet are found all over the body of the sea urchin, it appears that the entire adult sea urchin acts as a huge compound eye!

There are many other mysteries about the sensory world of animals. We know that many animals show a magnetic sense, but in most cases we do not know the details of the receptor.

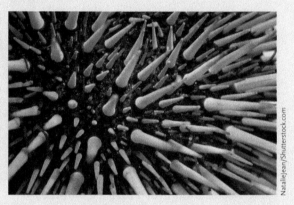

Figure 1

(a) The purple sea urchin *Strongylocentrotus purpuratus*. *(b)* Close-up showing the tube feet between the spines. The photoreceptors are located at the tips of the tube feet.

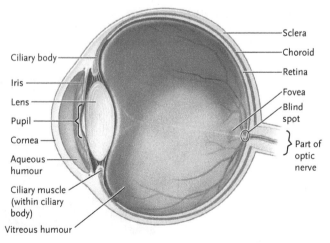

Figure 45.15

Structures of the human eye.

the retina. We can see distinctly only the image focused on the fovea; the surrounding image is what we term *peripheral vision*. Mammals and birds with eyes specialized for night vision have retinas containing mostly rods and lacking a defined fovea. Some fishes and many reptiles have cones generally distributed throughout their retina and very few rods.

The rods of mammals are much more sensitive than the cones to low-intensity light; in fact, they can respond to a single photon of light. This is why, in dim light, we can detect objects better by looking slightly to the side of the object. This action directs the image away from the cones in the fovea to the highly light-sensitive rods in surrounding regions of the retina.

a. Focusing on distant object

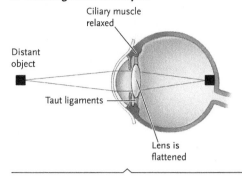

Distant object

Ciliary muscle relaxed

Taut ligaments

Lens is flattened

When the eye focuses on a distant object, the ciliary muscles relax, allowing the ligaments that support the lens to tighten. The tightened ligaments flatten the lens, bringing the distant object into focus on the retina.

b. Focusing on near object

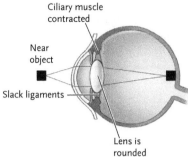

Near object

Ciliary muscle contracted

Slack ligaments

Lens is rounded

When the eye focuses on a near object, the ciliary muscles contract, loosening the ligaments and allowing the lens to become rounder. The rounded lens focuses a near object on the retina.

Figure 45.16
Accommodation in terrestrial vertebrates occurs when the lens changes shape to focus on distant **(a)** and near **(b)** objects.

Sensory Transduction by Rods and Cones: Converting Signals to Electrical Impulses. A photoreceptor cell has three parts:

- an outer segment, consisting of stacked, flattened, membranous discs;
- an inner segment, where the cell's metabolic activities occur; and
- the synaptic terminal, where neurotransmitter molecules are stored and released **(Figure 45.17a).**

The light-absorbing pigment of rods and cones, retinal, is bonded covalently to **opsins** to produce photopigments. The photopigments are embedded in the membranous discs of the photoreceptors' outer segments (Figure 45.17b). The retinal–opsin photopigment in rods is **rhodopsin.**

a. Structure of cones and rods

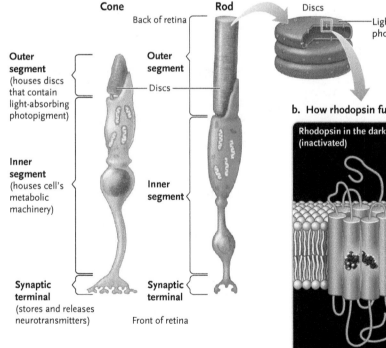

Cone   Rod   Discs

Back of retina

Light-absorbing photopigment

Outer segment (houses discs that contain light-absorbing photopigment)

Outer segment

Discs

Inner segment (houses cell's metabolic machinery)

Inner segment

Synaptic terminal (stores and releases neurotransmitters)

Synaptic terminal

Front of retina

b. How rhodopsin functions

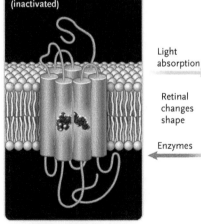

Rhodopsin in the dark (inactivated)

Light absorption

Retinal changes shape

Enzymes

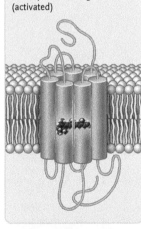

Rhodopsin in the light (activated)

cis-Retinal

trans-Retinal

Figure 45.17
Photoreceptors. Structure of cones and rods **(a)**, the photoreceptors of all mammals, and the location of photopigments in stacked, membranous discs. The photopigment rhodopsin (found in rods) **(b)**, which consists of the opsin protein retinal. In response to light, the retinal changes from a bent to a straight structure.

In the dark, the retinal segment of unstimulated rhodopsin is *cis*-retinal, an inactive form (see Figure 45.17b), and rods steadily release the neurotransmitter glutamate. When rhodopsin absorbs a photon of light, retinal converts to *trans*-retinal, the active form, and the rods *decrease* the amount of glutamate they release.

Rhodopsin is a membrane-embedded G protein–coupled receptor. An extracellular signal received by a G protein–coupled receptor activates the receptor, triggering a signal transduction pathway within the cell and generating a cellular response. Here, activated rhodopsin triggers a signal transduction pathway that leads to the closure of Na$^+$ channels in the plasma membrane **(Figure 45.18)**. Closure of the channels hyperpolarizes the photoreceptor's membrane, decreasing neurotransmitter release. The response is graded because as light absorption by photopigment molecules increases, the amount of neurotransmitter released is reduced proportionately. If light absorption decreases, neurotransmitter release by the photoreceptor increases proportionately. Transduction in rods works in the opposite way from most sensory receptors in which a stimulus increases neurotransmitter release.

Visual Processing in the Retina: Events at the Back of the Eye. In the vertebrate retina, the two types of photoreceptors are linked to a network of neurons that carry out initial integration and processing of visual information. The retina of mammals has four types of neurons **(Figure 45.19)**. There is a layer of **bipolar cells** just in front of the rods and cones. These neurons synapse with rods or cones at one end and with **ganglion cells**, a layer of neurons, at the other end. The axons of ganglion cells extend over the retina and collect at the back of the eyeball to form the optic nerve, which transmits action potentials to the brain. The point where the optic nerve exits the eye lacks photoreceptors. This *blind spot* can be several millimetres in diameter in humans. **Horizontal cells** connect photoreceptor cells, whereas **amacrine cells** connect bipolar and ganglion cells.

In the dark, the steady release of glutamate from rods and cones depolarizes some postsynaptic bipolar cells and hyperpolarizes others. In the light, the decrease in neurotransmitter release from rods and cones results in the depolarized bipolar cells becoming hyperpolarized and the hyperpolarized bipolar cells becoming depolarized.

Signals from the rods and cones may move vertically or laterally in the retina. Signals move vertically from the photoreceptors to bipolar cells and then to ganglion cells. Whereas the human retina has over 120 million photoreceptors, it has only about 1 million ganglion cells. This disparity is explained by the fact that each ganglion cell receives signals from a clearly defined set of photoreceptors constituting the *receptive field* for that cell. Therefore, stimulating numerous photoreceptors in a ganglion cell's receptive field results in only a single message to the brain from that cell. Receptive fields are typically circular and are of different sizes. Smaller receptive fields result in sharper images because they send more precise information to the brain about the location in the retina where the light was received.

Lateral movement of signals from a rod or cone proceeds to a horizontal cell and continues to bipolar cells with which the horizontal cell makes inhibitory connections. To understand this, consider a spot of light falling on the retina. Photoreceptors detect the light and send a signal to bipolar cells and horizontal cells. Horizontal cells inhibit more-distant bipolar cells that are outside the spot of light, causing the light spot to appear lighter and its surrounding dark area to appear darker. This type of visual processing is called **lateral inhibition** and serves both to sharpen the edges of objects and to enhance contrast in an image.

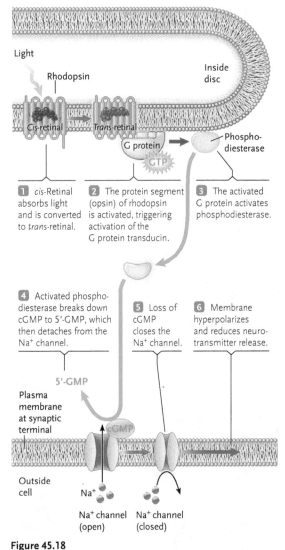

Figure 45.18

The signal transduction pathway that closes Na$^+$ channels in photoreceptor plasma membranes when rhodopsin absorbs light.

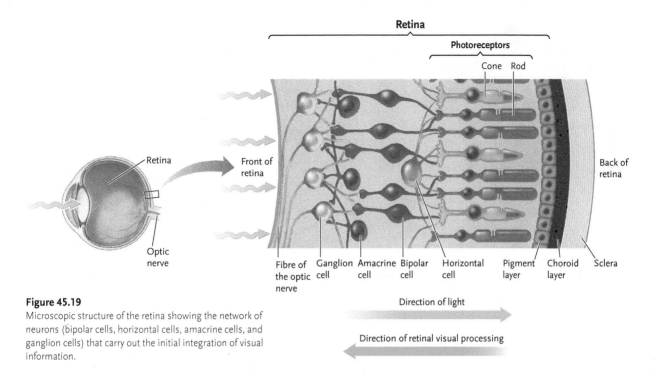

Retina

Photoreceptors

Cone Rod

Retina

Front of
retina

Optic
nerve

Fibre of
the optic
nerve

Ganglion
cell

Amacrine
cell

Bipolar
cell

Horizontal
cell

Pigment
layer

Choroid
layer

Sclera

Back of
retina

Direction of light

Direction of retinal visual processing

Figure 45.19

Microscopic structure of the retina showing the network of
neurons (bipolar cells, horizontal cells, amacrine cells, and
ganglion cells) that carry out the initial integration of visual
information.

45.4e Three Kinds of Opsin Pigments Underlie Colour Vision

Many invertebrates and some species in each class
of vertebrates have colour vision, which depends on
cones in the retina. Most mammals have two types
of cones, whereas humans and other primates have
three types. Each human or primate cone cell contains one of three **photopsins** in which retinal is
combined with different opsins. The three photopsins absorb light over different, but overlapping,
wavelength ranges, with peak absorptions at
445 nm (blue light), 534 nm (green light), and
570 nm (red light). The farther a wavelength is from
the peak colour absorbed, the less strongly the cone
responds. Having more types of cones translates
into better colour vision. Birds have four photopsins
and are able to distinguish shades of colour that
humans cannot.

Overlapping wavelength ranges for the three photoreceptors mean that light at any visible wavelength
stimulates at least two of three types of cones. Maximal
absorption by each type of cone at a different wavelength leads to differential stimulation of different
types of cones. These differences are relayed to the
visual centres of the brain, where they are integrated
into the perception of a colour corresponding to the
particular wavelength absorbed. Light stimulating all
three receptor types equally is seen as white.

Colour-blindness results from inherited defects in
opsin proteins of one or more of the three types of
cones. For example, people with a mutation preventing

cones from making a functional form of red-absorbing
opsin see orange, yellow, and red as the same grey or
greenish colour.

45.4f The Visual Cortex Generates Images in the Brain

Just behind the eyes, the optic nerves converge before
entering the base of the brain. A portion of each optic
nerve crosses over to the opposite side, forming the
optic chiasm (*chiasma* = crossing place). Most axons
enter the **lateral geniculate nuclei** in the thalamus,
where they synapse with interneurons leading to the
visual cortex **(Figure 45.20, p. 1114)**.

Because of the optic chiasm, the left half of the
image seen by both eyes is transmitted to the visual
cortex in the right cerebral hemisphere, and the
right half of the image is transmitted to the left
cerebral hemisphere. The right hemisphere thus
sees objects to the left of the centre of vision, and
the left hemisphere sees objects to the right of the
centre of vision. Communication between the right
and left hemispheres integrates this information
into a perception of the entire visual field seen by
the two eyes.

If you look at a nearby object with one eye and then
the other, you will notice that the point of view is
slightly different. Integration of the visual field by the
brain creates a single picture with a sense of distance
and depth. The greater the difference between the
images seen by the two eyes, the closer the object
appears to the viewer.

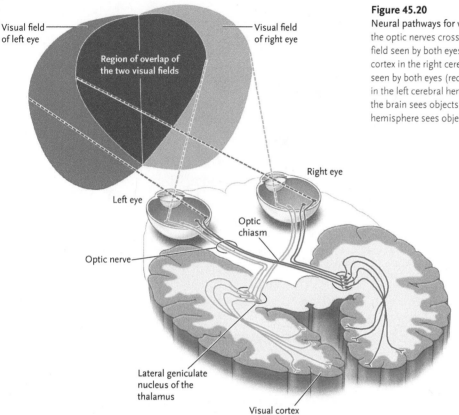

Visual field of left eye

Visual field of right eye

Region of overlap of the two visual fields

Right eye

Left eye

Optic chiasm

Optic nerve

Lateral geniculate nucleus of the thalamus

Visual cortex

Figure 45.20

Neural pathways for vision. Because half of the axons carried by the optic nerves cross over in the optic chiasma, the left half of the field seen by both eyes (green segment) is transmitted to the visual cortex in the right cerebral hemisphere. The right half of the field seen by both eyes (red segment) is transmitted to the visual cortex in the left cerebral hemisphere. As a result, the right hemisphere of the brain sees objects to the left of the centre of vision, and the left hemisphere sees objects to the right of the centre of vision.

different positions. They also correct for curvature of the water droplet's trajectory. Other fish also spit at aerial prey, and some birds hunt fish from above the water's surface; both deal with the problems of refraction from a different standpoint.

In humans, the two optic nerves together contain more than a million axons, more than all other afferent neurons of the body put together. Almost one-third of the grey matter of the cerebral cortex is devoted to visual information. These numbers give some idea of the complexity of the information integrated into the visual image formed by the brain and the importance of visual information for everyday activity.

Archerfish **(Figure 45.21)** live in fresh water and knock flying or resting insects onto the water's surface with spit droplets. The fish then catch and eat the insects. During the spitting attacks, the fishes' eyes are below the surface of the water, posing a potentially serious problem because of refraction, the deflection of rays of light at the air–water interface. Some evidence suggests that archerfish spit from directly under the prey, but further observations show that this is not always true. Archerfish correctly set their spitting angle to compensate for the refraction they experience at

STUDY BREAK

1. What is the "simplest" eye? Why is it an eye, and how does it differ from image-forming eyes?
2. What causes colour-blindness?
3. Why are compound eyes so adept at detecting motion?
4. What is accommodation?

45.5 Chemoreceptors

Chemoreceptors provide information about taste (gustation) and smell (olfaction), as well as measures of intrinsic levels of molecules such as oxygen, carbon dioxide, and hydrogen ions. All chemoreceptors probably work through membrane receptor proteins that are stimulated when they bind with specific molecules in their environment (internal or external) and generate action potentials in afferent nerves leading to the CNS. In this section, we only discuss sensing of external stimuli through taste and smell.

Figure 45.21

An archerfish, *Toxotes chatareus*, projecting spit at an insect prey.

A. & J. Visage/Photolibrary/Getty Images

ON THE ORIGIN OF SPECIES.

INTRODUCTION.

WHEN on board H.M.S. 'Beagle,' as naturalist, I was much struck with certain facts in the distribution of the inhabitants of South America, and in the geological relations of the present to the past inhabitants of that continent. These facts seemed to me to throw some light on the origin of species—that mystery of mysteries, as it has been called by one of our greatest philosophers. On my return home, it occurred to me, in 1837, that something might perhaps be made out on this question by patiently accumulating and reflecting on all sorts of facts which could possibly have any bearing on it. After five years' work I allowed myself to speculate on the subject, and drew up some short notes; these I enlarged in 1844 into a sketch of the conclusions, which then seemed to me probable: from that period to the present day I have steadily pursued the same object. I hope that I may be excused for entering on these personal details, as I give them to show that I have not been hasty in coming to a decision.

My work is now nearly finished; but as it will take me two or three more years to complete it, and as my health is far from strong, I have been urged to publish this Abstract. I have more especially been induced to do this, as Mr. Wallace, who is now studying the

B

natural history of the Malay archipelago, has arrived
at almost exactly the same general conclusions that I
have on the origin of species. Last year he sent me a
memoir on this subject, with a request that I would
forward it to Sir Charles Lyell, who sent it to the Lin-
nean Society, and it is published in the third volume
of the Journal of that Society. Sir C. Lyell and Dr.
Hooker, who both knew of my work—the latter having
read my sketch of 1844—honoured me by thinking it
advisable to publish, with Mr. Wallace's excellent memoir, some brief extracts from my manuscripts.

This Abstract, which I now publish, must necessarily
be imperfect. I cannot here give references and authorities for my several statements; and I must trust to
the reader reposing some confidence in my accuracy.
No doubt errors will have crept in, though I hope I have
always been cautious in trusting to good authorities
alone. I can here give only the general conclusions at
which I have arrived, with a few facts in illustration,
but which, I hope, in most cases will suffice. No one
can feel more sensible than I do of the necessity of hereafter publishing in detail all the facts, with references,
on which my conclusions have been grounded; and I
hope in a future work to do this. For I am well aware
that scarcely a single point is discussed in this volume
on which facts cannot be adduced, often apparently
leading to conclusions directly opposite to those at which
I have arrived. A fair result can be obtained only by
fully stating and balancing the facts and arguments on
both sides of each question; and this cannot possibly be
here done.

I much regret that want of space prevents my having
the satisfaction of acknowledging the generous assistance
which I have received from very many naturalists, some
of them personally unknown to me. I cannot, however,

let this opportunity pass without expressing my deep obligations to Dr. Hooker, who for the last fifteen years has aided me in every possible way by his large stores of knowledge and his excellent judgment.

In considering the Origin of Species, it is quite conceivable that a naturalist, reflecting on the mutual affinities of organic beings, on their embryological relations, their geographical distribution, geological succession, and other such facts, might come to the conclusion that each species had not been independently created, but had descended, like varieties, from other species. Nevertheless, such a conclusion, even if well founded, would be unsatisfactory, until it could be shown how the innumerable species inhabiting this world have been modified, so as to acquire that perfection of structure and coadaptation which most justly excites our admiration. Naturalists continually refer to external conditions, such as climate, food, &c., as the only possible cause of variation. In one very limited sense, as we shall hereafter see, this may be true; but it is preposterous to attribute to mere external conditions, the structure, for instance, of the woodpecker, with its feet, tail, beak, and tongue, so admirably adapted to catch insects under the bark of trees. In the case of the misseltoe, which draws its nourishment from certain trees, which has seeds that must be transported by certain birds, and which has flowers with separate sexes absolutely requiring the agency of certain insects to bring pollen from one flower to the other, it is equally preposterous to account for the structure of this parasite, with its relations to several distinct organic beings, by the effects of external conditions, or of habit, or of the volition of the plant itself.

The author of the 'Vestiges of Creation' would, I presume, say that, after a certain unknown number of

B 2

generations, some bird had given birth to a woodpecker, and some plant to the missletoe, and that these had been produced perfect as we now see them; but this assumption seems to me to be no explanation, for it leaves the case of the coadaptations of organic beings to each other and to their physical conditions of life, untouched and unexplained.

It is, therefore, of the highest importance to gain a clear insight into the means of modification and co-adaptation. At the commencement of my observations it seemed to me probable that a careful study of domesticated animals and of cultivated plants would offer the best chance of making out this obscure problem. Nor have I been disappointed; in this and in all other perplexing cases I have invariably found that our knowledge, imperfect though it be, of variation under domestication, afforded the best and safest clue. I may venture to express my conviction of the high value of such studies, although they have been very commonly neglected by naturalists.

From these considerations, I shall devote the first chapter of this Abstract to Variation under Domestication. We shall thus see that a large amount of hereditary modification is at least possible; and, what is equally or more important, we shall see how great is the power of man in accumulating by his Selection successive slight variations. I will then pass on to the variability of species in a state of nature; but I shall, unfortunately, be compelled to treat this subject far too briefly, as it can be treated properly only by giving long catalogues of facts. We shall, however, be enabled to discuss what circumstances are most favourable to variation. In the next chapter the Struggle for Existence amongst all organic beings throughout the world, which inevitably follows from the high geometrical ratio of their increase, will be treated of. This is the doctrine of Malthus, applied to the whole animal and vegetable kingdoms. As many more individuals of each species are born than can possibly survive; and as, consequently, there is a frequently recurring struggle for existence, it follows that any being, if it vary however slightly in any manner profitable to itself, under the complex and sometimes varying conditions of life, will have a better chance of surviving, and thus be *naturally selected*. From the strong principle of inheritance, any selected variety will tend to propagate its new and modified form.

This fundamental subject of Natural Selection will be treated at some length in the fourth chapter; and we shall then see how Natural Selection almost inevitably causes much Extinction of the less improved forms of life, and leads to what I have called Divergence of Character. In the next chapter I shall discuss the complex and little known laws of variation and of correlation of growth. In the four succeeding chapters, the most apparent and gravest difficulties on the theory will be given: namely, first, the difficulties of transitions, or in understanding how a simple being or a simple organ can be changed and perfected into a highly developed being or elaborately constructed organ; secondly, the subject of Instinct, or the mental powers of animals; thirdly, Hybridism, or the infertility of species and the fertility of varieties when intercrossed; and fourthly, the imperfection of the Geological Record. In the next chapter I shall consider the geological succession of organic beings throughout time; in the eleventh and twelfth, their geographical distribution throughout space; in the thirteenth, their classification or mutual affinities, both when mature and in an embryonic condition. In the last chapter I shall give a brief recapitulation of the whole work, and a few concluding remarks.

No one ought to feel surprise at much remaining as yet unexplained in regard to the origin of species and varieties, if he makes due allowance for our profound ignorance in regard to the mutual relations of all the beings which live around us. Who can explain why one species ranges widely and is very numerous, and why another allied species has a narrow range and is rare? Yet these relations are of the highest importance, for they determine the present welfare, and, as I believe, the future success and modification of every inhabitant of this world. Still less do we know of the mutual relations of the innumerable inhabitants of the world during the many past geological epochs in its history. Although much remains obscure, and will long remain obscure, I can entertain no doubt, after the most deliberate study and dispassionate judgment of which I am capable, that the view which most naturalists entertain, and which I formerly entertained—namely, that each species has been independently created—is erroneous. I am fully convinced that species are not immutable; but that those belonging to what are called the same genera are lineal descendants of some other and generally extinct species, in the same manner as the acknowledged varieties of any one species are the descendants of that species. Furthermore, I am convinced that Natural Selection has been the main but not exclusive means of modification.

males, in their weapons, means of defence, or charms; and have transmitted these advantages to their male offspring. Yet, I would not wish to attribute all such sexual differences to this agency: for we see peculiarities arising and becoming attached to the male sex in our domestic animals (as the wattle in male carriers, horn-like protuberances in the cocks of certain fowls, &c.), which we cannot believe to be either useful to the males in battle, or attractive to the females. We see analogous cases under nature, for instance, the tuft of hair on the breast of the turkey-cock, which can hardly be either useful or ornamental to this bird;—indeed, had the tuft appeared under domestication, it would have been called a monstrosity.

Illustrations of the action of Natural Selection.—In order to make it clear how, as I believe, natural selection acts, I must beg permission to give one or two imaginary illustrations. Let us take the case of a wolf, which preys on various animals, securing some by craft, some by strength, and some by fleetness; and let us suppose that the fleetest prey, a deer for instance, had from any change in the country increased in numbers, or that other prey had decreased in numbers, during that season of the year when the wolf is hardest pressed for food. I can under such circumstances see no reason to doubt that the swiftest and slimmest wolves would have the best chance of surviving, and so be preserved or selected,—provided always that they retained strength to master their prey at this or at some other period of the year, when they might be compelled to prey on other animals. I can see no more reason to doubt this, than that man can improve the fleetness of his greyhounds by careful and methodical selection, or by that unconscious selection which results from each man trying to keep the best dogs without any thought of modifying the breed.

Even without any change in the proportional numbers of the animals on which our wolf preyed, a cub might be born with an innate tendency to pursue certain kinds of prey. Nor can this be thought very improbable; for we often observe great differences in the natural tendencies of our domestic animals; one cat, for instance, taking to catch rats, another mice; one cat, according to Mr. St. John, bringing home winged game, another hares or rabbits, and another hunting on marshy ground and almost nightly catching woodcocks or snipes. The tendency to catch rats rather than mice is known to be inherited. Now, if any slight innate change of habit or of structure benefited an individual wolf, it would have the best chance of surviving and of leaving offspring. Some of its young would probably inherit the same habits or structure, and by the repetition of this process, a new variety might be formed which would either supplant or coexist with the parent form of wolf. Or, again, the wolves inhabiting a mountainous district, and those frequenting the lowlands, would naturally be forced to hunt different prey; and from the continued preservation of the individuals best fitted for the two sites, two varieties might slowly be formed. These varieties would cross and blend where they met; but to this subject of intercrossing we shall soon have to return. I may add, that, according to Mr. Pierce, there are two varieties of the wolf inhabiting the Catskill Mountains in the United States, one with a light greyhound-like form, which pursues deer, and the other more bulky, with shorter legs, which more frequently attacks the shepherd's flocks.

Let us now take a more complex case. Certain plants excrete a sweet juice, apparently for the sake of eliminating something injurious from their sap: this is effected by glands at the base of the stipules in some Leguminosæ, and at the back of the leaf of the common laurel. This juice, though small in quantity, is greedily sought by insects. Let us now suppose a little sweet juice or nectar to be excreted by the inner bases of the petals of a flower. In this case insects in seeking the nectar would get dusted with pollen, and would certainly often transport the pollen from one flower to the stigma of another flower. The flowers of two distinct individuals of the same species would thus get crossed; and the act of crossing, we have good reason to believe (as will hereafter be more fully alluded to), would produce very vigorous seedlings, which consequently would have the best chance of flourishing and surviving. Some of these seedlings would probably inherit the nectar-excreting power. Those individual flowers which had the largest glands or nectaries, and which excreted most nectar, would be oftenest visited by insects, and would be oftenest crossed; and so in the long-run would gain the upper hand. Those flowers, also, which had their stamens and pistils placed, in relation to the size and habits of the particular insects which visited them, so as to favour in any degree the transportal of their pollen from flower to flower, would likewise be favoured or selected. We might have taken the case of insects visiting flowers for the sake of collecting pollen instead of nectar; and as pollen is formed for the sole object of fertilisation, its destruction appears a simple loss to the plant; yet if a little pollen were carried, at first occasionally and then habitually, by the pollen-devouring insects from flower to flower, and a cross thus effected, although nine-tenths of the pollen were destroyed, it might still be a great gain to the plant; and those individuals which produced more and more pollen, and had larger and larger anthers, would be selected.

When our plant, by this process of the continued preservation or natural selection of more and more attractive flowers, had been rendered highly attractive to insects, they would, unintentionally on their part, regularly carry pollen from flower to flower; and that they can most effectually do this, I could easily show by many striking instances. I will give only one—not as a very striking case, but as likewise illustrating one step in the separation of the sexes of plants, presently to be alluded to. Some holly-trees bear only male flowers, which have four stamens producing a rather small quantity of pollen, and a rudimentary pistil; other holly-trees bear only female flowers; these have a full-sized pistil, and four stamens with shrivelled anthers, in which not a grain of pollen can be detected. Having found a female tree exactly sixty yards from a male tree, I put the stigmas of twenty flowers, taken from different branches, under the microscope, and on all, without exception, there were pollen-grains, and on some a profusion of pollen. As the wind had set for several days from the female to the male tree, the pollen could not thus have been carried. The weather had been cold and boisterous, and therefore not favourable to bees, nevertheless every female flower which I examined had been effectually fertilised by the bees, accidentally dusted with pollen, having flown from tree to tree in search of nectar. But to return to our imaginary case: as soon as the plant had been rendered so highly attractive to insects that pollen was regularly carried from flower to flower, another process might commence. No naturalist doubts the advantage of what has been called the " physiological division of labour;" hence we may believe that it would be advantageous to a plant to produce stamens alone in one flower or on one whole plant, and pistils alone in another flower or on another plant. In plants under culture and placed under new conditions of life, sometimes the male organs and sometimes the female organs become more or less impotent; now if we suppose this to occur in ever so slight a degree under nature, then as pollen is already carried regularly from flower to flower, and as a more complete separation of the sexes of our plant would be advantageous on the principle of the division of labour, individuals with this tendency more and more increased, would be continually favoured or selected, until at last a complete separation of the sexes would be effected.

Let us now turn to the nectar-feeding insects in our imaginary case: we may suppose the plant of which we have been slowly increasing the nectar by continued selection, to be a common plant; and that certain insects depended in main part on its nectar for food. I could give many facts, showing how anxious bees are to save time; for instance, their habit of cutting holes and sucking the nectar at the bases of certain flowers, which they can, with a very little more trouble, enter by the mouth. Bearing such facts in mind, I can see no reason to doubt that an accidental deviation in the size and form of the body, or in the curvature and length of the proboscis, &c., far too slight to be appreciated by us, might profit a bee or other insect, so that an individual so characterised would be able to obtain its food more quickly, and so have a better chance of living and leaving descendants. Its descendants would probably inherit a tendency to a similar slight deviation of structure. The tubes of the corollas of the common red and incarnate clovers (Trifolium pratense and incarnatum) do not on a hasty glance appear to differ in length; yet the hive-bee can easily suck the nectar out of the incarnate clover, but not out of the common red clover, which is visited by humble-bees alone; so that whole fields of the red clover offer in vain an abundant supply of precious nectar to the hive-bee. Thus it might be a great advantage to the hive-bee to have a slightly longer or differently constructed proboscis. On the other hand, I have found by experiment that the fertility of clover depends on bees visiting and moving parts of the corolla, so as to push the pollen on to the stigmatic surface. Hence, again, if humble-bees were to become rare in any country, it might be a great advantage to the red clover to have a shorter or more deeply divided tube to its corolla, so that the hive-bee could visit its flowers. Thus I can understand how a flower and a bee might slowly become, either simultaneously or one after the other, modified and adapted in the most perfect manner to each other, by the continued preservation of individuals presenting mutual and slightly favourable deviations of structure.

I am well aware that this doctrine of natural selection, exemplified in the above imaginary instances, is open to the same objections which were at first urged against Sir Charles Lyell's noble views on " the modern changes of the earth, as illustrative of geology;" but we now seldom hear the action, for instance, of the coast-waves, called a trifling and insignificant cause, when applied to the excavation of gigantic valleys or to the formation of the longest lines of inland cliffs. Natural selection can act only by the preservation and accumulation of infinitesimally small inherited modifications, each profitable to the preserved being; and as modern geology has almost banished such views as the excavation of a great valley by a single diluvial wave, so will natural selection, if it be a true principle, banish the belief of the continued creation of new organic beings, or of any great and sudden modification in their structure.

On the Intercrossing of Individuals.—I must here introduce a short digression. In the case of animals and plants with separated sexes, it is of course obvious that two individuals must always (with the exception of the curious and not well-understood cases of partheno-genesis) unite for each birth; but in the case of her-maphrodites this is far from obvious. Nevertheless I am strongly inclined to believe that with all hermaphrodites two individuals, either occasionally or habitually, concur for the reproduction of their kind. This view was first suggested by Andrew Knight. We shall presently see its importance; but I must here treat the subject with extreme brevity, though I have the materials prepared for an ample discussion. All vertebrate animals, all insects, and some other large groups of animals, pair for each birth. Modern research has much diminished the number of supposed hermaphrodites, and of real hermaphrodites a large number pair; that is, two indivi-duals regularly unite for reproduction, which is all that concerns us. But still there are many hermaphrodite animals which certainly do not habitually pair, and a vast majority of plants are hermaphrodites. What reason, it may be asked, is there for supposing in these cases that two individuals ever concur in reproduction? As it is impossible here to enter on details, I must trust to some general considerations alone.

In the first place, I have collected so large a body of facts, showing, in accordance with the almost universal belief of breeders, that with animals and plants a cross between different varieties, or between individuals of the same variety but of another strain, gives vigour and

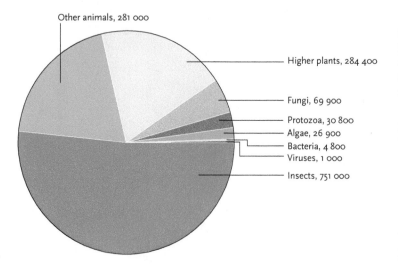

Figure 3.3

Diversity of life. The approximate numbers of species in different groups of organisms.

Other animals, 281 000
Higher plants, 284 400
Fungi, 69 900
Protozoa, 30 800
Algae, 26 900
Bacteria, 4 800
Viruses, 1 000
Insects, 751 000

When we group organisms by factors other than their taxonomic categories, we get a different picture of the diversity of life on Earth. One approach is to consider how organisms obtain carbon because carbon is the "backbone" of all organic molecules synthesized by an organism (see Chapter 47). Most plants are autotrophs (*auto* = self; *troph* = nourishment), which synthesize organic carbon molecules using inorganic carbon (CO_2). (Note that although CO_2 contains a carbon atom, oxides containing carbon are considered inorganic molecules.) All animals are heterotrophs, meaning that they obtain carbon from organic molecules, either from living hosts or from organic molecules in the products, wastes, or remains of dead organisms.

Organisms are also divided according to the source of the energy they use to drive biological activities. Chemotrophs (*chemo* = chemical; *troph* = nourishment) obtain energy by oxidizing inorganic or organic substances, whereas phototrophs obtain energy from light. Combining the carbon and energy sources allows us to group living organisms into four categories **(Table 3.1)**.

Prokaryotes show the greatest diversity in their modes of securing carbon and energy. Note that prokaryotes are the only representatives of two of the categories, chemoautotrophs and photoheterotrophs; see Chapter 21 to find out more about the amazing metabolic diversity that exists among prokaryotes.

STUDY BREAK

Describe the differences among heterotrophs, autotrophs, photoautotrophs, and chemoautotrophs. Provide an example of each.

3.2 Selection

Selection occurs when some force or phenomenon affects the survival of individual organisms. An unexpected spring frost can kill many plants in your garden. Only the cold-resistant plants survive the selective force (temperature). When you hear about an outbreak of some disease in a hospital or care facility, you are often seeing an example of the outcome of selection. Bacteria that are resistant to antibiotics, for example, can survive and reproduce, overwhelming the defences of individuals and institutions. The same can be true with the emergence of pests that are resistant to pesticides, whether the targets are weeds, parasites, or insects.

Selection occurs when a large population of individuals is exposed to a lethal factor and only resistant individuals survive to reproduce. If resistance is inherited, then the offspring of survivors will be resistant. If the resistant population is able to reproduce quickly, there is the potential for explosive growth of a population of individuals who are immune to the lethal factor. When the target pests are bacteria, some of which can double their populations in minutes, it does not take long for resistant pests to take over (see Chapter 45). Imagine having 10 million toxic bacteria in your body. You take an antibiotic that kills 99.99% of them. The remaining 1000 bacteria are resistant to the antibiotic.

Table 3.1	**Modes of nutrition among living organisms.**		
		Energy source	
		Oxidation of Molecules*	Light
Carbon source	CO_2	**CHEMOAUTOTROPH** Found in some bacteria and archaeans; not found in eukaryotes	**PHOTOAUTOTROPH** Found in some photosynthetic bacteria, in some proteins, and in plants
	Organic molecules	**CHEMOHETEROTROPH** Found in some bacteria and archaeans, and also in proteins, fungi, animals, and plants	**PHOTOHETEROTROPH** Found in some photosynthetic bacteria

*Inorganic molecules for chemoautotrophs and organic molecules for chemoheterotrophs.

If their population doubles every 20 minutes, you will have over 10 million (now resistant) bacteria within 5 hours.

The key factors behind selection are a selective force (pressure) and the capacity for explosive population growth. When these factors coincide, we can be overrun by pests, such as antibiotic-resistant bacteria in hospitals or health care facilities, weeds in crop fields, or insect pests. When this happens, the consequences for humans can be deadly.

Selection is the major force responsible for evolution and biodiversity. A recurring theme in selection is genetic variation in the population put to the test by some selection pressure. Here are three examples of selection in action.

3.2a Case 1, Syphilis: Migration and Emergence of a Disease

Treponematoses are diseases caused by bacteria in the genus *Treponema*. *Treponema pallidum pallidum* is the bacterium that causes syphilis, a venereal disease also known as "the pox." Often the first signs of syphilis are small, painless sores (chancres) at the site of contact. This can progress to secondary stages (rash, fever, fatigue) and, if untreated, to tertiary syphilis, with symptoms that can include disfigurement, neurological disorders, and cardiovascular problems. *Treponema pallidum pertenue* causes yaws, a skin disease that usually afflicts people in hot, humid areas. The extinct *Treponema carateum* caused pinta, a skin disease confined to South and Central America. Perhaps also extinct, *Treponema pallidum endemicum* caused bejel, endemic syphilis that was limited to hot, arid climates in the Middle East. Genetic evidence indicates that *T. pallidum pertenue* is an older subspecies of *T. pallidum* than *T. pallidum pallidum* is, meaning that whereas yaws has afflicted people for a long time, syphilis caused by *T. pallidum pallidum* is relatively new. Syphilis and other treponemal diseases, except pinta, leave distinct marks on the skeleton, which have allowed paleoanthropologists to document the incidence of these diseases in human skeletal remains and determine their prehistoric distribution.

The first outbreak of syphilis in Europe occurred in 1495, and since then, it has killed tens of thousands of people. Syphilis has long been thought to have originated in the New World. In 2008, genetic analyses supported the hypothesis that a new strain of *T. pallidum (T. pallidum pallidum)* emerged in Europe in 1495, brought from the New World by members of Columbus's crew.

The history of *T. pallidum* appears to have involved three steps:

- First, *T. pallidum* appeared as a nonvenereal infection and spread with humans throughout the Middle East, Europe, and the New World. At that point, the pathogen caused yaws, which was spread by skin-to-skin contact.

- Second, European explorers brought a strain of *T. pallidum* from the New World to Europe, where it emerged as the progenitor of the modern *T. pallidum pallidum* that caused syphilis. When clothed European explorers, such as Columbus and his crew, met unclothed natives in the New World, yaws (caused by *T. pallidum*) could not readily spread between the two groups of people because of the lack of skin-to-skin contact. But the explorers could be exposed to the lesions of yaws (and *T. pallidum*) during sex.

- Third, although the strains or subspecies of *T. pallidum* that caused yaws were thwarted by clothes, variants that occurred in the genital area could be transferred during sex. This meant success for the bacterium, and syphilis was the result.

The pivotal discovery giving genetic support to the theory that syphilis came from the New World emerged when a Canadian physician (Michael S. Silverman), working in isolated settlements in Guyana (South America), spotted lesions caused by yaws. He obtained samples of bacteria from the lesions and set the genetics side of the story in motion.

The key elements were genetic variation, differences in transmission of the disease-causing agent, and the opportunity for *T. pallidum pallidum* to spread widely due to people's sexual behaviour. In 2008, syphilis became more common, suggesting that the process is still in play.

3.2b Case 2, Evolution of Whales: A Change from Hoofed Mammal to Whale

The first fossil whales were found in rocks in south Asia dated to the Eocene, about 50 million years ago. Paleontologists had presumed that the ancestor of whales lived a hippopotamus-like existence, retreating to the water to avoid predators and going ashore at night to eat vegetation. The fossil evidence also indicated that whales and modern hoofed mammals (ungulates) shared a common ancestor and that hippopotomi are ungulates. But the oldest hippo ancestors are 15 million years old and have been found only in Africa, so timing and location mean that hippos are not close relatives of whales.

In 2007, Hans Thewissen and his colleagues reported evidence of an ungulate ancestor that was closely related to whales. The candidates, raccoon-sized species in the genus *Indohyus* (family Raoellidae), were Eocene fossils found in Kashmir (India). Thewissen and his colleagues presented several lines of evidence supporting the proposal that *Indohyus* was aquatic, lived a hippo-like existence, and shared a close ancestor with whales. *Indohyus* had dense bones and high levels of oxygen isotopes (O^{18}), two features indicating an aquatic lifestyle. *Indohyus* had crushing basins in their molar teeth, and the levels of carbon isotopes (C^{13}) suggested that they ate terrestrial plants. Raoellids also shared cochlear structures (see Chapter 34) with whales, notably the presence of a ridge called the "involucrum."

In the Eocene in what is now Kashmir, *Indohyus* lived an amphibious existence, entering the water to avoid predators and going ashore to eat vegetation. At some point, *Indohyus* species started to eat fish, which became the mainstay of their diet; this was also true of the earliest whales but not the living ones. Thewissen's proposal explains the development of an aquatic mammal from a terrestrial one, a herbivore to a piscivore.

Again, genetic variation, survival of individuals that used the water to avoid predation, and selection of strains of individuals that switched their diets to fish were the key elements.

3.2c Case 3, Climbing Plants: Reaching for the Light

Plants such as trees reach for the sun by growing tall, at least as tall as their neighbours. An alternative way for plants to get their share of sunlight is to climb on a physical support. Climbing plants are known as vines or lianas, and those that find suitable support often have biomass and reproductive output that matches or exceeds that of the trees on which they grow. Climbing plants are successful because they grow quickly, depend on reduced biomass of supporting structures (compared with trees), achieve higher leaf biomass, and thus outcompete other plants when it comes to reaching for the sun. At least 130 families of plants include climbing species, and vines represent at least 40% of the plant diversity in tropical forests. Whereas vines such as morning glories (*Ipomoea* spp.) are herbaceous, others, such as grapevines (*Vitus* spp.), are woody. Herbaceous vines grow readily on pioneer species of trees that are rarely robust enough to support woody vines.

In 2004, Ernesto Gianoli compared 48 groups of plants in which there was enough information about evolutionary relationships to assess the relative diversity of climber and nonclimber sister groups. In 38 cases, climbing taxa were more diverse than non-climbers. Gianoli concluded that climbing was a "key" development in plants because it resulted in a great increase in numbers of species.

The success and diversity of climbing plants are reflected in the variety of structures they use for climbing. Some use tendrils, modified stems or leaves, which coil around supporting structures. Others use modified roots, sometimes holdfasts, to attach to supports. In still others, the stem itself coils clockwise or anticlockwise around the support. Note that Charles Darwin was one of the first to study climbing plants.

STUDY BREAK

Selection is the force responsible for evolution and biodiversity. What key elements aid in the selection and survival of certain individuals and their genetic traits?

3.3 Evolution

Evolution, a gradual change in the characteristics of a population of organisms over time, can be the result of selection. Evolution is a central key to understanding the diversity of life on Earth (see Chapters 17, 18, 19, and 20). Although the theory of evolution is widely accepted today by educated people around the world, the levels of acceptance vary among countries **(Figure 3.4)**, perhaps reflecting variation in the degree to which science has been politicized. Teaching of evolution is not permitted in some educational jurisdictions. In this book, we consider evolution to be an organizing force in life and the foundation of modern biology. Understanding evolution is central to understanding the elements of biodiversity, but it does not mean believing or accepting that humans evolved from apes or from amoebas.

The theory of evolution explains both the unity and the diversity of all life; it tells us that all organisms alive today descended from a common ancestor, which explains why all organisms share features such as the use of adenosine triphosphate (ATP) as a cellular energy source, deoxyribonucleic acid (DNA) as genetic material, and plasma membranes composed of lipid bilayers. But evolution also tells us that species change over time as a result of natural selection. The central ideas of Darwin's theory of evolution by natural selection can be summarized as follows:

- Individual organisms in a population vary in many heritable traits.
- Any population has the potential to produce far more offspring than the environment can support. Competition for limited resources means that only some individuals survive.
- Some individuals in the population have traits that give them an advantage in their local environment; these organisms are more likely to survive and reproduce.

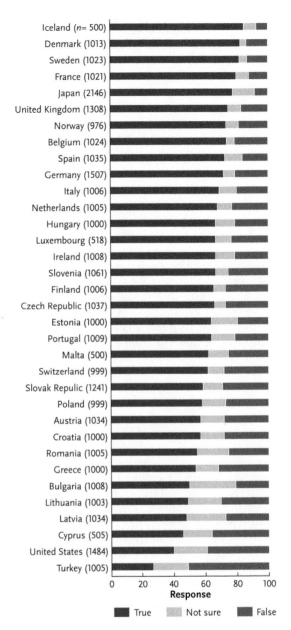

Iceland (*n*= 500)
Denmark (1013)
Sweden (1023)
France (1021)
Japan (2146)
United Kingdom (1308)
Norway (976)
Belgium (1024)
Spain (1035)
Germany (1507)
Italy (1006)
Netherlands (1005)
Hungary (1000)
Luxembourg (518)
Ireland (1008)
Slovenia (1061)
Finland (1006)
Czech Republic (1037)
Estonia (1000)
Portugal (1009)
Malta (500)
Switzerland (999)
Slovak Repulic (1241)
Poland (999)
Austria (1034)
Croatia (1000)
Romania (1005)
Greece (1000)
Bulgaria (1008)
Lithuania (1003)
Latvia (1034)
Cyprus (505)
United States (1484)
Turkey (1005)

0   20   40   60   80   100
Response

■ True   ■ Not sure   ■ False

Figure 3.4
Public acceptance of evolution based on surveys of people living in 34 countries. Low acceptance in the United States appears to reflect, in part, the politicization of science and the rise of fundamentalism.

- These organisms pass on favourable traits to their offspring. Over time, the incidence of the trait(s) will change in the population.

Different environments favour different traits. Thus, even though all organisms share a common ancestor, they have diverged over evolutionary time in response to the selection pressures of different environments. The process of adaptive radiation, discussed next, is an example of such divergence.

3.3a Adaptive Radiation: Diversification of Lineages of Life

In the history of life on Earth, organisms have had to overcome fundamental barriers that, once crossed, opened many new opportunities for diversification (for example, the cases above under *Selection*). The development of photosynthesis is another example of such a breakthrough. Organisms with the ability to convert solar energy into usable chemical energy survived and thrived as they exploited the "new" energy source. The appearance of oxygenic photosynthesis increased the concentrations of oxygen (a by-product of the process), which led to aerobic respiration and the ozone layer, which allowed organisms to colonize terrestrial environments by blocking harmful ultraviolet (UV) rays. Together, the changes caused by an increase in atmospheric oxygen triggered an extraordinary diversification of life. There is paleontological evidence of the relative timing of some fundamental changes in life (e.g., evolution of whales), and sometimes we know the underlying factors (again, the whales).

An organism may move into a new adaptive zone after a chance innovation allows it to use the environment in a unique way. The ability of plants to move onto land opened new opportunities for animals. The dehydration-resistant eggs of early reptiles enabled them to complete their life cycle on land, opening terrestrial habitats to them. The evolution of flowers that attract insect pollinators was a key innovation in the history of flowering plants.

An adaptive zone may open up after the demise of a successful group, for example, the replacement of the mammals Multituberculata by Rodentia (see Chapter 48). We know that a rich diversity of soft-bodied organisms thrived in Precambrian seas. But the beginning of the Cambrian, about 600 million years ago, is marked by the disappearance of many of the soft-bodied organisms and the appearance of an extraordinary diversity of life, including many species with skeletons. The change from soft- to hard-bodied is reflected in the fossil record, but the reasons for the switch in body form are not clear.

3.3b Islands: Showcases of Evolution

Adaptive radiations, therefore, occur when an evolutionary breakthrough allows diversification of life. Adaptive radiations are a recurring theme in the development of biodiversity. At one level, we can see it in the evolution of the fauna and flora of the Hawaiian Islands, arguably the most isolated landmasses in the world. When Captain Cook arrived on the islands in 1778, Hawaii had about 2000 species of higher plants that had arisen from about 275 ancestral stocks. There were also about 6500 species of insects descended from 250 ancestral stocks. There were 600 to 700 species in the genus *Drosophila* alone. Many plants on Hawaii have undergone adaptive radiations. Violets have become shrubs, lobelias are tree-like. These radiations have occurred in the absence of the plants normally filling the shrub and tree life styles. Biologists suspect that one ancestral insect species and one ancestral plant species gained access to Hawaii in each of the 25 000 to 100 000 years that the islands were "islands," that is, above water. Hawaii is a showcase of evolution and adaptive radiation. Recall that a species may arrive several times, so each arrival is not necessarily a new colonization event.

Islands elsewhere are well known as showcases of evolution and adaptive radiation. One celebrated case is the richness of the Galapagos Islands that so impressed Charles Darwin (see Chapter 20). But whether the setting is New Zealand, Madagascar, or Mauritius, the story repeats itself. As we will see in Chapter 48, island populations of animals and plants can be very vulnerable to extinction. Lamentably, Hawaii is also a showcase of the negative impact of humans on biodiversity.

Adaptive radiation on islands reminds us that species can be adapting to new ways of life at the same time in different parts of the world. The result is a mosaic of life, with many examples of parallel and convergent evolution (see Chapters 19 and 20, respectively).

3.3c Land: Organisms Conquer a New Frontier

The movement of organisms onto land presented many challenges (see Chapters 25, 26, and 27), and many "terrestrial" organisms actually live in films of water, so they have not forsaken an aquatic existence. Included on the list of challenges are matters of support, conservation of water, reproduction, and disposal of wastes. Other facts of life are also different for organisms living on land as opposed to in water.

Some of the differences between water and air include density and viscosity, which, in turn, affect rates of diffusion and availability of oxygen **(Table 3.2)**. Animals operating in water extract dissolved oxygen, although some photoautotrophs actually break water molecules

Table 3.2.	Gases in Water and in Air.		
		Water	Air
Viscosity		100x	x
Density		1000y	y
Diffusion rate		Low	High
O_2 mL.L^{-1}		0–10	100–130
CO_2 mL.L^{-1}		0–13	>100
O_2 extraction		<80%	25%
% of energy budget to run pump that drives breathing, whether air or water		20%	1–2%

Table 3.3.	The Impact of Temperature on Oxygen Availability for Goldfish (*Carassius Auratus*).	
	5° C	35° C
O_2 available	9 mL.L^{-1}	5 mL.L^{-1}
Goldfish need	8 mL.kg.h^{-1}	225 mL.kg.h^{-1}
Ventilation rate	1.3 L.kg.h^{-1}	60 L.kg.h^{-1}

The amount of oxygen available is further reduced in salt water.

in the process of photosynthesis. Animals that breathe air have more ready access to oxygen and spend less of their overall energy budget acquiring it than aquatic animals (see Table 3.2). A closer look at the availability of dissolved oxygen in water and the goldfish's need for oxygen **(Table 3.3)** makes it easy to recognize some of the drawbacks to living in water. Put simply, the warmer the water, the greater the goldfish's need for oxygen, which coincides with reduced amounts of dissolved oxygen.

Truly terrestrial plants and animals have more complex body designs than many of their aquatic counterparts. By the end of the Devonian, terrestrial plants had developed specialized sexual organs, stems with mechanisms for fluid transport, structural elements such as wood to provide mechanical support, roots for anchorage, leaves as sites of photosynthesis, stomata in the leaves to allow passage of CO_2 and O_2, and seeds **(Figure 3.5)**. Terrestrial animals of this period had skeletons for support and anchoring muscles (allowing locomotion), organs for gaseous exchange (breathing atmospheric oxygen), and systems for circulating materials within the body. Terrestrial animals and plants also had waterproof coverings to minimize the chances of desiccation. Terrestrial animals used nontoxic excretory products (urea and uric acid), whereas aquatic ones still relied heavily on ammonia.

3.3d Other Breakthroughs Underlying Adaptive Radiations

As you proceed through this book, look for other examples of breakthroughs that appeared to result in a radiation of organisms within a group (e.g., mammals or birds), or where different organisms adopted similar strategies. Examples include the insect traps of carnivorous plants, fungi, and spiders; the wings of bats, birds, insects, and pterosaurs; and the reinvasion of the oceans by reptiles and mammals.

See Chapters 17, 18, 19, and 20 for a more in-depth look at evolution and the ample evidence that has been gathered to support this theory.

Evolution is the idea behind representations of "trees of life" **(Figure 3.6)**. Traditional trees of life are designed to illustrate the relationships between organisms over time and may be presented in the context of a geologic time series (see the geologic time table in *The Chemical and Physical Foundations of Biology* pages).

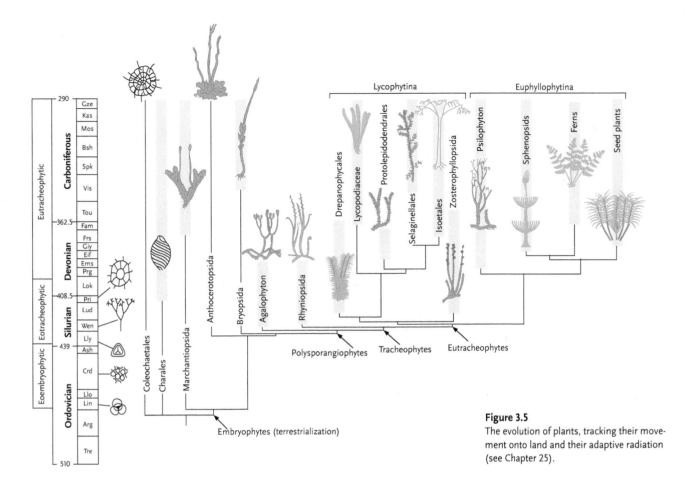

Figure 3.5
The evolution of plants, tracking their movement onto land and their adaptive radiation (see Chapter 25).

With the advent of the tools of molecular genetics (see Chapter 16), biologists have been able to prepare more detailed trees reflecting broader relationships. The example in **Figure 3.7, p. 56** shows that the diversity of life is almost overwhelming because of the broad coverage that can be achieved with genetic data, even though this tree presents only 191 species. One challenge to biologists is putting this diversity in context and appreciating the processes that have produced it.

STUDY BREAK

1. How does the theory of evolution explain the unity and diversity of all life?
2. What are the four central ideas of Darwin's theory of evolution by natural selection?
3. List advantages that oxygenic photosynthesis provided organisms living on Earth.

Figure 3.6
The tree of life. Darwin envisioned the history of life as a tree. Branching points represent the origins of new lineages; branches that do not reach the top represent extinct groups.

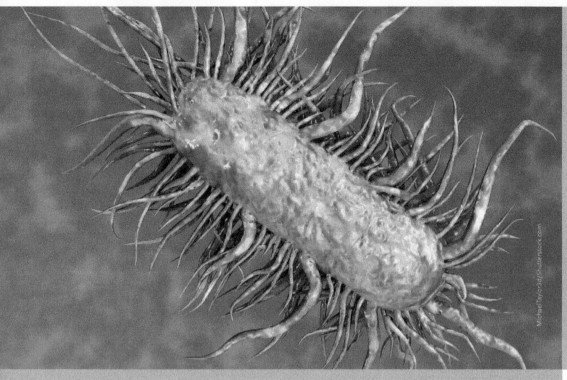

The bacterium *Escherichia coli*.

Bacteria and Archaea

WHY IT MATTERS

Who are you? What makes you "you"? Would you feel less like "you" if you knew that most of the cells in your body weren't human cells at all? The bacterial cells on and in our body outnumber our cells by ten to one. And given that, as Princeton University scientist Bonnie Bassler points out, the average person has about 30 000 human genes but more than 3 million bacterial genes, we are at most 1% human! But these bacteria aren't alien invaders—many of them may be crucial for making us unique individuals. There are about a hundred trillion bacteria of hundreds (or thousands) of different species lining your large intestine. When you were born, your gut was sterile, but immediately after birth, your intestines started to be colonized—the exact composition of these "pioneers" depends on where you were born and whether you were breastfed, among other factors. The early colonists were essential for the normal development of your gut as an infant, and throughout your life, your gut bacteria have continued to help you in many ways: they help digest your food, synthesize vitamin K for you, and produce antimicrobial factors to protect you from pathogens. The composition of your gut bacteria is more similar to that of your family than to people not related to you, but it is still unique to you; even identical twins, who share so much else, have different sets of gut bacteria. Recent research has revealed that the diversity of your gut bacteria plays a role in your odds of developing metabolic diseases and becoming obese, and may even be involved in your mental health.

CONCEPT FIX As you can tell from this introduction, not all or even most prokaryotic organisms are harmful! The idea that all bacteria cause disease is one of the major misconceptions about these organisms, but nothing could be farther from the truth: most known bacteria and members of the other group of prokaryotic organisms, archaea, play a crucial role in ecosystems, recycling nutrients and breaking down compounds that no other organisms can. Others carry out reactions important in food production, in industry (e.g., production of pharmaceutical products), and in **bioremediation** of polluted sites. ⬡

In this chapter, we first look at the structure and function of prokaryotic organisms, emphasizing the features that differentiate them from other organisms, and conclude with a look at the diversity of these fascinating organisms.

22.1 The Full Extent of the Diversity of Bacteria and Archaea Is Unknown

While reading this chapter, keep in mind that everything we know so far about bacteria and archaea is based on a tiny fraction of the total number of species. We have isolated and identified only about 6000 species, which may be as low as 1% of the total number. We know almost nothing about the prokaryotic organisms of entire habitats, such as the oceans, which make up 70% of Earth's surface. Why have we only identified so few, and why are we not even sure how many prokaryotic organisms there might be? In the past, we identified and classified bacteria and archaea based on external features (e.g., cell wall structure) and physiological differences, which meant that we had to be able to grow the organisms in culture. We have learned a great deal about the biology of some bacteria and archaea but have been unable to learn much about the majority of prokaryotic organisms, since they cannot be grown in culture (e.g., those that require extreme physicochemical conditions). Recently, molecular techniques have been developed that allow us to isolate and clone DNA from an environment and then analyze gene sequences; this means that we can now identify and characterize bacteria and archaea without having to culture them. This approach, known as **metagenomics**, now enables us to investigate the diversity of prokaryotic organisms in a wide range of environments. However, our understanding of the full extent of microbial diversity still faces other challenges, such as the fact that many environments (e.g., the deep ocean) are remote and thus very difficult and/or costly to sample.

22.1a Prokaryotic Organisms Make Up Two of the Three Domains of Life

Two of the three domains of living organisms, **Archaea** and **Bacteria**, consist of prokaryotic organisms (the third domain, **Eukarya**, includes all eukaryotes). Bacteria are the prokaryotic organisms most familiar to us, including those responsible for diseases of humans and other animals as well as those that we rely on for production of cheese, yogurt, chocolate, and other foods. Archaea are not as well known, as they were only discovered about 40 years ago. As you will see in this chapter, archaea share some cellular features with eukaryotes and some with bacteria but have still other features that are unique. Many of the archaea live under very extreme conditions that no other organisms, including bacteria, can survive.

22.2 Prokaryotic Structure and Function

We begin our survey by examining prokaryotic cellular structures and modes of reproduction, and how they obtain energy and nutrients.

In general, prokaryotic organisms are the smallest in the world (Figure 22.1). Few species are more than 1 to 2 μm long (although the longest is 600 μm long, which is larger than some eukaryotes!); from 500 to 1000 of them would fit side by side across the dot on this letter "i." Despite the small size of bacteria and archaea, they dominate life on Earth: current estimates of total prokaryotic diversity are in the billions of species, and their total collective mass (their **biomass**) on Earth exceeds that of animals and may be greater than that of all plant life. Prokaryotic organisms colonize every niche on Earth that supports life, and even occur deep in the Earth's crust. They also colonize other organisms—for example, huge numbers of bacteria inhabit the surfaces and cavities of a healthy human body, including the skin, mouth and nasal passages, and large intestine. As mentioned in "Why It Matters," collectively, the bacteria in and on your body outnumber all the other cells in your body. It is not surprising that the diversity of bacteria and archaea should be so much greater than that of eukaryotes because for about 3 billion years they were the only forms of life on Earth and so had time to diversify and expand into every habitat on Earth before the first eukaryotes appeared on the scene (see Chapter 2).

22.2a Prokaryotic Cells Appear Simple in Structure Compared with Eukaryotic Cells

Three cell shapes are common among prokaryotes: spiral, spherical (or **coccoid**; *coccus* = berry), and cylindrical (known as **rods**), but some archaea even have square cells (Figure 22.2).

At first glance, a typical prokaryotic cell seems much simpler than a eukaryotic cell (Figure 22.3, p. 484): images taken with standard electron microscopy typically reveal little more than a cell wall and plasma membrane surrounding cytoplasm with DNA concentrated in one region and ribosomes scattered throughout. The chromosome is not contained in a membrane-bound nucleus but is packed into an area of the cell called the **nucleoid**. Prokaryotic cells have no cytoplasmic organelles equivalent to the endoplasmic reticulum (ER) or Golgi complex of eukaryotic cells (see Chapter 2). With few exceptions, the reactions carried out by organelles in eukaryotes are distributed between the plasma membrane and the cytoplasmic solution of prokaryotic cells; this means that macromolecules such as proteins are very concentrated in the cytoplasm of these cells, making the cytoplasm quite viscous. This evident simplicity of prokaryotic cells led

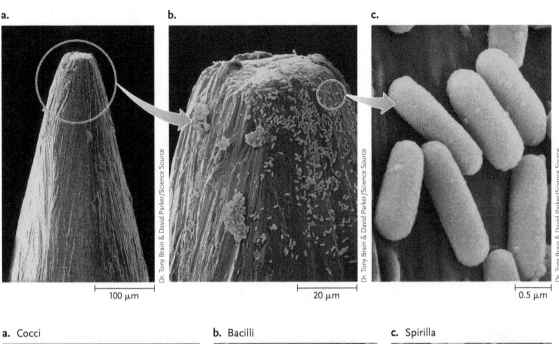

Figure 22.1
Bacillus bacteria on the point of a pin. Cells magnified **(a)** 70 times, **(b)** 350 times, and **(c)** 14 000 times.

100 μm

20 μm

0.5 μm

Dr. Tony Brain & David Parker/Science Source

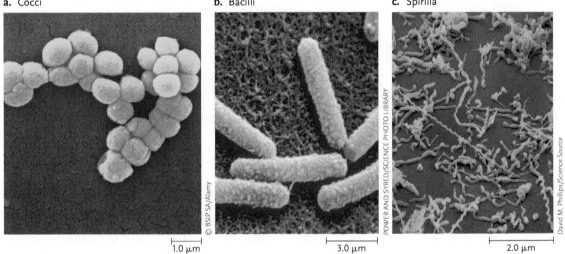

a. Cocci

b. Bacilli

c. Spirilla

1.0 μm

3.0 μm

2.0 μm

© BSIP SA/Alamy

POWER AND SYRED/SCIENCE PHOTO LIBRARY

David M. Phillips/Science Source

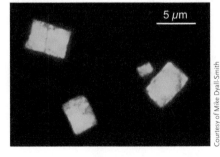

d. Square cells

5 μm

Courtesy of Mike Dyall-Smith

Figure 22.2
Common shapes of prokaryotic cells. **(a)** Scanning electron microscope (SEM) image of *Micrococcus*, a coccoid bacterium. **(b)** SEM image of *Salmonella*, a rod-shaped bacterium. **(c)** SEM image of *Spiroplasma*, a spiral bacterium. **(d)** Acridine orange–stained cells of *Haloquadratum walsbyi*, a square archaeon.

people to regard these cells as featureless and disorganized. However, the apparent simplicity of these cells is misleading. New microscopic techniques reveal that prokaryotic cells do have a cytoskeleton—not homologous to that of a eukaryote but serving some of the same functions—and have more sophisticated organization than was previously thought. In fact, recent research carried out by Laura van Niftrik of the Netherlands and her colleagues has identified a prokaryotic organelle! Certain bacteria that obtain energy by oxidizing ammonia have an internal membrane-bound compartment, where ammonia oxidation

Figure 22.3

The structure of a bacterial cell. The high concentration of ribosomes gives the cytoplasm a granular appearance.

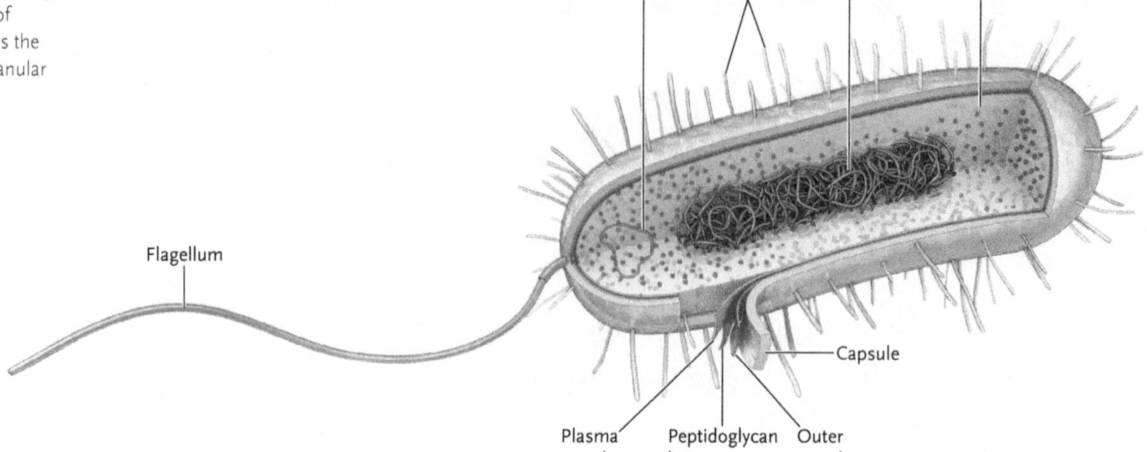

Plasmid · Pili · Condensed DNA molecule (in the nucleoid) · Cytoplasm containing ribosomes

Flagellum

Capsule

Plasma membrane · Peptidoglycan layer · Outer membrane

Cell wall

occurs. It was hypothesized that as ammonia oxidation proceeds inside this compartment, a proton-motive force could be generated across the membrane, generating ATP. Van Niftrik and her colleagues found that the membrane around this compartment does contain ATP synthase, supporting the above hypothesis. Thus, it appears that some prokaryotic cells have organelles with specialized functions.

Internal Structures. The genome of most prokaryotic cells consists of a single, circular DNA molecule, although some, such as the causative agent of Lyme disease (*Borrelia burgdorferi*), have a linear chromosome. Many prokaryotic cells also contain small circles of DNA called **plasmids (Figure 22.4)**, which generally contain genes for nonessential but beneficial functions such as antibiotic resistance. Plasmids replicate independently of the cell's chromosome and can be transferred from one cell to another, meaning that genes for antibiotic resistance are readily shared among prokaryotic cells, even among cells of different species. This *horizontal gene transfer* allows antibiotic resistance and other traits to spread very quickly in bacterial populations. Horizontal gene transfer also occurs when bacterial cells take up DNA from their environment (e.g., from other cells that have lysed) or when viruses transfer DNA from one bacterium to another (see Chapter 23). Evidence indicates that a virus transferred toxin-encoding genes from *Shigella dysenteriae* (which causes bloody diarrhea) to *E. coli,* resulting in the deadly O157:H7 strain responsible for serious illness or even death of people eating beef and other food contaminated with this bacterium.

Like eukaryotic cells, prokaryotic cells contain ribosomes. Bacterial ribosomes are smaller than eukaryotic ribosomes but carry out protein synthesis by essentially

the same mechanisms as those of eukaryotes (see Chapter 13). Archaeal ribosomes resemble those of bacteria in size but differ in structure; protein synthesis in Archaea is a combination of bacterial and eukaryotic processes, with some unique archaeal features. As a result, antibiotics that stop bacterial infections by targeting ribosome activity do not interfere with archaeal protein synthesis.

Prokaryotic Cell Walls. Most prokaryotic cells have a cell wall that lies outside their plasma membrane and protects the cell from lysing if subjected to hypotonic conditions or exposed to membrane-disrupting compounds such as detergents. The primary component of bacterial cell walls is **peptidoglycan,** a polymer of sugars and amino acids that forms linear chains. Peptide cross-linkages between the chains give the cell wall great strength and rigidity. The antibiotic penicillin prevents the formation of these cross-linkages, resulting in a weak cell wall that is easily ruptured, killing the cell **(Figure 22.5).**

Bacteria can be divided into two broad groups, Gram-positive and Gram-negative cells, based on their reaction to the **Gram stain procedure,** traditionally used as the first step in identifying an unknown bacterium.

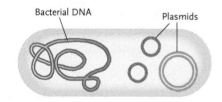

Bacterial DNA · Plasmids

Figure 22.4
Plasmids inside a prokaryotic cell.

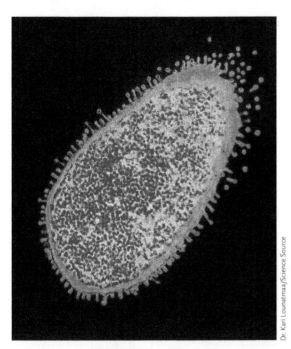

Figure 22.5
Image showing degradation of the cell wall following antibiotic treatment. The cell will eventually lyse, killing the bacterium.

Cells are first stained with crystal violet and then treated with iodine, which forms a complex with crystal violet. The cells are then rinsed with ethanol and counterstained with safranin. Some cells retain the crystal violet–iodine complex and thus appear purple when viewed under the microscope; these are termed Gram-positive cells. In other bacteria, ethanol washes the crystal violet–iodine complex out of the cells, which are colourless until counterstained with safranin; these Gram-negative cells appear pink under the microscope. The differential response to staining is related to

differences in cell wall structure: **Gram-positive** bacteria have cell walls composed almost entirely of a single, relatively thick layer of peptidoglycan **(Figure 22.6a).** This thick peptidoglycan layer retains the crystal violet–iodine complex inside the cell. **Gram-negative** cells have only a thin peptidoglycan layer in their walls, and the crystal violet–iodine complex is washed out. In contrast, the cell wall of Gram-negative bacteria has two distinct layers (Figure 22.6b), a thin peptidoglycan layer just outside the plasma membrane and an **outer membrane** external to the peptidoglycan layer. This outer membrane contains **lipopolysaccharides (LPSs)** and thus is very different from the plasma membrane. The outer membrane protects Gram-negative bacteria from potentially harmful substances in the environment; for example, it inhibits entry of penicillin. Therefore, Gram-negative cells are less sensitive to penicillin than are Gram-positive cells.

The cell walls of some archaea are assembled from a molecule related to peptidoglycan but with different molecular components and bonding structure. Others have walls assembled from proteins or polysaccharides instead of peptidoglycan. Archaea have a variable response to the Gram stain, so this procedure is not useful in identifying archaea.

The cell wall of many prokaryotic cells is surrounded by a layer of polysaccharides known as a **capsule (Figure 22.7, p. 486;** see also Figure 22.6). Capsules are "sticky" and play important roles in protecting cells in different environments. Cells with capsules are protected to some extent from desiccation, extreme temperatures, bacterial viruses, and harmful molecules such as antibiotics and antibodies. In many pathogenic bacteria, the presence or absence of the protective capsule differentiates infective from noninfective forms. For example, normal *Streptococcus pneumoniae* bacteria are capsulated and virulent, causing severe pneumonia in humans and other mammals. Mutant *S. pneumoniae* without capsules are nonvirulent and can easily be

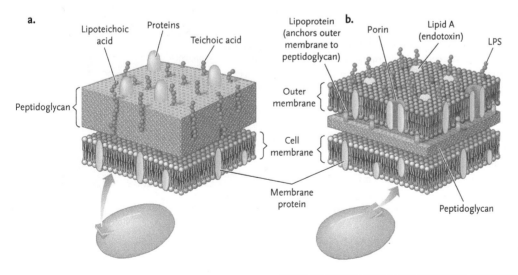

Figure 22.6
Cell wall structure in Gram-positive and Gram-negative bacteria. **(a)** The thick cell wall in Gram-positive bacteria. **(b)** The thin cell wall of Gram-negative bacteria has a thin peptidoglycan layer and outer membrane with lipopolysaccharides (LPSs). The uppermost part of LPS is the O antigen, a carbohydrate chain that elicits an antibody response in vertebrates exposed to Gram-negative bacteria such as *E. coli* O157:H7. More information on the toxic effects of lipid A, which embeds LPSs in the outer membrane, is provided on p. 489.

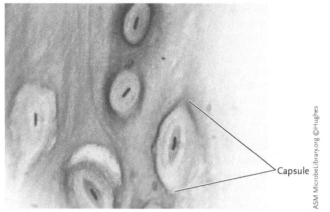

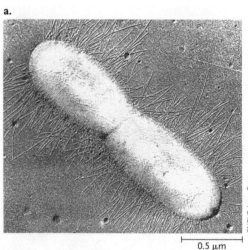

Capsule

ASM MicrobeLibrary.org ©Hughes

CNR/Science Source

0.5 μm

Figure 22.7
Capsules surrounding the cell wall of *Rhizobium*, a Gram-negative soil bacterium.

a.

b.

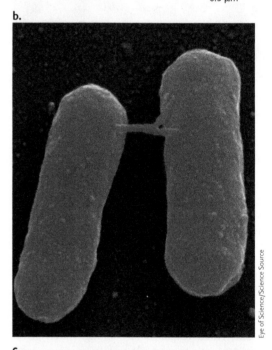

Eye of Science/Science Source

eliminated by the body's immune system if they are injected into mice or other animals.

Flagella and Pili. Many prokaryotic cells can move actively through liquids and even through films of liquid on a surface, most commonly via **flagella** (singular, *flagellum* = whip) extending from the cell wall (see Figure 22.3, p. 484). As outlined in Chapter 2, prokaryotic flagella are very different from eukaryotic flagella in both structure and pattern of movement. Prokaryotic flagella are made of rigid helical proteins, some of which act as a motor, rotating the flagellum much like the propeller of a boat. Archaeal flagella are superficially similar to bacterial flagella and carry out the same function, but the two types of flagella contain different components, develop differently, and are coded for by different genes.

Some prokaryotic cells have rigid shafts of protein called **pili** (singular, *pilus* = "hair") extending from their cell walls **(Figure 22.8a),** which enable them to adhere to or move along a surface. One type, called a *sex pilus*, not only allows bacterial cells to adhere to each other but also acts as a conduit for the transfer of plasmids from one cell to another (Figure 22.8b). Other types of pili enable bacteria to bind to animal cells. The bacterium that causes gonorrhea (*Neisseria gonorrhoeae*) uses pili to adhere to cells of the throat, eye, urogenital tract, or rectum in humans. In 2005, it was discovered that the pili of some bacteria (e.g., species of *Geobacter* and *Shewanella*) conduct electricity; these "nanowires" transfer electrons out of the cell onto minerals such as iron oxides in their environment (Figure 22.8c). Such electricity-generating bacteria hold promise for the development of microbial fuel cells as an alternative energy source.

Even though prokaryotes are simpler and less structurally diverse than eukaryotic cells, they are much more diverse metabolically, as we will now explore.

c.

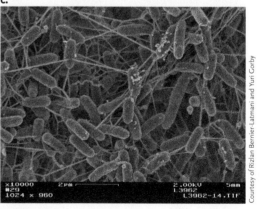

×10000 2 μm 2.00kV 5mm
#20 L3962
1024 × 960 L3962-14.TIF

Courtesy of Rizlan Bernier-Latmani and Yuri Gorby

Figure 22.8
(a) Pili extending from the surface of a dividing *E. coli* bacterium. **(b)** Sex pilus connecting two bacterial cells. **(c)** Nanowires (pili that conduct electricity) on *Shewanella oneidensis*. Note that these nanowires are much longer than the cells.

1. What features differentiate a prokaryotic cell from a eukaryotic cell? What features do both kinds of cells have?
2. How does the presence of a capsule affect the ability of the human body to mount an immune response to those bacteria?
3. How is a pilus similar to a flagellum? How is it different?
4. How does the amount of peptidoglycan in a bacterial cell wall relate to its Gram-stain reaction?

Table 22.1	Modes of Nutrition Used by Living Organisms		
Energy Source		Oxidation of Molecules*	Light
Carbon source	CO_2	**Chemoautotroph** Some bacteria and archaea; no eukaryotes	**Photoautotroph** Some bacteria, some protists, and most plants
	Organic molecules	**Chemoheterotroph** Some bacteria, archaea, and protists; also fungi, animals, and even some plants	**Photoheterotroph** Some bacteria

*Inorganic molecules for chemoautotrophs and organic molecules for chemoheterotrophs.

22.2b Prokaryotic Organisms Have the Greatest Metabolic Diversity of All Organisms

Organisms can be grouped into four modes of nutrition based on sources of energy and carbon (see **Table 22.1**).

In this approach to classification, we focus on carbon rather than other nutrients because carbon is the backbone of all organic molecules synthesized by an organism. Organisms such as plants that synthesize organic carbon molecules using inorganic carbon (CO_2) are **autotrophs** (*auto* = self; *troph* = nourishment). (Note that although CO_2 contains a carbon atom, oxides containing carbon are considered inorganic molecules.) All animals are **heterotrophs**, meaning that they obtain carbon from organic molecules, either from living hosts or from organic molecules in the products, wastes, or remains of dead organisms.

Organisms are also divided according to the source of the energy they use to drive biological activities. **Chemotrophs** (*chemo* = chemical) obtain energy by oxidizing inorganic or organic substances, whereas **phototrophs** obtain energy from light. Combining the carbon and energy sources allows us to group living organisms into four categories (Table 22.1).

Prokaryotic organisms (bacteria and archaea) show the greatest diversity in their modes of securing carbon and energy; they are the only representatives of two of the categories, chemoautotrophs and photoheterotrophs. **Photoheterotrophs** use light as an energy source and obtain carbon from organic molecules rather than from CO_2. **Chemoautotrophs** are commonly referred to as "lithotrophs" (*lithos* = rock, thus "rock-eaters"). As this name suggests, chemoautotrophs obtain energy by oxidizing inorganic substances such as hydrogen, iron, sulfur, ammonia, and nitrites and use CO_2 as their carbon source. Chemolithotrophs thrive in habitats such as deep-sea hydrothermal vents **(Figure 22.9)**, where reduced inorganic compounds are abundant. The ability of these organisms to harness energy from these compounds makes them the foundation upon which the rest of the vent community ultimately depends, just as terrestrial organisms rely on the ability of plants and other photoautotrophs to capture light energy.

We breathe oxygen to provide the final electron acceptor for the electrons we remove from our food and pass down an electron transport chain (ETC) to make ATP via aerobic respiration (Chapter 6). Some prokaryotic organisms also use oxygen as a final electron acceptor; like us, these are aerobic organisms or **aerobes**. Aerobes may be **obligate aerobes**; that is, they cannot survive without oxygen. But some prokaryotic organisms "breathe" metals, using metals as the final electron acceptor for electrons; these organisms obtain energy via anaerobic respiration. **Anaerobic respiration** can also involve other inorganic molecules, such as nitrate or sulfate, as the final electron acceptors. Only prokaryotic organisms are capable of this type of respiration. **Obligate anaerobes** are poisoned by oxygen and survive either by fermentation, in which organic molecules are the final electron acceptors, or by anaerobic respiration. **Facultative anaerobes** use O_2 when it is present, but under anaerobic conditions, they live by fermentation or anaerobic respiration. As you learned in Chapter 6, prokaryotic organisms carry out a wider

Figure 22.9
Hydrothermal vents on the ocean floor.

Dr. Ken Macdonald/Science Source

range of fermentation reactions than do eukaryotes; many of these fermentations are economically important to humans, for example, in the production of foods such as cheese, yogurt, and chocolate.

22.2c Bacteria and Archaea Play Key Roles in Biogeochemical Cycles

The ability of prokaryotic organisms to metabolize such a wide range of substrates makes them key players in the life-sustaining recycling of elements such as carbon, oxygen, and nitrogen. The pathway by which a chemical element moves through an ecosystem is known as a **biogeochemical cycle**. As an element flows through its cycle, it is transformed from one form to another; prokaryotic organisms are crucial in many of these transformations. We will look at the nitrogen cycle as an example of the key role prokaryotic organisms play in biogeochemical cycles.

Nitrogen is a component of proteins and nucleotides and so is of vital importance for all organisms. The largest source of nitrogen on Earth is the atmosphere, which is almost 80% nitrogen. Why can't we just use this abundant atmospheric nitrogen? Most organisms cannot make use of this nitrogen because they cannot break the strong triple bond between the two nitrogen atoms. Only some bacteria and archaea can break this bond, using the enzyme nitrogenase, and convert N_2 into forms that can be used by other organisms. In this conversion process, known as **nitrogen fixation**, N_2 is reduced to ammonia (NH_3). Ammonia is quickly ionized to ammonium (NH_4^+), which prokaryotic cells then use to produce nitrogen-containing molecules such as amino acids and nucleic acids. Nitrogen fixation is the only means of replenishing the nitrogen sources used by most organisms—in other words, all organisms rely on nitrogen fixed by bacteria. Examples of nitrogen-fixing bacteria are cyanobacteria and *Rhizobium* (which is symbiotic with plants; see Chapter 38).

Other prokaryotic organisms carry out **nitrification**, the oxidation of ammonium (NH_4^+) to nitrate (NO_3^-). This oxidation process is carried out in two steps by two types of nitrifiers, ammonia oxidizers and nitrate oxidizers, present in soil and water. Ammonium oxidizers convert ammonium to nitrite (NO_2^-), whereas nitrite oxidizers convert nitrite to nitrate. Nitrate is then taken up by plants and fungi and incorporated into their organic molecules. Animals obtain nitrogen in organic form by eating other organisms or each other.

In sum, nitrification makes nitrogen available to many other organisms, including plants, animals, and bacteria that cannot metabolize ammonia. The metabolic versatility of bacteria and archaea is one factor that accounts for their abundance and persistence on the planet; another factor is their impressive reproductive capacity.

22.2d Asexual Reproduction Can Result in Rapid Population Growth

In prokaryotic organisms, asexual reproduction is the normal mode of reproduction. In this process, a parent cell divides by binary fission into two daughter cells that are exact genetic copies of the parent **(Figure 22.10)**. Reproducing by binary fission means that under favourable conditions, populations of prokaryotic organisms can have very rapid exponential growth as one cell becomes two, two become four, and so on. Some prokaryotic cells can double their population size in only 20 minutes and will even begin a second round of cell division before the first round is complete; thus, one cell, given ideal conditions, can produce millions of cells in only a few hours.

These short generation times, combined with the small genomes (roughly one-thousandth the size of the genome of an average eukaryote), mean that prokaryotic organisms have higher mutation rates than do eukaryotic organisms. This translates to roughly 1000 times as many mutations per gene, per unit time, per individual as for eukaryotes. Genetic variability in prokaryotic populations, the basis for their diversity, derives largely from mutation and to a lesser degree from horizontal gene transfer (see Chapter 9). Further, the typically much larger populations of prokaryotic organisms compared with eukaryotes contribute to the much greater genetic variability in bacteria and archaea. In short, prokaryotic organisms have an enormous capacity to adapt, which is one reason for their evolutionary success.

As we have seen, the success of bacteria is beneficial to humans in many ways but can also be detrimental to us when dealing with successful pathogenic

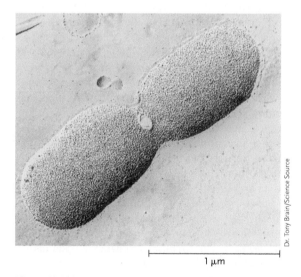

1 μm

Figure 22.10

E. coli cell dividing by binary fission. Note that a septum is forming between the two parent cells.

bacteria. In the next section, we investigate how some bacteria cause disease and how they are able to resist treatment with antibiotics.

22.2e Pathogenic Bacteria Cause Diseases by Different Mechanisms

Some bacteria produce **exotoxins**, toxic proteins that leak from or are secreted from the bacterium. For example, botulism food poisoning is caused by the exotoxin of the Gram-positive bacterium *Clostridium botulinum,* which grows in poorly preserved foods **(Figure 22.11).** The botulism exotoxin, botulin, is one of the most poisonous substances known: just a few nanograms can cause severe illness. What makes botulin so toxic? It produces muscle paralysis that can be fatal if the muscles that control breathing are affected. Interestingly, botulin is used under the brand name Botox for the cosmetic removal of wrinkles and in the treatment of migraine headaches and some other medical conditions. Exotoxins produced by certain strains of *Streptococcus pyogenes* have "superantigen properties" (i.e., overactivation of the immune system) that cause necrotizing fasciitis ("flesh-eating disease"). In 1994, Lucien Bouchard, who was then premier of Quebec, lost a leg to this disease.

Other bacteria cause disease through **endotoxins.** Endotoxins are the lipid A portion of the LPS molecule of the outer membrane of all Gram-negative bacteria, such as *E. coli, Salmonella,* and *Shigella.* When a Gram-negative cell lyses, the LPSs of the outer membrane are released; exposure to a specific component of this layer, known as lipid A, causes endotoxic shock. When Gram-negative bacteria enter the bloodstream, endotoxin overstimulates the host's immune system, triggering inflammation and an often lethal immune response. Endotoxins have different effects depending on the bacterial species and the site of infection.

22.2f Pathogenic Bacteria Commonly Develop Resistance to Antibiotics

An **antibiotic** is a natural or synthetic substance that kills or inhibits the growth of bacteria and other microorganisms. Prokaryotic organisms and fungi produce these substances naturally as defensive molecules, and we have also developed ways to synthesize several types of antibiotics. Different types of antibiotics have different modes of action: for example, streptomycins, produced by soil bacteria, block protein synthesis in their targets, whereas penicillins, produced by fungi, target the peptide cross-linkages in peptidoglycan, as described above.

How are bacteria able to block the actions of antibiotics? There are various mechanisms by which bacteria resist antibiotics **(Figure 22.12, p. 490).** For example, some bacteria are able to pump antibiotics out of the cell using membrane-bound pumps. They can also produce molecules that bind to the antibiotic or enzymes that break down the antibiotic, rendering it ineffective against its target. Alternatively, a simple mutation can result in a change in the structure of the antibiotic's target, so that the antibiotic cannot bind to it. Finally, bacteria can develop new enzymes or pathways that are not inhibited by the antibiotic.

Bacteria can develop resistance through mutations, but they can also acquire resistance via horizontal gene transfer (e.g., plasmid transfer). Taking antibiotics routinely in mild doses, or failing to complete a prescribed dosage, contributes to the spread of resistance by selecting strains that can survive in the presence of the drug. Prescription of antibiotics for

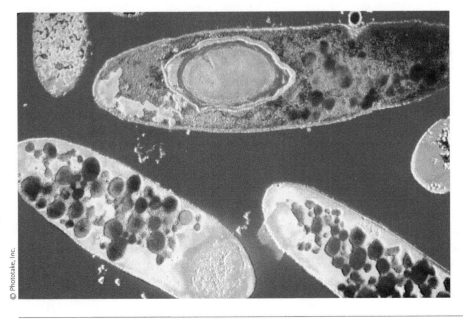

Figure 22.11
The bacterium *Clostridium butyricum,* one of the *Clostridium* species that produces the toxin botulin (colourized TEM). The large stained structure in the cells is a spore (a survival structure).

© Phototake, Inc.

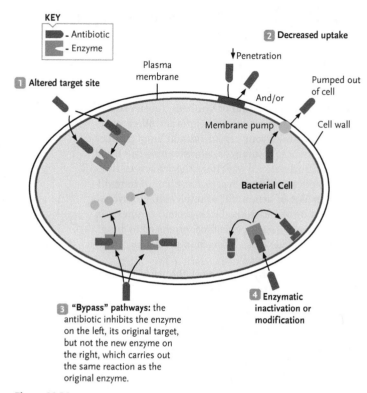

KEY

- Antibiotic
- Enzyme

1 Altered target site

Plasma membrane

2 Decreased uptake

↓ Penetration

And/or

Membrane pump

Pumped out of cell

Cell wall

Bacterial Cell

3 "Bypass" pathways: the antibiotic inhibits the enzyme on the left, its original target, but not the new enzyme on the right, which carries out the same reaction as the original enzyme.

4 Enzymatic inactivation or modification

Figure 22.12
Four major mechanisms of antibiotic resistance. See text for further explanation of each mechanism.

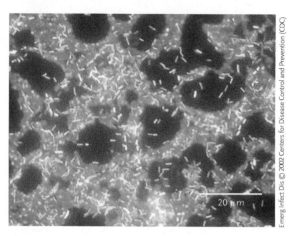

20 μm

Figure 22.13
Biofilm grown on a stainless steel surface.

colds and other virus-caused diseases can also promote bacterial resistance because viruses are unaffected by antibiotics, but the presence of antibiotics in your system can lead to resistance. Antibacterial agents that may promote resistance are also commonly included in such commercial products as soaps, detergents, and deodorants. Resistance is a form of evolutionary adaptation; antibiotics alter the bacterium's environment, conferring a reproductive advantage on those strains best adapted to the altered conditions.

The development of resistant strains has made tuberculosis, cholera, typhoid fever, gonorrhea, and other bacterial diseases difficult to treat with antibiotics. For example, as recently as 1988, drug-resistant strains of *Streptococcus pneumoniae*, which causes pneumonia, meningitis, and middle-ear infections, were practically unknown. Now, resistant strains of *S. pneumoniae* are common and increasingly difficult to treat.

22.2g In Nature, Prokaryotic Organisms May Live in Communities Attached to a Surface

Often, researchers grow bacteria and archaea as individuals in pure cultures. We have learned a lot about prokaryotic organisms from these pure cultures, but in nature, prokaryotic organisms rarely exist as individuals or as pure cultures. Instead, bacteria and

archaea live in communities where they interact in a variety of ways. One important type of community is known as a **biofilm**, which consists of a complex aggregation of microorganisms attached to a surface and surrounded by a film of polymers **(Figure 22.13).** Life in a biofilm offers several benefits: organisms can adhere to hospitable surfaces, they can live on the products of other cells, conditions within the biofilm promote gene transfer between species, and the biofilm protects cells from harmful environmental conditions (see "Life on the Edge" 22.3). Biofilms form on any surface with sufficient water and nutrients. For example, you're probably familiar with how slippery rocks in a stream can be when you try to step from one to the next; the slipperiness is due to biofilms on the rocks. Dental plaque is also a biofilm; if this biofilm spreads below the gum-line, it causes inflammation of the gums (gingivitis). Regular removal of plaque by brushing, flossing, and dental checkups helps prevent gingivitis.

Biofilms have practical consequences for humans, both beneficial and detrimental. On the beneficial side, for example, are the health effects each of us gains from the bacteria that live in biofilms in our gastrointestinal tracts. We also make use of biofilms in commercial applications: biofilms on solid supports are used in sewage treatment plants to process organic matter before the water is discharged, and they can be effective in bioremediating toxic organic molecules contaminating groundwater. But biofilms can also be harmful to human health. Biofilms adhere to many kinds of surgical equipment and supplies, including catheters, pacemakers, and artificial joints. Even if the bacteria colonizing these devices are not pathogenic, their presence is obviously not desirable given that these devices should be sterile. The presence of any Gram-negative bacteria is a concern, given their nature. As well, many heterotrophic bacteria will become opportunistic pathogens, given the right conditions. Biofilm infections are difficult to treat because bacteria in a biofilm

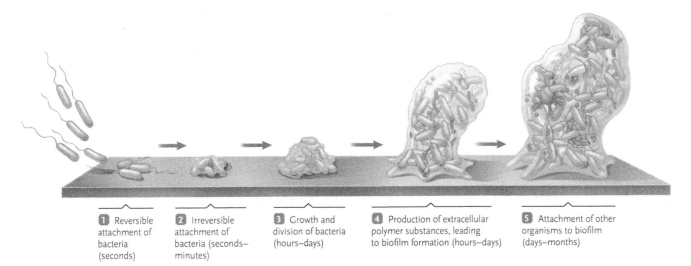

1 Reversible attachment of bacteria (seconds)

2 Irreversible attachment of bacteria (seconds–minutes)

3 Growth and division of bacteria (hours–days)

4 Production of extracellular polymer substances, leading to biofilm formation (hours–days)

5 Attachment of other organisms to biofilm (days–months)

Figure 22.14
Steps in the formation of a biofilm.

are up to 1000 times as resistant to antibiotics as are the same bacteria in liquid cultures. For example, outbreaks of the disease caused by *E. coli* O157:H7 have been caused by biofilms that are very difficult to wash off spinach, lettuce, and other produce.

How does a biofilm form? Imagine a surface, such as a rock in a stream, over which water is flowing **(Figure 22.14)**. Due to the nutrients in the water, the surface rapidly becomes coated with polymeric organic molecules, such as polysaccharides or glycoproteins. Once the surface is conditioned with organic molecules, free cells attach in a reversible manner in a matter of seconds (see Figure 22.14, step 1). If the cells remain attached, the association may become irreversible (step 2), at which point the cells grow and divide on the surface (step 3). Next, the physiology of the cells changes, and they begin to secrete *extracellular polymeric substances* (EPSs), slimy, gluelike substances similar to the molecules found in bacterial capsules. EPS extends between cells in the mixture, forming a matrix that binds cells to each other and anchors the complex to the surface, thereby establishing the biofilm (step 4). The slime layer entraps a variety of materials, such as dead cells and insoluble minerals. The physiological change accompanying the formation of a biofilm results from marked changes in a prokaryotic organism's gene expression pattern—in effect, the prokaryotic cells in a biofilm become very different organisms. Over time, other organisms are attracted to and join the biofilm; depending on the environment, these may include other bacterial species, algae, fungi, or protozoa producing diverse microbial communities (step 5). As described in "Molecule behind Biology" 22.1, on p. 492, prokaryotic organisms in a biofilm communicate with each other via **quorum sensing**; in fact, this communication is part of biofilm

formation—it allows cells to start secreting EPS when a high enough cell density is reached.

Much remains to be learned about how organisms form and interact within a biofilm and how changes in gene expression during the transition are regulated.

In the next two sections, we describe the major groups of prokaryotic organisms.

STUDY BREAK

1. What is the difference between a chemoheterotroph and a photoautotroph?
2. What is the difference between an obligate anaerobe and a facultative anaerobe?
3. What is the difference between nitrogen fixation and nitrification? Why are nitrogen-fixing prokaryotic organisms important?
4. What is binary fission?
5. What is the difference between an endotoxin and an exotoxin? Explain how they differ with respect to how they cause disease.
6. Explain four mechanisms by which bacteria protect themselves from antibiotics.
7. What is a biofilm? Give an example of a biofilm that is beneficial to humans and one that is harmful. What advantages do prokaryotic cells in a biofilm gain?
8. What is quorum sensing?

22.3 The Domain Bacteria

As for other organisms, classification of bacteria and archaeans has been revolutionized by molecular techniques that allow researchers to compare nucleic acid

N-Acyl-l-Homoserine Lactone

Most bacteria are social organisms that interact in many ways and display social behaviours, such as hunting for food in swarms, bioluminescence (see Chapter 1), biofilm formation, and virulence in pathogenic bacteria, such as the strain of *E. coli* O157:H7 responsible for "hamburger disease." These behaviours happen only when a critical population density is reached, meaning that bacteria must be able to sense the presence of other cells. How does a bacterial cell know that it is not alone? Bacteria use quorum sensing to communicate; this mechanism involves the release of signalling molecules into the environment. Accumulation of signalling molecules enables the cell to determine the density of other cells around it and respond accordingly; the response occurs after the signalling molecule is perceived by specific receptors on the cell's membrane and triggers activation of specific genes. Different bacterial species use different signalling molecules; for example, many Gram-negative bacteria use *N*-acyl-l-homoserine lactones (a lactone is a type of cyclic ester) such as that shown in **Figure 1.** Gram-positive cells also signal each other but use small peptides rather than lactones. If we can learn to "speak" or "translate" these bacterial languages, could we interfere with the social behaviours they control? The possibility has important implications for medical science given the role of these signals in processes such as the onset of virulence in pathogenic bacteria and communication within biofilms such as those that form on medical devices implanted in patients.

Figure 1
N-*Acyl-l-homoserine lactone* from *Vibrio fischeri.*

and protein sequences as tests of evolutionary related-ness. Ribosomal RNA (rRNA) sequences have been most widely used in the evolutionary studies of pro-karyotic organisms. Researchers have identified sev-eral evolutionary branches within each prokaryotic domain **(Figure 22.15)**, but these classifications will likely change in the future when full genomic sequences can be compared. We discuss the major groups of the domain Bacteria, which is much better characterized than the domain Archaea, in this sec-tion, and those of the domain Archaea in the next section.

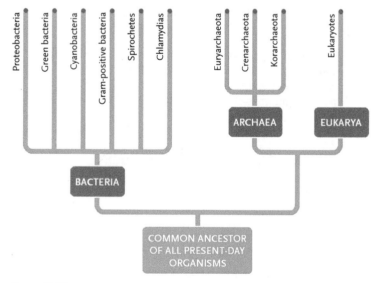

Figure 22.15
An abbreviated phylogenetic tree of Bacteria and Archaea.

22.3a Molecular Studies Reveal Numerous Evolutionary Branches in the Bacteria

Bacteria as a domain is much better characterized than Archaea: sequencing studies reveal that bacteria have several distinct and separate evolutionary branches. We restrict our discussion to six particularly important groups: proteobacteria, green bacteria, cyanobacteria, Gram-positive bacteria, spirochetes, and chlamydias (see Figure 22.15).

Proteobacteria: The Purple Bacteria and Their Relatives. This highly diverse group of Gram-negative bacteria likely evolved from a purple, photosynthetic ancestor. Their purple colour comes from their photo-synthetic pigment, a type of chlorophyll distinct from that of plants. Many present-day species are either pho-toautotrophs (the purple sulfur bacteria) or photohet-erotrophs (the purple nonsulfur bacteria); both groups carry out a type of photosynthesis that does not use water as an electron donor and does not release oxygen as a by-product.

Other present-day proteobacteria are **chemohetero-trophs** that are thought to have evolved as an evolutionary branch following the loss of photosynthetic capabilities in an early proteobacterium. The evolutionary ancestors of mitochondria are considered likely to have been ancient nonphotosynthetic proteobacteria.

Among the chemoheterotrophs classified with the proteobacteria are *E. coli*; plant pathogenic bacteria; and bacteria that cause human diseases such as bubonic plague, gonorrhea, and various forms of gas-troenteritis and dysentery. The proteobacteria also include both free-living and symbiotic nitrogen-fixing bacteria.

Myxobacteria are an unusual group of nonphotosynthetic proteobacteria that form colonies held together by the slime they produce. Enzymes secreted by the colonies digest "prey"—other bacteria, primarily—that become stuck in the slime. When environmental conditions become unfavourable, as when soil nutrients or water are depleted, myxobacteria form a fruiting body, a differentiated multicellular stage large enough to be visible to the naked eye (**Figure 22.16**). The fruiting body contains clusters of spores that are dispersed to form new colonies when the fruiting body bursts. Quorum sensing is involved in spore formation.

Helicobacter pylori, the cause of many gastric ulcers (see "People behind Biology" 22.2, p. 494), is also a proteobacterium.

Green Bacteria. This diverse group of photosynthetic Gram-negative bacteria is named for the chlorophyll pigments that give the cells their green colour (a different form of chlorophyll than that found in plants). Like the purple bacteria, they do not release oxygen as a by-product of photosynthesis. Also like the purple bacteria, some are photoautotrophs, whereas others are photoheterotrophs. The photoautotrophic green bacteria are fairly closely related to the Archaea and are usually found in hot springs, whereas the photoheterotrophic type is typically found in marine and high-salt environments.

Cyanobacteria. These Gram-negative photoautotrophs are blue-green in colour (**Figure 22.17**) and carry

a.

b.

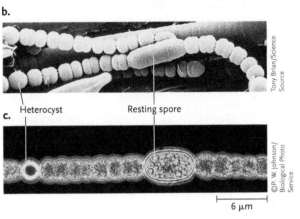

Heterocyst   Resting spore

c.

6 μm

Figure 22.17
Cyanobacteria. **(a)** A population of cyanobacteria covering the surface of a pond. **(b)** and **(c)** Chains of cyanobacterial cells. Some cells in the chains form spores. The heterocyst is a specialized cell that fixes nitrogen.

out photosynthesis by the same pathways and using the same chlorophyll as eukaryotic algae and plants. Like plants and algae, they release oxygen as a by-product of photosynthesis.

The direct ancestors of present-day cyanobacteria were the first organisms to use the water-splitting reactions of photosynthesis. As such, they were critical to the accumulation of oxygen in the atmosphere, which allowed the evolutionary development of aerobic organisms. Chloroplasts probably evolved from early cyanobacteria that were incorporated into the cytoplasm of primitive eukaryotes, which eventually gave rise to the algae and higher plants, as discussed in Chapter 26. Besides releasing oxygen, present-day cyanobacteria help fix nitrogen into organic compounds in aquatic habitats and act as symbiotic partners with fungi in lichens (see Chapter 25).

Gram-Positive Bacteria. This large group contains many species that live primarily as chemoheterotrophs. Some cause human diseases, including *Bacillus anthracis*, the causal agent of anthrax;

100 μm

Figure 22.16
The fruiting body of *Chondromyces crocatus*, a myxobacterium. Cells of this species collect together to form the fruiting body.

Barry Marshall, *University of Western Australia*; Robin Warren, *Royal Perth Hospital (retired)*

A few hours after you eat, you go to your doctor complaining of stomach pain, abdominal bloating, and nausea; most worryingly, you have started to vomit blood. Your doctor tells you that you have a gastric ulcer, a lesion in your stomach lining. If this visit to your doctor had occurred before the mid-1980s, your doctor would have explained that ulcers are caused by increased stomach acidity due to stress. The treatment? Drink lots of milk, take antacids, and give up alcohol and your favourite spicy foods—no more curries or chili that would aggravate your ulcer. This view of ulcers was accepted for years until two Australian physicians, Barry Marshall and Robin Warren, of the University of Western Australia, demonstrated that most ulcers are caused by a bacterial infection. Marshall and Warren observed that biopsies from patients with ulcers revealed large numbers of spiral-shaped bacterial cells in inflamed tissues. Together, the two physicians carried out a series of studies that demonstrated the link between ulcers and the presence of the bacterium; as you can see in **Table 1**, the bacterium was associated with almost all gastric and duodenal (part of the small intestine) ulcers. The bacterium was not known at the time but was later named *Helicobacter pylori*

Table 1	Association of Bacteria with Biopsy Samples	
Biopsy Appearance	Total Samples	Number (%) Associated with Bacteria
Gastric ulcer	22	18 (77%)
Duodenal ulcer	13	13 (100%)
Total	35	31 (89%)

(Figure 1). But despite Marshall and Warren having research published in respected medical journals, the medical community did not believe their findings—how could bacteria possibly survive in the very acidic conditions of the stomach? Out of frustration, and anxious to get proper treatment for his patients, Marshall drank a culture of *H. pylori*! After about a week, he developed severe abdominal pain and vomiting, and endoscopic examination of his stomach showed regions of inflammation teeming with *H. pylori*. Much to his disappointment, he did not develop ulcers, but he had made the point that *H. pylori* is pathogenic. Marshall and Warren also showed that antibiotics were effective in treating ulcers, and in 2005, they were awarded the Nobel Prize in Medicine. So how is *H. pylori* able to survive in the stomach? It is able to burrow deep into the mucus lining the stomach by means of its numerous flagella, and it produces urease, which converts urea into CO_2 and ammonia, making the region around its cells more basic.

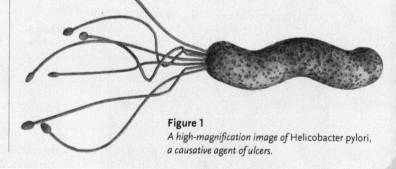

Figure 1
A high-magnification image of Helicobacter pylori, *a causative agent of ulcers.*

Figure 22.18
Streptococcus bacteria forming the long chains of cells typical of many species in this genus.

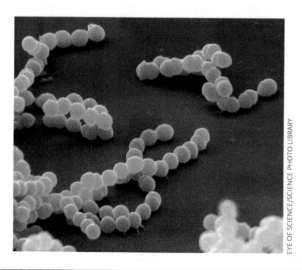

EYE OF SCIENCE/SCIENCE PHOTO LIBRARY

Staphylococcus, which causes some forms of food poisoning, toxic shock syndrome, pneumonia, and meningitis; and *Streptococcus* **(Figure 22.18)**, which causes strep throat, necrotizing fasciitis, and some forms of pneumonia. However, some Gram-positive bacteria are beneficial to humans; *Lactobacillus*, for example, carries out the lactic acid fermentation used in the production of pickles, sauerkraut, and yogurt. One unusual group of bacteria, the mycoplasmas, is placed among the Gram-positive bacteria by molecular studies even though they show a Gram-negative staining reaction. This staining reaction results because they are naked cells that secondarily lost their cell walls in evolution. Some mycoplasmas, with diameters from 0.1 to 0.2 μm, are the smallest known cells.

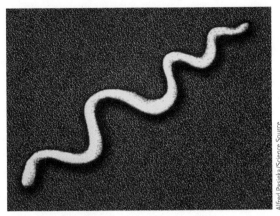

Figure 22.19
Treponema pallidum, a spirochete bacterium that causes syphilis (scanning electron microscope image).

Spirochetes. These organisms have helically spiralled flagella embedded in their cytoplasm, causing the cells to move in a twisting, corkscrew pattern **(Figure 22.19).** Their corkscrew movements enable them to move in viscous environments such as mud and sewage, where they are common. Some spirochetes are harmless inhabitants of the human mouth; another species, *Treponema pallidum*, is the cause of syphilis. Termites have symbiotic spirochetes in their intestines that enable them to digest cellulose.

Chlamydias. These bacteria are unusual because although they are Gram-negative and have cell walls with an outer membrane, they lack peptidoglycan. All the known chlamydias are intracellular parasites that cause various diseases in animals. One bacterium of this group, *Chlamydia trachomatis,* is responsible for one of the most common sexually transmitted infections of the urinary and reproductive tracts of humans and also causes trachoma, an infection of the cornea that is the leading cause of blindness in humans.

In this section, you have seen that bacteria thrive in nearly every habitat on Earth. However, some members of the second prokaryotic domain, the Archaea, the subject of the next section, live in habitats that are too forbidding even for bacteria.

STUDY BREAK

1. What methodologies have been used to classify prokaryotic organisms?
2. What were the likely characteristics of the evolutionary ancestor of present-day proteobacteria?
3. How does photosynthesis in photosynthetic proteobacteria differ from photosynthesis in cyanobacteria?

22.4 The Domain Archaea

The first Archaea were isolated from extreme environments, such as hot springs, hydrothermal vents on the ocean floor, and salt lakes **(Figure 22.20).** For that reason, these prokaryotes were called *extremophiles* (organisms that live in extreme environments). Subsequently, archaea have also been found living in less extreme environments.

Archaea share some cellular features with eukaryotes and some with bacteria and have other features that are unique **(Table 22.2, p. 496).**

22.4a Unique Characteristics of Archaea

Among their unique characteristics are certain features of their plasma membranes and cell walls. The lipid molecules in archaeal plasma membranes are unlike those in the plasma membranes of the majority of bacteria: there is a different linkage between glycerol and the hydrophobic tails, and the

a.

b.

Figure 22.20
Typically extreme archaeal habitats. (a) Highly saline water in Great Salt Lake, Utah, coloured red purple by archaeans. **(b)** Hot, sulfur-rich water in Emerald Pool, Yellowstone National Park, coloured brightly by the oxidative activity of archaea, which convert H_2S to elemental sulfur.

LIFE ON THE EDGE 22.3

Snottite Bacteria

Some of the most extreme and inhospitable environments on Earth are deep caves that have formed in sulfur-rich rocks. As water flows through these rocks, toxic H_2S gas is released at concentrations that can make the cave atmosphere toxic to humans, who cannot survive in the caves without gas masks. But extremophile bacteria and archaea thrive in these caves, including bacteria that grow in biofilms to form snottites **(Figure 1),** mucous stalactites that hang from the walls and ceiling of the cave. These bacteria obtain energy from H_2S and other sulfur compounds, producing sulfuric acid as a waste product that drips from the snottites. The biofilm that surrounds the bacteria protects them from the extremely acid environment (pH < 2) they have helped to create, but the acid eats away at the surrounding rock, enlarging the cave. In addition to actively contributing to cave formation, these extremophile bacteria are the foundation of the cave ecosystem. Their ability to convert inorganic chemicals such as H_2S into the organic molecules that make up their cells provides a source of organic carbon to other organisms, making them the base of the food web in such caves.

Figure 1
Snottites, Cueva de Villa Luz, Mexico.

Table 22.2	Characteristics of the Bacteria, Archaea, and Eukarya		
Characteristic	Bacteria	Archaea*	Eukarya
DNA arrangement	Single, circular in most, but some linear and/or multiple	Single, circular	Multiple linear molecules
Chromosomal proteins	Prokaryotic histonelike proteins	Five eukaryotic histones	Five eukaryotic histones
Genes arranged in operons	Yes	Yes	No
Nuclear envelope	No	No	Yes
Mitochondria	No	No	Yes
Chloroplasts	No	No	Yes
Peptidoglycan in cell wall	Present	Absent; some have pseudopeptidoglycan	Absent
Membrane lipids	Unbranched; linked by ester linkages	Branched; linked by ether linkage; may have polar heads at both ends	Unbranched; linked by ester linkages
RNA polymerase	Limited variations	Multiple types	Multiple types
Ribosomal proteins	Prokaryotic	Some prokaryotic, some eukaryotic	Eukaryotic
First amino acid placed in proteins	Formylmethionine	Methionine	Methionine
Aminoacyl–tRNA synthetases	Prokaryotic	Eukaryotic	Eukaryotic
Cell division proteins	Prokaryotic	Prokaryotic	Eukaryotic
Proteins of energy metabolism	Prokaryotic	Prokaryotic	Eukaryotic

*Given that very few Archaea have been identified or cultured, the information in this table is based on an extremely small data set.

tails are isoprenes rather than fatty acids (see Chapter 5). Also, some lipids have polar head groups at both ends. Why would such seemingly minor differences be significant? These unique lipids are more resistant to disruption, making the plasma membranes better suited to extreme environments. Similarly, the unique cell walls of archaea are more resistant to extremes than those of bacteria; some archaea can even survive being boiled in strong detergents!

Many archaea are chemoautotrophs, whereas others are chemoheterotrophs. Interestingly, no known member of the Archaea has been shown to be pathogenic.

22.4b Molecular Studies Reveal Three Evolutionary Branches in the Archaea

The phylogeny of Archaea is poorly developed relative to Bacteria and in quite a state of flux because a tremendous number of archaea have not been cultured, meaning that we have only metagenomic data for most of these organisms. Based on differences in rRNA sequence data, the domain Archaea is divided into three groups (see Figure 22.15, p. 492). Two major groups, the **Euryarchaeota** and the **Crenarchaeota**, contain archaea that have been cultured in the laboratory. The third group, the **Korarchaeota**, has been recognized solely on the basis of DNA taken from environmental samples.

Euryarchaeota. These organisms are found in various extreme environments. They include methanogens, extreme halophiles, and some extreme thermophiles, as described below.

Methanogens (methane generators) live in low-oxygen environments **(Figure 22.21)** and represent about one-half of all known species of Archaea. Methanogens are obligate anaerobes that live in the anoxic (oxygen-lacking) sediments of swamps, lakes,

RALPH ROBINSON, VISUALS UNLIMITED/SCIENCE PHOTO LIBRARY

5 μm

Figure 22.21
A colony of the methanogenic archaeon *Methanosarcina*, which lives in the sulfurous, waterlogged soils of marshes and swamps.

marshes, and sewage works, as well as in more moderate environments, such as the rumen of cattle and sheep, the large intestine of dogs and humans, and the hindgut of insects such as termites and cockroaches. Methanogens generate energy by converting various substrates such as carbon dioxide and hydrogen gas or acetate into methane gas, which is released into the atmosphere.

Halophiles are salt-loving organisms. Extreme halophilic Archaea live in highly saline environments such as the Dead Sea and on foods preserved by salting. They require a minimum NaCl concentration of about 1.5 M (about 9% solution) to survive and can live in a fully saturated solution (5.5 M, or 32%). Most are aerobic chemoheterotrophs, which obtain energy from sugars, alcohols, and amino acids using pathways similar to those of bacteria. Many extreme halophiles use light as a secondary energy source, supplementing the oxidations that are their primary source of energy.

Extreme thermophiles live in extremely hot environments such as hot springs and ocean floor hydrothermal vents. Their optimal temperature range for growth is 70 to 95°C, close to the boiling point of water. By comparison, no eukaryotic organism is known to live at a temperature higher than 60°C. Some extreme thermophiles are members of the Euryarchaeota, but most belong to the **Crenarchaeota**, the next group that we discuss.

Crenarchaeota. This group includes most of the extreme thermophiles, which have a higher optimal temperature range than those belonging to the Euryarchaeota. For example, the most thermophilic member of this group, *Pyrobolus*, dies below 90°C, grows optimally at 106°C, and can survive an hour of autoclaving at 121°C! *Pyrobolus* lives in ocean floor hydrothermal vents, where the pressure creates water temperatures greater than the boiling point of water on Earth's surface.

Also in this group are **psychrophiles** ("cold loving"), organisms that grow optimally in cold temperatures in the range from −10 to −20°C. These organisms are found mostly in the Antarctic and Arctic oceans, which are frozen most of the year, and in the intense cold at ocean depths.

Mesophilic members of the Crenarchaeota make up a large part of plankton found in cool, marine waters, where they are food sources for other marine organisms.

Korarchaeota. This group has been recognized solely on the basis of DNA samples obtained from marine and terrestrial hydrothermal environments. To date, no members of this group have been isolated and cultivated in the lab, and nothing is known about their physiology. Molecular data indicate that they are the oldest archaeal lineage.

Thermophilic archaea are important commercially. For example, they are very important in biotechnological applications as sources of enzymes that function under extreme physicochemical conditions (e.g., high temperature, high salinity).

In this chapter, we have focused on bacteria and archaea, whose metabolic diversity and environmental range and ecological importance belie their structural simplicity. In the next chapter, we look at still simpler entities: viruses, viroids, and prions, which are derived from living organisms and retain only some of the properties of life.

1. What distinguishes members of the Archaea from members of the Bacteria and Eukarya?
2. How does a methanogen obtain energy? In which group or groups of Archaea are methanogens found?
3. Where do extreme halophilic Archaea live? How do they obtain energy? In which group or groups of Archaea are the extreme halophiles found?
4. What are extreme thermophiles and psychrophiles?

Review

aplia™

To access course materials such as Aplia and other companion resources, please visit www.NELSONbrain.com.

22.1 The Full Extent of the Diversity of Bacteria and Archaea Is Unknown

- Bacteria and Archaea are the most abundant and diverse organisms on Earth; however, the vast majority of prokaryotic organisms have not been described because they cannot be cultured using standard techniques and because many environments are very difficult and/or expensive to access.
- Prokaryotic organisms make up two of the three domains of life, the Archaea and the Bacteria.

22.2 Prokaryotic Structure and Function

- Prokaryotic genomes typically consist of a single, circular DNA molecule packaged into the nucleoid (Figure 22.4). Many prokaryotic cells also contain plasmids, which replicate independently of the chromosome and can be passed to other cells.
- Gram-positive bacterial cell walls consist of a single, relatively thick peptidoglycan layer. Gram-negative bacteria have walls consisting of a relatively thin peptidoglycan sheath surrounded by an outer lipopolysaccharide (LPS) membrane (Figure 22.6).
- A polysaccharide capsule (Figures 22.3, and 22.7) surrounds many bacteria, protecting them and helping them adhere to surfaces.
- Archaea and bacteria show great diversity in their modes of obtaining energy and carbon. Two of the modes of nutrition found among eukaryotic organisms are also found in prokaryotic organisms (chemoheterotrophy and photoautotrophy), but two other modes are unique to prokaryotic organisms: chemoautotrophs obtain energy by oxidizing inorganic substrates and use carbon dioxide as their carbon source, and photoheterotrophs use light as a source of energy and obtain their carbon from organic molecules.

- Bacteria and Archaea use a range of pathways to transform energy: aerobic respiration, anaerobic respiration, and/or various forms of fermentation.
- Some bacteria and archaea are capable of nitrogen fixation, the conversion of atmospheric nitrogen to ammonia; others are responsible for nitrification, the conversion of ammonium to nitrate.
- Prokaryotic cells normally reproduce asexually by binary fission (Figure 22.10), which can result in very rapid population growth under favourable conditions.
- In nature, bacteria and archaea live in complex communities, such as biofilms (Figure 22.13).
- Pathogenic bacteria cause disease via exotoxins and endotoxins.
- Bacteria may develop resistance to antibiotics through mutation of their own genes or by acquiring resistance genes from other bacteria.

22.3 The Domain Bacteria

- Bacteria are divided into more than a dozen evolutionary branches, including Gram-negative proteobacteria, Gram-negative green bacteria, cyanobacteria, Gram-positive bacteria, spirochetes, and chlamydias.

22.4 The Domain Archaea

- A very large number of archaea have not been cultured, but we know that archaea have some features that are like those of bacteria, other features that are eukaryotic, and some that are unique (see Table 22.2).
- Archaea are classified into three groups: the Euryarchaeota (methanogens, extreme halophiles, and some extreme thermophiles); the Crenarchaeota (which includes most of the extreme thermophiles, but also some psychrophiles and mesophiles); and the Korarchaeota, known only from DNA samples.

Questions

Self-Test Questions

1. Which of the following structures is found in prokaryotic cells?
   a. cellulose cell wall
   b. ribosome
   c. mitochondria
   d. nuclear membrane

2. Which of the following statements about archaea is correct?
   a. Their cell walls contain peptidoglycan.
   b. Most are pathogens.
   c. Many are extremophiles.
   d. They have no traits in common with eukaryotic cells.

3. Which of the following statements accurately describes a plasmid?
   a. It can only replicate when the cell's chromosome replicates.
   b. It is a small circular piece of RNA outside a cell's chromosome.
   c. It is a small circular piece of DNA outside a cell's chromosome.
   d. It refers to a piece of DNA taken up from the environment by a prokaryotic cell.

4. You have isolated an unknown bacterium that produces a toxin and you are trying to determine if this is an endotoxin or an exotoxin. Which of the following features would be associated with the toxin, if it were an endotoxin?
   a. It would be secreted from the cell.
   b. It would be part of the cell wall.
   c. It would be part of the plasma membrane.
   d. It would be produced by an archaeon.

5. Place the following steps by which prokaryotic cells form a biofilm in the correct order:
   1. Cells grow and divide.
   2. The cells' physiology changes.
   3. Cells attach to a surface that is covered in organic polymers.
   4. Cells secrete extracellular polymers that "glue" the cells to the surface and to each other.
      a. 1, 2, 3, 4
      b. 2, 1,4, 3
      c. 4, 3, 1, 2
      d. 3, 1, 2, 4

6. You are growing a facultative anaerobic archaeon in culture under two conditions: one culture is in anaerobic conditions, and the other is in aerobic conditions. How would you expect the growth of the cells to compare between the two cultures?
   a. Growth would be greater in the culture in aerobic conditions.
   b. Growth would be greater in the culture in anaerobic conditions.
   c. Growth would be the same in both conditions.

7. A bacterium that oxidizes nitrite as its only energy source was found deep in a cave. How would you classify this bacterium, based on its carbon and energy source?
   a. as a chemolithotroph
   b. as a chemoheterotroph
   c. as a photoautotroph
   d. as a photoheterotroph

8. Which of the following processes converts ammonium (NH_4^+) into nitrate (NO_3^-)?
   a. nitrogen fixation
   b. ammonification
   c. nitrification
   d. denitrification

9. Which of the following groups of bacteria are all oxygen-producing photoautotrophs?
   a. spirochetes
   b. cyanobacteria
   c. proteobacteria
   d. green bacteria

10. Which of the following statements about chlamydias is correct?
    a. They lack peptidoglycan.
    b. They are Gram-positive.
    c. They are not pathogenic.
    d. They have no outer membrane in the cell wall.

Questions for Discussion

1. In the lab, you have isolated some prokaryotic cells that belong either to a Gram-positive bacterium or to an archaeon. What cellular (structural) features could you look for to determine which type of organism you have isolated? Indicate how that feature would differ between the two kinds of organism (assume that you have the necessary equipment to test for any cellular feature you want).

2. List several functions of the outer wall layer in Gram-negative bacteria.

3. You are doing research to develop new drugs and have developed a new antibiotic. This drug acts by inhibiting ribosome function in prokaryotic cells. When you test it on animal cells, however, you find that the growth of animal cells is inhibited. Explain why this drug inhibits the growth of animal cells.

4. How do bacteria resist antibiotics? Why do antibiotics lose their effectiveness so quickly?

5. In which nutritional class would you place a prokaryotic organism that uses glucose as its only energy and carbon source? What about an organism that uses elemental sulfur as an energy source and carbon dioxide as a carbon source? What is the energy source for phototrophic organisms?

A B cell and a T cell communicating by direct contact in the human immune system (computer image). Cell communication coordinates the cellular defence against disease.

Russell Kightley Media

8 Cell Communication

WHY IT MATTERS

Hundreds of aircraft, ranging from small private planes to huge passenger jets, approach and leave airports in Southern California. In addition to the large terminals in Los Angeles and San Diego, dozens of smaller airports are located in the vicinity. The aircraft that approach these airports are travelling at various speeds, entering from all points of the compass, and flying at different altitudes. Airplanes are also leaving the same airports with routes distributed over the same directions, speeds, and altitudes. A wrong turn, ascent, or descent by any one of the hundreds of planes could lead to disaster. Yet disasters are extremely rare. How are all these aircraft kept separate and routed to and from their airports safely and efficiently? The answer lies in a highly organized system of controllers, signals, and receivers.

As the aircraft thread their way along the various approach and departure routes, they follow directions arriving on a radio frequency unique to each aircraft. Instructions arriving on the frequency assigned to Piper 4879Z, a slow-moving two-seater headed for Montgomery Field near San Diego, keep this plane's path separate from that of "five-two heavy," a passenger jet, leaving the main San Diego air terminal. The flow of directing signals, followed individually by each aircraft in the vicinity, keeps the traffic unscrambled and moving safely.

The principle of the air control system is nothing new. An equivalent system of signals and tuned receivers evolved hundreds of millions of years ago as one of the developments that made multicellular life possible. Within a multicellular organism, the activities of individual cells are directed by molecular signals, such as hormones, that are released by controlling cells. Although the controlling cells release many signals, each receiving cell has receptors that are "tuned" to recognize only one or a few of the many signal molecules that circulate in its vicinity; other signals pass by without effect because the cell has no receptors for them.

When a cell binds a signal molecule via a receptor, it modifies its internal activities in accordance with the signal, coordinating its functions with the activities of other cells of the organism. The responses of the receiving cell may include changes in gene activity, protein synthesis, transport of molecules across the plasma membrane, metabolic reactions, secretion, movement, and division. In some cases, the response to a signal may be "suicide" or programmed death of the receiving cell **(Figure 8.1).** As part of its response, a cell may itself become a signaller and thus contribute to the organizational network by releasing signal molecules that modify the activity of other cell types. The total network of signals and responses allows multicellular organisms to grow, develop, reproduce, and compensate for environmental changes in an internally coordinated fashion.

This chapter describes the major pathways that form parts of the cell communication system based on both surface and internal receptors, including the links that tie the different response pathways into fully integrated networks. (Nerve communication in animals is discussed in Chapter 33.) This chapter concentrates primarily on the systems working in animals, particularly in mammals, from which most of our knowledge of cell communication has been developed. Nonetheless, the principles of cell communication illustrated by these pathways apply to most eukaryotic organisms, including plants, protists and fungi. (The plant communication and control systems are described in more detail in Chapter 31.) This discussion begins with a few fundamental principles that underlie the often complex networks of cell communication.

8.1 Cell Communication: An Overview

Communication is critical for the function and survival of cells that compose a multicellular animal. For example, the ability of cells to communicate with one another in a regulated way is responsible for the controlled growth and development of an animal, as well as the integrated activities of its tissues and organs.

Cells communicate with one another in three ways. Adjacent cells use direct channels of communication. In this rapid means of communication, small molecules and ions exchange directly between the two cytoplasms. In animal cells, the direct channels of communication are *gap junctions,* the specialized connections between the cytoplasms of adjacent cells (Chapter 32). The main role of gap junctions is to synchronize metabolic activities or electronic signals between cells in a tissue. For example, gap junctions play a key role in the spread of electrical signals from one cell to the next in cardiac muscle. In plant cells, the direct channels of communication are plasmodesmata (see Chapter 28). Small molecules moving between adjacent cells in plants include plant hormones that regulate growth. In this way, responses triggered by plant hormones are spread to other cells.

Cells also communicate through *specific contact between cells.* Certain cells have molecules on their surfaces that allow them to interact directly with other cells. Some cells use their surface molecules to recognize particular molecules on the surfaces of invading pathogens or parasites that signal them as foreign. The host cell then engulfs the invader. Cells also have on their surfaces *cell adhesion molecules,* integral membrane proteins that allow the cells to bind to other cells or to the extracellular matrix. There are many important functions of cell adhesion molecules, including roles in cell movement and coordinating tissue and organ formation as an embryo develops.

Finally, cells communicate through *intercellular* ("between cell") *chemical messengers.* This method is the most common means of cell communication. Here, one cell, the *controlling cell,* synthesizes a specific molecule that acts as a *signalling molecule* to affect the activity of another cell, the *target cell.* The target cell is not in contact with the cell that synthesizes the signalling molecule; rather, it is either nearby or at a distance away in the organism. For example, in response to stress, cells of the adrenal glands (located on top of the kidneys) secrete the hormone epinephrine into the bloodstream. Among its actions, epinephrine acts on target cells so that the amount of glucose in the blood increases.

Cell communication through intercellular chemical messengers is the focus of this chapter, and the

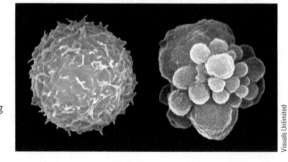

Figure 8.1
A normal cell (left) and a cell undergoing apoptosis (programmed cell death) (right).

Visuals Unlimited

epinephrine example is used to illustrate the principles involved. In the 1950s, Earl Sutherland and his research team at Case Western Reserve University, Cleveland, Ohio, began investigating this cell communication system. Sutherland discovered that the hormone epinephrine acts by activating an enzyme, glycogen phosphorylase, which catalyzes the production of glucose from glycogen. That is, the result of the secretion of epinephrine into the blood by adrenal gland cells is an increase in the amount of glucose in the blood. Sutherland's experiments showed that enzyme activation did not involve epinephrine directly but did require an unknown (at the time) cellular substance. Sutherland called the hormone the *first messenger* in the system and the unknown cellular substance the *second messenger.* He proposed that the following chain of reactions was involved: epinephrine (the first messenger) leads to the formation of the second messenger, which activates the enzyme for conversion of glycogen to glucose.

Sutherland's work was the foundation for research that developed our current understanding of this type of cell communication. In brief, a controlling cell releases a signal molecule that causes a response (affects the function) of target cells. Target cells

process the signal in the following three sequential steps (**Figure 8.2**):

1. **Reception.** Reception is the binding of a signal molecule with a specific receptor of target cells. Target cells have receptors that are specific for the signal molecule, which distinguishes them from cells that do not respond to the signal molecule. The signal molecules are often peptides or steroids, but many other types of molecules, such as amines, can act as chemical signals between cells. Each molecule will have a cellular receptor that is shaped to recognize and bind that molecule specifically **(Figure 8.3)**. Membrane receptors are normally embedded in the plasma membrane with a binding site for the signal molecule on the cell surface (see Figures 8.2 and 8.3a). Epinephrine, the first messenger in Sutherland's research, is an

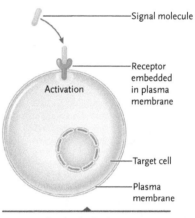

a. Reception by a cell-surface receptor

Some signal molecules bind to a receptor on the surface.

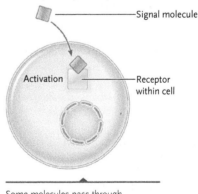

b. Reception by a receptor within cell

Some molecules pass through the plasma membrane and bind to their receptors in the cell.

Figure 8.2
The three stages of signal transduction: reception, transduction, and response (shown for a system using a surface receptor).

Figure 8.3
Reception **(a)** of a signal molecule by a receptor on the cell surface and **(b)** of a signal molecule by a receptor in the cell.

PEOPLE BEHIND BIOLOGY

Doug Storey

Bacterial cells are also able to communicate with each other via chemical signals, a communication system known as **quorum sensing** (see Chapter 21). In this method of communication, a growing population of bacteria produces signalling molecules (either peptides or lactones, depending on the type of bacterium) that accumulate in the environment around the cells. When the concentration of these signalling molecules reaches a critical threshold, they bind to protein receptors inside the bacterial cells. The complex formed by the signal molecule and the protein receptor then binds to specific regions of the cell's genome, activating certain genes. In this way, cells "know" that their population is large enough to perform some coordinated function and synthesize the proteins necessary to carry out that function. Behaviours that are regulated by quorum sensing include bioluminescence (see Chapter 1) and biofilm formation (see Chapter 21). In addition, quorum sensing also regulates pathogenesis as the bacteria begin to produce virulence factors (molecules that cause disease or create conditions needed for the pathogen to thrive inside the host). This last aspect of quorum sensing has important implications for our understanding of pathogenic bacteria—does quorum sensing occur in pathogenic bacteria infecting humans?

This is a question of great interest to Doug Storey, a microbiologist at the University of Calgary. Storey studies *Pseudomonas aeruginosa*, a bacterium that causes serious lung infections in people with cystic fibrosis (See chapter 5 for a discussion of this disease). Storey's research goal is to understand how *P. aeruginosa* is able to infect the lungs of CF patients and to look for new ways of fighting these infections. Of particular interest to Storey are the virulence factors produced by *P. aeruginosa*—what regulates the production of these factors? Does *P. aeruginosa* use quorum sensing to regulate levels of virulence factors when infecting host lungs? Recent research carried out by Storey and his collaborators indicates that the quorum-sensing system of *P. aeruginosa* does function in the lungs of CF patients and coordinates gene expression. This finding offers the potential for a new way to fight these lung infections: perhaps we can interfere with the bacterium's communication system and so prevent it from synthesizing virulence factors. We need to have a better understanding of the details of quorum sensing, but this is an exciting new tool in the fight against pathogenic infections.

---

amine that is recognized by a surface receptor on target cells. Receptors for some molecules are located within the cell (see Figure 8.3b). In this case, the signal molecule passes freely through the plasma membrane and interacts with its receptor within the cell. Steroid hormones such as testosterone and estrogen are examples of signal molecules that act on receptors within the cell. Many steroids also have separate actions via membrane receptors. Receptors at the cell surface, *membrane receptors,* usually involve rapid, short-lived events. Internal receptors often act directly on the genome (*nuclear receptors*), activating specific genes. These responses and reactions occur over a longer time.

Although the focus of this chapter is on eukaryotes, bacteria also engage in chemical communication (see *People Behind Biology*).

2. **Transduction.** Transduction is the process of changing the signal into the form necessary to cause the cellular response (see Figure 8.2). In other words, the binding of a signal molecule to its receptor is not directly responsible for the response. Transduction may occur in a single step, although more often it involves a cascade of reactions that include several different molecules, often referred to as a *signalling cascade.* For example, in Sutherland's work, after epinephrine bound to its surface receptor, the signal was transmitted through the plasma membrane into the cell, where transduction by a signalling cascade activated a molecule that triggered a cellular response. This molecule was Sutherland's *second messenger.*

3. **Response.** In the third and last stage, the transduced signal causes a specific cellular response. That response depends on the signal and the receptors on the target cell. In Sutherland's work, the response was the activation of the enzyme glycogen phosphorylase; the active enzyme catalyzed the conversion of stored glycogen to glucose.

The whole series of events from reception to response is called **signal transduction.** As explained in subsequent sections, signal transduction occurs by different mechanisms, depending on the receptor type. Earl Sutherland was awarded a Nobel Prize in 1971 for his research on the mechanisms of action of hormones.

STUDY BREAK

What accounts for the specificity of a cellular response in signal transduction?

8.2 Characteristics of Cell Communication Systems with Surface Receptors

Cell communication systems based on surface receptors have three components: (1) the extracellular signal molecules released by controlling cells, (2) the surface receptors on target cells that receive the signals, and (3) the internal response pathways triggered when receptors bind a signal.

8.2a Hormones and Neurotransmitters Are Extracellular Signal Molecules Recognized by Surface Receptors in Animals

Surface receptors in mammals and other vertebrates recognize and bind two major types of extracellular signal molecules: *hormones* and *neurotransmitters*. These signal molecules are released by control cells and enter the fluids that surround cells, including the blood circulation in animals with a circulatory system.

Hormones (see Chapter 35) are molecules, usually peptides or steroids, that are released by specialized gland cells such as the adrenal glands, by specialized nerve cells such as the pituitary, or by cells distributed in organs such as the liver or intestines. A special class of peptides, the growth factors, affects cell growth, division, and differentiation.

Neurotransmitters are molecules released by neurons that trigger activity in other neurons or other cells in the body; they include small peptides, individual amino acids or their derivatives, and other chemical substances. Some neurotransmitters affect only one or a few cells in the immediate vicinity of the neuron that releases the signal molecule, whereas others are released into the body circulation and act essentially as hormones, affecting many types of tissues. (Neurotransmitters are discussed in further detail in Chapter 33.)

Once signal molecules are released into the body's circulation, they remain for only a certain time. They are either broken down at a steady rate by enzymes in their target cells or in organs such as the liver, or they are excreted by the kidneys. The removal process ensures that the signal molecules are active only as long as controlling cells are secreting them.

8.2b Surface Receptors Are Integral Membrane Glycoproteins

The surface receptors that recognize and bind signal molecules are all glycoproteins—proteins with attached carbohydrate chains. They are integral membrane proteins that extend entirely through the plasma membrane (**Figure 8.4**). The signal-binding site of the receptor, which extends from the outer membrane surface, is folded in a way that closely fits the signal molecule. The fit, similar to the fit of an enzyme to its substrate, is specific, so a particular receptor binds only one type of signal molecule or a closely related group of signal molecules.

A signal molecule brings about specific changes to the receptor and therefore to the cells to which it binds. When a signal molecule binds to a surface receptor, the molecular structure of that receptor is changed so that it transmits the signal through the plasma membrane, activating the cytoplasmic end of the receptor. The activated receptor then initiates the first step in a cascade of molecular events—the signal transduction pathway—that triggers the cellular response (see Figure 8.2).

Animal cells typically have hundreds to thousands of surface receptors that represent many receptor types. Membrane receptors for a specific hormone may number from 500 to as many as 100 000 or more per cell. Different cell types contain distinct combinations of receptors, allowing them to react individually to the hormones and growth factors circulating in the extracellular fluids. The combination of surface receptors on particular cell types is not fixed but rather changes as cells develop. Changes also occur as normal cells are transformed into cancer cells.

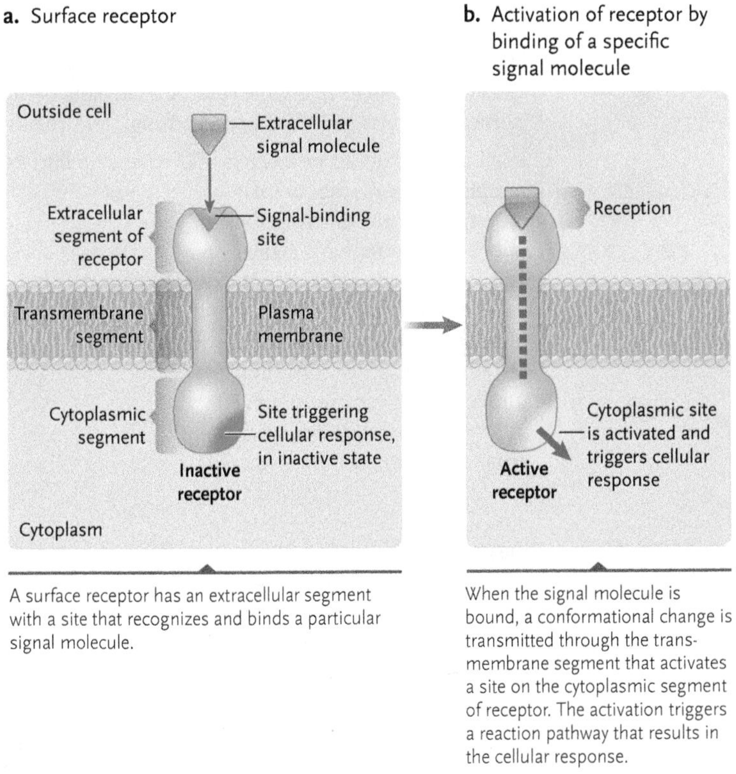

a. Surface receptor

b. Activation of receptor by binding of a specific signal molecule

A surface receptor has an extracellular segment with a site that recognizes and binds a particular signal molecule.

When the signal molecule is bound, a conformational change is transmitted through the transmembrane segment that activates a site on the cytoplasmic segment of receptor. The activation triggers a reaction pathway that results in the cellular response.

Figure 8.4
The mechanism by which a surface receptor responds when it binds a signal molecule.

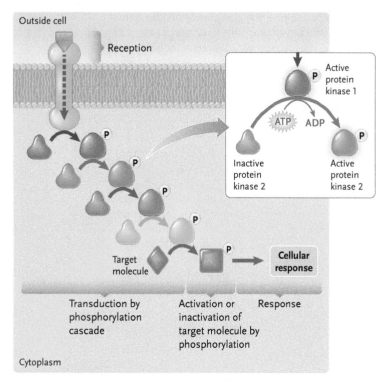

Figure 8.5
Phosphorylation, a key reaction in many signalling pathways.

Labels within figure:
- Outside cell
- Reception
- Active protein kinase 1
- ATP → ADP
- Inactive protein kinase 2
- Active protein kinase 2
- P
- Target molecule
- Cellular response
- Transduction by phosphorylation cascade
- Activation or inactivation of target molecule by phosphorylation
- Response
- Cytoplasm

8.2c The Signalling Molecule Bound by a Surface Receptor Triggers Response Pathways within the Cell

Signal transduction pathways triggered by surface receptors are common to all animal cells. At least parts of the pathways are also found in protists, fungi, and plants.

In all cases, binding of a signal molecule to a surface receptor triggers the cellular response without entering the cell. Experiments have shown that (1) a signal molecule produces no response if it is injected directly into the cytoplasm, and (2) unrelated molecules that mimic the structure of the normal extracellular signal molecule can trigger a full cellular response as long as they can bind to the recognition site of the receptor.

A second typical characteristic of signal transduction is that the signal is relayed inside the cell by **protein kinases**, enzymes that transfer a phosphate group from ATP to one or more sites on particular proteins (**Figure 8.5**). These phosphorylated proteins are

known as *target proteins* because they are the proteins modified by signalling pathways. The added phosphate groups either stimulate or inhibit the activity of the target proteins; the change in the target proteins' activity leads directly or indirectly to the cellular response. Often protein kinases act in a chain, called a *protein kinase cascade,* to pass along a signal. The first kinase catalyzes phosphorylation of the second, which then becomes active and phosphorylates the third kinase, and so on. The proteins that bring about the cellular response may be parts of the reaction pathways, enzymes of other cellular reactions, end targets of the signal transduction pathways (such as transport proteins), or, at the most fundamental level, proteins that regulate gene transcription.

The effects of protein kinases in the signal transduction pathways are balanced or reversed by another group of enzymes called **protein phosphatases**, which remove phosphate groups from target proteins. Unlike the protein kinases, which are active only when a surface receptor binds a signal molecule, most of the protein phosphatases are continuously active in cells. By continually removing phosphate groups from target proteins, the protein phosphatases quickly shut off a signal transduction pathway if its signal molecule is no longer bound at the cell surface.

A third characteristic of signal transduction pathways involving surface receptors is **amplification**—an increase in the magnitude of each step as a signal transduction pathway proceeds (**Figure 8.6**). Amplification occurs because many of the proteins that carry out individual steps in the pathways, including the protein kinases, are enzymes. Once activated, each enzyme can activate hundreds of proteins, including other enzymes, that enter the next step in the pathway. Generally, the more enzyme-catalyzed steps in a

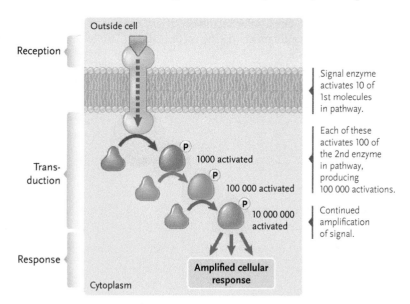

Figure 8.6
Amplification in signal transduction.

Labels within figure:
- Outside cell
- Reception
- Transduction
- Response
- Cytoplasm
- 1000 activated
- 100 000 activated
- 10 000 000 activated
- Amplified cellular response
- Signal enzyme activates 10 of 1st molecules in pathway.
- Each of these activates 100 of the 2nd enzyme in pathway, producing 100 000 activations.
- Continued amplification of signal.

response pathway, the greater the amplification. As a result, just a few extracellular signal molecules binding to their receptors can produce a full internal response. For similar reasons, amplification also occurs for signal transduction pathways that involve internal receptors.

As signal transduction runs its course, the receptors and their bound signal molecules are removed from the cell surface by endocytosis. Both the receptor and its bound signal molecule may be degraded in lysosomes after entering the cell. Alternatively, the receptors may be separated from the signal molecules and recycled to the cell surface, whereas only the signal molecules are degraded. Thus, surface receptors participate in an extremely lively cellular "conversation" with moment-to-moment shifts in the information.

The next two sections discuss two large families of surface receptors: the receptor tyrosine kinases and the G protein–coupled receptors.

STUDY BREAK

1. What are protein kinases, and how are they involved in signal transduction pathways?
2. How is amplification accomplished in a signal transduction pathway?

8.3 Surface Receptors with Built-in Protein Kinase Activity: Receptor Tyrosine Kinases

In the simplest form of signal transduction, the receptor itself has a protein kinase site at its cytoplasmic end. For this type of receptor, initiation of transduction occurs when two receptor molecules each bind a signal molecule in the reception step, move together in the membrane, and assemble into a pair called a *dimer* (Figure 8.7). Dimer assembly

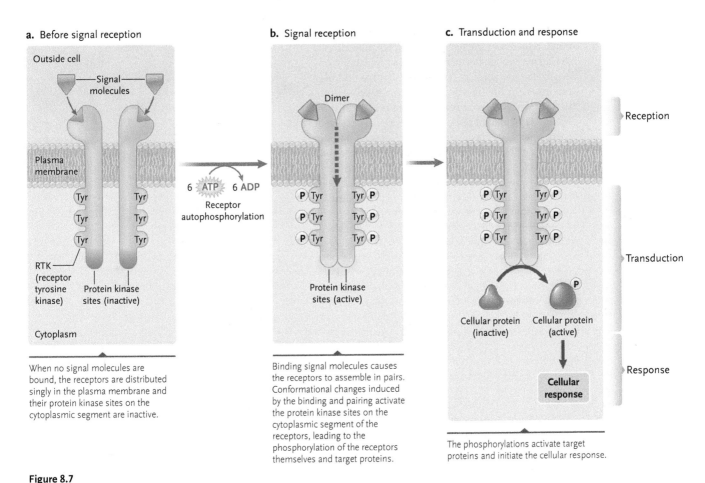

a. Before signal reception

When no signal molecules are bound, the receptors are distributed singly in the plasma membrane and their protein kinase sites on the cytoplasmic segment are inactive.

b. Signal reception

Binding signal molecules causes the receptors to assemble in pairs. Conformational changes induced by the binding and pairing activate the protein kinase sites on the cytoplasmic segment of the receptors, leading to the phosphorylation of the receptors themselves and target proteins.

c. Transduction and response

The phosphorylations activate target proteins and initiate the cellular response.

Figure 8.7
The action of receptors with built-in protein kinase activity leading to the phosphorylation of the receptors themselves and the subsequent phosphorylation of target proteins. These receptors are called receptor tyrosine kinases because they add phosphate groups to tyrosines in target proteins. These receptors combine into pairs (dimers) when they bind signal molecules; the assembly into a dimer transmits the signal that activates the cytoplasmic end of the receptors.

activates the receptor's protein kinase, which adds phosphate groups to sites on the receptor itself, a process known as *autophosphorylation*. Target proteins recognize and bind to the phosphorylated sites on the receptor and are then activated by being phosphorylated themselves. The total effect of the phosphorylations is to initiate the signal transduction pathway controlled by the receptor.

In autophosphorylation, the phosphate groups are added to tyrosine amino acids on the receptor. The protein kinase activity of the activated receptors also adds phosphate groups to tyrosines in the amino acid chains of target proteins. Because of this specificity of phosphorylation, the receptors in this group are called **receptor tyrosine kinases**. More than 50 receptor tyrosine kinases are known. In mammals, receptor tyrosine kinases fall into 14 different families, all related to one another in structure and amino acid sequence. Relatives of the mammalian receptors have been discovered in yeasts, *Drosophila*, and higher plants, indicating that the origin of the receptor tyrosine kinases is a single ancestral type that must have appeared before the evolutionary splits that led to the fungi, plants, and animals.

The cellular responses triggered by receptor tyrosine kinases are among the most important processes of animal cells. For example, the receptor tyrosine kinases binding the peptide hormone *insulin*, a regulator of carbohydrate metabolism, triggers diverse cellular responses, including effects on glucose uptake, the rates of many metabolic reactions, and cell growth and division. (The insulin receptor is exceptional because it is permanently in the dimer form.) Other receptor tyrosine kinases bind growth factors, including *epidermal growth factor*, *platelet-derived growth factor*, and *nerve growth factor*, which are all important peptide hormones that regulate cell growth and division in higher animals.

Hereditary defects in the insulin receptor are responsible for some forms of *diabetes*, a disease in which glucose accumulates in the blood because it cannot be absorbed in sufficient quantity by body cells. The inherited defects may impair the ability of the receptor to bind insulin or block its ability to trigger a cellular response. In either case, the cell is unresponsive to insulin and does not add sufficient glucose transporters to take up glucose.

STUDY BREAK

How does a receptor tyrosine kinase become activated?

8.4 G Protein–Coupled Receptors

A second large family of surface receptors, known as the **G protein–coupled receptors**, respond to a signal by activating an inner membrane protein called a G protein, which is closely associated with the cytoplasmic end of the receptor. About 1000 different G protein–coupled receptors have been identified; several hundred types are involved in recognizing and binding odour molecules as part of the sense of smell. Almost all of the receptors of this group are large glycoproteins built up from a single polypeptide chain anchored in the plasma membrane by seven segments of the amino acid chain that zigzag back and forth across the membrane seven times **(Figure 8.8)**.

Unlike receptor tyrosine kinases, these receptors lack built-in protein kinase activity.

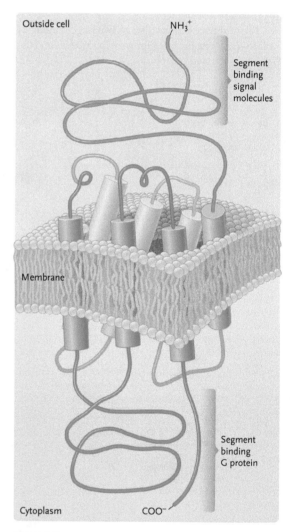

Figure 8.8

Structure of the G protein–coupled receptors, which activate separate protein kinases. These receptors have seven transmembrane α-helical segments (shown as cylinders) that zigzag across the plasma membrane. Binding of a signal molecule at the cell surface, by inducing changes in the positions of some of the helices, activates the cytoplasmic end of the receptor.

8.4a G Proteins Are Key Molecular Switches in Second-Messenger Pathways

The extracellular signal molecule in signal transduction pathways controlled by G protein–coupled receptors is termed the **first messenger**. Binding the first messenger by the receptor activates a site on the cytoplasmic end of the receptor (**Figure 8.9**, step 1). The active site of the receptor then activates the G protein associated with the cytoplasmic tail of the receptor by inducing the G protein to bind GTP, replacing the GDP that was bound to it (step 2). The G protein is an example of a *molecular switch* protein because it changes between inactive and active states. If GDP is bound to the G protein, the G protein is inactive, whereas if GTP is bound, it is active. In fact, G proteins are named because they use GDP and GTP to control their activities. The role of a switched-on G protein is to activate a plasma membrane–associated enzyme called the **effector** (step 3). In turn, the effector generates one or more internal, nonprotein signal molecules called **second messengers** (step 4). The second messengers directly or indirectly activate protein kinases, which elicit the cellular response by adding phosphate groups to specific target proteins (step 5). Thus, the entire control pathway operates through the following sequence:

first messenger → receptor → G proteins → effector → second messenger → protein kinases → target proteins effector

The separate protein kinases of these pathways all add phosphate groups to serine or threonine amino acids in their target proteins, which are typically

- enzymes catalyzing steps in metabolic pathways
- ion channels in the plasma and other membranes
- regulatory proteins that control gene activity and cell division

Cells can make a variety of G proteins, with each type activating a different cellular response. The pathway from first messengers to target proteins is common to all G protein–coupled receptors.

As long as a G protein–coupled receptor is bound to a first messenger, the receptor keeps the G protein active. The activated G protein, in turn, keeps the effector active in generating second messengers. If the first messenger is released from the receptor, or if the receptor is taken into the cell by endocytosis, GTP is hydrolyzed to GDP, which inactivates the G protein. As a result, the effector becomes inactive, turning "off" the response pathway.

The importance of G proteins to cellular metabolism is underscored by the fact that they are targets of toxins released by some infecting bacteria. The cholera toxin produced by *Vibrio cholerae*, the pertussis toxin that causes whooping cough produced by

Bordetella pertussis, and a toxin produced by a disease-causing form of *Escherichia coli* are all enzymes that modify the G proteins, making them continuously active and keeping their response pathways turned "on" at high levels. For example, the cholera toxin prevents a G protein from hydrolyzing GTP, keeping the G protein switched on and the pathway in a permanently active state. Among other effects, the pathway opens ion channels in intestinal cells, causing severe diarrhea through a massive release of salt and water from the body into the intestinal tract. Unless the resulting dehydration is relieved, death can result quickly. The *E. coli* toxin, which has similar but milder effects, is the cause of many cases of traveller's diarrhea.

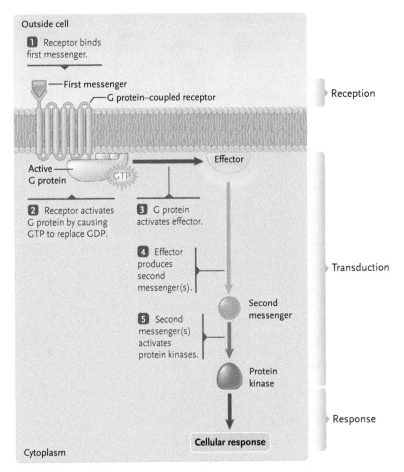

Figure 8.9

Response pathways activated by G protein–coupled receptors, in which protein kinase activity is separate from the receptor. The signal molecule is called the first messenger; the effector is an enzyme that generates one or more internal signal molecules called second messengers. The second messengers directly or indirectly activate the protein kinases of the pathway, leading to the cellular response.

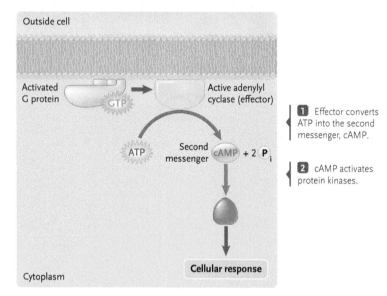

Outside cell

Activated G protein

GTP

Active adenylyl cyclase (effector)

1 Effector converts ATP into the second messenger, cAMP.

ATP

Second messenger (cAMP) + 2 P_i

2 cAMP activates protein kinases.

Cellular response

Cytoplasm

Figure 8.10

The operation of cAMP–response pathways. The second messenger of the pathway, cAMP, activates one or more cAMP-dependent protein kinases, which add phosphate groups to target proteins to initiate the cellular response.

8.4b Two Major G Protein–Coupled Receptor–Response Pathways Involve Different Second Messengers

Activated G proteins bring about a cellular response through two major receptor–response pathways in which different effectors generate different second messengers. One pathway involves the second messenger **cyclic AMP (cAMP)**, a relatively small, water-soluble molecule derived from ATP **(Figure 8.10)**. The effector that produces cAMP is the enzyme *adenylyl cyclase,* which converts ATP to cAMP **(Figure 8.11)**. cAMP diffuses through the cytoplasm and activates protein kinases that add phosphate groups to target proteins to initiate the cellular response. The other pathway involves two second messengers: **inositol triphosphate (IP₃)** and **diacylglycerol (DAG)**. The effector of this pathway, an enzyme called *phospholipase C,* produces both of these second

messengers by breaking down a membrane phospholipid **(Figure 8.12)**. IP₃ is a small, water-soluble molecule that diffuses rapidly through the cytoplasm. DAG is hydrophobic; it remains and functions in the plasma membrane.

The primary effect of IP₃ in animal cells is to activate transport proteins in the endoplasmic reticulum (ER), which release Ca^{2+} stored in the ER into the cytoplasm. The released Ca^{2+}, either alone or in combination with DAG, activates a protein kinase cascade that brings about the cellular effect.

Both major G protein–coupled receptor–response pathways are balanced by reactions that constantly eliminate their second messengers. cAMP is quickly degraded by *phosphodiesterase,* an enzyme that is continuously active in the cytoplasm (see Figure 8.11). The rapid elimination of the second messengers provides another highly effective off switch for the pathways, ensuring that protein kinases are inactivated quickly if the receptor becomes inactive. Still another off switch is provided by protein phosphatases that remove the phosphate groups added to proteins by the protein kinases.

As in the receptor tyrosine kinase pathways, the activities of the pathways controlled by cAMP and IP₃/DAG second messengers are also stopped by endocytosis of receptors and their bound extracellular signals. As with all cell signalling pathways, cells vary in their response to cAMP or IP₃/DAG pathways depending on the type of G protein–coupled receptors on the cell surface and the kinds of protein kinases present in the cytoplasm.

The cAMP pathway is limited to animals and some fungi. The IP₃/DAG pathway is universally distributed among eukaryotic organisms, including both vertebrate and invertebrate animals, fungi, and plants. The cAMP pathway occurs in animals and fungi, but its presence in plants is uncertain.

Specific Examples of Cyclic AMP Pathways. Many hormones act as first messengers for cAMP pathways in animals. The receptors that bind these hormones control such varied cellular responses as the uptake and oxidation of glucose, glycogen breakdown or synthesis,

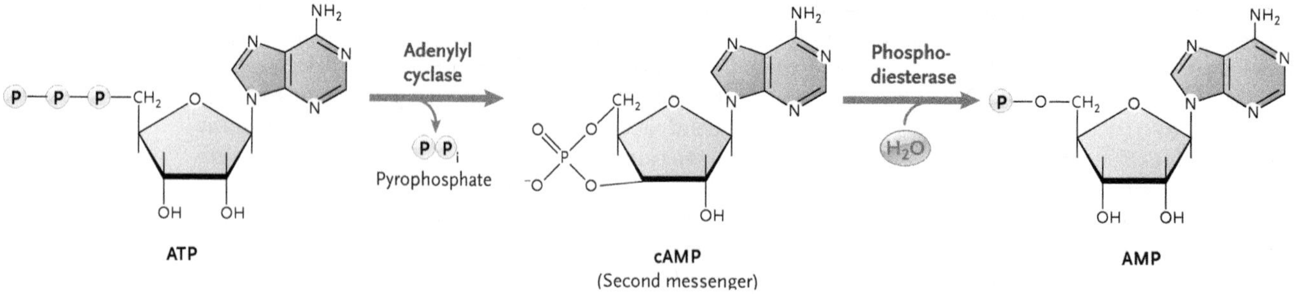

ATP

Adenylyl cyclase

P P_i
Pyrophosphate

cAMP
(Second messenger)

Phospho-diesterase

H₂O

AMP

Figure 8.11

cAMP. The second messenger, cAMP, is made from ATP by adenylyl cyclase and is broken down to AMP by phosphodiesterase.

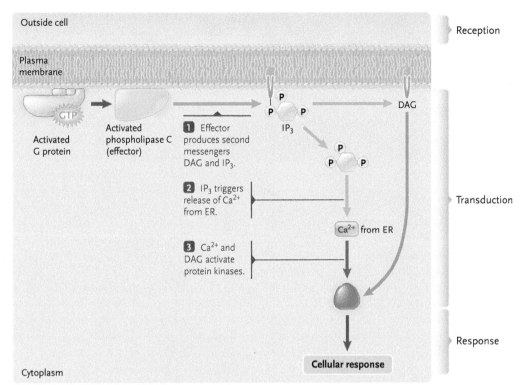

Outside cell

Plasma membrane

Activated G protein

Activated phospholipase C (effector)

1 Effector produces second messengers DAG and IP₃.

2 IP₃ triggers release of Ca²⁺ from ER.

3 Ca²⁺ and DAG activate protein kinases.

P P IP₃ P

DAG

P P P

Ca²⁺ from ER

Cellular response

Cytoplasm

Reception

Transduction

Response

Figure 8.12
The operation of IP₃/DAG receptor–response pathways. Two second messengers, IP₃ and DAG, are produced by the pathway. IP₃ opens Ca²⁺ channels in ER membranes, releasing the ion into the cytoplasm. The Ca²⁺, with DAG in some cases, directly or indirectly activates the protein kinases of the pathway, which add phosphate groups to target proteins to initiate the cellular response.

ion transport, the transport of amino acids into cells, and cell division.

A cAMP pathway is involved in the regulation of the level of glucose, the fundamental fuel of cells. When the level of blood glucose falls too low in mammals, cells in the pancreas release the peptide hormone glucagon. Binding of the hormone by a G protein–coupled glucagon receptor on the surface of liver cells triggers the cAMP pathway (see Figure 8.10). The cAMP produced activates a protein kinase cascade that amplifies the effects of the pathway at each step. Two enzymes are end targets of the protein kinase cascades. One enzyme is *glycogen phosphorylase*, which catalyzes the breakdown of glycogen into glucose units that pass from the liver cells into the bloodstream and increase the glucose level in the blood; it is activated by the cascades. The other enzyme is *glycogen synthase*, which adds glucose units to glycogen; it is inactivated by the cascades, ensuring that glucose is not converted back into glycogen in the liver cells.

Specific Examples of IP₃/DAG Pathways. The IP₃/DAG-response pathways are also activated by a large number of peptide hormones (including growth factors) and neurotransmitters, leading to responses as varied as sugar and ion transport, glucose oxidation, cell growth and division, and movements such as smooth muscle contraction.

Among the vertebrate hormones that activate the pathways are vasopressin, angiotensin, and norepinephrine. Vasopressin, also known as antidiuretic

hormone, helps the body conserve water by reducing the output of urine. Angiotensin helps maintain blood volume and pressure. Norepinephrine, together with epinephrine, brings about the fight-or-flight response in threatening or stressful situations.

Many growth factors operate through IP₃/DAG pathways. Defects in the receptors or other parts of the pathways that lead to higher-than-normal levels of DAG in response to growth factors are often associated with the progression of some forms of cancer. This is because DAG, in turn, causes an overactivity of the protein kinases responsible for stimulating cell growth and division. Also, plant substances in a group called *phorbol esters* resemble DAG so closely that they can promote cancer in animals by activating the same protein kinases.

In plants, IP₃/DAG pathways control responses to conditions such as water loss and changes in light intensity or salinity. Plant hormones—relatively small, nonprotein molecules such as *auxin* (a derivative of the amino acid tryptophan) and the *cytokinins* (derivatives of the nucleotide base adenine)—act as first messengers activating some of the IP₃/DAG pathways of these organisms.

Example of a Signalling Pathway That Combines a Receptor Tyrosine Kinase with a G Protein. Some pathways important in gene regulation link certain receptor tyrosine kinases to a specific type of G protein called Ras. When

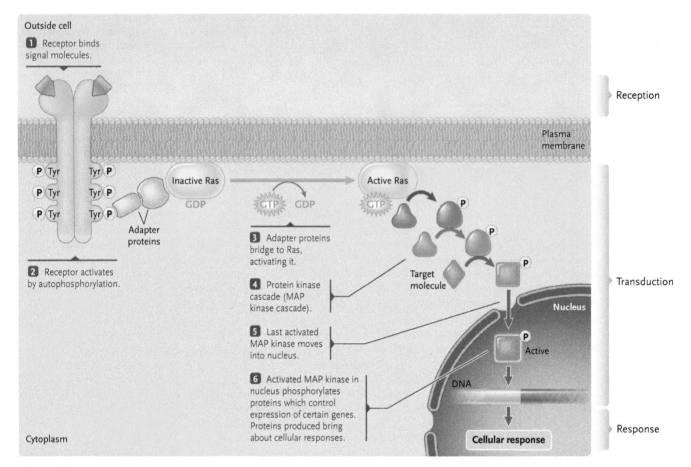

Figure 8.13
The pathway from receptor tyrosine kinases to gene regulation, including the G protein, Ras, and MAP kinase.

the receptor tyrosine kinase receives a signal (**Figure 8.13,** step 1), it activates by autophosphorylation (step 2). Adapter proteins then bind to the phosphorylated receptor and bridge to Ras, stimulating the activation of Ras (step 3). Like other G proteins, Ras is activated by binding GTP. The activated Ras sets in motion a phosphorylation cascade that involves a series of three enzymes known as *mitogen-activated protein kinases* (MAP kinases; step 4). The last MAP kinase in the cascade, when activated, enters the nucleus (step 5) and phosphorylates other proteins, which then change the expression of certain genes, particularly activating those involved in cell division (step 6). (A *mitogen* is a substance that controls cell division, hence the name of the kinases.) Changes in gene expression can have far-reaching effects on the cell, such as determining whether a cell divides or how frequently it divides. The Ras proteins are of major interest to investigators because of their role in linking receptor tyrosine kinases to gene regulation, as well as their major roles in the development of many types of cancer when their function is altered.

In this section, we have surveyed major response pathways linked to surface receptors that bind peptide hormones, growth factors, and neurotransmitters.

We now turn to the other major type of signal receptor: the internal receptors binding signal molecules.

STUDY BREAK

1. What is the role of the first messenger in a G protein–coupled receptor-controlled pathway?
2. What is the role of the effector?
3. For a cAMP second-messenger pathway, how is the pathway turned off if no more signal molecules are present in the extracellular fluids?

8.5 Pathways Triggered by Internal Receptors: Steroid Hormone Nuclear Receptors

Cells of many types have internal receptors that respond to signals arriving from the cell exterior. Unlike the signal molecules that bind to surface receptors, these signals, primarily, but not exclusively, steroid hormones, penetrate through the plasma membrane and bind to receptors in the cytoplasm. The receptor-hormone complex enters the nucleus and interacts directly with the genome. Although the receptors are often referred to as steroid nuclear receptors, other hormones can act via nuclear receptors. Thyroxine, a nonsteroidal hormone that has many developmental effects, including the control of development from tadpole to frog, acts via nuclear receptors. The internal receptors, called **steroid hormone receptors**, are typically control proteins that turn on specific genes when they are activated by binding a signal molecule.

The same steroid hormones that activate internal receptors may also have different effects when they activate membrane receptors. The membrane receptors may be on different cells or on the same cells.

8.5a Steroid Hormones Have Widely Different Effects That Depend on Relatively Small Chemical Differences

Steroid hormones are relatively small, nonpolar molecules derived from cholesterol, with a chemical structure based on four carbon rings. Steroid hormones combine with hydrophilic carrier proteins that mask their hydrophobic groups and hold them in solution in the blood and extracellular fluids. When a steroid hormone–carrier protein complex collides with the surface of a cell, the hormone is released and penetrates directly through the nonpolar part of the plasma membrane. On the cytoplasmic side, the hormone binds to its internal receptor.

The various steroid hormones differ only in the side groups attached to their carbon rings. Although the differences are small, they are responsible for highly distinctive effects. For example, the male and female sex hormones of mammals, testosterone and estrogen, respectively, which are responsible for many of the structural and behavioural differences between male and female mammals, differ only in minor substitutions in side groups at two positions. The differences cause the hormones to be recognized by different receptors, which activate specific regulatory DNA regions of target genes, leading to development of individuals as males or females.

8.5b The Response of a Cell to Steroid Hormones Depends on Its Internal Receptors and the Genes They Activate

Steroid nuclear hormone receptors are proteins with two major domains **(Figure 8.14)**. One domain recognizes and binds a specific steroid hormone. The other domain

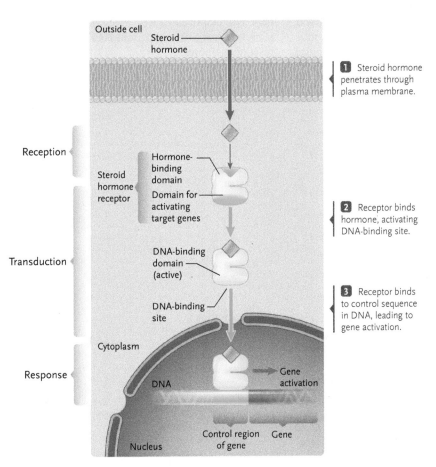

Figure 8.14
Pathway of gene activation by steroid hormone receptors.

1 Steroid hormone penetrates through plasma membrane.

2 Receptor binds hormone, activating DNA-binding site.

3 Receptor binds to control sequence in DNA, leading to gene activation.

Outside cell
Steroid hormone

Reception

Steroid hormone receptor

Hormone-binding domain

Domain for activating target genes

Transduction

DNA-binding domain (active)

DNA-binding site

Cytoplasm

Response

DNA

Gene activation

Control region of gene Gene

Nucleus

interacts with the regions of target genes that control their expression. When a steroid hormone combines with the hormone-binding domain, the gene activation domain changes shape, thus enabling the complex to bind to the DNA control regions of the target genes that the hormone affects. For most steroid hormone receptors, binding of the activated receptor to a gene control region activates that gene, although some may suppress the expression of the target gene.

Steroid hormones, like peptide hormones, are released by cells in one part of an organism and are carried by the organism's circulation to other cells. Whether a cell responds to a steroid hormone depends on whether it has a receptor for the hormone. For responses to steroids mediated by internal receptors, the type of response depends on the genes that are recognized and turned on by an activated receptor. Depending on the receptor type and the particular genes it recognizes, even the same steroid hormone can have highly varied effects on different cells.

Taken together, the various types of receptor tyrosine kinases, G protein–coupled receptors, and steroid hormone nuclear receptors prime cells to respond to a stream of specific signals that continuously fine-tune their function. How are the signals integrated within the cell and organism to produce harmony rather than chaos? The next section shows how the various signal pathways are integrated into a coordinated response. Not all receptors can be classified as surface receptors or internal receptors. The plant hormone ethylene acts via membrane receptors that are inside the cell (see *Molecule Behind Biology*).

STUDY BREAK

1. What distinguishes a steroid nuclear receptor from a receptor tyrosine kinase receptor or a G protein–coupled receptor?
2. By what means does a specific steroid hormone result in a specific cellular response?

8.6 Integration of Cell Communication Pathways

Cells are under the continual influence of many simultaneous signal molecules. The cell signalling pathways may communicate with one another to integrate their responses to cellular signals. The interpathway interaction is called **cross-talk**; a conceptual example that involves two second-messenger pathways is shown in **Figure 8.15**. A protein kinase in one pathway might phosphorylate a site on a target protein in another signal transduction pathway, activating or inhibiting that protein, depending on the site of the phosphorylation. The cross-talk can be extensive, resulting in a complex network of interactions between cell communication pathways.

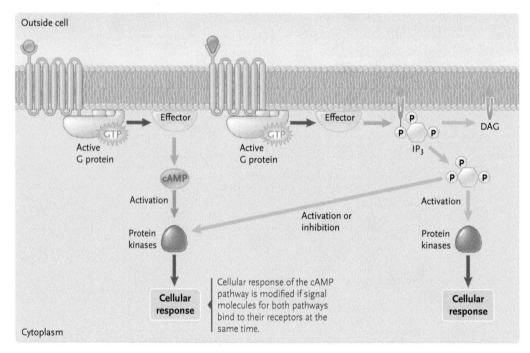

Figure 8.15
Cross-talk, the interaction between cell communication pathways to integrate the responses to signal molecules.

Ethylene

Ethylene is a structurally simple molecule that has dramatic effects on the physiology of plants throughout their life history. As discussed in Chapter 31, ethylene influences such fundamental physiological processes as seed germination, response to wounding, flowering, fruit ripening, and senescence. Several characteristics of ethylene and its action are interesting in the context of this chapter.

First, this molecule is strikingly simple in structure compared to the peptide or steroid hormones of animals and the auxin or cytokinin hormones of plants. Second, it is one of very few hormones that is a gas at physiological temperature (nitric oxide is another). It is soluble in both water and lipids, and as such, it can readily diffuse to, *and into*, target cells. Third, the receptors for ethylene are a family of membrane-bound proteins found not on the cell surface but within the cell on the ER. Fourth, whereas the membrane receptors discussed in this chapter have binding sites that protrude away from the membrane, the binding site for ethylene is within the transmembrane portion of the receptor protein. That is, ethylene diffuses inside the ER membrane to find its receptor. Fifth, in the absence of ethylene, the cascade of proteins involved in ethylene response is actively repressed and inactive. However,

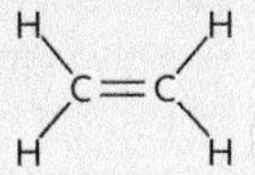

Figure 1
Ethylene: a gaseous plant hormone.

when ethylene binds a receptor, kinase activity and conformational changes activate the pathway, ultimately resulting in production of transcription factors that, in turn, regulate the expression of hundreds of genes.

Cross-talk often leads to modifications of the cellular responses controlled by the pathways. Such modifications fine-tune the effects of combinations of signal molecules binding to the receptors of a cell. For example, cross-talk between second-messenger pathways is involved in particular types of olfactory (smell) signal transduction in rats and probably in many animals. The two pathways involved are activated upon stimulation with distinct odours. One pathway involves cAMP as the second messenger, and the other involves IP_3. However, the two olfactory second-messenger pathways do not work independently; rather, they operate in an antagonistic way. That is, experimentally blocking key enzymes of one signal transduction cascade inhibits that pathway while simultaneously augmenting the activity of the other pathway. The cross-talk may be a way to refine the animal's olfactory sensory perception by helping discriminate different odour molecules more effectively.

Cross-talk networks may also involve inputs from other cellular response systems, such as those triggered by cell adhesion molecules as a result of specific contact between cells. Cell adhesion molecules are receptor-like glycoproteins in plasma membranes; they link cells together or bind them to molecules of the extracellular matrix. Many of these surface molecules also trigger cellular responses. For example, when the surface molecule *integrin* binds to another cell or to a molecule of the extracellular matrix, such as collagen, it triggers a cellular response, often including cross-talk steps that link the reactions to the cAMP and IP_3/DAG pathways. The responses triggered by the cell adhesion molecules include changes in the rate of cell division and gene activity and alterations in cell motility, development, and differentiation.

Direct channels of communication may also be involved in a cross-talk network. For example, gap junctions between the cytoplasms of adjacent cells admit ions and small molecules, including the Ca^{2+}, cAMP, and IP_3 second messengers released by the receptor–response pathways. Thus, one cell that receives a signal through its surface receptors can transmit the signal to other cells in the same tissue via the connecting gap junctions, thereby coordinating the functions of those cells. For instance, cardiac muscle cells are connected by gap junctions, and the Ca^{2+} flow regulates coordinated muscle fibre contractions.

The entire system integrating cellular response mechanisms, tied together by many avenues of cross-talk between individual pathways, creates a sensitively balanced control mechanism that regulates and coordinates the activities of individual cells into the working unit of the organism.

STUDY BREAK

What cell communication pathways might be integrated in a cross-talk network?

Intercellular signal molecules control many cellular activities; therefore, it is not surprising that many laboratories are extensively researching the mechanisms involved. Experimental goals include determining the molecular details of the receptor structures and how they interact with and change when a signal molecule binds, identifying and characterizing all of the components of the transduction steps, detailing how the final activated component of the transduction steps triggers the cellular responses, and understanding the regulation of signal transduction pathways.

What are the prospects for treating human diseases caused by signal transduction pathway malfunctions?
Receptor tyrosine kinase–mediated signalling is critical for cell growth, division, differentiation, and development. Some human diseases and developmental abnormalities result from mutations in the genes for receptor tyrosine kinases and from overexpression of those genes.

Examples are dwarfism, heritable cancer susceptibility, vein malformations, and piebaldism. Researchers are determining the exact nature of the receptor gene mutations in order to explore how the mutations cause the malfunctions of the signal transduction pathways. They have found that some mutations affect the ability of the receptor to form a dimer when the signal molecule binds, and others affect the kinase activity of the cytoplasmic side of the receptor. In fact, there are a surprisingly large number of different mutations that affect receptor tyrosine kinases, meaning that there are many ways that their functions can be affected. In terms of treating human diseases resulting from receptor tyrosine kinase mutations, research is at a relatively early stage. Prospects for therapeutic approaches to treat these diseases include developing anti–tyrosine kinase drugs. Clearly, an increased understanding of receptor tyrosine kinases' signalling and function is crucial for progress to be made in the diagnosis and treatment of human diseases resulting from mutations that cause abnormal regulation of receptor tyrosine kinase function.

Review

Go to CENGAGENOW™ at http://hed.nelson.com/ to access quizzing, animations, exercises, articles, and personalized homework help.

8.1 Cell Communication: An Overview

- Cells communicate with one another through direct channels of communication, specific contact between cells, and intercellular chemical messengers.

- In communication that involves an intercellular chemical messenger, a controlling cell releases a signal molecule that causes a response of target cells. To respond, the target cell must have a receptor for the specific signal molecule. The target cell processes the signal in three steps: reception, transduction, and response. The series of events from reception to response is called signal transduction.

8.2 Characteristics of Cell Communication Systems with Surface Receptors

- Cell communication systems based on surface receptors have three components: (1) extracellular signal molecules, (2) surface receptors that receive the signals, and (3) internal response pathways triggered when receptors bind a signal.

- The systems based on surface receptors respond to hormones and neurotransmitters.

- Hormones include peptides and steroids. A special class of peptide hormones is the growth factors, which affect cell growth, division, and differentiation. Neurotransmitters include small peptides, individual amino acids or their derivatives, and other chemical substances.

- Surface receptors are integral membrane proteins that extend entirely through the plasma membrane. Binding a signal molecule induces a molecular change in the receptor that activates its cytoplasmic end.

- Cellular response pathways operate by activating protein kinases. Phosphate groups added by the protein kinases stimulate or inhibit the activities of the target proteins,

thereby accomplishing the cellular response. The response is reversed by protein phosphatases that remove phosphate groups from target proteins. In addition, receptors are removed by endocytosis when signal transduction has run its course.

- Each step of a response pathway catalyzed by an enzyme is amplified because each enzyme can activate hundreds or thousands of proteins that enter the next step in the pathway. Amplification allows a full cellular response when a few signal molecules bind to their receptors.

8.3 Surface Receptors with Built-in Protein Kinase Activity: Receptor Tyrosine Kinases

- When receptor tyrosine kinases bind a signal molecule, it moves together with another protein kinase to form a dimer, activating the kinase. The active dimer adds phosphate groups to tyrosines in the receptor itself and to target proteins. The phosphate groups added to the cytoplasmic end of the receptor are recognition sites for proteins that are activated by binding to the receptor.

8.4 G Protein–Coupled Receptors

- In the pathways activated by G protein-coupled receptors, binding of the extracellular signal molecule (the first messenger) activates a site on the cytoplasmic end of the receptor.

- An activated receptor turns on a G protein, which acts as a molecular switch. The G protein is active when it is bound to GTP and inactive when it is bound to GDP.

- When a G protein is active, it switches on the effector of the pathway, an enzyme that generates small internal signal molecules called second messengers. The second messengers activate the protein kinases of the pathway.

- In one of the two major pathways triggered by G protein–coupled receptors, the effector, adenylyl cyclase, generates cAMP as second messenger. cAMP activates specific protein kinases.

- In the other major pathway, the activated effector, phospholipase C, generates two second messengers, IP$_3$ and DAG. IP$_3$ activates transport proteins in the ER, which release stored Ca^{2+} into the cytoplasm. The released Ca^{2+}, alone or in combination with DAG, activates specific protein kinases that add phosphate groups to their target proteins.

- Both the cAMP and IP$_3$/DAG pathways are balanced by reactions that constantly eliminate their second messengers. Both pathways are also stopped by protein phosphatases that continually remove phosphate groups from target proteins and by endocytosis of receptors and their bound extracellular signals.

- Some pathways important in gene regulation link certain receptor tyrosine kinases to a specific G protein called Ras. When the receptor binds a signal molecule, it phosphorylates itself, and adapter proteins then bind, bridging to Ras, activating it. Activated Ras turns on the MAP kinase cascade. The last MAP kinase in the cascade, when activated, phosphorylates target proteins in the nucleus, activating them to turn on specific genes. Many of those genes control cell division.

8.5 Pathways Triggered by Internal Receptors: Steroid Hormone Nuclear Receptors

- In addition to their effects on membrane receptors, steroid hormones also penetrate through the plasma membrane to bind to receptors within the cell. The internal receptors are regulatory proteins that turn on specific genes when they are activated by binding a signal molecule, thereby producing the cellular response.

- Steroid hormone nuclear receptors have a domain that recognizes and binds a specific steroid hormone and a domain that interacts with the controlling regions of target genes.

- Steroids may act on membrane and nuclear receptors in the same cells or on different cells. The type of response involving nuclear receptors depends on the genes that are turned on by an activated receptor.

8.6 Integration of Cell Communication Pathways

- In cross-talk, cell signalling pathways such as the cAMP and IP$_3$ pathways communicate with one another to integrate responses to cellular signals. Cross-talk may result in a complex network of interactions between cell communication pathways.

- Cross-talk often results in modifications of the cellular responses controlled by the pathways, fine-tuning the effects of combinations of signal molecules binding to the receptors of a cell.

- In animals, inputs from other cellular response systems, including cell adhesion molecules, as well as molecules arriving through gap junctions, also can become involved in the cross-talk network.

Questions

Self-Test Questions

1. In signal transduction, which of the following is *not* a target protein?
   a. proteins that regulate gene activity.
   b. hormones that activate the receptor.
   c. enzymes of pathways.
   d. transport proteins.
   e. enzymes of cell reactions.

2. A cell that responds to a signal molecule is distinguished from a cell that does not respond by the fact that it has
   a. a cell adhesion molecule.
   b. cAMP.
   c. a first-messenger molecule.
   d. a receptor.
   e. a protein kinase.

3. In a stepwise pathway activated by a small number of signal molecules binding to their receptors, which of the following enables enzymes to activate thousands of molecules?
   a. autophosphorylation.
   b. second-messenger enhancement.
   c. amplification.
   d. ion channel regulation.
   e. G protein turn-on.

4. Which of the following is *incorrect* about pathways activated by G protein–coupled receptors?
   a. The extracellular signal is the first messenger.
   b. When activated, plasma membrane–bound G protein can switch on an effector.

   c. Second messengers enter the nucleus.
   d. ATP converts to cAMP to activate protein kinases.
   e. Protein kinases phosphorylate molecules to change cellular activity.

5. Which of the following would *not* inhibit signal transduction?
   a. Phosphate groups are removed from proteins.
   b. Endocytosis acts on receptors and their bound signals.
   c. Receptors and signals separate.
   d. Receptors and bound signals enter lysosomes.
   e. Autophosphorylation targets the cytoplasmic portion of the receptor.

Questions for Discussion

1. Describe the possible ways in which a G-protein–coupled receptor pathway could become defective and not trigger any cellular responses.

2. What factors might have contributed to the evolution of two internal mechanisms: one using switching molecules that bind ATP and the other binding GTP?

3. What experiments would you do to determine whether a receptor is located on the cell surface or inside the cell?

equipment, and to Dr. G. E. R. Deacon and the captain and officers of R.R.S. *Discovery II* for their part in making the observations.

[1] Young, F. B., Gerrard, H., and Jevons, W., *Phil. Mag.*, **40**, 149 (1920).

[2] Longuet-Higgins, M. S., *Mon. Not. Roy. Astro. Soc., Geophys. Supp.*, **5**, 285 (1949).

[3] Von Arx, W. S., Woods Hole Papers in Phys. Ocearog. Meteor., **11** (3) (1950).

[4] Ekman, V. W., *Arkiv. Mat. Astron. Fysik. (Stockholm)*, **2** (11) (1905).

MOLECULAR STRUCTURE OF NUCLEIC ACIDS

A Structure for Deoxyribose Nucleic Acid

WE wish to suggest a structure for the salt of deoxyribose nucleic acid (D.N.A.). This structure has novel features which are of considerable biological interest.

A structure for nucleic acid has already been proposed by Pauling and Corey[1]. They kindly made their manuscript available to us in advance of publication. Their model consists of three intertwined chains, with the phosphates near the fibre axis, and the bases on the outside. In our opinion, this structure is unsatisfactory for two reasons : (1) We believe that the material which gives the X-ray diagrams is the salt, not the free acid. Without the acidic hydrogen atoms it is not clear what forces would hold the structure together, especially as the negatively charged phosphates near the axis will repel each other. (2) Some of the van der Waals distances appear to be too small.

Another three-chain structure has also been suggested by Fraser (in the press). In his model the phosphates are on the outside and the bases on the inside, linked together by hydrogen bonds. This structure as described is rather ill-defined, and for this reason we shall not comment on it.

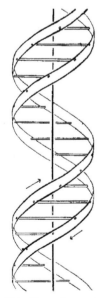

We wish to put forward a radically different structure for the salt of deoxyribose nucleic acid. This structure has two helical chains each coiled round the same axis (see diagram). We have made the usual chemical assumptions, namely, that each chain consists of phosphate diester groups joining β-D-deoxyribofuranose residues with 3′,5′ linkages. The two chains (but not their bases) are related by a dyad perpendicular to the fibre axis. Both chains follow right-handed helices, but owing to the dyad the sequences of the atoms in the two chains run in opposite directions. Each chain loosely resembles Furberg's[2] model No. 1 ; that is, the bases are on the inside of the helix and the phosphates on the outside. The configuration of the sugar and the atoms near it is close to Furberg's 'standard configuration', the sugar being roughly perpendicular to the attached base. There

This figure is purely diagrammatic. The two ribbons symbolize the two phosphate—sugar chains, and the horizontal rods the pairs of bases holding the chains together. The vertical line marks the fibre axis

is a residue on each chain every 3·4 A. in the z-direction. We have assumed an angle of 36° between adjacent residues in the same chain, so that the structure repeats after 10 residues on each chain, that is, after 34 A. The distance of a phosphorus atom from the fibre axis is 10 A. As the phosphates are on the outside, cations have easy access to them.

The structure is an open one, and its water content is rather high. At lower water contents we would expect the bases to tilt so that the structure could become more compact.

The novel feature of the structure is the manner in which the two chains are held together by the purine and pyrimidine bases. The planes of the bases are perpendicular to the fibre axis. They are joined together in pairs, a single base from one chain being hydrogen-bonded to a single base from the other chain, so that the two lie side by side with identical z-co-ordinates. One of the pair must be a purine and the other a pyrimidine for bonding to occur. The hydrogen bonds are made as follows : purine position 1 to pyrimidine position 1 ; purine position 6 to pyrimidine position 6.

If it is assumed that the bases only occur in the structure in the most plausible tautomeric forms (that is, with the keto rather than the enol configurations) it is found that only specific pairs of bases can bond together. These pairs are : adenine (purine) with thymine (pyrimidine), and guanine (purine) with cytosine (pyrimidine).

In other words, if an adenine forms one member of a pair, on either chain, then on these assumptions the other member must be thymine ; similarly for guanine and cytosine. The sequence of bases on a single chain does not appear to be restricted in any way. However, if only specific pairs of bases can be formed, it follows that if the sequence of bases on one chain is given, then the sequence on the other chain is automatically determined.

It has been found experimentally[3,4] that the ratio of the amounts of adenine to thymine, and the ratio of guanine to cytosine, are always very close to unity for deoxyribose nucleic acid.

It is probably impossible to build this structure with a ribose sugar in place of the deoxyribose, as the extra oxygen atom would make too close a van der Waals contact.

The previously published X-ray data[5,6] on deoxyribose nucleic acid are insufficient for a rigorous test of our structure. So far as we can tell, it is roughly compatible with the experimental data, but it must be regarded as unproved until it has been checked against more exact results. Some of these are given in the following communications. We were not aware of the details of the results presented there when we devised our structure, which rests mainly though not entirely on published experimental data and stereochemical arguments.

It has not escaped our notice that the specific pairing we have postulated immediately suggests a possible copying mechanism for the genetic material.

Full details of the structure, including the conditions assumed in building it, together with a set of co-ordinates for the atoms, will be published elsewhere.

We are much indebted to Dr. Jerry Donohue for constant advice and criticism, especially on interatomic distances. We have also been stimulated by a knowledge of the general nature of the unpublished experimental results and ideas of Dr. M. H. F. Wilkins, Dr. R. E. Franklin and their co-workers at

King's College, London. One of us (J. D. W.) has been aided by a fellowship from the National Foundation for Infantile Paralysis.

J. D. WATSON
F. H. C. CRICK
Medical Research Council Unit for the
Study of the Molecular Structure of
Biological Systems,
Cavendish Laboratory, Cambridge.
April 2.

[1] Pauling, L., and Corey, R. B., *Nature*, **171**, 346 (1953); *Proc. U.S. Nat. Acad. Sci.*, **39**, 84 (1953).
[2] Furberg, S., *Acta Chem. Scand.*, **6**, 634 (1952).
[3] Chargaff, E., for references see Zamenhof, S., Brawerman, G., and Chargaff, E., *Biochim. et Biophys. Acta*, **9**, 402 (1952).
[4] Wyatt, G. R., *J. Gen. Physiol.*, **36**, 201 (1952).
[5] Astbury, W. T., Symp. Soc. Exp. Biol. 1, Nucleic Acid, 66 (Camb. Univ. Press, 1947).
[6] Wilkins, M. H. F., and Randall, J. T., *Biochim. et Biophys. Acta*, **10**, 192 (1953).

Molecular Structure of Deoxypentose Nucleic Acids

WHILE the biological properties of deoxypentose nucleic acid suggest a molecular structure containing great complexity, X-ray diffraction studies described here (cf. Astbury[1]) show the basic molecular configuration has great simplicity. The purpose of this communication is to describe, in a preliminary way, some of the experimental evidence for the poly-nucleotide chain configuration being helical, and existing in this form when in the natural state. A fuller account of the work will be published shortly.

The structure of deoxypentose nucleic acid is the same in all species (although the nitrogen base ratios alter considerably) in nucleoprotein, extracted or in cells, and in purified nucleate. The same linear group of polynucleotide chains may pack together parallel in different ways to give crystalline[1-3], semi-crystalline or paracrystalline material. In all cases the X-ray diffraction photograph consists of two regions, one determined largely by the regular spacing of nucleotides along the chain, and the other by the longer spacings of the chain configuration. The sequence of different nitrogen bases along the chain is not made visible.

Oriented paracrystalline deoxypentose nucleic acid ('structure B' in the following communication by Franklin and Gosling) gives a fibre diagram as shown in Fig. 1 (cf. ref. 4). Astbury suggested that the strong 3·4-A. reflexion corresponded to the inter-nucleotide repeat along the fibre axis. The ~ 34 A. layer lines, however, are not due to a repeat of a polynucleotide composition, but to the chain con-figuration repeat, which causes strong diffraction as the nucleotide chains have higher density than the interstitial water. The absence of reflexions on or near the meridian immediately suggests a helical structure with axis parallel to fibre length.

Diffraction by Helices

It may be shown[5] (also Stokes, unpublished) that the intensity distribution in the diffraction pattern of a series of points equally spaced along a helix is given by the squares of Bessel functions. A uniform continuous helix gives a series of layer lines of spacing corresponding to the helix pitch, the intensity distribution along the nth layer line being proportional to the square of J_n, the nth order Bessel function. A straight line may be drawn approximately through

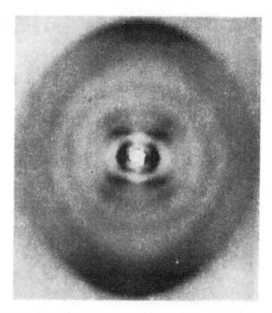

Fig. 1. Fibre diagram of deoxypentose nucleic acid from *B. coli.* Fibre axis vertical

the innermost maxima of each Bessel function and the origin. The angle this line makes with the equator is roughly equal to the angle between an element of the helix and the helix axis. If a unit repeats n times along the helix there will be a meridional reflexion (J_0^2) on the nth layer line. The helical configuration produces side-bands on this fundamental frequency, the effect[5] being to reproduce the intensity distribution about the origin around the new origin, on the nth layer line, corresponding to C in Fig. 2.

We will now briefly analyse in physical terms some of the effects of the shape and size of the repeat unit or nucleotide on the diffraction pattern. First, if the nucleotide consists of a unit having circular symmetry about an axis parallel to the helix axis, the whole diffraction pattern is modified by the form factor of the nucleotide. Second, if the nucleotide consists of a series of points on a radius at right-angles to the helix axis, the phases of radiation scattered by the helices of different diameter passing through each point are the same. Summation of the corresponding Bessel functions gives reinforcement for the inner-

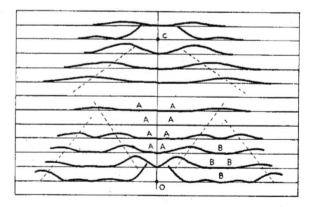

Fig. 2. Diffraction pattern of system of helices corresponding to structure of deoxypentose nucleic acid. The squares of Bessel functions are plotted about 0 on the equator and on the first, second, third and fifth layer lines for half of the nucleotide mass at 20 A. diameter and remainder distributed along a radius, the mass at a given radius being proportional to the radius. About C on the tenth layer line similar functions are plotted for an outer diameter of 12 A.

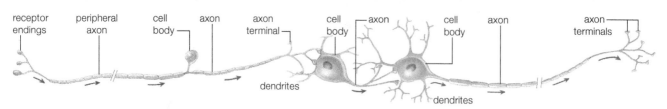

A Sensory neurons have a long axon with receptor endings at one end and axon terminals at the other.

B Interneurons have many dendrites and a short axon.

C Motor neurons have many dendrites and a long axon.

FIGURE 29.4 Typical structure of the three types of neurons. Arrows indicate the direction of information flow among them.

In vertebrate nervous systems, information typically flows from sensory neurons, to interneurons, to motor neurons (**FIGURE 29.4**). **Sensory neurons** are neurons that detect a stimulus such as light or touch. When activated by this stimulus, they usually signal an interneuron. **Interneurons** both receive signals from and send signals to other neurons. An interneuron may signal another interneuron or a motor neuron. **Motor neurons** control muscles and glands.

FIGURE 29.5 {**Animated**} The functional zones of a motor neuron.

❶ Dendrites and the cell body are the neuron's input zone. They receive chemical signals from another neuron and convert them to electrical signals.

❷ Electrical signals spread to a trigger zone at the start of an axon.

❸ If the electrical signals are sufficiently strong, they are conducted along the axon to its terminal endings.

❹ Axon terminals are a signal output zone. They release chemical signals that influence another cell. In the case of a motor neuron, signals affect a muscle cell or gland cell.

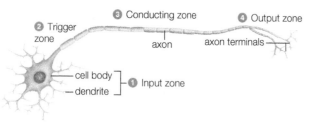

axon Of a neuron, a cytoplasmic extension that transmits electrical signals along its length and secretes chemical signals at its endings.
dendrite Of a motor neuron or interneuron, a cytoplasmic extension that receives chemical signals sent by other neurons and converts them to electrical signals.
interneuron Neuron that both receives signals from and sends signals to other neurons. Located mainly in the brain and spinal cord.
motor neuron Neuron that controls a muscle or gland.
sensory neuron Neuron that is activated when its receptor endings detect a specific stimulus, such as light or pressure.

All neurons have a cell body, a region that holds the nucleus and other organelles. Cytoplasmic extensions that project from the cell body send out and receive chemical signals. All neurons have one **axon**, a special cytoplasmic extension that transmits electrical signals along its length and releases chemical signals at its terminals. Some neurons also have **dendrites**, cytoplasmic extensions that receive chemical signals from other neurons.

Sensory neurons do not receive signals from other cells, so the axon is their only cytoplasmic extension. One end of this axon has receptor endings that detect a specific stimulus; the other has signal-sending axon terminals (**FIGURE 29.4A**).

Interneurons and motor neurons both receive and send signals, so they have dendrites as well as an axon. Most vertebrate interneurons are located entirely in the brain or spinal cord. They have a short axon (**FIGURE 29.4B**). Motor neurons have a cell body in the brain or spinal cord, and an axon that extends out to the muscle or gland they command (**FIGURE 29.4C**). Axons of some motor neurons extend from your spinal cord to your toes.

FIGURE 29.5 shows the functional zones of a motor neuron. The dendrites and cell body are an input zone, where the neuron receives chemical signals and converts them to electrical signals ❶. The part of the axon nearest the cell body is a trigger zone ❷. Arrival of an electrical signal here triggers signals that flow along the conducting zone of the axon ❸ to the axon terminals. Axon terminals are the output zone: They release signaling molecules that influence other cells ❹.

> **TAKE-HOME MESSAGE 29.2**
>
> All neurons have a cell body with organelles and an axon that sends chemical signals to other cells.
>
> Interneurons and motor neurons have signal-receiving dendrites. A sensory neuron has no dendrites. One end of its axon has receptor endings that detect a specific stimulus.

CREDITS: (4) From Starr/Taggart/Evers/Starr, Biology, 13E. © 2013 Cengage Learning; (5) © Cengage Learning.

RESTING POTENTIAL

Animals cells have an electric gradient across their plasma membrane; cytoplasmic fluid near this membrane has more negatively charged ions and proteins than extracellular fluid does. As in a battery, the separation of charge constitutes potential energy that we measure as voltage. The voltage across a cell's membrane is called **membrane potential**. Researchers measure membrane potential across a neuron's axon by inserting one electrode into the axon and another into the fluid just outside of it:

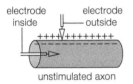

The membrane potential of a neuron that is not being excited is the **resting potential**. This potential is usually about –70 millivolts. (A millivolt [mV] is one-thousandth of a volt.) The negative sign indicates that the inside of the neuron is more negative than the outside.

Resting potential arises from the distribution of charged proteins and small ions. The cytoplasm of a neuron at rest has more negatively charged proteins than the extracellular fluid. Being large and charged, these proteins cannot diffuse across the lipid bilayer of the cell membrane. Positively charged potassium ions (K^+) and positively charged sodium ions (Na^+) also influence resting potential. These ions can move in and out of the neuron with the assistance of transport proteins.

Transport proteins called sodium–potassium pumps (Section 5.7) move two potassium ions into the cell for every three sodium ions they move out (**FIGURE 29.6A**). Because these pumps move more positively charged ions out of the cell than into it, they increase the charge gradient across the membrane. The pumps also contribute to concentration gradients for sodium and potassium ions across the membrane.

Sodium ions cannot cross a resting neuron's membrane, but potassium ions can. Some potassium ions leave the cell through passive transport proteins in the membrane (**FIGURE 29.6B**). Movement of potassium outward increases the charge difference across the membrane.

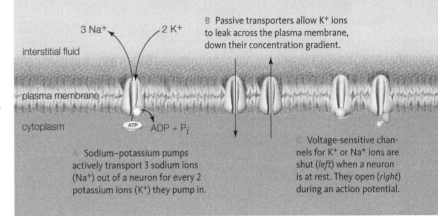

FIGURE 29.6 Transport proteins in a neuron's membrane.

B Passive transporters allow K^+ ions to leak across the plasma membrane, down their concentration gradient.

A Sodium–potassium pumps actively transport 3 sodium ions (Na^+) out of a neuron for every 2 potassium ions (K^+) they pump in.

C Voltage-sensitive channels for K^+ or Na^+ ions are shut (*left*) when a neuron is at rest. They open (*right*) during an action potential.

In summary, the cytoplasm of a resting neuron has more negatively charged proteins than interstitial fluid. It also has fewer sodium ions (Na^+) and more potassium ions (K^+). We illustrate the difference below, with the white minus sign representing negatively charged proteins:

interstitial fluid	150 Na^+	5 K^+	
plasma membrane			
cytoplasm	15 Na^+	150 K^+	65 —

ACTION POTENTIAL

Neurons and muscle cells are said to be "excitable" because they can undergo an **action potential**—an abrupt reversal in the electric gradient across the plasma membrane. The charge reversal occurs when sodium and potassium ions follow their concentration gradients through voltage-gated ion channels, which are passive transport proteins that open only during an action potential (**FIGURE 29.6C**). Neurons have voltage-gated channels in the membrane of their trigger zone and conducting zone. We continue our discussion of action potentials in the next section.

TAKE-HOME MESSAGE 29.3

The cytoplasm of a resting neuron is more negatively charged than extracellular fluid. The impermeability of the membrane to negatively charged proteins and the activity of transport proteins contribute to this resting potential.

A resting neuron also has concentration gradients for sodium and potassium across its membrane, with more sodium outside and more potassium inside.

A neuron can undergo an action potential, in which voltage-gated channels open and the membrane potential reverses abruptly.

---

action potential Abrupt reversal of the charge difference across a neuron membrane.
membrane potential Voltage difference across a cell membrane; arises from differences in charge on opposite sides of the membrane.
resting potential Membrane potential of a neuron at rest.

An action potential begins in a neuron's trigger zone, the part of the axon adjacent to the cell body (**FIGURE 29.7**). When a neuron is at rest, this region's gated channels for sodium and potassium are closed, and there are more negatively charged ions inside the axon than outside it ❶.

A stimulus such as a signal from another neuron shifts the membrane potential in the trigger zone. If the stimulus is large enough, the membrane potential reaches **threshold potential**, the potential at which gated sodium channels in the trigger zone open and an action potential begins.

A POSITIVE FEEDBACK MECHANISM

When gated sodium channels open in a trigger zone, they allow sodium ions (Na^+) to follow their concentration gradient and diffuse from interstitial fluid into the neuron's cytoplasm ❷. As these positively charged ions flow in, they make the cytoplasm more positively charged. This increase in charge causes gated sodium channels in nearby regions of membrane to open, which in turn allows more sodium ions to flow into the cytoplasm, and so on. This is an example of a **positive feedback mechanism**, in which an activity intensifies because of its own occurrence. Positive feedback ensures that an action potential is an all-or-nothing event: Once the membrane potential in the trigger zone reaches threshold level, an action potential always occurs.

A MAXIMUM VALUE

All action potentials are the same size. When an action potential is triggered, the axon's membrane potential quickly shoots up to about +30 mV (**FIGURE 29.8**). A positive

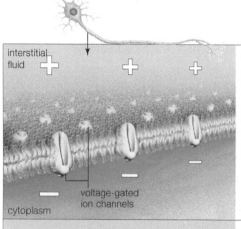

❶ Neuron's trigger zone at resting potential, with voltage-gated channels closed. White pluses and minuses indicate that the cytoplasm's charge is negative relative to that of interstitial fluid.

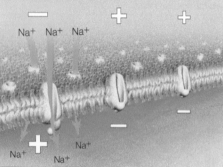

❷ Membrane potential reaches threshold, causing gated sodium (Na^+) channels to open. Na^+ flows through the channels from interstitial fluid into the cytoplasm. This inward flow of positively charged ions reverses the charge across the neuron membrane.

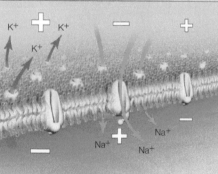

❸ High membrane potential causes gated Na^+ to close, and gated potassium (K^+) channels to open. K^+ flows out and membrane potential becomes negative. At the same time, diffusion of Na^+ ions in the neuron triggers opening of Na^+ gates in an adjacent region.

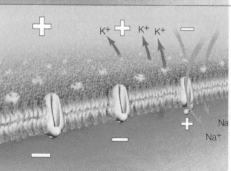

❹ The decline in voltage at the site of the original action potential causes gated potassium channels to shut. After an action potential occurs, gated sodium channels briefly become unable to open. As a result, an action potential moves in one direction only, toward the axon terminals.

FIGURE 29.7 {Animated} Membrane events during an action potential. The drawings illustrate one region of an axon membrane.

FIGURE 29.8 An action potential. This graph shows how the membrane potential reverses and then restores itself. Numbers on the graph correlate with the numbered graphics in **FIGURE 29.7**.

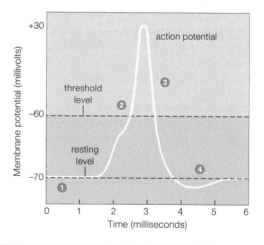

UNIT 6
**HOW ANIMALS
WORK**

CREDITS: (7) From Starr/Taggart/Evers/Starr, Biology, 13E. © 2013 Cengage Learning; (8) © Cengage Learning.

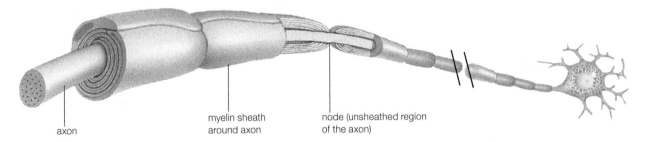

axon

myelin sheath
around axon

node (unsheathed region
of the axon)

FIGURE 29.9 Myelinated axon. Neuroglial cells produce the sheath that wraps around and insulates the axon.

membrane potential indicates that cytoplasm has more positively charged ions than interstitial fluid on the other side of the membrane. Membrane potential cannot exceed +30 mV, because when it reaches this level, gated sodium channels close, and gated potassium channels open ❸. As positively charged potassium ions (K⁺) diffuse out of the cell through the now-open channels, the axon's cytoplasm once again becomes more negatively charged than interstitial fluid. This decline in membrane potential causes gates on gated potassium channels to shut.

In summary, during an action potential, membrane potential rises from the resting potential to a peak value, then declines once again to resting potential. The whole process takes only a few milliseconds.

CONDUCTION ALONG AN AXON

An action potential is self-propagating and does not weaken with distance. It travels along an axon, affecting each patch of membrane only briefly. When voltage-gated sodium channels open, some of the sodium ions that rush inward diffuse into adjacent regions of cytoplasm. The arrival of positive ions raises the membrane potential in these regions to threshold level, setting in motion an action potential in adjacent patches of membrane ❹. Sodium channels open in one region of membrane after another, and the action potential moves along the axon from trigger zone to terminals. The action potential moves only in one direction because it cannot move backward. After a voltage-gated sodium channel closes, it cannot open for a brief period.

However, gated sodium channels in regions farther along the axon's membrane can and do swing open as these regions reach threshold.

Most vertebrate axons have associated neuroglial cells that increase the rate of conduction along the axon. The neuroglia make **myelin**, a fatty material that wraps around the axon (**FIGURE 29.9**). Ions cannot cross myelin, so a myelinated axon undergoes action potentials only at nodes, where there is no myelin. The membrane at each node contains many gated sodium channels. By jumping from node to node in a myelinated axon, an action potential can move as fast as 120 meters per second. By contrast, in unmyelinated axons, the maximum speed of conduction is about 10 meters per second.

Multiple sclerosis (MS) is a nervous system disorder that arises when white blood cells mistakenly attack and destroy myelin sheaths in the brain and spinal cord. As myelin becomes replaced by scar tissue, the speed at which action potentials travel declines. As a result, people with multiple sclerosis experience muscle weakness, fatigue, impaired coordination, numbness, and vision problems.

TAKE-HOME MESSAGE 29.4

An action potential begins in a neuron's trigger zone. When threshold potential is reached, gated sodium channels open and the charge difference across the membrane reverses. Self-propagating voltage reversals that do not weaken with distance occur at consecutive patches of membrane as the action potential travels toward axon terminals.

At each patch of membrane, an action potential ends when potassium ions flow out of the neuron, and the voltage difference across the membrane is restored. Action potentials move only toward axon terminals, because gated sodium channels cannot reopen immediately after an action potential.

Myelin-producing neuroglial cells that associate with most vertebrate neurons speed conduction of action potentials.

myelin Fatty material produced by neuroglial cells; insulates axons and thus speeds conduction of action potentials.
positive feedback mechanism A response intensifies the conditions that caused its occurrence.
threshold potential Neuron membrane potential at which gated sodium channels open, causing an action potential to occur.

CREDIT: (9) From Starr/Evers/Starr, Biology Today and Tomorrow with Physiology, 4E. © 2013 Cengage Learning.

TRANSMISSION, RECEPTION, TRANSDUCTION

Action potentials cannot pass directly from a neuron to another cell. Instead, signaling molecules relay signals between neurons or between a neuron and a muscle or gland. The region where an axon terminal sends chemical signals to a neuron, a muscle fiber, or a gland cell is a **synapse**. The signal-sending neuron at a synapse is called a presynaptic cell. A fluid-filled synaptic cleft about 20 nanometers wide separates its axon terminal from the input zone of a postsynaptic cell (the cell that receives the signal). For comparison, a hair is 100,000 nanometers wide.

FIGURE 29.10 illustrates how signals are transmitted at a **neuromuscular junction**, a synapse between a motor neuron and a skeletal muscle fiber. Action potentials travel along the neuron's axon to the axon terminals ❶. The terminals have vesicles filled with **neurotransmitter**, a type of signaling molecule that relays messages between cells at a synapse ❷. Neurotransmitter is made in the cell body, then moved to axon terminals where it is stored until an action potential arrives. Arrival of an action potential at an axon terminal triggers exocytosis; neurotransmitter-filled vesicles move to the plasma membrane and fuse with it, releasing the neurotransmitter into the synaptic cleft ❸.

The plasma membrane of a postsynaptic cell has receptor proteins that reversibly bind neurotransmitter ❹. Motor neurons release the neurotransmitter acetylcholine (ACh), and skeletal muscle has receptors for this molecule. Binding of ACh to one of these receptors causes a change in the receptor's shape. The receptor is also a passive transport protein, and when it changes shape, sodium ions can travel through it, from interstitial fluid into the muscle cell ❺.

Like a neuron, a muscle fiber can undergo an action potential. The influx of sodium caused by the binding of ACh drives the muscle fiber's membrane toward threshold potential. Once this threshold is reached, action potentials stimulate muscle contraction. We detail this process in Section 32.7.

After neurotransmitter molecules do their work, they must be removed from synaptic clefts to make way for new signals. Reuptake of neurotransmitter by presynaptic cells is part of this process. In addition, enzymes in the membrane of postsynaptic cells break down neurotransmitter. At a neuromuscular junction, the muscle cell membrane contains an enzyme that breaks down ACh.

SIGNAL AND RECEPTOR VARIETY

The effect a neurotransmitter has on a postsynaptic cell depends on the type of neurotransmitter and the type of receptor it binds to. For example, binding of ACh to receptors on skeletal muscle encourages muscle contraction, whereas binding of ACh to receptors on cardiac muscle inhibits contraction. The two types of muscle respond differently to ACh because they have different ACh receptors. ACh also acts in the brain, where it affects alertness and plays a role in memory.

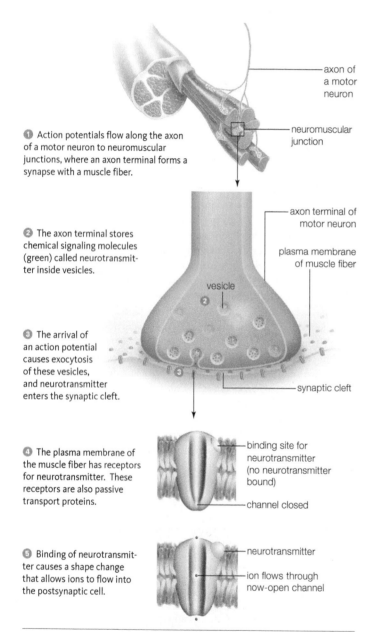

❶ Action potentials flow along the axon of a motor neuron to neuromuscular junctions, where an axon terminal forms a synapse with a muscle fiber.

axon of a motor neuron

neuromuscular junction

❷ The axon terminal stores chemical signaling molecules (green) called neurotransmitter inside vesicles.

axon terminal of motor neuron

plasma membrane of muscle fiber

vesicle

❸ The arrival of an action potential causes exocytosis of these vesicles, and neurotransmitter enters the synaptic cleft.

synaptic cleft

❹ The plasma membrane of the muscle fiber has receptors for neurotransmitter. These receptors are also passive transport proteins.

binding site for neurotransmitter (no neurotransmitter bound)

channel closed

❺ Binding of neurotransmitter causes a shape change that allows ions to flow into the postsynaptic cell.

neurotransmitter

ion flows through now-open channel

FIGURE 29.10 {Animated} Communication at a synapse. This example depicts what occurs at a neuromuscular junction, a synapse between an axon terminal of a motor neuron and the muscle fiber that the neuron controls.

CREDIT: (10) © Cengage Learning.

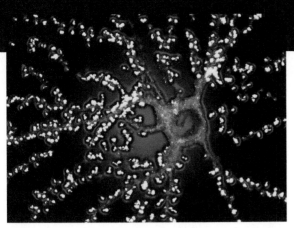

FIGURE 29.11 Synaptic density. This interneuron is stained with a yellow fluorescent dye that indicates the location of many synapses.

ACh is one of many vertebrate neurotransmitters. Norepinephrine and epinephrine (commonly known as adrenaline) are neurotransmitters that prepare the body to respond to stress or excitement. Dopamine influences reward-based learning and acts in fine motor control. Serotonin influences mood and memory. Glutamate is the main excitatory signal in the central nervous system. Endorphins are the body's natural pain relievers.

SYNAPTIC INTEGRATION

A postsynaptic cell typically receives messages from many neurons (FIGURE 29.11). An interneuron in the brain can be on the receiving end of hundreds to thousands of synapses. At each synapse, the incoming signal may be excitatory and push the membrane potential closer to threshold. Or the signal may be inhibitory and nudge the potential away from threshold. Through **synaptic integration**, a neuron sums all inhibitory and excitatory signals arriving at its input zone. When excitatory signals outweigh inhibitory ones, an action potential occurs.

neuromuscular junction Synapse between a neuron and a muscle.
neurotransmitter Chemical signal released by axon terminals.
synapse Region where a neuron's axon terminals transmit signaling molecules (neurotransmitter) to another cell.
synaptic integration The summation of excitatory and inhibitory signals by a postsynaptic cell.

TAKE-HOME MESSAGE 29.5

Action potentials travel to a neuron's axon terminals, where they cause release of neurotransmitter into the synaptic cleft.

A neurotransmitter is a type of signaling molecule that can have an excitatory or inhibitory effect on a postsynaptic cell.

The response of a postsynaptic cell is determined by the sum of all excitatory and inhibitory signals arriving at its input zone at the same time.

29.6 HOW DO DRUGS ACT AT SYNAPSES?

FIGURE 29.12 Commonly used psychoactive drugs. Alcohol, coffee, and nicotine. All alter the function of synapses in the brain.

Psychoactive drugs alter brain function by acting at synapses in the brain (FIGURE 29.12). They do so by a variety of mechanisms. Some drugs mimic a neurotransmitter's effect on a postsynaptic cell. For example, morphine and heroin bind to receptors for endorphins (natural pain relievers), and they elicit the same effects—pain relief and feelings of well-being. In other cases, binding of a drug prevents, rather than mimics, a neurotransmitter's actions. For example, caffeine binds to and inactivates receptors for adenosine, a neurotransmitter that causes drowsiness. Other drugs encourage or inhibit neurotransmitter release from a presynaptic cell. Alcohol makes us drowsy because it encourages adenosine release. Still other drugs interfere with reuptake of neurotransmitter from the synaptic cleft. For example, cocaine slows reuptake of several neurotransmitters, including dopamine.

Some prescription drugs can treat mental disorders by slowing reuptake of a neurotransmitter. Attention deficit hyperactivity disorder (ADHD), which impairs the ability to concentrate and to control impulses, is treated with drugs that slow dopamine reuptake. Depression is treated with drugs that inhibit reuptake of serotonin.

Drug addiction has many causes, but dopamine plays an important role in creating dependency. Behaviors such as eating, which enhances survival, or engaging in sex, which enhances reproduction, result in a surge of dopamine. This response helps individuals learn to repeat evolutionarily beneficial behaviors. When drugs cause dopamine release or prevent its reuptake, they hijack this ancient learning pathway. Drug users inadvertently teach themselves that the drug is essential to their well-being.

TAKE-HOME MESSAGE 29.6

Psychoactive drugs affect signal transmission in the brain by encouraging or inhibiting release of a neurotransmitter, blocking or mimicking its action, or affecting its reuptake.

CREDITS: (11) Courtesy of Riken Brain Science Institute; (12) Szasz-Fabian Jozsef/Shutterstock.com.

Properties of skeletal muscle arise from the composition and arrangement of its component fibers (FIGURE 32.13). As previously noted, a muscle is enclosed within a sheath of connective tissue ❶. This tissue extends beyond the muscle as a tendon. Additional connective tissue encloses bundles of muscle fibers that constitute the bulk of the muscle ❷. Each **skeletal muscle fiber** is a roughly cylindrical cell that runs parallel to the long axis of the muscle ❸. The muscle fiber forms before birth by the fusion of many embryonic cells, so it contains many nuclei, which are positioned at its outer edges. The fiber also contains large numbers of mitochondria, which supply the energy necessary for muscle contraction.

The bulk of the muscle fiber's interior is filled with thousands of threadlike **myofibrils** ❹. A myofibril consists of many identical contractile units, called **sarcomeres**, attached end to end. Each end of a sarcomere is delineated by a Z line, a mesh of cytoskeletal elements that attach the sarcomere to its neighbors. The Z stands for *zwischen*, the German word for "between," and refers to the fact that a sarcomere is the region between two Z lines.

A sarcomere contains parallel arrays of two types of protein filaments. Thick filaments at the sarcomere's center are flanked by thin filaments, which attach to the Z lines at the sarcomere's ends. Thick filaments consist of **myosin**, a motor protein (Section 4.9) that has a long tail and a clublike head with two binding sites. One of the sites can bind ATP and break it into ADP and phosphate, releasing energy in the process. The other binding site is for **actin**, a globular protein that is the main component of thin filaments. As you will learn in the next section, the head of a myosin molecule uses energy from ATP to bind to and move along an adjacent actin filament.

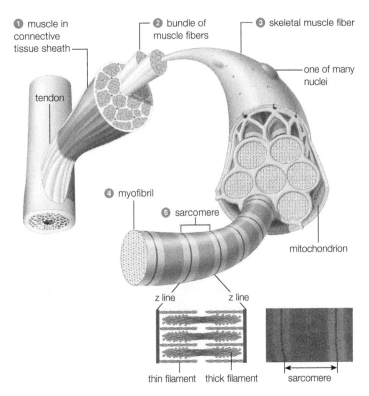

FIGURE 32.13 {Animated} Skeletal muscle components.

Skeletal muscle fibers, myofibrils, thin filaments, and thick filaments all run parallel with a muscle's long axis. As a result, all sarcomeres in all fibers of a skeletal muscle work together and pull in the same direction. Skeletal muscle and cardiac muscle appear striated because Z lines and other sarcomere components in all their fibers are aligned with one another. Smooth muscle fibers have sarcomeres too, but because these sarcomeres are not aligned, smooth muscle does not have a striped appearance.

actin Globular protein that plays a role in cell movements; the main component of thin filaments in myofibrils.
myofibril Within a muscle fiber, a threadlike contractile component made up of sarcomeres arranged end to end.
myosin ATP-dependent motor protein; comprises thick filaments in a sarcomere.
sarcomere Contractile unit of skeletal and cardiac muscle.
skeletal muscle fiber Multinucleated contractile cell that runs the length of a skeletal muscle.

TAKE-HOME MESSAGE 32.5

Sarcomeres are the basic units of contraction in skeletal muscle. Sarcomeres are lined up end to end in myofibrils that run parallel with muscle fibers. These fibers, in turn, run parallel with the whole muscle.

The parallel orientation of skeletal muscle components focuses a muscle's contractile force in a particular direction.

CREDITS: (13) bottom right photo, © Don Fawcett/Visuals Unlimited; top art, © Cengage Learning 2015; bottom left art, From Starr/Taggart/Evers/Starr, Biology, 13E. © 2013 Cengage Learning.

The **sliding-filament model** explains how interactions between thick and thin filaments bring about muscle contraction. Neither actin nor myosin filaments change length, and the myosin filaments do not change position. Instead, myosin heads bind to actin filaments and slide them toward the center of a sarcomere. As the actin filaments are pulled inward, the ends of the sarcomere are drawn closer together, and the sarcomere shortens:

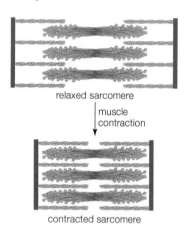

relaxed sarcomere

↓ muscle
contraction

contracted sarcomere

FIGURE 32.14 provides a step-by-step look at events during muscle contraction, starting with the sarcomere in a resting muscle fiber. In a relaxed sarcomere, sites where myosin could bind to actin are blocked. The myosin heads of thick filaments have bound ATP molecules and are in a low-energy conformation ❶. Removing a phosphate group (P_i) from a bound ATP energizes a myosin head in a manner analogous to stretching a spring ❷. The myosin head remains in a high-energy conformation, with bound ADP and phosphate, until a signal from the nervous system excites the muscle (a process we consider in the next section). When this signal arrives, myosin heads attach to actin. The attachment constitutes a cross-bridge between the thin and thick filaments ❸. Attachment releases a phosphate group from myosin and triggers a power stroke ❹. Like a stretched spring returning to its original shape, a myosin head snaps back toward the sarcomere center. As it does, it pulls the attached thin filament along with it.

During the power stroke, a myosin head releases bound ADP. Afterward, the head can bind to a new molecule of ATP and return to its low-energy conformation ❺. In the process, the myosin head releases its grip on actin, and the cross-bridge is lost. Loss of one cross-bridge does not allow a thin filament to slip backward because other cross-bridges hold it in place. During a contraction, many myosin heads repeatedly bind, move, and release an adjacent thin filament.

❶ In a relaxed sarcomere, myosin-binding sites on actin are blocked. The myosin heads have bound ATP, and are in their low-energy conformation.

❷ The myosin heads remove a phosphate group from the ATP. Absorbing energy released by breaking the phosphate bond boosts the myosin heads to a high-energy conformation. ADP and phosphate remain bound to each head.

❸ A signal from the nervous system opens up the myosin-binding sites on actin. Each myosin head attaches to actin and releases its bound phosphate group, thus forming a cross-bridge between thick and thin filaments.

❹ The release of the phosphate group triggers a power stroke, in which the myosin heads snap inward and release ADP. As the heads contract, they pull the attached thin filaments inward.

❺ Another ATP binds to each myosin head, causing it to release actin and return to its low-energy conformation.

FIGURE 32.14 {Animated} Sliding-filament model of muscle contraction.

---

sliding-filament model   Explanation of how interactions among actin and myosin filaments shorten a sarcomere and bring about muscle contraction.

TAKE-HOME MESSAGE 32.6

During muscle contraction, sarcomeres shorten when myosin binds to actin and pulls thin filaments toward the center of the sarcomeres.

Contraction does not change the length of muscle filaments or the position of thick (myosin) filaments.

MOTOR CORTEX AND MOTOR NEURONS

Most commands for voluntary movement originate in the portion of the cerebral cortex known as the primary motor cortex (Section 29.10). Signals from this brain region travel to and excite a motor neuron in the spinal cord (FIGURE 32.15 ❶). As you know, the axon of a such a neuron extends to a skeletal muscle and synapses with it at a neuromuscular junction ❷. When an action potential arrives at this junction, it triggers the release of the neurotransmitter acetylcholine (ACh).

Muscle fibers have receptors for ACh in their plasma membrane. Binding of ACH by these receptors triggers an action potential that travels along the muscle fiber's membrane, then down membrane extensions called transverse tubules or T tubules ❸. T tubules convey action potentials to the **sarcoplasmic reticulum**, a specialized endoplasmic reticulum that wraps around myofibrils and stores calcium ions. When an action potential arrives, the sarcoplasmic reticulum releases these ions into the muscle fiber's cytoplasm. The influx of calcium clears myosin-binding sites on actin filaments. Actin and myosin then interact, and muscle contraction gets under way. When contraction ends, calcium pumps in the sarcoplasmic reticulum's membrane actively transport the ions back into the organelle. As the calcium ion concentration in cytoplasm drops, myosin-binding sites become blocked again and the muscle fiber rests.

MOTOR UNITS

A motor neuron has many terminal endings, and each synapses on a different fiber inside a muscle. A motor neuron and all of the muscle fibers it synapses with constitute one **motor unit**. Stimulate a motor neuron, and all the muscle fibers in its motor unit contract. The nervous system cannot make only some fibers in a motor unit contract.

The mechanical force generated by a contracting muscle—the **muscle tension**—depends on the number of muscle fibers contracting. Some tasks require more muscle tension than others, so the number of muscle fibers controlled by a single motor neuron varies. In motor units that bring about small, fine movements such as those that control muscles that move the eye, one motor neuron synapses with only 5 or so muscle fibers. By contrast, muscles that must frequently exert a large amount of force, have many fibers per motor unit. For example, the biceps of the arm has about 700 muscle fibers per motor unit. Having many fibers pulling the same way at once increases the force a motor unit can generate.

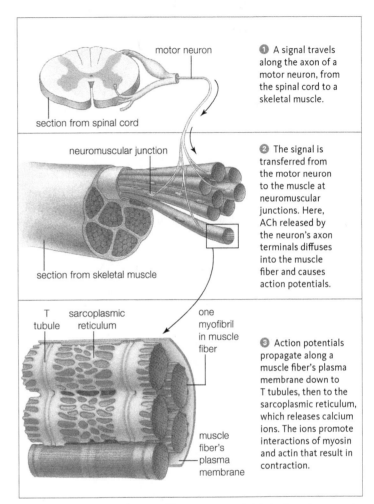

❶ A signal travels along the axon of a motor neuron, from the spinal cord to a skeletal muscle.

❷ The signal is transferred from the motor neuron to the muscle at neuromuscular junctions. Here, ACh released by the neuron's axon terminals diffuses into the muscle fiber and causes action potentials.

❸ Action potentials propagate along a muscle fiber's plasma membrane down to T tubules, then to the sarcoplasmic reticulum, which releases calcium ions. The ions promote interactions of myosin and actin that result in contraction.

FIGURE 32.15 {Animated} Nervous control of skeletal muscle contraction.

motor unit One motor neuron and the muscle fibers it controls.
muscle tension Force exerted by a contracting muscle.
sarcoplasmic reticulum Specialized endoplasmic reticulum in muscle cells; stores and releases calcium ions.

TAKE-HOME MESSAGE 32.7

Most commands for voluntary movement originate in the motor cortex. They reach a muscle by way of a motor neuron.

Arrival of an action potential at a neuromuscular junction excites a muscle fiber. T tubules convey the excitatory signal to the sarcoplasmic reticulum, which releases calcium ions. The rise in calcium ion concentration allows myosin to bind to actin so contraction can occur.

Each motor neuron synapses with multiple fibers in the same muscle.

CREDIT: (15) © Cengage Learning.

Appendix A
Answers to Self-Test Questions

Chapter 1
1. c 2. a 3. a 4. a 5. c 6. b 7. d 8. d 9. d 10. a

Chapter 2
1. b 2. e 3. d 4. d 5. c 6. b 7. d 8. a 9. b 10. a

Chapter 3
1. c 2. b 3. e 4. d 5. c 6. a 7. d 8. e 9. b 10. a

Chapter 4
1. c 2. d 3. d 4. b 5. d 6. c 7. b 8. a 9. c 10. d

Chapter 5
1. a 2. c 3. b 4. c 5. b 6. b 7. b 8. a 9. d 10. e

Chapter 6
1. a 2. c 3. d 4. d 5. c 6. a 7. b 8. c 9. e 10. d

Chapter 7
1. d 2. c 3. c 4. c 5. a 6. d 7. a 8. c 9. c 10. c

Chapter 8
1. c 2. d 3. c 4. a 5. b 6. b 7. b 8. d 9. b 10. b

Chapter 9
1. d 2. d 3. c 4. d 5. b 6. a 7. a 8. b 9. a 10. c

Chapter 10
1. c
2. (a) The CC parent produces all C gametes, and the Cc parent produces $1/2$ C and $1/2$ c gametes. All offspring would have coloured seeds—half homozygous CC and half heterozygous Cc. (b) Both parents produce $1/2$ C and $1/2$ c gametes. Of the offspring, three-fourths would have coloured seeds ($1/4$ CC + $1/2$ Cc) and one-fourth would have colourless seeds ($1/4$ cc). (c) The Cc parent produces $1/2$ C gametes and $1/2$ c gametes, and the cc parent produces all c gametes. Half of the offspring are coloured ($1/2$ Cc), and half are colourless ($1/2$ cc).
3. The genotypes of the parents are Tt and tt.
4. The taster parents could have a nontaster child, but nontaster parents are not expected to have a child who can taste PTC. The chance that they might have a taster child is $3/4$. The chance

of a nontaster child being born to the taster couple is $1/4$. Because each combination of gametes is an independent event, the chance of the couple having a second child, or any child, who cannot taste PTC is expected to be $1/4$.
5. (a) All A B (b) $1/2$ A B + $1/2$ a B (c) $1/2$ A b + $1/2$ a b (d) $1/4$ A B + $1/4$ A b + $1/4$ a B + $1/4$ a b
6. (a) All $AaBB$ (b) $AABB$ ($1/16$) + $AaBB$ ($1/8$) + $aaBB$ ($1/16$) + $AABb$ ($1/8$) + $AaBb$ ($1/4$) + $aaBb$ ($1/8$) + $AAbb$ ($1/16$) + $Aabb$ ($1/8$) + $aabb$ ($1/16$) (c) $AaBb$ ($1/4$) + $Aabb$ ($1/4$) + $aaBb$ ($1/4$) + $aabb$ ($1/4$) (d) $AABB$ ($1/4$) + $AABb$ ($1/4$) + $AaBB$ ($1/4$) + $AaBb$ ($1/4$)
7. (a) All A B C (b) $1/2$ A B c + $1/2$ a B c (c) $1/4$ A B C + $1/4$ A B c + $1/4$ a B C + $1/4$ a B c (d) $1/8$ A B C + $1/8$ A B c + $1/8$ A b C + $1/8$ A b c + $1/8$ a B C + $1/8$ a B c + $1/8$ a b C + $1/8$ a b c
8. This diagram is incorrect because it does not show that each gamete will contain one allele from each of the two genes involved in this cross. The gametes should be Mh, MH, mH, and mh.
9. Because the man can produce only 1 type of allele for each of the 10 genes, he can produce only 1 type of sperm cell with respect to these genes. The woman can produce 2 types of alleles for each of her 2 heterozygous genes, so she can produce $2 \times 2 = 4$ different types of eggs with respect to the 10 genes. In general, as the number of heterozygous genes increases, the number of possible types of gametes increases as $2n$, where $n =$ the number of heterozygous genes.
10. Use a standard testcross; that is, cross the guinea pig with rough, black fur with a double-recessive individual, rr bb (smooth, white fur). If your animal is homozygous RR BB, you would expect all the offspring to have rough, black fur.
11. One gene probably controls pod colour. One allele, for green pods, is dominant; the other allele, for yellow pods, is recessive.
12. The cross $RR \times Rr$ will produce $1/2$ RR and $1/2$ Rr offspring. The cross $Rr \times Rr$ will produce $1/4$ RR, $1/2$ Rr, and $1/4$ rr as combinations of alleles. However, the $1/4$ rr combination is lethal, so it does not appear among the offspring. Therefore, the offspring will be born with only two types, RR and Rr, with twice as many Rr as rr in a 1:2 ratio (or $1/3$ RR + $2/3$ Rr).
13. The parental cross is GG TT $RR \times gg$ tt rr. All offspring of this cross are expected to be tall plants with green pods and round seeds, or Gg Tt Rr. When crossed, this heterozygous F_1 generation is expected to produce eight

different phenotypes among the offspring: green-tall-round, green-dwarf-round, yellow-tall-round, green-tall-wrinkled, yellow-dwarf-round, green-dwarf-wrinkled, yellow-tall-wrinkled, and yellow-dwarf-wrinkled, in a 27:9:9:9:3:3:3:1 ratio.

14. The genotypes are bird 1, *Ff Pp;* bird 2, FF PP; bird 3, *Ff PP;* and bird 4, *Ff Pp.*

15. Yes, it can be determined that the child is not hers, because the father must be AB to have both an A and B child with a type O wife; none of the woman's children could have type O blood with an AB father.

16. The cross is expected to produce white, tabby, and black kittens in a 12:3:1 ratio.

17. The mother is homozygous recessive for both genes, and the father must be heterozygous for both genes. The child is homozygous recessive for both genes. The chance of having a child with normal hands is 1/2, and that of having a child with woolly hair is 1/2. Using the product rule of probability, the probability of having a child with normal hands and woolly hair is $1/2 \times 1/2 = 1/4$.

Chapter 11

1. All sons will be colour-blind, but none of the daughters will be. However, all daughters will be heterozygous carriers of the trait.

2. The chance that her son will be colour-blind is 1/2, regardless of whether she marries a normal or colour-blind male.

3. All of these questions can be answered from the pedigree. Polydactyly is caused by a dominant allele, and the trait is not sex linked. The genotypes of each person are as shown below:

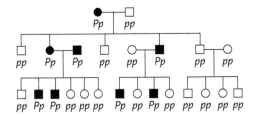

4. The sequence of the genes is *ADBC.*

5. Let the allele for wild-type grey body colour be b^+, and the allele for black body be b. Let the allele for wild-type red eye colour be p^+, and the allele for purple eyes be p. Then the parents are as follows:

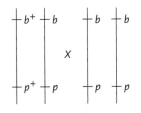

The F₁ flies with black bodies and red eyes are as follows:

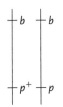

The flies with grey bodies and purple eyes are as shown:

6. The genes are linked by their presence on the same chromosome (an autosome), but they are not sex linked. Because the F₁ females must have produced 600 gametes to give these 600 progeny, and because 42 + 30 of these were recombinant, the percentage of recombinant gametes is 72/600, or 12%, which implies that 12 map units separate the two genes.

7. Because this trait is probably carried on the Y chromosome, which a man transmits to all his sons, all will have hairy ears. None of the daughters will have hairy ears because they do not have a Y chromosome.

8. You might suspect that a recessive allele is sex linked and is carried on one of the two X chromosomes of the female parent in the cross. When present on the single X of the male (or if present on both X's of a female), the gene is lethal.

Chapter 12

1. c 2. b 3. a 4. a 5. d 6. c 7. b 8. a 9. d 10. d

Chapter 13

1. c 2. a 3. d 4. b 5. d 6. b 7. b 8. c 9. a 10. b

Chapter 14

1. c 2. c 3. b 4. b 5. d 6. c 7. d 8. a 9. a 10. d

Chapter 15

1. c 2. d 3. a 4. a 5. a 6. b 7. a 8. d 9. c 10. b

Chapter 16

1. b 2. a 3. a 4. a 5. d 6. b 7. d 8. a 9. c 10. d

Chapter 17

1. c 2. c 3. d 4. b 5. c 6. b 7. a 8. b 9. d 10. d

Chapter 18

1.c 2. b 3. c 4. d 5. b 6. e 7. a 8. b 9. c 10. d

Chapter 19

1. a 2. e 3. e 4. d 5. d 6. e 7. b 8. c 9. a 10. b

Chapter 20

1. a 2. c 3. e 4. d 5. b 6. c 7. a 8. d 9. c 10. b

Chapter 21

1. d 2. c 3. d 4. d 5. c 6. a 7. c 8. d 9. b 10. c

Chapter 22

1. b 2. c 3. c 4. b 5. d 6. a 7. a 8. c 9. b 10. a

Chapter 23

1. c 2. a 3. a 4. c 5. d 6. b 7. c 8. c 9. d 10. d

Chapter 24

1. b 2. a 3. d 4. b 5. d 6. c 7. b 8. c 9. d 10. c

Chapter 25

1. c 2. b 3. d 4. b 5. b 6. c 7. d 8. c 9. a 10. c

Chapter 26

1. c 2. d 3. c 4. c 5. b 6. b 7. d 8. a 9. d 10. d

Chapter 27

1. c 2. d 3. d 4. d 5. b 6. d 7. c 8. b 9. c 10. d

Chapter 28

1. a 2. b 3. c 4. a 5. c 6. c 7. c 8. b 9. c 10. a

Chapter 29

1. a 2. b 3. b 4. c 5. a 6. a 7. a 8. d 9. d 10. a

Chapter 30

1. c 2. b 3. a 4. a 5. b 6. d 7. b 8. d 9. c 10. b

Chapter 31

1. d 2. c 3. a 4. d 5. d 6. a 7. c 8. d 9. c 10. a

Chapter 32

1. d 2. c 3. d 4. c 5. b 6. b 7. a 8. b 9. b 10. b

Chapter 33

1. c 2. d 3. b 4. b 5. c 6. d 7. b 8. b 9. b 10. b

Chapter 34

1. c 2. d 3. d 4. b 5. a 6. b 7. a 8. b 9. c 10. c

Chapter 35

1. d 2. c 3. a 4. c 5. d 6. c 7. b 8. c 9. c 10. c

Chapter 36

1. b 2. c 3. b 4. a 5. b 6. c 7. d 8. a 9. c 10. c

Chapter 37

1. e 2. c 3. d 4. c 5. b 6. c 7. a 8. d 9. a 10. e

Chapter 38

1. e 2. c 3. d 4. c 5. b 6. c 7. a 8. d 9. a 10. e

Chapter 39

1. a 2. b 3. e 4. a 5. d 6. b 7. d 8. c 9. d 10. c, e

Chapter 40

1. a, b, c, d, e 2. d 3. b 4. d 5. a, d, e 6. d 7. e
8. a, b, c, d 9. b, d 10. d

Chapter 41

1. a, d 2. d 3. a, c 4. d 5. d 6. d 7. b 8. a 9. c 10. b

Chapter 42

1. d 2. d 3. b 4. c 5. d 6. d 7. d 8. b 9. c 10. b

Chapter 43

1. a 2. c 3. e 4. c 5. a 6. d 7. a, b, c, d 8. b, c
9. a 10. c

Chapter 44

1. b, c, d, e 2. a, c, d 3. a, c 4. a, c 5. e 6. b 7. c, d
8. a 9. c 10. b

Chapter 45

1. a 2. d 3. b, d 4. c 5. e 6. a, b, c, d, e 7. d 8. b, d
9. a, b 10. b

Chapter 46

1. d 2. d 3. e 4. e 5. a, b 6. c 7. a, b 8. a 9. e 10. e

Chapter 47

1. b 2. c 3. a 4. b 5. d 6. c 7. d 8. b 9. c 10. b

Chapter 48

1. a 2. b 3. e 4. b 5. d 6. b 7. d 8. c 9. d 10. c

Chapter 1

1. e 2. d 3. b 4. a 5. e 6. d 7. e 8. d 9. d 10. e

Chapter 2

1. c 2. b 3. c 4. e 5. e 6. e 7. d 8. b 9. e 10. b

Chapter 3

1. c 2. c 3. b 4. a 5. b 6. b 7. b 8. e 9. e 10. c

Chapter 4

1. e 2. d 3. d 4. d 5. d 6. c 7. e 8. c 9. d 10. e

Chapter 5

1. d 2. a 3. e 4. d 5. d 6. e 7. c 8. b 9. a 10. c

Chapter 6

1. c 2. d 3. c 4. d 5. e 6. b 7. c 8. d 9. d 10. e

Chapter 7

1. e 2. c 3. a 4. b 5. e 6. b 7. c 8. e 9. c 10. b

Chapter 8

1. b 2. d 3. c 4. c 5. e

Chapter 9

1. c 2. b 3. d 4. b 5. b 6. d 7. a 8. b 9. b 10. c

Chapter 10

1. a 2. c 3. d 4. a 5. e 6. b 7. d 8. c 9. b 10. b 11. a 12. d 13. b

Chapter 11

1. (a) The CC parent produces all C gametes, and the Cc parent produces $1/2$ C and $1/2$ c gametes. All offspring would have coloured seeds—half homozygous CC and half heterozygous Cc. (b) Both parents produce $1/2$ C and $1/2$ c gametes. Of the offspring, three-fourths would have coloured seeds ($1/4$ $CC + 1/2$ Cc) and one-fourth would have colourless seeds ($1/4$ cc). (c) The Cc parent produces $1/2$ C gametes and $1/2$ c gametes, and the cc parent produces all c gametes. Half of the offspring are coloured ($1/2$ Cc) and half are colourless ($1/2$ cc).

2. The genotypes of the parents are Tt and tt.

3. The taster parents could have a nontaster child, but nontaster parents are not expected to have a child who can taste PTC. The chance that they might have a taster child is $3/4$. The chance of a nontaster child being born to the taster couple would be $1/4$. Because each combination of gametes is an independent event, the chance of the couple having a second child, or any child, who cannot taste PTC is expected to be $1/4$.

4. (a) All A B. (b) $1/2$ A $B + 1/2$ a B. (c) $1/2$ A $b + 1/2$ a b. (d) $1/4$ A $B + 1/4$ A $b + 1/4$ a $B + 1/4$ a b.

5. (a) All Aa BB. (b) $1/4$ AA $BB + 1/4$ AA $Bb + 1/4$ Aa $BB + 1/4$ Aa Bb. (c) $1/4$ Aa Bb _ $1/4$ Aa $bb + 1/4$ aa $Bb + 1/4$ aa bb. (d) $1/4$ Aa $Bb + 1/8$ AA $Bb + 1/8$ Aa $BB + 1/8$ Aa $bb + 1/8$ aa $Bb + 1/16$ AA $BB + 1/16$ AA $bb + 1/16$ aa $BB + 1/16$ aa bb.

6. (a) All A B C. (b) $1/2$ A B $c + 1/2$ a B c. (c) $1/4$ A B $C + 1/4$ A B $c + 1/4$ a B $C + 1/4$ a B c. (d) $1/8$ A B $C + 1/8$ A B $c + 1/8$ A b $C + 1/8$ A b $c + 1/8$ a B $C + 1/8$ a B $c + 1/8$ a b $C + 1/8$ a b c.

7. Because the man can produce only 1 type of allele for each of the 10 genes, he can produce only 1 type of sperm cell with respect to these genes. The woman can produce 2 types of alleles for each of her 2 heterozygous genes, so she can produce $2 \times 2 = 4$ different types of eggs with respect to the 10 genes. In general, as the number of heterozygous genes increases, the number of possible types of gametes increases as 2^n, where $n = $ the number of heterozygous genes.

8. Use a standard testcross; that is, cross the guinea pig with rough, black fur with a double recessive individual, rr bb (smooth, white fur). If your animal is homozygous RR BB, you would expect all the offspring to have rough, black fur.

9. One gene probably controls pod colour. One allele, for green pods, is dominant; the other allele, for yellow pods, is recessive.

10. The cross $RR \times Rr$ will produce $1/2$ RR and $1/2$ Rr offspring. The cross $Rr \times Rr$ will produce $1/4$ RR, $1/2$ Rr, and $1/4$ rr as combinations of alleles. However, the $1/4$ rr combination is lethal, so it does not appear among the offspring. Therefore, the offspring will be born with only two types, RR and Rr, with twice as many Rr as rr in a 1:2 ratio (or $1/3$ $RR + 2/3$ Rr).

11. The parental cross is GG TT $RR \times gg$ tt rr. All offspring of this cross are expected to be tall plants with green pods and round seeds, or Gg Tt Rr. When crossed, this heterozygous F1 generation is expected to produce eight different

Glossary

3′ end The end of a polynucleotide chain at which a hydroxyl group is bonded to the 3 carbon of a deoxyribose sugar. p. 268

5′ cap In eukaryotes, a guanine-containing nucleotide attached in a reverse orientation to the 5 end of pre-mRNA and retained in the mRNA produced from it. The 5′ cap on an mRNA is the site where ribosomes attach to initiate translation. p. 297

5′ end The end of a polynucleotide chain at which a phosphate group is bound to the 5 carbon of a deoxyribose sugar. p. 268

10 nm chromatin fibre The most fundamental level of chromatin packing of a eukaryotic chromosome, in which DNA winds for almost two turns around an eight-protein nucleosome core particle to form a nucleosome, and linker DNA extends between adjacent nucleosomes. The result is a beads-on-a-string type of structure with a 10 nm diameter. p. 283

30 nm chromatin fibre Level of chromatin packing of a eukaryotic chromosome in which histone H1 binds to the 10 nm chromatin fibre, causing it to package into a coiled structure about 30 nm in diameter and with about six nucleosomes per turn. Also referred to as a *solenoid*. p. 284

A site The site where the incoming aminoacyl-tRNA carrying the next amino acid to be added to the polypeptide chain binds to the mRNA. p. 302

abdomen In insects, the region behind the thorax. p. 622

abiotic Nonbiological, often in reference to physical factors in the environment. p. 53

abscisic acid (ABA) A plant hormone involved in the abscission of leaves, flowers, and fruits; dormancy of buds and seeds; and closing of stomata. p. 928

abscission In plants, the dropping of flowers, fruits, and leaves in response to environmental signals. p. 927

absorption spectrum Curve representing the amount of light absorbed at each wavelength. p. 149

absorptive nutrition Mode of nutrition in which an organism secretes digestive enzymes into its environment and then absorbs the small molecules thus produced. p. 541

accommodation A process by which the lens changes to enable the eye to focus on objects at different distances. p. 1108

acid Proton donor that releases H (and anions) when dissolved in water. p. F-18

acid-growth hypothesis A hypothesis to explain how the hormone auxin promotes the growth of plant cells; it suggests that auxin stimulates H pumps in the plasma membrane to move H from the cell interior into the cell wall, which increases wall acidity, making the wall expandable. p. 923

acetabulum Socket of hip joint, receives head of femur. p. 657

acid precipitation Rainfall with low pH, primarily created when gaseous sulfur dioxide (SO_2) dissolves in water vapour in the atmosphere, forming sulfuric acid. p. 909

acidity The concentration of H^+ in a water solution, compared with the concentration of OH^-. p. 93

acoelomate A body plan of bilaterally symmetrical animals that lack a body cavity (coelom) between the gut and the body wall. p. 596

acorn worms Sedentary marine animals living in U-shaped tubes or burrows in coastal sand or mud. p. 639

acquired immune deficiency syndrome (AIDS) A constellation of disorders that follows infection by the HIV virus. pp. 213, 507

acrosome A specialized secretory vesicle on the head of an animal sperm, which helps the sperm penetrate the egg. p. 992

acrosome reaction The process in which enzymes contained in the acrosome are released from an animal sperm and digest a path through the egg coats. p. 1007

action potential The abrupt and transient change in membrane potential that occurs when a neuron conducts an electrical impulse. p. 938

action spectrum Graph produced by plotting the effectiveness of light at each wavelength in driving photosynthesis. p. 150

activation energy The initial input of energy required to start a reaction. p. 85

activator A regulatory protein that controls the expression of one or more genes. pp. 316, 323

active immunity The production of antibodies in the body in response to exposure to a foreign antigen. p. 1281

active parental care Parents' investment of time and energy in caring for offspring after they are born or hatched. p. 687

active site The region of an enzyme that recognizes and combines with a substrate molecule. p. 87

active transport The mechanism by which ions and molecules move against the concentration gradient across a membrane, from the side with the lower concentration to the side with the higher concentration. pp. 109, 865

adaptation, evolutionary Characteristic or suite of characteristics that helps an organism survive longer or reproduce more under a particular set of environmental conditions; the accumulation of adaptive traits over time. p. 423

adaptation, sensory *See* sensory adaptation. p. 1099

adaptive (acquired) immunity A specific line of defence against invasion of the body in which individual pathogens are recognized and attacked to neutralize and eliminate them. p. 1267

adaptive radiation (diversification) A cluster of closely related species that are each adaptively specialized to a specific habitat or food source. p. 451

adaptive trait A genetically based characteristic, preserved by natural selection, that increases an organism's likelihood of survival or its reproductive output. pp. 398, 423

adaptive zone A part of a habitat that may be occupied by a group of species exploiting the same resources in a similar manner. p. 661

adductor muscle A muscle that pulls inward toward the median line of the body; in bivalve molluscs, it pulls the shell closed. p. 615

adenine A purine that base-pairs with either thymine in DNA or uracil in RNA. p. 268

adherens junction Animal cell junction in which intermediate filaments are the anchoring cytoskeletal component. p. 47

adhesion The adherence of molecules to the walls of conducting tubes, as in plants. p. 47

adipose tissue Connective tissue containing large, densely clustered cells called adipocytes that are specialized for fat storage. p. 954

adrenal cortex The outer region of the adrenal glands, which contains endocrine cells that secrete two major types of steroid hormones, the glucocorticoids and the mineralocorticoids. p. 1058

adrenal medulla The central region of the adrenal glands, which contains neurosecretory neurons that secrete the catecholamine hormones epinephrine and norepinephrine. p. 1058

adrenocorticotropic hormone (ACTH) A hormone that triggers hormone secretion by cells in the adrenal cortex. p. 1055

adult stem cells Mammalian stem cells that can differentiate into a limited number of cell types associated with the tissue in which they occur. p. 354

adventitious Formed in an unusual position. p. 853

adventitious root A root that develops from the stem or leaves of a plant. p. 853

aerobe An organism that requires oxygen for cellular respiration. p. 487

afferent arteriole The vessel that delivers blood to the glomerulus of the kidney. p. 1247

afferent neuron A neuron that transmits stimuli collected by a sensory receptor to an interneuron. 1070

African emergence hypothesis A hypothesis proposing that modern humans first evolved in Africa and then dispersed to other continents. p. 477

agar A gelatinous product extracted from certain red algae or seaweed used as a culture medium in the laboratory and as a gelling or stabilizing agent in foods. p. 532

agarose gel electrophoresis Technique by which DNA, RNA, or molecules are separated in a gel subjected to an electric field. p. 346

age structure A statistical description or graph of the relative numbers of individuals in each age class in a population. p. 683

age-specific fecundity The average number of offspring produced by surviving females of a particular age. p. 685

age-specific mortality The proportion of individuals alive at the start of an age interval that died during that age interval. p. 685

age-specific survivorship The proportion of individuals alive at the start of an age interval that survived until the start of the next age interval. p. 685

aggregate fruit A fruit that develops from multiple separate carpels of a single flower, such as a raspberry or strawberry. p. 891

albumin The most abundant protein in blood plasma, important for osmotic balance and pH buffering; also, the portion of an egg that serves as the main source of nutrients and water for the embryo. pp. 654, 970

alcohol A molecule of the form R—OH in which R is a chain of one or more carbon atoms, each of which is linked to hydrogen atoms. p. 100

alcohol fermentation Reaction in which pyruvate is converted into ethyl alcohol and CO_2 in a two-step series that also converts NADH into NAD^+. p. 137

aldosterone A mineralocorticoid hormone released from the adrenal cortex that increases the amount of Na reabsorbed from the urine in the kidneys and absorbed from foods in the intestine, reduces the amount of Na secreted by salivary and sweat glands, and increases the rate of K excretion by the kidneys, keeping Na and K balanced at the levels required for normal cellular function. p. 1059

algin Alginic acid, found in the cell walls of brown algae. p. 526

all-or-nothing principle The principle that an action potential is produced only if the stimulus is strong enough to cause depolarization to reach the threshold. p. 1075

allantoic membrane Forms from mesoderm and endoderm that has bulged outward from the gut and encloses the allantois. p. 1021

allantois In an amniote egg, an extraembryonic membrane sac that fills much of the space between the chorion and the yolk sac and stores the embryo's nitrogenous wastes. p. 1021

allele One of two or more versions of a gene. pp. 201, 220

allele frequency The abundance of one allele relative to others at the same gene locus in individuals of a population. p. 414

allergen A type of antigen responsible for allergic reactions, which induces B cells to secrete an overabundance of IgE antibodies. p. 1284

allopatric speciation The evolution of reproductive isolating mechanisms between two populations that are geographically separated. p. 435

allopolyploidy The genetic condition of having two or more complete sets of chromosomes from different parent species. p. 441

allosteric activator Molecule that converts an enzyme with an allosteric site, a regulatory site outside the active site, from the inactive form to the active form. p. 92

allosteric inhibitor Molecule that converts an enzyme with an allosteric site, a regulatory site outside the active site, from the active form to the inactive form. p. 92

allosteric regulation Specialized control mechanism for enzymes with an allosteric site, a regulatory site outside the active site, that may either slow or accelerate activity depending on the enzyme. p. 92

allosteric site A regulatory site outside the active site. p. 91

alpine tundra A biome that occurs on high mountaintops throughout the world, in which dominant plants form cushions and mats. p. 572

alternation of generations The regular alternation of mode of reproduction in the life cycle of an organism, such as the alternation between diploid (sporophyte) and haploid (gametophyte) phases in plants. pp. 563, 884

alternative hypothesis An explanation of an observed phenomenon that is different from the explanation being tested. p. 58

alternative splicing Mechanism that joins exons in different combinations to produce different mRNAs from a single gene. p. 299

altricial Helpless at birth. p. 668

altruism A behavioural phenomenon in which individuals appear to sacrifice their own reproductive success to help other individuals. p. 1181

alveolus (plural, alveoli) One of the millions of tiny air pockets in mammalian lungs, each surrounded by dense capillary networks. p. 1223

amacrine cell A type of neuron that forms lateral connections in the retina of the eye, connecting bipolar cells and ganglion cells. p. 1112

amino acid A molecule that contains both an amino and a carboxyl group. p. 32

amino group Group that acts as an organic base, consisting of a nitrogen atom bonded on one side to two hydrogen atoms and on the other side to a carbon chain. p. 80

aminoacyl–tRNA A tRNA linked to its "correct" amino acid, which is the finished product of charging. p. 302

aminoacyl–tRNA synthetase An enzyme that catalyzes aminoacylation. p. 302

aminoacylation The process of adding an amino acid to a tRNA. Also referred to as *charging*. p. 302

ammocoetes Larval lamprey eel. p. 645

ammonification A metabolic process in which bacteria and fungi convert organic nitrogen compounds into ammonia and ammonium ions; part of the nitrogen cycle. pp. 766, 911

amniocentesis Technique of prenatal diagnosis in which cells are obtained from the amniotic fluid. p. 258

amnion In an amniote egg, an extraembryonic membrane that encloses the embryo, forming the amniotic cavity and secreting amniotic fluid, which provides an aquatic environment in which the embryo develops. pp. 654, 1020

Amniota The monophyletic group of vertebrates that have an amnion during embryonic development. p. 1021

amniote (amniotic) egg A shelled egg that can survive and develop on land. p. 654

amoeboid Similar to an amoeba, particularly in type of movement. p. 601

amphipathic Containing a region that is hydrophobic and a region that is hydrophilic. p. 100

amplification An increase in the magnitude of each step as a signal transduction pathway proceeds. pp. 116, 1049

amygdala A grey-matter centre of the brain that works as a switchboard, routing information about experiences that have an emotional component through the limbic system. p. 1126

amyloplast Colourless plastid that stores starch in plants. p. 45

anabolic pathway Type of metabolic pathway in which energy is consumed to build complicated molecules from simpler ones; often called a biosynthetic pathway. p. 82

anabolic reaction Metabolic reaction that requires energy to assemble simple substances into more complex molecules. p. 121

anabolic steroid A steroid hormone that stimulates muscle development. p. 1060

anaerobe *See* facultative anaerobe and strict anaerobe.

anaerobic respiration The process by which molecules are oxidized to produce ATP via an electron transport chain and ATP synthase, but unlike aerobic respiration, oxygen is not the final electron acceptor. p. 487

anaphase The phase of mitosis during which the spindle separates sister chromatids and pulls them to opposite spindle poles. p. 175

anaphase-promoting complex (APC) An enzyme complex activated by M phase–promoting factor that controls the separation of sister chromatids and the onset of daughter chromosome separation in anaphase of mitosis. p. 183

anaphylactic shock A severe inflammation stimulated by an allergen, involving extreme swelling of air passages in the lungs, interfering with breathing, and massive leakage of fluid from capillaries, causing blood pressure to drop precipitously. p. 1285

anapsid (lineage Anapsida) A member of the group of amniote vertebrates with no temporal arches and no spaces on the sides of the skull (includes turtles). p. 655

Anapsida An extinct group of fossil fishes. p. 655

anatomy The study of the structures of organisms. p. 946

ancestral character A trait that was present in a distant common ancestor. p. 458

anchoring junction Cell junction that forms belts that run entirely around cells, "welding" adjacent cells together. p. 47

androgen One of a family of hormones that promote the development and maintenance of sex characteristics. pp. 1002, 1059

aneuploid An individual with extra or missing chromosomes. p. 253

angiosperm A flowering plant. Its egg-containing ovules mature into seeds within protected chambers called ovaries. p. 586

angiotensin A peptide hormone that raises blood pressure quickly by constricting arterioles in most parts of the body; it also stimulates release of the steroid hormone aldosterone. p. 1049

animal behaviour The responses of animals to specific internal and external stimuli. p. 1155

animal pole The end of the egg where the egg nucleus is located, which typically gives rise to surface structures and the anterior end of the embryo. p. 1015

Animalia The taxonomic kingdom that includes all living and extinct animals. p. 594

anion A negatively charged ion. pp. 1073, F-11

annual A herbaceous plant that completes its life cycle in one growing season and then dies. p. 840

annulus In ferns, a ring of thick-walled cells that nearly encircles the sporangium and functions in spore release. p. 579

antagonistic pair Two skeletal muscles, one of which flexes as the other extends to move joints. p. 1148

antenna complex (light-harvesting complex) In photosystems, the sites at which light is absorbed and converted into chemical energy during photosynthesis, an aggregate of many chlorophyll pigments and a number of carotenoid pigments that serve as the primary site of absorbing light energy in the form of photons. p. 151

antennal glands Excretory structures at the base of the antennae in some crustaceans. p. 624

anterior Indicating the head end of an animal. p. 596

anterior pituitary The glandular part of the pituitary, composed of endocrine cells that synthesize and secrete several tropic and nontropic hormones. p. 1053

anther The pollen-bearing part of a stamen. p. 885

antheridium (plural, antheridia) In plants, a structure in which sperm are produced. p. 572

Anthocerophyta The phylum comprising hornworts. p. 575

Anthophyta The phylum comprising flowering plants. p. 587

antibiotic A natural or synthetic substance that kills or inhibits the growth of bacteria and other microorganisms. p. 489

antibody A highly specific soluble protein molecule that circulates in the blood and lymph, recognizing and binding to antigens and clearing them from the body. p. 233

antibody-mediated immunity Adaptive immune response in which plasma cells secrete antibodies. p. 1273

anticodon The three-nucleotide segment in tRNAs that pairs with a codon in mRNAs. p. 300

antidiuretic hormone (ADH) A hormone secreted by the posterior pituitary that increases water absorption in the kidneys, thereby increasing the volume of the blood. p. 1056

antigen A foreign molecule that triggers an adaptive immunity response. p. 1273

antigen-presenting cell (APC) A cell that presents an antigen to T cells in antibody-mediated immunity and cell-mediated immunity. p. 1277

antigenic variation The process by which an infectious organism alters its surface proteins to evade a host immune response. Parasites such as the trypanosomes that cause sleeping sickness in humans have 10% of their genes dedicated to generating new surface glycoproteins. p. 1289

antimicrobial peptides Small, potent, broad-spectrum antibiotic peptides that are used by hosts collectively to eliminate bacterial and fungal pathogens. Some antimicrobial peptides may also act as immunomodulators. p. 1268

anti-Müllerian hormone Anti-Müllerian hormone (AMH) is used in testing fertility of women. The AMH gene encodes the protein. p. 1029

antiparallel Refers to strands of DNA that run in opposite directions. p. 269

antiport A secondary active transport mechanism in which a molecule moves through a membrane channel into a cell and powers the active transport of a second molecule out of the cell. Also referred to as *exchange diffusion*. p. 112

aorta A large artery from the heart that branches into arteries leading to all body regions except the lungs. p. 974

aortic body One of several small clusters of chemoreceptors, baroreceptors, and supporting cells located along the aortic arch that measures changes in blood pressure and the composition of arterial blood flowing past it. p. 1228

apical dominance Inhibition of the growth of lateral buds in plants due to auxin diffusing down a shoot tip from the terminal bud. p. 848

apical growth Growth from the tip of a cell or tissue. p. 542

apical meristem A region of unspecialized dividing cells at the shoot tips and root tips of a plant. pp. 568, 839

apical surface The outer surface of epithelial cells. p. 949

apicomplexan A group of parasitic organisms with specific structures in their apical complex to penetrate and enter the cells they parasitize. p. 522

apomixis In plants, the production of offspring without meiosis or formation of gametes. p. 896

apoplast The nonliving component of plant tissues, composed of cell walls and intercellular spaces. p. 868

apoplastic pathway The route followed by water moving through plant cell walls and intercellular spaces (the apoplast). *Compare* symplastic pathway. p. 868

apoptosis Programmed cell death. pp. 185, 1021

aposematic Refers to bright, contrasting patterns that advertise the unpalatability of poisonous or repellent species. p. 715

appendicular skeleton The bones constituting the pectoral (shoulder) and pelvic (hip) girdles and limbs of a vertebrate. p. 1146

appendix A fingerlike sac that extends from the cecum of the large intestine. p. 1206

applied ecology Application of ecological theory and principles to management of natural resources. p. 679

applied research Research conducted with the goal of solving specific practical problems. p. 340

aquaporin A specialized protein channel that facilitates diffusion of water through cell membranes. p. 865

aquatic succession A process in which debris from rivers and runoff accumulates in a body of fresh water, causing it to fill in at the margins. p. 737

aqueous humour A clear fluid that fills the space between the cornea and the lens of the eye. p. 1109

arbuscular mycorrhizas Symbiotic association between a glomeromycete fungus and the roots of a wide range of plants, including nonvascular, nonseed, and seed plants. p. 557

arbuscule Highly branched hypha produced inside root cells by arbuscular mycorrhizal fungi; nutrient exchange site between plant and fungus. p. 548

Archaea One of two domains of prokaryotes; archaeans have some unique molecular and biochemical traits, but they also share some traits with Bacteria and other traits with Eukarya. p. 482

archaeocytes A major group of the domain Archaea, members of which are found in different extreme environments. They include methanogens, extreme halophiles, and some extreme thermophiles. *See* Euryarchaeota. p. 601

archegonium (plural, archegonia) The flask-shaped structure in which bryophyte eggs form. p. 572

archenteron The central endoderm-lined cavity of an embryo at the gastrula stage, which forms the primitive gut. pp. 597, 1016

Archosauromorpha A diverse group of diapsids that comprises crocodilians, pterosaurs, and dinosaurs (including birds). p. 655

arctic tundra A treeless biome that stretches from the boreal forests to the polar ice cap in Europe, Asia, and North America. p. 572

arteries In vertebrates, vessels conducting blood away from the heart at relatively high pressure. pp. 231, 967

arteriole A branch from a small artery at the point where it reaches the organ it supplies. p. 977

artificial selection Selective breeding of animals or plants to ensure that certain desirable traits appear at higher frequency in successive generations. p. 398

ascocarp A reproductive body that bears or contains asci. p. 548

ascospore Spore formed by meiosis in the ascus, a saclike cell produced by ascomycete fungi. p. 549

ascus (plural, asci) A saclike cell in ascomycetes (sac fungi) in which meiosis gives rise to haploid sexual spores (meiospores). p. 548

asexual reproduction Any mode of reproduction in which a single individual gives rise to offspring without fusion of gametes, that is, without genetic input from another individual. *See also* vegetative reproduction. p. 989

assimilation efficiency The ratio of the energy absorbed from consumed food to the total energy content of the food. p. 752

association area One of several areas surrounding the sensory and motor areas of the cerebral cortex that integrate information from the sensory areas, formulate responses, and pass them on to the primary motor area. p. 1128

assumption of parsimony Assumption that the simplest explanation should be the most accurate. p. 459

aster Radiating array produced as microtubules extending from the centrosomes of cells grow in length and extent. p. 179

astrocyte A star-shaped glial cell that provides support to neurons in the vertebrate central nervous system. p. 1070

asymmetrical Characterized by a lack of proportion in the spatial arrangement or placement of parts. p. 596

atmosphere The component of the biosphere that includes the gases and airborne particles enveloping the planet. p. 13

atom The smallest unit that retains the chemical and physical properties of an element. p. F-9

atomic nucleus The nucleus of an atom, containing protons and neutrons. p. 121

atomic number The number of protons in the nucleus of an atom. p. F-9

ATP (adenosine triphosphate) The primary agent that couples exergonic and endergonic reactions. p. 7

ATP cycle Continued breakdown and resynthesis of ATP. p. 85

ATP synthase A membrane-spanning protein complex that couples the energetically favourable transport of protons across a membrane to the synthesis of ATP. p. 132

atrial siphon A tube through which invertebrate chordates expel digestive and metabolic wastes. p. 641

atriopore The hole in the body wall of a cephalochordate through which water is expelled from the body. p. 641

atrioventricular node (AV node) A region of the heart wall that receives signals from the sinoatrial node and conducts them to the ventricle. p. 976

atrioventricular valve (AV valve) A valve composed of endocardium and connective tissue between each atrium and ventricle that prevents backflow of blood from the ventricle to the atrium during emptying of the heart. p. 974

atrium (plural, atria) A body cavity or chamber surrounding the perforated pharynx of invertebrate chordates; also one of the chambers that receive blood returning to the heart. p. 641

autoimmune reaction The production of antibodies against molecules of the body. p. 1284

autonomic nervous system A subdivision of the peripheral nervous system that controls largely involuntary processes, including digestion, secretion by sweat glands, circulation of the blood, many functions of the reproductive and excretory systems, and contraction of smooth muscles in all parts of the body. p. 1092

autopolyploidy The genetic condition of having more than two sets of chromosomes from the same parent species. p. 441

autosomal dominant inheritance Pattern in which the allele that causes a trait is dominant, and only homozygous recessives are unaffected. p. 257

autosomal recessive inheritance Pattern in which individuals with a trait are homozygous for a recessive allele. p. 256

autosome Chromosome other than a sex chromosome. p. 246

autotroph An organism that produces its own food using CO_2 and other simple inorganic compounds from its environment and energy from the Sun or from oxidation of inorganic substances. pp. 63, 145, 487

auxin Any of a family of plant hormones that stimulate growth by promoting cell elongation in stems and coleoptiles, inhibit abscission, govern responses to light and gravity, and have other developmental effects. p. 919

auxotrophs Mutant strains that are unable to synthesize amino acids. p. 191

Avogadro's number The number 6.022×10^{23}, derived by dividing the atomic weight of any element by the weight of an atom of that element. p. F-18

Avr gene A gene in certain plant pathogens that encodes a product triggering a defensive response in the plant. p. 932

axial skeleton The bones constituting the head and trunk of a vertebrate: the cranium, vertebral column, ribs, and sternum (breastbone). pp. 641, 1146

axillary buds Embryonic shoots that develop where a leaf meets the stem. p. 847

axon The single elongated extension of a neuron that conducts signals away from the cell body to another neuron or an effector. p. 1069

axon hillock A junction with the cell body of a neuron from which the axon arises. p. 1069

axon terminal A branch at the tip of an axon that ends as a small, buttonlike swelling. p. 1069

axopods Slender, raylike strands of cytoplasm supported internally by long bundles of microtubules. p. 527

B cell A lymphocyte that recognizes antigens in the body. p. 1273

B-cell receptor (BCR) The receptor on B cells that is specific for a particular antigen. p. 1273

backbone (spine) Vertebral column of vertebrates. p. 641

background extinction rate The average rate of extinction of taxa through time. p. 781

Bacteria One of the two domains of prokaryotes; collectively, bacteria are the most metabolically diverse organisms. p. 482

bacterial chromosome DNA molecule in bacteria in which hereditary information is encoded. p. 285

bacterial flagellum *See* flagellum. p. 33

bacteriophage A virus that infects bacteria. Also referred to as a *phage*. pp. 196, 266, 502

bacteroid A rod-shaped or branched bacterium in the root nodules of nitrogen-fixing plants. p. 912

balanced polymorphism The maintenance of two or more phenotypes in fairly stable proportions over many generations. p. 421

bark The tough outer covering of woody stems and roots, comprising all the living and nonliving tissues between the vascular cambium and the stem surface. p. 856

Barr body The inactive, condensed X chromosome seen in the nucleus of female mammals. p. 250

basal body Structure that anchors cilia and flagella to the surface of a cell. p. 45

basal lamina A membrane secreted at the inner surface of epithelial cells. p. 949

basal nucleus (plural, basal nuclei) One of several grey-matter centres that surround the thalamus on both sides of the brain and moderate voluntary movements directed by motor centres in the cerebrum. p. 1126

basal surface The inner surface of epithelial cells. p. 949

base Proton acceptor that reduces the H^+ concentration of a solution. p. F-19

base-pair mismatch An error in the assembly of a new nucleotide chain in which bases other than the correct ones pair together. p. 280

base-pair substitution mutation A particular mutation involving a change from one base pair to another in DNA. p. 310

basement membrane A membrane at the inner surface of epithelia in vertebrates. It consists of the basal lamina and a layer of connective tissue. p. 949

basic research Research conducted to search for explanations about natural phenomena to satisfy curiosity and advance collective knowledge of living systems. p. 340

basidiocarp A fruiting body of a basidiomycete; mushrooms are examples. p. 553

basidiospore A haploid sexual spore produced by basidiomycete fungi. p. 553

basidium (plural, basidia) A small, club-shaped structure in which sexual spores of basidiomycetes arise. p. 550

basilar membrane A stiff structural element within the cochlea. p. 1106

basophil A type of leukocyte that is induced to secrete histamine by allergens. p. 1284

Batesian mimicry The form of defence in which a palatable or harmless species resembles an unpalatable or poisonous one. p. 716

behavioural isolation A prezygotic reproductive isolating mechanism in which two species do not mate because of differences in courtship behaviour; also known as ethological isolation. p. 431

biennial A plant that completes its life cycle in two growing seasons and then dies; limited secondary growth occurs in some biennials. p. 840

bilateral symmetry The body plan of animals in which the body can be divided into mirror image right and left halves by a plane passing through the midline of the body. p. 596

bilayer A membrane with two molecular layers. p. 28

bile A mixture of substances including bile salts, cholesterol, and bilirubin that is made in the liver, stored in the gallbladder, and used in the digestion of fats. p. 1197

binary fission Prokaryotic cell division—splitting or dividing into two parts. p. 169

binomial Relating to or consisting of two names or terms. p. 427

binomial nomenclature The naming of species with a two-part scientific name, the first indicating the genus and the second indicating the species. p. 427

biodiversity The richness of living systems as reflected in genetic variability within and among species, the number of species living on Earth, and the variety of communities and ecosystems. p. 780

biofilm A microbial community consisting of a complex aggregation of microorganisms attached to a surface. p. 490

biogeochemical cycle Any of several global processes in which a nutrient circulates between the abiotic environment and living organisms. p. 488

biogeography The study of the geographic distributions of plants and animals. p. 392

bioinformatics Field that fuses biology with mathematics and computer science and is used for the analysis of genome sequences. p. 368

biological clock An internal time-measuring mechanism that adapts an organism to recurring environmental changes. p. 938

biological evolution The process by which some individuals in a population experience changes in their DNA and pass those modified instructions to their offspring. p. 392

biological lineage An evolutionary sequence of ancestral organisms and their descendants. p. 401

biological magnification The increasing concentration of nondegradable poisons in the tissues of animals at higher trophic levels. p. 757

biological research The collective effort of individuals who have worked to understand how living systems function. p. F-2

biological species concept The definition of species based on the ability of populations to interbreed and produce fertile offspring. p. 429

bioluminescent Refers to an organism that glows or releases a flash of light, particularly when disturbed. p. 521

biomass The dry weight of biological material per unit area or volume of habitat. pp. 482, 750

biome A large-scale vegetation type and its associated microorganisms, fungi, and animals. p. F-49

bioremediation Applications of chemical and biological knowledge to decontaminate polluted environments. p. 481

biosphere All regions of Earth's crust, waters, and atmosphere that sustain life. p. 7

biota The total collection of organisms in a geographic region. p. 773

biotechnology The manipulation of living organisms to produce useful products. p. 339

biotic Biological, often in reference to living components of the environment. p. 53

bipedalism The habit in animals of walking upright on two legs. p. 469

bipolar cell A type of neuron in the retina of the eye that connects the rods and cones with the ganglion cells. p. 1112

blade The expanded part of a leaf that provides a large surface area for absorbing sunlight and carbon dioxide. p. 850

blastocoel A fluid-filled cavity in the blastula embryo. p. 1015

blastocyst An embryonic stage in mammals; a single cell–layered hollow ball of about 120 cells with a fluid-filled blastocoel in which a dense mass of cells is localized to one side. p. 1025

blastodisc A disclike layer of cells at the surface of the yolk produced by early cleavage divisions. p. 1019

blastomere A small cell formed during cleavage of the embryo. p. 1015

blastopore The opening at one end of the archenteron in the gastrula that gives rise to the mouth in protostomes and the anus in deuterostomes. p. 597

blastula The hollow ball of cells that is the result of cleavage divisions in an early embryo. p. 1015

blending theory of inheritance Theory suggesting that hereditary traits blend evenly in offspring through mixing of the blood of the two parents. p. 218

blood A fluid connective tissue composed of blood cells suspended in a fluid extracellular matrix, plasma. p. 952

blood–brain barrier A specialized arrangement of capillaries in the brain that prevents most substances dissolved in the blood from entering the cerebrospinal fluid and thus protects the brain and spinal cord from viruses, bacteria, and toxic substances that may circulate in the blood. p. 1124

bolting Rapid formation of a floral shoot in plant species that form rosettes, such as lettuce. p. 925

bolus The food mass after chewing. p. 1201

bone The densest form of connective tissue, in which living cells secrete the mineralized matrix of collagen and calcium salts that surrounds them; forms the skeleton. p. 953

book lungs Pocketlike respiratory organs found in some arachnids consisting of several parallel membrane folds arranged like the pages of a book. p. 622

boreal forest A biome that is a circumpolar expanse of evergreen coniferous trees in Europe, Asia, and North America. p. 557

Bowman's capsule An infolded region at the proximal end of a nephron that cups around the glomerulus and collects the water and solutes filtered out of the blood. p. 1246

brain A single, organized collection of nervous tissue in an organism's head that forms the control centre of the nervous system and major sensory structures. p. 1089

brain hormone A peptide hormone secreted by neurosecretory neurons in the brain of insects. p. 1064

brain stem A stalklike structure formed by the pons and medulla, along with the midbrain, which connects the forebrain with the spinal cord. p. 1124

brassinosteroid Any of a family of plant hormones that stimulate cell division and elongation and differentiation of vascular tissue. p. 927

bronchiole One of the small, branching airways in the lungs that lead into the alveoli. p. 1225

bronchus (plural, **bronchi**) An airway that leads from the trachea to the lungs. p. 1225

brown adipose tissue A specialized tissue in which the most intense heat generation by nonshivering thermogenesis takes place. p. 1258

Bryophyta The phylum of nonvascular plants, including mosses and their relatives. p. 574

bryophyte A general term for plants (such as mosses) that lack internal transport vessels. p. 572

budding A mode of asexual reproduction in which a new individual grows and develops while attached to the parent. pp. 542, 989

buffer Substance that compensates for pH changes by absorbing or releasing H^+. p. 347

bulbourethral gland One of two pea-sized glands on either side of the prostate gland that secrete a mucous fluid that is added to semen. p. 1003

bulk feeder An animal that consumes sizable food items whole or in large chunks. p. 1195

bulk flow The group movement of molecules in response to a difference in pressure between two locations. p. 869

bulk-phase endocytosis (pinocytosis) Mechanism by which extracellular water is taken into a cell together with any molecules that happen to be in solution in the water. p. 112

C-terminal end The end of an amino acid chain with a —COO group. p. 300

Ca^{2+} pump (calcium pump) Pump that pushes Ca^{2+} from the cytoplasm to the cell exterior and from the cytosol into the vesicles of the endoplasmic reticulum. p. 109

cadherin (calcium-dependent adhesion molecule) A cell surface protein responsible for selective cell adhesions that require calcium ions to set up adhesions. p. 1032

calcitonin A nontropic peptide hormone that lowers the level of Ca^{2+} in the blood by inhibiting the ongoing dissolution of calcium from bone. p. 1057

callus An undifferentiated tissue that develops on or around a cut plant surface or in tissue culture. p. 897

Calvin cycle *See* light-independent reaction. p. 7

CAM plant A C_4 plant that runs the Calvin and C_4 cycles at different times to circumvent photorespiration. CAM stands for "crassulacean acid metabolism." p. 161

capillary The smallest-diameter blood vessel, with a wall that is one cell thick, which forms highly branched networks well adapted for diffusion of substances. p. 967

capsid *See* coat. p. 501

capsule An external layer of sticky or slimy polysaccharides coating the cell wall in many prokaryotes. pp. 32, 485

carapace A protective outer covering that extends backward behind the head on the dorsal side of an animal, such as the shell of a turtle or lobster. p. 624

carbon cycle The global circulation of carbon atoms, especially via the processes of photosynthesis and respiration. p. 760

cardiac cycle The systole–diastole sequence of the heart. p. 974

cardiac muscle The contractile tissue of the heart. p. 954

carnivore An animal that primarily eats other animals. p. 670

carotenoid Molecule of yellow-orange pigment by which light is absorbed in photosynthesis. p. 19

carpel The reproductive organ of a flower that houses an ovule and its associated structures. p. 885

carrageenan A chemical extracted from the red alga *Eucheuma* that is used to thicken and stabilize paints, dairy products such as pudding and ice cream, and many other creams and emulsions. p. 532

carrier An individual who carries a mutant allele and could pass it on to offspring but does not display its symptoms. p. 249

carrier protein Transport protein that binds a specific single solute and transports it across the lipid bilayer. p. 106

carrying capacity The maximum size of a population that an environment can support indefinitely. p. 691

Cartagena Protocol on Biosafety An international agreement that promotes biosafety as it relates to genetically modified organisms. p. 359

cartilage A tissue composed of sparsely distributed chondrocytes surrounded by networks of collagen fibres embedded in a tough but elastic matrix of the glycoprotein. p. 953

Casparian strip A thin, waxy, impermeable band that seals abutting cell walls in roots; the strip helps control the type and amount of solutes that enter the stele by blocking the apoplastic pathway at the endodermis and forcing substances to pass through cells (the symplast). p. 868

caspase A protease involved in programmed cell death. p. 185

catabolic pathway Type of metabolic pathway in which energy is released by the breakdown of complex molecules to simpler compounds. p. 82

catabolic reaction Cellular reaction that breaks down complex molecules such as sugar to make their energy available for cellular work. p. 85

catalyst Substance with the ability to accelerate a spontaneous reaction without being changed by the reaction. p. 86

catastrophism The theory that Earth has been affected by sudden, violent events that were sometimes worldwide in scope. p. 393

catecholamine Any of a class of compounds derived from the amino acid tyrosine that circulates in the bloodstream, including epinephrine and norepinephrine. p. 1058

cation A positively charged ion. p. F-11

cation exchange Replacement of one cation with another, as on a soil particle. p. 908

CD4$^+$ T cell A type of T cell in the lymphatic system that has CD4 receptors on its surface. This type of T cell binds to an antigen-presenting cell in antibody-mediated immunity. p. 1277

CD8$^+$ T cell A type of T cell in the lymphatic system that has CD8 receptors on its surface. This type of T cell binds to an antigen-presenting cell in cell-mediated immunity. p. 1281

cDNA library The entire collection of cloned cDNAs made from the mRNAs isolated from a cell. p. 344

cecum A blind pouch formed at the junction of the large and small intestines. p. 1206

cell Smallest unit with the capacity to live and reproduce. p. 1

cell adhesion molecule A cell surface protein responsible for selectively binding cells together. pp. 47, 1032

cell body The portion of the neuron containing genetic material and cellular organelles. p. 1069

cell centre *See* centrosome. p. 42

cell culture A living cell grown in a laboratory vessel. p. 173

cell cycle The sequence of events during which a cell experiences a period of growth followed by nuclear division and cytokinesis. p. 69

cell differentiation A process in which changes in gene expression establish cells with specialized structure and function. p. 883

cell expansion A mechanism that enlarges the cells in specific directions in a developing organ. p. 894

cell junction Junction that seals the spaces between cells and provides direct communication between cells. p. 47

cell lineage Cell derivation from the undifferentiated tissues of the embryo. p. 1035

cell-mediated immunity An adaptive immune response in which a subclass of T cells—cytotoxic T cells—becomes activated and, with other cells of the immune system, attacks host cells infected by pathogens, particularly those infected by a virus. p. 1273

cell plate In cytokinesis in plants, a new cell wall that forms between the daughter nuclei and grows laterally until it divides the cytoplasm. p. 176

cell theory Three generalizations yielded by microscopic observations: all organisms are composed of one or more cells, the cell is the smallest unit that has the properties of life, and cells arise only from the growth and division of preexisting cells. p. 28

cell wall A rigid external layer of material surrounding the plasma membrane of cells in plants, fungi, bacteria, and some protists, providing cell protection and support. p. 32

cellular respiration The process by which energy-rich molecules are broken down to produce energy in the form of ATP. p. 121

cellular senescence Loss of proliferative ability over time. p. 184

cellular slime mould Any of a variety of primitive organisms of the phylum Acrasiomycota, especially of the genus *Dictyostelium*; the life cycle is characterized by a slimelike amoeboid stage and a multicellular reproductive stage. p. 529

cellulose One of the primary constituents of plant cell walls, formed by chains of carbohydrate subunits. p. 837

centimorgan *See* map unit. p. 244

central canal The central portion of the vertebral column in which the spinal cord is found. p. 1090

central nervous system (CNS) One of the two major divisions of the nervous system containing the brain and spinal cord. p. 1068

central vacuole A large, water-filled organelle in plant cells that maintains the turgor of the cell and controls movement of molecules between the cytosol and sap. pp. 46, 866

centriole A cylindrical structure consisting of nine triplets of microtubules in the centrosomes of most animal cells. pp. 42, 178

centromere A specialized chromosomal region that connects sister chromatids and attaches them to the mitotic spindle. p. 174

centrosome (cell centre) The main microtubule organizing centre of a cell, which organizes the microtubule cytoskeleton during interphase and positions many of the cytoplasmic organelles. pp. 42, 178

cephalization The development of an anterior head where sensory organs and nervous system tissue are concentrated. p. 596

cephalothorax The anterior section of an arachnid, consisting of a fused head and thorax. p. 622

cerebellum The portion of the brain that receives sensory input from receptors in muscles and joints, from balance receptors in the inner ear, and from the receptors of touch, vision, and hearing. p. 1125

cerebral cortex A thin outer shell of grey matter covering a thick core of white matter within each hemisphere of the brain; the part of the forebrain responsible for information processing and learning. p. 1124

cerebrospinal fluid Fluid that circulates through the central canal of the spinal cord and the ventricles of the brain, cushioning the brain and spinal cord from jarring movements and impacts, as well as nourishing the CNS and protecting it from toxic substances. p. 1123

cervix The lower end of the uterus. p. 961

channel protein Transport protein that forms a hydrophilic channel in a cell membrane through which water, ions, or other molecules can pass, depending on the protein. p. 106

chaperone protein (chaperonin) "Guide" protein that binds temporarily with newly synthesized proteins, directing their conformation toward the correct tertiary structure and inhibiting incorrect arrangements as the new proteins fold. p. F-36

character A heritable characteristic. p. 218

character displacement The phenomenon in which allopatric populations are morphologically similar and use similar resources, but sympatric populations are morphologically different and use different resources; may also apply to characters influencing mate choice. p. 721

charging *See* aminoacylation. p. 302

charophyte A member of the group of green algae most similar to the algal ancestors of land plants. p. 533

checkpoint Internal control of the cell cycle that prevents a critical phase from beginning until the previous phase is complete. p. 181

chelicerae The first pair of fanglike appendages near the mouth of an arachnid, used for biting prey and often modified for grasping and piercing. p. 622

chemical bond Link formed when atoms of reactive elements combine into molecules. p. F-11

chemical equation A chemical reaction written in balanced form. p. F-14

chemical reaction A reaction that occurs when atoms or molecules interact to form new chemical bonds or break old ones. p. F-14

chemical signal Any secretion from one cell type that can alter the behaviour of a different cell that bears a receptor for it; a means of cell communication. p. 529

chemical synapse A type of communicating connection between two neurons or a neuron and an effector cell in which an electrical impulse arriving at an axon terminal of the presynaptic cell triggers release of a neurotransmitter that crosses the gap and binds to a receptor on the postsynaptic cell, triggering an electrical impulse in that cell. p. 1073

chemiosmosis Ability of cells to use the proton-motive force to do work. p. 132

chemoautotroph An organism that obtains energy by oxidizing inorganic substances such as hydrogen, iron, sulfur, ammonia, nitrites, and nitrates and uses carbon dioxide as a carbon source. p. 487

chemoheterotroph An organism that oxidizes organic molecules as an energy source and obtains carbon in organic form. p. 487

chemokine A protein secreted by activated macrophages that attracts other cells, such as neutrophils. p. 1269

chemoreceptor A sensory receptor that detects specific molecules or chemical conditions such as acidity. p. 1077

chemotroph An organism that obtains energy by oxidizing inorganic or organic substances. p. 487

chiasmata *See* crossover. p. 208

chitin A polysaccharide that contains nitrogen and is present in the cell walls of fungi and the exoskeletons of arthropods. p. 47

chlorophyll Molecule of green pigment that absorbs photons of light in photosynthesis. p. 7

chloroplast The site of photosynthesis in plant cells. p. 45

chlorosis An abnormal yellowing of plant tissues due to lack of chlorophyll; a sign of nutrient deficiency or infection by a pathogen. p. 905

choanocyte One of the inner layer of flagellated cells lining the body cavity of a sponge. p. 601

choanoflagellata A group of minute, single-celled protists found in water; the flask-shaped body has a collar of closely packed microvilli that surrounds the single flagellum by which it moves and takes in food. p. 531

cholesterol The predominant sterol of animal cell membranes. p. 102

chondrocyte A cartilage-producing cell. p. 953

chorion In an amniote egg, an extraembryonic membrane that surrounds the embryo and yolk sac completely and exchanges oxygen and carbon dioxide with the environment; becomes part of the placenta in mammals. p. 1020

chorionic villus (plural, **villi**) One of many treelike extensions from the chorion, which greatly increase the surface area of the chorion. p. 1027

chorionic villus sampling Technique of prenatal diagnosis in which cells are obtained from portions of the placenta that develop from tissues of the embryo. p. 258

chromatids One half of a replicated chromosome. Each chromatid is one double helix of DNA. p. 170

chromatin remodelling Process in which the state of the chromatin is changed so that the proteins that initiate transcription can bind to their promoters. p. 327

chromatin The structural building block of a chromosome, which includes the complex of DNA and its associated proteins. pp. 35, 283

chromoplast Plastid containing red and yellow pigments. p. 45

chromosomal protein The histone and nonhistone protein associated with DNA structure and regulation in the nucleus. p. 283

chromosome The nuclear unit of genetic information, consisting of a DNA molecule and associated proteins. p. 170

chromosome alterations Changes in the structure of chromosomes involving insertion, deletion, inversion, or translocation of significant amounts of DNA sequence. p. 439

chromosome segregation The equal distribution of daughter chromosomes to each of the two cells that result from cell division. p. 171

chromosome theory of inheritance The principle that genes and their alleles are carried on the chromosomes. p. 228

chylomicron A small triglyceride droplet covered by a protein coat. p. 1205

chyme Digested content of the stomach released for further digestion in the small intestine. p. 1203

ciliary body A fine ligament in the eye that anchors the lens to a surrounding layer of connective tissue and muscle. p. 1109

cilium Motile structure, extending from a cell surface, that moves a cell through fluid or fluid over a cell. p. 43

circadian rhythm Any biological activity that is repeated in cycles, each about 24 hours long, independent of any shifts in environmental conditions. pp. 16, 938

circulatory system An organ system consisting of a fluid, a heart, and vessels for moving important molecules, and often cells, from one tissue to another. p. 965

circulatory vessel An element of the circulatory system through which fluid flows and carries nutrients and oxygen to tissues and removes wastes. p. 611

circumcision Removal of the prepuce for religious, cultural, or hygienic reasons. p. 1004

cisternae (singular, cisterna) Membranous channels and vesicles that make up the endoplasmic reticulum. p. 36

citric acid cycle Series of reactions in which acetyl groups are oxidized completely to carbon dioxide and some ATP molecules are synthesized. Also referred to as *Krebs cycle* and *tricarboxylic acid cycle*. p. 126

clade A monophyletic group of organisms that share homologous features derived from a common ancestor. p. 461

cladistics An approach to systematics that uses shared derived characters to infer the phylogenetic relationships and evolutionary history of groups of organisms. p. 461

cladogenesis The evolution of two or more descendent species from a common ancestor. p. 457

cladogram A branching diagram in which the endpoints of the branches represent different species of organisms, used to illustrate phylogenetic relationships. p. 461

claspers A pair of organs on the pelvic fins of male crustaceans and sharks, which help transfer sperm into the reproductive tract of the female. p. 648

class A Linnaean taxonomic category that ranks below a phylum and above an order. p. 428

class II major histocompatibility complex (MHC) A collection of proteins that present antigens on the cell surface of an antigen-presenting cell in an antibody-mediated immune response. p. 1277

classical conditioning A type of learning in which an animal develops a mental association between two phenomena that are usually unrelated. p. 1159

classification An arrangement of organisms into hierarchical groups that reflect their relatedness. p. 428

clathrin The network of proteins that coat and reinforce the cytoplasmic surface of cell membranes. p. 114

cleavage Mitotic cell divisions of the zygote that produce a blastula from a fertilized ovum. pp. 596, 1015

climate The weather conditions prevailing over an extended period of time. p. 160

climax community A relatively stable, late successional stage in which the dominant vegetation replaces itself and persists until an environmental disturbance eliminates it, allowing other species to invade. p. 735

cline A pattern of smooth variation in a characteristic along a geographic gradient. p. 434

clitoris The structure at the junction of the labia minora in front of the vulva, homologous to the penis in the male. p. 999

clonal expansion The proliferation of the activated CD4 T cell by cell division to produce a clone of cells. p. 1278

clonal selection The process by which a lymphocyte is specifically selected for cloning when it encounters a foreign antigen from among a randomly generated, enormous diversity of lymphocytes with receptors that specifically recognize the antigen. p. 1279

clone An individual genetically identical to an original cell from which it descended. pp. 171, 191

closed circulatory system A circulatory system in which the fluid, blood, is confined in blood vessels and is distinct from the interstitial fluid. pp. 616, 966

clumped dispersion A pattern of distribution in which individuals in a population are grouped together. p. 681

cnidocyte A prey-capturing and defensive cell in the epidermis of cnidarians. p. 603

coactivator (mediator) In eukaryotes, a large multiprotein complex that bridges between activators at an enhancer and proteins at the promoter and promoter proximal region to stimulate transcription. p. 324

coat The protective layer of protein that surrounds the nucleic acid core of a virus in free form. *See* capsid. p. 501

coated pit A depression in the plasma membrane that contains receptors for macromolecules to be taken up by endocytosis. p. 114

coccoid Spherical prokaryotic cell. p. 482

cochlea A snail-shaped structure (in vertebrates) in the inner ear containing the organ of hearing. p. 1106

codominance Condition in which alleles have approximately equal effects in individuals, making the alleles equally detectable in heterozygotes. p. 232

codon Each three-letter word (triplet) of the genetic code. p. 292

coelom A fluid-filled body cavity in bilaterally symmetrical animals that is completely lined with derivatives of mesoderm. p. 596

coelomate A body plan of bilaterally symmetrical animals that have a coelom. p. 596

coenzymes Organic cofactors that include complex chemical groups of various kinds. p. 89

coevolution The evolution of genetically based, reciprocal adaptations in two or more species that interact closely in the same ecological setting. pp. 588, 711

cofactor An inorganic or organic nonprotein group that is necessary for catalysis to take place. p. 88

cohesion The high resistance of water molecules to separation. p. F-16

cohesion–tension mechanism of water transport A model of how water is transported from roots to leaves in vascular plants; the evaporation of water from leaves pulls water up in the xylem by creating a continuous negative pressure (tension) that extends to roots. p. 870

cohesion–tension theory of water transport *See* cohesion-tension mechanism of water transport. p. 870

cohort A group of individuals of similar age. p. 685

coleoptile A protective sheath that covers the shoot apical meristem and plumule of the embryo in monocots, such as grasses, as it pushes up through soil. p. 892

coleorhiza A sheath that encloses the radicle of an embryo until it breaks out of the seed coat and enters the soil as the primary root. p. 893

collagen Fibrous glycoprotein—very rich in carbohydrates—embedded in a network of proteoglycans. p. 951

collecting duct A location where urine leaving individual nephrons is processed further. p. 1245

collenchyma One of three simple plant tissues. Flexibly supports rapidly growing plant parts. Its elongated cells are alive at maturity and often collectively form strands or a sheathlike cylinder under the dermal tissue of growing shoot regions and leaf stalks. p. 842

colon The main part of the large intestine. p. 1206

colony Multiple individual organisms of the same species living in a group. p. 516

combinatorial gene regulation The combining of a few regulatory proteins in particular ways so that the transcription of a wide array of genes can be controlled and a large number of cell types can be specified. p. 325

commaless The sequential nature of the words of the nucleic acid code, with no indicators such as commas or spaces to mark the end of one codon and the beginning of the next. p. 294

commensalism A symbiotic interaction in which one species benefits and the other is unaffected. pp. 722, 1267

community Populations of all species that occupy the same area. p. 315

community ecology The ecological discipline that examines groups of populations occurring together in one area. p. 680

companion cell A specialized parenchyma cell that is connected to a mature sieve tube member by plasmodesmata and assists sieve tube members with both the uptake of sugars and the unloading of sugars in tissues. p. 846

comparative genomics A technique for discovering relatedness among organisms by considering the similarity of their respective genome sequences. p. 364

comparative morphology Analysis of the structure of living and extinct organisms. p. 393

compass orientation A wayfinding mechanism that allows animals to move in a particular direction, often over a specific distance or for a prescribed length of time. p. 1171

competitive exclusion principle The ecological principle stating that populations of two or more species cannot coexist indefinitely if they rely on the same limiting resources and exploit them in the same way. p. 717

competitive inhibition Inhibition of an enzyme reaction by an inhibitor molecule that resembles the normal substrate closely enough that it fits into the active site of the enzyme. p. 90

complement system A nonspecific defence mechanism activated by invading pathogens, made up of more than 30 interacting soluble plasma proteins circulating in the blood and interstitial fluid. p. 1271

complementary base-pairing Feature of DNA in which the specific purine–pyrimidine base pairs A–T (adenine–thymine) and G–C (guanine–cytosine) occur to bridge the two sugar–phosphate backbones. p. 269

complementary DNA (cDNA) A DNA molecule that is complementary to an mRNA molecule, synthesized by reverse transcriptase. p. 344

complete digestive system A digestive system with a mouth at one end, through which food enters, and an anus at the other end, through which undigested waste is voided. p. 610

complete metamorphosis The form of metamorphosis in which an insect passes through four separate stages of growth: egg, larva, pupa, and adult. p. 629

compound A molecule whose component atoms are different. p. F-8

compound eye The eye of most insects and some crustaceans, composed of many-faceted, light-sensitive units called ommatidia fitted closely together, each with its own refractive system and each forming a portion of an image. pp. 622, 1108

concentration The number of molecules or ions of a substance in a unit volume of space. p. F-18

concentration gradient The concentration difference that drives diffusion. p. 105

conduction The flow of heat between atoms or molecules in direct contact. pp. 1079, 1252

cone In the vertebrate eye, a photoreceptor in the retina that is specialized for detection of different wavelengths (colours). In cone-bearing plants, a cluster of sporophylls. pp. 577, 1109

conformation The overall three-dimensional shape of a protein. p. 88

conformational change Alteration in the three-dimensional shape of a protein. p. 1137

conformers Animals having internal environments that change as the external environment changes. p. 958

conidium (plural, conidia) An asexually produced fungal spore. p. 549

Coniferophyta The major phylum of cone-bearing gymnosperms, most of which are substantial trees; includes pines, firs, and other conifers. p. 583

conjugation In bacteria, the process by which a copy of part of the DNA of a donor cell moves through the cytoplasmic bridge into the recipient cell where genetic recombination can occur. In ciliate protozoans, a process of sexual reproduction in which individuals of the same species temporarily couple and exchange genetic material. p. 193

connective tissue Tissue with cells scattered through an extracellular matrix; forms layers in and around body structures that support other body tissues, transmit mechanical and other forces, and in some cases act as filters. p. 951

conodont An abundant, bonelike fossil dating from the early Paleozoic era through the early Mesozoic era, now described as a feeding structure of some of the earliest vertebrates. p. 645

consciousness Awareness of oneself, one's identity, and one's surroundings, with understanding of the significance and likely consequences of events. p. 1129

conservation biology An interdisciplinary science that focuses on the maintenance and preservation of biodiversity. p. 419

consumer An organism that consumes other organisms in a community or ecosystem. p. 728

contact inhibition The inhibition of movement or proliferation of normal cells that results from cell–cell contact. p. 183

contractile vacuole A specialized cytoplasmic organelle that pumps fluid in a cyclical manner from within the cell to the outside by alternately filling and then contracting to release its contents at various points on the surface of the cell. p. 517

control Treatment that tells what would be seen in the absence of the experimental manipulation. p. F-3

convection The transfer of heat from a body to a fluid, such as air or water, that passes over its surface. p. 1252

convergent evolution The evolution of similar adaptations in distantly related organisms that occupy similar environments. p. 403

coral reef A structure made from the hard skeletons of coral animals or polyps; found largely in tropical and subtropical marine environments. p. 604

core The nucleic acid centre of a virus in the free form. p. 284

corepressor In the regulation of gene expression in bacteria, a regulatory molecule that combines with a repressor to activate it and shut off an operon. p. 319

cork A nonliving, impermeable secondary tissue that is one element of bark. p. 855

cork cambium A lateral meristem in plants that forms periderm, which in turn produces cork. p. 855

cornea The transparent layer that forms the front wall of the eye, covering the iris. p. 1108

corona The ciliated crownlike organ at the anterior end of rotifers used for feeding or locomotion. p. 610

corpus callosum A structure formed of thick axon bundles that connect the two cerebral hemispheres and coordinate their functions. p. 1127

corpus luteum Cells remaining at the surface of the ovary during the luteal phase; the structure acts as an endocrine gland, secreting several hormones: estrogens, large quantities of progesterone, and inhibin. p. 1000

cortex Generally, an outer, rindlike layer. In mammals, the outer layer of the brain, the kidneys, or the adrenal glands. In plants, the outer region of tissue in a root or stem lying between the epidermis and the vascular tissue, composed mainly of parenchyma. pp. 381, 667, 911

cortical granule A secretory vesicle just under the plasma membrane of an egg cell. p. 995

cortisol The major glucocorticoid steroid hormone secreted by the adrenal cortex, which increases blood glucose by promoting breakdown of proteins and fats. p. 1059

cotranslational import A mechanism in which proteins end up on the inside (lumen) of the endoplasmic reticulum (ER) as they are translated by ribosome associated with the ER. p. 308

cotransport *See* symport. p. 112

cotyledon A leaf of a seed plant embryo; also known as a seed leaf. p. 892

countercurrent exchange A mechanism in which the water flowing over the gills moves in a direction opposite to the flow of blood under the respiratory surface (can also apply to transfer of heat). p. 1222

coupled reaction Reaction that occurs when an exergonic reaction is joined to an endergonic reaction, producing an overall reaction that is exergonic. p. 84

courtship display A behaviour performed by males to attract potential mates or to reinforce the bond between a male and a female. pp. 397, 431

covalent bond Bond formed by electron sharing between atoms. p. F-12

cranial nerve A nerve that connects the brain directly to the head, neck, and body trunk. p. 642

cranium The part of the skull that encloses the brain. p. 641

crassulacean acid metabolism (CAM) A biochemical variation of photosynthesis that was discovered in a member of the plant family Crassulaceae. Carbon dioxide is taken up and stored during the night to allow the stomata to remain closed during the daytime, decreasing water loss. pp. 161, 875

Crenarchaeota A major group of the domain Archaea, separated from the other archaeans based mainly on rRNA sequences. p. 497

crista (plural, **cristae**) Fold that expands the surface area of the inner mitochondrial membrane. p. 41

critical period A restricted stage of development early in life during which an animal has the capacity to respond to specific environmental stimuli. p. 1159

crop Of birds, an enlargement of the digestive tube where the digestive contents are stored and mixed with lubricating mucus. p. 823

cross-pollination Fertilization of one plant by a different plant. p. 219

crossing-over The recombination process in meiosis, in which chromatids exchange segments. p. 208

crossover Site of recombination during meiosis. Also referred to as a *chiasmata*. p. 208

cryptochrome A light-absorbing protein that is sensitive to blue light and that may also be an important early step in various light-based growth responses. p. 934

cupula In certain mechanoreceptors, a gelatinous structure with stereocilia extending into it that moves with pressure changes in the surrounding water; movement of the cupula bends the stereocilia, which triggers release of neurotransmitters. p. 1101

cuticle The outer layer of plants and some animals, which helps prevent desiccation by slowing water loss. pp. 564, 847

Cycadophyta A phylum of palmlike gymnosperms known as cycads; the pollen-bearing and seed-bearing cones (strobili) occur on separate plants. p. 583

cyclic AMP (cAMP) In particular signal transduction pathways, a second messenger that activates protein kinases, which elicit the cellular response by adding phosphate groups to specific target proteins. cAMP functions in one of two major G protein–coupled receptor response pathways. p. 318

cyclic electron transport An electron transport pathway associated with photosystem I in photosynthesis that produces ATP without the synthesis of NADPH. p. 155

cyclin In eukaryotes, protein that regulates the activity of Cdk (cyclin-dependent kinase) and controls progression through the cell cycle. p. 181

cyclin-dependent kinase (Cdk) A protein kinase that controls the cell cycle in eukaryotes. p. 181

cytochrome Protein with a heme prosthetic group that contains an iron atom. p. 125

cytokine A molecule secreted by one cell type that binds to receptors on other cells and, through signal transduction pathways, triggers a response. In innate immunity, cytokines are secreted by activated macrophages. p. 1269

cytokinesis Division of the cytoplasm into two daughter cells following the nuclear division stage of mitosis. p. 176

cytokinin A hormone that promotes and controls growth responses of plants. p. 925

cytoplasm All parts of the cell that surround the central nuclear or nucleoid region. p. 30

cytoplasmic determinants The mRNA and proteins stored in the egg cytoplasm that direct the first stages of animal development in the period before genes of the zygote become active. p. 1014

cytoplasmic inheritance Pattern in which inheritance follows that of genes in the cytoplasmic organelles, mitochondria, or chloroplasts. p. 259

cytoplasmic streaming Intracellular movement of cytoplasm. p. 43

cytosine A pyrimidine that base-pairs with guanine in nucleic acids. p. 268

cytoskeleton The interconnected system of protein fibres and tubes that extends throughout the cytoplasm of a eukaryotic cell. p. 30

cytosol Aqueous solution in the cytoplasm containing ions and various organic molecules. p. 30

cytotoxic T cell A T lymphocyte that functions in cell-mediated immunity to kill body cells infected by viruses or transformed by cancer. p. 1283

daily torpor A period of inactivity and lowered metabolic rate that allows an endotherm to conserve energy when environmental temperatures are low. p. 1260

dalton A standard unit of mass, about 1.66×10^{24} g. p. 333

day-neutral plant A plant that flowers without regard to photoperiod. p. 940

decomposer A small organism, such as a bacterium or fungus, that feeds on the remains of dead organisms, breaking down complex biological molecules or structures into simpler raw materials. p. 145

dehydration synthesis reaction Reaction during which the components of a water molecule are removed, usually as part of the assembly of a larger molecule from smaller subunits. Also referred to as a *condensation reaction*. p. F-21

degeneracy (redundancy) The feature of the genetic code in which, with two exceptions, more than one codon represents each amino acid. p. 294

deletion Chromosomal alteration that occurs if a broken segment is lost from a chromosome. p. 251

demographic transition model A graphic depiction of the historical relationship between a country's economic development and its birth and death rates. p. 701

demography The statistical study of the processes that change a population's size and density through time. p. 684

denaturation A loss of both the structure and function of a protein due to extreme conditions that unfold it from its conformation. p. F-36

dendrite The branched extension of the nerve cell body that receives signals from other nerve cells. p. 1069

dendritic cell A type of phagocyte, so called because it has many surface projections that resemble dendrites of neurons, that engulfs a bacterium in infected tissue by phagocytosis. p. 1277

denitrification A metabolic process in which certain bacteria convert nitrites or nitrates into nitrous oxide and then into molecular nitrogen, which enters the atmosphere. p. 766

density dependent Description of environmental factors for which the strength of their effect on a population varies with the population's density. p. 694

density independent Description of environmental factors for which the strength of their effect on a population does not vary with the population's density. p. 696

deoxyribonucleic acid (DNA) The large, double-stranded, helical molecule that contains the genetic material of all living organisms. p. 264

deoxyribose A five-carbon sugar to which the nitrogenous bases in nucleotides of DNA link covalently. p. F-37

depolarized State of the membrane (which was polarized at rest) as the membrane potential becomes less negative. p. 1074

deposit feeder An animal that consumes particles of organic matter from the solid substrate on which it lives. p. 1195

derived character A new version of a trait found in the most recent common ancestor of a group. p. 458

dermal tissue system The plant tissue system that comprises the outer tissues of the plant body, including the epidermis and periderm; it serves as a protective covering for the plant body. p. 841

dermis The skin layer below the epidermis; it is packed with connective tissue fibres such as collagen, which resist compression, tearing, or puncture of the skin. p. 1256

descent with modification Biological evolution. p. 400

desert A sparsely vegetated biome that forms where precipitation averages less than 25 cm per year. p. 750

desmosome Anchoring junction for which microfilaments anchor the junction in the underlying cytoplasm. p. 47

determinate cleavage A type of cleavage in protostomes in which each cell's developmental path is determined as the cell is produced. p. 597

determinate growth The pattern of growth in most animals in which individuals grow to a certain size and then their growth slows dramatically or stops. p. 839

determination Mechanism in which the developmental fate of a cell is set. p. 1017

detritivore An organism that extracts energy from the organic detritus (refuse) produced at other trophic levels. p. 594

deuterostome A division of the Bilateria in which blastopore forms the anus during development and the mouth appears later (includes Echinodermata and Chordata). p. 596

development A series of programmed changes encoded in DNA, through which a fertilized egg divides into many cells that are ultimately transformed into an adult, which is itself capable of reproduction. p. 2

diabetes mellitus A disease that results from problems with insulin production or action. p. 1060

diapsid (lineage Diapsida) A member of a group within the amniote vertebrates with a skull with two temporal arches. Their living descendants include lizards and snakes, crocodilians, and birds. p. 655

diastole The period of relaxation and filling of the heart between contractions. p. 974

diatom Photosynthetic single-celled organisms with a glassy silica shell; also called bacillariophytes. p. 524

differentiation Follows determination and involves the establishment of a cell-specific developmental program in the cells. Differentiation results in cell types with clearly defined structures and functions. p. 1017

diffusion The net movement of ions or molecules from a region of higher concentration to a region of lower concentration. p. 105

digestion The splitting of carbohydrates, proteins, lipids, and nucleic acids in foods into chemical subunits small enough to be absorbed into the body fluids and cells of an animal. p. 1189

dihybrid A zygote produced from a cross that involves two characters. p. 225

dihybrid cross A cross between two individuals that are heterozygous for two pairs of alleles. p. 225

dikaryon The life stage in certain fungi in which a cell contains two genetically distinct haploid nuclei. p. 553

dikaryotic hyphae Hyphae containing two separate nuclei in one cell. p. 549

dioecious Having male flowers and female flowers on different plants of the same species. p. 885

diphyodont Having two generations of teeth, milk (baby) teeth and adult teeth. p. 667

diploblastic An animal body plan in which adult structures arise from only two cell layers, the ectoderm and the endoderm. p. 595

diploid An organism or cell with two copies of each type of chromosome in its nucleus. p. 170

direct neurotransmitter A neurotransmitter that binds directly to a ligand-gated ion channel in the postsynaptic membrane, opening or closing the channel gate and altering the flow of a specific ion or ions in the postsynaptic cell. p. 1082

directional selection A type of selection in which individuals near one end of the phenotypic spectrum have the highest relative fitness. p. 412

discontinuous replication Replication in which a DNA strand is formed in short lengths that are synthesized in the direction opposite to DNA unwinding. p. 275

dispersal 1. The movement of organisms away from their place of origin, as well as the movement from one breeding site to another; 2. The movement of material that is used by an organism to move to the next stage in their life cycle. p. 601

dispersed duplication Gene copies that are found in different places in the genome, often on two different chromosomes. p. 382

dispersion The spatial distribution of individuals within a population's geographic range. p. 681

disruptive selection A type of natural selection in which extreme phenotypes have higher relative fitness than intermediate phenotypes. p. 414

dissociation The separation of water to produce hydrogen ions and hydroxide ions. p. 1230

distal convoluted tubule The tubule in the human nephron that drains urine into a collecting duct that leads to the renal pelvis. p. 1246

disturbance climax (disclimax) community An ecological community in which regular disturbance inhibits successional change. p. 740

DNA *See* deoxyribonucleic acid. p. 264

DNA chip *See* DNA microarray. p. 376

DNA fingerprinting Technique in which DNA samples are used to distinguish between individuals of the same species. p. 349

DNA helicase An enzyme that catalyzes the unwinding of DNA template strands. p. 274

DNA hybridization Technique in which a gene or sequence of interest is identified in a set of clones when it base-pairs with a single-stranded DNA or RNA molecule called a nucleic acid probe. p. 344

DNA ligase In DNA replication, an enzyme that seals the nicks left after RNA primers are replaced with DNA. p. 276

DNA methylation Process in which a methyl group is added enzymatically to cytosine bases in the DNA. p. 327

DNA microarray A solid surface divided into a microscopic grid of thousands of spaces each containing thousands of copies of a DNA probe. DNA microarrays are used commonly for analysis of gene activity and for detecting differences between cell types. Also referred to as a *DNA chip*. p. 376

DNA polymerase An enzyme that assembles complementary nucleotide chains during DNA replication. p. 271

DNA polymerase I A specialized polymerase responsible for removing RNA primers and replacing them with DNA. p. 276

DNA polymerase III The main, "general-purpose" polymerase for replicating DNA. p. 276

DNA repair mechanism Mechanism to correct base-pair mismatches that escape proofreading. p. 282

DNA technologies Techniques to isolate, purify, analyze, and manipulate DNA sequences. p. 339

domain In protein structure, a distinct, large structural subdivision produced in many proteins by the folding of the amino acid chain. In systematics, the highest taxonomic category; a group of cellular organisms with characteristics that set it apart as a major branch of the evolutionary tree. pp. 104, 428

domestication Selective breeding of other species to increase desirable characteristics in progeny. p. 808

dominance The masking effect of one allele over another. p. 221

dominance hierarchy A social system in which the behaviour of each individual is constrained by that individual's status in a highly structured social ranking. p. 1178

dominant Refers to the allele expressed when more than one allele is present. p. 221

dormancy A period in the life cycle in which biological activity is suspended. pp. 894, 941

dorsal Indicating the back side of an animal. p. 596

dorsal lip of the blastopore A crescent-shaped depression rotated clockwise 90° on the embryo surface that marks the region derived from the grey crescent, to which cells from the animal pole move as gastrulation begins. p. 1018

double fertilization The characteristic feature of sexual reproduction in flowering plants. In the embryo sac, one sperm nucleus unites with the egg to form a diploid zygote from which the embryo develops, and another unites with two polar nuclei to form the primary endosperm nucleus. p. 890

double helix Two nucleotide chains wrapped around each other in a spiral. p. 2

double-helix model Model of DNA consisting of two complementary sugar–phosphate backbones. p. 269

duodenum A short region of the small intestine where secretions from the pancreas and liver enter a common duct. p. 1204

duplication Chromosomal alteration that occurs if a segment is broken from one chromosome and inserted into its homologue. p. 251

E site The site where an exiting tRNA binds prior to its release from the ribosome. p. 302

ecdysis Shedding of the cuticle, exoskeleton, or skin; moulting. p. 600

ecdysone A steroid hormone that controls cuticle formation in insects and crustaceans and possibly nematodes. p. 1049

echolocation A behaviour in which an animal compares echoes of sounds it produced to the original signals. Differences between pulses and echoes allow location of obstacles and prey. p. 1097

ecological community An assemblage of species living in the same place. p. 680

ecological efficiency The ratio of net productivity at one trophic level to net productivity at the trophic level below it. p. 752

ecological isolation A prezygotic reproductive isolating mechanism in which species that live in the same geographic region occupy different habitats. p. 431

ecological niche The resources a population uses and the environmental conditions it requires over its lifetime. p. 717

ecological pyramid A diagram illustrating the effects of energy transfer from one trophic level to the next. p. 754

ecological succession A somewhat predictable series of changes in the species composition of a community over time. p. 561

ecology The study of the interactions between organisms and their environments. p. 679

ecosystem A group of biological communities interacting with their shared physical environment. p. 749

ecosystem ecology An ecological discipline that explores the cycling of nutrients and the flow of energy between the biotic components of an ecological community and the abiotic environment. p. 680

ecotone A wide transition zone between adjacent communities. p. 725

ectoderm The outermost of the three primary germ layers of an embryo, which develops into epidermis and nervous tissue. pp. 595, 1015

ectomycorrhiza A mycorrhiza that grows between and around the young roots of trees and shrubs but does not enter root cells. p. 557

ectoparasite A parasite that lives on the exterior of its host organism. p. 609

ectotherm An animal that obtains its body heat primarily from the external environment. p. 1253

effector In signal transduction, a plasma membrane–associated enzyme, activated by a G protein, that generates one or more second messengers. In homeostatic feedback, the system that returns the condition to the set point if it has strayed away. pp. 960, 1070

effector T cell A cell involved in effecting—bringing about—the specific immune response to an antigen. p. 1278

efferent arteriole The arteriole that receives blood from the glomerulus. p. 1247

efferent neuron A neuron that carries the signals indicating a response away from the interneuron networks to the effectors. p. 1070

egg cell The female reproductive cell. p. 888

eggs Nonmotile gametes. p. 990

Elasmobranchii Cartilaginous fishes, including the skates and rays. p. 647

elastin A rubbery protein in some connective tissues that adds elasticity to the extracellular matrix. It is able to return to its original shape after being stretched, bent, or compressed. p. 952

electrical signalling A means of animal communication in which a signaller emits an electric discharge that can be received by another individual. p. 1167

electrical synapse A mechanical and electrically conductive link between two abutting neurons that is formed at the gap junction. p. 1072

electrocardiogram (ECG) Graphic representation of the electrical activity within the heart, detected by electrodes placed on the body. p. 977

electrochemical gradient A difference in chemical concentration and electric potential across a membrane. pp. 111, 1073

electromagnetic spectrum The range of wavelengths or frequencies of electromagnetic radiation extending from gamma rays to the longest radio waves and including visible light. p. 4

electron Negatively charged particle outside the nucleus of an atom. p. 5

electron microscope Microscope that uses electrons to illuminate the specimen. p. 29

electron shell In chemistry and physics, may be thought of as an orbit followed by electrons around an atom's nucleus. Also known as *principal energy level*. p. F-10

electron transfer system Stage of cellular respiration in which high-energy electrons produced from glycolysis, pyruvate oxidation, and the citric acid cycle are delivered to oxygen by a sequence of electron carriers. p. 162

electronegativity The measure of an atom's attraction for the electrons it shares in a chemical bond with another atom. p. F-13

electroreceptor A specialized sensory receptor that detects electrical fields. pp. 648, 1121

element A pure substance that cannot be broken down into simpler substances by ordinary chemical or physical techniques. p. F-8

elongation factor Proteins that promote various steps in the elongation of peptides during translation. p. 305

embryo An organism in its early stage of reproductive development, beginning in the first moments after fertilization. p. 47

embryo sac The female gametophyte of angiosperms, within which the embryo develops; it usually consists of seven cells: an egg cell, an endosperm mother cell, and five other cells with fleeting reproductive roles. p. 888

embryonic stem cell Stem cells in the mammalian embryo that can differentiate into any cell type. p. 354

emigration The movement of individuals out of a population. p. 684

endangered species A species in immediate danger of extinction throughout all or a significant portion of its range. p. 419

endemic species A species that occurs in only one place on Earth. p. 785

endergonic process Reaction that can proceed only if free energy is supplied. p. 79

endocrine gland Any of several ductless secretory organs that secrete hormones into the blood or extracellular fluid. pp. 950, 1047

endocrine system The system of glands that release their secretions (hormones) directly into the circulatory system. p. 1046

endocytic vesicle Vesicle that carries proteins and other molecules from the plasma membrane to destinations within the cell. p. 38

endocytosis In eukaryotes, the process by which molecules are brought into the cell from the exterior involving a bulging in of the plasma membrane that pinches off to form an endocytic vesicle. p. 38

endoderm The innermost of the three primary germ layers of an embryo, which develops into the gastrointestinal tract and, in some animals, the respiratory organs. pp. 595, 1015

endodermis The innermost layer of the root cortex; a selectively permeable barrier that helps control the movement of water and dissolved minerals into the stele. pp. 854, 868

endomembrane system In eukaryotes, a collection of interrelated internal membranous sacs that divide a cell into functional and structural compartments. pp. 36, 68

endoparasite A parasite that lives in the internal organs of its host organism. p. 723

endoplasmic reticulum (ER) In eukaryotes, an extensive interconnected network of cisternae that is responsible for the synthesis, transport, and initial modification of proteins and lipids. p. 36

endorphin One of a group of small proteins occurring naturally in the brain and around nerve endings that bind to opiate receptors and thus can raise the pain threshold. p. 1055

endoskeleton A supportive internal body structure, such as bones, that provides support. p. 1146

endosperm Nutritive tissue inside the seeds of flowering plants. p. 890

endosporous Pattern of development in some plants (e.g., seed plants) in which the gametophyte develops inside the spore wall. p. 580

endosymbiosis A symbiotic association in which one symbiont or partner lives inside the other. p. 66

endotherm An animal that obtains most of its body heat from internal physiological sources. p. 1253

endothermic Refers to reactions that absorb energy. pp. 78, 667

endotoxin A lipopolysaccharide released from the outer membrane of the cell wall when a bacterium dies and lyses. p. 489

energy The capacity to do work. p. 75

energy budget The total amount of energy that an organism can accumulate and use to fuel its activities. p. 686

energy coupling The process by which ATP is brought in close contact with a reactant molecule involved in an endergonic reaction, and when the ATP is hydrolyzed, the terminal phosphate group is transferred to the reactant molecule. p. 84

energy levels Regions of space within an atom where electrons are found. Also referred to as *energy shells*. p. 121

enhancer In eukaryotes, a region at a significant distance from the beginning of a gene, containing regulatory sequences that determine whether the gene is transcribed at its maximum possible rate. p. 322

enterocoelom In deuterostomes, the body cavity pinched off by outpocketings of the archenteron. p. 598

enthalpy Potential energy in a system. p. 78

entropy Disorder, in thermodynamics. p. 77

envelope Outer glycoprotein layer surrounding the capsid of some viruses, derived in part from host cell plasma membrane. p. 501

enveloped virus A virus that has a surface membrane derived from its host cell. p. 502

enzymatic hydrolysis A process in which chemical bonds are broken by the addition of H^+ and OH^-, the components of a molecule of water. p. 1195

enzyme Protein that accelerates the rate of a cellular reaction. p. 86

eosinophil A type of leukocyte that targets extracellular parasites too large for phagocytosis in the inflammatory response. p. 1269

epiblast The top layer of the blastodisc. p. 1019

epicotyl The upper part of the axis of an early plant embryo, located between the cotyledons and the first true leaves. p. 893

epidermis A complex tissue that covers an organism's body in a single continuous layer or sometimes in multiple layers of tightly packed cells. pp. 603, 846, 1256

epididymis A coiled storage tubule attached to the surface of each testis. p. 1003

epigenetics The study of changes to gene expression that do not arise from changes in the DNA sequence (i.e., mutations). Epigenetic changes may arise from chemical modification of bases (e.g., methylation), chromatin remodelling, protein or RNA binding, etc. p. 1041

epiglottis A flaplike valve at the top of the trachea. p. 1202

epinephrine A nontropic amine hormone secreted by the adrenal medulla. p. 1058

epiphyte A plant that grows independently on other plants and obtains nutrients and water from the air. p. 913

epistasis Interaction of genes, with one or more alleles of a gene at one locus inhibiting or masking the effects of one or more alleles of a gene at a different locus. p. 234

epithelial tissue Tissue formed of sheetlike layers of cells that are usually joined tightly together, with little extracellular matrix material between them. They protect body surfaces from invasion by bacteria and viruses and secrete or absorb substances. p. 949

epitope The small region of an antigen molecule to which B-cell receptors or T-cell receptors bind. p. 1274

equilibrium theory of island biogeography A hypothesis suggesting that the number of species on an island is governed by a give and take between the immigration of new species to the island and the extinction of species already there. p. 741

ER (endoplasmic reticulum) lumen The enclosed space surrounded by a cisterna. p. 36

erythrocyte A red blood cell that contains hemoglobin, a protein that transports O2 in blood. p. 970

erythropoietin (EPO) A hormone that stimulates stem cells in bone marrow to increase erythrocyte production. p. 971

esophagus A connecting passage of the digestive tube. p. 638

essential element Any of a number of elements required by living organisms to ensure normal reproduction, growth, development, and maintenance. p. 903

essential fatty acid Any fatty acid that the body cannot synthesize but needs for normal metabolism. p. 1190

essential nutrient Any of the essential amino acids, fatty acids, vitamins, and minerals required in the diet of an animal. p. 1190

estivation Seasonal torpor in an animal that occurs in summer. p. 1261

estradiol A form of estrogen. p. 1060

estrogen Any of the group of female sex hormones. p. 1059

ethology A discipline that focuses on how animals behave. p. 1159

ethylene A plant hormone that helps regulate seedling growth; stem elongation; the ripening of fruit; and the abscission of fruits, leaves, and flowers. p. 926

euchromatin In eukaryotes, regions of loosely packed chromatin fibres in interphase nuclei. p. 285

eudicot A plant belonging to the Eudicotyledones, one of the two major classes of angiosperms; their embryos generally have two seed leaves (cotyledons), and their pollen grains have three grooves. pp. 587, 840

Eukarya The domain that includes all eukaryotes, organisms that contain a membrane-bound nucleus within each of their cells; all protists, plants, fungi, and animals. p. 482

eukaryote Organism in which the DNA is enclosed in a nucleus. p. 31

eukaryotic chromosome A DNA molecule, with its associated proteins, in the nucleus of a eukaryotic cell. p. 35

euploid An individual with a normal set of chromosomes. p. 253

Euryarchaeota A major group of the domain Archaea, members of which are found in different extreme environments. They include methanogens, extreme halophiles, and some extreme thermophiles. p. 497

eusocial A form of social organization, observed in some insect species, in which numerous related individuals—a large percentage of them sterile female workers—live and work together in a colony for the reproductive benefit of a single queen and her mate(s). p. 1181

eustachian tube A duct leading from the air-filled middle ear to the throat that protects the eardrum from damage caused by changes in environmental atmospheric pressure. p. 1106

evaporation Heat transfer through the energy required to change a liquid to a gas. p. 1252

evolution The main unifying concept in biology, explaining how the diversity of life on Earth arose and how species change over time in response to changes in their abiotic and biotic environment. p. 392

evolutionary developmental biology A field of biology that compares the genes controlling the developmental processes of different animals to determine the evolutionary origin of morphological novelties and developmental processes. p. 456

evolutionary divergence A process whereby natural selection or genetic drift causes populations to become more different over time. p. 399

exchange diffusion *See* antiport. p. 112

excitatory postsynaptic potential (EPSP) The change in membrane potential caused when a neurotransmitter opens a ligand-gated Na^+ channel and Na^+ enters the cell, making it more likely that the postsynaptic neuron will generate an action potential. p. 1085

excretion The process that helps maintain the body's water and ion balance while ridding the body of metabolic wastes. p. 587

exergonic process Reaction that has a negative ΔG because it releases free energy. p. 79

exocrine gland A gland that is connected to the epithelium by a duct and that empties its secretion at the epithelial surface. p. 950

exocytosis In eukaryotes, the process by which a secretory vesicle fuses with the plasma membrane and releases the vesicle contents to the exterior. p. 38

exodermis In the roots of some plants, an outer layer of root cortex that may limit water losses from roots and help regulate the absorption of ions. p. 854

exon An amino acid–coding sequence present in pre-mRNA that is retained in a spliced mRNA that is translated to produce a polypeptide. p. 298

exon shuffling Molecular evolutionary process that combines exons of two or more existing genes to produce a gene that encodes a protein with an unprecedented function. p. 382

exoskeleton A hard external covering of an animal's body that blocks the passage of water and provides support and protection. pp. 620, 1145

exothermic Refers to processes that release energy. p. 78

exotoxin A toxic protein that leaks from or is secreted from a bacterium and interferes with the biochemical processes of body cells in various ways. p. 489

experimental data Information that describes the result of a careful manipulation of the system under study. p. 415

experimental variable The variable to which any difference in observations of experimental treatment subjects and control treatment subjects is attributed. p. F-3

exploitative competition Form of competition in which two or more individuals or populations use the same limiting resources. p. 717

exponential (model of population growth) Model that describes unlimited population growth. p. 689

expression vector A plasmid that can not only carry cloned genes but also drive their expression. p. 352

external fertilization The process in which sperm and eggs are shed into the surrounding water, occurring in most aquatic invertebrates, bony fishes, and amphibians. p. 993

external gill A gill that extends out from the body and lacks a protective covering. p. 1222

extinction The death of the last individual in a species or the last species in a lineage. p. 781

extracellular digestion Digestion that takes place outside body cells, in a pouch or tube enclosed within the body. p. 603

extracellular fluid The fluid occupying the spaces between cells in multicellular animals. p. 958

extracellular matrix (ECM) A molecular system that supports and protects cells and provides mechanical linkages. pp. 47, 948

extra-embryonic membrane A primary tissue layer extended outside the embryo that conducts nutrients from the yolk to the embryo, exchanges gases with the environment outside the egg, or stores metabolic wastes removed from the embryo. p. 1020

eye The organ animals use to sense light. p. 9

F pilus Structure on the cell surface that allows an F^+ donor bacterial cell to attach to an F^- recipient bacterial cell. Also referred to as a *sex pilus*. p. 193

F^+ cell Donor cell in conjugation between bacteria. p. 193

F^- cell Recipient cell in conjugation between bacteria. p. 193

F_1 generation The first generation of offspring from a genetic cross. p. 219

F_2 generation The second generation of offspring from a genetic cross. p. 220

facilitated diffusion Mechanism by which polar and charged molecules diffuse across membranes with the help of transport proteins. p. 106

facilitation hypothesis A hypothesis that explains ecological succession, suggesting that species modify the local environment in ways that make it less suitable for themselves but more suitable for colonization by species typical of the next successional stage. p. 737

facultative anaerobe An organism that can live in the presence or absence of oxygen, using oxygen when it is present and living by fermentation under anaerobic conditions. pp. 139, 487

familial (hereditary) cancer Cancer that runs in a family. p. 333

family A Linnaean taxonomic category that ranks below an order and above a genus. p. 428

family planning program A program that educates people about ways to produce an optimal family size on an economically feasible schedule. p. 702

fast block (to polyspermy) The barrier set up by the wave of depolarization triggered when sperm and egg fuse, making it impossible for other sperm to enter the egg. p. 994

fast muscle fibre A muscle fibre that contracts relatively quickly and powerfully. p. 1142

fat Neutral lipid that is semisolid at biological temperatures. p. 99

fat-soluble vitamin A vitamin that dissolves in liquid fat or fatty oils, in addition to water. p. 1193

fate mapping Mapping of adult or larval structures onto the region of the embryo from which each structure developed. p. 1035

fatty acid One of two components of a neutral lipid, containing a single hydrocarbon chain with a carboxyl group linked at one end. p. 39

feather A sturdy, lightweight structure of birds, derived from scales in the skin of their ancestors. p. 662

feces Condensed and compacted digestive contents in the large intestine. p. 1207

feedback inhibition In enzyme reactions, regulation in which the product of a reaction acts as a regulator of the reaction. Also referred to as *end-product inhibition*. p. 92

fermentation Process in which electrons carried by NADH are transferred to an organic acceptor molecule rather than to the electron transfer system. p. 137

fertilization The fusion of the nuclei of an egg and sperm cell, which initiates development of a new individual. pp. 199, 990

fetus A developing human from the eighth week of gestation onward, at which point the major organs and organ systems have formed. p. 1025

fibre In sclerenchyma, an elongated, tapered, thick-walled cell that gives plant tissue its flexible strength. p. 843

fibrin A protein necessary for blood clotting; fibrin forms a weblike mesh that traps platelets and red blood cells and holds a clot together. p. 973

fibrinogen A plasma protein that plays a central role in the blood-clotting mechanism. p. 970

fibroblast The type of cell that secretes most of the collagen and other proteins in the loose connective tissue. p. 952

fibronectin A class of glycoproteins that aids in the attachment of cells to the extracellular matrix and helps hold the cells in position. p. 952

fibrous connective tissue Tissue in which fibroblasts are sparsely distributed among dense masses of collagen and elastin fibres that are lined up in highly ordered, parallel bundles, producing maximum tensile strength and elasticity. p. 952

fibrous root system A root system that consists of branching roots rather than a main taproot; roots tend to spread laterally from the base of the stem. p. 853

filament In flowers, the stalk of a stamen, which supports the anther. p. 885

filtration The nonselective movement of some water and a number of solutes—ions and small molecules, but not large molecules such as proteins—into the proximal end of the renal tubules through spaces between cells. p. 1238

first law of thermodynamics The principle that energy can be transferred and transformed but cannot be created or destroyed. p. 76

fission The mode of asexual reproduction in which the parent separates into two or more offspring of approximately equal size. p. 989

fixed action pattern A highly stereotyped instinctive behaviour; when triggered by a specific cue, it is performed over and over in almost exactly the same way. p. 1156

flagellum (plural, flagella) A long, threadlike, cellular appendage responsible for movement; found in both prokaryotes and eukaryotes, but with different structures and modes of locomotion. pp. 43, 486, 601

flame cell The cell that forms the primary filtrate in the excretory system of many bilateria. The urine is propelled through ducts by the synchronous beating of cilia, resembling a flickering flame. p. 608

flower The reproductive structure of angiosperms, consisting of floral parts grouped on a stem; the structure in which seeds develop. p. 586

fluid feeder An animal that obtains nourishment by ingesting liquids that contain organic molecules in solution. p. 1194

fluid mosaic model Model proposing that the membrane consists of a fluid phospholipid bilayer in which proteins are embedded and float freely. p. 98

follicle The ovum and follicle cells. p. 1000

follicle cell A cell that grows from ovarian tissue and nourishes the developing egg. p. 993

follicle-stimulating hormone (FSH) The pituitary hormone that stimulates oocytes in the ovaries to continue meiosis and become follicles. During follicle enlargement, FSH interacts with luteinizing hormone to stimulate follicular cells to secrete estrogens. p. 1055

food chain A depiction of the trophic structure of a community; a portrait of who eats whom. p. 357

food web A set of interconnected food chains with multiple links. p. 572

forebrain The largest division of the brain, which includes the cerebral cortex and basal ganglia. It is credited with the highest intellectual functions. p. 1090

foreskin A loose fold of skin that covers the glans of the penis. *See* prepuce. p. 1004

fossil The remains or traces of an organism of a past geologic age embedded and preserved in Earth's crust. p. 12

founder effect An evolutionary phenomenon in which a population that was established by just a few colonizing individuals has only a fraction of the genetic diversity seen in the population from which it was derived. p. 419

fovea The small region of the retina around which cones are concentrated in mammals and birds with eyes specialized for daytime vision. p. 1109

fragmentation A type of vegetative reproduction in plants in which cells or a piece of the parent break off and then develop into new individuals. pp. 895, 989

frameshift mutation Mutation in a protein-coding gene that causes the reading frame of an mRNA transcribed from the gene to be altered, resulting in the production of a different, and nonfunctional, amino acid sequence in the polypeptide. p. 310

free energy The energy in a system that is available to do work. p. 75

freeze-fracture technique Technique in which experimenters freeze a block of cells rapidly and then fracture the block to split the lipid bilayer and expose the hydrophobic membrane interior. p. 99

fruit A mature ovary, often with accessory parts, from a flower. pp. 586, 891

fruiting body In some fungi, a stalked, spore-producing structure such as a mushroom. p. 529

functional genomics The study of the functions of genes and of other parts of the genome. p. 364

functional groups The atoms in reactive groups. p. F-22

fundamental niche The range of conditions and resources that a population can possibly tolerate and use. p. 721

furculum Wishbone in birds. p. 661

furrow In cytokinesis, a groove that girdles the cell and gradually deepens until it cuts the cytoplasm into two parts. p. 176

G protein–coupled receptor In signal transduction, a surface receptor that responds to a signal by activating a G protein. p. 1049

G0 phase The phase of the cell cycle in eukaryotes in which many cell types stop dividing. p. 172

G1 phase The initial growth stage of the cell cycle in eukaryotes, during which the cell makes proteins and other types of cellular molecules but not nuclear DNA. p. 171

G2 phase The phase of the cell cycle in eukaryotes during which the cell continues to synthesize proteins and grow, completing interphase. p. 171

gallbladder The organ that stores bile between meals, when no digestion is occurring. p. 1205

gametangium (plural, **gametangia**) A cell or organ in which gametes are produced. pp. 546, 572

gamete A haploid cell; an egg or sperm. Haploid cells fuse during sexual reproduction to form a diploid zygote. pp. 199, 595

gametic isolation A prezygotic reproductive isolating mechanism caused by incompatibility between the sperm of one species and the eggs of another; may prevent fertilization. p. 432

gametogenesis The formation of male and female gametes. p. 990

gametophyte An individual of the haploid generation produced when a spore germinates and grows directly by mitotic divisions in organisms that undergo alternation of generations. pp. 200, 526, 563, 884

ganglion A functional concentration of nervous system tissue composed principally of nerve cell bodies, usually lying outside the central nervous system. pp. 608, 640

ganglion cell A type of neuron in the retina of the eye that receives visual information from photoreceptors via various intermediate cells such as bipolar cells, amacrine cells, and horizontal cells. p. 1112

gap gene In *Drosophila* embryonic development, the first activated set of segmentation genes that progressively subdivide the embryo into regions, determining the segments of the embryo and the adult. p. 1037

gap junction Junction that opens direct channels allowing ions and small molecules to pass directly from one cell to another. p. 48

gastric juice A substance secreted by the stomach that contains the digestive enzyme pepsin. 1202

gastrodermis The derivative of endoderm that lines the gastrovascular cavity of radially symmetrical animals and forms the epithelial lining of the midgut in bilaterally symmetrical anmals. p. 603

gastrovascular cavity A saclike body cavity with a single opening, a mouth, which serves both digestive and circulatory functions. p. 602

gastrula The developmental stage resulting when the cells of the blastula migrate and divide once cleavage is complete. p. 1015

gastrulation The second major process of early development in most animals, which produces an embryo with three distinct primary tissue layers. p. 1015

gated channel Ion transporter in a membrane that switches between open, closed, and intermediate states. p. 106

gemma (plural, **gemmae**) Small cell mass that forms in cuplike growths on a thallus. p. 574

gemmules Clusters of cells with a resistant covering that allows them to survive unfavourable conditions. p. 602

gene A unit containing the code for a protein molecule or one of its parts, or for functioning RNA molecules such as tRNA and rRNA. p. 30

gene flow The transfer of genes from one population to another through the movement of individuals or their gametes. p. 418

gene-for-gene recognition A mechanism in which plants can detect an attack by a specific pathogen; the product of a specific plant gene interacts with the product of a specific pathogen gene, triggering the plant's defensive response. p. 932

gene pool The sum of all alleles at all gene loci in all individuals in a population. p. 414

gene therapy Correction of genetic disorders using genetic engineering techniques. p. 354

general transcription factor (basal transcription factor) In eukaryotes, a protein that binds to the promoter of a gene in the area of the TATA box and recruits and orients RNA polymerase II to initiate transcription at the correct place. p. 322

generalized compartment model A model used to describe nutrient cycling in which two criteria—organic versus inorganic nutrients and available versus unavailable nutrients—define four compartments where nutrients accumulate. p. 759

generalized transduction Transfer of bacterial genes between bacteria using virulent phages that have incorporated random DNA fragments of the bacterial genome. p. 196

generation time The average time between the birth of an organism and the birth of its offspring. p. 684

generative cell A cell in the pollen grain (male gametophyte) of seed plants that will give rise to sperm. p. 886

genetic code The nucleotide information that specifies the amino acid sequence of a polypeptide. p. 292

genetic counselling Counselling that allows prospective parents to assess the possibility that they might have a child affected by a genetic disorder. p. 258

genetic drift Random fluctuations in allele frequencies as a result of chance events; usually reduces genetic variation in a population. p. 418

genetic engineering The use of DNA technologies to alter genes for practical purposes. p. 339

genetic equilibrium The point at which neither the allele frequencies nor the genotype frequencies in a population change in succeeding generations. p. 415

genetic recombination The process by which the combinations of alleles for different genes in two parental individuals become shuffled into new combinations in offspring individuals. p. 190

genetic screening Biochemical or molecular tests for identifying inherited disorders after a child is born. p. 259

genetically modified organism (GMO) A transgenic organism. p. 359

genome The entire collection of DNA sequence for a given organism. p. 67

genomic imprinting Pattern of inheritance in which the expression of a nuclear gene is based on whether an individual organism inherits the gene from the male or the female parent. p. 259

genomic library A collection of clones that contains a copy of every DNA sequence in a genome. p. 344

genotype The genetic constitution of an organism. p. 221

genotype frequency The percentage of individuals in a population possessing a particular genotype. p. 414

genus A Linnaean taxonomic category ranking below a family and above a species. p. 427

geographic range The overall spatial boundaries within which a population lives. p. 680

germ cell An animal cell that is set aside early in embryonic development and gives rise to the gametes. pp. 991, 1020

germ layer The layers (up to three) of cells produced during the early development of the embryo of most animals. p. 595

germ-line gene therapy Therapy in which a gene is introduced into germ-line cells of an animal to correct a genetic disorder. p. 355

gestation The period of mammalian development in which the embryo develops in the uterus of the mother. p. 668

gibberellin Any of a large family of plant hormones that regulate aspects of growth, including cell elongation. p. 924

gill A respiratory organ formed as an evagination of the body that extends outward into the respiratory medium. p. 611

gill arch One of the series of curved supporting structures between the slits in the pharynx of a chordate. p. 646

gill slit One of the openings in the pharynx of a chordate through which water passes out of the pharynx. p. 640

Ginkgophyta A plant phylum with a single living species, the ginkgo (or maidenhair) tree. p. 583

gizzard The part of the digestive tube that grinds ingested material into fine particles by muscular contractions of the wall. p. 1195

gland A cell or group of cells that produces and releases substances nearby, in another part of the body, or to the outside. p. 950

glans A soft, caplike structure at the end of the penis, containing most of the nerve endings producing erotic sensations. p. 1004

glial cell A nonneuronal cell contained in the nervous tissue that physically supports and provides nutrients to neurons, provides electrical insulation between them, and scavenges cellular debris and foreign matter. pp. 955, 1070

globulin A plasma protein that transports lipids (including cholesterol) and fat-soluble vitamins; a specialized subgroup of globulins, the immunoglobulins, constitute antibodies and other molecules contributing to the immune response. p. 970

glomerulus A ball of blood capillaries surrounded by Bowman's capsule in the human nephron. p. 1246

glucagon A pancreatic hormone with effects opposite to those of insulin: it stimulates glycogen, fat, and protein degradation. p. 1060

glucocorticoid A steroid hormone secreted by the adrenal cortex that helps maintain the blood concentration of glucose and other fuel molecules. p. 1058

glycocalyx A carbohydrate coat covering the cell surface. p. 32

glycogen Energy-providing carbohydrates stored in animal cells. p. 135

glycolysis Stage of cellular respiration in which sugars such as glucose are partially oxidized and broken down into smaller molecules. p. 125

Gnathostomata The group of vertebrates with movable jaws. p. 644

Golgi complex In eukaryotes, the organelle responsible for the final modification, sorting, and distribution of proteins and lipids. p. 37

Golgi tendon organ A proprioceptor of tendons. p. 1103

gonad A specialized gamete-producing organ in which the germ cells collect. Gonads are the primary source of sex hormones in vertebrates: ovaries in the female and testes in the male. p. 1059

gonadotropin A hormone that regulates the activity of the gonads (ovaries and testes). p. 1055

gonadotropin-releasing hormone (GnRH) A tropic hormone secreted by the hypothalamus that causes the pituitary to make luteinizing hormone (LH) and follicle-stimulating hormone (FSH). p. 1060

graded potential A change in membrane potential that does not necessarily trigger an action potential. p. 1085

gradualism The view that Earth and its living systems changed slowly over its history. p. 395

Gram-negative Describing bacteria that do not retain the stain used in the Gram stain procedure. p. 485

Gram-positive Describing bacteria that appear purple when stained using the Gram stain technique. p. 485

Gram stain procedure A procedure of staining bacteria to distinguish between types of bacteria with different cell wall compositions. p. 484

granum (plural, **grana**) Structure in the chloroplasts of higher plants formed by thylakoids stacked one on top of another. p. 46

gravitropism A directional growth response to Earth's gravitational pull that is induced by mechanical and hormonal influences. p. 934

greater vestibular gland One of two glands located slightly below and to the left and right of the opening of the vagina in women. They secrete mucus to provide lubrication, especially when the woman is sexually aroused. p. 999

greenhouse effect A phenomenon in which certain gases foster the accumulation of heat in the lower atmosphere, maintaining warm temperatures on Earth. p. 764

grey crescent A crescent-shaped region of the underlying cytoplasm at the side opposite the point of sperm entry exposed after fertilization when the pigmented layer of cytoplasm rotates toward the site of sperm entry. p. 1018

grey matter Areas of densely packed nerve cell bodies and dendrites in the brain and spinal cord. p. 1123

gross primary productivity The rate at which producers convert solar energy into chemical energy. p. 750

ground meristem The primary meristematic tissue in plants that gives rise to ground tissues, mostly parenchyma. p. 849

ground tissue system One of the three basic tissue systems in plants; includes all tissues other than dermal and vascular tissues. p. 841

growth factor Any of a large group of peptide hormones that regulates the division and differentiation of many cell types in the body. p. 1047

growth hormone (GH) A hormone that stimulates cell division, protein synthesis, and bone growth in children and adolescents, thereby causing body growth. p. 1055

guanine A purine that base-pairs with cytosine in nucleic acids. p. 268

guard cell Either of a pair of specialized crescent-shaped cells that control the opening and closing of stomata in plant tissue. p. 847

guttation The exudation of water from leaves as a result of strong root pressure. p. 872

gymnosperm A seed plant that produces "naked" seeds not enclosed in an ovary. p. 581

H^+ pump *See* proton pump. p. 109

habitat fragmentation A process in which remaining areas of intact habitat are reduced to small, isolated patches. p. 653

habitat The specific environment in which a population lives, as characterized by its biotic and abiotic features. p. 680

habituation The learned loss of responsiveness to stimuli. p. 1159

half-life The time it takes for half of a given amount of a radioisotope to decay. p. F-10

haplodiploidy A pattern of sex determination in insects in which females are diploid and males are haploid. p. 1182

haploid An organism or cell with only one copy of each type of chromosome in its nuclei. p. 170

Hardy–Weinberg principle An evolutionary rule of thumb that specifies the conditions under which a population of diploid organisms achieves genetic equilibrium. p. 415

harvesting efficiency The ratio of the energy content of food consumed to with the energy content of food available. p. 752

head-foot In molluscs, the region of the body that provides the major means of locomotion and contains concentrations of nervous system tissues and sense organs. p. 611

heartwood The inner core of a woody stem; composed of dry tissue and nonliving cells that no longer transport water and solutes and may store resins, tannins, and other defensive compounds. p. 856

heat of vaporization The heat required to give water molecules enough energy of motion to break loose from liquid water and form a gas. p. F-16

heat-shock protein (HSP) Any of a group of chaperone proteins that are present in all cells in all life forms. They are induced when a cell undergoes various types of environmental stresses such as heat, cold, and oxygen deprivation. p. 933

heavy chain The heavier of the two types of polypeptide chains that are found in immunoglobulin and antibody molecules. p. 1274

helical virus A virus in which the protein subunits of the coat assemble in a rodlike spiral around the genome. p. 502

helper T cell A clonal cell that assists with the activation of B cells. p. 1278

hemocoel A cavity in the body of some coelomic invertebrates (arthropods and some molluscs) filled with blood. The hemocoel displaces the coelom, which persists as a small chamber surrounding the gonads or heart. p. 596

hemolymph The circulatory fluid of invertebrates with open circulatory systems, including molluscs and arthropods. pp. 611, 965

hepatic portal vein The blood vessel that leads to capillary networks in the liver. p. 1206

Hepatophyta The phylum that includes liverworts and their bryophyte relatives. p. 573

herbicide A compound that, at proper concentration, kills plants. p. 921

herbivore An animal that obtains energy and nutrients primarily by eating plants. p. 712

herbivory The interaction between herbivorous animals and the plants they eat. p. 712

hermaphroditism The mechanism in which both mature egg-producing and mature sperm-producing tissue are present in the same individual. p. 997

heterochromatin In eukaryotes, regions of densely packed chromatin fibres in interphase nuclei. p. 285

heterodont Having different teeth specialized for different jobs. p. 667

heterosporous Producing two types of spores, "male" microspores and "female" megaspores. p. 570

heterotroph An organism that acquires energy and nutrients by eating other organisms or their remains. pp. 63, 487, 594

heterozygote An individual with two different alleles of a gene. p. 221

heterozygote advantage An evolutionary circumstance in which individuals that are heterozygous at a particular locus have higher relative fitness than either homozygote. p. 421

heterozygous The state of possessing two different alleles of a gene. p. 221

Hfr cell A special donor cell that can transfer genes on a bacterial chromosome to a recipient bacterium. p. 195

hibernation Extended torpor during winter. p. 1260

hindbrain The lower area of the brain that includes the brain stem, medulla oblongata, and pons. p. 1090

hippocampus A grey-matter centre that is involved in sending information. 1126

histone A small, positively charged (basic) protein that is complexed with DNA in the chromosomes of eukaryotes. p. 283

histone code A regulatory mechanism for altering chromatin structure and, therefore, gene activity, based on signals in histone tails represented by chemical modification patterns. p. 327

Holocephali The chimeras, another group of cartilaginous fishes. p. 647

homeobox A region of a homeotic gene that corresponds to an amino acid section of the homeodomain. p. 394

homeodomain An encoded transcription factor of each protein that binds to a region in the promoters of the genes whose transcription it regulates. p. 1039

homeostasis A steady internal condition maintained by responses that compensate for changes in the external environment. pp. 946, 1236

homeostatic mechanism Any process or activity responsible for homeostasis. p. 946

homeotic gene Any of the family of genes that determines the structure of body parts during embryonic development. p. 1039

hominin A member of a monophyletic group of primates, characterized by an erect bipedal stance, that includes modern humans and their recent ancestors. p. 469

hominoid (Hominoidea) The monophyletic group of primates that includes apes and humans. p. 469

homologous Similar. p. 190

homologous genes Genes that are related by descent from a common ancestor. p. 369

homologous traits Characteristics that are similar in two species because they inherited the genetic basis of the trait from their common ancestor. p. 402

homoplasies Characteristics shared by a set of species, often because they live in similar environments, but not present in their common ancestor; often the product of convergent evolution. p. 458

homosporous Producing only one type of spore. p. 570

homozygote An individual with two copies of the same allele. p. 221

homozygous State of possessing two copies of the same allele. p. 221

horizon A noticeable layer of soil, such as topsoil, with a distinct texture and composition that varies with soil type. p. 907

horizontal cell A type of neuron that forms lateral connections among photoreceptor cells in the retina of the eye. p. 1112

hormone A signalling molecule secreted by a cell that can alter the activities of any cell with receptors for it; in animals, typically a molecule produced by one tissue and transported via the bloodstream to another specific tissue to alter its physiological activity. pp. 326, 918, 1046

host A species that is fed upon by a parasite. p. 66

host race A population of insects that may be reproductively isolated from other populations of the same species as a consequence of their adaptation to feed on a specific host plant species. p. 438

human chorionic gonadotropin (hCG) A hormone that keeps the corpus luteum in the ovary from breaking down. p. 1008

human immunodeficiency virus (HIV) A retrovirus that causes acquired immune deficiency syndrome (AIDS). p. 213

humus The organic component of soil remaining after decomposition of plants and animals, animal droppings, and other organic matter. p. 906

hybrid breakdown A postzygotic reproductive isolating mechanism in which hybrids are capable of reproducing, but their offspring have either reduced fertility or reduced viability. p. 433

hybrid inviability A postzygotic reproductive isolating mechanism in which a hybrid individual has a low probability of survival to reproductive age. p. 432

hybrid sterility A postzygotic reproductive isolating mechanism in which hybrid offspring cannot form functional gametes. p. 432

hybrid zone A geographic area where the hybrid offspring of two divergent populations or species are common. p. 436

hybridization When two species interbreed and produce fertile offspring. p. 427

hydration shell A shell of any chemical species that acts as a solvent and surrounds a solute species. When the solvent is water it is often referred to as a *hydration shell* or *hydration sphere*. A classic example is when water molecules form a sphere around a metal ion. F-17

hydrocarbon Molecule consisting of carbon linked only to hydrogen atoms. p. 100

hydrogen bond Noncovalent bond formed by unequal electron sharing between hydrogen atoms and oxygen, nitrogen, or sulfur atoms. p. F-13

hydrogeologic cycle The global cycling of water between the ocean, the atmosphere, land, freshwater ecosystems, and living organisms. p. 760

hydrolysis Reaction in which the components of a water molecule are added to functional groups as molecules are broken into smaller subunits. p. F-21

hydrophilic Refers to polar molecules that associate readily with water. p. F-13

hydrophobic Refers to nonpolar substances that are excluded by water and other polar molecules. p. F-13

hydroponic culture A method of growing plants not in soil but with the roots bathed in a solution that contains water and mineral nutrients. p. 902

hydrostatic skeleton A structure consisting of muscles and fluid that, by themselves, provide support for the animal or part of the animal; no rigid support, such as a bone, is involved. pp. 596, 1143

hydroxyl group Group consisting of an oxygen atom linked to a hydrogen atom on one side and to a carbon chain on the other side. p. 268

hymen A thin flap of tissue that partially covers the opening of the vagina. p. 999

hyomandibular bones Bones that support the hyoid and throat. p. 646

hyperpolarized The condition of a neuron when its membrane potential is more negative than the resting value. p. 1074

hypersensitive response A plant defence that physically cordons off an infection site by surrounding it with dead cells. p. 930

hyperthermia The condition resulting when the heat gain of the body is too great to be counteracted. p. 1259

hypertonic Solution containing dissolved substances at higher concentrations than the cells it surrounds. p. 109

hypha (plural, hyphae) Any of the threadlike filaments that form the mycelium of a fungus. pp. 524, 542

hypoblast The bottom layer of a blastodisc. p. 1019

hypocotyl The region of a plant embryo's vertical axis between the cotyledons and the radicle. p. 893

hypodermis The innermost layer of the skin that contains larger blood vessels and additional reinforcing connective tissue. p. 1257

hypothalamus The portion of the brain that contains centres regulating basic homeostatic functions of the body and contributing to the release of hormones. p. 1126

hypothermia A condition in which the core temperature falls below normal for a prolonged period. p. 1259

hypothesis A "working explanation" of observed facts. p. F-2

hypotonic Solution containing dissolved substances at lower concentrations than the cells it surrounds. p. 108

imbibition The movement of water into a seed as the water molecules are attracted to hydrophilic groups of stored proteins; the first step in germination. p. 894

immigration Movement of organisms into a population. p. 684

immune privilege The situation in which certain sites in the body tolerate the presence of an antigen without mounting an inflammatory immune response. These sites include the brain, eyes, and testicles. p. 1282

immune response The defensive reactions of the immune system. p. 1267

immune system The combined defences, innate and acquired, a body uses to eliminate infections. p. 1266

immunoglobulin A specific protein substance produced by plasma cells to aid in fighting infection. p. 970

immunological memory The capacity of the immune system to respond more rapidly and vigorously to the second contact with a specific antigen than to the primary contact. p. 1280

immunological tolerance The process that protects the body's own molecules from attack by the immune system. p. 1283

imperfect flower A type of incomplete flower that has stamens or carpels, but not both. p. 885

imprinting The process of learning the identity of a caretaker and potential future mate during a critical period. p. 1159

inbreeding A special form of nonrandom mating in which genetically related individuals mate with each other. p. 420

incisors Flattened, chisel-shaped teeth of mammals, located at the front of the mouth, that are used to nip or cut food. p. 464

incomplete dominance Condition in which the effects of recessive alleles can be detected to some extent in heterozygotes. p. 229

incomplete metamorphosis In certain insects, a life cycle characterized by the absence of a pupal stage between the immature and adult stages. p. 629

incurrent siphon A muscular tube that brings water containing oxygen and food into the body of an invertebrate. p. 615

incus The second of the three sound-conducting middle ear bones in vertebrates, located between the malleus and the stapes. p. 1105

independent assortment Mendel's principle that the alleles of the genes that govern two characters segregate independently during formation of gametes. p. 226

indeterminate cleavage A type of cleavage, observed in many deuterostomes, in which the developmental fates of the first few cells produced by mitosis are not determined as soon as cells are produced. p. 597

indeterminate growth Growth that is not limited by an organism's genetic program, so that the organism grows for as long as it lives; typical of many plants. *Compare* determinate growth. p. 839

indirect neurotransmitter A neurotransmitter that acts as a first messenger, binding to a G protein–coupled receptor in the postsynaptic membrane, which activates the receptor and triggers generation of a second messenger such as cyclic AMP or other processes. p. 1082

inducer Concerning regulation of gene expression in bacteria, a molecule that turns on the transcription of the genes in an operon. p. 317

inducible operon Operon whose expression is increased by an inducer molecule. p. 317

induction A mechanism in which one group of cells (the inducer cells) causes or influences another nearby group of cells (the responder cells) to follow a particular developmental pathway. p. 1016

infection thread In the formation of root nodules on nitrogen-fixing plants, the tube formed by the plasma membrane of root hair cells as bacteria enter the cell. p. 912

inflammation The heat, pain, redness, and swelling that occur at the site of an infection. p. 1268

inflorescence The arrangement of flowers on a stem. p. 883

ingestion The feeding methods used to take food into the digestive cavity. p. 1189

inheritance The transmission of DNA (i.e., genetic information) from one generation to the next. p. 187

inhibin A peptide that, in females, is an inhibitor of follicle-stimulating hormone (FSH) secretion from the pituitary, thereby diminishing the signal for follicular growth. In males, inhibin inhibits FSH secretion from the pituitary, thereby decreasing spermatogenesis. p. 1000

inhibiting hormone (IH) A hormone released by the hypothalamus that inhibits the secretion of a particular anterior pituitary hormone. p. 1053

inhibition hypothesis A hypothesis suggesting that new species are prevented from occupying a community by whatever species are already present. p. 737

inhibitory postsynaptic potential (IPSP) A change in membrane potential caused when hyperpolarization occurs, pushing the neuron farther from threshold. p. 1085

initiator codon *See* start codon. p. 294

innate immunity A nonspecific line of defence against pathogens that includes inflammation, which creates internal conditions that inhibit or kill many pathogens, and specialized cells that engulf or kill pathogens or infected body cells. p. 1266

inner boundary membrane Membrane lying just inside the outer boundary membrane of a chloroplast, enclosing the stroma. p. 46

inner cell mass The dense mass of cells within the blastocyst that will become the embryo. p. 1025

inner ear That part of the ear, particularly the cochlea, that converts mechanical vibrations (sound) into neural messages that are sent to the brain. p. 1106

inner mitochondrial membrane Membrane surrounding the mitochondrial matrix. p. 41

inorganic molecule Molecule without carbon atoms in its structure. p. F-20

inositol triphosphate (IP3) In particular, signal transduction pathways, a second messenger that activates transport proteins in the endoplasmic reticulum to release Ca^{2+} into the cytoplasm. IP3 is involved in one of two major G protein–coupled receptor response pathways. p. 919

insertion sequence (IS) A transposable element that contains only genes for its transposition. p. 211

insight learning A phenomenon in which animals can solve problems without apparent trial-and-error attempts at the solution. p. 1159

instar The stage between successive moults in insects and other arthropods. p. 628

instinctive behaviour A genetically "programmed" response that appears in complete and functional form the first time it is used. p. 1155

insulin A hormone secreted by beta cells in the islets of Langerhans, acting mainly on cells of nonworking skeletal muscles, liver cells, and adipose tissue (fat) to lower blood glucose, fatty acid, and amino acid levels and promote the storage of those molecules. pp. 1060, 1207

insulin-like growth factor (IGF) A peptide that directly stimulates growth processes. p. 1055

integral membrane protein Protein embedded in a phospholipid bilayer. p. 103

integration The sorting and interpretation of neural messages and the determination of the appropriate response(s). p. 1069

integrator In homeostatic feedback, the control centre that compares a detected environmental change with a set point. p. 960

integument Skin. In plants, the outer layer of an ovule. pp. 886, 1256

interference competition Form of competition in which individuals fight over resources or otherwise harm each other directly. p. 717

interferon A cytokine produced by infected host cells affected by viral dsRNA, which acts on both the infected cell that produces it, an autocrine effect, and neighbouring uninfected cells, a paracrine effect. p. 1272

interkinesis A brief interphase separating the two meiotic divisions. p. 202

intermediate disturbance hypothesis Hypothesis proposing that species richness is greatest in communities that experience fairly frequent disturbances of moderate intensity. p. 735

intermediate filament A cytoskeletal filament about 10 nm in diameter that provides mechanical strength to cells in tissues. p. 42

intermediate-day plant A plant that flowers only when day length falls between the values for long-day and short-day plants. p. 940

internal fertilization The process in which sperm are released by the male close to or inside the entrance of the reproductive tract of the female. p. 994

internal gill A gill located within the body that has a cover providing physical protection for the gills. Water must be brought to internal gills. p. 1222

interneuron A neuron that integrates information to formulate an appropriate response. p. 1070

internode The region between two nodes on a plant stem. p. 847

interphase The first stage of the mitotic cell cycle, during which the cell grows and replicates its DNA before undergoing mitosis and cytokinesis. p. 171

interspecific competition The competition for resources between species. p. 717

interstitial fluid The fluid occupying the spaces between cells in multicellular animals. p. 958

intertidal zone The shoreline that is alternately submerged and exposed by tides. p. 563

intestine The portion of the digestive system where organic matter is hydrolyzed by enzymes secreted into the digestive tube. As muscular contractions of the intestinal wall move the mixture along, cells lining the intestine absorb the molecular subunits produced by digestion. pp. 32, 93

intracellular digestion The process in which cells take in food particles by endocytosis. p. 603

intraspecific competition The dependence of two or more individuals in a population on the same limiting resource. p. 693

intrinsic rate of increase The maximum possible per capita population growth rate in a population living under ideal conditions. p. 691

intron A non–protein-coding sequence that interrupts the protein-coding sequence in a eukaryotic gene. Introns are removed by splicing in the processing of pre-mRNA to mRNA. p. 298

invagination The process in which cells changing shape and pushing inward from the surface produce an indentation, such as the dorsal lip of the blastopore. p. 33

inversion Chromosomal alteration that occurs if a broken segment reattaches to the same chromosome from which it was lost, but in reversed orientation, so that the order of genes in the segment is reversed with respect to the other genes of the chromosome. p. 252

invertebrate An animal without a vertebral column. p. 9

inverted repeat Enables the transposase enzyme to identify the ends of the transposable element when it catalyzes transposition. p. 211

involution The process by which cells migrate into the blastopore. p. 1018

ion A positively or negatively charged atom. pp. 8, F-11

ionic bond Bond that results from electrical attractions between atoms that have lost or gained electrons. p. 105

iris Of the eye, the coloured muscular membrane that lies behind the cornea and in front of the lens, which by opening or closing determines the size of the pupil and hence the amount of light entering the eye. p. 1108

islets of Langerhans Endocrine cells that secrete the peptide hormones insulin and glucagon into the bloodstream. p. 1060

isotonic Refers to the state of equal concentration of water inside and outside cells. p. 109

isotope A distinct form of the atoms of an element, with the same number of protons but a different number of neutrons. p. F-9

jasmonate Any of a group of plant hormones that help regulate aspects of growth and responses to stress, including attacks by predators and pathogens. p. 929

juvenile hormones A family of fatty acid hormones that govern metamorphosis and reproduction in insects and crustaceans. p. 1063

karyogamy In plants, the fusion of two sexually compatible haploid nuclei after cell fusion (plasmogamy). p. 543

karyotype A characteristic of a species consisting of the shapes and sizes of all of the chromosomes at metaphase. p. 175

keeled sternum The ventrally extended breastbone of a bird to which the flight muscles attach. p. 661

ketone Molecule in which the carbonyl group is linked to a carbon atom in the interior of a carbon chain. p. 1061

keystone species A species that has a greater effect on community structure than its numbers might suggest. p. 732

kin selection Altruistic behaviour to close relatives, allowing them to produce proportionately more surviving copies of the altruist's genes than the altruist might otherwise have produced on its own. p. 1180

kinesis A change in the rate of movement or the frequency of turning movements in response to environmental stimuli. p. 1169

kinetic energy The energy of motion. p. 75

kinetochore A specialized structure consisting of proteins attached to a centromere that mediates the attachment and movement of chromosomes along the mitotic spindle. p. 174

kingdom A Linnaean taxonomic category that ranks below a domain and above a phylum. p. 428

kingdom Animalia The taxonomic kingdom that includes all living and extinct animals. p. 594

kingdom Fungi The taxonomic kingdom that includes all living or extinct fungi. p. 543

kingdom Plantae The taxonomic kingdom encompassing all living or extinct plants. p. 564

Korarchaeota A group of Archaea recognized solely on the basis of rRNA coding sequences in DNA taken from environmental samples. p. 497

Krebs cycle *See* citric acid cycle. p. 129

K-selected species Long-lived, slow-reproducing species that thrive in more stable environments. p. 697

labia majora A pair of fleshy, fat-padded folds that partially cover the labia minora. p. 999

labia minora Two folds of tissue that run from front to rear on either side of the opening to the vagina. p. 999

lactate fermentation Reaction in which pyruvate is converted into lactate. p. 137

lagging strand A DNA strand assembled discontinuously in the direction opposite to DNA unwinding. p. 276

lagging strand template The DNA template strand for the lagging strand. p. 276

larva (larval form) A sexually immature stage in the life cycle of many animals that is morphologically distinct from the adult. p. 595

larynx The voice box. p. 1225

latent phase The time during which a virus remains in the cell in an inactive form. p. 506

lateral bud A bud on the side of a plant stem from which a branch may grow. p. 848

lateral geniculate nuclei Clusters of neurons located in the thalamus that receive visual information from the optic nerves and send it on to the visual cortex. p. 1113

lateral inhibition Visual processing in which lateral movement of signals from a rod or cone proceeds to a horizontal cell and continues to bipolar cells with which the horizontal cell makes inhibitory connections, serving both to sharpen the edges of objects and enhance contrast in an image. p. 1112

lateral line system The complex of mechanoreceptors along the sides of some fishes and aquatic amphibians that detect vibrations in the water. pp. 648, 1101

lateral meristem A plant meristem that gives rise to secondary tissue growth. *Compare* primary meristem. p. 839

lateral root A root that extends away from the main root (or taproot). p. 852

lateralization A phenomenon in which some brain functions are more localized in one of the two hemispheres. p. 1129

leaching The process by which soluble materials in soil are washed into a lower layer of soil or are dissolved and carried away by water. p. 901

leading strand A DNA strand assembled in the direction of DNA unwinding. p. 276

leading strand template The "old" DNA used as a template for synthesis of "new" DNA in the direction of DNA unwinding. p. 276

leaf primordium (plural, primordia) A lateral outgrowth from the apical meristem that develops into a young leaf. p. 851

learned behaviour A response of an animal that depends on having a particular kind of experience during development. p. 1155

learning A process in which experiences stored in memory change the behavioural responses of an animal. p. 1129

left aortic arch In mammals, leads blood way from the heart to the aorta. p. 667

leghemoglobin An iron-containing, red-pigmented protein produced in root nodules during the symbiotic association between *Bradyrhizobium* or *Rhizobium* and legumes. p. 912

lek A display ground where males each possess a small territory from which they court attentive females. p. 1176

lens The transparent, biconvex intraocular tissue that helps bring rays of light to a focus on the retina. p. 1108

Lepidosauromorpha A monophyletic lineage of diapsids that includes both marine and terrestrial animals, represented today by sphenodontids, lizards, and snakes. p. 655

leukocyte A white blood cell, which eliminates dead and dying cells from the body, removes cellular debris, and participates in defending the body against invading organisms. p. 971

Leydig cell A cell that produces the male sex hormones. p. 1002

lichen A single vegetative body that is the result of an association between a fungus and a photosynthetic partner, often an alga. p. 555

life cycle The sequential stages through which individuals develop, grow, maintain themselves, and reproduce. p. 517

life history The lifetime pattern of growth, maturation, and reproduction that is characteristic of a population or species. p. 686

life table A chart that summarizes the demographic characteristics of a population. p. 685

ligament A fibrous connective tissue that connects bones to each other at a joint. p. 952

ligand-gated ion channel A channel that opens or closes when a specific chemical, such as a neurotransmitter, binds to the channel. p. 1082

light The portion of the electromagnetic spectrum that humans can detect with their eyes. p. 4

light chain The lighter of the two types of polypeptide chains found in immunoglobulin and antibody molecules. p. 1274

light-independent reaction The second stage of photosynthesis, in which electrons are used as a source of energy to convert inorganic CO_2 to an organic form. Also referred to as the *Calvin cycle*. p. 156

light microscope Microscope that uses light to illuminate the specimen. p. 29

lignin A tough, rather inert polymer that strengthens the secondary walls of various plant cells and thus helps vascular plants grow taller and stay erect on land. p. 837

limbic system A functional network formed by parts of the thalamus, hypothalamus, and basal nuclei, along with other nearby grey-matter centres—the amygdala, hippocampus, and olfactory bulbs—sometimes called the "emotional brain." p. 1126

limiting nutrient An element in short supply within an ecosystem, the shortage of which limits productivity. p. 750

linkage The phenomenon of genes being located on the same chromosome. p. 241

linkage map Map of a chromosome showing the relative locations of genes based on recombination frequencies. p. 243

linked genes Genes on the same chromosome. p. 241

linker A short segment of DNA extending between one nucleosome and the next in a eukaryotic chromosome. p. 283

lipopolysaccharide (LPS) A large molecule that consists of a lipid and a carbohydrate joined by a covalent bond. p. 485

loam Any well-aerated soil composed of a mixture of sand, clay, silt, and organic matter. p. 906

locus The particular site on a chromosome at which a gene is located. p. 229

logistic (model of population growth) Model of population growth that assumes that a population's per capita growth rate decreases as the population gets larger. p. 689

long-day plant A plant that flowers in spring when dark periods become shorter and day length becomes longer. p. 939

long-term memory Memory that stores information from days to years or even for life. p. 1129

long-term potentiation A long-lasting increase in the strength of synaptic connections in activated neural pathways following brief periods of repeated stimulation. p. 1130

loop of Henle In mammals, a U-shaped bend of the proximal convoluted tubule. p. 1246

loose connective tissue A tissue formed of sparsely distributed cells surrounded by a more or less open network of collagen and other glycoprotein fibres. p. 952

lophophore The circular or U-shaped fold with one or two rows of hollow, ciliated tentacles that surrounds the mouth of brachiopods, bryozoans, and phoronids and is used to gather food. p. 607

loss of imprinting A phenomenon in which the imprinting mechanism for a gene does not work, resulting in both alleles of the gene being active. p. 260

lumbar vertebrae In mammals, the vertebrae from the thoracic (bearing ribs) to the sacral (junction with pelvis). p. 670

lumen The inside of the digestive tube. p. 1047

lung One of a pair of invaginated respiratory surfaces, buried in the body interior where they are less susceptible to drying out; the organs of respiration in mammals, birds, reptiles, and most amphibians. p. 1223

luteinizing hormone (LH) A hormone secreted by the pituitary that stimulates the growth and maturation of eggs in females and the secretion of testosterone in males. p. 1055

Lycophyta The plant phylum that includes club mosses and their close relatives. p. 577

lymph The interstitial fluid picked up by the lymphatic system. p. 981

lymph node One of many small, bean-shaped organs spaced along the lymph vessels that contain macrophages and other leukocytes that attack invading disease organisms. p. 983

lymphatic system An accessory system of vessels and organs that helps balance the fluid content of the blood and surrounding tissues and participates in the body's defences against invading disease organisms. p. 981

lymphocyte A leukocyte that carries out most of its activities in the tissues and organs of the lymphatic system. Lymphocytes play major roles in immune responses. p. 983

lysed Refers to a cell that has ruptured or undergone lysis. p. 504

lysogenic cycle Cycle in which the DNA of the bacteriophage is integrated into the DNA of the host bacterial cell and may remain for many generations. pp. 197, 505

lysosome Membrane-bound vesicle containing hydrolytic enzymes for the digestion of many complex molecules. p. 38

lytic cycle The series of events from infection of one bacterial cell by a phage through the release of progeny phages from lysed cells. pp. 196, 504

M phase–promoting factor A complex of M cyclin and cyclin-dependent kinase 1 (Cdk1). The complex initiates mitosis and orchestrates some of its key events. p. 182

macroevolution Large-scale evolutionary patterns in the history of life, producing major changes in species and higher taxonomic groups. p. 401

macromolecule A very large molecule assembled by the covalent linkage of smaller subunit molecules. p. 53

macronucleus In ciliophorans, a single large nucleus that develops from a micronucleus but loses all genes except those required for basic "housekeeping" functions of the cell and for ribosomal RNAs. p. 521

macronutrient In humans, a mineral required in amounts ranging from 50 mg to more than 1 g per day. In plants, a nutrient needed in large amounts for normal growth and development. pp. 903, 1190

macrophage A phagocyte that takes part in nonspecific defences and adaptive immunity. p. 1268

magnetoreceptor A receptor found in some animals that navigate long distances that allows them to detect and use Earth's magnetic field as a source of directional information. p. 1121

magnification The ratio of an object as viewed to its real size. p. 29

major histocompatibility complex A large cluster of genes encoding the MHC proteins. p. 1277

malleus The outermost of the sound-conducting bones of the middle ear in vertebrates. p. 1105

malnutrition A condition resulting from a diet that lacks one or more essential nutrients. p. 1190

Malpighian tubule The main organ of excretion and osmoregulation in insects, helping them maintain water and electrolyte balance. p. 626

mammary glands Specialized organs of female mammals that produce energy-rich milk, a watery mixture of fats, sugars, proteins, vitamins, and minerals. pp. 329, 1013, 1055

mandible In arthropods, one of the paired head appendages posterior to the mouth used for feeding. In vertebrates, the lower jaw. p. 624

mantle One or two folds of the body wall that lines the shell and secretes the substance that forms the shell in molluscs. p. 611

mantle cavity The protective chamber produced by the mantle in many molluscs. p. 611

map unit The unit of a linkage map, equivalent to a recombination frequency of 1%. Also referred to as a *centimorgan*. p. 244

marsupium An external pouch on the abdomen of many female marsupials, containing the mammary glands, and within which the young continue to develop after birth. p. 997

mass number The total number of protons and neutrons in the atomic nucleus. p. F-9

mast cell A type of cell dispersed through connective tissue that releases histamine when activated by the death of cells, caused by a pathogen at an infection site. p. 1269

mastax The toothed grinding organ at the anterior of the digestive tract in rotifers. p. 610

maternal chromosome The chromosome derived from the female parent of an organism. p. 201

maternal-effect gene One of a class of genes that regulate the expression of other genes expressed by the mother during oogenesis and that control the polarity of the egg and, therefore, of the embryo. p. 1037

mating systems The social systems describing how males and females pair up. p. 1175

mating type A genetically defined strain of an organism (such as a fungus) that can only mate with an organism of the opposite mating type; mating types are often designated + and −. p. 540

matter Anything that occupies space and has mass. p. F-8

maxilla (plural, maxillae) One of the paired head appendages posterior to the mouth used for feeding in arthropods. pp. 624, 646

mechanical isolation A prezygotic reproductive isolating mechanism caused by differences in the structure of reproductive organs or other body parts. p. 432

mechanoreceptor A sensory receptor that detects mechanical energy, such as changes in pressure, body position, or acceleration. The auditory receptors in the ears are examples of mechanoreceptors. p. 1077

medusa (plural, medusae) The tentacled, usually bell-shaped, free-swimming sexual stage in the life cycle of a coelenterate. p. 603

megapascal A unit of pressure used to measure water potential. p. 865

megaspore A plant spore that develops into a female gametophyte; usually larger than a microspore. pp. 570, 886

meiocytes Cells that are destined to divide by meiosis. p. 201

meiosis The division of diploid cells to haploid progeny, consisting of two sequential rounds of nuclear and cellular division. pp. 170, 199, 990

meiosis I The first division of the meiotic cell cycle in which homologous chromosomes pair and undergo an exchange of chromosome segments, and then the homologous chromosomes separate, resulting in two cells, each with the haploid number of chromosomes and with each chromosome still consisting of two chromatids. p. 201

meiosis II The second division of the meiotic cell cycle in which the sister chromatids in each of the two cells produced by meiosis I separate and segregate into different cells, resulting in four cells each with the haploid number of chromosomes. p. 201

melanocyte-stimulating hormone (MSH) A hormone secreted by the anterior pituitary that controls the degree of pigmentation in melanocytes. p. 1055

melanotic encapsulation The mechanism by which hemocytes move toward and form a capsule around pathogens that are too big to phagocytose. The capsule may then be melanized by the deposition of phenolic compounds that further isolate the pathogen. p. 1268

melatonin A peptide hormone secreted by the pineal gland that helps maintain daily biorhythms. p. 1062

membrane attack complexes An abnormal activation of the complement (protein) portion of the blood, forming a cascade reaction that brings blood proteins together, binds them to the cell wall, and then inserts them through the cell membrane. p. 1271

membrane potential An electrical voltage that measures the potential inside a cell membrane relative to the fluid just outside; it is negative under resting conditions and becomes positive during an action potential. pp. 111, 1073

memory The storage and retrieval of a sensory or motor experience or a thought. p. 1124

memory B cell In antibody-mediated immunity, a long-lived cell expressing an antibody on its surface that can bind to a specific antigen. A memory B cell is activated the next time the antigen is encountered, producing a rapid secondary immune response. p. 1279

memory cell An activated lymphocyte that circulates in the blood and lymph, ready to initiate a rapid immune response on subsequent exposure to the same antigen. p. 1273

memory helper T cell In cell-mediated immunity, a long-lived cell differentiated from a helper T cell, which remains in an inactive state in the lymphatic system after an immune reaction has run its course and is ready to be activated on subsequent exposure to the same antigen. p. 1280

meninges Three layers of connective tissue that surround and protect the spinal cord and brain. p. 1123

menstrual cycle A cycle of approximately 1 month in the human female during which an egg is released from an ovary and the uterus is prepared to receive the fertilized egg; if fertilization does not occur, the endometrium breaks down, which releases blood and tissue breakdown products from the uterus to the outside through the vagina. p. 1000

meristem An undifferentiated, permanently embryonic plant tissue that gives rise to new cells forming tissues and organs. p. 839

mesenteries Sheets of loose connective tissue, covered on both surfaces with epithelial cells, which suspend the abdominal organs in the coelom and provide lubricated, smooth surfaces that prevent chafing or abrasion between adjacent structures as the body moves. pp. 596, 952

mesoderm The middle layer of the three primary germ layers of an animal embryo, from which the muscular, skeletal, vascular, and connective tissues develop. pp. 595, 1015

mesoglea A layer of gel-like connective tissue separating the gastrodermis and epidermis in radially symmetrical animals. It contains widely dispersed amoeboid cells. p. 603

mesohyl The gelatinous middle layer of cells lining the body cavity of a sponge. p. 601

mesophyll The ground tissue located between the two outer leaf tissues, composed of loosely packed parenchyma cells that contain chloroplasts. p. 851

messenger RNA (mRNA) An RNA molecule that serves as a template for protein synthesis. p. 292

metabolism The biochemical reactions that allow a cell or organism to extract energy from its surroundings and use that energy to maintain itself, grow, and reproduce. p. 82

metagenomics The study of all DNA sequences, regardless of origin, isolated "in bulk" from ecosystems such as decaying animals, ocean water, termite gut, etc. pp. 380, 482

metamorphosis A reorganization of the form of certain animals during postembryonic development. pp. 602, 1057

metanephridium (plural, metanephridia) The excretory tubule of most annelids and molluscs. p. 617

metaphase The phase of mitosis during which the spindle reaches its final form and the spindle microtubules move the chromosomes into alignment at the spindle midpoint. p. 175

micelle A sphere composed of a single layer of lipid molecules. p. 100

microclimate The abiotic conditions immediately surrounding an organism. p. 737

microevolution Small-scale genetic changes within populations, often in response to shifting environmental circumstances or chance events. pp. 401, 410

micronucleus In ciliophorans, one or more diploid nuclei that contain a complete complement of genes, functioning primarily in cellular reproduction. p. 521

micronutrient Any mineral required by an organism only in trace amounts. pp. 903, 1190

micropyle A small opening at one end of an ovule through which the pollen tube passes prior to fertilization. p. 886

microRNAs (miRNAs) Small RNAs that regulate gene expression by binding to specific mRNAs and decreasing their translation. p. 329

microscope Instrument of microscopy with different magnifications and resolutions of specimens. p. 29

microscopy Technique for producing visible images of objects that are too small to be seen by the human eye. p. 28

microspore A plant spore from which a male gametophyte develops; usually smaller than a megaspore. pp. 570, 583, 885

microtubule A cytoskeletal component formed by the polymerization of tubulin into rigid, hollow rods about 25 nm in diameter. p. 41

microtubule organizing centre (MTOC) An anchoring point near the centre of a eukaryotic cell from which most microtubules extend outward. p. 178

microvilli Fingerlike projections forming a brush border in epithelial cells that cover the villi. p. 601

midbrain The uppermost of the three segments of the brain stem, serving primarily as an intermediary

between the rest of the brain and the spinal cord. p. 1090

middle ear The air-filled cavity containing three small, interconnected bones: the malleus, incus, and stapes. p. 1105

migration The predictable seasonal movement of animals from the area where they are born to a distant and initially unfamiliar destination, returning to their birth site later. p. 1171

mimic The species in Batesian mimicry that resembles the model. p. 716

mimicry A form of defence in which one species evolves an appearance resembling that of another. p. 716

mineralocorticoid A steroid hormone secreted by the adrenal cortex that regulates the levels of Na and K in the blood and extracellular fluid. p. 1059

minimal medium A growth medium containing the minimal ingredients that enable a nonmutant organism, such as *E. coli,* to grow. p. 191

mismatch repair Repair system that removes mismatched bases from newly synthesized DNA strands. p. 282

missense mutation A base-pair substitution mutation in a protein-coding gene that results in a different amino acid in the encoded polypeptide than the normal one. p. 310

mitochondrial matrix The innermost compartment of the mitochondrion. p. 41

mitochondrion Membrane-bound organelle responsible for synthesis of most of the ATP in eukaryotic cells. p. 40

mitosis Nuclear division that produces daughter nuclei that are exact genetic copies of the parental nucleus. p. 170

mitotic spindle The complex of microtubules that orchestrate the separation of chromosomes during mitosis. p. 174

mobile elements Particular segments of DNA that can move from one place to another; they cut and paste DNA backbones using a type of recombination that does not require homology. p. 210

model The species in Batesian mimicry that is resembled by the mimic. p. 716

model organism An organism with characteristics that make it a particularly useful subject of research because it is likely to produce results widely applicable to other organisms. p. F-52

modern synthesis A unified theory of evolution developed in the middle of the twentieth century. p. 401

molarity (M) The number of moles of a substance dissolved in 1 L of solution. p. F-18

molars Posteriormost teeth of mammals, with a broad chewing surface for grinding food. p. 464

mole (mol) The atomic weight of an element or the molecular weight of a compound. p. F-18

molecular clock A technique for dating the time of divergence of two species or lineages, based on the number of molecular sequence differences between them. p. 471

molecular weight The weight of a molecule in grams, equal to the total mass number of its atoms. p. F-18

molecule A unit composed of atoms combined chemically in fixed numbers and ratios. p. F-12

monoclonal antibody An antibody that reacts only against the same segment (epitope) of a single antigen. p. 1283

monocot A plant belonging to the Monocotyledones, one of the two major classes of angiosperms; monocot embryos have a single seed leaf (cotyledon) and pollen grains with a single groove. pp. 587, 840

monocyte A type of leukocyte that enters damaged tissue from the bloodstream through the endothelial wall of the blood vessel. p. 1268

monoecious Having both "male" flowers (which possess only stamens) and "female" flowers (which possess only carpels). pp. 601, 885

monogamy A mating system in which one male and one female form a long-term association. p. 1175

monohybrid An F_1 heterozygote produced from a genetic cross that involves a single character. p. 221

monohybrid cross A genetic cross between two individuals that are each heterozygous for the same pair of alleles. p. 221

monomers Identical or nearly identical subunits that link together to form polymers during polymerization. p. 59

monophyletic taxon A group of organisms that includes a single ancestral species and all of its descendants. p. 459

monosaccharides The smallest carbohydrates, containing three to seven carbon atoms. p. 85

monotreme A lineage of mammals that lay eggs instead of bearing live young. p. 668

morphological species concept The concept that all individuals of a species share measurable traits that distinguish them from individuals of other species. p. 428

morphology The form or shape of an organism or part of an organism. p. 66

morula The first stage of animal development, a solid ball or layer of blastomeres. p. 1015

mosaic evolution The tendency of characteristics to undergo different rates of evolutionary change within the same lineage. p. 458

motif A highly specialized region in a protein produced by the three-dimensional arrangement of amino acid chains within and between domains. p. 323

motile Capable of self-propelled movement. p. 595

motor neuron An efferent neuron that carries signals to skeletal muscle. p. 1070

motor unit A block of muscle fibres that is controlled by branches of the axon of a single efferent neuron. p. 1141

moult-inhibiting hormone (MIH) A peptide neurohormone secreted by cells in the eyestalks (extensions of the brain leading to the eyes). p. 1063

mRNA splicing Process that removes introns from pre-mRNAs and joins exons together. p. 298

mucosa The lining of the gut that contains epithelial and glandular cells. p. 1198

Müllerian duct The bipotential primitive duct associated with the gonads that leads to a cloaca. p. 1029

Müllerian mimicry A form of defence in which two or more unpalatable species share a similar appearance. p. 716

multicellular organism Individual consisting of interdependent cells. p. 28

multigene family A family of homologous genes in a genome. The members of a multigene family have all evolved from one ancestral gene, and therefore have similar DNA sequences and produce proteins with similar structures and functions. p. 383

multiple alleles More than two different alleles of a gene. p. 232

multiple fruit A fruit that develops from several ovaries in multiple flowers; examples are pineapples and mulberries. p. 891

multiregional hypothesis A hypothesis proposing that after archaic humans migrated from Africa to many regions on Earth, their different populations evolved into modern humans simultaneously. p. 477

muscle fibre A bundle of elongated, cylindrical cells that make up skeletal muscle. pp. 954, 1134

muscle spindle A stretch receptor in muscle; a bundle of small, specialized muscle cells wrapped with the dendrites of afferent neurons and enclosed in connective tissue. p. 1103

muscle tissue Cells that have the ability to contract (shorten) forcibly. p. 954

muscle twitch A single, weak contraction of a muscle fibre. p. 1140

muscularis The muscular coat of a hollow organ or tubular structure. p. 1198

mutation A spontaneous and heritable change in DNA. pp. 282, 310, 417

mutualism A symbiotic interaction between species in which both partners benefit. pp. 541, 722, 1267

mycelium A network of branching hyphae that constitutes the body of a multicellular fungus. pp. 524, 542

mycobiont The fungal component of a lichen. p. 555

mycorrhiza A mutualistic symbiosis in which fungal hyphae associate intimately with plant roots. pp. 548, 910

myoblast An undifferentiated muscle cell. p. 1036

myofibril A cylindrical contractile element about 1 m in diameter that runs lengthwise inside the muscle fibre cell. p. 1135

myogenic heart A heart that maintains its contraction rhythm with no requirement for signals from the nervous system. p. 976

myoglobin An oxygen-storing protein closely related to hemoglobin. p. 1142

N-terminal end The end of a polypeptide chain with an —NH_3 group. p. 300

Na^+/K^+ pump Pump that pushes 3 Na^+ out of the cell and 2 K^+ into the cell in the same pumping cycle. Also referred to as the *sodium–potassium pump*. p. 110

nastic movement In plants, a reversible response to nondirectional stimuli, such as mechanical pressure or humidity. p. 937

natural killer (NK) cell A type of lymphocyte that destroys pathogen-infected cells. p. 1271

natural selection The evolutionary process by which alleles that increase the likelihood of survival and the reproductive output of the individuals that carry them become more common in subsequent generations. p. 398

natural theology A belief that knowledge of God may be acquired through the study of natural phenomena. p. 392

navigation A wayfinding mechanism in which an animal moves toward a specific destination, using both a compass and a "mental map" of where it is in relation to the destination. p. 1171

negative feedback The primary mechanism of homeostasis, in which a stimulus—a change in the external or internal environment—triggers a response that compensates for the environmental change. p. 959

negative pressure breathing Muscular contractions that expand the lungs, lowering the pressure of the air in the lungs and causing air to be pulled inward. p. 1223

nematocyst A coiled thread, encapsulated in a cnidocyte, that cnidarians fire at prey or predators, sometimes releasing a toxin through its tip. p. 603

nephron A specialized excretory tubule that contributes to osmoregulation and carries out excretion, found in all vertebrates. p. 1243

nerve A bundle of axons enclosed in connective tissue and all following the same pathway. p. 1069

nerve cord A bundle of nerves that extends from the central ganglia to the rest of the body, connected to smaller nerves. p. 1089

nerve net A simple nervous system that coordinates responses to stimuli but has no central control organ or brain. pp. 603, 1088

nervous tissue Tissue that contains neurons, which serve as lines of communication and control between body parts. p. 955

net primary productivity The chemical energy remaining in an ecosystem after a producer's cellular respiration is deducted. p. 750

neural crest A band of cells that arises early in the embryonic development of vertebrates near the region where the neural tube pinches off from the ectoderm; later, the cells migrate and develop into unique structures. p. 1021

neural plate Ectoderm thickened and flattened into a longitudinal band, induced by notochord cells. p. 1021

neural signalling The process by which an animal responds appropriately to a stimulus. p. 1069

neural tube A hollow tube in vertebrate embryos that develops into the brain, spinal cord, spinal nerves, and spinal column. p. 1090

neurogenic heart A heart that beats under the control of signals from the nervous system. p. 976

neuromuscular junction The junction between a nerve fibre and the muscle it supplies. p. 1136

neuron An electrically active cell of the nervous system responsible for controlling behaviour and body functions. pp. 955, 1047, 1069

neuronal circuit The connection between axon terminals of one neuron and the dendrites or cell body of a second neuron. p. 1070

neuropile The region of a ganglion in which branching axons and dendrites make interconnections. p. 1089

neurosecretory neuron A neuron that releases a neurohormone into the circulatory system when appropriately stimulated. p. 1047

neurotransmitter A chemical released by an axon terminal at a chemical synapse. p. 1071

neurulation The process in vertebrates by which organogenesis begins with development of the nervous system from ectoderm. p. 1021

neutral mutation hypothesis An evolutionary hypothesis that some variation at gene loci coding for enzymes and other soluble proteins is neither favoured nor eliminated by natural selection. p. 425

neutron Uncharged particle in the nucleus of an atom. p. F-9

neutrophil A type of phagocytic leukocyte that attaches to blood vessel walls in massive numbers when attracted to the infection site by chemokines. p. 1269

nitrification A metabolic process in which certain soil bacteria convert ammonia or ammonium ions into nitrites that are then converted by other bacteria to nitrates, a form usable by plants. pp. 488, 766, 911

nitrogen cycle A biogeochemical cycle that moves nitrogen between the huge atmospheric pool of gaseous molecular nitrogen and several much smaller pools of nitrogen-containing compounds in soils, marine and freshwater ecosystems, and living organisms. p. 762

nitrogen fixation A metabolic process in which certain bacteria and cyanobacteria convert molecular nitrogen into ammonia and ammonium ions, forms usable by plants. pp. 488, 762, 911

nitrogenous base A nitrogen-containing molecule with the properties of a base. p. 83

nociceptor A sensory receptor that detects tissue damage or noxious chemicals; their activity registers as pain. p. 1077

node The point on a stem where one or more leaves are attached. p. 847

node of Ranvier The gap between two Schwann cells, which exposes the axon membrane directly to extracellular fluids. p. 1070

nondisjunction The failure of homologous pairs to separate during the first meiotic division or of chromatids to separate during the second meiotic division. p. 252

nonhistone protein All of the proteins associated with DNA in a eukaryotic chromosome that are not histones. p. 285

nonsense codon *See* stop codon. p. 294

nonsense mutation A base-pair substitution mutation in a gene in which the base-pair change results in a change from a sense codon to a nonsense codon in the mRNA. The polypeptide translated from the mRNA is shorter than the normal polypeptide because of the mutation. p. 310

nonshivering thermogenesis The generation of heat by oxidative mechanisms in nonmuscle tissue throughout the body. p. 1258

nonvascular plant *See* bryophyte. p. 567

norepinephrine A nontropic amine hormone secreted by the adrenal medulla. p. 1058

notochord A flexible rodlike structure constructed of fluid-filled cells surrounded by tough connective tissue, which supports a chordate embryo from head to tail. p. 640

nucellus The inner part of an ovule, containing the embryo sac; equivalent to a megasporangium. p. 886

nuclear envelope In eukaryotes, membranes separating the nucleus from the cytoplasm. p. 33

nuclear localization signal A short amino acid sequence in a protein that directs the protein to the nucleus. p. 309

nuclear pore Opening in the membrane of the nuclear envelope through which large molecules, such as RNA and proteins, move between the nucleus and the cytoplasm. p. 35

nuclear pore complex A large, octagonally symmetrical, cylindrical structure that functions to exchange molecules between the nucleus and cytoplasm and prevents the transport of material not meant to cross the nuclear membrane. A nuclear pore—a channel through the complex—is the path for the exchange of molecules. p. 35

nucleoid The central region of a prokaryotic cell with no boundary membrane separating it from the cytoplasm, where DNA replication and RNA transcription occur. pp. 31, 169, 285, 482

nucleolus The nuclear site of rRNA transcription, processing, and ribosome assembly in eukaryotes. p. 35

nucleoplasm The liquid or semiliquid substance within the nucleus. p. 35

nucleosome The basic structural unit of chromatin in eukaryotes, consisting of DNA wrapped around a histone core. p. 283

nucleosome core particle An eight-protein particle formed by the combination of two molecules each of H2A, H2B, H3, and H4, around which DNA winds for almost two turns. p. 283

nucleosome remodelling complex A multiprotein structure that moves, or modifies, nucleosomes in such a way that exposes promoters to the transcription machinery. p. 321

nucleotide The monomer of nucleic acids consisting of a five-carbon sugar, a nitrogenous base, and a phosphate. p. F-37

nucleus The central region of eukaryotic cells, separated by membranes from the surrounding cytoplasm, where DNA replication and messenger RNA transcription occur. p. 31

null model A conceptual model that predicts what one would see if a particular factor had no effect. p. 415

nutrition The processes by which an organism takes in, digests, absorbs, and converts food into organic compounds. p. 1189

obligate aerobe A microorganism that must use oxygen for cellular respiration and requires oxygen in its surroundings to support growth. p. 487

obligate anaerobe A microorganism that cannot use oxygen and can grow only in the absence of oxygen. p. 487

ocellus (plural, **ocelli**) The simplest eye, which detects light but does not form an image. p. 1108

Okazaki fragments Relatively short segments of DNA synthesized on the lagging strand at a replication fork. p. 275

olfactory bulb A grey-matter centre that relays inputs from odour receptors to both the cerebral cortex and the limbic system. p. 1126

oligodendrocyte A type of glial cell that populates the central nervous system and is responsible for producing myelin. p. 1070

oligosaccharin A complex carbohydrate that in plants serves as a signalling molecule and as a defence against pathogens. p. 929

ommatidium (plural, **ommatidia**) A faceted visual unit of a compound eye. p. 1108

omnivore An animal that feeds at several trophic levels, consuming plants, animals, and other sources of organic matter. p. 1000

oncogene A gene that, when deregulated, is capable of inducing one or more characteristics of cancer cells. pp. 185, 333

one gene–one enzyme hypothesis Hypothesis showing the direct relationship between genes and enzymes. p. 292

one gene–one polypeptide hypothesis Restatement of the one gene–one enzyme hypothesis, taking into account that some proteins consist of more than one polypeptide and not all proteins are enzymes. p. 292

oocyte A developing gamete that becomes an ootid at the end of meiosis. p. 601

oogenesis The process of producing eggs. p. 992

oogonium (plural, **oogonia**) A cell that enters meiosis and gives rise to gametes, produced by mitotic divisions of the germ cells in females. p. 991

open circulatory system An arrangement of internal transport in some invertebrates in which the vascular fluid, hemolymph, is released into sinuses, bathing organs directly, and is not always retained within vessels. pp. 611, 965

open reading frames (ORFs) Segments of DNA sequence that contain start and stop codons. Such sequences are candidate genes. p. 369

operant conditioning A form of associative learning in which animals learn to link a voluntary activity, an operant, with its favourable consequences, the reinforcement. p. 1159

operator A DNA regulatory sequence that controls transcription of an operon. p. 315

operculum A lid or flap of the bone serving as the gill cover in some fishes. pp. 615, 649

operon A cluster of prokaryotic genes and the DNA sequences involved in their regulation. p. 315

opsin One of several different proteins that bond covalently with the light-absorbing pigment of rods and cones (retinal). p. 1111

optic chiasm Location just behind the eyes where the optic nerves converge before entering the base of the brain, withth a portion of each optic nerve crossing over to the opposite side. p. 1113

optimal foraging theory A set of mathematical models that predict the diet choices of animals as they encounter a range of potential food items. p. 712

oral hood Soft fleshy structure at the anterior end of a cephalochordate that frames the opening of the mouth. p. 641

orbital The region of space where the electron "lives" most of the time. p. F-10

order A Linnaean taxonomic category of organisms that ranks above a family and below a class. p. 428

organ Two or more different tissues integrated into a structure that carries out a specific function. pp. 836, 947

organ of Corti An organ within the cochlear duct that contains the sensory hair cells detecting sound vibrations transmitted to the inner ear. p. 1106

organ system The coordinated activities of two or more organs to carry out a major body function such as movement, digestion, or reproduction. p. 947

organelles The nucleus and other specialized internal structures and compartments of eukaryotic cells. p. 30

organic molecule Molecule based on carbon. p. 30

organismal ecology An ecological discipline in which researchers study the genetic, biochemical, physiological, morphological, and behavioural adaptations of organisms to their abiotic environments. p. 680

organogenesis The development of the major organ systems, giving rise to a free-living individual with the body organization characteristic of its species. p. 1015

origin of replication (ori) A specific region at which replication of a bacterial chromosome commences. p. 169

osculum (plural, **oscula**) An opening in a sponge through which water is expelled. p. 601

osmoconformer An animal in which the osmolarity of the cellular and extracellular solutions matches the osmolarity of the environment. p. 1237

osmolality A measure of the osmotic concentration of a solution. It is measured in osmoles (the number of solute molecules and ions) per kilogram of solvent. p. 1237

osmolarity The total solute concentration of a solution, measured in osmoles—the number of solute molecules and ions (in moles)—per litre of solution. p. 1237

osmoregulator An animal that uses control mechanisms to keep the osmolarity of cellular and extracellular fluids the same but at levels that may differ from the osmolarity of the surroundings. p. 1237

osmosis The passive transport of water across a selectively permeable membrane in response to solute concentration gradients, a pressure gradient, or both. pp. 108, 865

osteoblast A cell that produces the collagen and mineral of bone. p. 954

osteoclast A cell that removes bone minerals and recycles them through the bloodstream. p. 954

osteocyte A mature bone cell. p. 954

osteon The structural unit of bone, consisting of a minute central canal surrounded by osteocytes embedded in concentric layers of mineral matter. p. 954

ostracoderm One of an assortment of extinct, jawless fishes that were covered with bony armour. p. 645

otolith One of many small crystals of calcium carbonate embedded in the otolithic membrane of the hair cells. p. 1102

outer boundary membrane A smooth membrane that surrounds a chloroplast, enclosing the stroma. p. 46

outer ear The external structure of the ear, consisting of the pinna and meatus. p. 1105

outer membrane In Gram-negative bacteria, an additional boundary membrane that covers the peptidoglycan layer of the cell wall. p. 485

outer mitochondrial membrane The smooth membrane covering the outside of a mitochondrion. p. 40

outgroup comparison A technique used to identify ancestral and derived characters by comparing the group under study with more distantly related species that are not otherwise included in the analysis. p. 458

oval window An opening in the bony wall that separates the middle ear from the inner ear. p. 1106

ovarian cycle The cyclic events in the ovary leading to ovulation. p. 999

ovary In animals, the female gonad, which produces female gametes and reproductive hormones. In flowering plants, the enlarged base of a carpel in which one or more ovules develop into seeds. pp. 885, 991, 1060

overnutrition The condition caused by excessive intake of specific nutrients. p. 1190

oviduct The tube through which the egg moves from the ovary to the outside of the body. p. 993

oviparous Referring to animals that lay eggs containing the nutrients needed for development of the embryo outside the mother's body. p. 996

ovoviviparous Referring to animals in which fertilized eggs are retained within the body and the embryo develops using nutrients provided by the egg; eggs hatch inside the mother. p. 996

ovulation The process in which oocytes are released into the oviducts as immature eggs. p. 999

ovule In plants, the structure in a carpel in which a female gametophyte develops and fertilization takes place. pp. 582, 885

ovum (plural, **ova**) A female sex cell, or egg. p. 992

oxidation The removal of electrons from a substance. p. 62

oxidative phosphorylation Synthesis of ATP in which ATP synthase uses an H^+ gradient built by the electron transfer system as the energy source to make the ATP. p. 132

oxidized Refers to a substance from which the electrons are removed during oxidation. p. 122

oxytocin A hormone that stimulates the ejection of milk from the mammary glands of a nursing mother. p. 1056

P generation The parental individuals used in an initial cross. p. 220

P site The site in the ribosome where the tRNA carrying the growing polypeptide chain is bound. p. 302

pacemaker cell A specialized cardiac muscle cell in the upper wall of the right atrium that sets the rate of contraction in the heart. p. 976

pairing Process in meiosis in which homologous chromosomes come together and pair. Also referred to as *synapsis*. p. 202

pair-rule genes In *Drosophila* embryonic development, the set of segmentation regulatory genes activated by gap genes that divide the embryo into units of two segments each. p. 1038

pancreas A mixed gland composed of an exocrine portion that secretes digestive enzymes into the small intestine and an endocrine portion, the islets of Langerhans, that secretes insulin and glucagon. p. 1060

parapatric speciation Speciation between populations with adjacent geographic distributions. p. 436

paraphyletic taxon A group of organisms that includes an ancestral species and some, but not all, of its descendants. p. 459

parapodium (plural, **parapodia**) A fleshy lateral extension of the body wall of aquatic annelids, used for locomotion and gas exchange. p. 618

parasite An organism that feeds on the tissues of or otherwise exploits its host. p. 516

parasitism A symbiotic interaction in which one species, the parasite, uses another, the host, in a way that is harmful to the host. pp. 541, 723

parasitoid An insect species in which a female lays eggs in the larva or pupa of another insect species, and her young consume the tissues of the living host. p. 1290

parasympathetic division The division of the autonomic nervous system that predominates during quiet, low-stress situations, such as while relaxing. p. 1093

parathyroid gland One of a pair of glands that produce parathyroid hormone (PTH) (found only in tetrapod vertebrates). p. 1057

parathyroid hormone (PTH) The hormone secreted by the parathyroid glands in response to a fall in blood Ca^{2+} levels. p. 1057

parental Phenotypes identical to the original parental individuals. p. 170

parental investment The time and energy devoted to the production and rearing of offspring. p. 1012

parthenogenesis A mode of asexual reproduction in which animals produce offspring by the growth and development of an egg without fertilization. pp. 610, 989

partial diploid A condition in which part of the genome of a haploid organism is diploid. Recipients in bacterial conjugation between an Hfr and an F cell become partial diploids for part of the Hfr bacterial chromosome. p. 195

partial pressure The individual pressure exerted by each gas within a mixture of gases. p. 1218

parturition The process of giving birth. p. 1028

passive immunity The acquisition of antibodies as a result of direct transfer from another person. p. 1281

passive parental care The amount of energy invested in offspring—in the form of the energy stored in eggs or seeds or energy transferred to developing young through a placenta—before they are born. p. 687

passive transport The transport of substances across cell membranes without expenditure of energy, as in diffusion. pp. 105, 865

paternal chromosome The chromosome derived from the male parent of an organism. p. 201

pathogenesis-related (PR) protein A hydrolytic enzyme that breaks down components of a pathogen's cell wall. p. 930

pattern formation The arrangement of organs and body structures in their proper three-dimensional relationships. p. 1036

pectoral girdle A bony or cartilaginous structure in vertebrates that supports and is attached to the forelimbs. p. 641

pedicellariae Small pincers at the base of short spines in starfishes and sea urchins. p. 638

pedigree Chart that shows all parents and offspring for as many generations as possible, the sex of individuals in the different generations, and the presence or absence of a trait of interest. p. 249

pedipalps The second pair of appendages in the head of chelicerates. p. 622

pellicle A layer of supportive protein fibres located inside the cell, just under the plasma membrane, providing strength and flexibility instead of a cell wall. p. 517

pelvic girdle A bony or cartilaginous structure in vertebrates that supports and is attached to the hindlimbs. p. 641

pepsin An enzyme made in the stomach that breaks down proteins. p. 93

pepsinogen The inactive precursor molecule for pepsin. p. 308

peptide bond A link formed by a dehydration synthesis reaction between the —NH2 group of one amino acid and the —COOH group of a second. p. 302

peptidoglycan A polymeric substance formed from a polysaccharide backbone tied together by short polypeptides, which is the primary structural molecule of bacterial cell walls. p. 484

peptidyl transferase An enzyme that catalyzes the reaction in which an amino acid is cleaved from the tRNA in the P site of the ribosome and forms a peptide bond with the amino acid on the tRNA in the A site of the ribosome. p. 305

peptidyl–tRNA A tRNA linked to a growing polypeptide chain containing two or more amino acids. p. 304

per capita growth rate The difference between the per capita birth rate and the per capita death rate of a population. p. 690

perception The conscious awareness of our external and internal environments derived from the processing of sensory input. p. 1099

perennial A plant in which vegetative growth and reproduction continue year after year. p. 840

perfusion The flow of blood or other body fluids on the internal side of the respiratory surface. p. 1220

pericarp The fruit wall. p. 891

pericycle A tissue of plant roots, located between the endodermis and the phloem, which gives rise to lateral roots. p. 854

periderm The outermost portion of bark; consists of cork, cork cambium, and secondary cortex. p. 856

peripheral membrane protein Protein held to membrane surfaces by noncovalent bonds formed with the polar parts of integral membrane proteins or membrane lipids. p. 105

peripheral nervous system (PNS) All nerve roots and nerves (motor and sensory) that supply the muscles of the body and transmit information about sensation (including pain) to the central nervous system. p. 1055

peristalsis The rippling motion of muscles in the intestine or other tubular organs characterized by the alternate contraction and relaxation of the muscles that propel the contents onward. p. 1198

peritoneum The thin tissue derived from mesoderm that lines the abdominal wall and covers most of the organs in the abdomen. p. 596

peritubular capillary A capillary of the network surrounding the glomerulus. p. 1246

permafrost Perpetually frozen ground below the topsoil. p. 263

peroxisome Microbody that produces hydrogen peroxide as a by-product. p. 308

petal Part of the corolla of a flower, often brightly coloured. p. 885

petiole The stalk by which a leaf is attached to a stem. p. 850

phage *See* bacteriophage. pp. 266, 502

phagocytosis Process in which some types of cells engulf bacteria or other cellular debris to break them down. pp. 39, 114, 1268

pharynx The throat. In some invertebrates, a protrusible tube used to bring food into the mouth for passage to the gastrovascular cavity; in mammals, the common pathway for air entering the larynx and food entering the esophagus. pp. 609, 1225

phenotype The outward appearance of an organism. p. 221

phenotypic variation Differences in appearance or function between individual organisms. p. 410

pheromone A distinctive volatile chemical released in minute amounts to influence the behaviour of members of the same species. p. 405

phloem The food-conducting tissue of a vascular plant. pp. 567, 844

phloem sap The solution of water and organic compounds that flows rapidly through the sieve tubes of flowering plants. p. 877

phosphate group Group consisting of a central phosphorus atom held in four linkages: two that bind —OH groups to the central phosphorus atom, a third that binds an oxygen atom to the central phosphorus atom, and a fourth that links the phosphate group to an oxygen atom. p. 74

phosphodiester bond The linkage of nucleotides in polynucleotide chains by a bridging phosphate group between the 5 carbon of one sugar and the 3 carbon of the next sugar in line. p. 268

phospholipid A phosphate-containing lipid. p. 99

phosphorus cycle A biogeochemcial cycle in which weathering and erosion carry phosphate ions from rocks to soil and into streams and rivers, which eventually transport them to the ocean, where they are slowly incorporated into rocks. p. 768

photoautotroph A photosynthetic organism that uses light as its energy source and carbon dioxide as its carbon source. p. 145

photobiont The photosynthetic component of a lichen. p. 555

photoheterotroph An organism that uses light as the ultimate energy source but obtains carbon in organic form rather than as carbon dioxide. p. 487

photons Discrete particles or packets of energy. p. 5

photoperiodism The response of plants to changes in the relative lengths of light and dark periods in their environment during each 24 hour period. p. 938

photophosphorylation The synthesis of ATP coupled to the transfer of electrons energized by photons of light. p. 154

photopigment Light-absorbing pigment. p. 1108

photopsin One of three photopigments in which retinal is combined with different opsins. p. 1113

photoreceptor A sensory receptor that detects the energy of light. p. 1077

photorespiration A process that metabolizes a by-product of photosynthesis. p. 158

photosynthesis The conversion of light energy to chemical energy in the form of sugar and other organic molecules. p. 145

photosystem A large complex into which the light-absorbing pigments for photosynthesis are organized with proteins and other molecules. p. 147

photosystem I In photosynthesis, a protein complex in the thylakoid membrane that uses energy absorbed from sunlight to synthesize NADPH. p. 151

photosystem II In photosynthesis, a protein complex in the thylakoid membrane that uses energy absorbed from sunlight to synthesize ATP. p. 151

phototroph An organism that obtains energy from light. p. 487

phototropism The tendency of a plant shoot to bend toward a source of light. p. 920

PhyloCode A formal set of rules governing phylogenetic nomenclature. p. 461

phylogenetic species concept A concept that seeks to delineate species as the smallest aggregate population that can be united by shared derived characters. p. 429

phylogenetic tree A branching diagram depicting the evolutionary relationships of groups of organisms. p. 455

phylogeny The evolutionary history of a group of organisms. p. 455

phylum (plural, phyla) A major Linnaean division of a kingdom, ranking above a class. p. 428

physiology The study of the functions of organisms—the physicochemical processes of organisms. pp. 946, 1296

phytoalexin A biochemical that functions as an antibiotic in plants. p. 930

phytochrome A blue-green pigmented plant chromoprotein involved in the regulation of light-dependent growth processes. p. 938

phytoplankton Microscopic, free-flowing aquatic plants and protists. p. 516

pigment A molecule that can absorb photons of light. p. 5

piloting A wayfinding mechanism in which animals use familiar landmarks to guide their journey. p. 1171

pilus (plural, **pili**) A hair or hairlike appendage on the surface of a prokaryote. pp. 33, 486

pinacoderm In sponges, an unstratified outer layer of cells. p. 601

pineal gland A light-sensitive, melatonin-secreting gland that regulates some biological rhythms. p. 1061

pinna The external structure of the outer ear, which concentrates and focuses sound waves. p. 1105

pinocytosis *See* bulk-phase endocytosis. p. 112

pith The soft, spongelike, central cylinder of the stems of most flowering plants, composed mainly of parenchyma. p. 849

pituitary A gland consisting mostly of two fused lobes suspended just below the hypothalamus by a slender stalk of tissue that contains both neurons and blood vessels; it interacts with the hypothalamus to control many physiological functions, including the activity of some other glands. p. 1053

placenta A specialized temporary organ that connects the embryo and fetus with the uterus in mammals, mediating the delivery of oxygen and nutrients. Analagous structures occur in other animals. pp. 668, 996

plasma The clear, yellowish fluid portion of the blood in which cells are suspended. Plasma consists of water, glucose and other sugars, amino acids, plasma proteins, dissolved gases, ions, lipids, vitamins, hormones and other signal molecules, and metabolic wastes. pp. 958, 970

plasma cell A large antibody-producing cell that develops from B cells. p. 1278

plasma membrane The outer limit of the cytoplasm responsible for the regulation of substances moving into and out of cells. pp. 29, 102

plasmid A DNA molecule in the cytoplasm of certain prokaryotes, which often contains genes with functions that supplement those in the nucleoid and can replicate independently of the nucleoid DNA and be passed along during cell division. pp. 286, 484

plasmodesma (plural, **plasmodesmata**) A minute channel that perforates a cell wall and contains extensions of the cytoplasm that directly connect adjacent plant cells. p. 837

plasmodial slime mould A slime mould of the class Myxomycetes. p. 529

plasmodium The composite mass of plasmodial slime moulds consisting of individual nuclei suspended in a common cytoplasm surrounded by a single plasma membrane. p. 529

plasmogamy The sexual stage of fungi during which the cytoplasms of two genetically different partners fuse. p. 543

plasmolysis Condition due to outward osmotic movement of water, in which plant cells shrink so much that they retract from their walls. p. 867

plastids A family of plant organelles. p. 45

plastron The ventral part of the shell of a turtle. p. 659

platelet An oval or rounded cell fragment enclosed in its own plasma membrane, which is found in the blood; they are produced in red bone marrow by the division of stem cells and contain enzymes and other factors that take part in blood clotting. p. 973

pleiotropy Condition in which single genes affect more than one character of an organism. p. 236

pleura The double layer of epithelial tissue covering the lungs. p. 1225

ploidy The number of chromosome sets of a cell or species. p. 171

plumule The rudimentary terminal bud of a plant embryo located at the end of the hypocotyl, consisting of the epicotyl and a cluster of tiny foliage leaves. p. 893

poikilohydric Having little control over internal water content. p. 565

polar body A nonfunctional cell produced in oogenesis. p. 991

polar covalent bond Bond in which electrons are shared unequally. p. F-13

polar nucleus In the embryo sac of a flowering plant, one of two nuclei that migrate into the centre of the sac, become housed in a central cell, and eventually give rise to endosperm. p. 888

polar transport Unidirectional movement of a substance from one end of a cell (or other structure) to the other. p. 922

polarity The unequal distribution of yolk and other components in a mature egg. p. 1015

pollen grain The male gametophyte of a seed plant. pp. 582, 886

pollen sac The microsporangium of a seed plant, in which pollen develops. p. 589

pollen tube A tube that grows from a germinating pollen grain through the tissues of a carpel and carries the sperm cells to the ovary. p. 582

pollination The transfer of pollen to a flower's reproductive parts by air currents or on the bodies of animal pollinators. p. 582

poly(A) tail The string of A nucleotides added posttranscriptionally to the 3 end of a pre-mRNA molecule and retained in the mRNA produced from it that enables the mRNA to be translated efficiently and protects it from attack by RNA-digesting enzymes in the cytoplasm. p. 298

polyandry A polygamous mating system in which one female mates with multiple males. p. 1175

polygamy A mating system in which either males or females may have many mating partners. p. 1175

polygenic inheritance Inheritance in which several to many different genes contribute to the same character. p. 235

polygyny A polygamous mating system in which one male mates with many females. p. 1175

polyhedral virus A virus in which the coat proteins form triangular units that fit together like the parts of a geodesic sphere. p. 502

polymerase chain reaction (pCR) Process that amplifies a specific DNA sequence from a DNA mixture to an extremely large number of copies. p. 345

polymorphic development The production during development of one or more morphologically distinct forms. p. 595

polymorphism The existence of discrete variants of a character among individuals in a population. p. 411

polyp The tentacled, usually sessile stage in the life cycle of a coelenterate. p. 603

polypeptide The chain of amino acids formed by sequential peptide bonds. p. F-30

polyphyletic taxon A group of organisms that belong to different evolutionary lineages and do not share a recent common ancestor. p. 459

polyploid An individual with one or more extra copies of the entire haploid complement of chromosomes. p. 253

polyploidy The condition of having one or more extra copies of the entire haploid complement of chromosomes. p. 439

polysaccharide Chain with more than 10 linked monosaccharide subunits. p. 32

polysome The entire structure of an mRNA molecule and the multiple associated ribosomes that are translating it simultaneously. p. 306

population All individuals of a single species that live together in the same place and time. p. 410

population bottleneck An evolutionary event that occurs when a stressful factor reduces population size greatly and eliminates some alleles from a population. p. 418

population density The number of individuals per unit area or per unit volume of habitat. p. 680

population ecology The ecological discipline that focuses on how a population's size and other characteristics change in space and time. p. 680

population genetics The branch of science that studies the prevalence and variation in genes among populations of individuals. p. 401

population size The number of individuals in a population at a specified time. p. 680

positive feedback A mechanism that intensifies or adds to a change in internal or external environmental condition. p. 961

positive pressure breathing A gulping or swallowing motion that forces air into the lungs. p. 1223

posterior Indicating the tail end of an animal. p. 596

posterior pituitary The neural portion of the pituitary, which stores and releases two hormones made by the hypothalamus, antidiuretic hormone and oxytocin. p. 1053

postsynaptic cell The neuron or the surface of an effector after a synapse that receives the signal from the presynaptic cell. p. 1071

postsynaptic membrane The plasma membrane of the postsynaptic cell. p. 1082

posttranslational import A process for sorting proteins that are translated on cytosolic ribosomes and then moved into organelles. p. 309

postzygotic isolating mechanism A reproductive isolating mechanism that acts after zygote formation. p. 431

potential energy Stored energy. p. 75

precocial Born with fur and quickly mobile. p. 668

precursor mRNA (pre-mRNA) The primary transcript of a eukaryotic protein-coding gene, which is processed to form messenger RNA. p. 297

predation The interaction between predatory animals and the animal prey they consume. p. 712

prediction A statement about what the researcher expects to happen to one variable if another variable changes. p. F-3

pregnancy The period of mammalian development in which the embryo develops in the uterus of the mother. p. 1025

premolars Teeth located in pairs on each side of the upper and lower jaws of mammals, positioned behind the canines and in front of the molars. p. 668

prenatal diagnosis Techniques in which cells derived from a developing embryo or its surrounding tissues or fluids are tested for the presence of mutant alleles or chromosomal alterations. p. 258

prepuce Foreskin; a loose fold of skin that covers the glans of the penis. p. 1004

pressure flow mechanism In vascular plants, pressure that builds up at the source end of a sieve tube system and pushes solutes by bulk flow toward a sink, where they are removed. p. 878

presynaptic cell The neuron with an axon terminal on one side of the synapse that transmits the signal across the synapse to the dendrite or cell body of the postsynaptic cell. p. 1071

presynaptic membrane The plasma membrane of the axon terminal of a presynaptic cell, which releases neurotransmitter molecules into the synapse in response to the arrival of an action potential. p. 1082

prezygotic isolating mechanism A reproductive isolating mechanism that acts prior to the production of a zygote, or fertilized egg. p. 431

primary active transport Transport in which the same protein that transports a substance also hydrolyzes ATP to power the transport directly. p. 109

primary cell layers The ectoderm, mesoderm, and endoderm layers that form the embryonic tissues. p. 1015

primary cell wall The initial cell wall laid down by a plant cell. p. 837

primary consumer A herbivore, a member of the second trophic level. p. 1190

primary endosymbiosis In the model for the origin of plastids in eukaryotes, the first event in which a eukaryotic cell engulfed a photosynthetic cyanobacterium. p. 535

primary growth The growth of plant tissues derived from apical meristems. *Compare* secondary growth. p. 839

primary immune response The response of the immune system to the first challenge by an antigen. p. 1281

primary meristem Root and shoot apical meristems, from which a plant's primary tissues develop. *Compare* lateral meristem. p. 848

primary motor area The area of the cerebral cortex that runs in a band just in front of the primary somatosensory area and is responsible for voluntary movement. p. 1127

primary plant body The portion of a plant that is made up of primary tissues. p. 839

primary producer An autotroph, usually a photosynthetic organism, a member of the first trophic level. p. 145

primary somatosensory area The area of the cerebral cortex that runs in a band across the parietal lobes of the brain and registers information on touch, pain, temperature, and pressure. p. 1127

primary structure The sequence of amino acids in a protein. pp. 104, F-31

primary succession Predictable change in species composition of an ecological community that develops on bare ground. p. 735

primary tissue A plant tissue that develops from an apical meristem. p. 839

primase An enzyme that assembles the primer for a new DNA strand during DNA replication. p. 275

primer A short nucleotide chain made of RNA that is laid down as the first series of nucleotides in a new DNA strand or made of DNA for use in the polymerase chain reaction (pCR). p. 275

primitive groove In the development of birds, the sunken midline of the primitive streak that acts as a conduit for migrating cells to move into the blastocoel. p. 1020

primitive streak In the development of birds, the thickened region of the embryo produced by cells of the epiblast streaming toward the midline of the blastodisc. p. 1019

principle of independent assortment Mendel's principle that the alleles of the genes that govern two characters segregate independently during formation of gametes. p. 226

principle of monophyly A guiding principle of systematic biology that defines monophyletic taxa, each of which contains a single ancestral species and all of its descendants. p. 459

principle of segregation Mendel's principle that the pairs of alleles that control a character segregate as gametes are formed, with half the gametes carrying one allele and the other half carrying the other allele. p. 221

prion An infectious agent that contains only protein and does not include a nucleic acid molecule. p. 509

probability The possibility that an outcome will occur if it is a matter of chance. p. 222

procambium The primary meristem of a plant that develops into primary vascular tissue. p. 849

product An atom or molecule leaving a chemical reaction. p. F-14

product rule Mathematical rule in which the final probability is found by multiplying individual probabilities. p. 223

production efficiency The ratio of the energy content of new tissue produced to the energy assimilated from food. p. 753

progesterone A female sex hormone that stimulates growth of the uterine lining and inhibits contractions of the uterus. p. 1060

progestin A class of sex hormones synthesized by the gonads of vertebrates and active predominantly in females. p. 1059

proglottid One of the segmentlike repeating units that constitute the body of a tapeworm. p. 609

prokaryote Organism in which the DNA is suspended in the cell interior without separation from other cellular components by a discrete membrane. p. 28

prokaryotic chromosome A single, typically circular DNA molecule. p. 32

prolactin (pRL) A peptide hormone secreted by the anterior pituitary that stimulates breast development and milk secretion in mammals. pp. 1029, 1055

prometaphase A transition period between prophase and metaphase during which the microtubules of the mitotic spindle attach to the kinetochores and the chromosomes shuffle until they align in the centre of the cell. p. 174

promiscuity A mating system in which individuals do not form close pair bonds, and both males and females mate with multiple partners. p. 1175

promoter The site to which RNA polymerase binds for initiating transcription of a gene. p. 296

promoter proximal elements Regulatory sequence within the promoter proximal region, a region upstream of a eukaryotic protein-coding gene. Regulatory proteins bind to promoter proximal elements. p. 322

promoter proximal region Upstream of a eukaryotic gene, a region containing regulatory sequences for transcription called promoter proximal elements. p. 322

proofreading mechanism Mechanism of DNA polymerase to back up and remove mispaired nucleotides from a newly synthesized DNA strand. p. 280

propagation (conduction) In animal nervous systems, the concept that the action potential does not need further trigger events to keep going. p. 1079

prophage A viral genome inserted in the host cell DNA. pp. 197, 505

prophase The beginning phase of mitosis during which the duplicated chromosomes within the nucleus condense from a greatly extended state into compact, rodlike structures. p. 173

proprioceptor A mechanoreceptor that detects stimuli used in the central nervous system to maintain body balance and equilibrium and to monitor the position of the head and limbs. p. 1101

prostaglandin One of a group of local regulators derived from fatty acids that are involved in paracrine and autocrine regulation. p. 1002

prostate gland An accessory sex gland in males that adds a thin, milky fluid to the semen and adjusts the pH of the semen to the level of acidity best tolerated by sperm. p. 1003

protein Molecules that carry out most of the activities of life, including the synthesis of all other biological molecules. A protein consists of one or more polypeptides depending on the protein. p. 2

protein kinase Enzyme that transfers a phosphate group from ATP to one or more sites on particular proteins. p. 116

protein phosphatase Enzyme that removes phosphate groups from target proteins. p. 116

proteome The complete set of proteins that can be expressed by the genome of an organism. p. 376

proteomics The study of the proteome. p. 376

protist Organism currently classified in the kingdom Protista. p. 513

protobiont The term given to a group of abiotically produced organic molecules that are surrounded by a membrane or membranelike structure. p. 60

protoderm The primary meristem that will produce stem epidermis. p. 848

proton Positively charged particle in the nucleus of an atom. p. F-9

proton-motive force Stored energy that contributes to ATP synthesis and to the cotransport of substances to and from mitochondria. p. 132

proton pump Pump that moves hydrogen ions across membranes and pushes hydrogen ions across the plasma membrane from the cytoplasm to the cell exterior. Also referred to as H^+ *pump*. p. 7

protonema The structure that arises when a liverwort or moss spore germinates and eventually gives rise to a mature gametophyte. p. 574

protonephridium The simplest form of invertebrate excretory tubule. p. 1241

proto-oncogene A gene that encodes various kinds of proteins that stimulate cell division. Mutated proto-oncogenes contribute to the development of cancer. p. 333

protostome A division of the Bilateria in which the blastopore forms the mouth during development of the embryo and the anus appears later. p. 596

prototrophs Strains that are able to synthesize the necessary amino acids. p. 191

provirus The inserted viral DNA. p. 213

proximal convoluted tubule The tubule between the Bowman's capsule and the loop of Henle in the nephron of the kidney, which carries and processes the filtrate. p. 1246

pseudocoelom A fluid- or organ-filled body cavity between the gut (a derivative of endoderm) and the muscles of the body wall (a derivative of mesoderm). p. 596

pseudocoelomate A body plan of bilaterally symmetrical animals with a body cavity that lacks a complete lining derived from mesoderm. p. 596

pseudogene A gene that is very similar to a functional gene at the DNA sequence level but that has one or more inactivating mutations that prevent it from producing a functional gene product. p. 368

pseudopod (plural, **pseudopodia**) A temporary cytoplasmic extension of a cell. p. 517

psychrophile An archaean or bacterium that grows optimally at temperatures in the range of -10 to $-20°C$. p. 497

Pterophyta The plant phylum of ferns and their close relatives. p. 577

pulmonary circuit The circuit of the cardiovascular system that supplies the lungs. p. 968

pulvinus (plural, **pulvini**) A jointlike, thickened pad of tissue at the base of a leaf or petiole; flexes when the leaf makes nastic movements. p. 937

Punnett square Method for determining the genotypes and phenotypes of offspring and their expected proportions. p. 224

pupa The nonfeeding stage between the larva and adult in the complete metamorphosis of some insects, during which the larval tissues are completely reorganized within a protective cocoon or hardened case. p. 629

pupil The dark centre in the middle of the iris through which light passes to the back of the eye. p. 1108

purine A type of nitrogenous base with two carbon–nitrogen rings. p. 58

pyramid of biomass A diagram that illustrates differences in standing crop biomass in a series of trophic levels. p. 754

pyramid of energy A diagram that illustrates the amount of energy that flows through a series of trophic levels. p. 754

pyramid of numbers A diagram that illustrates the number of individual organisms present in a series of trophic levels. p. 755

pyrimidine A type of nitrogenous base with one carbon–nitrogen ring. p. 58

qualitative variation Variation that exists in two or more discrete states, with intermediate forms often being absent. p. 411

quantitative trait A character that displays a continuous distribution of the phenotype involved, typically resulting from several to many contributing genes. p. 235

quantitative variation Variation that is measured on a continuum (such as height in human beings) rather than in discrete units or categories. p. 410

quorum sensing The use of signalling molecules by prokaryotes to communicate and to coordinate their behaviour. p. 491

R gene A resistance gene in a plant; dominant R alleles confer enhanced resistance to plant pathogens. p. 932

r-selected species A short-lived species adapted to function well in a rapidly changing environment. p. 697

radial cleavage A cleavage pattern in deuterostomes in which newly formed cells lie directly above and below other cells of the embryo. p. 596

radial symmetry A body plan of organisms in which structures are arranged regularly around a central axis, like spokes radiating out from the centre of a wheel. p. 602

radiation The transfer of heat energy as electromagnetic radiation. p. 1252

radicle The rudimentary root of a plant embryo. p. 892

radioactivity The giving off of particles of matter and energy by decaying nuclei. p. 266

radioisotope An unstable, radioactive isotope. p. 267

radiometric dating A dating method that uses measurements of certain radioactive isotopes to calculate the absolute ages in years of rocks and minerals. p. 55

radula The tooth-lined "tongue" of molluscs that scrapes food into small particles or drills through the shells of prey. p. 611

random dispersion A pattern of distribution in which the individuals in a population are distributed unpredictably in their habitat. p. 682

rapid eye movement (REM) sleep The period during deep sleep when the delta wave pattern is replaced by rapid, irregular beta waves characteristic of the waking state. The person's heartbeat and breathing rate increase, the limbs twitch, and the eyes move rapidly behind the closed eyelids. p. 1130

reabsorption The process in which some molecules (e.g, glucose and amino acids) and ions are transported by the transport epithelium back into the body fluid (animals with open circulatory systems) or into the blood in capillaries surrounding the tubules (animals with closed circulatory systems) as the filtered solution moves through the excretory tubule. p. 1050

reactants The atoms or molecules entering a chemical reaction. p. F-14

reaction centre Part of photosystems I and II in chloroplasts of plants. In the light-dependent reactions of photosynthesis, the reaction centre receives light energy absorbed by the antenna complex in the same photosystem. p. 151

reading frame A particular grouping of triplet bases read by transfer RNA during translation. pp. 294, 304

realized niche The range of conditions and resources that a population actually uses in nature. p. 721

receptacle The expanded tip of a flower stalk that bears floral organs. p. 885

reception In signal transduction, the binding of a signal molecule with a specific receptor in a target cell. p. 1069

receptor-mediated endocytosis The selective uptake of macromolecules that bind to cell surface receptors concentrated in clathrin-coated pits. p. 112

receptor protein Protein that recognizes and binds molecules from other cells that act as chemical signals. p. 49

recessive An allele that is masked by a dominant allele. p. 221

reciprocal altruism Form of altruistic behaviour in which individuals help nonrelatives if they are likely to return the favour in the future. p. 1181

recognition protein Protein in the plasma membrane that identifies a cell as part of the same individual or as foreign. p. 504

recombinant Phenotype with a different combination of traits from those of the original parents. p. 195

recombinant DNA DNA from two or more different sources joined together. p. 340

recombination frequency In the construction of linkage maps of diploid eukaryotic organisms, the percentage of testcross progeny that are recombinants. p. 203

rectum The final segment of the large intestine. p. 1206

red tide A growth in dinoflagellate populations that causes red, orange, or brown discoloration of coastal ocean waters. p. 521

redox reaction Coupled oxidation–reduction reaction in which electrons are removed from a donor molecule and simultaneously added to an acceptor molecule. p. 122

reduced Refers to a substance that receives electrons during reduction. p. 122

reduction The addition of electrons to a substance. p. 122

reflex A programmed movement that takes place without conscious effort, such as the sudden withdrawal of a hand from a hot surface. p. 1123

refractory period A period that begins at the peak of an action potential and lasts a few milliseconds, during which the threshold required for generation of an action potential is much higher than normal. p. 1075

regulators Animals that maintain factors of the internal environment in a relatively constant state. p. 958

regulatory protein DNA-binding protein that binds to a regulatory sequence and affects the expression of an associated gene or genes. p. 315

reinforcement 1. The enhancement of reproductive isolation that had begun to develop while populations were geographically separated; 2. Encouraging or establishing a pattern of behaviour using a positive or negative stimulus. pp. 436, 1159

relative abundance The relative commonness of populations within a community. p. 414

relative fitness The number of surviving offspring that an individual produces compared with the number left by others in the population. p. 420

release factor A protein that recognizes stop codons in the A site of a ribosome translating an mRNA and terminates translation. Also referred to as the *termination factor*. p. 306

releasing hormone (RH) A peptide neurohormone that controls the secretion of hormones from the anterior pituitary. p. 1053

renal artery An artery that carries bodily fluids into the kidney. p. 1245

renal cortex The outer region of the mammalian kidney that surrounds the renal medulla. p. 1245

renal medulla The inner region of the mammalian kidney. p. 1245

renal pelvis The central cavity in the kidney where urine drains from collecting ducts. p. 1245

renal vein The vein that routes filtered blood away from the kidney. p. 1245

renaturation The reformation of a denatured protein into its folded, functional state. p. F-36

replica plating Technique for identifying and counting genetic recombinants in conjugation, transformation, or transduction experiments in which the colony pattern on a plate containing solid growth medium is pressed onto sterile velveteen and transferred to other plates containing different combinations of nutrients. p. 191

replicates Multiple subjects that receive either the same experimental treatment or the same control treatment. p. F-3

replication bubble A structure resulting from bidirectional DNA replication from a given origin. Two forks, travelling in opposite directions, create a bubble. p. 276

replication fork The region of DNA synthesis where the parental strands separate and two new daughter strands elongate. p. 275

replication origin The site at which DNA replication begins. *See* origin of replication. p. 193

repressible operon Operon whose expression is prevented by a repressor molecule. p. 319

repressor A regulatory protein that prevents the operon genes from being expressed. p. 316

reproduction The process in which a parent or parents produce offspring. p. 989

reproductive isolating mechanism A biological characteristic that prevents the gene pools of two species from mixing. p. 430

reproductive strategy A set of behaviours that lead to reproductive success. p. 989

residual volume The air that remains in lungs after exhalation. p. 1227

resolution The minimum distance two points in a specimen can be separated and still be seen as two points. p. 29

resource partitioning The use of different resources or the use of resources in different ways by species living in the same place. p. 721

respiratory medium The environmental source of O_2 and the sink for released CO_2. For aquatic animals, the respiratory medium is water; for terrestrial animals, it is air. p. 1220

respiratory surface A layer of epithelial cells that provides the interface between the body and the respiratory medium. p. 1219

response In signal transduction, the last stage in which the transduced signal causes the cell to change according to the signal and to the receptors on the cell. In the nervous system, the output resulting from the integration of neural messages. p. 1069

resting potential A steady negative membrane potential exhibited by the membrane of a neuron that is not stimulated—that is, not conducting an impulse. p. 1073

restriction endonuclease (restriction enzyme) An enzyme that cuts DNA at a specific sequence. p. 341

restriction fragment A DNA fragment produced by cutting a long DNA molecule with a restriction enzyme. p. 341

restriction fragment length polymorphisms (RFLPs) When comparing different individuals, restriction enzyme–generated DNA fragments of different lengths from the same region of the genome. p. 349

retina A light-sensitive membrane lining the posterior part of the inside of the eye. p. 1108

retrotransposon A transposable element that transposes via an intermediate RNA copy of the transposable element. p. 212

retrovirus A virus with an RNA genome that replicates via a DNA intermediate. p. 213

reverse transcriptase An enzyme that uses RNA as a template to make a DNA copy of the retrotransposon. Reverse transcriptase is used to make DNA copies of RNA in test tube reactions. p. 212

reversible Refers to a reaction may go from left to right or from right to left, depending on conditions. p. 80

rhizoid A modified hypha that anchors a fungus to its substrate and absorbs moisture. p. 572

rhizome A horizontal, modified stem that can penetrate a substrate and anchor the plant. p. 577

rhodopsin The retinal–opsin photopigment. p. 1111

rhynchocoel A coelomic cavity that contains the proboscis of nemerteans. p. 611

ribonucleic acid (RNA) A polymer assembled from repeating nucleotide monomers in which the five-carbon sugar is ribose. Cellular RNAs are mRNA (which is translated to produce a polypeptide), tRNA (which brings an amino acid to the ribosome for assembly into a polypeptide during translation), and rRNA (which is a structural component of ribosomes). The genetic material of some viruses is RNA. p. 28

ribose A five-carbon sugar to which the nitrogenous bases in nucleotides link covalently. p. F-37

ribosomal RNA (rRNA) The RNA component of ribosomes. p. 32

ribosome A ribonucleoprotein particle that carries out protein synthesis by translating mRNA into chains of amino acids. pp. 32, 292, 302

ribosome binding site In translation initiation in prokaryotes, a sequence just upstream of the start codon that directs the small ribosomal subunit to bind and orient correctly for the complete ribosome to assemble and start translating in the correct spot. p. 304

ribozyme An RNA-based catalyst that is part of the biochemical machinery of all cells. p. 61

ribulose-1,5-bisphosphate (RuBP) carboxylase/oxygenase (rubisco) An enzyme that catalyzes the key reaction of the Calvin cycle, carbon fixation, in which CO_2 combines with RuBP (ribulose 1,5-bisphosphate) to form 3-phosphoglycerate. p. 157

ring species A species with a geographic distribution that forms a ring around uninhabitable terrain. p. 433

RNA interference (RNAi) The phenomenon of silencing a gene posttranscriptionally by a small, single-stranded RNA that is complementary to part of an mRNA. p. 329

RNA polymerase An enzyme that catalyzes the assembly of nucleotides into an RNA strand. p. 292

RNA-seq A technique for whole transcriptome sequencing. One method converts mRNA to cDNA for next-generation sequencing. p. 376

rod In the vertebrate eye, a type of photoreceptor in the retina that is specialized for detection of light at low intensities. pp. 482, 1109

root An anchoring structure in land plants that also absorbs water and nutrients and (in some plant species) stores food. p. 568

root cap A dome-shaped cell mass that forms a protective covering over the apical meristem in the tip of a plant root. p. 853

root hair A tubular outgrowth of the outer wall of a root epidermal cell; root hairs absorb much of a plant's water and minerals from the soil. p. 847

root nodule A localized swelling on a root in which symbiotic nitrogen-fixing bacteria reside. p. 912

root pressure The pressure that develops in plant roots as the result of osmosis, forcing xylem sap upward and out through leaves. *See also* guttation. p. 872

root system An underground (or submerged) network of roots with a large surface area that favours the rapid uptake of soil water and dissolved mineral ions. pp. 568, 839

rough ER Endoplasmic reticulum with many ribosomes studding its outer surface. p. 36

round window A thin membrane that faces the middle ear. p. 1106

ruminant An animal that has a complex, four-chambered stomach. p. 103

S phase The phase of the cell cycle during which DNA replication occurs. p. 171

saccule A fluid-filled chamber in the vestibular apparatus that provides information about the position of the head with respect to gravity (up versus down), as well as changes in the rate of linear movement of the body. p. 1102

salicylic acid (SA) In plants, a chemical synthesized following a wound that has multiple roles in plant defences, including interaction with jasmonates in signalling cascades. p. 929

salivary amylase A substance that hydrolyzes starches to the disaccharide maltose. p. 1201

salivary gland A gland that secretes saliva through a duct on the inside of the cheek or under the tongue; the saliva lubricates food and begins digestion. p. 1201

saltatory conduction A mechanism that allows small-diameter axons to conduct impulses rapidly. p. 1080

saprotroph An organism nourished by dead or decaying organic matter. p. 540

sapwood The newly formed outer wood located between heartwood and the vascular cambium. Compared with heartwood, it is wet, lighter in colour, and not as strong. p. 856

sarcomere The basic unit of contraction in a myofibril. p. 1136

saturated fatty acid Fatty acid with only single bonds linking the carbon atoms. p. 101

savannah A biome comprising grasslands with few trees, which grows in areas adjacent to tropical deciduous forests. p. 727

schizocoelom In protostomes, the body cavity that develops as inner and outer layers of mesoderm separate. p. 598

Schwann cell A type of glial cell in the peripheral nervous system that wraps nerve fibres with myelin and also secretes regulatory factors. p. 1070

scientific method An investigative approach in which scientists make observations about the natural world, develop working explanations about what they observe, and then test those explanations by collecting more information. p. F-2

sclereid A type of sclerenchyma cell; sclereids are typically short and have thick, lignified walls. p. 843

sclerenchyma A ground tissue in which cells develop thick secondary walls, which are commonly lignified and perforated by pits through which water can pass. p. 843

sclerotium Tough mass of hyphae, often serving as a survival or overwintering structure. p. 550

scolex The anterior (head) of a tapeworm, adapted for fastening the worm to the intestinal epithelium of its host. p. 609

scrotum The baglike sac in which the testes are suspended in many mammals. p. 1002

second law of thermodynamics Principle that for any process in which a system changes from an initial to a final state, the total disorder of the system and its surroundings always increases. p. 77

second messenger In particular, in signal transduction pathways, an internal, nonprotein signal molecule that directly or indirectly activates protein kinases, which elicit the cellular response. p. 919

secondary active transport Transport indirectly driven by ATP hydrolysis. p. 109

secondary cell wall A layer added to the cell wall of plants that is more rigid and may become many times thicker than the primary cell wall. p. 837

secondary consumer A carnivore that feeds on herbivores, a member of the third trophic level. p. 1190

secondary endosymbiosis In the model for the origin of plastids in eukaryotes, the second event, in which a nonphotosynthetic eukaryote engulfed a photosynthetic eukaryote. p. 535

secondary growth Plant growth that originates at lateral meristems and increases the diameter of older roots and stems. *Compare* primary growth. p. 839

secondary immune response The rapid immune response that occurs during the second (and subsequent) encounters of the immune system of a mammal with a specific antigen. p. 1281

secondary metabolite Organic compound not required for the growth or survival of an organism; tends to be biologically active. p. 543

secondary productivity Energy stored in new consumer biomass as energy is transferred from producers to consumers. p. 752

secondary structure Regions of alpha helix, beta strand, or random coil in a polypeptide chain. pp. 104, F-31

secondary succession Predictable changes in species composition in an ecological community that develops after existing vegetation is destroyed or disrupted by an environmental disturbance. p. 737

secondary tissue In plants, the tissue that develops from lateral meristems. p. 839

secretory vesicle Vesicle that transports proteins to the plasma membrane. p. 38

seed The structure that forms when an ovule matures after a pollen grain reaches it and a sperm fertilizes the egg. p. 582

seed coat The outer protective covering of a seed. p. 892

segment polarity genes In *Drosophila* embryonic development, the set of segmentation regulatory genes activated by pair-rule genes that set the boundaries and anterior–posterior axis of each segment in the embryo. p. 1039

segmentation The production of body parts and some organ systems in repeating units. p. 599

segmentation genes Genes that work sequentially, progressively subdividing the embryo into regions, determining the segments of the embryo and the adult. p. 1037

segregate *See* principle of segregation. p. 221

segregation The separation of the pairs of alleles that control a character as gametes are formed. p. 169

selective cell adhesion A mechanism in which cells make and break specific connections to other cells or to the extracellular matrix. p. 1016

selectively permeable Membranes that selectively allow, impede, or block the passage of atoms and molecules. p. 60

self-fertilization (self-pollination) Fertilization in which sperm nuclei in pollen produced by anthers fertilize egg cells housed in the carpel of the same flower. Self-fertilization can also occur in hermaphroditic animals. pp. 420, 888

self-incompatibility In plants, the inability of a plant's pollen to fertilize ovules of the same plant. p. 888

semen The secretions of several accessory glands in which sperm are mixed prior to ejaculation. 1003

semicircular canal A part of the vestibular apparatus that detects rotational (spinning) motions. p. 1102

semiconservative replication The process of DNA replication in which the two parental strands separate and each serves as a template for the synthesis of new progeny double-stranded DNA molecules. p. 270

semilunar valve (SL valve) A flap of endocardium and connective tissue reinforced by fibres that prevent the valve from turning inside out. p. 974

seminal vesicle A vesicle that secretes seminal fluid. p. 1003

seminiferous tubule One of the tiny tubes in the testes where sperm cells are produced, grow, and mature. p. 1002

senescence The biologically complex process of aging in mature organisms that leads to the death of cells and eventually the whole organism. p. 926

sense codon A codon that specifies an amino acid. p. 302

sensitization Increased responsiveness to mild stimuli after experiencing a strong stimulus; one of the simplest forms of memory. p. 1130

sensor A tissue or organ that detects a change in an external or internal factor such as pH, temperature, or the concentration of a molecule such as glucose. p. 959

sensory adaptation A condition in which the effect of a stimulus is reduced if it continues at a constant level. p. 1099

sensory hair cell A hair cell that sends impulses along the auditory nerve to the brain when alternating changes of pressure agitate the basilar membrane on which the organ of Corti rests, moving the hair cells. p. 1101

sensory neuron A neuron that transmits stimuli collected by their sensory receptors to interneurons. p. 1070

sensory receptor (transducer) A receptor formed by the dendrites of afferent neurons or by specialized receptor cells making synapses with afferent neurons that pick up information about the external and internal environments of the animal. p. 1075

sensory transduction The conversion of a stimulus into a change in membrane potential. p. 1076

sepal One of the separate, usually green parts forming the calyx of a flower. p. 885

septum (plural, septa) A thin partition or cross wall that separates body segments. pp. 542, 617

sequential hermaphroditism The form of hermaphroditism in which individuals change from one sex to the other. p. 997

serosa The serous membrane: a thin membrane lining the closed cavities of the body; has two layers with a space between that is filled with serous fluid. p. 1199

Sertoli cell One of the supportive cells that completely surrounds developing spermatocytes in the seminiferous tubules. Follicle-stimulating hormone stimulates Sertoli cells to secrete a protein and other molecules that are required for spermatogenesis. p. 1002

sessile Unable to move from one place to another. p. 595

set point The level at which the condition controlled by a homeostatic pathway is to be maintained. p. 960

seta (plural, setae) A chitin-reinforced bristle that protrudes outward from the body wall in some annelid worms. p. 617

sex chromosomes Chromosomes that are different in male and female individuals of the same species. p. 203

sex-linked gene Gene located on a sex chromosome. p. 246

sex pilus *See* F pilus. p. 193

sex ratio The relative proportions of males and females in a population. p. 684

sexual dimorphism Differences in the size or appearance of males and females. p. 1176

sexual reproduction The mode of reproduction in which male and female parents produce offspring through the union of egg and sperm generated by meiosis. pp. 199, 989

sexual selection A form of natural selection established by male competition for access to females and by the females' choice of mates. p. 405

shoot system The stems and leaves of a plant. pp. 568, 839

short-day plant A plant that flowers in late summer or early autumn when dark periods become longer and light periods become shorter. p. 939

short interfering RNAs (siRNAs) Small RNA molecules that regulate expression of certain genes by binding to their mRNA and reducing translation. p. 329

short-term memory Memory that stores information for seconds. p. 1129

sieve tube A series of phloem cells joined end to end, forming a long tube through which nutrients are transported; seen mainly in flowering plants. p. 846

sieve tube member Any of the main conducting cells of phloem that connect end to end, forming a sieve tube. p. 844

sign stimulus A simple cue that triggers a fixed action pattern. p. 1156

signal peptide A short segment of amino acids to which the signal recognition particle binds, temporarily blocking further translation. A signal peptide is found on polypeptides that are sorted to the endoplasmic reticulum. Also referred to as *signal sequence*. p. 309

signal recognition particle (SRP) Protein–RNA complex that binds to signal sequences and targets polypeptide chains to the endoplasmic reticulum. p. 309

signal sequence *See* signal peptide. p. 309

signal transduction The series of events by which a signal molecule released from a controlling cell causes a response (affects the function) of target cells with receptors for the signal. Target cells process the signal in the three sequential steps of reception, transduction, and response. p. 9

silencing Phenomenon in which methylation of cytosines in eukaryotic promoters inhibits transcription and turns the genes off. p. 327

silent mutation A base-pair substitution mutation in a protein-coding gene that does not alter the amino acid specified by the gene. p. 310

simple diffusion Mechanism by which certain small substances diffuse through the lipid part of a biological membrane. p. 105

simple fruit A fruit that develops from a single ovary; in many of them, at least one layer of the pericarp is fleshy and juicy. p. 891

simulation modelling An analytical method in which researchers gather detailed information about a system and then create a series of mathematical equations that predict how the components of the system interact and respond to change. p. 770

simultaneous hermaphroditism A form of hermaphroditism in which individuals develop functional ovaries and testes at the same time. p. 997

single-lens eye An eye type that works by changing the amount of light allowed to enter into the eye and by focusing this incoming light with a lens. p. 1108

single-stranded binding protein (SSB) Protein that coats single-stranded segments of DNA, stabilizing the DNA for the replication process. p. 275

sink Any region of a plant where organic substances are being unloaded from the sieve tube system and used or stored. p. 877

sinoatrial node (SA node) The region of the heart that controls the rate and timing of cardiac muscle cell contraction. p. 976

sinus (plural, **sinuses**) A body space that surrounds an organ. p. 611

siRNA-induced silencing complex (siRISC) A group of proteins, recruited when siRNA binds to mRNA, that degrade the target mRNA. p. 330

sister chromatid One of two exact copies of a chromosome duplicated during replication. p. 171

skeletal muscle A muscle that connects to bones of the skeleton, typically made up of long and cylindrical cells that contain many nuclei. p. 954

sliding DNA clamp A protein that encircles the DNA and binds to the DNA polymerase to tether the enzyme to the template, thereby making replication more efficient. p. 272

slime layer A coat typically composed of polysaccharides that is loosely associated with bacterial cells. p. 32

slow block (to polyspermy) The process in which enzymes released from cortical granules alter the egg coats within minutes after fertilization so that no other sperm can attach and penetrate to the egg. p. 994

slow muscle fibre A muscle fibre that contracts relatively slowly and with low intensity. p. 1142

small interfering RNA (siRNA) A class of single-stranded RNAs that cause RNA interference. p. 323

small ribonucleoprotein particle A complex of RNA and proteins. p. 298

smooth ER Endoplasmic reticulum with no ribosomes attached to its membrane surfaces. Smooth ER has various functions, including synthesis of lipids that become part of cell membranes. p. 37

smooth muscle A relatively small and spindle-shaped muscle cell in which actin and myosin molecules are arranged in a loose network rather than in bundles. p. 955

social behaviour The interactions that animals have with other members of their species. p. 469

sodium–potassium pump *See* Na^+/K^+ pump. p. 110

soil solution A combination of water and dissolved substances that coats soil particles and partially fills pore spaces. p. 907

solenoid *See* 30 nm chromatin fibre. p. 284

solute The molecules of a substance dissolved in water. p. 105

solution Substance formed when molecules and ions separate and are suspended individually, surrounded by water molecules. p. F-17

solvent The water in a solution in which the hydration layer prevents polar molecules or ions from reassociating. p. F-17

somatic cell Any of the cells of an organism's body other than reproductive cells. pp. 199, 991

somatic embryo A plant embryo that is genetically identical to the parent because it arose through asexual means. p. 896

somatic gene therapy Gene therapy in which genes are introduced into somatic cells. p. 355

somatic nervous system A subdivision of the peripheral nervous system controlling body movements that are primarily conscious and voluntary. p. 1091

somites Paired blocks of mesoderm cells along the vertebrate body axis that form during early vertebrate development and differentiate into dermal skin, bone, and muscle. p. 1022

soredium (plural, soredia) A specialized cell cluster produced by lichens, consisting of a mass of algal cells surrounded by fungal hyphae; soredia function like reproductive spores and can give rise to a new lichen. p. 555

sorus (plural, sori) A cluster of sporangia on the underside of a fern frond; reproductive spores arise by meiosis inside each sporangium. p. 578

source In plants, any region (such as a leaf) where organic substances are being loaded into the sieve tube system of phloem. p. 877

source population In metapopulation analyses, a population that is either stable or increasing in size. p. 738

Southern blot analysis Technique in which labelled probes are used to detect specific DNA fragments that have been separated by gel electrophoresis. p. 349

spatial summation The summation of excitatory postsynaptic potentials produced by firing of different presynaptic neurons. p. 1087

specialized transduction Transfer of bacterial genes between bacteria using temperate phages that have incorporated fragments of the bacterial genome as they make the transition from the lysogenic cycle to the lytic cycle. pp. 196, 506

speciation The process of species formation. p. 427

species A group of populations in which the individuals are so closely related in structure, biochemistry, and behaviour that they can successfully interbreed. p. 427

species cluster A group of closely related species recently descended from a common ancestor. p. 436

species composition The particular combination of species that occupy a site. p. 730

species diversity A community characteristic defined by species richness and the relative abundance of species. p. 727

species richness The number of species that live within an ecological community. p. 726

specific epithet The species name in a binomial. p. 427

specific heat The amount of heat required to increase the temperature of a given quantity of water. p. F-16

sperm Motile gamete. p. 990

spermatocyte A developing gamete that becomes a spermatid at the end of meiosis. p. 813

spermatogenesis The process of producing sperm. p. 992

spermatogonium (plural, spermatogonia) A cell that enters meiosis and gives rise to gametes, produced by mitotic divisions of the germ cells in males. p. 991

spermatozoon (plural, spermatozoa) Also called sperm; a haploid cell that develops into a mature sperm cell when meiosis is complete. p. 992

sphincter A powerful ring of smooth muscle that forms a valve between major regions of the digestive tract. p. 1201

spinal cord A column of nervous tissue located within the vertebral column and directly connected to the brain. p. 1090

spinal nerve A nerve that carries signals between the spinal cord and the body trunk and limbs. p. 1123

spindle The structure that separates sister chromatids and moves them to opposite spindle poles. p. 170

spindle pole One of the pair of centrosomes in a cell undergoing mitosis from which bundles of microtubules radiate to form the part of the spindle from that pole. p. 174

spinneret A modified abdominal appendage from which spiders secrete silk threads. p. 623

spiracle An opening in the chitinous exoskeleton of an insect through which air enters and leaves the tracheal system. p. 1221

spiral cleavage The cleavage pattern in many protostomes in which newly produced cells lie in the space between the two cells immediately below them. p. 596

spiral valve A corkscrew-shaped fold of mucous membrane in the digestive system of elasmobranchs, which slows the passage of material and increases the surface area available for digestion and absorption. p. 648

spliceosome A complex formed between the pre-mRNA and small ribonucleoprotein particles, in which mRNA splicing takes place. p. 298

spongocoel The central cavity in a sponge. p. 601

spontaneous reaction Chemical or physical reaction that occurs without outside help. p. 79

sporadic (nonhereditary) cancer Cancer that is not inherited. p. 333

sporangium (plural, sporangia) A single-celled or multicellular structure in fungi and plants in which spores are produced. pp. 545, 570

spore A haploid reproductive structure, usually a single cell, that can develop into a new individual without fusing with another cell; found in plants, fungi, and certain protists. pp. 200, 884

sporophyll A specialized leaf that bears sporangia (spore-producing structures). p. 577

sporophyte An individual of the diploid generation produced through fertilization in organisms that undergo alternation of generations; it produces haploid spores. pp. 200, 526, 563, 883

squalene A liver oil found in sharks that is lighter than water, which increases their buoyancy. p. 648

stability The ability of a community to maintain its species composition and relative abundances when environmental disturbances eliminate some species from the community. p. 725

stabilizing selection A type of natural selection in which individuals expressing intermediate phenotypes have the highest relative fitness. p. 413

stamen A "male" reproductive organ in flowers, consisting of an anther (pollen producer) and a slender filament. p. 885

standing crop biomass The total dry weight of plants present in an ecosystem at a given time. p. 750

stapes The smallest of three sound-conducting bones in the middle ear of tetrapod vertebrates. pp. 652, 1105

starch Energy-providing carbohydrates stored in plant cells. p. 45

start codon The first codon read in an mRNA in translation—AUG. Also referred to as the *initiator codon*. p. 294

statocyst A mechanoreceptor in invertebrates that senses gravity and motion using statoliths. p. 1101

statolith A movable starch- or carbonate-containing stonelike body involved in sensing gravitational pull. pp. 934, 1101

stele The central core of vascular tissue in roots and shoots of vascular plants; it consists of the xylem and phloem together with supporting tissues. p. 854

stem cell Undifferentiated cells in most multicellular organisms that can divide without differentiating and also can divide and differentiate into specialized cell types. p. 353

stereocilia Microvilli covering the surface of hair cells clustered in the base of neuromasts. p. 1101

steroid A type of lipid derived from cholesterol. p. 326

steroid hormone receptor Internal receptor that turns on specific genes when it is activated by binding a signal molecule. p. 326

steroid hormone response element The DNA sequence to which the hormone receptor complex binds. p. 326

sterol Steroid with a single polar —OH group linked to one end of the ring framework and a complex, nonpolar hydrocarbon chain at the other end. p. 102

sticky end End of a DNA fragment, with a single-stranded structure that can form hydrogen bonds with a complementary sticky end on any other DNA molecule cut with the same enzyme. p. 341

stigma The receptive end of a carpel where deposited pollen germinates. p. 885

stimulus A component of a negative feedback control system maintaining homeostasis, specifically an environmental change that triggers a response. p. 959

stoma (plural, stomata) The opening between a pair of guard cells in the epidermis of a plant leaf or stem, through which gases and water vapour pass. pp. 565, 847

stomach The portion of the digestive system in which food is stored and digestion begins. p. 48

stop codon A codon that does not specify amino acids. The three nonsense codons are UAG, UAA, and UGA. Also referred to as the *nonsense codon* and *termination codon*. p. 294

stretch receptor A proprioceptor in the muscles and tendons of vertebrates that detects the position and movement of the limbs. p. 980

strict aerobe Cell with an absolute requirement for oxygen to survive, unable to live solely by fermentations. p. 139

strict anaerobe Organism in which fermentation is the only source of ATP. p. 139

strobilus *See* cone (of a plant). p. 577

stroma An inner compartment of a chloroplast, enclosed by two boundary membranes and containing a third membrane system. p. 46

stromatolite Fossilized remains of ancient cyanobacterial mats that carried out photosynthesis by the water-splitting reaction. p. 63

style The slender stalk of a carpel situated between the ovary and the stigma in plants. p. 885

suberin A waxy, waterproof substance present in cork cells. pp. 856, 868

submucosa A thick layer of elastic connective tissue that contains neuron networks and blood and lymph vessels. p. 1198

subsoil The region of soil beneath the topsoil that contains relatively little organic matter. p. 907

subspecies A taxonomic subdivision of a species. p. 433

substrate The particular reacting molecule or molecular group that an enzyme catalyzes. p. 23

substrate-level phosphorylation An enzyme-catalyzed reaction that transfers a phosphate group from a substrate to ADP. p. 126

succession The change from one community type to another. p. 735

sugar–phosphate backbone Structure in a polynucleotide chain that is formed when deoxyribose sugars are linked by phosphate groups in an alternating sugar–phosphate–sugar–phosphate pattern. p. 268

sum rule Mathematical rule in which the final probability is found by summing individual probabilities. p. 223

surface tension The force that places surface water molecules under tension, making them more resistant to separation than the underlying water molecules. p. F-16

survivorship curve Graphic display of the rate of survival of individuals over a species' life span. p. 685

suspension (filter) feeder An animal that ingests small food items suspended in water. pp. 601, 1195

suspensor In seed plants, a stalklike row of cells that develops from a zygote and helps position the embryo close to the nourishing endosperm. p. 892

swim bladder A gas-filled internal organ that helps fish maintain buoyancy. p. 649

symbiont An organism living in symbiosis with another organism; the symbionts are not usually closely related. p. 540

symbiosis An interspecific interaction in which the ecological relations of two or more species are intimately tied together. p. 66

symmetry (adj., symmetrical) Exact correspondence of form and constituent configuration on opposite sides of a dividing line or plane. p. 595

sympathetic division Division of the autonomic nervous system that predominates in situations involving stress, danger, excitement, or strenuous physical activity. p. 1093

sympatric Occupying the same spaces at the same time. p. 680

sympatric speciation Speciation that occurs without the geographic isolation of populations. p. 438

symplast The living component of plant tissue, composed of protoplasts interconnected by plasmodesmata. p. 868

symplastic pathway The route taken by water that moves through the cytoplasm of plant cells (the symplast). *Compare* apoplastic pathway. p. 868

symport The transport of two molecules in the same direction across a membrane. Also referred to as *cotransport*. p. 107

synapse A site where a neuron makes a communicating connection with another neuron or an effector such as a muscle fibre or gland. p. 1071

synapsid One of a group of amniotes with one temporal arch on each side of the head, which includes living mammals. p. 655

synapsis *See* pairing. p. 202

synaptic cleft A narrow gap that separates the plasma membranes of the presynaptic and postsynaptic cells. p. 1073

systemic acquired resistance A plant defence response to microbial invasion; defensive chemicals including salicylic acid may spread throughout a plant, rendering healthy tissues less vulnerable to infection. p. 932

systemic circuit In amphibians, the branch of a double blood circuit that receives oxygenated blood and provides the blood supply for most of the tissues and cells of a body. p. 968

systemin A plant peptide hormone that functions in defence responses to wounds. p. 929

systems biology An area of biology that studies the organism as a whole to unravel the integrated and interacting network of genes, proteins, and biochemical reactions responsible for life. p. 364

systole The period of contraction and emptying of the heart. p. 974

T cell A lymphocyte produced by the division of stem cells in the bone marrow and then released into the blood and carried to the thymus. T cells participate in adaptive immunity. p. 1273

T-cell receptor (TCR) A receptor that covers the plasma membrane of a T cell, specific for a particular antigen. p. 1273

T-even bacteriophage Virulent bacteriophages, T2, T4, and T6, that have been valuable for genetic studies of bacteriophage structure and function. p. 504

T (transverse) tubule The tubule that passes in a transverse manner from the sarcolemma across a myofibril of striated muscle. p. 1136

tactile signal A means of animal communication in which the signaller uses touch to convey a message to the signal receiver. p. 1167

taiga *See* boreal forest. p. 751

taproot system A root system consisting of a single main root from which lateral roots can extend; often stores starch. p. 852

TATA box A regulatory DNA sequence found in the promoters of many eukaryotic genes transcribed by RNA polymerase II. pp. 295, 321

taxis A behavioural response that is directed either toward or away from a specific stimulus. p. 1169

taxon (plural, taxa) A name designating a group of organisms included within a category in the Linnaean taxonomic hierarchy. p. 428

taxonomic hierarchy A system of classification based on arranging organisms into ever more inclusive categories. p. 428

taxonomy The science of the classification of organisms into an ordered system that indicates natural relationships. p. 427

telomerase An enzyme that adds telomere repeats to chromosome ends. p. 279

telomeres Repeats of simple-sequence DNA that maintain the ends of linear chromosomes. p. 279

telophase The final phase of mitosis, during which the spindle disassembles, the chromosomes decondense, and the nuclei re-form. p. 175

temperate bacteriophage Bacteriophage that may enter an inactive phase (lysogenic cycle) in which the host cell replicates and passes on the bacteriophage DNA for generations before the phage becomes active and kills the host (lytic cycle). pp. 197, 504

temperate deciduous forest A forested biome found at low to middle altitudes at temperate latitudes, with warm summers, cold winters, and annual precipitation between 75 and 250 cm. p. 726

temperate grassland A nonforested biome that stretches across the interiors of most continents, where winters are cold and snowy and summers are warm and fairly dry. p. 751

temperate rain forest A coniferous forest biome supported by heavy rain and fog, which grows where winters are mild and wet and the summers are cool. p. 525

template A nucleotide chain used in DNA replication for the assembly of a complementary chain. p. 212

template strand The DNA strand that is copied into an RNA molecule during gene transcription. p. 292

temporal isolation A prezygotic reproductive isolating mechanism in which species live in the same habitat but breed at different times of day or different times of year. p. 431

temporal summation The summation of several excitatory postsynaptic potentials produced by successive firing of a single presynaptic neuron over a short period of time. p. 1087

tendon A type of fibrous connective tissue that attaches muscles to bones. p. 952

terminal bud A bud that develops at the apex of a shoot. p. 847

termination codon *See* stop codon. p. 294

termination factor *See* release factor. p. 306

terminator Specific DNA sequence for a gene that signals the end of transcription of a gene. Terminators are common for prokaryotic genes. p. 296

territory A plot of habitat, defended by an individual male or a breeding pair of animals, within which the territory holders have exclusive access to food and other necessary resources. p. 1160

tertiary consumer A carnivore that feeds on other carnivores, a member of the fourth trophic level. p. 729

testcross A genetic cross between an individual with the dominant phenotype and a homozygous recessive individual. p. 224

testis (plural, **testes**) The male gonad. In male vertebrates, secretes androgens and steroid hormones that stimulate and control the development and maintenance of male reproductive systems. pp. 991, 1059

testosterone A hormone produced by the testes, responsible for the development of male secondary sex characteristics and the functioning of the male reproductive organs. pp. 1002, 1059

tetanus A situation in which a muscle fibre cannot relax between stimuli, and twitch summation produces a peak level of continuous contraction. p. 1140

tetrad Homologous pair consisting of four chromatids. p. 202

Tetrapoda A monophyletic lineage of vertebrates that includes animals with four feet, legs, or leglike appendages. pp. 461, 644

thalamus A major switchboard of the brain that receives sensory information and relays it to the regions of the cerebral cortex concerned with motor responses to sensory information of that type. p. 1126

thallus (plural, **thalli**) A plant body not differentiated into stems, roots, or leaves. pp. 555, 573

theory A broadly applicable idea or hypothesis that has been confirmed by every conceivable test. p. F-4

thermal acclimatization A set of physiological changes in ectotherms in response to seasonal shifts in environmental temperature, allowing the animals to attain good physiological performance at both winter and summer temperatures. p. 1256

thermodynamics The study of the energy flow during chemical and physical reactions. p. 75

thermoreceptor A sensory receptor that detects the flow of heat energy. p. 1077

thermoregulation The control of body temperature. p. 1251

thick filament A type of filament in striated muscle composed of myosin molecules; they interact with thin filaments to shorten muscle fibres during contraction. p. 1135

thigmomorphogenesis A plant response to a mechanical disturbance, such as frequent strong winds; includes inhibition of cellular elongation and production of thick-walled supportive tissue. p. 936

thigmotropism Growth in response to contact with a solid object. p. 936

thin filament A type of filament in striated muscle composed of actin, tropomyosin, and troponin molecules; interacts with thick filaments to shorten muscle fibres during contraction. p. 1135

thorax The central part of an animal's body, between the head and the abdomen. p. 624

threshold potential In signal conduction by neurons, the membrane potential at which the action potential fires. p. 1074

thylakoids Flattened, closed sacs that make up a membrane system within the stroma of a chloroplast. p. 46

thymine A pyrimidine that base-pairs with adenine. p. 268

thymus An organ of the lymphatic system that plays a role in filtering viruses, bacteria, damaged cells, and cellular debris from the lymph and bloodstream and in defending the body against infection and cancer. p. 983

thyroid gland A gland located beneath the voice box (larynx) that secretes hormones regulating growth and metabolism. p. 1056

thyroid-stimulating hormone (TSH) A hormone that stimulates the thyroid gland to grow in size and secrete thyroid hormones. p. 1055

thyroxine (T4) The main hormone of the thyroid gland, responsible for controlling the rate of metabolism in the body. p. 1056

Ti (tumour-inducing) plasmid A plasmid used to make transgenic plants. p. 357

tidal volume The volume of air entering and leaving the lungs during inhalation and exhalation. p. 1226

tight junction Region of tight connection between membranes of adjacent cells. p. 48

time lag The delayed response of organisms to changes in environmental conditions. p. 693

tissue A group of cells and intercellular substances with the same structure that function as a unit to carry out one or more specialized tasks. p. 947

tolerance hypothesis Hypothesis asserting that ecological succession proceeds because competitively superior species replace competitively inferior ones. p. 739

tonoplast The membrane that surrounds the central vacuole in a plant cell. pp. 46, 866

topoisomerase An enzyme that relieves the overtwisting and strain of DNA ahead of the replication fork. p. 275

topsoil The rich upper layer of soil where most plant roots are located; it generally consists of sand, clay particles, and humus. p. 907

torpor A sleeplike state produced when a lowered set point greatly reduces the energy required to maintain body temperature, accompanied by reductions in metabolic, nervous, and physical activity. p. 1260

torsion The realignment of body parts in gastropod molluscs that is independent of shell coiling. p. 615

totipotency The ability to develop into any type of cells. p. 666

totipotent Having the capacity to produce cells that can develop into or generate a new organism or body part. pp. 601, 895

trace element An element that occurs in organisms in very small quantities (0.01%); in nutrition, a mineral required by organisms only in small amounts. p. 1191

trachea In insects, an extensively branched, air-conducting tube formed by invagination of the outer epidermis of the animal and reinforced by rings of chitin. In vertebrates, the windpipe, which branches into the bronchi. p. 1225

tracheal system A branching network of tubes that carries air from small openings in the exoskeleton of an insect to tissues throughout its body. p. 626

tracheid A conducting cell of xylem, usually elongated and tapered. p. 844

traditional evolutionary systematics An approach to systematics that uses phenotypic similarities and differences to infer evolutionary relationships, grouping species that share both ancestral and derived characters. p. 460

trait A particular variation in a genetic or phenotypic character. p. 218

transcription The mechanism by which the information encoded in DNA is made into a complementary RNA copy. p. 292

transcription factors Proteins that recognize and bind to the TATA box and then recruit the polymerase. pp. 296, 321

transcription initiation complex Combination of general transcription factors with RNA polymerase II. p. 322

transcription unit A region of DNA that transcribes a single primary transcript. pp. 296, 316

transcriptome The complete set of RNA transcripts from a given cell under given conditions. p. 376

transcriptomics The study of the transcriptome. p. 376

transduction In cell signalling, the process of changing a signal into the form necessary to cause the cellular response. In prokaryotes, the process in which DNA is transferred from donor to recipient bacterial cells by an infecting bacteriophage. p. 196

transfer cell Any of the specialized cells that form when large amounts of solutes must be loaded or unloaded into the phloem; they facilitate the short-distance transport of organic solutes from the apoplast into the symplast. p. 878

transfer RNA (tRNA) The RNA that brings amino acids to the ribosome for addition to the polypeptide chain. p. 66

transformation The conversion of the hereditary type of a cell by the uptake of DNA released by the breakdown of another cell. pp. 196, 266

transgenic Refers to an organism that has been modified to contain genetic information from an external source. p. 352

transit sequence A part of a gene sequence that targets the protein product to an organelle, endoplasmic lumen, etc. p. 309

transition state An intermediate arrangement of atoms and bonds that both the reactants and the products of a reaction can assume. p. 85

translation The use of the information encoded in the RNA to assemble amino acids into a polypeptide. p. 292

translocation In genetics, a chromosomal alteration that occurs if a broken segment is attached to a different, nonhomologous chromosome. In vascular plants, the long-distance transport of substances by xylem and phloem. pp. 252, 877

transmission In neural signalling, the sending of a message along a neuron and then to another neuron or to a muscle or gland. p. 1069

transpiration The evaporation of water from a plant, principally from the leaves. p. 869

transport The controlled movement of ions and molecules from one side of a membrane to the other. p. 7

transport epithelium A layer of cells with specialized transport proteins in their plasma membranes. p. 1238

transport protein A protein embedded in the cell membrane that forms a channel allowing selected polar molecules and ions to pass across the membrane. p. 30

transposable element (TE) A sequence of DNA that can move from one place to another within the genome of a cell. p. 210

transposase An enzyme that catalyzes some of the reactions inserting or removing the transposable element from the DNA. p. 211

transposition Mechanism of movement of transposable elements involving nonhomologous recombination. p. 210

transposon A bacterial transposable element with an inverted repeat sequence at each end enclosing a central region with one or more genes. p. 211

trichocyst A dartlike protein thread that can be discharged from a surface organelle for defence or to capture prey. p. 521

trichome A single-celled or multicellular outgrowth from the epidermis of a plant that provides protection and shade and often gives the stems or leaves a hairy appearance. p. 847

triglyceride A nonpolar compound produced when a fatty acid binds by a dehydration synthesis reaction at each of glycerol's three —OH-bearing sites. p. 135

triiodothyronine (T3) A hormone secreted by the thyroid gland that regulates metabolism. p. 1056

trimester A division of human gestation, three months in length. p. 1025

triploblastic An animal body plan in which adult structures arise from three primary germ layers: endoderm, mesoderm, and ectoderm. p. 595

trochophore The small, free-swimming, ciliated aquatic larva of various invertebrates, including certain molluscs and annelids. p. 614

trophic cascade The effects of predator–prey interactions that reverberate through other population interactions at two or more trophic levels in an ecosystem. p. 757

trophic level A position in a food chain or web that defines the feeding habits of organisms. p. 728

trophoblast The outer single layer of cells of the blastocyst. p. 1025

trophozoite Motile, feeding stage of *Giardia* and other single-celled protists. p. 513

tropic hormone A hormone that regulates hormone secretion by another endocrine gland. p. 1053

tropical deciduous forest A tropical forest biome that occurs where winter drought reduces photosynthesis and most trees drop their leaves seasonally. p. 751

tropical forest Any forest that grows between the Tropics of Capricorn and Cancer, a region characterized by high temperature and rainfall and thin, nutrient-poor topsoil. p. 582

tropical rain forest A dense tropical forest biome that grows where some rain falls every month, mean annual rainfall exceeds 250 cm, mean annual temperature is at least 25°C, and humidity is above 80%. p. 557

tropism The turning or bending of an organism or one of its parts toward or away from an external stimulus, such as light, heat, or gravity. p. 920

true-breeding Refers to an individual that passes traits without change from one generation to the next. p. 219

tube cell The cell in a pollen grain (male gametophyte) of a seed plant that will give rise to the pollen tube. p. 886

tumour suppressor gene A gene that encodes proteins that inhibit cell division. p. 333

turgid A cell with high internal hydrostatic pressure. p. 867

turgor pressure The internal hydrostatic pressure within plant cells; the normal fullness or tension produced by the fluid content of plant and animal cells. p. 867

turnover rate The rate at which one generation of producers in an ecosystem is replaced by the next. p. 755

tympanum A thin membrane in the auditory canal that vibrates back and forth when struck by sound waves. pp. 652, 1105

umbilical cord A long tissue with blood vessels linking the embryo and the placenta. p. 355

umbilicus Navel; the scar left when the short length of umbilical cord still attached to the infant after birth dries and shrivels within a few days. p. 1027

undernutrition A condition in animals in which intake of organic fuels is inadequate or whose assimilation of such fuels is abnormal. p. 1190

undulating membrane In parabasalid protists, a fin-like structure formed by a flagellum buried in a fold of the cytoplasm that facilitates movement through thick and viscous fluids. An expansion of the plasma membrane in some flagellates that is usually associated with a flagellum. p. 520

uniform dispersion A pattern of distribution in which the individuals in a population are evenly spaced in their habitat. p. 682

uniformitarianism The concept that the geologic processes that sculpted Earth's surface over long periods of time—such as volcanic eruptions, earthquakes, erosion, and the formation and movement of glaciers—are exactly the same as the processes observed today. p. 395

universal A feature of the nucleic acid code, with the same codons specifying the same amino acids in all living organisms. p. 294

unreduced gamete A gamete that contains the same number of chromosomes as a somatic cell. p. 441

unsaturated Fatty acid with one or more double bonds linking the carbons. p. 100

ureter The tube through which urine flows from the renal pelvis to the urinary bladder. p. 1245

urethra The tube through which urine leaves the bladder. In most animals, the urethra opens to the outside. p. 1245

urinary bladder A storage sac located outside the kidneys. p. 1245

uterine cycle The menstrual cycle. p. 1000

uterus A specialized saclike organ in which the embryo develops in viviparous animals. p. 996

utricle A fluid-filled chamber of the vestibular apparatus that provides information about the position of the head with respect to gravity (up versus down), as well as changes in the rate of linear movement of the body. p. 1102

vaccination The process of administering a weakened form of a pathogen to patients as a means of giving them immunity to subsequent infection, and disease, caused by that pathogen. p. 1266

valence electron An electron in the outermost energy level of an atom. p. F-10

van der Waals forces Weak molecular attractions over short distances. p. F-14

variable An environmental factor that may differ among places or an organismal characteristic that may differ among individuals. p. 412

vas deferens (plural, **vasa deferentia)** The tube through which sperm travel from the epididymis to the urethra in the male reproductive system. p. 1003

vascular bundle A cord of plant vascular tissue; often multistranded with both xylem and phloem. p. 849

vascular cambium A lateral meristem that produces secondary vascular tissues in plants. p. 855

vascular plant A plant with xylem, phloem, and usually well-developed roots, stems, and leaves. p. 567

vascular tissue In plants, tissue that transports water and nutrients or the products of photosynthesis through the plant body. p. 567

vascular tissue system One of the three tissue systems in plants that provide the foundation for plant organs; it consists of transport tubes for water and nutrients. p. 841

vegetal pole The end of the egg opposite the animal pole, which typically gives rise to internal structures such as the gut and the posterior end of the embryo. p. 1015

vegetative reproduction Asexual reproduction in plants by which new individuals arise (or are created) without seeds or spores; examples include fragmentation from the parent plant or the use of cuttings by gardeners. p. 895

vein In a plant, a vascular bundle that forms part of the branching network of conducting and supporting tissues in a leaf or other expanded plant organ. In an animal, a vessel that carries the blood back to the heart. pp. 852, 967

veliger A second larva that occurs after the trochophore in some molluscs. p. 599

ventilation The flow of the respiratory medium (air or water, depending on the animal) over the respiratory surface. p. 1220

ventral Indicating the lower or "belly" side of an animal. p. 596

ventricle In the brain, an irregularly shaped cavity containing cerebrospinal fluid. In the heart, a chamber that pumps blood out of the heart. p. 1090

venule A capillary that merges into the small veins leaving an organ. p. 977

vernalization The stimulation of flowering by a period of low temperature. p. 940

vesicle A small, membrane-bound compartment that transfers substances between parts of the endomembrane system. p. 36

vessel In plants, one of the tubular conducting structures of xylem, typically several centimetres long; most angiosperms and some other vascular plants have xylem vessels. p. 844

vessel member Any of the short cells joined end to end in tubelike columns in xylem. p. 844

vestibular apparatus The specialized sensory structure of the inner ear of most terrestrial vertebrates that is responsible for perceiving the position and motion of the head and, therefore, for maintaining equilibrium and for coordinating head and body movements. p. 1102

vestigial structure An anatomical feature of living organisms that no longer retains its function. p. 393

virion A complete virus particle. p. 503

viroid A plant pathogen that consists of strands or circles of RNA, smaller than any viral DNA or RNA molecule, that have no protein coat. p. 509

virulent bacteriophage Bacteriophage that kills its host bacterial cells during each cycle of infection. pp. 196, 504

virus An infectious agent that contains either DNA or RNA surrounded by a protein coat. p. 266

visceral mass In molluscs, the region of the body containing the internal organs. p. 611

visual signal A means of communication in which animals use facial expressions or body language to send messages to other individuals. p. 1166

vital capacity The maximum tidal volume of air that an individual can inhale and exhale. p. 1227

vitamin An organic molecule required in small quantities that the animal cannot synthesize for itself. p. 1190

vitamin D A steroidlike molecule that increases the absorption of Ca^{2+} and phosphates from ingested food by promoting the synthesis of a calcium-binding protein in the intestine; it also increases the release of Ca^{2+} from bone in response to parathyroid hormone. p. 1057

vitelline coat A gel-like matrix of proteins, glycoproteins, or polysaccharides immediately outside the plasma membrane of an egg cell. p. 993

vitreous humour The jellylike substance that fills the main chamber of the eye, between the lens and the retina. p. 1109

viviparous Referring to animals that retain the embryo within the mother's body and nourish it during at least early embryo development. pp. 668, 996

voltage-gated ion channel A membrane-embedded protein that opens and closes as the membrane potential changes. p. 1075

vulva The external female sex organs. p. 999

water lattice An arrangement formed when a water molecule in liquid water establishes an average of 3.4 hydrogen bonds with its neighbours. p. F-15

water potential The potential energy of water, representing the difference in free energy between pure water and water in cells and solutions; it is the driving force for osmosis. p. 865

watershed An area of land from which precipitation drains into a single stream or river. p. 761

water-soluble vitamin A vitamin with a high proportion of oxygen and nitrogen able to form hydrogen bonds with water. p. 1193

wavelength The distance between two successive peaks of electromagnetic radiation. p. 4

wetland A highly productive ecotone often at the border between a freshwater biome and a terrestrial biome. p. 586

white matter The myelinated axons that surround the grey matter of the central nervous system. p. 1123

wilting The drooping of leaves and stems caused by a loss of turgor. p. 867

wobble hypothesis Hypothesis stating that the complete set of 61 sense codons can be read by fewer than 61 distinct tRNAs because of particular pairing properties of the bases in the anticodons. p. 302

Wolffian duct A bipotential primitive duct associated with the gonads that leads to a cloaca. p. 1029

wood The secondary xylem of trees and shrubs, lying under the bark and consisting largely of cellulose and lignin. p. 855

X chromosome Sex chromosome that occurs paired in female cells and single in male cells. p. 246

X-linked recessive inheritance Pattern in which displayed traits are due to inheritance of recessive alleles carried on the X chromosome. p. 257

X-ray diffraction Method for deducing the position of atoms in a molecule. p. 268

xylem The plant vascular tissue that distributes water and nutrients. p. 843

xylem sap The dilute solution of water and solutes that flows in the xylem. p. 869

Y chromosome Sex chromosome that is paired with an X chromosome in male cells. p. 203

yeast A single-celled fungus that reproduces by budding or fission. p. 28

yolk The portion of an egg that serves as the main energy source for the embryo. p. 654

yolk sac In an amniote egg, an extraembryonic membrane that encloses the yolk. p. 1020

zero population growth A circumstance in which the birth rate of a population equals the death rate. p. 691

zona pellucida A gel-like matrix of proteins, glycoproteins, or polysaccharides immediately outside the plasma membrane of the egg cell. p. 993

zone of cell division The region in a growing root that consists of the root apical meristem and the actively dividing cells behind it. p. 853

zone of elongation The region in a root where newly formed cells grow and elongate. p. 854

zone of maturation The region in a root above the zone of elongation where cells do not increase in length but may differentiate further and take on specialized roles. p. 854

zooplankton Small, usually microscopic, animals that float in aquatic habitats. p. 516

zygospore A multinucleate, thick-walled sexual spore in some fungi that is formed from the union of two gametes. p. 545

zygote A fertilized egg. pp. 199, 595, 992

Index

Classical conditioning, **1159**
Classical endocrine regulation, **1046–1047, 1046i**
Classical neural regulation, 1046i
Classification, **428**
  animal, 599–601
  phylogeny, 459, 459i, 460i
Classification schemes, 392
Clathrin, **114**
Clay soils, **906**, 908
Cleavage, **596**, 1015–1017, 1015i, 1016i, 1017–1021, 1017i,
    1018i, 1019i, 1020i, 1021i, 1042
Cleome droserifolia, 686
Cliff Swallows, 1178
Climate, **807**, 813
Climax community, **735**
Clinal variation, **434–435**
Cline, **434**
Clitoris, **999**
Clonal expansion, **1278**
Clonal selection, 1280i
Clone, **340**
Cloning, 356i, **1035**
Cloning vectors, **342**, 343i, 344, 348
Closed circulatory systems, **616**, 965–966, 966i,
    967–968, 967i
Closed system, **75–76**, 76i
Clotting factor, **355**
Club fungi, 552i
Club-winged Manakins, **1166**
Clumped dispersion, **681–682**
Cnidaria, phylum, **603–606**
  body plan, 603f
  predation, 604f
Cnidarians, **1088–1089**, 1088i
Cnidocyte, **603**
CO_2-concentrating mechanisms, **158–162**, 159i, 160i,
    161i, 162i, 165
Coactivator, **324**
Coal Tit, 1170, 1170i
Coat, **501**
Coated pit, **114**
Cobalt, as essential animal nutrient, 1191–1192b
Cobra lily, 913, 914i
Cocaine, 1084–1085t
Coccoid, **482**
Cochlea, **1106**
Cockroach, 1239
Codominance, **232**
Codons, **368–369**
Coelom, **596**
Coelomate, **596**
Coenzymes, **1190–1191**
Coevolution, **588**, 590i
Cofactor, **88**
Cohen, Stanley N., 342
Cohesion, **F-16**
Cohesion-tension mechanism, of water transport,
    870–871, 870i, 872
Cohesiveness of species, **429**
Cohn, Martin J., 403
Coho salmon case history, 1305–1306, 1305i, 1310
Cohort, **685**
Cold receptors, **1256**

Cold-water marine teleosts, **1254**
Coleoptile, **892**
Coleorhiza, **893**
Collagen, **49**, 49f
Collecting duct, **1245**
Collecting ducts, 1248t, **1250**
Collenchyma, **842–843**
Colon, **1206**
  See also Large intestine
Colony, **989**
Colony Collapse Disorder (CCD), **883**
Colour
  in animals, 18–19
  in plants, 19–20
Columnar cells, **950**, 950i
Combinatorial gene regulation, **324–325**, 325i
Combustion
  cellular respiration as controlled, 122–123
  oxidation of glucose by, 123i
  of propane, 86i
Commaless, **294**
Commensalism, **722**
Common cactus-finch, 397i
Common names, 427
Common Ravens, 1168–1169
Communication
  animal behaviour and, 1165–1169, 1166i, 1167i, 1168i,
    1186–1187
  body language, 477
  H. neandertalensis versus H. sapien, 468
  symbolism and syntax, 476
Community, **315**
Community ecology, **680**
Companion cell, **846**
Comparative genomics, **379–381**
Comparative morphology, **393**, 393i, 402
Compass orientation, **1172–1173**
Competitive exclusion principle, **717**
Competitive inhibition, **90–92**, 91i
Complement system, **1268**, 1271
Complementary base-pairing, **269**
Complementary DNA (cDNA), **344**, 344i, 348, 370
Complete digestive system, **610**
Complete metamorphosis, **629**
Complex tissues, **841**
Compound eye, 451b, **622**
Concentration, **F-18**
Concentration gradient, **105**
Concentration of CO_2 homeostasis and, 959
Concentration of O_2 homeostasis and, 959
Concentration of waste chemicals, homeostasis and, 959
Concentration of water and NaCl, homeostasis and, 959
Conduction, **1079**
Cones, **577**, 581i, 583
Confocal laser scanning microscopy, 30i
Conformation, **88**
Conformational change, **1137**
Conformers, **958**
Conidium (plural, conidia), 549, 550, 551i
Coniferophyta, 576t, 583
Coniferyl alcohol, 567b
Conine, **827**, 827i
Conium maculatum, 827

Development, **2**
  animals. *See* Animal development
  thyroid hormones and, 1056–1057, 1057*i*
Devonian period, 448*t*
  gymnosperms in, 581
  plants during, 577
  rapid diversification of plants in, 570
Diabetes mellitus, **1060**–1061
Diaphragm, in mammalian respiratory system,
    1225–1226, 1226*i*, 1228*i*
Diapsid, **660**–661
  extinct, 655–659
  living, 660*f*
Diapsida, **655**
Diarrhea, **1207**
Diastole, **974**
Diastolic blood pressure, **977**
Diatom, **524**
Diazepam (Valium), 1084–1085*t*
Dideoxy sequencing, **366**–367, 366*i*
Diencephalon, **1090**–1091, 1090*i*
Diet, brain size related to, **808**, 808*i*
Difference, in meiosis, 200–201
Differentiation, **898**, 1017, 1034–1035
Diffusion, **105**
  across membranes, 80*i*
  exchanging gas by simple, 1221
  Fick's equation of, 1219
  passive transport based on, 105, 105*i*, 106*i*
Diffusion coefficient, **1219**
Digestion, **1197**–1207, 1214–1215
Digestive processes
  in animals, 1195–1197, 1196*i*, 1197*i*, 1214
  regulation of, 1207–1209, 1207*i*, 1215
Digestive system, 956–957*i*, **1197**–1207, 1198*b*, 1199*i*
Digger wasps, 1172, 1172*i*
Dihybrid, **225**
Dihybrid cross, **225**
Dikaryon, **553**
Dikaryotic hyphae, **549**
Dikaryotic mycelium, **553**
Dinoflagellates, **23**
Dinosaurs, 401, 402*i*, 657*f*, 658*f*
Dioecious, **885**, 886*i*
Diphyodont, **667**
Diploblastic, **595**
Diploid, **170**
Diploid megasporocyte, **886**
Diploid stage (of life cycle), **200**, 563, 569, 569*i*, 574*i*, 579*i*,
    584*i*, 589*i*, 844*i*, 883–884
Diploidy, 420–421
Direct neurotransmitters, **1082**–1083, 1082*i*
Directional selection, **412**, 413*i*
Discontinuous replication, **275**
Disease, **1266**
Disease defences, **1265**–1266, 1292–1293
  adaptive immunity, 1272–1283, 1291–1292
  innate immunity, 1268–1272, 1291
  against invasion, 1266–1267, 1291
  malfunctions and failures of immune system,
    1283–1285, 1292
  in other organisms, 1285–1288, 1292
  parasite-host interactions, 1290–1291

  parasites, 1288–1290, 1292
  pathogens, 1288–1290, 1292
  vaccines, 1290–1291
Diseasome, **379**
Dishevlled gene, 1158*b*
Disk, **629**
Disorder, **77**
Dispersal, **477**–479, 1183
Dispersal agents, **418**
Dispersal stage, **601**
Dispersed duplication, **382**
Dispersion, **77**–78, 77*i*
Dispersion, population, **681**–683, 682*f*
Dispersive replication model, **270**
Display order, as characteristic of life, 54*i*
Disruptive selection, 399*b*, 399*i*, 413*i*, **414**
Dissociation, **1230**
Distal convoluted tubule, **1246**, 1246*i*, 1248*t*, 1249–1250
Distal end, **1238**
Distal-less (DLX), **405**
Distribution, **680**, 681–683
Disturbance climax (disclimax) community, **740**
Diversification, **389**
Diversity of Animals 1: Sponges, Radiata, Platyhel-
    minthes, and Protostomes
  animal phylogeny and classification, 599–601
  ecdysozoan protostomes, 619–629
  key innovations in animal evolution, 595–599
  lophotrochozoan protostomes, 606–619
  metazoans with radial symmetry, 602–606
  phylum Porifera, 601–602
  what is an animal?, 594–595
Diversity of Animals 2: Deuterostomes: Vertebrates and
    Their Closest Relatives
  agnathans: hagfishes and lampreys, conodonts, and
    ostracoderms, 644–646
  amniote origin and Mesozoic radiations, 654–659
  Aves: birds, 661–666
  deuterostomes, 635
  early tetrapods and modern amphibians, 651–654
  evolutionary convergence and mammalian diversity:
    tails to teeth, 670–672
  jawed fishes, 646–651
  living diapsids: sphenodontids, squamates, and
    crocodilians, 660–661
  Mammalia: monotremes, marsupials, and placentals,
    666–670
  phylum Chordata, 640–642
  phylum Echinodermata, 636–639
  phylum Hemichordata, 639–640
  subclass Testudinata: turtles and tortoises, 659–660
  vertebrate origin and diversification, 642–644
Diving reflex, 982*b*
Division, in cell cycles, **168**–169, 168*i*, 187
DLX *(distal-less)*, **405**
DNA. *See* Deoxyribonucleic acid (DNA)
DNA chips, **376**
  See also DNA microarrays
DNA cloning, **340**–348, 341*i*
DNA double helix, **269**–270, 270*i*
DNA fingerprinting, **349**–351
DNA helicase, **274**
DNA hybridization, **344**, 345*i*, 348

DNA ligase, 279*t*, **342**, 348
DNA methylation, **327**
DNA microarrays, **363**, 376, 377*i*, 381, 942*b*
DNA molecule, **269**
DNA packing, histones and, **283**, 284*i*
DNA polymerase, **271**–274, 275, 275*i*, 276*i*, 280–282, 282*i*
DNA polymerase I, 279*t*
DNA polymerase III, 279*t*
DNA repair mechanisms, **282**, 283*i*
DNA replication, 272*i*, **287**
    mechanisms to correct errors in, 280–283, 287
    multiple enzmes in, 276, 278*i*
    proteins of, 279*t*
DNA sequencing, **340**, 345*i*, 365–368
    taxonomic uses, 430*b*
    whale studies, 409–410
    wooly mammoth lineage, 404*b*, 404*i*
DNA synthesis, **274**–275
DNA technologies, **339**
    application of, 348–361
    DNA cloning. *See* DNA cloning
    as subject of public concern, 359–360
    why it matters, 339–340
DNA-directed RNA synthesis, **294**–296, 295*i*, 311
Dobbenstein, B., 308–309
Dodders, **913**, 914*i*
Dogbane, 403
Dogs
    domestication of, 809, 820
    selective breeding, 397–398
Do-it-yourself (DIY) biology, 339
Dolly (cloned sheep), 356, 356*i*
Dolphins, 393, 393*i*, 1181
Domains, **65**–66
Domestication, **830**
    of Atlantic salmon, 820–821
    of barley, 816, 816*i*, 817*i*
    of cats, 825, 826*i*
    of cattle, 813, 814*i*, 821
    of corn, 816, 817–818, 818*i*
    of cotton, 814, 814*i*, 821
    cultivation without domestication, 821
    of dogs, 809, 820
    of genus *Brassica*, 823*b*, 823*i*, 824*i*
    of grapes, 818
    of honeybees, 814
    of lentils, 816–817
    for more than one use, 821
    of plants in Solonaceae family, 818–820, 818*i*
    rationale for species selection, 813–821, 830–831
    of rice, 812–813, 812*i*, 815–816, 816*i*
    of squash, 818, 820, 820*i*
    timing and locations of, 808–813, 809*i*, 810*i*, 811*i*, 812*i*, 813, 816*i*, 817*i*, 830
    of wheat, 809–810, 810*i*, 815, 816, 816*i*, 819*b*
    yeast, 814–815
Dominance, **1178**–1179
Dominance hierarchy, **1178**
Dominant, **221**
Dominant alleles, 221
Dopamine, 1084–1085*t*
Dormancy, **894**, 941, 942*i*, 943*i*
Dorsal, **596**

Dorsal aspect, **596**
Dorsal lip of the blastopore, **1018**
D'Ortous de Mairan, Jean-Jacques, 16
Double blood circuits, **968**–969, 968*i*
Double fertilization, **890**
Double helix, **2**
Double-helix model, **269**–270, 270*i*
Double-stranded DNA, six reading frames of, 369*t*
Down syndrome, **253**–254, 254*i*
Downey, Richard Keith, 815*b*
Driscoll, Carlos A., 825
Dromaeosaurus, 401, 402*i*
Drosophila spp. (fruit fly), 241, 242*i*, 244, 245*i*, 247–249, 247*i*, 248*i*, 249–250, 250*i*, 439, 992, 1274*b*
    embryogenesis in, 1036–1037, 1037*i*
    gametic isolation, 432
    hybrid breakdown, 433
    infection of, 1267
    reproductive systems of, 993*i*
Drosopterin, 247*b*
Drugs
    affecting neurotransmission, 1084–1085*t*
    effects on antibody-mediated immunity of, 1281
Dry rot, **554**
Duboule, Denis, 394*b*
Duchenne muscular dystrophy, **349**
Duck-billed platypus, 428*i*
Ducks, sexual selection, 440, 440*i*
Dugesia, 1241, 1241*i*
Dumb rabies, **678**
Dung, fossilized, **476**
Duodenum, **1203**–1204, 1204*i*
Duplication, **251**–252, 252*i*
Dvl gene, 1158*b*

E

E. coli, **32**, 32*i*, 505–506, 505*i*, 690, 1289, 1296
    comparison of K12 and human genomes, 372*t*
    genetic engineering of to make insulin, 353
    genetic recombination in, 191–192, 193*i*, 194*i*
    genome of, 371–372, 371*i*
    Hershey-Chase experiments, 266
    transforming of DNA into, 342, 353*i*
    transforming of plasmids into, 343*i*
    use of DNA fingerprinting in testing for, 350
    use of to make protein, 352
E site, **302**
"Eagle" alarm, **476**
Earth, **55**–56, 56*i*, 395
Earthworms, **618**, 618*f*, 1144*i*, 1195, 1196, 1197*i*
Ecdysis, **600**, 621*f*
Ecdysone, 1049, 1064*i*
Ecdysozoan protostome, **619**–629
Echinodermata, phylum, **636**–639, 637*f*
Echinoderms, **1089**–1090, 1144
Echinoidea, class, 638–639
Echolocation, **1163**, 1163*i*, 1164*b*
Eclectus parrot, 18–19, 19*i*
Ecological community, **680**
Ecological efficiency, **752**
Ecological isolation, **431**, 431*t*
Ecological light pollution, 20–21, 21*i*
Ecological niche, **717**

Gill-water interface, 1254
Ginkgoes, 571i, **582**, 583–584
Ginkgophyta, 576t, **583**
Ginseng, **827**
Ginsenosides, **827**
Girth, meristems and, 839–840
Gizzard, **1195**
Glands, **950**, 951i
Glans, **1004**
Glenoid fossa, **475**, 475f
Glial cells, **955–956**, 1070–1071, 1071i
Globulins, **970**
Glomeromycetes, 544t, **557**
Glomeromycota, **544**, 544i, 544t, 547–548
Glomerulus, **1246**, 1246i
Glowing tobacco plant, 357
Glucagon, **1049**, 1060–1061, 1061i
Glucocorticoids, **1059**, 1059i
Glucose
    breakdown of, 79i
    oxidation of, 123i, 135i
    pancreatic islets of Langerhans and, 1060–1061, 1060i
    splitting of, 125–126, 125i, 141
Glucose-dependent insulinotropic peptide (GIP), **1208**
Glutamate, 1084–1085t
Glycocalyx, **32**
Glycogen, **135**
Glycolysis, **125**
    linking to citric acid cycle, 126, 128i
    as phase of cellular respiration, 124, 124i
    reactions of, 125–126, 125i, 126i, 127i
Glyphosate (Roundup), **358**
Glyptodont, **396**, 396i
Gnathostomata, **644**
Gnathostome, 647f
Gnetophytes, 576t, **583**, 584, 585i
Gnetum, **584**
Golgi, Camillo, 37
Golgi complex, 40i, **309**
Golgi tendon organ, **1103**
Golig complex, **37–38**, 38i
Gonadal development, **1029**, 1029i
Gonadal sex hormones, **1059–1060**, 1060i, 1066
Gonadotropin-releasing hormone (GnRH), **1000**, 1060, 1162
Goose bumps, **1258**
Gooseberry, 1039
Gorilla, 472b, 475f
Gorilla gorilla, 472b, 475f
Gossypium arboreum, 814
Gossypium barbadense, 814
Gossypium herbaceum, 814, 814i
Gossypium hirsutum, 814
Gould, James L., 1169
Graded potentials, **1074**, 1074i
Gradual change, **392**
Gradualism, **395**
Grafting, **818**
Grain, **893**
Gram stain procedure, **484**
Gram-negative bacteria, **1267**, 1269b
Gram-positive bacteria, **1267**, 1269b
Grandmother effect, 206b

Grant, Peter, 399b
Grant, Rosemary, 399b
Granum (plural, grana), **46**
Grapes, domestication of, 818
Graptopsalatsia nigrofusca, 621f
Grasshopper mice, 404, 405i
Grasshoppers, 828, 1196, 1197i
Gravitropisms, **934–936**, 935i
Great ape, 472b
Greater horseshoe bat, 1098i
Greater vestibular gland, **999**
Green revolution, **807**
Greenhouse effect, **764**
Greenish warbler, 434
Grey crescent, **1018**
Grey matter, **1123**
Grey whales, 1171, 1172, 1175
Grey wolf, 1180
Greylag Geese, 1159, 1159i
Grieder, Carol, 280
Griffith, Fred, 196
Griffith, Frederick, 264–265, 265i
Grip, 475, 475f, 476f
Gross primary productivity, **750**
Ground meristem, **852**
Ground tissue system, **841**
Ground tissues, **841–843**, 842i, 842t
Group living, **1177–1180**
Growth
    abscisic acid (ABA) and, 928
    auxins and, 924–925
    brassinosteroids and, 927–928
    in cell cycles, 168–169, 168i, 187
    as characteristic of life, 54i
    jasmonates and, 929
    oligosaccharins and, 929
    plants, 836–841, 860
    population. *See* Population growth
    in roots, 853–854, 854i
Growth factor, **1047**
Growth hormone (GH), **1055**
Guanine, **268**
Guard cells, **874**, 874i
Gull, 678
Guppy, 405, 688–689f, 998–999b
Gurdon, John B., 1034–1035
Gut layers, in mammals, **1197–1201**, 1199i
Gutless animals, **1209**
Guttation, **872**
Gymnophonia, **654**
Gymnosperms, 568t, **570**, 571i, 576t, 581–585

H
H⁺ pump, **109**
H zone, 1135i, **1136**, 1136i
Habitable zone, **56–57**, 57i
Habitat, **680**
Habitat fragmentation, **653**
Habituation, **1159**
Hacke, Uwe, 876b
Hadean eon, 448t
Haeckel, Ernst, 595, **679**
Hafted tool, **475**

Hagfish, 644–646, 645f
Haikouichthys, 643
Hair follicles, 1257, 1257i
Haldane, John, 57
Half-life, F-10
Half-siblings, 1180, 1180i
Hall, Brian K., 1023b
Hallucigenia, 593, 594f
Halobacterium, 8, 8i
Halteres, 1101i
Hamilton, William D., 1180, 1181, 1183
Hammerheaded bat, 405, 406i
Hamner, Karl, 939
Hand, 475, 475f
Hand axe, 471f
Haplodiploidy, 1182, 1182i
Haploid stage (of life cycle), 200, 563, 569, 574i, 579i, 584i, 589i, 844i, 883–884
HapMap Consortium, 373
Hardy, G. H., 415
Hardy-Weinberg Principle, 415, 415b–416b, 418–419, 420
Harlequin frog, 545i
Hartwell, Leland, 181
Harvesting efficiency, 752
Haustorial roots, 913
Hawaii
    fruit fly speciation, 437b
    whale populations, 410
Hawthorn (*Crataegus* spp.), 438, 439i
Hayes, Mickey, 240, 241i
Hayflick, Leonard, 184
Hayflick factors, 184
Haynes, Robert, 284
HbA allele (hemoglobin), 421
HbS allele (sickle cell), 421, 421i
HCl, 1208
Head, 1136, 1136i
Head-foot, 611
Hearing
    in invertebrates, 1104, 1104i
    mechanoreceptors and, 1131
    in vertebrates, 1105–1106
Heart, 968–969, 969i, 973–974, 973i, 974i
    arterial blood pressure cycles, 977
    cardiac cycle, 976–977, 976i
    cycle of contraction and relaxation, 974, 975i, 976
Heart rate, 980
Heartwood, 856
Heat exchanges, with environment, 1252, 1252i
Heat of vaporization, F-16
Heat-shock proteins (HSP), 933
Heat-shock responses, as plant chemical defence, 930t
Heavy chain, 1274
Hebert, Paul, 430b
Height, meristems and, 839–840
Heinrich, Bernd, 1169
Helical virus, 502
Helicases, 274–275, 276i, 279t
Helicobacter pylori, 1203
Helper T cell, 1278
Heme, 972b
Hemichordata, phylum, 639–640
Hemlock tree, 557i

Hemocoel, 596
Hemocytes, 970
Hemoglobin (*HbA* allele), 378, 421, 971, 972b, 1228–1230, 1229i, 1232b
Hemoglobin-O_2 equilibrium curve, 1229, 1229i
Hemolymph, 611
Hemophilia, 249–250
Hepadnavirus, 503t
Hepatic portal vein, 1206
Hepatitis A virus, 503t
Hepatophyta, 571i, 573–574, 576t
Herbicide, 921
Herbivore, 712
Herbivory, 712
Heritable changes, 401, 405
Heritable variation, 410, 417
Hermaphroditism, 997, 997i
Herpes simplex virus, 503t
Herrick, James, 217
Herring Gull, 1156–1157, 1156i
Herrmann, Esther, 1183
Hershey, Alfred D., 266, 267i
Hesperornis, 666f
Heterochromatin, 285
Heterodont, 667
Heterosporous, 570, 577, 580, 581, 582
Heterotroph, 594–595
Heterotrophic bacteria, 540
Heterotrophic eukaryotes, 540
Heterotrophs, 562
Heterozygote advantage, 421, 421i
Heterozygotes, 232, 255–257
Heterozygous, 221
Heun, Manfred, 816
Hexapoda, subphylum, 625–630
Hexokinase, 87, 88i
Hfr cells, 195
Hibernation, 1260–1261
Hibiscus, 590i
Higashiyama, Tetsuya, 889b
High-affinity state, 91–92
Himantura haophraya, 648
Hindbrain, 1090
Hippocampus, 1126
Hirudinea, class, 618, 619f
Histamine, 1269
Histone code, 327
Histone deacetylase, 327
Histones, 283
    chromatin fibers and, 284, 284i
    DNA packing and, 283, 284i
Historical biogeography, 401–402
"Historical" constraint, 1296
History of life, 467
    evolution of birds, 461–464, 463i, 466
    fossils, 447–452, 449i, 450i, 451i, 464–465, 466
    geological time scale, 446–447, 447–448i, 466
    importance of, 445–446
    parallelism and convergence, 464, 465i, 466
    phylogeny, 455–461, 459i, 460i, 464–465, 466
    prehistoric organisms, 453–455, 453i, 454i, 455i, 466
HIV, 1286–1287b
HLA-B*73 allele, 479

Inhibitory postsynaptic potential (IPSP), **1085**–1087, 1087*i*
Initiation, **302**–304, 304*i*
Initiation codon, **368**
Initiator codon. *See* Start codon
Innate immune system, **1266**
Innate immunity, **1268**–1272, 1268*i*, 1291
Inner boundary membrane, **46**
Inner cell mass, **1025**
Inner ear, **1106**
Inner membrane, **146**
Inner mitochondrial membrane, **41**
Inocybe fastigiata (fungus), 539*i*
Inorganic molecule, **F-20**
Inositol triphosphate (IP3), **919**
Insects
    body plan, 627*f*
    cardenolides, toxicity of, 403, 405*i*
    development, 628*f*
    digestion in, 1196, 1197*i*
    diversity, 626*f*
    gas exchange in, 1221–1222
    hormones and development in, 1063, 1064*i*
    juvenile hormone, 629*f*
    mouthparts, 627*f*
    muscles in flying, 1143*i*
    physiology, 628*f*
    sodium-potassium pump, 403
Inserted DNA viruses, **373**
Insertion sequence (IS), **210**–211
Insight learning, **1159**
Instar, **628**
Instinct, animal behaviour and, **1156**–1158, 1186
Instinctive behaviour, **1155**
Insulin, 353, 1060–1061, 1061*b*, 1061*i*
Insulin-like growth factor (IGF), 1061*b*
Integral membrane protein, **103**
Integration, **1069**–1070, 1070*i*
Integrator, **960**
Integument, **886**
Integumentary system, **956**–957*i*
Interactome, **379**
Intercostal muscles, in mammalian respiratory system, 1226*i*
Interference competition, **717**
Interferon, **1272**
Interkinesis, **203**
Interleuken, **828**, 1278
Intermediate disturbance hypothesis, **735**
Intermediate filament proteins, **41**–43
Intermediate filaments, **41**–43
Intermediate-day plant, **940**
Intermembrane space, **146**
Internal environment, **1235**–1236, 1263–1264
    ectothermy, 1254–1256, 1263
    endothermy, 1256–1261, 1263
    osmoregulation and excretion, 1236–1239, 1262
    osmoregulation and excretion in invertebrates, 1240–1242, 1262
    osmoregulation and excretion in mammals, 1244–1251, 1262–1263
    osmoregulation and excretion in nonmammalian vertebrates, 1243–1244, 1262
    thermoregulation, 1251–1253, 1263

Internal fertilization, **994**, 997*b*
Internal fluid environment, **947**
Internal gills, **1222**, 1222*i*
International Genetically Engineered Machine Competition (iGEM), **339**
International HapMap Project, **373**
Interneuron, **1070**
Internode, **850**
Interphase, **171**–173, 172*i*
Interspecific competition, **717**
Interspecific hybrids, 433*i*
Interstitial fluid, **958**
Intertidal zones, **563**
Intestinal bacteria, **1207**
Intestine, **32**
Intracellular digestion, **603**, 1195
Intraspecific competition, **693**
Intravenous immunoglobulin (IVIG), **1281**, 1289
Intrinsic rate of increase, **691**
Introns, **298**–299, 344, 352, 373, 384
Invagination, **33**
Inversion, **252**, 252*i*
Invertebrate muscle, **955**
Invertebrates, **9**
    ectothermy in, 1254
    endocrine systems in, 1062–1064, 1066
    eyes of, 1108, 1109*i*
    hearing in, 1104, 1104*i*
    movements in, 1142–1143, 1143*i*
    nervous systems, 1088*i*
    odours and, 1115
    as osmoconformers, 1240, 1240*i*
    osmoregulation and excretion in, 1240–1242, 1262
    as osmoregulators, 1240, 1240*i*
Inverted repeat, **211**
Involution, **1018**–1019
Iodine, as essential animal nutrient, 1191–1192*b*
Ionic bond, **105**
Ionizing radiation, **14**
Ions, **8**
    in plasma, 970
    roots taking up by active transport, 868–869
Iris, **1108**
Iron
    as essential animal nutrient, 1191–1192*b*
    as essential plant nutrient, 904*t*, 905
Irrigation, **807**, 825, 825*i*
Irritable bowel disease, **828**
Islets of Langerhans, 1051*i*, 1052–1053*t*, **1066**
Isolated system, **75**, 76*i*
Isoosmotic, **1237**
Isotonic, **109**
Isotope, **F-9**
Isthmus of Panama, 435, 435*i*

J

Jackrabbits, 1258
Jacob, François, 169, 315–317
Jarrows, 1170–1171, 1170*i*
Jasmonates, 919*t*, **929**, 929–930, 930*t*
Jawed fish, **646**–651, 646*f*
Jeffreys, Alec, 349
Jenner, Edward, 1265–1266, 1281

Membrane attack, **1271**
Membrane fusion, **1007**–1008
Membrane potential, **111**
Membrane surface receptors, **114**, 116
Memory, **1129**–1130, 1133
   long-term, 1129–1130
   short-term, 1129–1130
Memory B cell, **1279**
Memory cell, **1273**
Memory cytotoxic T cells, **1283**
Memory helper T cells, **1280**
Mendel, Gregor, 241, 243, 400, 411
   garden peas experiments, 218–229, 218*i*, 219*i*, 220*i*,
     222*i*, 224*i*, 225*i*, 226*i*, 237
   modifications to hypothesis of, 229–236, 237
Meninges, **1123**
Menstrual cycle, **1000**–1002, 1003*i*, 1260
Menten, Maud, 87*b*
Meosphyll, **851**
Meristem tissue, **568**
Meristems, **839**–840, 840*i*
Meselson, Matthew, 270–271, 273*i*
Mesencephalon, **1090**–1091, 1090*i*
Mesenteries, **1201**
Mesentery, **596**
Mesoderm, 394*b*, **595**, 1016*t*, 1022*i*, 1033*b*
Mesoglea, **603**
Mesohyl, **601**
Mesozoic beaver, 428*i*
Mesozoic era, 448*t*
   as age of gymnosperms, 583
   cycads in, 581
   extinctions during, 587
Messenger RNA (mRNA), **32**
Messner, Rheinhold, 1232*b*
Metabolic suppression, in Bar-Headed Geese, 1302
Metabolic waste, from animals, 1238–1239, 1239*i*
Metabolic water, **1238**–1239
Metabolism, **82**, 95
   ATP hydrolysis, 83–84, 83*i*
   catabolic and anabolic pathways, 82, 83*i*
   controlling with noncompetitive regulation,
     92–93, 93*i*
   energy coupling, 84, 84*i*
   pancreatic islets of Langerhans and, 1060–1061, 1060*i*
   regenerating ATP, 84–85, 85*i*
   thyroid hormones and, 1056–1057, 1057*i*
Metabolome, **379**
Metacarpal, **475**
Metagenomics, **380**–381
Metamorphosis, **602**
   complete, 629
   incomplete, 629
Metanephridium (plural, metanephridia), **617**, 1241,
   1241*i*
Metaphase, **175**, 175*i*
Metaphase I, **203**, 205*i*
Metaphase II, **203**, 205*i*
Metastasis, **333**
Metatarsal, 474*f*
Metatherians, **997**
Metazoan, **602**–606
Metchnikoff, Élie, 1287*b*

Metencephalon, **1090**–1091, 1090*i*
Meteorites, **52**
Methane, combustion of, 78*i*
Methylation, of DNA, **327**
Methylphenidate (Ritalin), 1084–1085*t*
Mexican cavefish, 22, 23*i*
Mice, house, 412
Micelle, **100**
Michel, Andrew P., 439
Microbodies, **309**
Microclimate, **737**
Microevolution, **401**, 409–410, 409–424, **410**, 424–425
   adaptation, 423–424
   evolutionary agents, 417–420
   maintenance of variation, 420–423
   population genetics, 414–417
   variation in natural populations, 410–414
Microfilaments, **41**–43, 1031, 1031*i*
Micronucleus, **521**
Micronutrients, **902**–904, 904*t*
Microphage, 1270*i*
Microphylls, **569**, 569*i*
Microplana termitophaga, **608**
Micropyle, **886**
MicroRNAs (miRNAs), **329**–330, 329*i*
Microscope, **29**
Microscopic nature, of cells, **28**–29
Microscopic tubules, excretion and, **1238**, 1238*i*
Microscopy, **28**
Microspore mother cells, **885**
Microspores, **570**, 570*i*, 580, 582, 583, 584*i*, 885–886
Microsporocytes, 584*i*, **885**
Microtubule organizing centre (MTOC), **178**
Microtubules, **41**, 1031, 1031*i*
Microvilli, **1203**–1204, 1204*i*, 1205
Midbrain, **1090**
Middle ear, **1105**
Middle lamella, **47**
Miescher, Joahnn Friedrich, 264
Migration, **1171**
   animal behaviour and, 1171–1175, 1171*i*, 1172*i*, 1173*i*,
     1174*i*, 1187
   in Bar-Headed Geese, 1304–1305, 1304*i*
   reasons for, 1173–1175, 1174*i*
Mildew, 551*i*
Milk, for the young, **1028**–1029
Milkweed (*Asclepias* spp.), **403**, 405*i*, 827*i*
Miller, Stanley, 57–58
Miller-Urey experiment, **57**–58, 58*i*
Milliosmoles, **1237**
Mimicry, **716**
Mimosa pudica, **936**, 937*i*
Mineralcorticoids, **1059**, 1059*i*
Minerals
   availability of in soil, 908–909, 908*i*
   long-distance transport of in xylem, 869–875, 880
Minimal medium, **191**
Miocene epoch, 447*t*
Miracadium, 613*f*
MiRNA genes, 334, 374
Mismatch repair, **282**, 283*i*
Missense mutation, **310**
Mitchell, Peter, 133

Multiple alleles, in populations, **232**–233, 233*i*
Multiple fruits, **891**, 892*i*
Multiple sclerosis, **1081**, 1284
Multipotent, **895**
Multiregional hypothesis, **477**–478
Multistep progression of cancer, 335, 335*i*
Murchison meteorite, **58**, 59*i*
Muscle fibre, **954**
Muscle spindles, 1104*i*
Muscle tissue, **954**
Muscle twitch, **1140**
Muscle-bone interactions, in vertebrates, **1149**–1151,
    1149*i*, 1151*i*
Muscles, **1134**–1135, 1153, 1225–1226, 1228*i*
Muscular system, **956**–957*i*
Muscularis, **1198**
Mushrooms, cultivation of, 821
Musk ox, 1294
Muskoxen, 1178, 1178*i*
Mustela nigripes, 683*f*
Mutant alleles, **241**
Mutations, **391**, 417, 417*t*
    effect on protein structure and function, 309–311,
        310*i*, 311*i*
    types, 417
Mutualism, **541**, 555
Mycelium, **542**
Mycelium of leaf litter, 542*i*
Mycelium of mushroom-forming fungus, 542*i*
Mycobiont, **555**
Mycoplasma mycoides, **360**
Mycorrhizae, **910**–911
Mycorrhizas, 547*i*, **548**, 551, 556–558, 557*i*, 565, 566*i*
Myelencephalon, **1090**–1091, 1090*i*
Myelin sheaths, **1070**
Myelinated neurons, 1072*i*
Myllokunmingia, **643**
Myoblast, **1036**
Myoclonic epilepsy, 259*t*
MyoD, **1036**, 1036*i*
Myofibrils, **1135**, 1135*i*
Myogenic heart, **976**
Myoglobin, **385**, 385*b*, 972*b*, 1141–1142
Myosins, **42**
Myriapoda, subphylum, **625**, 625*f*
Myrtle warbler, 428*i*
Mytilus, **289**, 290*i*

N

Na+ channels, **1083**
NADH, converting potential energy in, **130**, 131*i*
Na-K ATPase (sodium-potassium pump), **403**
Na+/K+ pump, **110**
Naked mole rats, 1183, 1185*b*
NASA Kepler Mission, **71**
Nasal passages, in mammalian respiratory system, 1226*i*
Nastic movements, **936**–938, 937*i*
National Center for Biotechnology Information, **369**
Natural experiment, **680**
Natural killer (NK) cells, **1272**
Natural selection, **396**–399, 398, 564, 1098, 1157
    constraints, 423–424
        Darwin's observations and inferences, 398*i*

    directional, 412, 413*i*
    disruptive, 413*i*, 414
    evidence of evolution, 401
    as evolutionary agent, 417*t*, 420
    fitness, 403
    phenotypic variation, 410–414
    relative fitness, 420
    stabilizing, 413–414, 413*i*
Natural selection, human use of, **807**–832, 827*i*, 831–832
    chemicals from plants and animals, 827–828,
        827*i*, 831
    complications, 825–827, 825*i*, 826*i*, 827*i*, 831
    contamination of crops, 825–826, 827*i*
    domestication of plants and animals, 808–821, 809*i*,
        810*i*, 811*i*, 812*i*, 814*i*, 815*b*, 815*i*, 816*i*, 817*i*, 818*i*,
        819*b*, 820*i*, 821*i*, 823–824, 823*i*, 824*i*, 830
    feeding people and keeping them healthy, 829*b*
    future of, 829–830, 831
    increasing yields, 821–823, 822*i*, 824*i*, 831
    molecular farming, 828, 828*i*, 829, 829*b*, 831
    why it matters, 807–808
Natural theology, **392**
Nautilus, 616
Navarro, Arcadi, 472*b*
Navigation, **1171**
    challenge of, 1173
    magnetoreception and, 1120
Neandertal. *See Homo neandertalensis*
Necrotizing fasciitis, **1289**
Nectar, **588**
Nectar guides, **588**
Nectocaris, **446**, 446*i*
Nedelcu, Aurora, 207
Negative feedback, **959**
Negative feedback control, 1058*i*
Negative feedback mechanisms
    blood and, 971
    homeostasis and, 959–961, 959*i*, 961*i*
    in reproduction, 1006*i*
Negative gene regulation, **319**–320, 320*i*
Negative pressure breathing, **1223**
Nematocyst, **603**
Nematoda, phylum, **619**–621, 620*f*
Nematodes, bacteria and, **1289**–1290
Nematode-trapping fungus, 549*i*
Nemertea, phylum, **611**, 611*f*
Neogene period, 447*t*
Neolithic Period, **808**
Nephrons, 1246*i*
    hyperosmotic urine from, 1247
    specialized functions of, 1246
Nerve cells, **955**
    See also Neurons
Nerve cord, **1089**
Nerve impulses
    action potentials and, 1079–1080, 1079*i*
    neurotransmitters and, 1082–1083, 1082*i*
Nerve net, **603**
Nerves, **1069**
Nervous system, **956**–957*i*, **1021**–1022, 1022*i*
Nervous tissue, **955**–957, 956*i*
Net primary productivity, **750**
Networks, **1094**–1095

Parietal cells, **1202**, 1203*i*

Parietal lobe, **1126**–**1127**, 1127*i*

Paroxetine (Paxil), 1084–1085*t*

Parsley, **827**

Parthenogenesis, **610**, 989–990

Partial diploid, **195**

Partial pressure, **1218**

Parturition, **1028**

Passive diffusion, osmosis as, **1236**–**1237**, 1237*i*

Passive immunity, **1281**

Passive membrane transport, **105**–**109**, 105*i*, 106*i*, 107*i*, 108*i*, 118

Passive parental care, **687**

Passive transport, **105**

Paternal chromosome, **201**

Paternity, DNA fingerprinting in testing of, **350**

Paterson, Eric, 910

Pathogen-associated molecular patterns (PAMPs), **1267**

Pathogenesis-related (PR) proteins, **930**, 930*t*, 1266

Pathogenic viruses, **1271**–**1272**

Pathogens, **33**

　　host responses and, 1288–1290, 1292

　　organisms and, 1267

Pathways, **82**

　　for movement of water into roots, 868, 868*i*

　　physiological integration within, 1295–1296

Pattern formation, **1036**

Pattern recognition receptors (PRRs), **1267**

Peacock spider, 1166, 1166*i*

Peacocks, 1176–1177, 1177*i*

Pearl fish, 639

Pearson, Keir, 1150*b*

Pectoral girdle, **641**

Pedicellariae, **638**

Pedigree, **249**

Pedipalps, **622**

Pellicle, **517**

Pelvic girdle, **641**

Pelvis, **473**–**474**, 475–476

Penfield, Wilder, 1128

Penicillin, 91*b*

Penicillium, 543, 549, 551*i*

Penis, **1003**–**1004**, 1245*i*, 1246

Pepsinogen, 1203*i*, **1208**

Peptide bond, **302**

Peptide hormones, 1047–1048

Peptidoglycan, **484**

Peptidyl transferase, **305**

Peptidyl-tRNA, **304**

Per capita growth rate, **690**

Perception, **1099**

Perennials, **840**

Perfusion, **1220**

Pericarp, **891**

Pericycle, **854**

Periderm, **856**

Peripheral membrane protein, **105**

Peripheral nervous system (PNS), **1055**, 1091–1093, 1092*i*, 1123–1124, 1123*i*

Peristalsis, **1198**, 1199, 1201*i*

Peritoneum, **596**

Peritubular capillaries, **1246**, 1246*i*

Permafrost, 263

Permian period, 448*t*, 581

Peroxisome, **308**

Personal Genome Project, **363**, 364

Personal genomics, **374**

Pest control, **825**

Pesticide, **825**

Petal, **885**

Petiole, **850**

Petroselinum crispum, **827**

PH

　　effect on enzyme activity of, 93, 93*i*

　　homeostasis and, 959

　　of soil, 909

Phage. *See* Bacteriophage

Phage lambda, **196**–**198**, 198*i*

Phagocytosis, **39**, 115*i*, 1268

Phalanges, **475**

Phanerozoic eon, 447*t*, 448*t*

Pharmacogenomics, **374**

Pharming, **355**, 359

Pharyngeal jaws, 1213*i*

Pharynx, **609**

　　in humans, 1198*b*

　　in mammalian respiratory system, 1226*i*

　　in mammals, 1225, 1226*i*

Phase-constant microscopy, 30*i*

Phencyclidine (PCP, or angel dust), 1084–1085*t*

Phenotype, **221**

Phenotypic variation, **401**, 410–412

　　causes, 411–412

　　directional selection, 412, 413*i*

　　disruptive selection, 413*i*, 414

　　maintenance, 420–423

　　natural selection, 410–414

　　qualitative, 411

　　quantitative, 410

　　stabilizing selection, 413–414, 413*i*

Phenylketonuria (PKU), **256**, 349

Phenylthiocarbamide (PTC), **232**

Pheromone, **405**

Philippine tarsier, 22, 22*i*

Phloem, **567**, 844, 846

　　nutrients transported in, 910

　　transporting organic substances in, 876–879, 878*i*, 880

Phloem sap, **877**

Phoronida, phylum, **607**

Phosphate group, **74**

Phosphodiester bond, **268**

Phospholipids, **100**–**101**, 100*i*, 101*i*, 1192

Phosphorous cycle, **768**

Phosphorus

　　as essential animal nutrient, 1191–1192*b*

　　as essential plant nutrient, 904*t*, 905

Phosphorylation, **116**, 116*i*, 378

Phosphorylation cascade, **116**

Photinus brimleyi (firefly), 431*i*

Photinus carolinus (firefly), 431*i*

Photinus collustrans (firefly), 431*i*

Photinus consanguineus (firefly), 431*i*

Photinus consimilis (firefly), 431*i*

Photinus granulatus (firefly), 431*i*

Photinus ignitus (firefly), 431*i*

Photinus marginellus (firefly), 431*i*

Ring canal, **638**
Ring species, **433**–434, 434*i*
Ringworm, 549
Ripening fruit, **927**
Rising, James, 438*i*
Ritualized, **1166**
RNA
    connection between DNA, protein and, 290–294, 311
    flow of information from DNA to, 60–61, 60*i*
    replaced by DNA, 61–62
RNA interference (RNAi), **375**, 1271–1272
RNA polymerase, **292**
RNA primers, **275**, 276*i*
RNA synthesis, **294**–296, 295*i*
RNA-seq (whole-transcriptome sequencing), **376**, 381
Rods and cones, **482**
    in mammals and birds, 1109–1112, 1110*i*, 1111*i*, 1113*i*
    sensory transduction by, 1111–1112, 1111*i*, 1112*i*
Rolling circle, **195**
Rolling circle replication, 286*i*
Romalea microptera, **828**
Root cap, **853**
Root hair, **847**
Root nodules, **912**
    beneficial effect of, 912*i*
    formation of in legumes, 913*i*
Root pressure, **872**
Root systems, **568**, 852–854, 861
    absorbing essential nutrients through, 909–910
    in plants, 836, 839
Root xylem, **868**
Roots, **568**
    adaptations of for obtaining and absorbing nutrients, 909–914, 915
    pressure in, 872, 872*i*
    secondary growth in, 857, 860*i*
    secretions from, 910
    taking up ions by active transport, 868–869
    transporting solutes by, 868–869, 868*i*, 879–880
    transporting water by, 868–869, 868*i*, 879–880
Root-soil interactions, **907**–909, 907*i*, 908*i*
Rosa acicularis (wild rose), 587*i*
Roscovotine, **185**
Rosmarinus officinalis, **827**, 827*i*
Rotifera, phylum, **609**–611, 610*f*
Rough ER, **36**–37, 37*i*
Round window, **1106**
Roundworm, 619–621, 620*f*
Rowan, William, 1062*b*
Royal Kingbird, 1166
Royal penguins, 1178, 1179*i*
RRNA genes, 374
R-selected species, **697**
Rubisco, **157**–158, 158–159, 158*i*, 159*i*
RuBP carboxylase/oxygenase (rubisco), **378**
Ruminants, 1200–1201*b*

S

S allele, **889**
S bacteria, 264–266
S phase, **171**
S. pyogenes, **1289**
Saccule, **1102**

Sachs, Julius von, 902–903, 903*i*
Sage Grouse, 1176, 1176*i*
Salamander, 434, 434*i*, 652–654
Salem witch trials, possible connection of to lysergic acid, 550, 551
Salicylic acid (SA), 811*b*, 919*t*, 930*t*, 932*b*
Salivary amylase, 1212*b*
Salivary glands, 1198*b*, **1201**
Salix, 811*b*
Salk, Jonas, 1281
Salmo salar, domestication of, 820–821
Salt glands, **1243**, 1243*i*, 1244, 1244*i*
Saltatory conduction, **1080**–1082, 1081*i*
Sand dollar, 638–639
Sandy soils, **906**
Sanger, Frederick, 365, 366
Saprotrophs, **540**, 545, 548, 554
Sapwood, **856**
Sarcomeres, **1136**–1140, 1139*i*, 1140*i*
Sarcopterygii, class, **649**–651, 651*f*
Saturated fatty acid, **101**
Saunders, Charles E., 819*b*
Saurischian dinosaur, 657*f*, 658*f*
Savannah, **727**
Scanning electron microscopy (SEM), 30*i*
Scapula, **475**, 475*f*
Scarlet monkey-flower, 432, 432*i*, 440*b*
Scherer, Stephen, 375*b*, 468
Schizocoelom, **598**
Schleiden, Matthias, 27
Schluter, Dolf, 422*b*
Schriver, Charles, 237
Schwann, Theodor, 27
Schwann cells, **1070**, 1081
Scientific method, **F-2**
Sclereids, **843**
Sclerenchyma, **843**, 843*i*
Sclerotiz/sclerotium, **550**, 551, 551*i*
Scolex, **609**
Scott, Becky, 1230*b*
Scrotum, **1002**
Scyphozoa, class, **604**, 605*f*
Sea anemones, 1144*i*, **1196**
Sea cucumber, 639
Sea lily, 639
Sea squirt, 640–641, 641*f*
Sea star, 638*f*
Sea turtles, magnetic sense in, 1122*i*
Sea urchins, 638–639, 1017–1018, 1017*i*
Seals, 1258
Seasonal change, **392**
Second law of thermodynamics, **77**
Second messengers, **919**, 1082–1083, 1082*i*
Secondary active transport, **109**, 112, 112*i*
Secondary cell wall, **837**
Secondary consumer, **1190**
Secondary contact, **436**
Secondary endosymbiosis, **535**
Secondary growth, **855**–860, 856*i*, 857*i*, 858*i*, 861
Secondary immune response, **1281**
Secondary mesenchyme, **1018**
Secondary metabolites, **542**, 930–931
Secondary productivity, **752**

Single blood circuits, **968**–969, 968*i*

Single nucleotide polymorphism (SNP), **373**, 374

Single-character crosses, **219**–222

Single-lens eye, **11**, 11*i*, 12*i*

Single-stranded binding proteins (SSbs), **275**, 279*t*

Sinks, **877**–879, 877*i*

Sinoatrial node (SA node), **976**

Sinus (plural, sinuses), **611**

Siphon, **615**

SiRNA-induced silencing complex (siRISC), **330**

Sister chromatid, **171**

Site-directed mutagenesis, **360**

Size, of cells, **28**–29

Skeletal muscle, **954**–955, 955*i*, 1135
   in antagonistic pairs, 1149*i*
   dividing control among motor units, 1140–1141, 1141*i*
   somatic system and, 1091–1092
   striated appearance of, 1135–1136
   in vertebrates, 1152

Skeletal systems, **956**–957*i*, **1143**–1145, 1144*i*, 1145–1146, 1146*i*, 1147*i*, 1152

Skeletons, **1134**–1135, 1153
   Australopithecus afarensis, 474*f*
   human, 473*f*
   importance of, 452
   mammals, 1147*i*

Skin, **1100**, 1100*i*
   controlling heat transfer with environment with, 1256–1257, 1257*i*
   human, 1257*i*
   physiological and behavioural responses to changes in, 1257*i*, 1259*i*
   in terrestrial mammals, 1250–1251, 1250*i*

Slagsvold, Tore, 1159

Slash and burn farming, **812**, 812*i*

Sliding clamp, 279*t*

Sliding DNA clamp, **272**

Sliding filament mechanism, **1136**–1140, 1139*i*, 1140*i*

Slime layer, **32**

Slow block (to polyspermy), **994**

Slow muscle fibres, **1141**–1142, 1141*t*

Small interfering RNA (siRNA), **323**

Small intestine, 1198*b*, **1203**–1206, 1204*i*, 1205*i*, 1206*i*, 1281

Small nuclear RNA, **298**

Small ribonucleoprotein particle, **298**

Small RNAs, regulation of gene expression by, **329**–330

Small-diameter axons, **1080**–1082, 1081*i*

Smallpox, **1265**–1266, 1290

Smith, Michael, 360*b*

Smooth ER, **36**–37, 37*i*

Smooth muscle, **955**, 955*i*

Snails, 410*i*, 421, 423, 439

Snakes, **402**–403, 402*i*, 660–661, 1213–1214, 1213*i*, 1255

Snapdragon, 414, 414*t*, 415*b*–416*b*

Snow geese, 411*i*, 420

Snow plant, 913, 914*i*

Social behaviour, 1182*b*
   animal behaviour and, 1177–1180, 1178*i*, 1179*i*, 1187
   human, 1183–1184, 1183*i*, 1184*i*

Social network, **476**

Sodium-potassium pump (Na-K ATPase), **110**–111, 110*i*, 111*i*, 403, 1191–1192*b*

Soil, **906**, 914–915
   components of, 906
   influences on features of, 906–907, 907*i*
   particle size, 906
   root-soil interactions, 907–909, 907*i*, 908*i*

Soil horizons, **907**, 907*i*

Soil solution, **907**

Solanum aethiopicum, domestication of, 819

Solanum lycopersicum, domestication of, 818, 818*i*, 819

Solanum macrocarpum, domestication of, 819

Solanum melongena, domestication of, 818, 818*i*, 819

Solanum tuberosum, domestication of, 818–819, 818*i*

Solar tracking, **938**

Solemya genus, **1209**

Solenoid, **284**

Solonaceae family, domestication of, 818–820, 818*i*

Solutes, **105**
   movement of in plants, 864–867, 864*i*, 879
   transporting by roots, 868–869, 868*i*, 879–880

Solution, **F-17**

Solvent, **F-17**

Somatic cell nuclear transfer (SCNT), **356**

Somatic (body) cells, **353**

Somatic embryo, **896**

Somatic embryogenesis, **897**

Somatic gene therapy, **355**

Somatic nervous system, **1091**

Somatic system, **1091**–1092

Somites, **1022**

Song thrush, 423

Songbirds, 1155, 1155*i*, 1166, 1166*i*

Sordino, Paolo, 394*b*

Soredia (plural, soredium), **555**, 556*i*

Sorus (plural, sori), **578**, 579*i*

Sossin, Wayne, 615

Sound, **1104**

Source population, **738**

Sources, **877**–879, 877*i*

South American intertidal mollusc, 1254

South American rhea, 393*i*

Southern, Edward, 349

Southern blot analysis, **349**, 351*i*

Space, animal behaviour and, **1169**–1171, 1187

Spalax, 22

Sparrow, 434*i*, 1155–1156, 1160, 1168, 1169, 1173–1175, 1175*i*

Spatial senses, **1100**–1104, 1100*i*, 1131

Spatial separation, 163*i*

Spatial summation, **1141**

Spawning, **987**

Spear, 475

Specialized cells, **947**–948

Specialized excretory tubules, role in osmoregulation, **1241**–1242, 1241*i*, 1242*i*

Specialized transduction, **196**

Speciation, **427**
   allopatric, 435–436, 435*i*
   genetic mechanisms, 439–443
   geographical variation, 433–435
   parapatric, **436**, 436–438
   sympatric, **438**, 438–439

Species, 427–429
  concepts, 428–429
  nomenclature, 427–428
Species clusters, 436, 436i
Species composition, 730
Species concept, 479
Species diversity, 727
Species name, 427
Species richness, 726
Specific epithet, 427
Specific heat, F-16
Specific response, 1267
Spemann, Hans, 1032, 1034b
Spermatazoa, 992, 992i
Spermatocyte, 813
Spermatogenesis, 991–992, 1002
Spermatogonium (plural, spermatogonia), 991
Spermatophyta, 571i
Spermatozoon (plural, spermatozoa), 992, 992i
Sphenodon, 655, 660
Sphenodon punctatus, 660
Sphenodontid, 660–661
Sphincter muscles, 1245, 1245i
Sphincters, 1201
Spinal cord, 1123–1124, 1123i
Spinal nerve, 1123
Spindle, 170
Spindle connections, 176i
Spindle pole, 174
Spine, 641
Spinneret, 623
Spiracles, 1221–1222, 1221i
Spiral cleavage, 596
Spiral valve, 648
Spliceosome, 298
Sponges, 1195
  See also Porifera, phylum
"Spongiform," 509–510, 510i
Spongocoel, 601
Spongy mesophyll, 851
Spontaneous processes, free energy and, 78–80, 94–95
Spontaneous reaction, 79
Sporadic (nonhereditary) cancer, 333
Sporangium (plural, sporangia), 545, 570, 574i, 577, 577i, 578, 580i, 584i
Spores, 543, 547i, 550, 551i, 563
Sporophylls, 577, 583, 586
Sporophytes, 200, 563, 569i, 570, 572, 573i, 575, 579i, 582, 883–884
Spruce budworm, 1261b
Squalene, 648
Squamate, 660–661
Squamous cells, 950, 950i
Squash, domestication of, 818, 820, 820i
SRY gene, 246–247
Stability, 725
Stabilizing selection, 413–414, 413i
Stahl, Franklin, 270–271, 273i
Stalked-eyed fly, 405, 406i
Stamen, 885
Standing crop biomass, 750
Stapes, 652
Starch, 45

Starfish, 638, 1268, 1268i
Star-nosed mole, 1164–1165, 1165i
Stars, using for celestial navigation, 1173, 1173i
Start codon, 294
Statocyst, 1101i
Statolith, 934
Stele, 854
Stem cells, 183–184, 183i, 353, 1271i
Stems, 847–850, 850i, 851i, 924–925
Stereocilia, 1101
Sterile parts, of flowers, 885, 885i
Sternum, 661
Steroid hormone receptor, 326
Steroid hormone regulation, 326, 326i
Steroid hormone response element, 326
Steroid hormones, 1048, 1058–1059
Sterol, 102
Stevan Arnold, 1157–1158
Sticky ends, 341
Sticky traps, 390, 390i
Stigma, 885
Stimuli response, 54i
Stimulus, 959
  constant, 1099
  perception of, 1099–1100
  strength of, 1099
Stoma (plural, stomata), 161i, 565, 565i, 572, 583, 874–875
Stomach, 48
  in humans, 1198b, 1202–1203, 1203i, 1205i
  in mammals, 1225, 1226i
Stomatal movements, 872, 874–875
Stone axe, 475
Stone cutting tool, 475
Stop codons, 369
Storey, Ken, 1255b
Stratified epithelia, 950, 950i
Stress, 1063b
Stress proteins, 1300b
Stretch receptors, in vertebrates, 1103–1104, 1104i
Strict aerobe, 139
Strict anaerobe, 139
Striped skunk, 1166
Strobili/strobilus, 570i, 577, 580i
  See also Cone
Stroke volume, 980
Stroma, 46
Stromatolites, 63, 63i, 146
Structure
  of cells, 28–31
  of chromatin, 327–328, 328i
  of DNA, 267–270, 287
  flowering plants, 885–888, 898–899
  plants, 836–841, 837i, 860
  skeletal muscle, 1152
Sturtevant, Alfred, 241
Style, 885
Suberin, 856
Submucosa, 1198, 1203i
Subordinance, 1179
Subsistence farmers, 807
Subsoil, 907
Subspecies, 433, 433i

Temperate rain forest, 525
Temperature
  ectothermy and, 1256
  effect on enzyme activity of, 93–94, 94i
  effect on membrane fluidity, 101
  homeostasis and, 959
  optimal organismal performance and, 1251–1252, 1252i
  photorespiration and, 160, 161i, 161t
Temperature bacteriophage, 197
Template, **212**
Template strand, **292**
Temporal isolation, **431**, 431t
Temporal lobe, **1126**–1127, 1127i
Temporal separation, 163i
Temporal summation, **1087**
10nm chromatin fibre, **283**
Tendons, **1135**, 1135i
Tendrils, **936**
Terminal bud, **847**
Terminal electron acceptor, in anaerobic respiration, **138**–139
Termination, **302**
Termination codons, **369**
  See also Stop codons
Termination factor. *See* Release factor
Termination stage, of translation, **306**
Terminator, **296**
Termite-eating flatworm, **1210**–1211, 1211i
Termites, **54**, 55i, 613f
Terrestrial amphibians, excretions from, **1244**
Terrestrial environments, **1223**–1224, 1224i, 1236
Terrestrial mammals, water-conserving adaptations in, **1250**–1251, 1250i
Terrestrial osmoregulators, **1240**
Territorial behaviour, **1171**
Territory, **1160**
Tertiary consumer, **729**
Testcross, **224**, 224i
Testis (plural, testes), 1051i, 1052–1053t, **1059**–1060, 1060i
Testosterone, **1002**
Testudinata, subclass, **659**–660, 659f
Tetanus, **1140**, 1140i
Tetanus toxin, 1084–1085t
Tetrad, **202**
Tetrahymena, **1063**
Tetraploids, **253**
Tetrapoda, **644**
Tetrapods, 394b, **651**–654, 652f
T-even bacteriophage, **504**, 504i
TGA, **369**
Thalamus, **1091**, 1126
Thallus (plural, thalli), **555**, 556i, 573, 573i
Theory, **F-4**
Thermal acclimitization, **1256**
Thermodynamics, **75**
Thermodynamics, laws of
  energy and, 75–78, 77i, 94
  life and, 95
Thermoreceptors, **1117**–1119, 1132, 1251, 1256
Thermoregulation, **1251**, 1263
  ectothermic animals, 1253, 1253i

endothermic animals, 1253, 1253i
  heat exchanges with environment, 1252, 1252i
  optimal physiological performance and, 1251–1252, 1252i
Thermostat, as a negative feedback mechanism, **960**–961, 961i
Theta waves, **1130**
Thick filaments, **1136**–1140, 1139i, 1140i
Thigmotropism and thigmomorphogenesis, **936**, 936i
Thin air, 1232b
Thin filaments, **1136**–1140, 1139i, 1140i
Thorax, **624**
Thorpe, S.K.S., 474
Threat display, **1168**, 1168i
3' end, **268**, 269
3-D structure, of fossils, 450b
Threespine stickleback, 422b, 422i
Threshold potential, **1074**
Throat, in mammals, **1225**, 1226i
Throwing, **475**
Thrush, **549**
Thylakoid lumen, **146**
Thylakoid membranes, **146**, 154i
Thylakoids, **46**
Thymine, **268**
Thymus, **983**
Thyroid gland, 1051i, 1052–1053t, **1065**
Thyroid hormones, **1056**–1057, 1057i, 1258
Thyroid-releasing hormone (TRH), **1048**, 1048i
Thyroid-stimulating hormone (TSH), **1048**, 1048i
Thyroxine (T$_4$), **1056**–1057
Ti (tumour-inducing) plasmid, **357**, 358i
Tidal volume, **1226**
Tight junctions, **48**, 48i
Tilghman, Shirley, 327b
Time, telling with light, **15**–18, 25
Time lag, **693**
Timing, of reproduction, 1001b
Tinbergen, Niko, 1172, 1172i
Tissue culture, propagating plants asexually using, **897**, 897i
Tissue diffusion, in Bar-Headed Geese, 1304
Tissue layers, 1016t
Tissues, **595**
  animal, 595
  lymphoid, 983
Tissues, animal, **947**–948, 949i, 962
  epithelial, 949–951
  muscle tissue, 954–955, 955i
  nervous, 955–957, 956i
  support from, 951–954
Toad, 652–654
Tobacco
  cultivation of, 828
  domestication of, 819
  uses for, 828i
Tobacco hawkmoth, 1254
Tobacco hornworm, 1045–1046
Tolerance hypothesis, **739**
Toll-receptors, **1267**
Tomatoes, domestication of, 818, 818i, 819
Tonegawa, Susumu, 1275b

Tongues
    forked, 1118*i*
    human, 1116*i*
Tonoplast, 46
Tool, 475
Top-down theory, 662
Topoisomerase, 279*t*
Topsoil, 907
Torpor, 1260
Torsion, 615
Tortoise, 397*i*, 659–660, 659*f*
Totipotency, 601
Totipotent, 601
Touch, receptors for, 1100, 1100*i*
Townes, P.L., 1032, 1033*b*
TP53 gene, 333–334
Trace element, 1191
Trachea, 1221, 1221*i*
    in mammalian respiratory system, 1226*i*
    in mammals, 1225, 1226*i*
Tracheal system, 626
Tracheids, 843, 844*i*, 845*b*
Traditional evolutionary systematics, 459–461, 460*i*
Trait, 218
Trans fats, 103*b*
Transcription, 322–324, 323*i*
    DNA-directed RNA synthesis, 294–296, 295*i*, 311
    gene to polypeptide, 292
    of *lac* operon, 317–319, 318*i*
    operon as a unit of, 315–316, 316*i*, 317*i*
    in prokaryotic and eukaryotic cells, 293*i*
    regression of, 324
    regulation of in eukaryotes, 321–328, 336
    supporting theory of endosymbiosis, 67
    of *trp* operon, 319–320, 320*i*
Transcription factors, 296
Transcription initiation, 321–326
Transcription initiation complex, 322
Transcription unit, 296
Transcriptome, 376
Transcriptomics, 376–379
Transducing phage, 196
Transduction, 196
    as DNA source for recombination, 196–198, 197*i*
    in signal pathway, 114
Transfer cell, 878
Transfer RNA (tRNA), 66
Transformation, 196, 265
Transforming DNA (T DNA), 357
Transforming principle, 265
Transgene, 352
Transgenic, 352, 354*i*
Transgenic crops, 357–359, 358*i*, 359
Transit sequence, 309
Transition state, 89
Translation, 292
    gene to polypeptide, 292
    mRNA-directed polypeptide synthesis, 300–311, 300*i*, 311–312
    in prokaryotic and eukaryotic cells, 293*i*
    supporting theory of endosymbiosis, 67
Translational regulation, 328–332, 336
Translocation, 252

as chromosomal alterations, 252, 252*i*
    moving organic solutes by, 876–877
Transmembrane protein, 103–104, 104, 104*i*
Transmembrane (TM) region, 385
Transmission, 1069–1070, 1070*i*
Transmission electron microscopy (TEM), 30*i*
Transpiration, 869
Transport, 7
    in animals. *See* Circulatory system
    in plants. *See* Plants
Transport epithelium, 1238
Transport mechanisms, characteristics of, 110*t*
Transport proteins, 106, 107*i*
Transportation, as key function of membrane proteins, 103
Transposable element (TE), 210–211, 211–212, 211*i*
Transposable element sequences, 373
Transposase, 211
Transposition, 210
Transposons, 210–211, 212, 212*i*
Tree frogs, 1239, 1243–1244, 1244*i*
Tree of life, 455, 456*i*
Tree ring formation, 858*i*
Trematoda, class, 609, 609*f*
Triassic period, 448*t*, 586–587
Trichocyst, 521
Trichomes, 389*i*, 390*i*
Triglyceride, 135
Triiodothyronine (T3), 1056
Trillium, 587*i*
Trilobita, subphylum, 622, 622*f*
Trimester, 1025
Trimethylamine oxide, 1243
Triploblastic body plan, 595
Triploids, 253
Tripoblastic, 595
Triticale (grass), 586*i*
Trivers, Robert, 1181
TRNA structure, 300–302, 301*i*
Trochophore, 614
Trocophore, 614, 614*f*
Trophic cascade, 757
Trophic level, 728
Trophoblast, 1025
Trophozoite, 513
Tropic hormone, 1053
Tropical deciduus forest, 751
Tropical forests, 582
Tropical orchid, 913, 914*i*
Tropical rain forests, 557, 901–902
Tropism, 920
True-breeding, 219
Tryptophan biosynthesis, 319–320, 320*i*
Tsui, Lap-Chee, 117*b*
Tuatara, 655, 660
Tube cell, 886
Tube foot, 638
Tuber, 850
Tumour necrosis factor (TNF), 1288
Tumour suppressor genes, 333–334, 334*i*
Tundra plants, 1294, 1295*i*
Tunicate, 640–641, 641*f*
Tunnicliffe, Verena, 619*f*

Villi, **1203**–1204, 1204*i*
Viral DNA, 1286–1287*b*
Viral envelope proteins, 1286–1287*b*
Viral RNA, 1286–1287*b*
Virion, **503**
Viroids, **509**–510, 511
Virulent bacteriophage, **504**, 504*i*
Viruses, **501**–503, 502*i*, 503*t*
   affecting bacterial, animal, and plant cells, 511
   characteristics of, 511
   evolving from cellular DNA/RNA, 509, 511
   preventing, 506, 508–509, 511
   prions, 509–510, 511
   structure of, 501*i*
   treating, 506, 508–509, 511
   viroids, 509–510, 511
   wasps and, 1290
Visceral mass, **611**
Visible light, **5**
Vision, photoreceptors and, **1107**–1114, 1111*i*, 1131–1132
Visual cortex, **1113**–1114, 1114*i*
Visual processing, in retina, **1112**, 1113*i*
Visual signal, **1166**
Vital capacity, **1227**
Vitamin A (retinol), 1193*b*
Vitamin B, **1193**
Vitamin B$_1$ (thiamine), 1193*b*
Vitamin B$_2$ (riboflavin), 1193*b*
Vitamin B$_6$ (pyridoxine), 1193*b*
Vitamin B$_{12}$ (cobalamin), 1193*b*
Vitamin C (ascorbic acid), **1193**, 1193*b*
Vitamin D (calciferol), **14**–15, 1193, 1193*b*
Vitamin E (tocopherol), 1193*b*
Vitamin K (napthoquinone), **1193**, 1193*b*
Vitamins, **1190**
   as essential elements for animals, 1190–1191
   as essential elements for humans, 1192–1193
   sources, functions, and effects of deficiencies in
      humans, 1193*b*
Vitelline coat, **993**
Vitis vinifera sylvestris, **818**
Vitreous humour, **1109**
Viviparous animals, **997**–998, 998–999*b*
Viviparousness, **668**
VKORC1 gene, **374**
Voltage, **111**
Voltage-gated ion channels, **1073**
Volume, of cells, 31*i*
Volume and pressure of plasma, homeostasis and, **959**
Von Tschermak, Erich, 228
Vulpes vulpes, **678**
Vulva, **999**

W

Waggle dance, **1168**, 1168*i*
Walcott, Charles, 593
Wald, George, 13, 70
Wallace, Alfred Russel, 392, 399, 400
Waller, Augustus, 964–965, 977
Warbler finch, 397*i*, 399
Warfarin, **374**
Warm receptors, **1256**

Wasp, 413
Wasps, viruses and, 1290
Water
   aquatic environments, 1242*b*
   availability of in soil, 907–908, 907*i*
   conserving in plants, 875, 875*i*
   converting O$_2$ to, 139*i*
   food production and, 808
   long-distance transport of in xylem, 869–875, 880
   movement of in plants, 864–867, 864*i*, 879
   movement of organisms back to, 453–455, 454*i*
   transporting by roots, 868–869, 868*i*, 879–880
   use in agriculture, 825, 825*i*
Water balance, **1236**
Water lattice, **F-15**
Water potential, **865**–866, 866*i*
Water strider, 405
Water vascular system, **638**
Waterproof frog, 653*f*
Watershed, **761**
Water-soluble vitamins, **1193**, 1193*b*
Watson, James D., 2, 264, 267–270, 269–270, 270–280, 271*i*
Wavelength, **4**
Weaver ant, 593
Weight control, 1210*b*
Weinberg, Wilhelm, 415
Weis-Fogh, Torkel, 952*b*
Weiss, Samuel, 951*b*
Welwitschia, **584**, 585*i*, 859*b*
Went, Fritz, 920–921, 923*i*
Wetlands, **586**
Whale, humpback, 409, 409*i*
Whales, 1258
Wheat
   domestication of, 809–810, 810*i*, 816, 816*i*, 817*i*, 819*b*
   yields, 822*i*
Wheat *(Triticum aestivum)*, 442, 442*i*
Wheat *(Triticum searsii)*, 442*i*
Wheat *(Triticum tauschii)*, 442*i*
Whippoorwill, 1166
White matter, **1123**
White Pelicans, 1178
White pine, 584*i*
Whole-genome duplication (WGD), **382**
Whole-genome shotgun sequencing, **365**, 365*i*
Whole-transcriptome sequencing, **376**
Whyte, Lyle, 65*b*
Wiebe, John P., 1006*b*
Wiebe, Karen, 1159
Wieschaus, Eric, 1036–1037
Wigge, Philip A., 942*b*
Wigglesworth, V.B., 628*f*, 629*f*
Wild dogs, 1179
Wild emmer, 442*i*
"Wild-type" alleles, **241**
Wilkins, Maurice H.F., 268, 269–270
Willow trees, 811*b*
Wilmut, Ian, 356, 356*i*, 1035
Wilson, Margo, 1184
Wilting, **867**
Wingless/Wnt pathway, 1158*b*